PHENAZINES

G. A. SWAN

King's College, Newcastle upon Tyne, England

D. G. I. FELTON

*British-American Tobacco Company, Ltd.,
Millbrook, Southhampton, England*

1957

INTERSCIENCE PUBLISHERS INC., NEW YORK

INTERSCIENCE PUBLISHERS LTD., LONDON

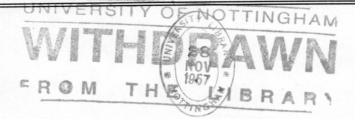

Library of Congress Catalog Card Number 57–6111

INTERSCIENCE PUBLISHERS, INC., 250 Fifth Avenue, New York 1, N.Y.

For Great Britain and Northern Ireland:

Interscience Publishers Ltd., 88/90 Chancery Lane, London, W.C. 2

PRINTED IN THE NETHERLANDS

The Chemistry of Heterocyclic Compounds

The chemistry of heterocyclic compounds is one of the most complex branches of organic chemistry. It is equally interesting for its theoretical implications, for the diversity of its synthetic procedures, and for the physiological and industrial significance of heterocyclic compounds.

A field of such importance and intrinsic difficulty should be made as readily accessible as possible, and the lack of a modern detailed and comprehensive presentation of heterocyclic chemistry is therefore keenly felt. It is the intention of the present series to fill this gap by expert presentations of the various branches of heterocyclic chemistry. The subdivisions have been designed to cover the field in its entirety by monographs which reflect the importance and the interrelations of the various compounds, and accommodate the specific interests of the authors.

Research Laboratories   ARNOLD WEISSBERGER
Eastman Kodak Company
Rochester, New York

Preface

This monograph is divided into two parts. The first deals with the phenazines and their quaternary derivatives (phenazinium compounds) which do not carry any condensed rings. Part II deals with the derivatives that have other carbocyclic or heterocyclic rings fused to the phenazine nucleus. Phenazine itself is conveniently represented by structure I (but see Chapter II:1,C). *The Ring Index* (*R. I.*) enumeration and ciphering are used throughout, although many papers (including current ones) use the alternative numbering shown in II. Beilstein employs II; but *Chemical Abstracts* indexes

(I)   (II)

phenazine derivatives according to I, although in the abstracts themselves the compounds are generally numbered according to II if the original paper does likewise. General methods for the synthesis of phenazine and its non-quaternary, non-condensed derivatives are collected together in Chapter I.

The phenazines include many dyestuffs of great commercial importance, and also a few compounds of natural occurrence, namely, certain bacterial pigments. In the case of dyestuffs described in the *Colour Index* (*C. I.*), the reference number in the latter work is usually given. In view of the biological importance of the bacterial pigments, and of the fairly extensive study that has been made of synthetic phenazines biologically, we decided to include a separate chapter on these aspects. As all but a very few of the compounds concerned belong to Part I, this chapter (XI) has been included at the end of that part, immediately following Chapter X, which deals with the chemistry of the bacterial pigments.

After making a comprehensive survey of almost all the phenazine compounds described in the literature, we decided that it would not be reasonable to include every such compound in the text, or even in the form of tables. Thus, many phenazines have been prepared merely as derivatives of *o*-quinones or *o*-diamines and are of very little intrinsic interest. Many others are unsatisfactorily described, frequently in the patent literature. We have therefore mentioned specifically in the text only compounds that appear to us to be likely to be of some potential interest, although in many cases we have included literature references in which descriptions of additional compounds are given. Again, we have not included every known patent, but have mentioned what appear to be the more important ones. In these respects, we realize that our judgment will be the object of criticism by at least some readers. In exercising discretion in this way, it is perhaps inevitable that our conclusions will be different from those of a chemist engaged exclusively in, for example, dyestuff chemistry. We should make clear at the outset that our approach has been that of general organic chemists and we hope that this will lead to the volume having an appeal to the widest possible circle. We shall welcome criticisms of fact or emphasis from those especially qualified to give it.

It may be mentioned here that difficulty has sometimes been encountered in obtaining satisfactory nitrogen values on phenazine derivatives. Recently, however, a description of a micro-method for the determination of nitrogen, which is claimed to give good results on such compounds, has been published (W. C. Alford in *Analytical Chemistry*, volume 24, page 881 (1952)).

During the last few years, there has been a considerable revival of interest in phenazine and its derivatives, the study of substitution in phenazine-N-oxides in particular having opened up the way to the synthesis of hitherto difficultly accessible compounds. As a considerable number of papers appeared between the time when our manuscript was completed and the data when the proofs were ready, we have included reference to these in an addendum, covering the literature up to approximately September, 1956. We wish to record our thanks to the publishers for their general cooperation throughout the whole period of the preparation of this book. Both publishers and printers also deserve a word of thanks for their patience.

Finally, we should like to thank Professor H. McIlwain for making some helpful suggestions on Chapter XI and Professor G. R. Clemo, F.R.S., who initially suggested that we should write this monograph.

G. A. SWAN

D. G. I. FELTON

February, 1957

Contents

Contents

PART I

Phenazine Systems Not Carrying Condensed Rings

G. A. SWAN

CHAPTER I

General Methods for the Synthesis of Phenazine, Its Homologs and Derivatives Not Containing Condensed Nuclei

1.   Merz,[1] in 1886, discovered a method of formation which leaves little doubt as to the basic ring structure of the phenazines. It consists in heating an aromatic o-diamine with pyrocatechol at 200–210°, in a sealed tube, and was applied to the synthesis of 2-methylphenazine by Merz and to that of phenazine itself (I) by Ris.[2] The reaction proceeds via the intermediate dihydrophenazine, which readily splits off hydrogen:

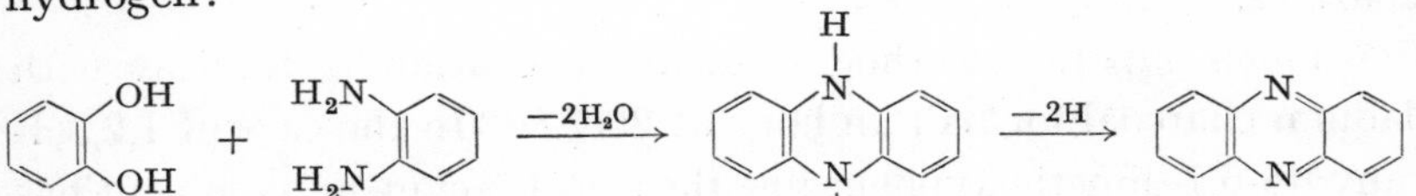

$$\text{(1)}$$

$$\text{(I)}$$

According to Campbell, Le Fèvre, Le Fèvre and Turner,[3] who have repeated several of the earlier phenazine syntheses, this method is extremely unsatisfactory. More recently, however, Morley[4] has reported that the sole product of the reaction is 5,10-dihydrophenazine, but oxidative sublimation gives phenazine in 55% overall yield from o-phenylenediamine. In fact, this now appears to be the best method for the preparation of phenazine or dihydrophenazine. See also, Chapter V:2A.

2.   The condensation of o-quinone with o-phenylenediamine in ethereal solution in the presence of anhydrous sodium sulfate is reported by Kehrmann and Mermod[5] to give a 35% yield of phenazine:

$$\text{(structure)} + \text{(structure)} \xrightarrow{-2H_2O} \quad I \qquad (2)$$

The method is due to Hinsberg[6] and Witt.[7] Later Diepolder[8] condensed 4,5-dimethyl-o-quinone with o-phenylenediamine in acetic acid solution and obtained 2,3-dimethylphenazine. A similar condensation between 3-methyl-o-phenylenediamine and o-quinone gives 1-methylphenazine.[9] Various phenazine derivatives have been prepared in this manner, the required o-quinone usually being obtained by oxidation of the corresponding catechol derivative with lead dioxide and not isolated in a state of purity. See also reference 10.

3. Clemo and McIlwain[11] obtained phenazine by condensing 1,2-cyclohexanedione with o-phenylenediamine in acetic acid solution in the presence of sodium acetate and dehydrogenating the resulting 1,2,3,4-tetrahydrophenazine by refluxing with iodine in acetic acid solution:

$$\text{(structure)} + \text{(structure)} \xrightarrow{-2H_2O} \text{(structure)} \xrightarrow{-4H} \quad I \qquad (3)$$

This synthesis is also applicable to a number of substituted phenazines.

A much superior method of dehydrogenation is to heat with palladium charcoal for half an hour at 200°.[4, 12] In the case of 1,2,3,4-tetrahydro-6,7-dimethoxyphenazine the use of p-cymene as solvent has been recommended.[13] The dehydrogenation cannot be effected by sulfur, selenium, Raney nickel or chloranil,[4, 12] but zinc dust distillation has been used in the conversion of octahydrophenazine into phenazine.[14] 1,2,3,4-Tetrahydro-6,8-dimethoxyphenazine is extremely resistant to dehydrogenation.[15]

Condensations of the type shown in Equation (3) had previously been described by Borsche[16] (Equation (4)) and by Landolt.[17]

$$\text{(structure)} + \text{(structure)} \longrightarrow \text{(structure)} \qquad (4)$$

4. Phenazines can be obtained by heating o-aminodiphenylamines with lead oxide, for example:

$$+ 2\,PbO \longrightarrow I + 2\,Pb + 2\,H_2O \qquad (5)$$

The method was discovered in 1890 by Nietzki and Ernst,[18] who prepared 2,8-diaminophenazine from 2,4,4'-triaminodiphenylamine and deaminated the product to phenazine *via* the diazo reaction. Phenazine itself was prepared from 2-aminodiphenylamine (obtainable by the condensation of 1-chloro-2-nitrobenzene with aniline, followed by reduction) by Fischer and Heiler;[19, 20] and more recent workers[3] obtained satisfactory yields, especially if the vapors of the base were led in a nitrogen stream over the red-hot lead oxide (40–55%).[3, 21] This method has also been applied to the synthesis of a number of phenazine derivatives, although 2-amino-2'-methoxydiphenylamine yields phenazine itself.[9]

Waterman and Vivian[22, 23] found that the procedure of reduction of the *o*-nitrodiphenylamine to the amino compound, followed by oxidation to the phenazine, could with advantage be replaced by one in which the nitro compound is treated with a reagent that caused the abstraction of oxygen, without supplying hydrogen to the reaction, so that cyclization might ensue directly. Thus, by heating 2-nitrodiphenylamine with iron filings for 30 minutes at 280–300°, a 46% yield of phenazine was obtained:

$$+ Fe \longrightarrow I + FeO + H_2O \qquad (6)$$

The ease with which the reaction occurs and the stability of the product permits a wide range of reducing agents to be employed, for example, red phosphorus, sulfur or lead; even activated carbon is capable of effecting the cyclization with little difficulty. Ferrous oxalate is also a suitable cyclizing agent; but the proportion used must be carefully controlled to obtain the highest yield of product.[24]

Certain derivatives of phenazine have also been prepared in this manner; but, in the case of 2,2'-dinitro- and 2-methoxy-2'-nitro-diphenylamines, elimination of an *o*-group occurs, and phenazine itself results.[22, 23, 25] Halogen atoms (except fluorine) undergo partial elimination in either *o*- or *p*- positions.[26] In general, it appears that an alkoxy group is eliminated in preference to a hydrogen atom, whenever both are in the appropriate position for reaction, for example:

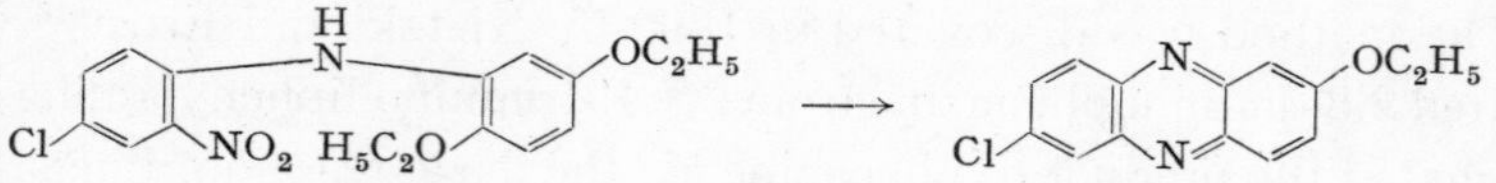

(7)

The formation of isomers has been observed, for example 4-chloro-3'-ethoxy-2-nitrodiphenylamine yields a mixture of 7-chloro-2-ethoxy-(II) and 8-chloro-1-ethoxy-phenazine (III).[24]

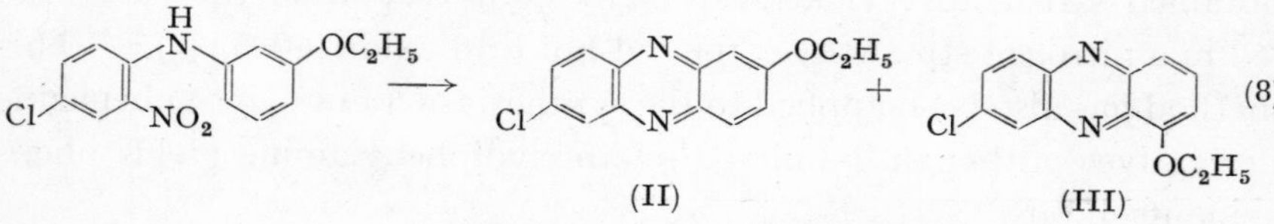

(8)

(II) (III)

In the reaction on 3,4-dimethoxy-2'-nitrodiphenylamine, only one isomer (IV) has been isolated.[25]

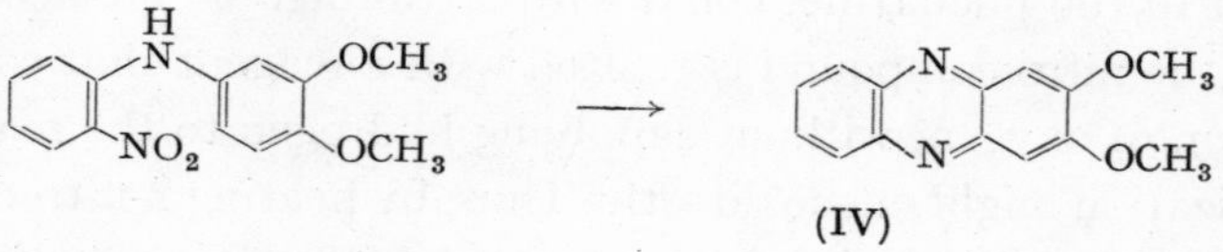

(9)

(IV)

Kehrmann and Havas[27] claimed to have obtained a 60–70% yield of phenazine by heating a mixture of 2-nitrodiphenylamine, 2-amino-diphenylamine and sodium acetate at 250–300°, followed by distillation with superheated steam (only traces were formed in the absence of sodium acetate); but later workers obtained low yields.[3, 28]

5. Very good yields of phenazine are also claimed by Eckert and Steiner[29] by the reduction of 2,2'-dinitrodiphenylamine (obtained by condensing 1-bromo-2-nitrobenzene with *o*-nitroaniline) with stannous chloride, followed by oxidation of the resulting semiquinonoid salt (see Chapter III:2B) with hydrogen peroxide, permanganate or other oxidizing agent:

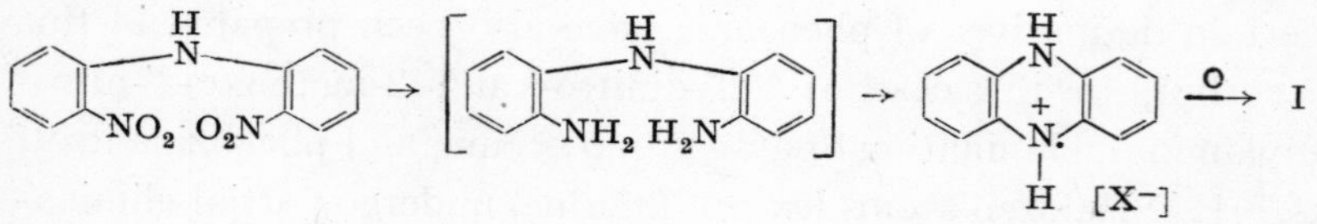

(10)

What appears to be a good and fairly generally applicable synthesis of phenazines has been described by Tomlinson[30] namely, the oxidation by ferric chloride of 2,2'-diaminodiphenylamines (prepared by reduction of the corresponding dinitro compounds with zinc dust and acetic acid) in dilute hydrochloric acid solution, the yields being almost quantitative. This method has also been used by other workers[13, 31, 32]; and zinc dust distillation or treatment with sodium sulfide have also been used for converting 2,2'-dinitrodiphenylamines into phenazines.[33]

6. A phenazine (V) has also been obtained as follows[34]:

$$\xrightarrow[\text{HCl}]{\text{C}_2\text{H}_5\text{OH}} \quad (11)$$

(V)

Related to this is the recent extension by King, Clark and Davis[15] of Crippa's[35] synthesis of quinoxalines from o-phenylazoanilines and ketomethylene compounds to the preparation of tetrahydrophenazines. By heating a solution of 2-p-tolylazo-p-toluidine in excess of cyclohexanone under reflux for two hours in the presence of a drop of concentrated hydrochloric acid, a 45% yield of 1,2,3,4-tetrahydro-7-methylphenazine (VI) was obtained.

$$+ \quad \longrightarrow \quad + \text{ H}_2\text{O} + \text{ArNH}_2 \quad (12)$$

(VI)

Attempts to prepare 1,3-dihydroxyphenazines from phloroglucinol in a similar manner were, however, unsuccessful.

7. The formation of phenazine from o-bromoaniline by boiling in nitrobenzene solution with potassium carbonate and copper is described by Hillemann[36]; the intermediate dihydrophenazine could not be isolated.

$$\xrightarrow{-2\,\text{HBr}} \quad \xrightarrow{-2\,\text{H}} \text{I} \quad (13)$$

8. Wohl and Aue[37] made the interesting observation that phenazines are formed by the reaction of aromatic mononitro compounds with aromatic monoamines in the presence of dry, finely powdered sodium hydroxide (or a mixture with potassium hydroxide) at 140°. Thus, nitrobenzene and aniline yield phenazine (30%); but 60% of the aniline is converted into azobenzene. If the sodium hydroxide is very dry and the reaction is carried out at as low a temperature as possible (110–120°), phenazine-5-oxide is isolated. Wohl[38-40] explained the reaction by postulating rearrangement of the nitrobenzene, under the influence of alkali, into o-nitrosophenol (o-quinone-monoxime) (VII), which condenses with the aniline; and the resulting intermediate either can be oxidized by excess of nitrobenzene to phenazine-5-oxide, or can go over to phenazine by loss of water:

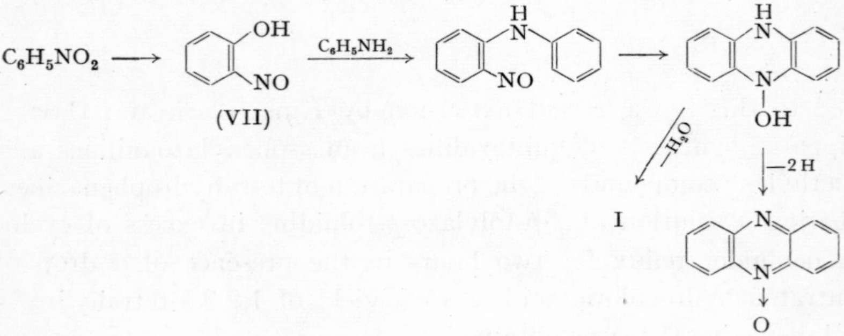

p-Nitrosodiphenylamine has been isolated from such a reaction.[38]

The o-nitrosophenol is accompanied by its p-isomer, recognized by isolation of a small amount of p-nitrophenol in the absence of aniline. It has not been established with absolute certainty which of the two nitrogen atoms bears the oxygen atom in an unsymmetrical phenazine N-oxide synthesized by this method, although it seems extremely probable that it is the nitrogen atom originally in the nitro group which eventually bears the oxygen atom in the N-oxide.[41] (See Chapter XII:3,E(1).)

On the other hand Bradley and Leete[42] have suggested a direct anionoid attack by aniline in the o-position of the nitrobenzene:

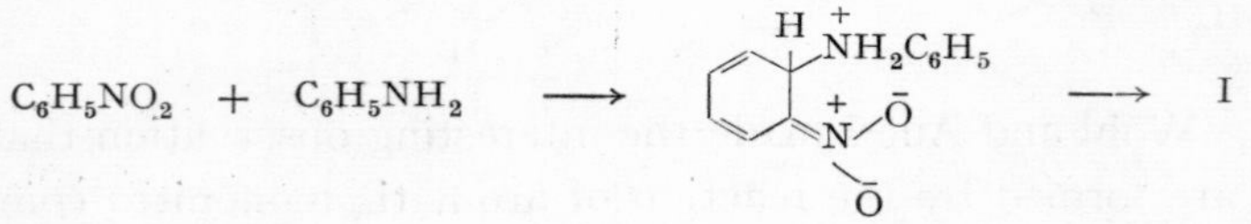

And moreover, Abramova and Postovskii[43] have recently shown that
o-nitrosophenol does not react with aniline under the Wohl-Aue conditions; these authors put forward a mechanism similar to that suggested
by Bradley and Leete. They also showed that phenazine could be
obtained in 30–32% yield by treating aniline with sodamide, to give
the sodio derivative, and heating this with nitrobenzene in xylene at
140–145°.

According to later workers,[3] as a preparative method for phenazine,
this is tedious and gives poor yields. For the preparation of phenazine-
5-oxide by this method, the use of an inert solvent (such as benzene),
with a molecular ratio of nitrobenzene:aniline of not less than 1 is
recommended.[41, 44, 45] If aniline is replaced by p-toluidine, 2-phenazine-
carboxylic acid-10-oxide is obtained.[46]

Zerevitinov and Ostromislenski[47] similarly obtained phenazine by
the action of barium oxide or hydroxide on nitrobenzene, and suggested
that it is formed by condensation of the intermediates, nitrosobenzene
and o-nitrophenol, both of which are known to be formed by the action
of alkalis on nitrobenzene.[48]

Wohl's method cannot be applied to o-nitroanilines, since these
are unstable to the alkaline treatment; however, if a mixture of
o-nitroaniline and aniline hydrochloride is fused with zinc chloride at
180–185°, the reaction occurs in a different manner and 2-amino-
phenazine (VIII) is formed.[49]

$$\underset{}{\text{(o-nitroaniline)}} \quad + \quad \underset{}{\text{(aniline)}} \quad \longrightarrow \quad \underset{\text{(VIII)}}{\text{(2-aminophenazine)}} \qquad (16)$$

This latter reaction does not occur if the p-position of the aniline
is blocked as in p-toluidine; and poor yields are obtained using diethyl-
aniline or o-toluidine. Formanilide may be used instead of aniline; and
the reaction can be applied to 1-naphthylamine.

Wohl's method failed in the case of o-nitroanisole and o-anisidine.[13]
The latter reaction yielded phenazine itself; but the condensation
without loss of substituent groups has recently been accomplished by
Serebryanyĭ,[50, 51] who has prepared a considerable number of alkoxy-
and dialkoxy-phenazines in low yields by the interaction of various

aromatic amines with o-nitroanisole or o-nitrophenetole in the presence of potassium hydroxide at room temperature. This modification has also been studied by Pachter and Kloetzel,[52] who thus prepared 1,6-dimethoxyphenazine and 1,6-dichlorophenazine. In this way, the phenazines (not their oxides) are obtained.

9. Although phenazine itself is obtained directly from aniline at high temperatures (Chapter II:1,B), this is not a general reaction for preparing phenazine derivatives. Malaviya and Dutt[53] claimed to obtain phenazine by the action of tropical sunlight for 135 days on a solution of aniline in dilute hydrochloric acid and also various substituted derivatives in a similar manner; but their results require verification.[13] The fluorescence produced when a film of aniline at — 180° is subjected to ultraviolet radiation of wavelength 200–220 mμ has been attributed to phenazine formed by photodehydrogenation.[54]

The action of bleaching powder on 2-naphthylamine leads to naphthazine formation; but, in the case of aromatic amines in general, azo compounds (not phenazines) result.[55] See also Chapter IV:3 and XV:3A.

10. The following reactions are probably of little value as preparative methods for phenazines.[56–59]

$$C_6H_5N_2X + CH_3COCH_2CO_2C_2H_5 \longrightarrow \underset{N.NHC_6H_5}{CH_3COCCO_2C_2H_5} + \underset{N.NHC_6H_5}{C_6H_5N\!=\!NCCO_2C_2H_5}$$

$$\text{Hot mineral acid} \Big\downarrow \tag{17}$$

$$C_6H_5NH_2 + \text{benzotriazole} + I$$

$$C_6H_5N_2X + CH_3COCO_2H \longrightarrow \underset{N.NHC_6H_5}{C_6H_5N\!=\!NCN\!=\!NC_6H_5} + \underset{N.NHC_6H_5}{C_6H_5N\!=\!NCCOCO_2H}$$

$$\text{Boiling HCl} \Big\downarrow \tag{18}$$

$$\text{Some } I$$

11. The formation of phenazine N-oxides by the action of concentrated sulfuric acid on p-substituted derivatives of nitrosobenzene in acetic acid at 20° has been explained by Bamberger and Ham[60] as follows:

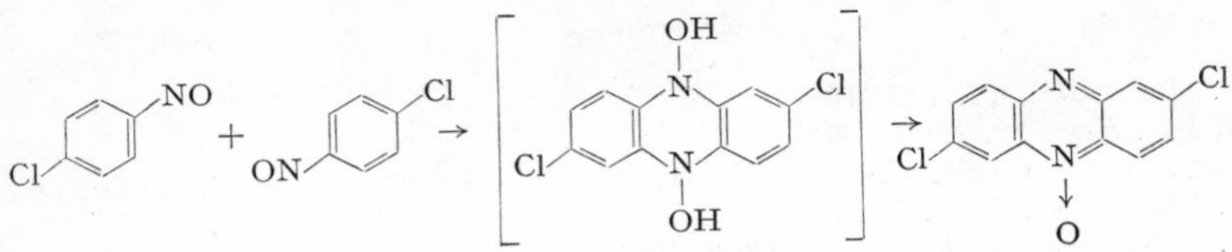

(19)

The N-oxides are reduced to the free phenazines by the action of stannous chloride and hydrochloric acid.

12. The formation of 2,3-diamino derivatives of phenazine by oxidation of aromatic o-diamines under mild conditions (ferric chloride) was established by Fischer and Hepp,[61] although the reaction had been carried out in 1871 by Griess,[62, 63] and further investigated by others.[64-66] The reaction can also be brought about by the use of cyanogen iodide.[67] See also Chapter VI:3,B.

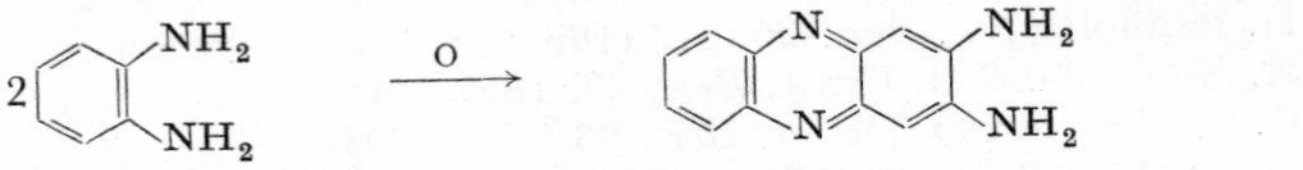

(20)

In the case of 3,4-diaminoguaiacol, a phenazine (IX) is formed by atmospheric oxidation.[68]

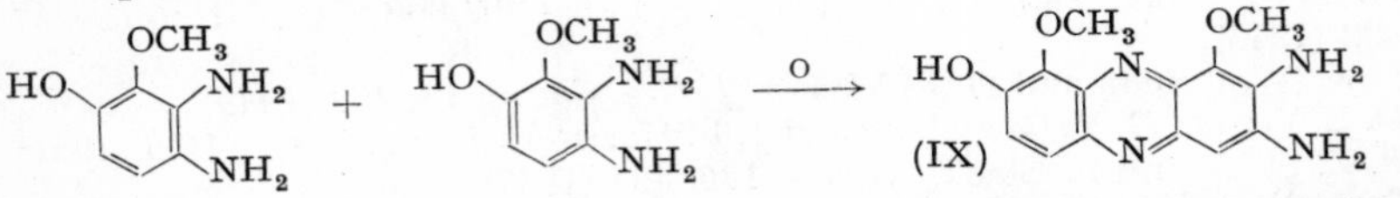

(21)

A similar reaction is the formation of 2,3-diaminophenazine by the action of o-quinonedioxime (X) or o-dinitrosobenzene (XI) on o-phenylenediamine in acetic acid solution.[69]

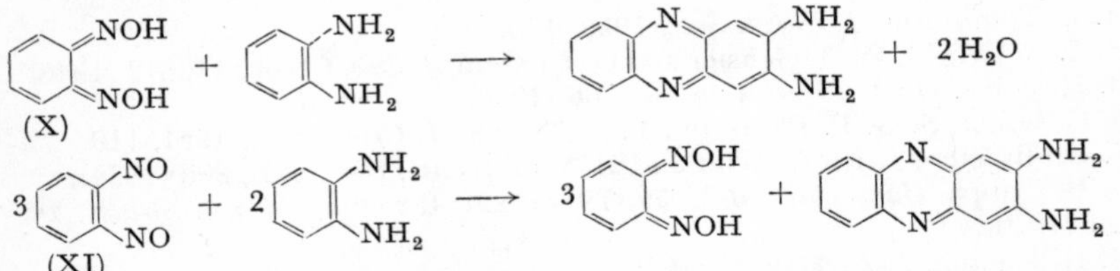

(22)

In the case of N,N'-dialkyl derivatives of o-phenylenediamine, phenazinium compounds (XII) result.[70-74]

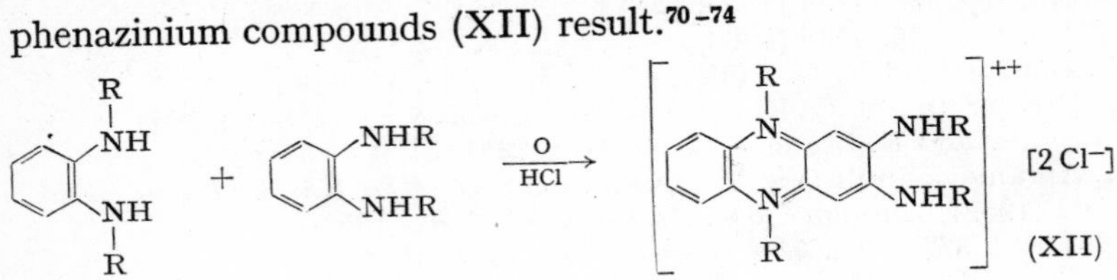

(23)

References

1. V. Merz, *Ber.*, **19**, 725 (1886).
2. C. Ris, *Ber.*, **19**, 2206 (1886).
3. I. G. M. Campbell, C. G. Le Fèvre, R. J. W. Le Fèvre and E. E. Turner, *J. Chem. Soc.*, **1938**, 404.
4. J. S. Morley, *J. Chem. Soc.*, **1952**, 4008.
5. F. Kehrmann and C. Mermod, *Helv. Chim. Acta*, **10**, 62 (1927).
6. O. Hinsberg, *Ber.*, **18**, 1228 (1885).
7. O. N. Witt, *Ber.*, **19**, 914 (1886).
8. E. Diepolder, *Ber.*, **42**, 2916 (1909).
9. H. McCombie, H. A. Scarborough and W. A. Waters, *J. Chem. Soc.*, **1928**, 353.
10. G. Stein and J. Weiss, *J. Chem. Soc.*, **1951**, 3265.
11. G. R. Clemo and H. McIlwain, *J. Chem. Soc.*, **1934**, 1991.
12. G. R. Clemo and H. McIlwain, *J. Chem. Soc.*, **1936**, 258.
13. G. R. Clemo and A. F. Daglish, *J. Chem. Soc.*, **1950**, 1481.
14. M. Godchot and M. Mousseron, *Compt. rend.*, **190**, 442 (1930).
15. F. E. King, N. G. Clark and P. M. H. Davis, *J. Chem. Soc.*, **1949**, 3012.
16. W. Borsche, *Wallach-Festschrift*, 301; through *Chem. Zentr.*, **1909**, II, 1549.
17. H. Landolt (Jr.), *Ber.*, **25**, 842 (1892).
18. R. Nietzki and O. Ernst, *Ber.*, **23**, 1852 (1890).
19. O. Fischer and O. Heiler, *Ber.*, **26**, 378 (1893).
20. O. Fischer, *Ber.*, **29**, 1873 (1896).
21. B. M. Mikhaïlov and A. N. Blokhina, *Izvest. Akad. Nauk S.S.S.R., Otdel. Khim. Nauk*, **1950**, 304; through *Chem. Abstracts*, **44**, 9452 (1950).
22. H. C. Waterman and D. L. Vivian, U. S. Pat. 2,292,808; *Chem. Abstracts*, **37**, 892 (1943).
23. H. C. Waterman and D. L. Vivian, *J. Org. Chem.*, **14**, 289 (1949).
24. D. L. Vivian, G. Y. Greenberg and J. L. Hartwell, *J. Org. Chem.*, **16**, 1 (1951).
25. P. Z. Slack and R. Slack, *Nature*, **160**, 437 (1947).
26. D. L. Vivian and J. L. Hartwell, *J. Org. Chem.*, **18**, 1065 (1953).
27. F. Kehrmann and E. Havas, *Ber.*, **46**, 341 (1913).
28. F. Kögl and J. J. Postowsky, *Ann.*, **480**, 280 (1930).
29. A. Eckert and K. Steiner, *Monatsh.*, **35**, 1153 (1914); through *Chem. Zentr.*, **1915**, I, 202.
30. M. L. Tomlinson, *J. Chem. Soc.*, **1939**, 158.
31. R. C. Elderfield, W. J. Gensler and O. Birstein, *J. Org. Chem.*, **11**, 812 (1946).
32. B. Hegedüs, *Helv. Chim. Acta*, **33**, 766 (1950).
33. G. G. Coker, S. G. P. Plant and P. B. Turner, *J. Chem. Soc.*, **1951**, 110.
34. F. Krollpfeiffer (with G. Wolf and H. Walbrecht), *Ber.*, **67B**, 908 (1934).
35. G. B. Crippa, *Gazz. chim. ital.*, **59**, 330 (1929); through *Chem. Abstracts*, **24**, 121 (1930).
36. H. Hillemann, *Ber.*, **71B**, 42 (1938).
37. A. Wohl and W. Aue, *Ber.*, **34**, 2442 (1901).
38. A. Wohl, *Ber.*, **36**, 4135 (1903).
39. A. Wohl, *Ber.*, **36**, 4139 (1903).
40. J. F. Bunnett and R. E. Zahler, *Chem. Revs.*, **49**, 377 (1951).
41. I. J. Pachter and M. C. Kloetzel, *J. Am. Chem. Soc.*, **74**, 971 (1952).
42. W. Bradley and E. Leete, *J. Chem. Soc.*, **1951**, 2129.
43. E. I. Abramova and I. Ya. Postovskiĭ, *Zhur. Obshcheĭ Khim.* (*J. Gen. Chem.*), **22**, 502 (1952); through *Chem. Abstracts*, **47**, 2182 (1953).
44. U. S. Pat. 2,332,179; *Chem. Abstracts*, **38**, 1534 (1944).

45. S. Maffei, S. Pietra and A. Cattaneo, *Gazz. chim. ital.*, **83**, 327 (1953).
46. S. Maffei, S. Pietra and A. M. Rivolta, *Ann. chim. (Rome)*, **42**, 519 (1952).
47. T. Zerevitinov and I. Ostromislenski, *Ber.*, **44**, 2402 (1911).
48. A. Wohl, *Ber.*, **32**, 3486 (1899).
49. A. Wohl and M. Lange, *Ber.*, **43**, 2186 (1910).
50. S. B. Serebryanyĭ, *Zhur. Obshcheĭ Khim. (J. Gen. Chem.)*, **20**, 1629 (1950); through *Chem. Abstracts*, **45**, 2009 (1951).
51. S. B. Serebryanyĭ, V. P. Chernetskiĭ and A. I. Kiprianov, *Doklady Akad. Nauk S.S.S.R.*, **70**, 645 (1950); through *Chem. Abstracts*, **45**, 4249 (1951).
52. I. J. Pachter and M. C. Kloetzel, *J. Am. Chem. Soc.*, **73**, 4958 (1951).
53. B. K. Malaviya and S. Dutt, *Proc. Acad. Sci. United Provinces Agra Oudh. India*, **4**, 319 (1935); through *Chem. Abstracts*, **30**, 1056 (1936).
54. A. N. Terenin, *Acta Physicochim. U.R.S.S.*, **13**, 1 (1940); through *Chem. Abstracts*, **35**, 1701 (1941).
55. W. Meigen and W. Norman, *Ber.*, **33**, 2711 (1900).
56. E. Bamberger and E. Wheelwright, *Ber.*, **25**, 3201 (1892).
57. E. Bamberger and E. Wheelwright, *J. prakt. Chem.*, (2), **65**, 123 (1902); through *Chem. Soc. Abstracts*, **82**, (i), 406 (1902).
58. E. Bamberger and J. Müller, *Ber.*, **27**, 147 (1894).
59. E. Bamberger and J. Müller, *J. prakt. Chem.*, (2), **64**, 199 (1901); through *Chem. Soc. Abstracts*, **80**, (i), 778 (1901).
60. E. Bamberger and W. Ham, *Ann.*, **382**, 82 (1911).
61. O. Fischer and E. Hepp, *Ber.*, **22**, 355 (1889).
62. P. Griess, *J. prakt. Chem.*, (2), **3**, 143 (1871); through *J. Chem. Soc.*, **24**, 562 (1871).
63. P. Griess, *Ber.*, **5**, 192 (1872).
64. H. Salkovski, *Ann.*, **173**, 39 (1874).
65. C. Rudolph, *Ber.*, **12**, 2211 (1879).
66. F. Wiesinger, *Ann.*, **224**, 353 (1884).
67. H. Hubner, *Ber.*, **9**, 774 (1876).
68. F. Fichter and J. Schwab, *Ber.*, **39**, 3339 (1906).
69. T. Zincke and P. Schwarz, *Ann.*, **307**, 28 (1899).
70. O. Fischer, *Ber.*, **37**, 552 (1904).
71. O. Fischer (with O. Veiel), *Ber.*, **38**, 320 (1905).
72. O. Fischer and O. Jonas, *Ber.*, **27**, 2782 (1894).
73. O. Fischer, *Ber.*, **37**, 552 (1904).
74. F. Krollpfeiffer, W. Graulich and A. Rosenberg, *Ann.*, **542**, 1 (1939).

CHAPTER II

Phenazine and Its Homologs

1. Phenazine (R.I. 1905)

A. Physical Constants

Phenazine, $C_{12}H_8N_2$, crystallizes from ethanol in bright yellow, glistening needles,[1] but is precipitated from its alcoholic solution by the careful addition of water as colorless needles.[2] Its melting point is given by most authors as 171°, although recently determined values are 173–4°[3] and 174.7–176.3° (corr.).[4] Its boiling point is 339°.[5] It sublimes without decomposition, and is volatile in steam, with an odor reminiscent of oil of cinnamon.[1] Its density is 1.33 g./ml.[6] The dipole moment of phenazine is zero[7,8] and its pK_a value is 1.23 ± 0.10 ($M/3000$).[3] It is soluble in 50 parts of cold ethanol, readily soluble in hot ethanol, rather difficultly soluble in ether or benzene and almost insoluble in cold water.[1] Light absorption: $\lambda_{max.}$, 250, 365 mμ; log $\varepsilon_{max.}$, 5.1, 4.15; $\lambda_{min.}$ 230, 290 mμ; log $\varepsilon_{min.}$, 4.1, 2.4.[9-12] Light absorption in ethanolic hydrogen chloride solution $\lambda_{max.}$, 270, 380 mμ; log $\varepsilon_{max.}$, 4.8, 4.3; $\lambda_{min.}$, 230, 305 mμ; log $\varepsilon_{min.}$, 4.0, 2.6. The light absorption in concentrated sulfuric acid solution has also been studied.[13,14] The fluorescence of a mixture of anthracene and phenazine has been investigated, and phenazine here acts as an exciton quencher.[15] The fluorescence bands produced by x-ray irradiation of phenazine have also been measured.[16] The crystal structure of phenazine has been investigated by optical and x-ray methods.[6,17] The monoclinic unit cell (space group No. 14, P2₁/a) contains two molecules and has dimensions a = 13.22 A., b = 5.061 A., c = 7.088 A., β = 109° 13′. The heat of combustion of phenazine is 1480.4 kcal./mole and the resonance energy has been calculated as 105 kcal./mole.[5,18]

14

B. Preparation and Importance

Phenazine was discovered in 1873 by Claus,[1] who obtained it in 18% yield by distilling calcium azobenzoate with calcium hydroxide; he named it "azophenylene" and assigned to it structure II. The general methods for the synthesis of phenazine and its derivatives have been discussed in Chapter I; of these, the best for the preparation of phenazine itself appear to be those of Ris as modified by Morley (Chapter I:1), Waterman and Vivian (Chapter I:4) and Tomlinson (Chapter I:5).

Schichuzki,[19] in 1874, obtained azobenzene and phenazine by the action of hot lead oxide on aniline; and Bernthsen[20] observed the formation of phenazine when aniline was passed through a red-hot tube. More recently, the conversion of aniline into phenazine by thallic oxide at temperatures varying from 250–500° and varying molecular ratios of oxygen:aniline has been studied by Brown and Frishe.[21] The highest yield of phenazine obtained was about 15% (30% conversion). The use of amino mercury compounds in the presence of selenium or sulfur for the conversion of aniline to phenazine has also been studied.[22]

Although many phenazine derivatives are of great commercial importance, the parent base appears to be of no value up to the present time. Phenazine is inferior to phenothiazine in inhibiting viscosity changes and acid production in bis(2-ethylhexyl) sebacate used as a turbo-jet lubricant.[23(b)] Phenazine acts as a sensitizer for film formers such as rubber hydrochlorides and nitrocelluloses, under the action of ultraviolet radiation; an unknown photoöxide is thought to be involved.[23(c)]

C. Structure

Phenazine is isomeric with benzo[c]cinnoline (I) and Claus gave consideration to both rival structures, in view of the formation from

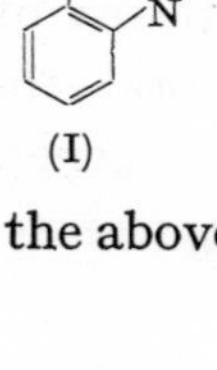

(I)

calcium azobenzoate, although the above structure was very soon ruled

out for phenazine. The various syntheses already given and the formation of quinoxaline-2,3-dicarboxylic acid in 80% yield by oxidation of
phenazine with aqueous permanganate at water-bath temperature[23(a)]
leave no doubt as to the nuclear structure, the only point requiring
further consideration being the distribution of the single and double
bonds. In the earlier period, the controversy centered around whether
phenazine possessed the "symmetrical" (II) or the "unsymmetrical"

(II)   (III)   (IV)   (V)   (VI)

(III) structure; and attempts (which would not now be considered
valid) to differentiate between these depended on whether dihydrophenazine formed a mono- or a di-acetyl derivative. Thus, it was
thought that, depending upon whether phenazine were II or III, its
dihydro derivative would be V or VI, the former of which should yield
a diacetyl derivative (IX), while the latter should give only a monoacetyl compound (VII). Actually, with acetic anhydride in the cold, a
monoacetyl derivative (colorless rhombohedra, m.p. 255°) is obtained,
whereas on heating, especially in the presence of a trace of zinc chloride,
a diacetyl derivative (prisms, m.p. 180°) is formed.[11, 24-30] It was
therefore suggested that phenazine had the "unsymmetrical" structure
(III) and that isomerization occurred on heating with acetic anhydride:

(VII)   (VIII)   (IX)

Later, the zero dipole moment was used as an argument in favor
of the "symmetrical" structure (II) for phenazine.[7]

However, in terms of the theory of resonance, phenazine could be
represented as a resonance hybrid, the principal structures involved
being III, IV and II, although in general, throughout this volume, the
base will, for convenience, be represented by only one of these formulas.

Dihydrophenazine has structure V, which is, of course, capable of forming either a mono- or a di-acetyl derivative, (VIII) and (IX), respectively. The close structural relationship between phenazine, acridine and anthracene is clearly seen, the resonance energies of these compounds being, 105, 106 and 105 kcal./mole, respectively.[18] The electronic charge distribution on the different atoms of the phenazine molecule has been discussed by Pullman.[31] The bond lengths shown in X have been calculated by the method of molecular orbitals; XI shows experimentally determined values.[17] The zero dipole moment is in keeping with a planar, symmetrical structure.

(X) (XI)

D. Salts and Addition Compounds

Phenazine dissolves in concentrated sulfuric acid with a red color; in moderately dilute mineral acids, it dissolves to a golden yellow colored solution, from which it is largely reprecipitated by water, on account of hydrolysis of the salts.[1, 32] The very low basicity of phenazine may be due to the facts: (a) that the second nitrogen atom introduced into acridine is electron-attracting and therefore base-weakening, and (b) that in the base an opportunity exists for the formation of exactly equivalent dipolar structures (as in II if the central N–N bond is regarded as an electrovalence) which may strengthen the resonance of this species at the expense of the ion.[3] Phenazine may be regarded as a vinylog of azobenzene.

Numerous salts have been described, some of which are shown in Table I. These are usually monoacidic and weakly colored; although the diperchlorate is a deep red powder with a bluish glance, readily hydrolyzed by water.[33] Phenazine forms certain halogen addition compounds[34] and with 1,3,5-trinitrobenzene it yields an addition compound (1:1) that separates from ethanol as yellow needles, m.p. 151–153°.[35] It also forms double compounds with pyrocatechol (m.p.

184°), resorcinol (m.p. 213.5°) and hydroquinone (m.p. 232° (dec.)), all crystallizing as yellow needles.[2] Addition compounds with nitrophenols are also known.[36,37]

E. Phenazine-5-oxide

Phenazine-5-oxide (phenazine N-oxide), $C_{12}H_8ON_2$, the formation of which has been discussed in Chapter I:8 crystallizes from ethanol as yellowish-red needles, m.p. 226.5°, and can be sublimed, largely unchanged, in a vacuum at 240–250°. The action of heat on this compound at 260–280° or sublimation in the presence of iron filings at 240–250° yields phenazine. It is recovered unchanged after being boiled for a short time with acetic anhydride; but long boiling leads to phenazine. Likewise, no change results from a short heating of the solution in concentrated sulfuric acid, whereas phenazine is formed on longer heating. In the case of some derivatives, the oxygen atom can be removed by boiling with aniline and sodium acetate.[38] Reduction with sodium amalgam in ethanol, or with zinc and hydrochloric acid yields dihydrophenazine.[39]

Wohl[40] formulated phenazine-5-oxide as XII, by analogy with the azoxy compounds; but the substance is now represented as XIII. The

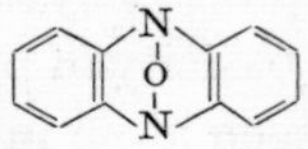

(XII) 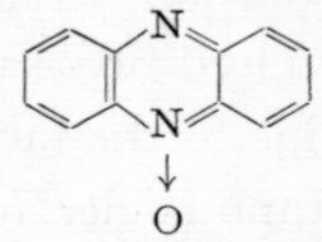   (XIII)

proof of the latter (unsymmetrical) structure was furnished by the formation of 1-methylphenazine-5-oxide (XIV), m.p. 142°, from nitro-

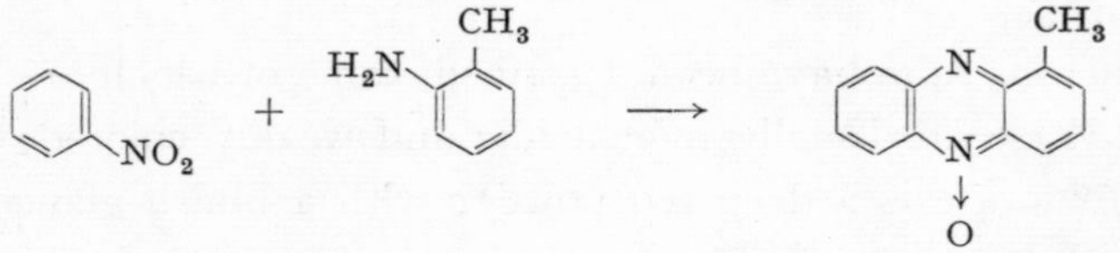

(XIV)

benzene and o-toluidine and that of the isomeric 4-methylphenazine-5-oxide (XV), m.p. 158°, from aniline and o-nitrotoluene, by condensation in the presence of sodamide; instead of only one compound, according to the Wohl formulation.[23(a)]

Phenazine-5-oxide forms an unstable hydrochloride and a di-bromide.[40]

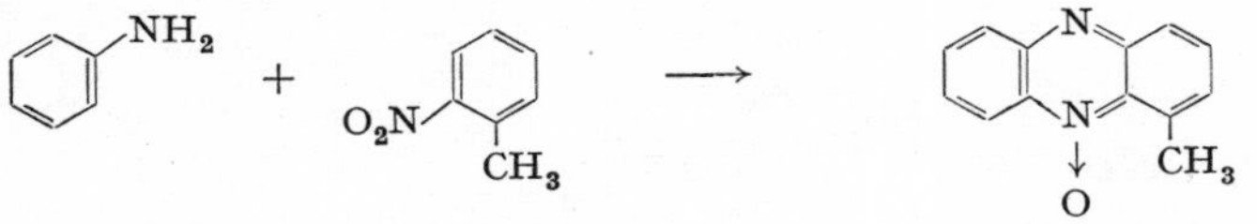

(XV)

F. Phenazine-5,10-dioxide

Phenazine-5,10-dioxide (phenazine di-N-oxide), $C_{12}H_8O_2N_2$ (XVI), separates from ethanol as orange-red needles, m.p. 204° (gas evolution), after turning brown at 150°. It is formed when phenazine is treated with hydrogen peroxide in acetic acid (16 hours at 50°)[41,42] or with

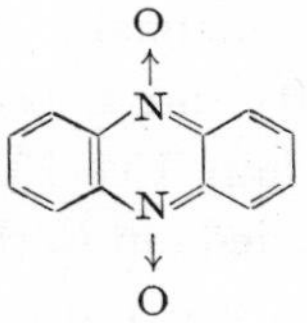

(XVI)

sodium perbenzoate in cold chloroform.[23(a)] It is decomposed to phenazine by heating with acetic anhydride or iron filings, or even (slowly) by heating alone or in solution at 100°, and liberates iodine from potassium iodide in the presence of acid. The infrared absorption spectrum of the compound has been recorded.[43]

2. Phenazinium Compounds

A. Structure

The phenazinium (formerly phenazonium) salts are quaternary compounds formed by the addition of a univalent hydrocarbon residue and a univalent acid residue to a nitrogen atom of phenazine or one of its derivatives, for example XVIII. Many such compounds have been described.[44-46]

As in the case of phenazine itself, it has been disputed whether the phenazinium compounds should be given the "symmetrical" (XVII) or "unsymmetrical" (XVIII) formulation. However, the molecule is

(XVII)   (XVIII)   (XIX)

best represented as a resonance hybrid, the principal structures involved being XVIII and XIX.

Those in which R is alkyl are usually obtained by the direct addition of alkyl halides or dialkyl sulfates to the phenazine.

B. 5-Methylphenazinium Methyl Sulfate

5-Methylphenazinium methyl sulfate (phenazine methosulfate) (XX) is obtained by heating phenazine with methyl sulfate in nitrobenzene for 7 minutes at 100° and is precipitated by ether, forming yellow prisms (from ethanol), m.p. 155–157°,[28, 47] or 198° (dec.) on rapid heating.[30] If the reaction is carried out in the absence of solvent (2 hours at 100°) or at a higher temperature, dark green crystals, m.p. 185–186° (dec.), are obtained, due to the substitution of a methyl group into one of the benzene rings, and formation of a semiquinone.[47] Treatment of 5-methylphenazinium methylsulfate in aqueous solution with potassium iodide gives a semiquinonoid iodide, forming bluish leaflets from ethanol (presumably due to the reducing action of hydriodic acid).[28, 48, 49] (See Chapter III:2A.)

The absorption spectra of various phenazinium salts have been measured.[9, 10, 14]

These quaternary compounds are reactive to anionoid substitution. Thus, Kehrmann and Havas[28] demonstrated that 5-methylphenazinium methyl sulfate reacted with ammonia in the presence of air with the formation of 2-amino-10-methylphenazinium methyl sulfate (XXI; but see Chapter VII:1,C(2)) and suggested that with oxygen alone it might yield 10-methyl-2(10)-phenazinone (2-keto-10-methyl-2,10-dihydrophenazine) (XXII), the methyl analog of aposafranone. This suggestion was proved correct by McIlwain[50] by the isolation of the product of atmospheric oxidation in the presence of a little sodium carbonate (reaction time: one week) and its comparison with 10-methyl-2(10)-phenazinone, prepared by the method of Kehrmann and Cherpillod[51];

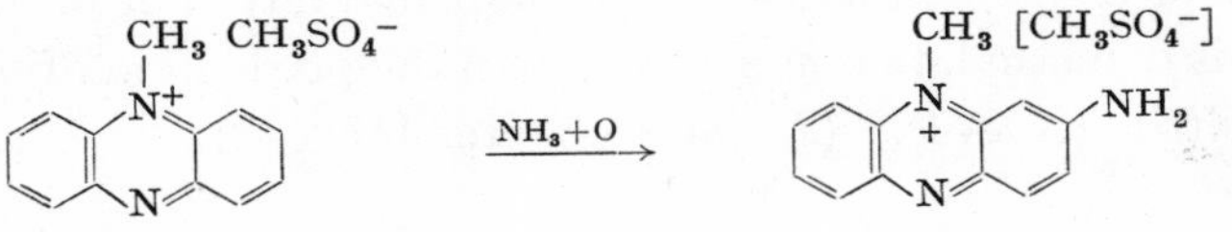

(XX)   (XXI)

the yield varied with temperature, but was never greater than 5%, the bulk of the product being phenazine. Compound **XXII** separates from water as dark red prisms, m.p. 200°. By the action of hydrogen peroxide on an alkaline solution of this compound at 80°, 2-phenazinol (2-hydro-xyphenazine) (**XXIII**) is obtained. 5-Methylphenazinium hydroxide,

(XX) $\longrightarrow$

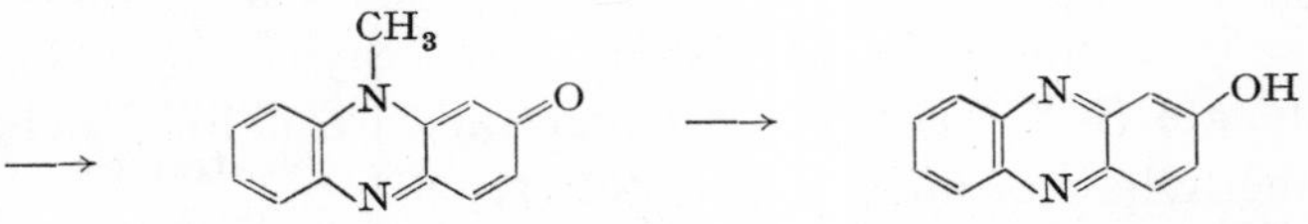

(XXII)   (XXIII)

presumably the intermediate product of the reaction between the methylphenazinium salts and alkali, is unstable even in the absence of air; in aqueous solution, a precipitate of phenazine and 5-methyl-5,10-dihydrophenazine is formed and formaldehyde is also produced:[28,50]

$$2 C_{13}H_{11}N_2OH \rightarrow C_{12}H_8N_2 + C_{13}H_{12}N_2 + CH_2O + H_2O$$

Under the influence of visible light, oxidation of the 5-methyl-phenazinium salts occurs more rapidly and produces mainly 5-methyl-1(5)-phenazinone (1-keto-5-methyl-1,5-dihydrophenazine or pyo-cyanine) (**XXIV**) (45%) and phenazine (47%), together with small amounts of 1-phenazinol and 10-methyl-2(10)-phenazinone.[50] (See also Chapter X:1,D.)

(XX) $\longrightarrow$

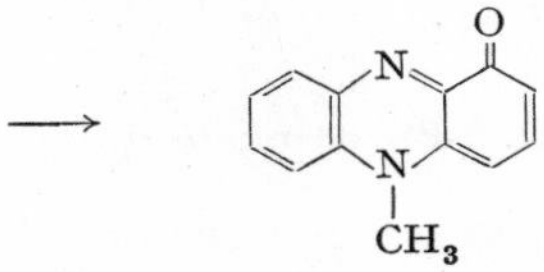

(XXIV)

The reaction between 5-methylphenazinium methyl sulfate and sodium cyanide in concentrated aqueous solution gives a 60% yield of 10-methyl-5,10-dihydrophenazine-2-carbonitrile (XXV) (the relative positions of the substituents in this compound have not been proved); but this is demethylated on heating, with the production of phenazine-2-carbonitrile (XXVI).[50] (See also Chapter III:2,C.)

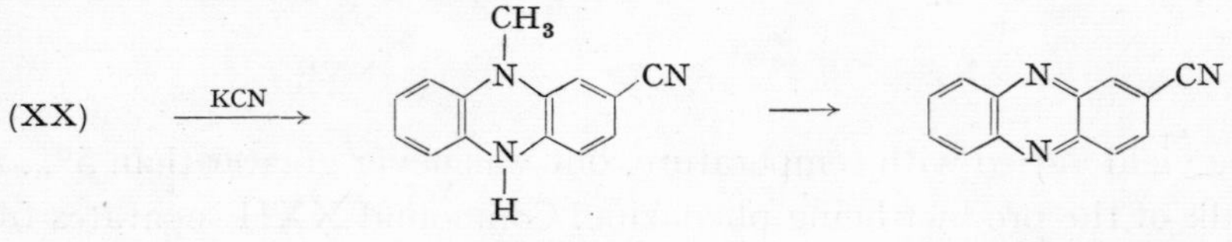

(XX) $\xrightarrow{\text{KCN}}$ (XXV)   (XXVI)

The reaction of 5-methylphenazinium methyl sulfate with sodium sulfite produces a mixture of mono- and di-sulfonic acids; the former can be separated by the lesser solubility of its sodium salt in water. This is assumed to be sodium 10-methyl-5,10-dihydrophenazine-2-sulfonate (XXVII) and, on oxidation with iodine, yields an internal *N*-methylphenazinium salt (XXVIII):[50]

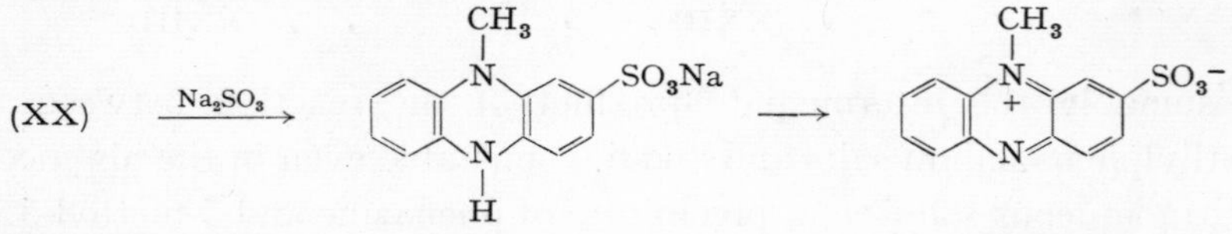

(XX) $\xrightarrow{\text{Na}_2\text{SO}_3}$ (XXVII)   (XXVIII)

C. 5-Ethylphenazinium Ethyl Sulfate

5-Ethylphenazinium ethyl sulfate (phenazine ethosulfate) (XVIII, R = C_2H_5, X = $C_2H_5SO_4$) does not lose its alkyl group with the facility of the 5-methyl compound; and is comparable with the 5-phenyl derivatives in stability and, like those compounds, forms 10-ethyl-2(10)-phenazinone in excellent yield by oxidation in alkaline solution. Photochemical oxidation, on the other hand, yields 5-ethyl-1(5)-phenazinone, without by-products.[50] See also reference 76.

D. 5-Phenylphenazinium Compounds

These are very important as they are closely related to the safranine and induline dyestuffs. The nitrate (XXX, X = NO_3) separates from ethanol as brownish-yellow crystals, m.p. 192°, readily soluble in water and ethanol with an orange-yellow color.[52] The ferric chloride double salt separates from acetic acid as reddish-brown needles, m.p. 186°, almost insoluble in saturated ferric chloride solution and in 20% hydrochloric acid and is used for isolation.[52] The chloride dissolves in concentrated sulfuric acid with a yellowish-red color.[53] The absorption spectrum has been measured in sulfuric acid solution.[10]

These compounds were first prepared by Kehrmann[53] by deamination of aposafranine (XXIX) *via* the diazo reaction. They are usually encountered in the form of salts. The corresponding phenazinium bases possess strongly basic properties (for example, they form carbonates[54]), but are unstable and are not generally obtainable in analytically pure form. Thus, on treating 5-phenylphenazinium chloride with sodium hydroxide, the free base is not obtained, the product being aposafranone (10-phenyl-2(10)-phenazinone) (XXXI). The action of ammonia in the

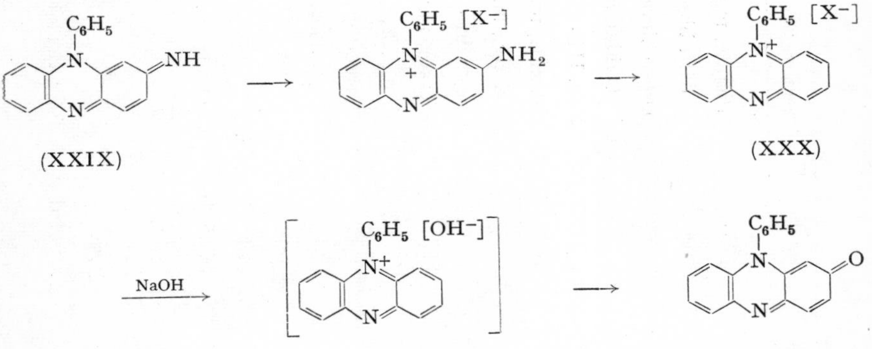

presence of air on the 5-phenylphenazinium salts likewise leads to the introduction of an amino group, with the re-formation of aposafranine, a reaction which recalls that between aniline and quinones, which leads to the simultaneous formation of anilinoquinones and hydroquinones, the latter being readily oxidizable. If the aposafranine is then acetylated and again treated with ammonia, a second amino group is introduced, yielding acetylphenosafranine (XXXII). Primary and secondary amines behave similarly;[53] [55] and hydroxylamine likewise

TABLE I. Phenazine and Its Homologs

Name of compound	M.p. (°C.)	Salts, derivatives, remarks	Ref.
Phenazine	175–6 (corr.)	Picrate, m.p. 181°. Monohydrochloride, dark blue-green needles Diperchlorate, deep red with bluish glance. Oxides, v. II:1,E and F. Hydro-derivs., v. III	v. II:1
1-Methylphenazine	108	5-Oxide, m.p. 142° 1,2,3,4-Tetrahydro-deriv., m.p. 37° 5,10-Diacetyl-5,10-dihydro-, m.p. 189°	11, 23 (a), 59–61, 75
2-Methylphenazine	117	Picrate, m.p. 168° 5,6,7,8-Tetrahydro-deriv., m.p. 81° 5,10-Dihydro-, m.p. 307°, mono-acetate, m.p. 222°, diacetate, m.p. 134°. 5,10-Dioxide, m.p. 165–166°	11, 27, 62–66, 75
1,6-Dimethylphenazine	160		67
2,3-Dimethylphenazine	173		68
2,7-Dimethylphenazine	162.5–163	5-Oxide, m.p. 204–205°	67, 69
2,8-Dimethylphenazine	155		70–72
1,2,3,4-Tetramethylphenazine	217		73
1,2,3,4,6,7,8,9-Octamethylphenazine	279		73
3-tert-Octylphenazine	150–151	Bactericidal properties	74

introduces the –NHOH group,[56] the product being of the betaine type, and alloted *The Ring Index* Number 2593.

$$(XXX) \xrightarrow[O]{NH_3} (XXIX) \rightarrow \qquad \rightarrow \qquad (XXXII)$$

The reduction of these compounds has been investigated.[56] (See Chapter III:1,E) For homologs, see references 57 and 58.

Although the phenazinium salts are colored, they become useful dyestuffs only on the introduction of amino groups into the molecule.

3. Homologs of Phenazine

The more important known homologs of phenazine are listed in Table I. In general, these form yellow needles and their behavior towards sulfuric acid is similar to that of the parent compound.

References

1. A. Claus, *Ann.*, **168**, 1 (1873).
2. T. Zerevitinov and I. Ostromislenski, *Ber.*, **44**, 2402 (1911).
3. A. Albert, R. Goldacre and J. Phillips, *J. Chem. Soc.*, **1948**, 2240.
4. H. C. Waterman and D. L. Vivian, *J. Org. Chem.*, **14**, 289 (1949).
5. A. Albert and J. B. Willis, *Nature*, **157**, 341 (1946).
6. R. G. Wood and G. Williams, *Phil. Mag.*, (7), **31**, 115 (1941).
7. E. Bergmann, L. Engel and H. Meyer, *Ber.*, **65B**, 446 (1932).
8. I. G. M. Campbell, C. G. Le Fèvre, R. J. W. Le Fèvre and E. E. Turner, *J. Chem. Soc.*, **1938**, 404.
9. A. Hantzsch, *Ber.*, **49**, 511 (1916).
10 (a). F. Kehrmann, E. Havas and E. Grandmougin, *Ber.*, **47**, 1881 (1914).
10 (b). D. Rădulescu and G. Ostrogovich, *Ber.*, **64B**, 2233 (1931).
10 (c). S. Dutt, *J. Chem. Soc.*, **1926**, 1171.
11. L. Birkofer, *Chem. Ber.*, **85**, 1023 (1952).
12. G. M. Badger, J. H. Seidler and B. Thomson, *J. Chem. Soc.*, **1951**, 3207.
13. F. Reitzenstein and F. Andre, *J. prakt. Chem.*, (2), **87**, 97 (1913).
14. F. Kehrmann and M. Sandoz, *Helv. Chim. Acta*, **1**, 270 (1918).
15. E. J. Bowen, E. Mikiewicz and F. W. Smith, *Proc. Phys. Soc. (London)*, **62A**, 26 (1949).
16. B. B. Ray, H. Bose and K. Das Gupta, *Science and Culture*, **5**, 568 (1940); through *Chem. Abstracts*, **34**, 5757 (1940).
17. F. H. Herbstein and G. M. J. Schmidt, *Nature*, **169**, 323 (1952); *Bull. Research Council Israel*, **1**, 123 (1951); *Chem. Abstracts*, **46**, 2871 (1952).

18. J. B. Willis, *Trans. Faraday Soc.*, **43**, 97 (1947).
19. Schichuzki, *Ber.*, **7**, 1454 (1874).
20. A. Bernthsen, *Ber.*, **19**, 3256 (1886).
21. O. W. Brown and W. C. Frishe, *J. Phys. & Colloid Chem.*, **51**, 1394 (1947).
22 (a). P. S. Pischimuka, *J. Gen. Chem. U.S.S.R.*, **10**, 305 (1940); through *Chem. Abstracts*, **34**, 7915 (1940).
22 (b). P. S. Pishchimuka, *Zhur. Obshcheĭ Khim.* (*J. Gen. Chem.*), **21**, 1689 (1951).
23 (a). Z. V. Pushkareva and G. I. Agibalova, *J. Gen. Chem. U.S.S.R.*, **8**, 151 (1938); through *Chem. Abstracts*, **32**, 5404 (1938) and *Chem. Zentr.*, **1939**, I, 4327.
23 (b). C. M. Murphy, H. Ravner and N. L. Smith, *Ind. Eng. Chem.*, **42**, 2478 (1950).
23 (c). G. A. Schröter, *Kunststoffe*, **41**, 291 (1951); through *Chem. Abstracts*, **45**, 10650 (1951).
24. M. Tichvinski and L. Volochovich, *J. Russ. Phys. Chem. Soc.*, **37**, 8 (1905); through *Chem. Zentr.*, **1905**, I, 1263.
25. N. Shcherbina, *J. Russ. Phys. Chem. Soc.*, **38**, 613 (1906); through *Chem. Zentr.*, **1906**, II, 1621.
26. O. Hinsberg, *Ber.*, **38**, 2800 (1905).
27. O. Hinsberg and H. Garfunkel, *Ann.*, **292**, 258 (1896).
28. F. Kehrmann and E. Havas, *Ber.*, **46**, 341 (1913).
29. Z. V. Pushkareva and I. Y. Postovskiĭ, *J. Gen. Chem. U.S.S.R.*, **8**, 158 (1938); through *Chem. Abstracts*, **32**, 5405 (1938) and *Chem. Zentr.*, **1939**, I, 4328.
30. J. S. Morley, *J. Chem. Soc.*, **1952**, 4008.
31 (a). A. Pullman, *Rev. Sci.*, **86**, 219 (1948); *Chem. Abstracts*, **43**, 2095 (1949).
31 (b). H. H. Jaffé, *J. Chem. Phys.*, **20**, 1554 (1952).
32. E. Bamberger and E. Wheelwright, *Ber.*, **25**, 3201 (1892).
33. K. A. Hofmann, A. Metzler and K. Höbold, *Ber.*, **43**, 1080 (1910).
34. A. Claus, *Ber.*, **8**, 600 (1875).
35. S. G. Sastry, *J. Chem. Soc.*, **109**, 270 (1916).
36. A. Chrétien and P. Laurent, *Compt. rend.*, **195**, 792 (1932).
37. P. Laurent, *Ann. chim.*, (11), **10**, 397 (1938).
38. I. J. Pachter and M. C. Kloetzel, *J. Am. Chem. Soc.*, **74**, 971 (1952).
39. A. Wohl and W. Aue, *Ber.*, **34**, 2442 (1901).
40. A. Wohl, *Ber.*, **36**, 4139 (1903).
41. G. R. Clemo and H. McIlwain, *J. Chem. Soc.*, **1938**, 479.
42. H. McIlwain, *J. Chem. Soc.*, **1943**, 322.
43. G. R. Clemo and A. F. Daglish, *J. Chem. Soc.*, **1950**, 1481.
44. K. Yamada and N. Hasebe, *J. Soc. Chem. Ind., Japan*, **40**, Suppl. binding 218 (1937); through *Chem. Abstracts*, **31**, 6663 (1937).
45. K. Yamada and N. Hasebe, *J. Soc. Chem. Ind., Japan*, **41**, Suppl. binding 160 (1938); through *Chem. Abstracts*, **32**, 7042 (1938).
46. K. Yamada and N. Hasebe, *J. Soc. Chem. Ind., Japan*, **41**, Suppl. binding 290-B (1938); through *Chem. Abstracts*, **33**, 1740 (1939).
47. H. Hillemann, *Ber.*, **71B**, 34 (1938).
48. F. Kehrmann and E. Havas, *Ber.*, **46**, 2820 (1913).
49. O. Fischer and E. Franck, *Ber.*, **26**, 179 (1893).
50. H. McIlwain, *J. Chem. Soc.*, **1937**, 1704.
51. F. Kehrmann and F. Cherpillod, *Helv. Chim. Acta*, **7**, 973 (1924).
52. F. Kehrmann and W. Shaposhnikov, *Ber.*, **29**, 2967 (1896).
53. F. Kehrmann, *Ber.*, **29**, 2316 (1896).
54. W. Shaposhnikov, *J. Russ. Phys. Chem. Soc.*, **29**, 535 (1897); through *Chem. Zentr.*, **1898**, I, 722.

55. F. Kehrmann and W. Shaposhnikov, *Ber.*, **30**, 2620 (1897).
56. F. Kehrmann (with H. Becker and A. Capatina), *Ann.*, **322**, 67 (1902).
57. F. Kehrmann and A. Wetter, *Ber.*, **31**, 966 (1898).
58. N. Orlov, *J. Russ. Phys. Chem. Soc.*, **42**, 939 (1910); through *Chem. Zentr.*, **1910**, II, 1761.
59. H. McCombie, H. A. Scarborough and W. A. Waters, *J. Chem. Soc.*, **1928**, 353.
60. G. R. Clemo and H. McIlwain, *J. Chem. Soc.*, **1934**, 1991.
61. C. Mermod, *Helv. Chim. Acta*, **18**, 362 (1935).
62. V. Merz, *Ber.*, **19**, 725 (1886).
63. A. Bernthsen and H. Schweitzer, *Ann.*, **236**, 332 (1886).
64. O. Fischer, *Ber.*, **29**, 1873 (1896).
65. F. Kehrmann and C. Mermod, *Helv. Chim. Acta*, **10**, 62 (1927).
66. F. E. King, N. G. Clark and P. M. H. Davis, *J. Chem. Soc.*, **1949**, 3012.
67. B. K. Malaviya and S. Dutt, *Proc. Acad. Sci. United Provinces Agra Oudh, India*, **4**, 319 (1935); through *Chem. Abstracts*, **30**, 1056 (1936).
68. E. Diepolder, *Ber.*, **42**, 2916 (1909).
69. E. Bamberger and W. Ham, *Ann.*, **382**, 82 (1911).
70. O. Fischer, *Ber.*, **27**, 2773 (1894).
71. F. Krollpfeiffer (with G. Wolf and H. Walbrecht), *Ber.*, **67B,** 908 (1934).
72. M. L. Tomlinson, *J. Chem. Soc.*, **1939**, 158.
73. L. I. Smith and L. R. Hac, *J. Am. Chem. Soc.*, **56**, 477 (1934).
74. U. S. Pat. 2,483,838; *Chem. Abstracts*, **44**, 2035 (1950).
75. S. Maffei, S. Pietra and A. M. Rivolta, *Ann. chim. (Rome)*, **42**, 519 (1952).
76. S. B. Serebryanyĭ, *Zhur. Obshchei Khim.*, **22**, 2203 (1952); through *Chem. Abstracts*, **48**, 680 (1954).

CHAPTER III

Hydrogenated Derivatives
of Phenazine

1. Dihydrophenazines

A. 5,10-Dihydrophenazine

This compound (I) separates from acetone solution by dilution with light petroleum as colorless leaflets that are almost insoluble in water and benzene and slightly soluble in cold ethanol.[1] It may be

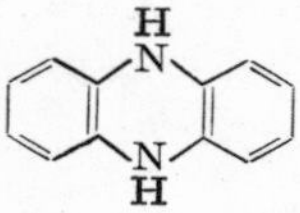

(I)

sublimed in a vacuum or recrystallized in the absence of air; but it is partly oxidized to phenazine by usual manipulation in air.[2] Its melting point has been given as 210–212° (dec.), by many authors,[3-5] although this appears to be due to oxidation to phenazhydrin; the true melting point of dihydrophenazine in sealed tubes filled with nitrogen is 317°,[6] or in evacuated tubes, 280° (dec.).[2] According to Claus,[1] it dissolves in concentrated sulfuric acid to give a red solution, which becomes green on dilution; but according to Kehrmann and Havas[7] the solution in sulfuric acid is intensely yellow and on dilution yields a colorless precipitate of the dihydrophenazine.

It is obtained by passing hydrogen sulfide into a solution of phenazine in alcoholic ammonia,[1] by reduction of phenazine with sodium dithionite in alcoholic sodium hydroxide solution[8] or by reduction with lithium aluminum hydride[6,9] or with hydrogen in the presence of palladium[6]; and can be reoxidized very readily to phenazine

by, for example, ammoniacal silver oxide solution.[10] See also Chapters
I:1 and III:2,D.

The mono- and di-acetyl derivatives have already been mentioned
(Chapter II:1,C). Other derivatives are also known.[2] For a discussion
of the deeply colored products at a stage of oxidation intermediate
between those in phenazine and dihydrophenazine, see Chapter III:2.

B. 5,10-Dihydro-5-methylphenazine

This compound (II) separates from a mixture of benzene and light
petroleum as white needles, m.p. 164° (in the absence of oxygen). It is
easily oxidized and, in the presence of air, its melting point is approximately 130° (dec.). It is soluble in ethanol, benzene, ether and chloroform, but insoluble in water. It can be obtained from 5-methylphen-
azinium salts by reduction with zinc dust and hydrochloric acid.[2, 11]

(II)

C. 5-Ethyl-5,10-dihydrophenazine

This dihydrophenazine forms colorless prisms, m.p. 99° (in
nitrogen).[12]

D. 5,10-Dihydro-5,10-dimethylphenazine

This compound (IV) separates from benzene, ethanol or propanol
as colorless prisms, m.p. 153°, and has a dipole moment of 0.4 D, which
suggests a folded structure such as (III).[13]

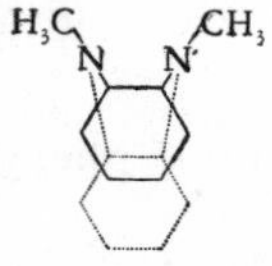

(III)

It has been prepared in the following ways:

(1) By the action of methylmagnesium iodide on 5-methyl-

phenazinium iodide[14] or methylsulfate[12,13] (the chloride gives only a low yield) in an atmosphere of nitrogen.

(2) By treatment of 5,10-dihydro-5-methylphenazine with ethyl lithium in benzene solution for 15 hours at 65°, followed by shaking with methyl iodide for two days:[14]

(3) When a solution of phenazine in ethylene glycol dimethyl ether is shaken with sodium for 35 hours in a sealed tube, it becomes brick-red and a brick-red precipitate of the disodium derivative of 5,10-dihydrophenazine separates (see also reference 15). By treatment of the resulting mixture with methyl iodide, IV is obtained in 60% yield, with the recovery of 17% of unchanged phenazine.[16]

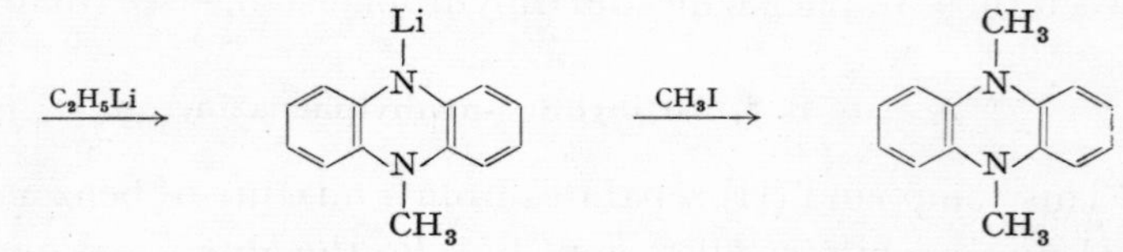

(4) By condensation of 1,2-cyclohexanedione with N,N'-dimethyl-o-phenylenediamine, with or without isolation of the intermediate 2,3,5,10-tetrahydro-5,10-dimethylphenazine (V), which readily loses two hydrogen atoms to yield (IV).[17] See also Chapter III:3E.

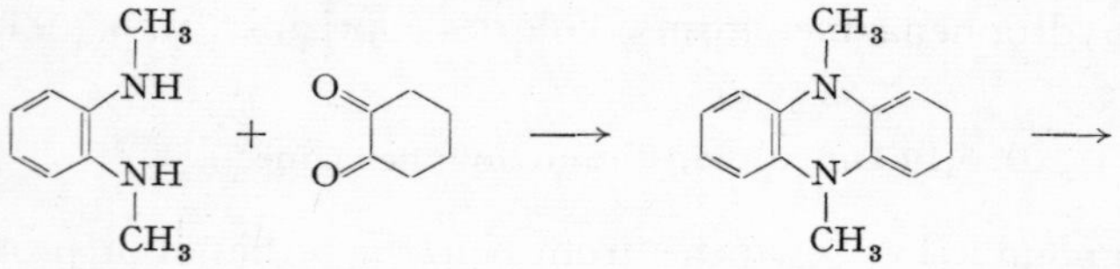

Attempts to effect a similar condensation between pyrocatechol and N,N'-dimethyl-o-phenylenediamine were unsuccessful.[14]

E. 5,10-Dihydro-5-phenylphenazine

This compound (VI) forms greyish-yellow leaflets, m.p. 143° (in an atmosphere of carbon dioxide), and is unstable in dilute acids. It is obtained from the ferric chloride double salt of 5-phenylphenazinium chloride by reduction with stannous chloride and hydrochloric acid:[18]

(VI)

F. 5,10-Diaryl-5,10-dihydrophenazines (Perazines)

In 1908, Wieland[19] prepared the first compound of this class and named the simplest member, that is 5,10-dihydro-5,10-diphenyl-phenazine, "perazine" (VIII). Tetra-arylhydrazines undergo fission in the presence of acidic reagents:

$$R_2N.NR_2 + H X \rightarrow R_2NH + R_2NX$$

When X is halogen, the compound R_2NX is unstable and, if R is a p-substituted phenyl group, two molecules will unite to give a perazine, although the dehydrogenating properties of R_2NX lead also to substitution of halogen:

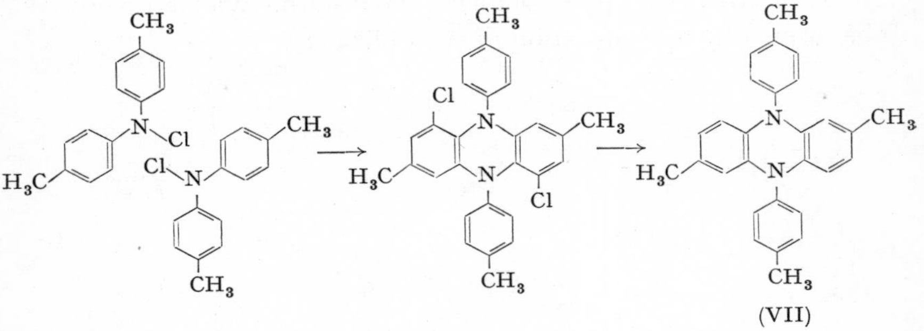

(VII)

Thus, when tetra-p-tolylhydrazine in chloroform solution is treated with a solution of hydrogen chloride in ether, and benzene is added to the mixture, green needles of a dihydrochloride separate. Decomposition of the latter with alkali gives a product Wieland formulated as 1,6-dichloro-5,10-dihydro-3,8-dimethyl-5,10-di-p-tolylphenazine, which sublimes without decomposition and which separates from xylene as lustrous, garnet-red prisms, decomposing at temperatures above 360°. Treatment of this compound in xylene with a solution of sodium in amyl alcohol affords 5,10-dihydro-2,7-dimethyl-5,10-di-p-tolylphenazine (VII), which separates from a mixture of benzene and ethanol as lustrous, orange-yellow needles, m.p. 274ᶜ, readily soluble in benzene with a weak fluorescence, difficultly soluble in acetic acid and ether, and almost insoluble in ethanol and light petroleum.

Wieland[20] also showed that tetraphenylhydrazine is partially dissociated when boiled in toluene solution; the resulting $(C_6H_5)_2N$ radical is unstable and undergoes further transformations. The solution develops a green color; but this rapidly changes to brown. If, after the solution has been boiled for 30 minutes (the same result can be achieved by keeping the mixture for several months at room temperature), the toluene is removed under reduced pressure, and the residue is treated with ether, a crystalline product (Z) separates, and the remaining solution contains diphenylamine and 2-anilinotriphenylamine (IX). The action of bromine on the latter gives rise to a salt which, when reduced with zinc dust and acetic acid, also yields Z. The latter separates from a mixture of benzene and ethanol as colorless needles, m.p. 172–175°, almost insoluble in ethanol and acetic acid, sparingly soluble in cold benzene or ether, but more soluble in chloroform. Wieland believed Z to be formed by a dismutation of the radicals:

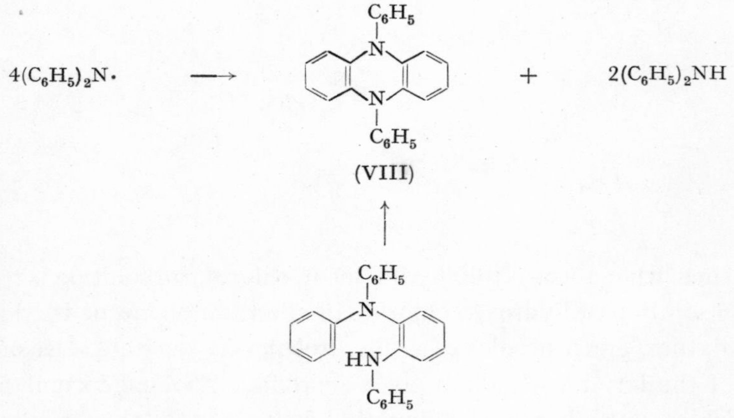

$$4(C_6H_5)_2N\cdot \longrightarrow \qquad + \qquad 2(C_6H_5)_2NH$$

(VIII)

(IX)

and to be 5,10-dihydro-5,10-diphenylphenazine (VIII), that is, perazine itself (or "phenoperazine"), although the molecular weight found in benzene solution was 919, instead of 334, corresponding to the formula

$C_{24}H_{18}N_2$. The latter anomaly was ascribed to association. This formulation was criticized by Kehrmann and Micewicz[21] as Z in concentrated sulfuric acid in the presence of an oxidizing agent gives a blue color, while VII gives an orange-red color. Wieland,[22] however, suggested that the blue color was due to oxidation at the free p-position of the phenyl groups of Z. In this connection, it should be mentioned that, in an earlier paper, the same author[23] had already described the production of a blue color from a compound he formulated as 5,10-dihydro-5,10-di-p-tolylphenazine (X). But as no structural proof was given for the latter compound, which was obtained from 1,2-diphenyl-1,2-di-p-tolylhydrazine, it might well be the isomeric 5,10-dihydro-2,7-dimethyl-5,10-diphenylphenazine (XI):

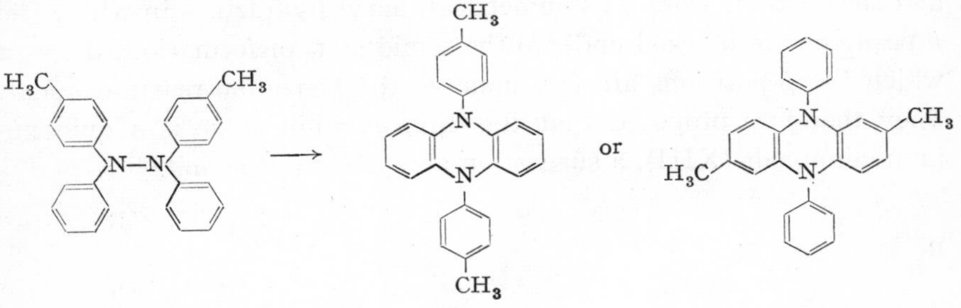

(X)   (XI)

Compound Z is also obtained by the action of the 2-(2',4',6'-trinitrophenyl)-1,1-diphenylhydrazyl radical on tetraphenylhydrazine in boiling toluene,[24] and by the action of heat on N-nitrosodiphenylamine (prepared by treating a toluene solution of tetraphenylhydrazine with nitric oxide).[20,25] In spite of the above-mentioned anomalies, it seems likely that Z does, in fact, possess the structure (VIII) assigned to it by Wieland, although further investigation on these compounds is still required.

Perazines are also formed by the oxidation of diphenylamine derivatives with potassium permanganate in acetone[19,26] or with lead dioxide and by the action of hydrogen chloride on diphenylhydroxylamine derivatives in ethereal solution,[27,28] as follows:

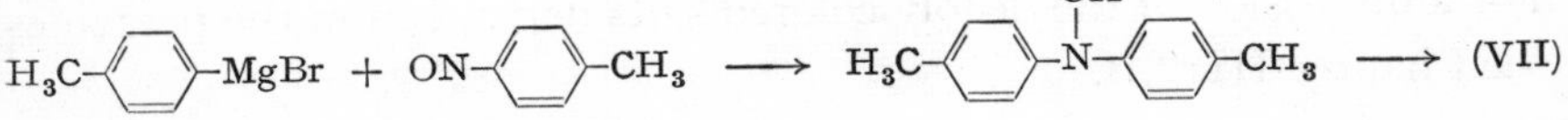

Wieland[20] suggested that the blue compound obtained by treating diphenylamine with concentrated sulfuric acid and an oxidizing agent is an *o*-quinonoid derivative of perazine (XII) formed as follows:

$$(C_6H_5)_2NH \xrightarrow{\ O\ } (C_6H_5)_2N-N(C_6H_5)_2 \xrightarrow{\ H_2O\ } (C_6H_5)_2NH + (C_6H_5)_2NOH \rightarrow (VIII)$$

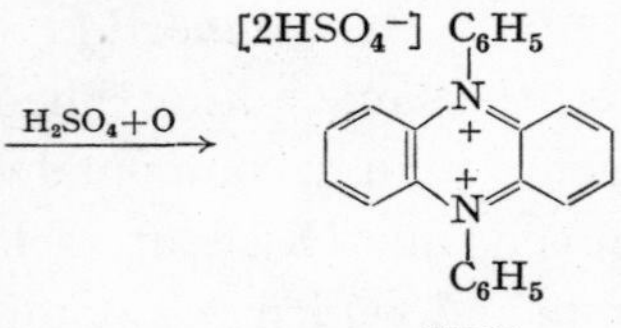

(XII)

However, Kehrmann and Micewicz[21] pointed out that Jacobson had shown that, whereas symmetrical diaryl hydrazines in which the *p*-positions are blocked undergo the semidine transformation, those in which the *p*-positions are free undergo the benzidine rearrangement. They therefore proposed that the diphenylamine blue is a quinone-immonium salt (XIII), a suggestion accepted by Wieland.[22]

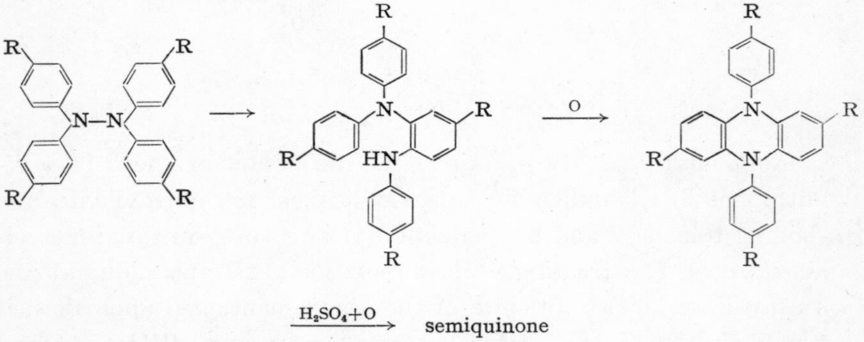

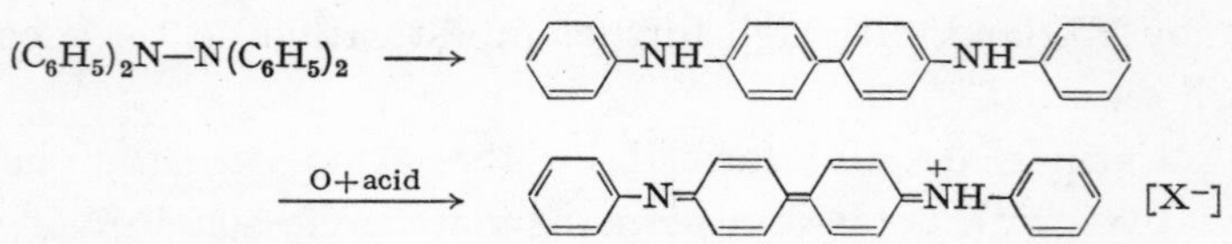

(XIII)

The more important known perazines are listed in Table II. For a discussion of the deeply colored salts derived from the perazines, see Chapter III:2,B.

TABLE II. 5,10-Diaryl-5,10-dihydrophenazines

Substituents in 5,10-dihydrophenazine	Appearance	M.p. (°C.)	Salts produced under oxidizing conditions	Ref.
5,10-Diphenyl-	Colorless needles	172–175	Green hydrochloride. Green salt with Br$_2$	20, 23
5,10-Di-p-tolyl-		> 315 (darkens 267)		23
5,10-Bis(p-nitrophenyl)-	Red brown	183 (sinters 154)		23
2,7-Dimethyl-5,10-di-p-tolyl-	Orange-yellow needles	274	Green	19, 21, 27, 28
5,10-Dianisyl-2,7-dimethoxy-	Light yellow needles	292	Hydrochloride, green needles, giving red-violet solutions	19, 23, 26, 29
5,10-Bis(p-chlorophenyl)-2,7-dimethoxy-	Yellow needles	281 (dec.) (darkens 244)	Violet	29
5,10-Bis(4-biphenylyl)-2,7-diphenyl-	Yellow needles	> 345	Blue solution in conc. H$_2$SO$_4$	30, 31
1,6-Dichloro-3,8-dimethyl-5,10-di-p-tolyl-	Garnet-red prisms	> 360 (dec.)	Dark green. Violet-red product with Br$_2$	19
5,10-Bis(4-biphenylyl)-1,6-dichloro-3,8-diphenyl-	Yellow needles	> 380	Violet	31
2,7-Dimethoxy-5,10-diphenyl-	Yellow			29

2. The Phenazhydrins,
Phenazyls and Semiquinones

A. Historical

Claus,[1] in 1873, found that the salts of the colorless 5,10-dihydro-phenazine on being heated tend to split off hydrogen and suggested that the resulting deeply colored products were salts derived from a structure such as XIV. The same author found that the addition of

$$
\underset{(XIV)}{\overset{\displaystyle \text{NH}\underset{\diagdown C_6H_4 \diagup}{\overset{\diagup C_6H_4 \diagdown}{}} \text{N—N} \overset{\diagup C_6H_4 \diagdown}{\underset{\diagdown C_6H_4 \diagup}{}} \text{NH}}{}}
$$

bromine to an alcoholic solution of dihydrophenazine produced an immediate deep blue color (due, he suggested, to the dihydrobromide of XIV); but on the continued addition of bromine, the solution turned yellow, due to the further oxidation to phenazine hydrobromide. Similar deeply colored products are also obtained by reduction of phenazine in acid solution. Kehrmann,[32] in 1905, found that 5,10-dihydro-5-phenylphenazine could be oxidized by air in the presence of acids to give an intensely green compound that crystallized from ethanol. When this was boiled with water, it was decomposed to 5,10-dihydro-5-phenylphenazine and a phenazinium compound. Also Hantzsch[11] showed the formation of a green salt by the action of bromine (1 mole) on 5,10-dihydro-5-methylphenazine.

Kehrmann and Danecki,[33, 34] in 1914, by reduction of 5-methyl-phenazinium methylsulfate with stannous chloride in hydrochloric acid, followed by addition of potassium iodide to the reaction mixture, obtained a dark green crystalline product, which they formulated as $C_{13}H_{11}N_2I.C_{13}H_{13}N_2I.H_2O$. This could be recrystallized quickly from ethanol, but on long standing in ethanol in the presence of air it was oxidized to the normal methiodide $C_{13}H_{11}N_2I$, which forms reddish-brown prisms, giving yellow solutions. Hantzsch[11] showed that reduction of the 5-methylphenazinium salts with zinc and hydrochloric acid in the absence of oxygen gave the colorless 5,10-dihydro-5-methyl-phenazine; but in the presence of air this was oxidized to the above-mentioned green salts. Attempts to isolate the free base corresponding to these salts led to decomposition with the formation of 5,10-dihydro-5-methylphenazine and (probably) a 5-methylphenazinium salt. Hantzsch also observed the formation of the green salts by simply treating 5-methylphenazinium chloride with alcoholic hydrogen chloride.

In these and various other deeply colored products it is now clear that we have either a state of oxidation intermediate between the phenazine and the dihydrophenazine, or an addition compound of the two. This quinhydrone-like nature of these compounds was not, however, accepted at first by Hantzsch,[35,36] who preferred to attribute the experimental results to chromo-isomerism. But after a polemical controversy with Kehrmann (for a summary of which see Kehrmann[37]), Hantzsch,[11] in 1916, suggested a free radical structure (the semiquinone) in view of the presence of two absorption bands in the ultraviolet, a phenomenon which is observed neither in the fully reduced nor in the fully oxidized form, and is absent also in compounds of a doubtless bimolecular, meriquinonoid structure. He failed, however, to find any representative of this group suitable for a determination of the molecular weight by the methods then available.

B. Semiquinones of the Phenazine Series

There are numerous aromatic or heterocyclic compounds on an oxidation level intermediate between a quinone and a hydroquinone, or between a diimine and a diamine, or between a phenazine and a dihydrophenazine, etc. In each case, we have the alternative possibilities of either a free radical structure (a semiquinone), or a molecular compound of the two forms (a meriquinone*). Theoretically the difference can easily be detected by molecular weight measurements; but, in actual practice, such measurements can be very unreliable because of association or for other reasons (for example, in freezing point determinations, the solubility of the solute may be exceeded). Thus it was not until the potentiometric studies of Michaelis and his collaborators and of Elema had been carried out that the free radical

* There is some confusion in the literature in the use of the term "meriquinone", but we are, in this volume, using the terminology indicated above (see Weitz [108]).

nature of such compounds was clearly demonstrated. Later, in certain cases, magnetic measurements have provided additional proof, the semiquinones being paramagnetic and the meriquinones diamagnetic in the solid state (although they may be paramagnetic in solution due to dissociation).

The solubility of phenazine itself in water is too low for a complete potentiometric study in aqueous buffer solutions. It gives most satisfactory results in 50% acetic acid solution.[38, 39] The initially colorless solution is reduced by hydrogen in the presence of colloidal palladium and, after passing through an intensely green phase, it finally becomes colorless again on reaching the dihydro state. It is then titrated with p-quinone, dissolved in the same solvent. The curve shows two distinctly separated steps which agree perfectly in shape with two one-electron titration curves, the normal potentials amounting to —0.086 and +0.254 volts in this solvent, which has an (apparent) pH of 1.26. Thus it is clear that the intermediate compound (the semiquinone) is a radical with an odd number of electrons and of the same molecular size as the fully oxidized or the fully reduced forms, and not a bimolecular meriquinone. The above work shows no evidence that the radicals might undergo a partial dimerization in the way that triphenylmethyl partly associates to hexaphenylethane. The explanation of this is found in the fact that the semiquinone is not only a radical, but also a cation, and hence will repel a like radical-cation; and Michaelis and Hill[38] considered that the semiquinone would be incapable of existence (or, at any rate, would have only a very short lifetime) except in acid solution. They represented the stable cation present in the semiquinones by XV, which is intended to mean that the odd electron is shared equally by the two nitrogen atoms; and considered the neutral free radical (XVI) to be unstable. In terms of the resonance theory, in the semiquinone we have a resonance hybrid involving structures

(XV)   (XVI)   (XVII)   (XVIII)

XVII and XVIII, giving increased stability. As a result of polarographic investigations, Kaye and Stonehill[40] have recently confirmed that the phenazine semiquinone is stable only in strongly acid solution.

Several derivatives of phenazine are sufficiently soluble in water to allow a complete set of experiments in aqueous buffer solutions over a wide range of pH. Two examples investigated by Michaelis are pyocyanine,[41-43] and 1-phenazinol (1-hydroxyphenazine).[41] Pyocyanine (XIX) is a blue compound (red in acid solution) that gives rise to a colorless fully reduced form. On being oxidized at pH 11, the color of

(XIX)   (XX)

the latter turns blue directly; but if the pH is below 8 it passes through a green phase (the semiquinone). This means that, in strongly alkaline solution, we have one two-electron step (without the formation of a semiquinone); but in acid solution we have two one-electron steps (with semiquinone formation), and the results of the potentiometric titrations are in agreement with these ideas. Within the physiological pH range 6-8, an appreciable amount of the semiquinone is capable of existence at a suitable oxidation-reduction potential. Similar work has also been carried out by Elema[44]; and a polarographic investigation of pyocyanine has been done by Cattaneo and Sartori.[45] Anomalous results observed in the polarographic curves of pyocyanine, phenosafranine, etc., have been attributed to adsorption phenomena.[46,47]

In the case of 1-phenazinol, the oxidized form is lemon yellow between pH 1 and 11; it turns red at pH 1 and cherry-red at pH > 11. The semiquinonoid form in all those pH ranges where it exists is green. The reduced form is very slightly yellow, almost colorless. A series of titration curves at constant pH was made over a wide range of pH, both by oxidizing the reduced form and by reducing the oxidized form. Polarographic investigations have been carried out by Müller,[48,49] who has also demonstrated the existence of a tautomeric form.[50] 2-Phenazinol has been investigated by Preisler and Hempelmann.[51]

Similar conclusions have been reached with the system chloro-raphine-oxychlororaphine (the latter being XX) by Elema.[52] Here again, in acid solution we have two one-electron steps in the reduction, the intermediate being emerald green; but in the pH range 4–10 a normal two-electron step process occurs, without the production of a green color. Polarographic studies have also been carried out on this system.[53]

Kuhn and Schön[54] have isolated the semiquinone of pyocyanine in the form of the perchlorate and demonstrated that this has para-magnetic properties, thus confirming its radical nature. Also, by measuring the velocity of diffusion in water and in benzene, they showed that pyocyanine in these solvents is monomolecular. For a fuller discussion of pyocyanine and chlororaphine see Chapter X. Paramagnetism has also been shown in the case of the semiquinone (as the chlorostannite) derived from dibenzo[a, c]phenazine.[55(a), (b)]

It is remarkable that, not only in the phenazines proper, but also in the group of quaternary phenazinium compounds (safranines), semi-quinones are not observed except in extremely acid solution in com-pounds containing one or more free amino group in the benzene rings (with one or two rather doubtful or unstable exceptions), despite the fact that many such compounds are soluble in water. Thus, Michaelis and Hill[38] investigated nine assorted compounds of this type and in no case did they find two-step reduction to occur. On the other hand, two-step reduction was observed in the cases of 1-methoxyphenazine and of rosinduline GG (rosindone monosulfonate), in addition to examples already discussed. Similarly, Meyer and Treadwell[55(c)] in their studies of the redox potentials of various dyes at different pH values found no evidence for the production of semiquinones by safranine or neutral red. However, in the case of the safranines and neutral red, the existence of a semiquinone can be demonstrated in strongly acid solution.[56] Thus, if the dye is dissolved in concentrated hydrochloric acid, it gives a blue to green solution; this must be diluted with water until it just becomes blue. The addition of a reducing agent (chromous chloride or zinc dust) then causes a change first to intense green (the semiquinone), then to almost colorless (the leuco dye). On addition of potassium persulfate, these color changes are reversed. Since the color of the oxidized form of the dye in concentrated sulfuric or hydrochloric acid solution is green, the acidity has to be lowered just to such an extent as to make it blue-violet; otherwise, no visible color change occurs on reduction of the dye to the semiquinonoid state.

The semiquinone forms are, in general, green in the phenazine derivatives and red to violet in the benzophenazine compounds. The deeply colored salts obtained by Claus[1] from 5,10-dihydrophenazine are of this nature, as are the various products of Kehrmann,[32-34] and Hantzsch,[11] mentioned above, and the intermediate "quinhydrone" (in fact, not a quinhydrone at all) in the phenazine synthesis of Eckert and Steiner.[57]

Finally, the 5,10-dihydro-5,10-diphenylphenazines (perazines, this chapter:1,F) deserve special mention. Although these compounds are not basic in properties (for example, VII does not form salts with hot aqueous acids[19]), in the presence of air and acids they are rapidly oxidized to yield green salts. Likewise, perazine is converted by bromine into an intensely green product, which (like the above) is reduced by zinc dust and acetic acid back to the original perazine.[20] The action of sodium dichromate and acetic acid on di-p-tolylamine gives rise to the same green hydrochloride as can be obtained by atmospheric oxidation of 5,10-dihydro-2,7-dimethyl-5,10-di-p-tolylphenazine (VII) in the presence of hydrogen chloride in ether.[21] At first, Wieland[19,20] represented the salts obtained with hydrochloric acid in air by the p-quinonoid structure (XXI) and those obtained using bromine as being o-quinonoid (XXII). Later, however, after he had become convinced

(XXI)   (XXII)   (XXIII)

that the formulation of the green hydrochlorides involved oxidation, he formulated these as meriquinones (XXIII). Doubtless, however, these substances are semiquinones and their formation can be represented as follows:

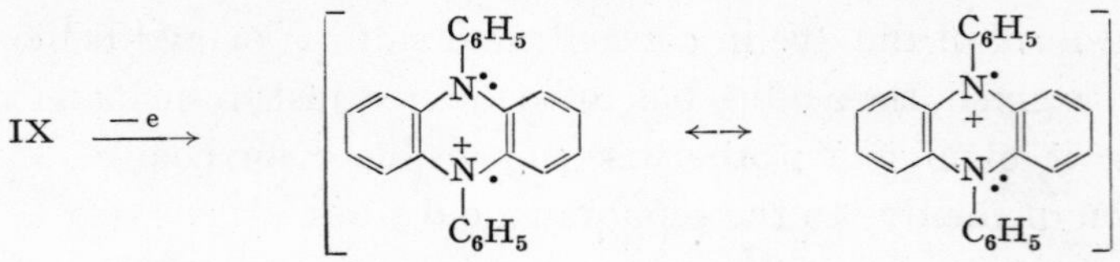

IX $\xrightarrow{-e}$

(XXIV)   (XXV)

The ion-radical (XXIV) would be stabilized by resonance with the (equivalent) structure XXV. Kehrmann and Micewicz[21] claimed that the action of ferric chloride on the green (semiquinonoid) salts caused further oxidation to the holoquinonoid salts (XXII), but this lacks confirmation.

C. The Phenazyls

These are the free radical bases, the salts of which are the semi-quinones, and, as mentioned above, Michaelis regarded these bases as being incapable of stable existence. However, in 1937, McIlwain[12] prepared examples of this class of compounds, although it should be mentioned that a number of compounds prepared by earlier workers (notably Kehrmann and his collaborators) are almost certainly also phenazyls. All well-authenticated phenazyls are of the type XXVI, where R is not a hydrogen atom.

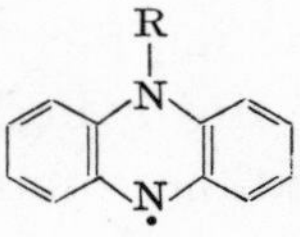

(XXVI)

By the oxidation of 5-ethyl-5,10-dihydrophenazine in ether or benzene solution with lead dioxide in the presence of anhydrous sodium sulfate, McIlwain obtained 10-ethyl-5(10)-phenazyl (XXVI, R $= C_2H_5$), isolated by concentration and cooling of the red, filtered solution, as an intensely red crystalline precipitate, m.p. 102°. Values obtained for the molecular weight and iodine equivalent agreed with the formula $C_{14}H_{13}N_2$. Qualitative evidence for the production of a phenazyl by the oxidation of 5,10-dihydro-5-methylphenazine in non-aqueous solution was also obtained, but it was not possible to isolate the red product in a pure state, owing to its decomposition with the formation of phenazine (compare Hantzsch's attempts to isolate the free base from the green salt obtained by partial reduction of 5-methylphenazinium methyl sulfate—the corresponding semiquinone[11]).

10-Ethyl-5(10)-phenazyl was prepared in the absence of water; certain other phenazyls have, however, been prepared under aqueous conditions. Thus, McIlwain[12] obtained N-methylphenazyl-2-nitrile (XXVII) as a by-product in the preparation of the corresponding dihydrophenazine derivative, by the action of sodium cyanide on 5-methylphenazinium methyl sulfate in concentrated aqueous solution

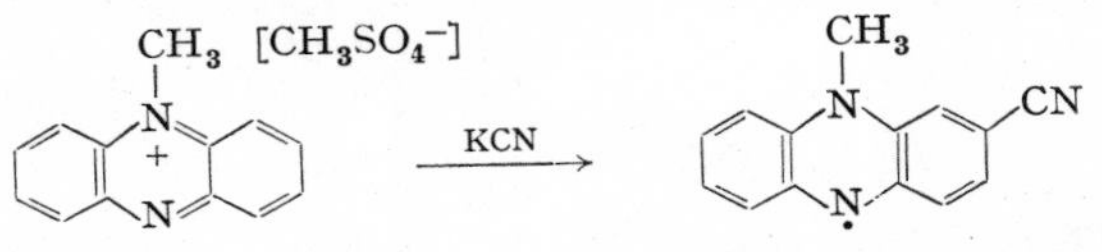

(XXVII)

(in dilute solution, the main product was phenazine). This phenazyl crystallizes from chloroform as deep blue needles, m.p. 145°, gives a blue-green solution in organic solvents and dissolves in dilute mineral acids to give the emerald-green semiquinone. It is converted into the corresponding dihydrophenazine compound on reduction; and the reverse change is brought about by oxidation under a variety of conditions. The dihydro compound requires two equivalents of iodine in oxidation to the holoquinonoid salt; and the blue compound, like the semiquinone, consumes one equivalent of iodine per phenazine nucleus. As the color of this blue nitrile persists in solution, McIlwain determined the molecule size by measurement of the molecular weight ebullioscopically in chloroform and obtained values agreeing with the formula $C_{14}H_{10}N_3$.

The internal semiquinonoid salt (betaine) of N-methylphenazyl-2-sulfonic acid (XXVIII) was prepared by treatment of an acidified solution of sodium N-methyl-5,10-dihydrophenazine-2-sulfonate with

(XXVIII)

potassium persulfate.[12] It is green and its melting point is above 300°. (In XXVII and XXVIII the relative positions of the N-methyl group and CN or SO_3^- groups, respectively, were not proved.)

In 1893, Kehrmann and Messinger[58] condensed picryl chloride with N-methyl-o-phenylenediamine and, after boiling the product (XXIX) with sodium acetate in alcoholic solution, obtained a compound

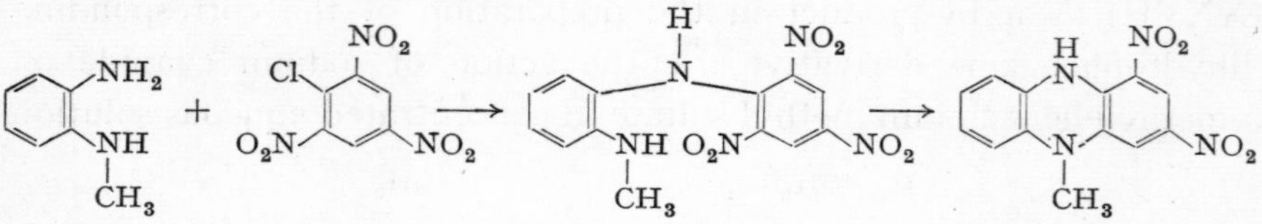

they considered to be 5,10-dihydro-5-methyl-1,3-dinitrophenazine (XXX). They also prepared the corresponding 5-ethyl-, 5-benzyl- and 5-phenyl- compounds. However, whereas true 5,10-dihydrophenazines are usually colorless, these substances form dark violet crystals with a coppery luster, and decompose at temperatures of about 240°. (In the case of the 5-methyl compound, two absorption maxima occur in the visible region at 538 and 581 mμ.[59]) It is therefore highly probable that they are, in fact, phenazyls (XXXI), for even hydrogen bonding between the 1-nitro group and the 10-hydrogen atom could scarcely make the compound violet. Kehrmann and y Punti[60] similarly prepared a compound, separating from nitrobenzene as black-violet

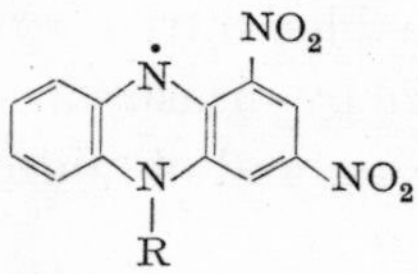

(XXXI)

needles, m.p. 265°, which they formulated as 5,10-dihydro-1,3,8-trinitro-5-phenylphenazine, and which, again, is probably the free phenazyl. Reduction with stannous chloride and hydrochloric acid in acetic acid solution yielded what was thought to be 1,3,8-triamino-5,10-dihydro-5-phenylphenazine, although this was isolated only in the form of a tin double salt. Likewise Kehrmann and Effront[61] prepared the alleged 5-methyl-1-nitro-, 1-nitro-5-phenyl- and 1-amino-3-nitro-5-

phenyl-(5,10-dihydrophenazines), the last mentioned being very unstable; but the properties of the products seem to be in better accord with the phenazyl formulation.

The stability of the phenazyls (as opposed to their salts, the semiquinones) appears to be dependent on the presence of a substituent attached to one of the nitrogen atoms, as in XXXII. In the free

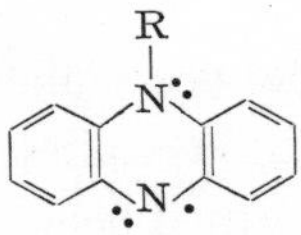

(XXXII) 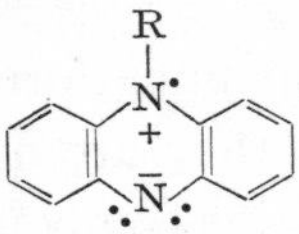   (XXXIII) 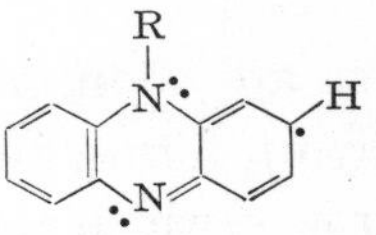   (XXXIV)

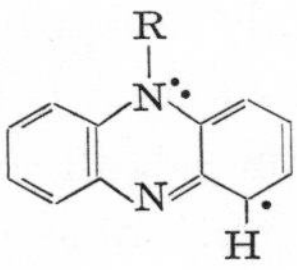

(XXXV) 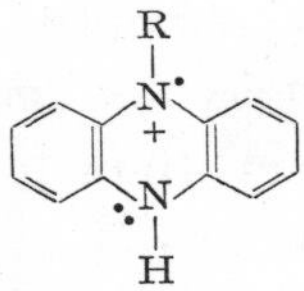   (XXXVI) 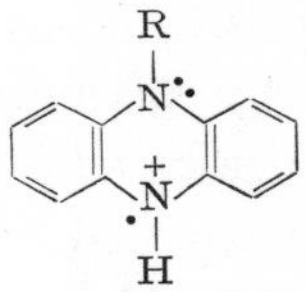   (XXXVII)

phenazyl of this type, the radical might be stabilized by resonance with structure XXXIII and structures such as XXXIV, XXXV, etc. Of these, XXXIII, involving the separation of opposite charges on the two nitrogen atoms, is unlikely to contribute much to the resonance hybrid. However, in acid solution, after a proton has become attached, instead of XXXIII we obtain XXXVI, in which there is no charge separation; this form can therefore contribute considerably to the resonance hybrid, together with XXXVII (which is equivalent to XXXVI when R = H), as well as structures analogous to XXXIV, XXXV, etc. This, together with the effect mentioned in Chapter III:2,B (namely, the electrostatic repulsion between the radical-cations) is presumably the reason why the semiquinones (when R may be H or alkyl, etc.) are most stable in acid solution. In the free phenazyls (when R must not be H), virtually all those known which appear to be stable under aqueous conditions seem to contain either CN or NO_2 groups substituted in one or both of the benzenoid rings (one containing one NO_2 and one NH_2 groups being very unstable[61]). It seems, therefore, not unlikely that the presence of CN and NO_2 groups may stabilize the phenazyl radicals. Comparison with the case of other radicals at present tells one little, for while hexa-*p*-nitrophenylethane and hexa-*p*-biphenylethane are much more highly dissociated than hexaphenylethane, it appears that tetra-*p*-biphenylylhydrazine is somewhat less dissociated than tetraphenylhydrazine and that 1,2-diphenyl-1,2-*p*-nitrophenylhydrazine is not dissociated at all.[62–63]

D. The Phenazhydrins

These are addition compounds formed between phenazines and their dihydro forms, that is, they are meriquinones analogous to the quinhydrones, which are addition compounds formed between quinones and hydroquinones. Clemo and McIlwain,[64] in 1934, found that the phenazhydrins could easily be obtained as highly crystalline purple or blue prisms by mixing equimolecular amounts of their components in concentrated alcoholic solution; thus, phenazine + dihydrophenazine gave a phenazhydrin, $C_{12}H_8N_2.C_{12}H_{10}N_2$, forming blue prisms, m.p. 209° (dec.). Schlenk and Bergmann[15] had obtained what appears to be the same product in 1928, although they described it as blue needles, m.p. 224–226°. They treated an ethereal solution of the potassium ketyl derived from 4-phenylbenzophenone with an excess of phenazine and obtained a brown-violet precipitate, which they formulated as a quinhydrone type of compound, formed from one mole of phenazine and one mole of the dipotassium derivative of dihydrophenazine. The action of water on the product yielded the phenazhydrin. Recently, Morley[2] reported the isolation of the two forms, melting at 209° and 225°, respectively. The former modification has also been obtained by the reduction of phenazine with lithium aluminum hydride.[9]

The possibility of the existence of such compounds had been envisaged much earlier, and, in fact, it had been suggested that the green salts obtained by partial reduction of phenazine, or oxidation of dihydrophenazine, were of this type. However, Hantzsch in 1916 stated, from an optical comparison of the green salts with the quinhydrones, that the two classes of compounds were structurally different, and suggested that the former were free radicals, as discussed in Chapter III.2.A. Thus the true phenazhydrins were not definitely recognized until the work of Schlenk and Bergmann and of Clemo and McIlwain, although, as will be mentioned later, one or two compounds that may possibly be phenazhydrins were already described in the literature.

The true phenazhydrins are, on the whole, similar to the quinhydrones and give pale yellow solutions in light petroleum or ethanol, which indicates dissociation and so prevents the determination of their molecular weights; but they crystallize from these solvents and give analytical results required for the bimolecular complex. Both the 5- and 10-hydrogen atoms appear to be involved in combination; 5,10-dihydro-5-methylphenazine does not form a complex with phenazine,[17] so the hydrogen-bonded structure (XXXVIII) was suggested.[64] If the resonance theory of hydrogen bonding is adopted, then phenazhydrin

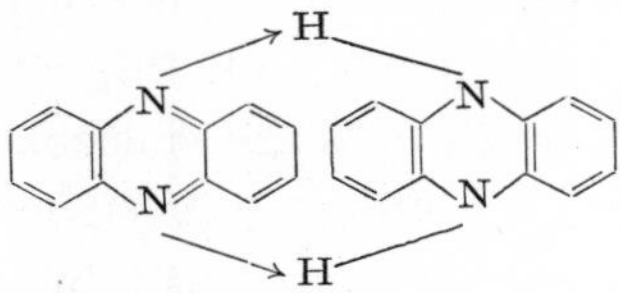

(XXXVIII)

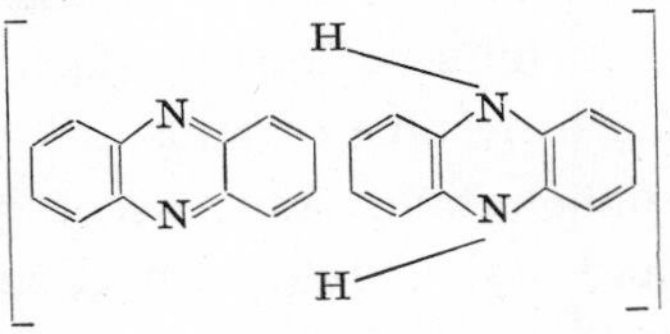

(XXXIX) 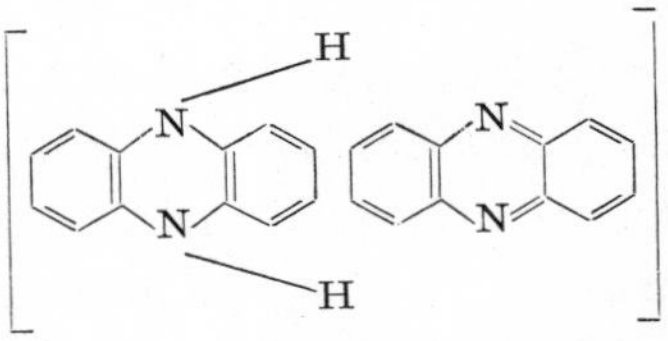   (XL)

can be regarded as a resonance hybrid involving structures **XXXIX** and **XL**. This implies that the two phenazine nuclei are held together in parallel planes, the two hydrogen atoms used to bind them together being midway between and equally attached to the two nuclei; presumably the complex would be further stabilized by overlapping of the π orbitals of the two phenazine nuclei. However, in the case of quinhydrone, it has recently been shown by the use of isotopes that the two hydrogen atoms involved in the analogous hydrogen bonding are not equally bound to the two nuclei.[65, 66] Other recent work on the structure of quinhydrone and other molecular compounds[67–70] is also of interest in this connection; and the exact structure of phenazhydrin must be regarded as not definitely established.

The phenazhydrins formed by (a) phenazine and 5,10-dihydro-1-methylphenazine and (b) 5,10-dihydrophenazine and 1-methylphenazine are identical, and form prisms, m.p. 159°.[64] This indicates the establishment of an oxidation-reduction equilibrium between each phenazine and its dihydro form, with the formation of the most stable complex, and corresponds to the related phenomenon in the quinhydrones (compare Hunter[71]). In the above case, the most stable state is methylphenazine-dihydrophenazine, for it is methylphenazine that is removed from the complex by steam-distillation in the first instance, while phenazine comes over freely only after the addition of an oxidizing agent such as ferric chloride.

According to two recent communications of Dufraisse, Étienne and Toromanoff,[72(a)] phenazine and dihydrophenazine form two different compounds by reaction in the molecular ratios of 1:1 and 3:1, respectively; the former is blue, m.p. 255–256° and the latter violet, m.p. 216–217°. These were also obtained by the action of light on solutions of phenazine in primary or secondary alcohols, the latter being oxidized to aldehydes or ketones. Thus, a solution of phenazine in isopropanol when irradiated for a few minutes deposits dark violet crystals, but these are gradually replaced by blue crystals and finally by colorless crystals of 5,10-dihydrophenazine. Also, according to Toromanoff,[72(b)] 1-methylphenazine and its 5,10-dihydro derivative (m.p. 176–178°) form a compound in the ratio 3:1 (violet-red, m.p. 170–172°). The same author showed that 2-methylphenazine and its 5,10-dihydro derivative (m.p. 295–297°) form compounds in the ratio 3:1 (violet-black, m.p. 163–165°) and 1:1 (blue, m.p. 217–220°).

The exact structure of a compound formulated by the earlier workers[58, 73] as 5,10-dihydro-1,3-dinitrophenazine is uncertain. This was obtained by cyclization (in naphthalene at 200–205°) of the condensation product of picryl chloride and o-phenylenediamine (a later claim[7] to have obtained the same compound by reduction of 1,3-dinitrophenazine is discredited in view of later work refuting the nature of the supposed dinitrophenazine; see Chapter IV:3). It separates from ethyl benzoate (in which it gives a blue-violet solution) as coppery leaflets. The color of the compound is certainly not in keeping with a dihydrophenazine structure and suggests a phenazyl, although every well-authenticated phenazyl carries a substituent on one of its nitrogen atoms. When substituents are lacking on the nitrogen atoms, presumably the radicals either dismutate or dimerize to give a phenazhydrin. However, the phenazhydrins in solution are usually dissociated and not deeply colored. It is possible that the presence of the two nitro groups stabilizes the radical sufficiently to allow of the existence of the phenazyl in this case.

Also, by the action of aniline on 2,4,6,2',4',6'-hexanitroazobenzene, Leemann and Grandmougin[74] in 1908 obtained, among other products, a substance that separates from chlorobenzene or xylene as blue-violet, lustrous leaflets, to which they attributed structure XLI, and for which they found molecular weight values agreeing with the bimolecular structure. Again, the suggested formulation is unsatisfactory, but it is not clear whether the compound is a phenazyl or a phenazhydrin.

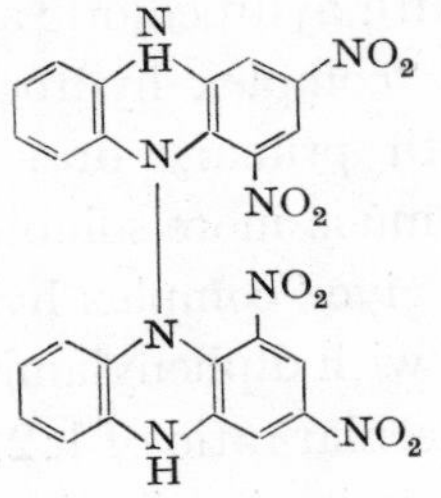

(XLI)

Pushkareva and Postovskiĭ[5] have investigated the oxidation of 5-acetyl-5,10-dihydrophenazine with anhydrous ferric chloride in cold chloroform solution and have concluded that, in the intermediate stage of oxidation, the radical is stabilized by coördination with a molecule of the dihydro compound to form a black-violet complex, m.p. 137°

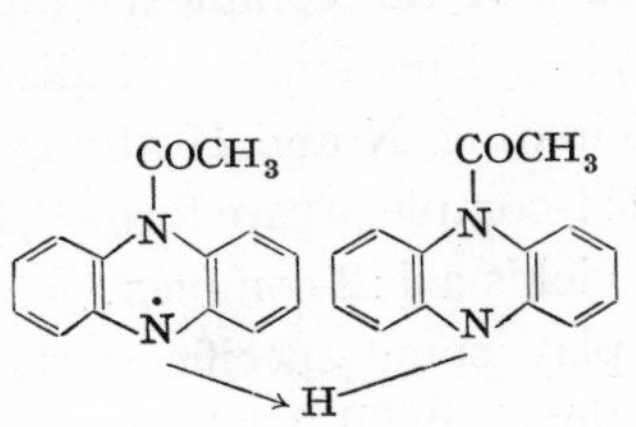

(XLII) 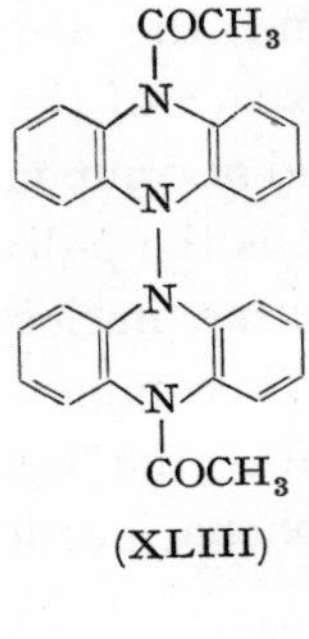   (XLIII)

(XLII) in analogy with the flavin compounds described by Kuhn and Ströbele.[75(a)] They also isolated an orange-colored product, m.p. 193–194°, which they formulated as the dimer (XLIII); on alkaline hydrolysis, this yielded phenazine. It is not clear why it is necessary to employ 2 and 4 molecular proportions of ferric chloride, respectively, to obtain XLII and XLIII. It has been reported recently that all known monoacetyl dihydrophenazine derivatives become red on standing in air, particularly in alcoholic solution, due to the formation of a phenazyl.[75(b)]

E. Complexes Formed between Phenazine and Primary or Secondary Aromatic Bases

The true phenazhydrins, described above, are much less soluble than their components in such solvents as ethanol or light petroleum and are green to purple. With hydrochloric acid they form what Clemo and McIlwain described as "complex hydrochlorides." But phenazine also forms complexes with primary or secondary aromatic bases, although the products are much more soluble than the phenazhydrins, are orange-red and do not give "complex hydrochlorides".[17]

Thus phenazine forms with diphenylamine a loosely bound orange colored complex in the molecular ratio of 1:2, although no combination occurs with N-methyldiphenylamine (indicating that the N-hydrogen atom performs a function in complex formation that the N-methyl group cannot). Phenazine and o-phenylenediamine form a 1:1 complex; but N,N'-dimethyl-o-phenylenediamine does not combine (perhaps due to the mutual repulsion of the two methyl groups orientating them, and hence also the N-hydrogen atoms, on opposite sides of the plane of the benzene rings). The nature of the complexes formed between phenazine and the various phenylenediamines indicates that an approach in space of the participating N and H atoms is necessary: with the o- and m-compounds, 1:1-complexes are formed, but under the same conditions the p-diamine yields a 1:2-complex.

The benzene nuclei also play some specific part, sterically or electronically, in complex formation. Thus, 1,2,3,4-tetrahydrophenazine (which contains the quinoxaline nucleus) does not combine with 5,10-dihydrophenazine; nor will 1,2,3,4,4a,5,10,10a-octahydrophenazine (which contains two cyclic imino groups between one benzenoid and one reduced ring) combine with phenazine or its tetrahydro compound. No complex is formed between either the octa- or tetra-hydro compounds and diphenylamine. Neither carbazole nor acridine gives complexes comparable with the phenazhydrins; but the latter does yield equi-molecular compounds with bases such as diphenylamine.[76]

F. Complex Salts of the Phenazhydrins

As mentioned in Chapter III.2,D, the replacement of one or both of the hydrogen atoms attached to the nitrogen atom of 5,10-dihydro-phenazine by other groups (for example, methyl) inhibits the formation of phenazhydrins. However, by the addition of alcoholic hydrogen chloride to an alcoholic solution of phenazine and 5,10-dihydro-5-methylphenazine in equimolecular proportions, Clemo and McIlwain[17] obtained what they described as a "complex hydrochloride," which was precipitated from the dark green solution by the addition of ether as green needles, m.p. $ca.$ 225° (dec.) and which was formulated as $C_{12}H_8N_2.C_{13}H_{12}N_2.2\,HCl$. Likewise, 5,10-dihydro-5,10-dimethylphen-azine yielded a product forming dark green needles, m.p. 225–230° (dec.), formulated as $C_{12}H_8N_2.C_{14}H_{14}N_2.2\,HCl$. Treatment of these with alkali yielded a mixture of the constituent bases. Also, by the addition of picric acid to the dark solution formed by mixing solutions of phen-azine and 5,10-dihydro-5,10-dimethylphenazine, Hillemann[14] obtained a picrate, as dark green needles, decomposing at 190°. Clemo and McIlwain represented the reactions involved as follows:

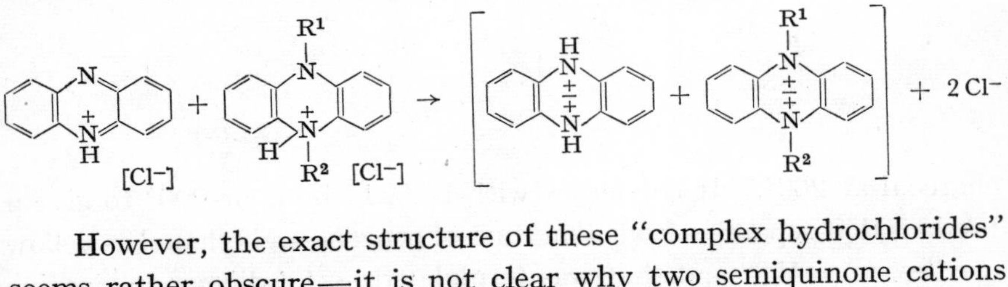

However, the exact structure of these "complex hydrochlorides" seems rather obscure—it is not clear why two semiquinone cations differing only by one or two methyl groups should form a complex, doubly charged cation. Also, the evidence of the existence of this complex is rather slight, resting as it does on the percentage of chlorine in the salt and on the decomposition by alkali of the product derived from phenazine and 5,10-dihydro-5-methylphenazine into its constituent bases. Moreover, these authors[14, 17] also observed that the oxidative demethylation of 5,10-dihydro-5-methylphenazine and of 5,10-dihydro-5,10-dimethylphenazine on exposure of the hydrochlorides to air or on the addition of oxidizing agents, followed by treatment with alkali, yielded phenazine. It therefore seems not impossible that the alleged complex hydrochlorides are, in fact, semiquinones (hydrochlorides), derived from the methylated dihydrophenazines.

G. Conclusion

Finally, one may suppose that in solution, as in the case of quinhydrone,[77] a rather complex equilibrium mixture may be present, involving here the phenazine, the dihydrophenazine, the phenazyl and the phenazhydrin, together with their respective cations, depending upon the pH of the solution.

3. Tetrahydrophenazines

A. 1,2,3,4-Tetrahydrophenazine

This compound (XLIV) separates from light petroleum as faintly yellow plates, m.p. 92.5° and is obtained by the condensation of 1,2-cyclohexanedione with o-phenylenediamine in boiling acetic acid solution in the presence of sodium acetate.[2, 64] It is dehydrogenated to phenazine by the action of iodine in acetic acid[64] or of palladium

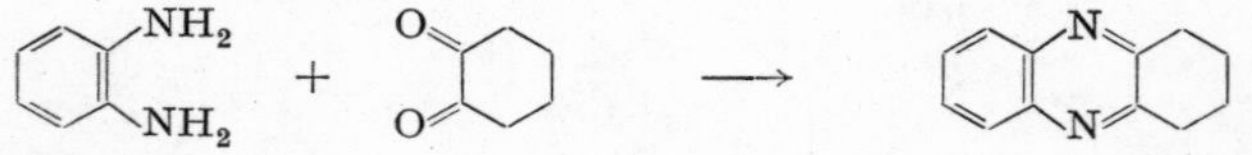

(XLIV)

charcoal at 200°.[78] It condenses with benzaldehyde at 200° to give a product that separates from a mixture of benzene and ethanol as yellow needles, m.p. 158° and that was formulated as 1,4-dibenzylphenazine (XLV), rather than the isomeric dibenzylidene compound (XLVI), because of its resistance to dehydrogenation. In the case of p-nitrobenzaldehyde and p-dimethylaminobenzaldehyde, both mono- and

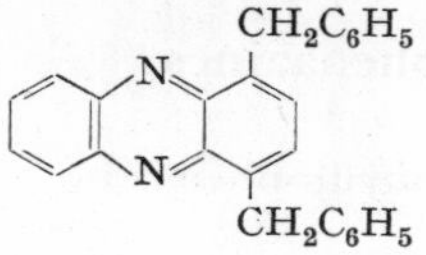

(XLV) 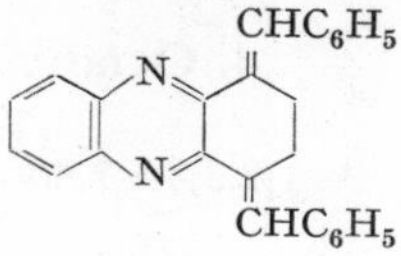   (XLVI)

di-condensation products have been isolated.[79] The reactivity of the 1- and 4-methylene groups has numerous analogies in heterocyclic chemistry (for example, 2- and 4-picolines) and is increased by quaternization of the base.[2]

B. 1,2,3,4-Tetrahydro-1-methylphenazine

This compound, m.p. 37°, b.p. 160–165°/20 mm., is similarly prepared from 3-methyl-1,2-cyclohexanedione and is dehydrogenated to 1-methylphenazine.[64]

C. 1,2,3,4-Tetrahydro-2-methylphenazine

This compound is a bright yellow oil, b.p. 147°/0.1 mm., obtained from 4-methyl-1,2-cyclohexanedione and is dehydrogenated to 2-methylphenazine.[17]

D. 1,2,3,4-Tetrahydro-7-methylphenazine

This compound, m.p. 78°, is obtained by the condensation of 1,2-cyclohexanedione with 3,4-diaminotoluene.[17]

E. 2,3,5,10-Tetrahydro-5,10-dimethylphenazine

This compound (V) separates from ethanol as colorless plates, m.p. 78°, and is formed by the condensation of 1,2-cyclohexanedione with N,N'-dimethyl-o-phenylenediamine in aqueous hydrochloric acid (5 minutes, reflux).[17] When a solution of this tetrahydro compound is exposed to the air for some days, or when an acetic acid solution is warmed in the open for 30 minutes, the bulk of the material is converted into a resin; but some 5,10-dihydro-5,10-dimethylphenazine is produced. The latter is the product obtained by condensing 1,2-cyclohexanedione with N,N'-dimethyl-o-phenylenediamine in acetic acid solution in the presence of sodium acetate (40 minutes, reflux).

4. Octahydrophenazines

A. 1,2,3,4,6,7,8,9-Octahydrophenazine

This compound (*sym*-octahydrophenazine) (XLVIII) was obtained
in 1924 by Wallach,[80] although at that time he believed his product to
be the 1,2,3,4,4a,6,7,8,9,9a-decahydro-compound (XLVII), later[81]
amending his view as to the structure. It was also prepared in 1925 by
Godchot,[82] who stated that it had been obtained in 1922 by G. Plancher.
It separates from acetone as colorless, triclinic prisms, m.p. 109°, is
volatile in steam, can be sublimed without decomposition and shows a
blue fluorescence in solution.

Wallach[80,81] obtained this compound by reduction of the dioxime
of 1,2-cyclohexanedione with zinc dust in alkaline solution, followed by
oxidation (for example, with hydrogen peroxide, or by atmospheric
oxidation). The reaction presumably proceeds *via* isonitrosocyclo-
hexanone, the reduction of which is known to yield octahydrophenazine.[83]

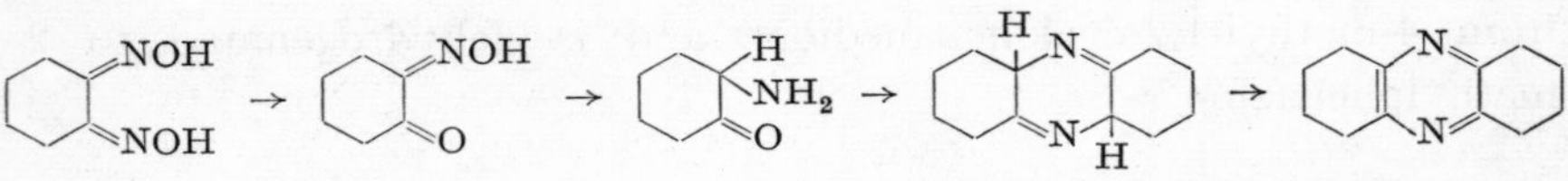

(XLVII)   (XLVIII)

It is also obtained from 1,2-cyclohexanedione by treatment with
zinc and an ammoniacal methanolic solution of nickel sulfate, the
reduction being brought about by the active nickel precipitated.[84,85]
A small amount of *sym*-octahydrophenazine is formed by boiling
cyclohexene pseudonitrosite (XLIX) with ethyl acetoacetate and zinc
dust.[86] The compound was prepared in 25% yield by Godchot[82,87] by

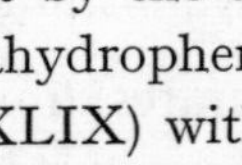

(XLIX)

the action of ammonia on 2-chlorocyclohexanone in ethanol; although
Smith[88] increased the yield to 37% by adding the ammonia rapidly,
and allowing the reaction to proceed for six days. It is obtained in 7%

yield by heating cyclohexanoneoxime-O-sulfonate with hydrogen chloride in dioxane.[88] It is also formed by vapor phase hydrogenation of 1,2,3,4-tetrahydrophenazine with a nickel catalyst (prepared from

nickel nitrate) at 180° or by similar treatment of cis- or trans-1,2,3,4,4a,5,10,10a-octahydrophenazine.[78]

The above syntheses, the dehydrogenation to phenazine by palladium charcoal at 200°[78] and the oxidation by alkaline permanganate to pyrazine-2,3,5,6-tetracarboxylic acid (L)[88] leave no doubt

(L)

as to the assignment of structure XLVIII to this substance. The failure of the compound to yield an N-nitroso derivative or a ferric chloride color reaction are also in keeping with this formulation.[78]

Numerous salts of **XLVIII** have been described. The melting point of the hydrochloride has been reported as 116–117° (mono-salt)[82] and 159–160° (sinters 150°)[83] and of the picrate as 167–168°,[82,87] 165° (dec.)[83] and 162–163°.[88] The monomethiodide is produced by heating the base in methanol with methyl iodide in a sealed tube for six hours at 100°, and forms yellow prisms, m.p. 175°.[79] The chloroaurate separates from ethanol as yellow needles, m.p. 145–146°.[88]

B. *cis*-and *trans*-1,2,3,4,4a,5,10,10a-Octahydrophenazines

These isomeric compounds are shown as (LI) and (LII). Clemo and McIlwain[89] have recorded the constants shown in Table III. In preparing a considerable quantity of 1,2,3,4-tetrahydrophenazine by the condensation of 1,2-cyclohexanedione with o-phenylenediamine, these authors[78] isolated a small amount of the *cis*-octahydrophenazine, m.p. 147°, as a by-product, which must have been formed through reduction before or during the condensation, as the tetrahydro compound could not be converted into the octahydro product by treatment

TABLE III

Compound		Crystal form	M.p. (°C.)	d^{20}	d^{182}	n_D^{20a}	Soly. at 20°C., % (w/v)	
							in ethanol	in ether
LI	cis-	Colorless plates	147	1.1949	1.0064	1.6182	18.1	19.1
LII	trans-	Colorless plates	156	1.1989	0.9982	1.6146	23.6	17.8

[a] The refractive index of each isomer was calculated from values obtained for solutions in pyridine of several concentrations, which obeyed the mixture law.

TABLE IV. α-, β- and γ-Tetradecahydrophenazines

Base	M.p. of base (°C.)	Dinitroso deriv. and m.p. (°C.)	Dipicrate m.p. (°C.)	Dibenzoyl deriv. m.p. (°C.)	Platinichloride (°C.)	Aurichloride (°C.)	Hydrochloride
α, colorless needles	135[a]	Yellow prisms, 168	278	234–5	dec. 240	dec. 220	White prisms
β, colorless needles	95[b]	183	252		dec. 230	dec. 210	Prisms, dec. 200°
γ, colorless needles	62	Yellow prisms, 107	242		dec. 260	dec. ca. 200	Plates, dec. ca. 240°

[a] A hydrate, m.p. 132°, appears also to exist.

[b] Various authors have recorded values of about 106° for the melting point of the β-isomer; but this figure appears to represent the melting point of the carbonate, which is readily formed on exposure of the base to the atmosphere.

with either o-phenylenediamine or 1,2-cyclohexanedione (see also reference 2). The same authors also obtained the trans-octahydro-phenazine, m.p. 156° (in the earlier paper, given erroneously as 150°) by reduction of the tetrahydro compound with sodium amalgam[17] or with sodium and ethanol,[78] or by catalytic vapor phase hydrogenation at 180° in the presence of a nickel catalyst prepared from nickel hydroxide (the use of a catalyst prepared from nickel nitrate gave 1,2,3,4,6,7,8,9-octahydrophenazine).[78] On the other hand, liquid phase hydrogenation in acetic acid solution, in the presence of platinum, palladium, or the catalyst prepared from nickel hydroxide yielded the cis-octahydro-phenazine, m.p. 147°[78]; and reduction with sodium and ethanol in the presence of acetic acid also produced mainly the cis-compound (trans-, in the absence of acetic acid).[89]

(LI)   (LII)

These two geometrical isomers are both dehydrogenated smoothly to phenazine, in the presence of palladium at 200°. Both yield di-N-nitroso derivatives (cis, m.p. 109°; trans, m.p. 126°), from which it follows that the central heterocyclic ring is in each case reduced; and both give the ferric chloride color reaction characteristic of substituted o-phenylenediamines. The cis- and trans-isomers are not interconverted by acidic or basic reagents; although at 180°, in the presence of hydrogen and a catalyst prepared from nickel hydroxide, the cis- is converted into the trans-(presumably more stable) form. (Using a catalyst prepared from nickel nitrate, either the cis- or trans-form is isomerized to 1,2,3,4,6,7,8,9-octahydrophenazine.)

The modes of formation described above suggest that the compound, m.p. 147° is the cis- and that of m.p. 156° is the trans-isomer. Thus Skita,[90] investigating homocyclic compounds, made the generalization that, in the hydrogenation of an unsaturated compound, reduction under acidic and neutral or alkaline conditions led to the production of the cis- and trans-isomer, respectively. The trans-isomer should, theoretically, be resolvable into optically active forms; but attempts to resolve both isomers failed.[89] However, the physical constants for the two isomers are in agreement with the suggested relationship. Thus the work of von Auwers[91] on ethylenic and homocyclic geometrical isomers has shown that the *cis*-compound usually possesses the higher boiling point, density and refractive index. In addition, the melting point of the *cis*-compound is lower than that of the *trans*, although melting point and solubility are not certain criteria of the configurations of geometrical isomers. The densities of the octahydrophenazine isomers determined in the liquid state are in agreement with the von Auwers-Skita rule; in the solid state, the *trans* compound is the denser.

The pK_a value for the *trans* isomer is 4.62 in aqueous ethanol (50%).[92] A number of derivatives have been prepared.[2]

5. Tetradecahydrophenazines

Three tetradecahydrophenazines (designated α, β and γ), which give the derivatives shown in Table IV, have been described. By reduction of *sym*-octahydrophenazine under a variety of conditions (sodium and ethanol,[87,93] aluminum amalgam,[87] hydrogen and nickel at $140–170°$[87,89,93] or hydrogen and platinum in acetic acid[87,89,93]) α-tetradecahydrophenazine, m.p. 135° is produced. Under the last mentioned conditions, it is accompanied by the β- (m.p. 95°) and γ- (m.p. 62°) isomers. α-Tetradecahydrophenazine is also obtained by hydrogenation of 1,2,3,4-tetrahydrophenazine or of the *cis*- or *trans*-octahydrophenazines (LI) and (LII).[89] It is unchanged by treatment with hydrogen in the presence of nickel; but, under the same conditions, the β- and γ-compounds can be converted into the α-isomer.[89] Hydrogenation of phenazine in acetic acid in the presence of platinum yields the β-isomer.[94] The α-isomer is also obtained, besides other products, by reduction with sodium and ethanol of the dioxime of 1,2-cyclohexanedione.[95]

```
+  +   +  −   +  −   −  −   −  +
+  +   +  −   +  +   +  +   +  −
```

(LIII)   (LIV)   (LV)   (LVI)   (LVII)   (LVIII)

Separation of a mixture of the three isomers can be achieved by conversion to the urates, that of the β-isomer being the least soluble;

the more soluble urate mixture is then basified and the mixture of the α- and γ-bases is separated by fractional crystallization from light petroleum.[89] For isolation of the α-form, the formation of the (+) tartrate is also of value.[89]

The three isomers are smoothly dehydrogenated in the presence of palladium charcoal at 200° to phenazine. A consideration of the structures of the possible isomers of LIII shows that in only two of these are the hydrogen atoms of both ring junctions arranged in the cis configuration; in the production of this mixture of isomers, therefore, the platinum-acetic acid reagent has deviated from the Skita rule in at least one instance. However, shaking in acetic acid in the presence of platinum under the conditions of the hydrogenation does not cause the isomerization of any of these compounds. The observations that the α-isomer is the product of reduction under a variety of different conditions and is the sole product of isomerizations in the tetradeca-hydrophenazines indicates it to be a very stable compound. In comparable cases of cis-trans isomerism, the trans is usually the more stable product. It appears probable, therefore, that the α-isomer possesses at least one trans junction. Also, as the α-isomer can be obtained by hydrogenation of both cis- and trans-octahydrophenazines, isomerization must have occurred during at least one of these reactions. Clemo and McIlwain suggested structure LVII for the α-isomer and LIV and LV for the β- and γ-isomers. Attempted resolutions of the tetradeca-hydrophenazines were unsuccessful; and this negative evidence would be in agreement with these structures, although it cannot be taken as reliable evidence, especially in view of the failure to resolve the trans-octahydrophenazine. It may be noted that Johnson[96] has recently concluded that, in the analogous series of perhydroanthracenes, the following is the order of stability:

$$LVII > LVI > LV > LVIII > LIV$$

6. Hydrophenazines Derived from Camphor, etc.

A. Introduction

The hydrophenazines derived from camphor and similar terpenoid compounds provide an interesting series of isomers based on the position both of alkyl substituents and of hydrogen atoms. They are all derived from 1,4,6,9-dimethanophenazine (LIX), *R. I.* 2890.

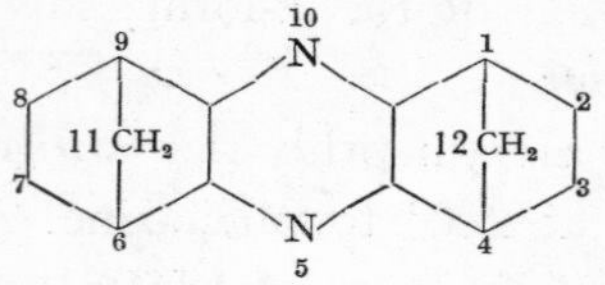

(LIX)

B. 1,2,3,4,4a,6,7,8,9,9a-Decahydro-1,6,11,11,12,12-hexamethyl-1,4,6,9-dimethanophenazine

Known also as dihydrodicamphenepyrazine, this compound (LX) is obtained by heating 3-aminocamphor on the water-bath for five hours[97] or longer,[98] or by exposing it to summer temperatures for several days,[97] when autocondensation occurs. It crystallizes from ether or light petroleum as colorless prisms, m.p. 116°, and yields a monohydrochloride, which forms long, flat prisms, m.p. 258°. It is readily hydrolyzed by acid to 3-aminocamphor, thus substantiating the structure given to it; and is oxidized by various reagents (for example, ferric chloride) to the corresponding pyrazine (LXI).[97]

C. 1,2,3,4,6,7,8,9-Octahydro-1,6,11,11,12,12-hexamethyl-1,4,6,9-dimethanophenazine

Known also as dicamphenepyrazine (LXI), this compound separates from ethanol as long, colorless needles, m.p. 159°,[86] b.p. 326°/748 mm.,[97] $[\alpha]_D = 55.5°$ in chloroform[99] and forms an aurichloride, m.p. 240° (dec.) and a mercurichloride, m.p. 249° (dec.). It is a weak base, readily reduced by tin and hydrochloric acid to LX; and with methyl iodide it yields a monomethiodide. Reduction under more vigorous conditions (sodium and ethanol) yields the corresponding piperazine (LXII).

D. 1,2,3,4,4a,5,5a,6,7,8,9,9a,10,10a-Tetradecahydro-1,6,11,11,12,12-hexamethyl-1,4,6,9-dimethanophenazine

This compound (dicamphenepiperazine) (LXII) is a fairly strong base, m.p. 147°, and yields a hydrochloride forming slender needles, m.p. $>$ 275°, a picrate as thin plates, m.p. 235° (dec.) and an N,N'-dinitroso compound, m.p. 215°.[97]

E. 1,2,3,4,5a,6,7,8,9,10a-Decahydro-1,6,11,11,12,12-hexamethyl-1,4,6,9-dimethanophenazine

This compound (epidihydrodicamphenepyrazine) (LXIII) is an isomer of LX, differing only in the position of the hydrogen atoms. It is a colorless solid, m.p. 163°, $[\alpha]_D = 425.5°$ in chloroform, and yields a picrate forming canary-yellow leaflets or prisms, m.p. 177°, $[\alpha]_D = 250.9°$. It was obtained in 1912 by Forster and Spinner[99] by the autocondensation of 2-aminoepicamphor, which occurs very rapidly in a desiccator or in 15–20 hours at 50°. That the isomerism of LX and LXIII is due solely to the position of the double bonds follows from the oxidation of both by ferric chloride to LXI.

F. 1,2,3,4,6,7,8,9-Octahydro-1,9,11,11,12,12-hexamethyl-1,4,6,9-dimethanophenazine

This compound (isodicamphenepyrazine) (LXIV) is a second isomer of LXI obtained by Einhorn and Jahn,[100] who heated a mixture of 3-aminocamphor and its hydrochloride in a sealed tube at 220–230°, when they obtained a mixture of LXI and the less soluble LXIV, which were separated by fractional crystallization from acetone. The base forms prisms, m.p. 204.5–205°, the picrate, yellow needles, m.p. 204–206°, and the methiodide, yellow needles, decomposing at 260°. Determination of the structure of the compound is due to Rupe and di Vignano.[101]

G. 1,2,3,4,4a,6,7,8,9,9a-Decahydro-1,9,11,11,12,12-hexamethyl-1,4,6,9-dimethanophenazine

Known also as isodihydrodicamphenepyrazine (LXV), this compound forms colorless crystals, m.p. 71–72°, b.p. 197–198°/12.5 mm., $[\alpha]_D^{20} = 387.63°$ (benzene), 330.2° (chloroform), which cannot be recrystallized.

Rupe and di Vignano[98, 101] showed that the action of methylamine on camphorquinone under pressure gave a mixture of methylaminocamphor, methylaminoepicamphor and a high-boiling resin that contained the "isodicamphenepyrazine" (LXIV) of Einhorn and Jahn[100] and a third isomer of LX, namely LXV, which was separated by means of its very insoluble picrate, golden needles, m.p. 196.5°. Compound LXV was also obtained by the condensation of camphorquinone with either the α-diaminocamphane of Duden[102] or the β-compound described by Rupe and Bohny.[103] The isomerism of LXV was not due to the position of double bonds in this case, since oxidation, which could be effected by nitrous and nitric acids, ferric chloride or cupric acetate, afforded LXIV and not LXI. The syntheses above are ambiguous for a structural determination; but Rupe and di Vignano showed that LXV was split smoothly by acid hydrolysis to give a mixture of 3-amino-camphor and 2-aminoepicamphor, and, on standing for a month the reaction was reversed and LXV was re-formed. Consequently they allotted LXV the structure shown. (A possible alternative structure, LXVI, was excluded because of the absence of active hydrogen.) These authors also conclude: (*a*) that the isomer LXIV of Einhorn and Jahn must arise from an isomerization of half the 3-aminocamphor to its epi-isomer, brought about by the elevated temperature employed, and (*b*) that, since in their own condensation experiments with camphor-quinone and diaminocamphane LXV is formed exclusively, it follows that a rearrangement of the double bonds must have occurred and also that the "iso" series must be the more stable when compared with its isomer (LX), etc.

With methyl iodide in methanol, LXV yields a monomethiodide, which decomposes at 245–246°, but which on prolonged heating at 240° loses methyl iodide, yielding LXIV. The methohydroxide similarly loses methanol to yield LXIV.

H. 1,2,3,4,4a,5,6,7,8,9,10,10a-Dodecahydro-1,9,11,11,12,12-hexamethyl-1,4,6,9-dimethanophenazine

This is shown in formula LXVII. Reduction of LXV by sodium and ethanol yields a tetrahydropyrazine (plates, m.p. 113.5–114.5°), confirmed by the analyses of several derivatives, such as the mono-perchlorate (decomposes at 231–233°) and the monohydriodide (brown-ish-yellow plates, m.p. > 310°). This product is a weak base and, since it forms an N,N'-dinitroso compound (m.p. 144–145° (dec.)), is presumably LXVII. Methylation of LXVII yields an N,N'-dimethyl compound, which forms colorless plates, m.p. 86–87°, $[\alpha]_D^{20} = 64.88°$, and which forms a monopicrate (deep yellow plates, m.p. 151–153° (dec.)).

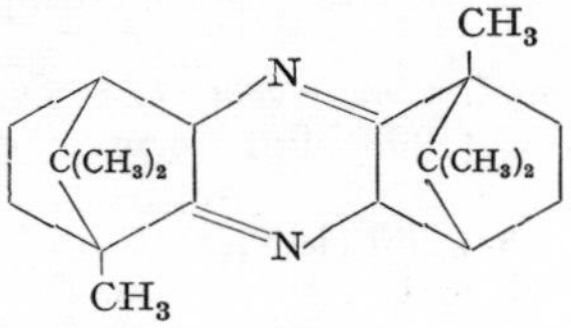

(LX)

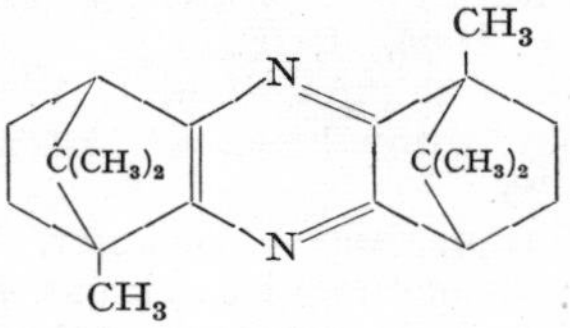

(LXI)

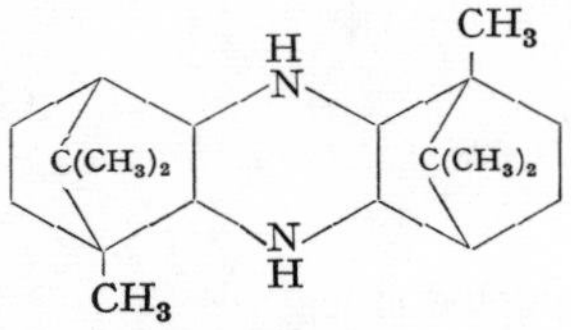

(LXII)

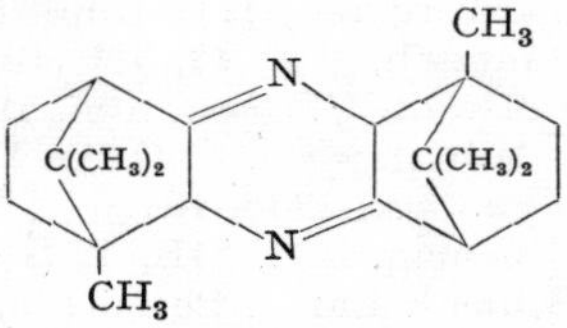

(LXIII)

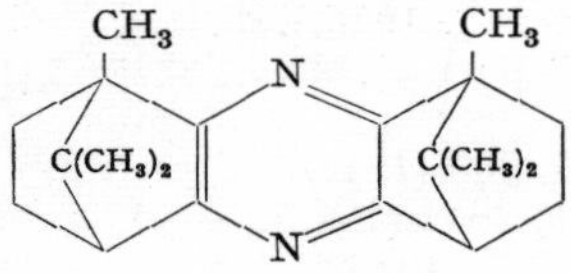

(LXIV)

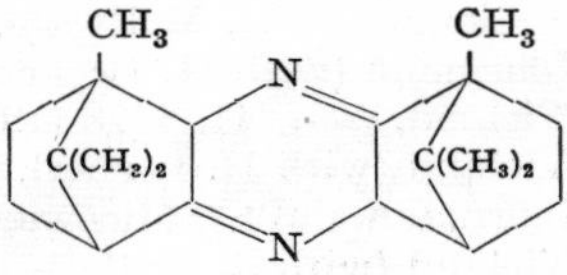

(LXV)

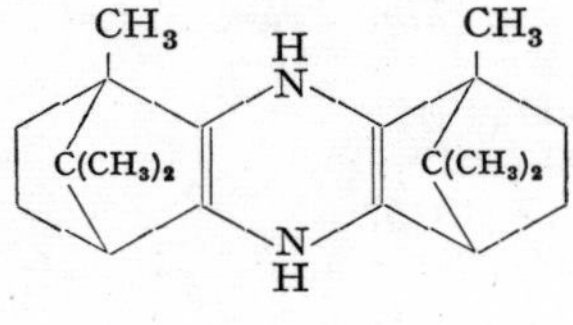

(LXVI)

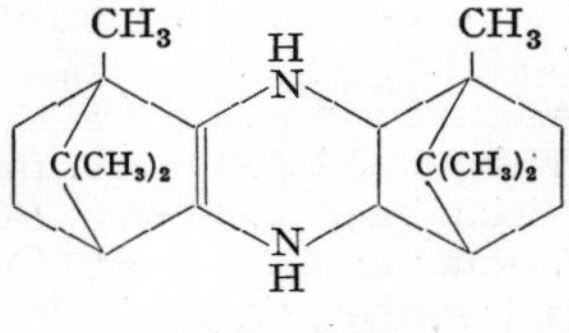

(LXVII)

I. Other Related Compounds

A number of other hydrophenazines derived from terpenoid sources are described in the literature.[104–107] These are formed by the condensation of camphorquinone, or other terpenoid quinones, with o-diamines; and, in many cases, there is ambiguity about the structure, since condensation might occur in two directions, although in no case have two compounds been isolated.

References

1. A. Claus, *Ann.*, **168**, 1 (1873).
2. J. S. Morley, *J. Chem. Soc.*, **1952**, 4008.
3. M. M. Tichvinski and L. Volochovich, *J. Russ. Phys. Chem. Soc.*, **37**, 8 (1905); through *Chem. Zentr.*, **1905**, I, 1263.
4. N. Shcherbina, *J. Russ. Phys. Chem. Soc.*, **38**, 613 (1906); through *Chem. Zentr.*, **1906**, II, 1621.
5. Z. V. Pushkareva and I. Y. Postovskiï, *J. Gen. Chem. U.S.S.R.*, **8**, 158 (1938); through *Chem. Abstracts*, **32**, 5405 (1938) and *Chem. Zentr.*, **1939** I, 4328.
6. L. Birkofer and A. Birkofer, *Chem. Ber.*, **85**, 286 (1952).
7. F. Kehrmann and E. Havas, *Ber.*, **46**, 341 (1913).
8. R. Scholl, *Monatsh.*, **39**, 231 (1918); through *Chem. Zentr.*, **1918**, II, 621.
9. F. Bohlmann, *Chem. Ber.*, **85**, 390 (1952).
10. O. Hinsberg and H. Garfunkel, *Ann.*, **292**, 258 (1896).
11. A. Hantzsch, *Ber.*, **49**, 511 (1916).
12. H. McIlwain, *J. Chem. Soc.*, **1937**, 1704.
13. I. G. M. Campbell, C. G. Le Fevre, R. J. W. Le Fevre and E. E. Turner, *J. Chem. Soc.*, **1938**, 404.
14. H. Hilleman, *Ber.*, **71B**, 42 (1938).
15. W. Schlenk and E. Bergmann, *Ann.*, **463**, 306 (1928).
16. B. M. Mikhaïlov and A. N. Blokhina, *Izvest. Akad. Nauk S.S.S.R., Otdel Khim. Nauk*, **1950**, 304; through *Chem. Abstracts*, **44**, 9452 (1950).
17. G. R. Clemo and H. McIlwain, *J. Chem. Soc.*, **1935**, 738.
18. F. Kehrmann (with H. Becker and A. Capatina), *Ann.*, **322**, 67 (1902).
19. H. Wieland, *Ber.*, **41**, 3478 (1908).
20. H. Wieland (with H. Lecher), *Ann.*, **381**, 200 (1911).
21. F. Kehrmann and St. Micewicz, *Ber.*, **45**, 2641 (1912).
22. H. Wieland (with C. Müller), *Ber.*, **46**, 3295 (1913).
23. H. Wieland and H. Lecher, *Ann.*, **392**, 156 (1912).
24. S. Goldschmidt and K. Renn, *Ber.*, **55B**, 628 (1922).
25. M. Marqueyrol and D. Florentin, *Bull. soc. chim. France, Mém.*, (IV), **11**, 804 (1912).
26. H. Wieland and H. Lecher, *Ber.*, **45**, 2600 (1912).
27. H. Wieland and A. Roseeu, *Ber.*, **45**, 494 (1912).
28. H. Wieland and A. Roseeu, *Ber.*, **48**, 1117 (1915).
29. H. Wieland and A. Süsser, *Ann.*, **392**, 169 (1912).
30. W. Bülow, *Ber.*, **57**, 1431 (1924).
31. H. Wieland and A. Süsser, *Ann.*, **381**, 217 (1911).
32. F. Kehrmann, *Ber.*, **38**, 3777 (1905).
33. F. Kehrmann and A. Danecki, *Ber.*, **47**, 279 (1914).
34. F. Kehrmann, *Ber.*, **48**, 1931 (1915).
35. A. Hantzsch, *Ber.*, **46**, 1925 (1913).
36. A. Hantzsch, *Ber.*, **46**, 682 (1913).
37. F. Kehrmann, *Ber.*, **49**, 1207 (1916).
38. L. Michaelis and E. S. Hill, *J. Am. Chem. Soc.*, **55**, 1481 (1933).
39. L. Michaelis, *Chem. Revs.*, **16**, 243 (1935).
40. R. C. Kaye and H. I. Stonehill, *J. Chem. Soc.*, **1952**, 3240.
41. L. Michaelis, E. S. Hill and M. P. Schubert, *Biochem. Z.*, **255**, 66 (1932).
42. E. Friedheim and L. Michaelis, *J Biol Chem.*, **91**, 355 (1931).
43. L. Michaelis, *J. Biol. Chem.*, **92**, 211 (1931).

44. B. Elema, *Rec. trav. chim.*, **50**, 807, (1931).
45. C. Cattaneo and G. Sartori, *Gazz. chim. ital.*, **72**, 38 (1942); through *Chem. Abstracts*, **37**, 650 (1943).
46. R. Brdička, *Coll. Czech. Chem. Communs.*, **12**, 522 (1947); through *Chem. Abstracts*, **42**, 5355 (1948).
47. M. Voriskova, *Coll. Czech. Chem. Communs.*, **12**, 607 (1947); through *Chem. Abstracts*, **42**, 5354 (1948).
48. O. H. Müller, *Ann. N. Y. Acad. Sci.*, **40**, Art. 2, 91 (1940); through *Chem. Abstracts*, **35**, 2798 (1941).
49. O. H. Müller, *Cold Springs Harbor Symposia on Quantitative Biology*, **7**, 59 (1939).
50. O. H. Müller, *J. Biol. Chem.*, **145**, 425 (1942).
51. P. W. Preisler and L. H. Hempelmann, *J. Am. Chem. Soc.*, **59**, 141 (1937).
52. B. Elema, *Rec. trav. chim.*, **52**, 569 (1933).
53. C. Cattaneo, G. Sartori and M. Morellini, *Gazz. chim. ital.*, **77**, 381 (1947); through *Chem. Abstracts*, **42**, 3018 (1948).
54. R. Kuhn and K. Schön, *Ber.*, **68B**, 1537 (1935).
55 (a). L. Pauling, *The Nature of the Chemical Bond*, Cornell University Press, 1942, p. 279.
55 (b). A. N. Holden, W. A. Yager and F. R. Merritt, *J. Chem. Phys.*, **19**, 1319 (1951).
55 (c). H. W. Meyer and W. D. Treadwell, *Helv. Chim. Acta*, **35**, 1444 (1952).
56. L. Michaelis, *J. Am. Chem. Soc.*, **58**, 1816 (1936).
57. A. Eckert and K. Steiner, *Monatsh.*, **35**, 1153 (1914); through *Chem. Zentr.*, **1915**, I, 202.
58. F. Kehrmann and J. Messinger, *Ber.*, **26**, 2372 (1893).
59. F. Kehrmann and H. Goldstein, *Helv. Chim. Acta*, **4**, 26 (1921).
60. F. Kehrmann and J. R. y Punti, *Ber.*, **44**, 2622 (1911).
61. F. Kehrmann and J. Effront, *Helv. Chim. Acta*, **4**, 517 (1921).
62. H. Wieland, *Die Hydrazine*, Enke, Stuttgart, 1913, p. 72.
63. G. W. Wheland, *Advanced Organic Chemistry*, 2nd ed., Wiley, New York, 1949, p. 729.
64. G. R. Clemo and H. McIlwain, *J. Chem. Soc.*, **1934**, 1991.
65 (a). I. P. Gragerov and G. P. Miklukhim, *Doklady Akad. Nauk S.S.S.R.*, **62**, 79 (1948); through *Chem. Abstracts*, **43**, 452 (1949).
65 (b). A. I. Brodskiï and I. P. Gragerov, *Doklady Akad. Nauk S.S.S.R.*, **79**, 277 (1951); through *Chem. Abstracts*, **45**, 9938 (1951).
66. A. A. Bothner-By, *J. Am. Chem. Soc.*: (a) **73**, 4228 (1951); (b) **75**, 728 (1953).
67 (a). K. Nakamoto, *J. Am. Chem. Soc.*, **74**, 1739 (1952).
67 (b). R. S. Mulliken, *J. Phys. Chem.*, **56**, 801 (1952).
68. R. S. Mulliken, *J. Am. Chem. Soc.*, **74**, 811 (1952).
69. J. Landauer and H. McConnell, *J. Am. Chem. Soc.*, **74**, 1221 (1952).
70 (a). S. C. Abrahams, *J. Am. Chem. Soc.*, **74**, 2692 (1952).
70 (b). S. C. Wallwork and T. T. Harding, *Nature*, **171**, 40 (1953).
71. L. Hunter, *Ann. Reports Progress Chem.*, **43**, 147 (1946).
72 (a). C. Dufraisse, A. Étienne and E. Toromanoff, *Compt. rend.*, **232**, 2379 (1951); **235**, 758 (1952); *Bull. soc. chim. France, Mém.*, **1953**, 140.
72 (b). E. Toromanoff, *Compt. rend.* **236**, 300 (1953).
73. H. Leemann and E. Grandmougin, *Ber.*, **41**, 1306 (1908).
74. H. Leemann and E. Grandmougin, *Ber.*, **41**, 1295 (1908).
75 (a). R. Kuhn and R. Ströbele, *Ber.*, **70**, 753 (1937).
75 (b). L. Birkofer, *Chem. Ber.*, **85**, 1023 (1952).

76. O. Blum, *Ber.*, **62**, 881 (1929).
77. G. W. Wheland, *Advanced Organic Chemistry*, 2nd ed., Wiley, New York, 1949, p. 56.
78. G. R. Clemo and H. McIlwain, *J. Chem. Soc.*, **1936**, 258.
79. H. McIlwain, *J. Chem. Soc.*, **1937**, 1701.
80. O. Wallach (with A. Weissenborn), *Ann.*, **437**, 148 (1924).
81. O. Wallach, *Nach. Ges. Wiss. Göttingen, math. physik. Klasse*, **1927**, 238; *Chem. Abstracts*, **22**, 2168 (1928).
82. M. Godchot, *Compt. rend.*, **180**, 444 (1925).
83. A. Treibs and D. Dinelli, *Ann.*, **517**, 152 (1935).
84. H. Mousseron, *Bull. soc. chim. France, Mém.*, (5), **12**, 70 (1945).
85. M. Mousseron and P. Froger (with R. Granger), *Bull. soc. chim. France, Mém.*, **1947**, 843.
86. A. Treibs (with F. Dornberger), *Ann.*, **524**, 285 (1936).
87. M. Godchot and M. Mousseron, *Bull. soc. chim. France, Mém.*, (4), **51**, 360 (1932).
88. P. A. S. Smith, *J. Am. Chem. Soc.*, **70**, 323, (1948).
89. G. R. Clemo and H. McIlwain, *J. Chem. Soc.*, **1936**, 1698.
90. A. Skita, *Ann.*, **431**, 1 (1923).
91. K. von Auwers, *Ann.*, **420**, 92 (1920).
92. J. S. Morley, *J. Chem. Soc.*, **1952**, 4002.
93. M. Godchot and M. Mousseron, *Compt. rend.*, **190**, 442 (1930).
94. M. Godchot and M. Mousseron, *Bull. soc. chim. France, Mém.*, (4), **51**, 528 (1932).
95. F. M. Jaeger and L. Bijkerk, *Proc. Acad. Sci. Amsterdam*, **40**, 12 (1937); through *Chem. Zentr.*, **1937**, II, 1196.
96. W. S. Johnson, *Experientia*, **7**, 315 (1951); *J. Am. Chem. Soc.*, **75**, 1498 (1953).
97. P. Duden, *Ann.*, **307**, 207 (1899).
98. H. Rupe and A. T. di Vignano, *Helv. Chim. Acta*, **20**, 1078 (1937).
99. M. O. Forster and H. Spinner, *J. Chem. Soc.*, **101**, 1340 (1912).
100. A. Einhorn and S. Jahn, *Ber.*, **35**, 3657 (1902).
101. H. Rupe and A. T. di Vignano, *Helv. Chim. Acta*, **20**, 1097 (1937).
102. Ger. Pat. 160,108; *Chem. Zentr.*, **1905**, II, 178.
103. H. Rupe and P. Bohny, *Helv. Chim. Acta*, **19**, 1305 (1936).
104. A. Heckendorn, *Helv. Chim. Acta*, **12**, 50 (1929).
105. B. K. Singh and B. Bhutnath, *J. Indian Chem. Soc.*, **8**, 623 (1931); through *Chem. Abstracts*, **26**, 1917 (1932).
106. L. I. Smith and L. H. Hac, *J. Am. Chem. Soc.*, **58**, 229 (1936).
107. R. N. Chakravarti, *J. Indian Chem. Soc.*, **21**, 319 (1944); *Chem. Abstracts*, **39**, 2499 (1945).
108. E. Weitz, *Angew. Chem.*, **66**, 658 (1954).

CHAPTER IV

Substitution Products of Phenazine
(Excluding Hydroxy and Amino Compounds)

1. Introduction

Phenazine is very unreactive towards the usual (cationoid) reagents employed in aromatic substitution; and hence, in the preparation of substitution products, the substituents are generally introduced into the intermediate before cyclization to the phenazine ring system. However, a few direct substitution products of phenazine are known. The substitution in the phenazine-N-oxides has been little explored.

2. Halogen Derivatives

Table V shows the known mono- and di-halogen substituted products of phenazine, which usually crystallize as yellow needles and about which little more need be said. Direct substitution of chlorine in phenazine in hydrochloric acid solution gives rise to the 1-chloro-, 1,4-dichloro-, 1,4,6-trichloro- and 1,4,6,9-tetrachloro-derivatives, the orientations of which have been proved synthetically.[1(a)] 1-Chlorophenazine[1(b)] is highly resistant to a variety of anionoid reagents, but 2-chlorophenazine is considerably more reactive. Thus, with aqueous alcoholic potassium hydroxide (3 days reflux) it gives 2-ethoxyphenazine in 88% yield; and with ammonium hydroxide at 175° it forms 2-aminophenazine.[2] The conversion of the phenazine into its 5,10-dioxide renders the halogen more labile; thus 2-chlorophenazine-5,10-dioxide (I) on treatment with alcoholic potassium hydroxide readily yields 2-phenazinol-5,10-dioxide, which can be reduced to 2-phenazinol (II) by means of sodium dithionite.[3, 4] 2-Chlorophenazine-5-oxide likewise yields

2-ethoxyphenazine-5-oxide in 91% yield (24 hours reflux); but the
10-oxide yields a mixture of 2-phenazinol-10-oxide and 2-ethoxy-

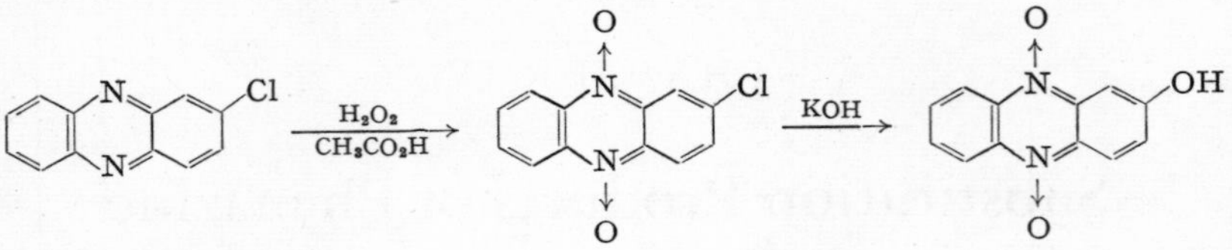

(I)

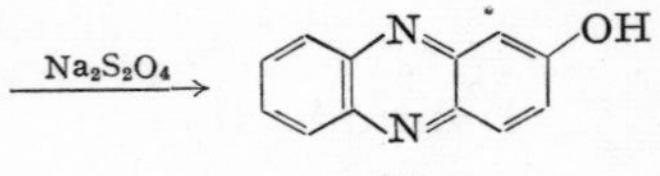

(II)

phenazine-10-oxide. 1-Chlorophenazine-5-oxide is less reactive than
either of the two preceding oxides, being comparable in reactivity to
2-chlorophenazine. The action of alkali on 2,7-dichlorophenazine-5-
oxide (III) leads to replacement of the 7-chlorine atom.[2]

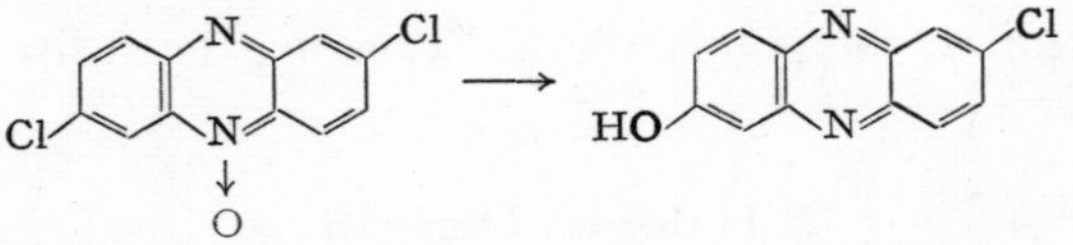

(III)

The only other halogen substitution products of the phenazines to
deserve special discussion are those related to the N-phenylphenazinium
salts and which are obtained from oxygen-containing substances
derived from the safranines and indulines by the action of phosphorus
pentachloride (compare the formation of chloropyridines from the
pyridones). 2-Chloro-10-phenylphenazinium chloride (aposafranone
chloride) (V) separates from a mixture of ethanol and ether in brownish-
yellow crystals with a blue iridescence and is readily soluble in water.
It is formed by the action of phosphorus pentachloride (1 mole) in
phosphoryl chloride solution on aposafranone (IV).[5] It reacts with

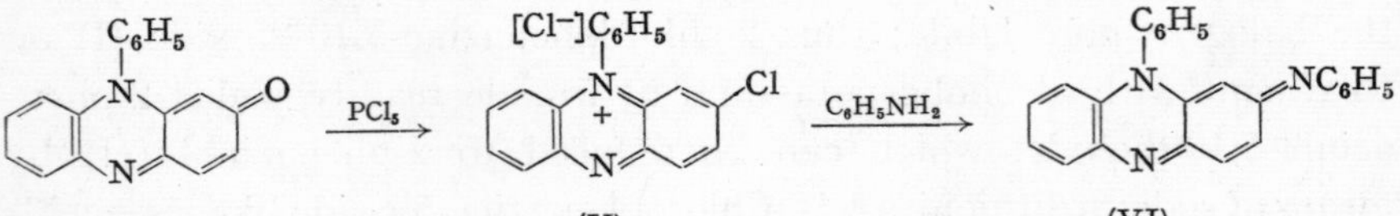

(IV)   (V)   (VI)

potassium iodide to form the less soluble 2-chloro-10-phenylphenazinium iodide[6] and with ammonia in aqueous solution or with aniline, on warming in ethanol, to form aposafranine and phenylaposafranine

TABLE V. Halogen Substitution Products of Phenazine

Substituents	M.p.(°C.)	Derivatives	Ref.
1-Chloro-	122–123	Chloroaurate, m.p. 232–234° (dec.); 5-oxide, m.p. 159–160°	1(b), 2
2-Fluoro-	180.8–181.2		45
2-Chloro-	137.7–138.9 (corr.)	5,10-Dioxide, red-orange needles, m.p. 190–191° (corr.); 5-oxide, m.p. 178°; 10-oxide, m.p. 175–176°	2, 3, 11, 12, 45, 48
2-Bromo-	149–150		11, 45
2-Iodo-	169.5–170		45
2,7-Difluoro-		5-Oxide, m.p. 150° (dec.), sublimes/110° in vacuo	13
1,3-Dichloro-	187		46
1,4-Dichloro-	194–195		1(a)
1,6-Dichloro-	266–267		14
2,7-Dichloro-	266–268	5-Oxide, yellow needles, m.p. 237.5–238° (dec.); 5,10-dioxide, red-orange, explodes at 220°	2, 4, 15, 47
x,y-Dichloro-	144		16
2,7-Dibromo-	244.5–245	5-Oxide, m.p. 242.5°	15
2,7-Diiodo-	235	5-Oxide, m.p. 241° (dec.)	15
1,4,6-Trichloro-	215		1(a)
1,2,3,4-Tetrachloro-	235		17, 46
1,2,4,7-Tetrachloro-	167		46
1,2,4,8-Tetrachloro-	211		46
1,3,4,6-Tetrachloro-	207		46
1,3,6,8-Tetrachloro-	223		46
1,4,6,8-Tetrachloro-	210		46
1,4,6,9-Tetrachloro-	325		1(a)

(VI),[5, 6] respectively. Thus, one chlorine atom is ionic and the other is reactive and easily exchangeable. The electrical conductivity has been studied by Hantzsch and Osswald.[7]

2,8-Dichloro-10-phenylphenazinium chloride (VIII), which separates from ethanol as reddish-yellow needles, readily soluble in water, is likewise formed from phenosafranol (VII).[8] Here, all the chlorine atoms exhibit a different reactivity. One is ionic and is exchanged with other ions. A second chlorine atom is reactive and is readily replaced by other groups; thus, by boiling with aqueous sodium acetate solution,

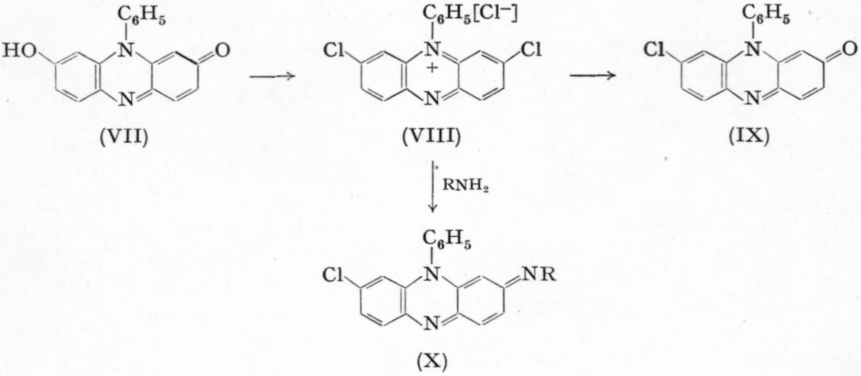

C_6H_5

HO—[N]—O

(VII)

$\longrightarrow$

$C_6H_5[Cl^-]$

Cl—[N+]—Cl

(VIII)

$\longrightarrow$

C_6H_5

Cl—[N]—O

(IX)

(VIII) $\downarrow$ RNH$_2$

C_6H_5

Cl—[N]—NR

(X)

8-chloro-10-phenyl-2(10)-phenazinone (IX) is produced. The remaining chlorine atom is not replaced by OH even with 50% alcoholic potassium hydroxide solution in a sealed tube at 150°. The dichlorophenazinium salts react immediately in the cold with bases, one chlorine atom being displaced, giving X. To displace the other chlorine atom, strong heating with excess of base has to be resorted to.[9] For an example of the replacement of NO_2 by Cl in a phenazine derivative, see reference 10.

3. Nitro Derivatives

Claus[18] claimed to have prepared a mononitrophenazine, forming yellow-green needles, m.p. 209–210° and which could be sublimed without decomposition, by boiling phenazine with a mixture of fuming nitric and sulfuric acids. Under different conditions, he obtained a red dinitro compound, m.p. 131°, which did not sublime. Later investigators appear to have been unable to repeat this work. Kehrmann and Havas,[19] however, using a mixture of concentrated nitric and sulfuric acids at a temperature of 130°, claimed a 66% yield of 1,3-dinitrophenazine, crystallizing from xylene as straw-yellow needles, decomposing above 200° with darkening. Since the entry of the second nitro group into the benzene ring already containing one such group is very unlikely, Albert and Duewell[20] attempted to repeat this work. The product, after being freed from phenazine (by extraction with hot, dilute hydrochloric acid) crystallized from acetic acid as yellow crystals that began to melt at 177°, but left a small residue that melted at 250°; crystallization from various solvents failed to separate this mixture. Analysis suggested that this product consisted of a mixture of mono- (mainly) and di-nitrophenazines. It was therefore reduced (with hydrogen and Raney nickel at room temperature and atmospheric pressure in acetone); the resulting mixture of dihydrophenazine derivatives rapidly absorbed oxygen, giving 1-aminophenazine, together with small amounts of two other substances, apparently diaminophenazines. Both of the latter substances were red; one decomposed above 250° and gave a yellow color with sulfuric acid, the other melted at 214° and is probably 1,9-diaminophenazine. Neither is identical with any of the four known diaminophenazines (1,3; 2,3; 2,7; 2,8).

A red, crystalline compound, m.p. 192–195°, probably 1-nitro-phenazine (XI), was obtained by Preston, Tucker and Cameron[21] by heating 2,6-dinitrodiphenylamine-4-carboxylic acid with quinoline and copper powder.

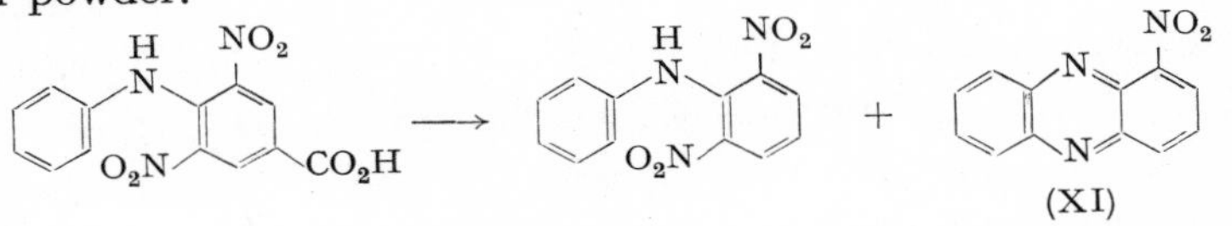

Nitration of 5,10-diacetyl-5,10-dihydrophenazine in acetic acid with concentrated nitric acid on the water-bath affords a mixture of 5,10-diacetyl-5,10-dihydro-2-nitrophenazine (XII) (pale yellow prisms, m.p. 166°, reduced by stannous chloride in hydrochloric acid to 2-aminophenazine) and 2-nitrophenazine (XIII) (yellow, m.p. 214°; sublimes without decomposition).[19]

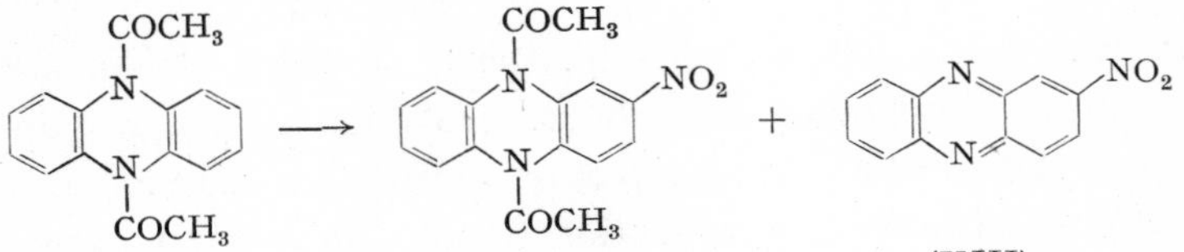

Nitration of phenazine-5-oxide has been reported to yield two dinitrophenazine-5-oxides, m.p. 240° and 269°, respectively.[22] The earlier claim[23] to have obtained a dinitrophenazine by the action of bleaching powder on *m*-nitraniline was shown to be erroneous; the product is actually a dinitroazobenzene.[24]

Nitration of 2-methoxyphenazine gives 2-methoxy-1-nitrophenazine, m.p. 233°. Nitration of 2-phenazinol (2-hydroxyphenazine) with potassium nitrate and concentrated sulfuric acid below 5° yields 1-nitro-2-phenazinol, m.p. 223° (XIV), the structure of which has been proved as follows:[25]

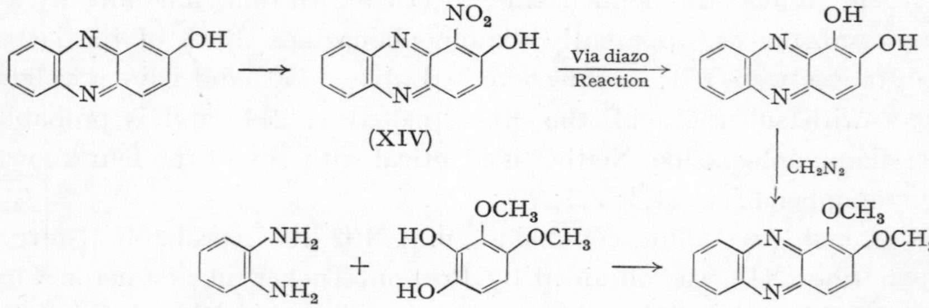

(XIV)

The action of alkali on 1'-methylamino-2,6-dinitrodiphenylamine gives a product (see Chapter III:2,C) that on treatment with ferric chloride affords a 1-nitro-5-methylphenazinium salt (that is, the methosalt derived from 1-nitrophenazine) (XV). Analogous di- and tri-nitro compounds are similarly obtained.[26, 27]

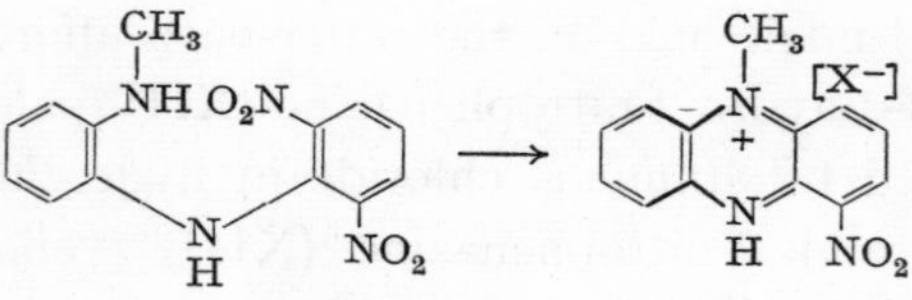

(XV)

Addendum. 1-Nitrophenazine (m.p. 195°), 1,6-dinitrophenazine (m.p. 343°) and 1,9-dinitrophenazine (m.p. 273°) have been obtained by Maffei and Aymon[49] by direct nitration of phenazine. In each case the orientation was proved by reduction to the amino- or diamino- compounds and the latter were converted into the known 1,6- and 1,9-dimethoxyphenazine. 2-Nitrophenazine (m.p. 226°) was prepared by cyclization of 2,4-diaminodiphenylamine.

4. Sulfones

2-Phenazyl-phenylsulfone (XVI) crystallizes from acetic acid in yellow lustrous leaflets m.p. 244°, and is precipitated when phenazine is warmed to 30–40° in alcoholic hydrogen chloride solution with benzene sulfinic acid (0.5 mole). Its formation has been used in support of the quinonoid conception of the phenazine nucleus, as benzenesulfinic acid reacts similarly with quinones.[28]

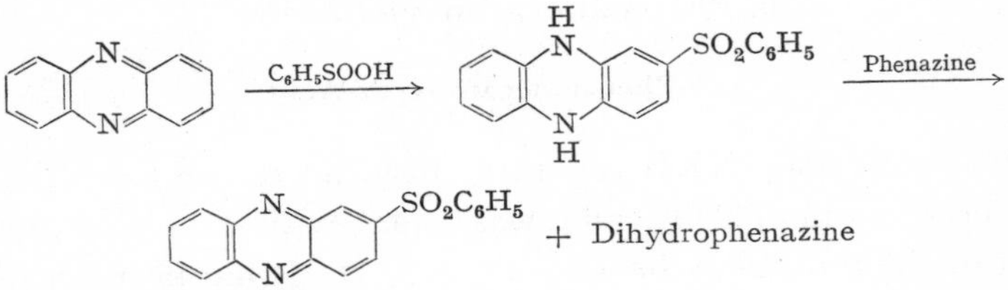

5. Sulfonic Acids

Maffei[29] has made an extensive study of the sulfonation of phenazine; very energetic conditions are necessary to bring about the reaction. Monosulfonation is best effected with oleum containing 50–70% of sulfur trioxide in the presence of mercuric sulfate at 160–170° for seven hours; but some phenazine remains unattacked and polysulfonic acids are also produced. The resulting 2-phenazinesulfonic acid (XVII), which probably exists as a betaine, is brilliant yellow and decomposes above 380°. When its sodium salt is heated with potassium cyanide at

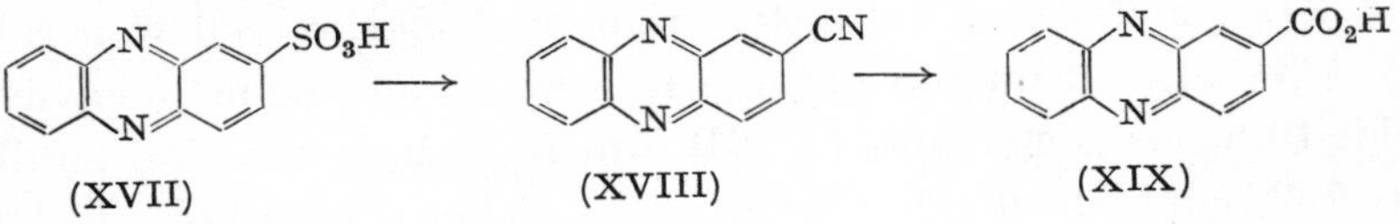

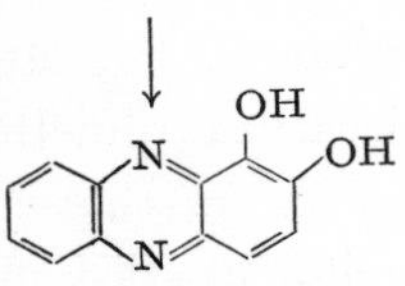

150°, phenazine-2-carbonitrile (XVIII) is formed; the structure is proved by hydrolysis with alcoholic sodium hydroxide to 2-phenazinecarboxylic acid (XIX). The fusion of sodium 2-phenazinesulfonate with potassium hydroxide gives a 25% yield of 1,2-phenazinediol (XX) (compare the formation of alizarin). Distillation of the alkali salts of the sulfonic acid yields phenazine, but the sulfonic acid group cannot be replaced by NH_2 or NO_2 (with ammonium hydroxide or sodamide, or with nitric acid, repectively). See also Chapter II:2,B.

6. Phenazinecarboxylic Acids

A. 1-Phenazinecarboxylic Acid

This compound (XXI) separates from acetic acid or ethanol as yellow needles, m.p. 239°, and was isolated first as a degradation product of chlororaphine (see Chapter X:2,D). It has been synthesized by Kögl and Postowsky[30] by the interaction of anthranilic acid and nitrobenzene in the presence of sodium hydroxide at 145–160°, and by Clemo and McIlwain[31] by the oxidation of 1-methylphenazine with chromium trioxide in acetic acid. Later workers[32] found the latter

(XXI)

method satisfactory; but were unable to repeat the preparation of Kögl. Its amide separates from methanol as bright yellow needles, m.p. 241°; and its methyl ester from methanol as yellow needles, m.p. 123–124°.[33] Reduction of the latter with lithium aluminum hydride yields 1-phenazinemethanol (XXII), which sublimes as yellow needles, m.p. 132°, and which can be oxidized to 1-phenazinecarboxyaldehyde (XXIII) (yellow needles, m.p. 175°, from 80% methanol). The latter compound can also be obtained from phenazine-1-carboxydimethyl-amide by reduction with lithium aluminum hydride; its thiosemi-carbazone separates from 94% ethanol as orange-yellow needles, m.p. 241°.[33–35] From the methyl ester, by the action of hydroxylamine, phenazine-1-hydroxamic acid (yellow needles, m.p. 207° from ethanol-dioxan) can also be obtained and by the action of hydrazine, phenazine-

1-carbonhydrazide (silky yellow needles, m.p. 231° from 70% ethanol) which gives a benzenesulfonyl derivative, m.p. 233°.[36]

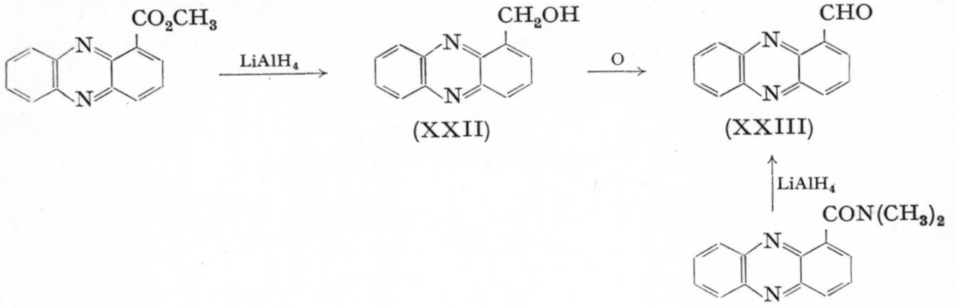

B. 2-Phenazinecarboxylic Acid

This compound (XXIV) separates from acetone as yellow needles, m.p. 292–293°, and can be sublimed. It was synthesized by Kögl, Tönnis and Groenewegen[37] by condensing o-bromonitrobenzene with 3,4-diaminobenzoic acid in an Ullmann reaction, reducing the resulting diphenylamine derivative with stannous chloride and hydrochloric acid and oxidizing the product with hydrogen peroxide. Clemo and McIlwain[38] also prepared it by oxidation of 2-methylphenazine. When a mixture of nitrobenzene and p-toluidine is subjected to the modified Wohl-Aue reaction, 2-phenazinecarboxylic acid-10-oxide (m.p. 263°) is obtained.[36] The corresponding 5,10-dioxide decomposes at 280° and is readily reduced by sodium dithionite to 2-phenazinecarboxylic acid. The amide separates from acetone as pale yellow lozenges m.p. 312°. For its nitrile see Chapters II:2,B and IV:5. 8-Methylphenazine-2-carbonitrile separates from ethanol as pale yellow plates, m.p. 248°, and the corresponding 8-chloro-compound from amyl alcohol as pale yellow needles, m.p. 317°.[39]

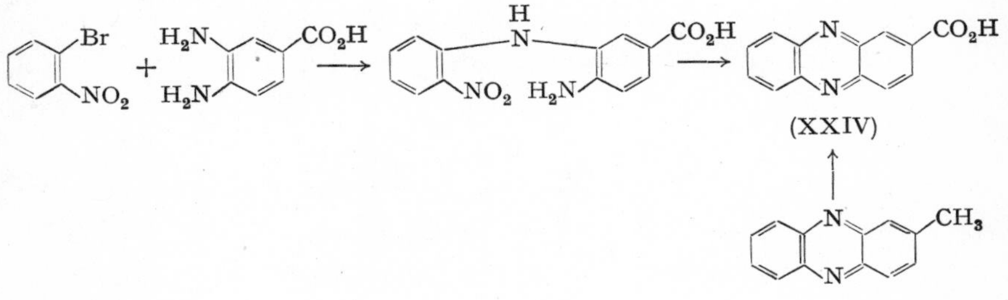

Addendum.   Pietra, Maffei and Rivolta[50] have, by standard methods, prepared the following derivatives of 2-phenazinecarboxylic acid: methyl ester, m.p. 153°; diethylamide, m.p. 97.5–98°; hydrazide, m.p. 269–270° (dec.); azide, m.p. 135° (dec.). Degradation of the latter yielded 2-aminophenazine.

C. Phenazinedicarboxylic Acids

The formation of phenazine-1,6-dicarboxylic acid (m.p. > 300°) by the action of tropical sunlight on a solution of anthranilic acid in dilute hydrochloric acid has been claimed.[40] This acid has also been synthesized by Birkofer and Widmann,[36] by the Wohl-Aue reaction on a mixture of *o*-nitrobenzoic acid and anthranilic acid at 50–85°. These authors state that it is soluble in concentrated sulfuric acid with a red coloration, but very sparingly soluble in organic solvents; at 300–320° it carbonizes without melting. The diethyl ester separates from ethanol as green needles, m.p. 143°. The synthesis of phenazine-2,7-dicarboxylic acid (dichloride, yellow needles from benzene, m.p. 214°; no analytical data given) by Schubert[41] is described in Chapter IV: 7.

7. Sirius Light Yellow R. R. (C. I. 814)

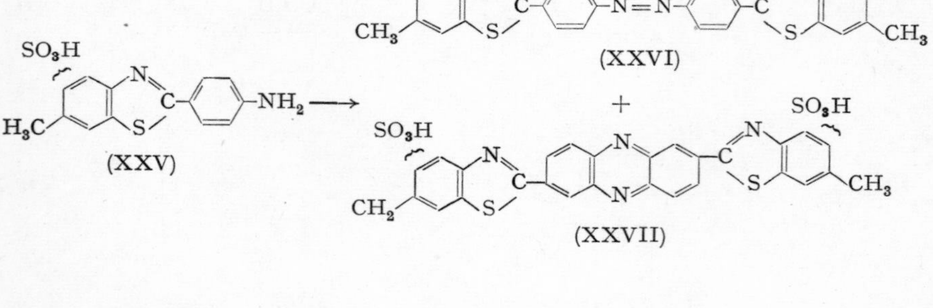

This light-fast dye, which is also known as Naphthamine Yellow N or Chlorazol Fast Yellow B, is obtained by the oxidation of de-hydrothio-*p*-toluidinesulfonic acid (XXV) with sodium hypochlorite. An azo structure (XXVI) (or perhaps the corresponding azoxy structure) was suggested for it[42]; but the work of Schubert[41] has shown the dye to consist of a mixture of XXVI with a phenazine derivative (XXVII) (the positions of the sulfonic acid groups in the molecule have not been definitely established). Thus, on reduction with stannous chloride and hydrochloric acid, it yields a deep violet, crystalline precipitate (25% the weight of the dye) and the filtrate contains dehydrothio-p-toluidinesulfonic acid (60%), the latter arising by splitting of the azo component. The violet compound is oxidized by nitrous or nitric acid to an orange-yellow dye, which can be reduced back to the violet compound by stannous chloride and hydrochloric acid and is, presumably, a phenazine semiquinone (see Chapter III:2,B). A product apparently identical with that isolated from the dye was synthesized in the following way, although the intermediate stages were not all satisfactorily characterized and analyzed:

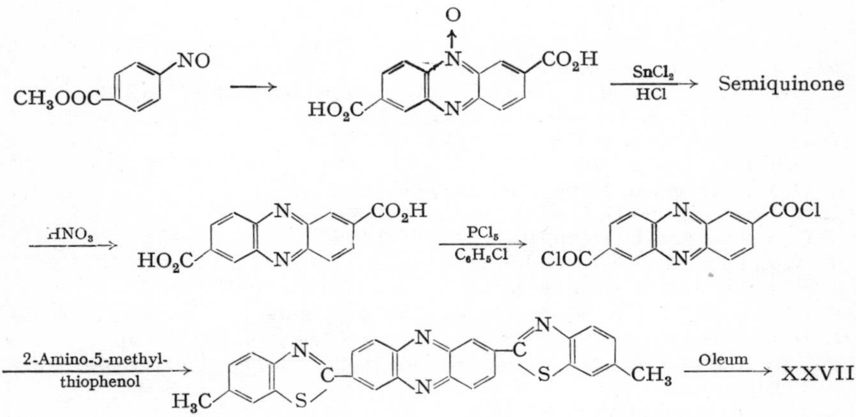

8. Arsonic Acids

The oxidation of p-aminobenzenearsonic acid in sulfuric acid with ammonium persulfate is reported to yield phenazine-2,7-diarsonic acid (XXVIII), which forms light brown leaflets, m.p. > 300°, and has little effect on trypanosomes.[43] Apart from the analytical data, the only evidence for the phenazine structure of this compound is the production of a blood-red color with concentrated sulfuric acid (see Chapter I:9).

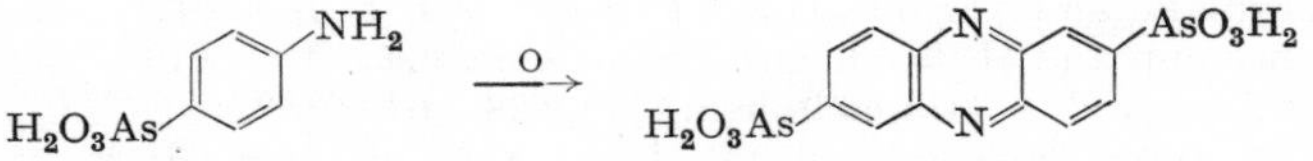

(XXVIII)

Karrer[44] prepared 2-(or 3)-dimethylaminophenazine-8-arsonic acid (XXIX) by condensing 3,4-dinitrosobenzenearsonic acid with dimethylaniline. The corresponding 9-arsonic acid and 2,3-diaminophenazine-7-arsonic acid were prepared similarly.

References

1(a). S. Maffei, S. Pietra and A. Cattaneo, *Gazz. chim. ital.*, **83**, 327 (1953).
1(b). F. Wrede and O. Mühlroth, *Ber.*, **63B**, 1931 (1930).
2. I. J. Pachter and M. C. Kloetzel, *J. Am. Chem. Soc.*, **74**, 971 (1952).
3. D. L. Vivian, *J. Am. Chem. Soc.*, **71**, 1139 (1949).
4. D. L. Vivian, *J. Am. Chem. Soc.*, **73**, 457 (1951).
5. O. Fischer and E. Hepp, *Ber.*, **30**, 1827 (1897).
6. O. Fischer and E. Hepp, *Ber.*, **33**, 1485 (1900).
7. A. Hantzsch and G. Osswald, *Ber.*, **33**, 278 (1900).
8. O. Fischer and E. Hepp, *Ber.*, **31**, 299 (1898).
9. K. Balls, J. T. Hewitt and S. H. Newman, *J. Chem. Soc.*, **101**, 1840 (1912).
10. H. Leemann and E. Grandmougin, *Ber.*, **41**, 1295 (1908).
11. H. McCombie, H. A. Scarborough and W. A. Waters, *J. Chem. Soc.*, **1928**, 353.
12. H. C. Waterman and D. L. Vivian, *J. Org. Chem.*, **14**, 289 (1949).
13. I. J. Rinkes, *Chem. Weekblad*, **16**, 206 (1919); through *Chem. Zentr.*, **1919**, I, 820.
14. I. J. Pachter and M. C. Kloetzel, *J. Am. Chem. Soc.*, **73**, 4958 (1951).
15. E. Bamberger and W. Ham, *Ann.*, **382**, 82 (1911).
16. A. Claus, *Ber.*, **8**, 600 (1875).
17. L. Horner and H. Merz, *Ann.*, **570**, 89 (1950).
18. A. Claus, *Ber.*, **8**, 37 (1875).
19. F. Kehrmann and E. Havas, *Ber.*, **46**, 341 (1913).
20. A. Albert and H. Duewell, *J. Soc. Chem. Ind. London*, **66**, 11 (1947).
21. R. W. G. Preston, S. H. Tucker and J. M. L. Cameron, *J. Chem. Soc.*, **1942**, 500.
22. A. Wohl, *Ber.*, **36**, 4139 (1903).
23. Ger. Pat. 78,748; *Frdl.*, **4**, 372 (1894–97).
24. W. Meigen and W. Norman, *Ber.*, **33**, 2711 (1900).
25. B. Hegedüs, *Jubilee Vol. Emil Barell*, **1946**, 388; *Chem. Abstracts*, **41**, 6262 (1947).
26. F. Kehrmann and J. Effront, *Helv. Chim. Acta*, **4**, 517 (1921).
27. F. Kehrmann and H. Goldstein, *Helv. Chim. Acta*, **4**, 26 (1921).
28. O. Hinsberg and A. Himmelschein, *Ber.*, **29**, 2019 (1896).
29. S. Maffei, *Gazz. chim. ital.*, **80**, 651 (1950); through *Chem. Abstracts*, **45**, 9063 (1951).

30. F. Kögl and J. J. Postowsky, *Ann.*, **480**, 280 (1930).
31. G. R. Clemo and H. McIlwain, *J. Chem. Soc.*, **1934**, 1991.
32. O. Schales, S. S. Schales, and D. A. Friedman, *Arch. Biochem.*, **6**, 329 (1945).
33. L. Birkofer and A. Birkofer, *Chem. Ber.*, **85**, 286 (1952).
34. L. Birkofer, *Angew. Chem.*, **64**, 111 (1952).
35. L. Birkofer, *Chem. Ber.*, **85**, 1023 (1952).
36. L. Birkofer and A. Widmann, *Chem. Ber.*, **86**, 1295 (1953).
37. F. Kögl and B. Tönnis (with H. J. Groenewegen), *Ann.*, **497**, 265 (1932).
38. G. R. Clemo and H. McIlwain, *J. Chem. Soc.*, **1935**, 738.
39. G. G. Coker, S. G. P. Plant and P. B. Turner, *J. Chem. Soc.*, **1951**, 110.
40. B. K. Malaviya and S. Dutt, *Proc. Acad. Sci. United Provinces Agra Oudh.*, *India*, **4**, 319 (1935); through *Chem. Abstracts*, **30**, 1056, (1936).
41. M. Schubert, *Ann.*, **558**, 10 (1947).
42. H. E. Fierz-David, *Helv. Chim. Acta*, **27**, 1 (1944).
43. M. Barrowcliff, F. L. Pyman and F. G. P. Remfry, *J. Chem. Soc.*, **93**, 1893 (1908).
44. P. Karrer, *Ber.*, **46**, 249 (1913).
45. D. L. Vivian and J. L. Hartwell, *J. Org. Chem.*, **18**, 1065 (1953).
46. S. Maffei, S. Pietra and A. Cattaneo, *Gazz. chim. ital.*, **83**, 812 (1953).
47. G. Heller, W. Dietrich and G. Reichardt, *J. prakt. Chem.*, [2], **118**, 144 (1928).
48. S. Maffei, S. Pietra and A. Cattaneo, *Gazz. chim. ital.*, **84**, 746 (1954).
49. S. Maffei and M. Aymon, *Gazz. chim. ital.*, **84**, 667 (1954).
50. S. Pietra, S. Maffei and A. Rivolta, *Ann. chim. (Rome)*, **43**, 227 (1953); through *Chem. Abstracts*, **48**, 11426 (1954).

CHAPTER V

Hydroxy and Keto Derivatives
of Phenazine

1. Introduction

The hydroxyphenazines are tautomeric substances. Thus, 1-phenazinol (I) is tautomeric with 1(5H)-phenazinone (II); and 2-phenazinol (III) is tautomeric with 2(10H)-phenazinone or 2,10-dihydro-2-ketophenazine (IV), which Kehrmann[1] termed "phenazone,"

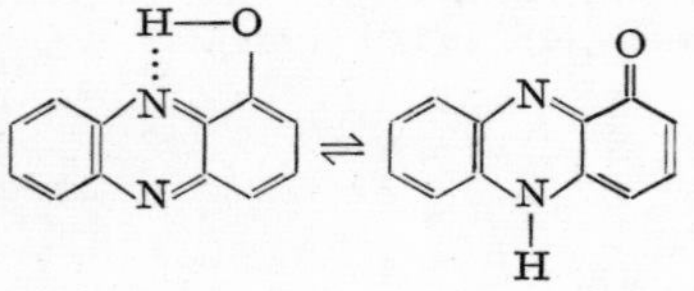

(I)   (II)

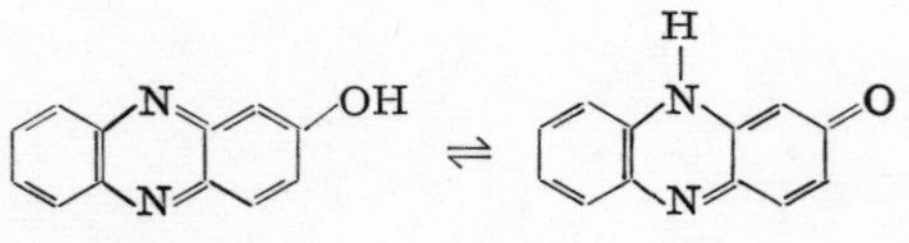

(III)   (IV)

although unfortunately the latter name is also applied to benzo[c]-cinnoline and to antipyrine. The introduction of the auxochromic hydroxyl group converts the azines into coloring matters, to which the name "eurhodols" has been applied.[2] These are of no technical importance.

2. Monohydroxy and Monoketo Derivatives

The more important known monohydroxy- and monoalkoxy-phenazines are listed in Table VI. For convenience in tabulation, the phenazinols are there named as hydroxyphenazines.

A. 1-Phenazinol

1-Phenazinol, 1-hydroxyphenazine or hemipyocyanine (I) separates from ethanol as orange crystals, m.p. 157–158°, and can be sublimed. Its absorption in the ultraviolet and infrared suggests that it exists exclusively in the phenazinol form, which is stabilized by hydrogen-bonding,[3,125] but see Chapter III:2,b. In the presence of copper ions, 1-phenazinol polymerizes to form a fibrous substance, which has been investigated under the electron microscope.[125] 1-Phenazinol gives red solutions in mineral acids and in alkali, the latter being decolorized by carbon dioxide. It occurs in cultures of *Pseudomonas aeruginosa* (see Chapter XI:2) and was first obtained in 1928 by Wrede and Strack[4,5] by demethylation of its methyl ether (VI) (see Chapter X:1,D); a recent paper describes the preparation of this compound by heating pyrogallol (V) with o-phenylenediamine in a sealed tube.[6] A good

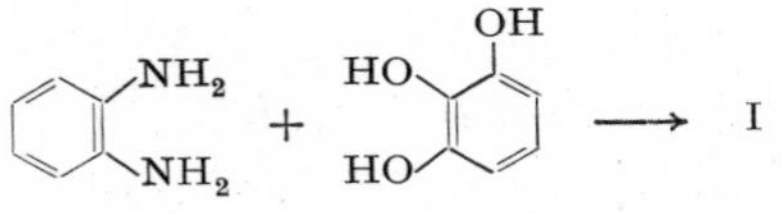

(V)

preparative method seems to be that of Hegedüs[7]: heating 1-amino-phenazine with dilute sulfuric acid or (better) dilute phosphoric acid under pressure at 150–160° (yield: 53%). See also reference 130.

When 1-phenazinol is heated at 180–185° with phenol in the presence of ammonia and cupric acetate, it gives 1-aminophenazine.[8]

1-Methoxyphenazine (VI) separates from ethanol as bright yellow needles, m.p. 169°, and is obtained by condensing 3-methoxy-o-quinone with o-phenylenediamine.[9] The quinone has an oxidizing action on the diamine, so that, besides resinous products, 2,3-diaminophenazine is

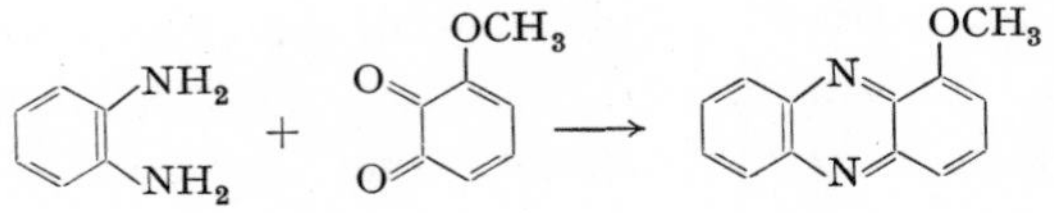

(VI)

also formed; the optimum yield of VI (33%) is obtained in very dilute solutions. For 5-ethyl-1(5)-phenazinone see Chapter II:2,C.

B. 2-Phenazinol

Known also as 2-hydroxyphenazine (III), this compound separates from ethanol as golden-yellow crystals, m.p. 253–254° (unsharp),[10] and sublimes as a yellow powder.[11] Solutions of the base in alkali are orange-red and those in concentrated sulfuric acid are dichroic, being olive-green in thin layers and ·blood-red in thick layers; on dilution with water, the color changes to golden yellow.[12] It was first prepared in 1924 by Kehrmann and Cherpillod[12,13] by the condensation of 2-hydroxyquinone (VII) with o-phenylenediamine. It has also been

(VII)

obtained by heating 2-aminophenazine with 15% hydrochloric acid at 180°[14] and by boiling 2-chlorophenazine-5,10-dioxide with aqueous-alcoholic sodium hydroxide solution, followed by reduction with alkaline sodium dithionite (see Chapter IV:2).[10,15] See also reference 130 and Chapter II:2,B.

2-Methoxyphenazine separates from water as yellow needles, m.p. 123°,[16,17] although a preparation crystallized from light petroleum is reported to melt at 112°.[11] The best methods of preparation appear to be those of Tomlinson[16] and of Waterman and Vivian,[17] although this compound has also been obtained by the action of diazomethane on 2-phenazinol.[11]

A comparison of the ultraviolet spectra of 2-phenazinol (III) and 2-methoxyphenazine shows the former to be tautomeric with 2(10H)-phenazinone (IV). In alcoholic solution, the former structure predominates; but, in water, the deeper color of the latter is apparent.[3] In the case of certain derivatives of 2-phenazinol, such as 1,3,4-trimethyl-2-phenazinol, the two tautomeric forms have been isolated, one being yellow (phenolic) and the other violet (keto). The transition from one form to the other can be followed colorimetrically and depends on the nature of the solvent; hence it has been investigated as a method for the analysis of organic solvent mixtures.[18,19] The effect of the solvent on the color and fluorescence of such compounds has been investigated

TABLE VI. Monohydroxy and Monoalkoxy Derivatives of Phenazine

Substituents	Appearance	M.p. (°C.)	Derivatives, etc.	Ref.
1-Hydroxy-	Orange	157–158	Acetyl, yellow needles, m.p. 123°; 5,10-dioxide, red prisms, m.p. 189–190°; 5-oxide, orange needles, m.p. 190° (dec.)	4–8, 85–89, 126, 127, 130
1-Methoxy-	Yellow needles	169	Mono-N-oxide, golden plates, m.p. 196–198°, dec. 210°; methosulfate, red, m.p. 201° (dec.)	5, 9, 85, 123, 126, 128–130
1-Ethoxy-	Yellow	130	Picrate, red, m.p. 195°; 5-oxide, yellow needles, m.p. 192°; mono-N-oxide. m.p. 181–182°, dec. 214–217°	89, 90, 123
2-Hydroxy-	Yellow needles	253–254 (unsharp)	Acetyl, pale yellow, m.p. 152°; 5,10-dioxide, orange-red, darkens 236°; 10-oxide, yellow, m.p. 258°	10–15, 89, 126, 127, 130
2-Methoxy-	Yellow needles	123 or 112	N-Oxide, yellow needles, m.p. 175–176°	11, 16, 17, 91, 126, 128
2-Ethoxy-	Yellow needles	114–115	5-Oxide, yellow needles, m.p. 155°; 10-oxide, needles, m.p. 171°, or prisms, m.p. 168°	89, 130
1-Phenoxy-3-methyl-	Yellow needles	100.5–101.8		92
1-Methoxy-6-methyl-	Yellow needles	190	Picrate, red-brown, m.p. 178–179°	90
1-Ethoxy-6-methyl-	Yellow needles	161.5–162.5	Picrate, red, m.p. 171°	90
1-Methoxy-8-methyl-	Yellow	182–182.5		90
1-Ethoxy-8-methyl-	Yellow	141–141.5	Picrate, m.p. 197° (dec.)	90
1-Methoxy-8-chloro-	Yellow needles	209–211	Conc. $H_2SO_4 \rightarrow$ deep green color	93
1-Ethoxy-8-chloro-	Yellow needles	149–150	Conc. $H_2SO_4 \rightarrow$ deep green color	93
2-Hydroxy-3-methyl-	Brown-yellow needles	295 or 263 (dec.)		19, 94

(Table continued)

TABLE VI (*continued*)

Substituents	Appearance	M.p. (°C.)	Derivatives, etc.	Ref.
2-Hydroxy-7-(or 8)-methyl-	Orange-red	248	Acetyl, pale yellow, m.p. 207°	12
2-Methoxy-8-methyl-	Yellow needles	135		16
2-Hydroxy-1-nitro-	Yellow	223	Acetyl, yellow needles, m.p. 198°	11
2-Methoxy-1-nitro-	Yellow	233		11
2-Hydroxy-7-nitro-	Red-brown needles		Acetyl, m.p. 224–227°. Conc. $H_2SO_4 \rightarrow$ dichroic soln.; $H_2O \rightarrow$ orange	95
2-Hydroxy-8-nitro-	Orange		Acetyl, m.p. 211°	95
2-Hydroxy-7-chloro-	Yellow needles	270.5–271.5° (dec.)	5-Oxide, dec. 260°	15, 89, 130
2-Hydroxy-7-bromo-	Yellow needles	256–258 (dec.)		130
2-Hydroxy-8-chloro-	Yellow needles	277–278.5 (dec.)		130
2-Hydroxy-8-bromo-	Yellow needles	249–251 (dec.)		130
2-Methoxy-7-chloro-	Yellow needles	173–174	10-Oxide, m.p. 207° (dec.); 5-oxide, m.p. 209° (dec.)	89, 93
2-Methoxy-7-bromo-	Yellow needles	172–174		130
2-Ethoxy-7-chloro-	Yellow needles	183–184 (sint. 180)	Conc. $H_2SO_4 \rightarrow$ deep violet; 10-oxide, m.p. 213–214° (dec.)	89, 93
2-Ethoxy-7-bromo-	Yellow needles	164–166		130
2-Methoxy-8-chloro-	Yellow needles	151–152		93
2-Methoxy-8-bromo-	Yellow needles	155–156		130
2-Ethoxy-8-chloro-	Yellow needles	171–172		93
2-Ethoxy-8-bromo-	Yellow needles	168–170		130
2-Phenoxy-8-chloro-	Yellow prisms or plates	176–177		130

spectroscopically. Thus, in the case of 1,3,4-trimethyl-2-phenazinol these properties are connected with the absorption band in the visible region (526 mμ). The intensity of this band increases with the polarity of the solvent (ethyl acetate < methanol < acetic acid), the color of the solution thus deepening (yellow, red, dark red); but the fluorescence correspondingly decreases in intensity. Hydrogen bonding between the solvent and the oxygen atom of the phenazinol is thus probably concerned in the color-change.[20,124]

C. Aposafranone

Aposafranone, 10-phenyl-2(10)-phenazinone (IX), is the *N*-phenyl derivative of IV and is formed from aposafranine (VIII) by exchange of NH for O. It was first prepared by Jaubert[21] in 1895. A compound termed "benzeneindone" and formulated as IX by Fischer and Hepp[22,23] was later shown to possess a different structure.[24]

It separates from benzene as ruby-red leaflets with a golden luster, m.p. 242°,[25] or from ethanol as needles with a greenish luster, m.p. 248–249°,[26] readily soluble in ethanol and difficultly soluble in hot water, giving a magenta solution. Its solution in concentrated sulfuric acid is dichroic, being green in thin layers, but red in thick layers.[21,26] Solutions in dilute mineral acids are reddish-yellow. It is very feebly basic in properties and does not form an acetate.[27]

It is obtained from aposafranine (VIII) by heating the aqueous solution at 180° under pressure[24] or by the action of 75% sulfuric acid,[21] or by boiling for a few minutes with very dilute sodium hydroxide solution[28] (alcoholic potassium hydroxide yields 3-hydroxy-10-phenyl-2(10)-phenazinone (XXIV)).[24] Aposafranone is also obtained in 50% yield by the action of dilute sodium hydroxide solution in the presence of air on the 5-phenylphenazinium salts[25,29] (see Chapter II:2 D). Synthetically, it is prepared by heating 2-anilino-2',4'-dinitrodiphenylamine (XI) in benzoic acid solution,[26] and in very low yield, by the condensation of hydroxyquinone (VII) with 2-aminodiphenylamine (XII).[12]

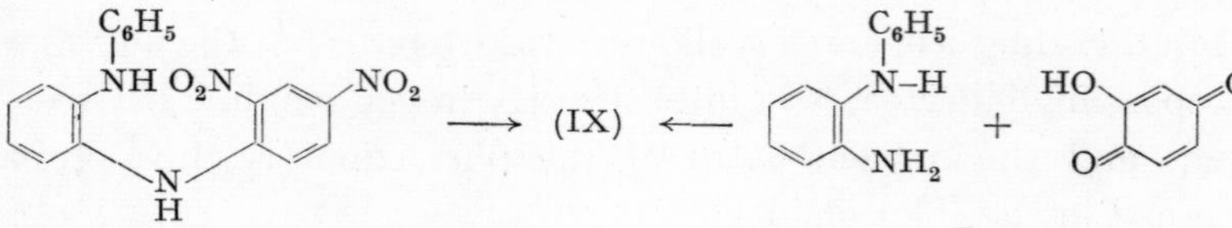

The rival merits of the p-quinonoid keto (IX) and the o-quinonoid phenol-betaine formulas, the modern version of the latter being X, have been discussed.[30,31] The failure of isorosindone (see Chapter XIV:2,C,(2)) to react with phenylmagnesium bromide even at 130–140° was thought by Decker and Würsch[31] to favor the latter structure. In fact, aposafranone is probably a resonance hybrid involving structures IX and X.

The action of phosphorus pentachloride (1 mole) in phosphoryl chloride solution on aposafranone yields 2-chloro-10-phenylphenazinium chloride (aposafranone chloride)[32] (see Chapter IV:2). With anionoid reagents, such as ammonia (in concentrated alcoholic solution in the presence of ammonium chloride under pressure at 140°)[33] and aniline (in the presence of aniline hydrochloride),[24] aposafranone undergoes substitution in position 3, yielding the corresponding amino or anilino derivative, respectively. The action of hydroxylamine, at first believed to yield aposafranone oxime,[34,35] in fact leads to the isomeric 3-aminoaposafranone.[33] (For analogous cases, see references 36 and 37.)

Derivatives of apoethosafranone (10-ethyl-2(10)-phenazinone) are also known.[38,39] See also Chapter II:2,C.

D. 3-Hydroxy-10-phenylphenazinium Salts

Prasindones is the name used by Kehrmann[40,41] in reference to compounds isomeric with the aposafranones but having the oxygen atom in the p-position to the phenylated nitrogen atom. The simplest prasindone (XIII) has not been isolated, although its salts, 3-hydroxy-10-phenylphenazinium salts (XIV), exist.

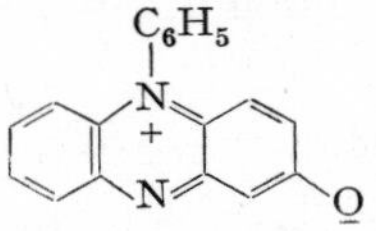

(XIII) 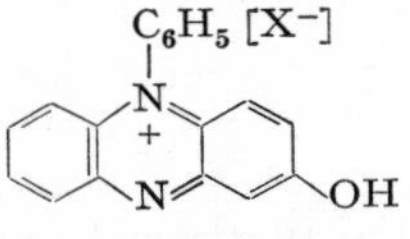   (XIV)

The name "prasindones" (from πράσιος = leek green) was suggested because, in contrast to the red compounds of the aposafranone type, these bases are blue or green in color. The salts are yellowish- or brownish-red. Solutions of the platinichloride in concentrated sulfuric acid are dichroic (olive-green in thin layers and red in thick layers); but become yellowish-red on dilution.

The salts of the simple prasindones are obtained by the condensation of 4-amino-5-hydroxy-o-quinone with 2-aminodiphenylamine hydrochloride in alcoholic solution, followed by diazotization and deamination of the product (XV) with ethanol. Theoretically, the

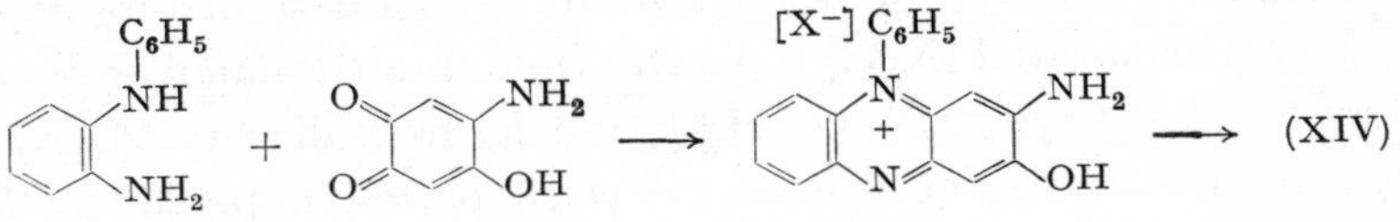

(XV)

initial condensation might proceed in either of two ways, leading to the aposafranone or prasindone types; but actually the latter is formed almost quantitatively. The action of dimethyl sulfate in nitrobenzene

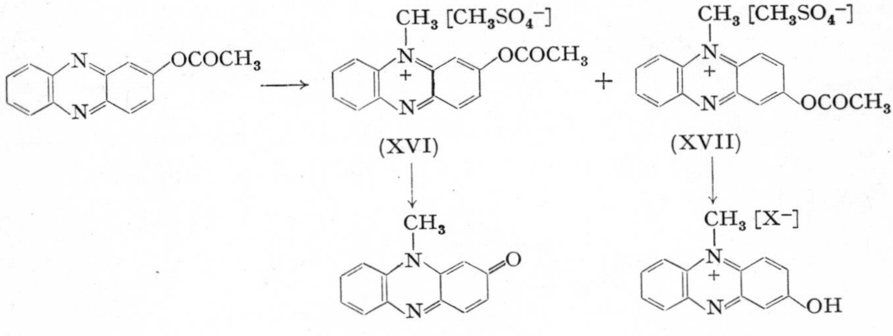

(XVI)   (XVII)

(XVIII)   (XIX)

solution on 2-acetoxyphenazine leads to the formation of the two isomeric products XVI and XVII which, when boiled with water, yield compounds XVIII and XIX, which are analogous to aposafranone and prasindone salts, respectively.[12, 13]

3. Derivatives Containing Two Oxygen Atoms

A. Phenazinediols

Ten dihydroxyphenazines are theoretically capable of existence, and all have been synthesized either as the free dihydroxy compound or as the dimethyl ether, mainly as a result of their interest in connection with the structure of iodinin (see Chapter X:3,D). These, together with a few derivatives, are listed in Table VII. In most cases, the methods of preparation used are merely adaptations of methods described in Chapter I and the only representative of the group calling for special mention here is the 2,3-compound. The demethylation of methoxy-phenazines to the free hydroxy compounds by the action of aluminum chloride in benzene appears to be a useful preparative method.[42]

2,3-Phenazinediol (XXI) separates from dilute ethanol as reddish-yellow needles, $C_{12}H_8O_2N_2.0.5H_2O$, and forms a diacetyl derivative that separates from benzene as yellowish plates, m.p. 230°.[43] It is formed from 2,3-diaminophenazine by heating with concentrated hydrochloric acid in a sealed tube,[43] and has also been synthesized from 2,5-dihydroxyquinone (XX) by condensation with o-phenylenedi-amine.[44]

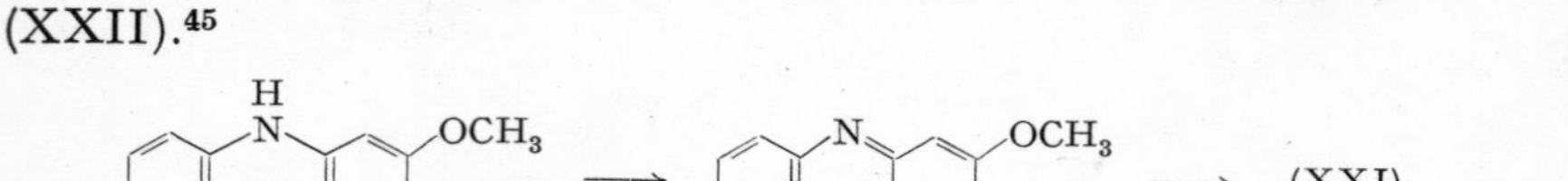

(XX)   (XXI)

It is also obtained by demethylation of 2,3-dimethoxyphenazine (XXIII), synthesized from 3',4'-dimethoxy-2-nitrodiphenylamine (XXII).[45]

(XXII)   (XXIII)   (XXI)

TABLE VII. Dihydroxy and Dialkoxy Derivatives of Phenazine

Substituents	Appearance	M.p. (°C.)	Derivatives, etc.	Ref.
1,2-Dihydroxy-	Orange needles	261 or 270–275	Diacetyl, yellow needles, m.p. 168°	11, 96
1,2-Dimethoxy-	Yellow or orange needles	145–146 or 138–139	5,6,7,8-Tetrahydro-, pale brown needles, m.p. 82–83° (picrate, m.p. 128° dec.)	11, 42, 45, 97, 98
1,3-Dihydroxy-	Orange-red needles	275	Diacetyl, white needles, m.p. 163°	99
1,3-Dimethoxy-			5,6,7,8-Tetrahydro-, yellow needles, m.p. 119°	42
1,4-Dihydroxy-	Red needles	230	Diacetyl, tarnished-gold needles, m.p. 193.5–194°	42
1,4-Dimethoxy-	Orange or red needles	185	5,6,7,8-Tetrahydro-, yellow needles, m.p. 152°	42, 45
1,6-Dihydroxy-	Yellow plates or golden needles	280–281	Diacetyl, m.p. 240–241°; 5,10-dioxide, see Chapter X:3,D	98, 100, 101, 121, 122
1,6-Dimethoxy-	Yellow needles	249–250	Does not form a picrate in alcohol	90, 98, 101–103, 121
1,6-Diethoxy-	Yellow	190	Mono-N-oxide, m.p. 170–172°	90, 100, 123
1-Methoxy-6-ethoxy-	Yellow	179		90
1,7-Dihydroxy-	Brown-yellow	305–306 (dec.) in sealed tube	Diacetyl, m.p. 148–149°	122
1,7-Dimethoxy-		175	Picrate, m.p. 258°; methosulfate, red, m.p. > 300°	103, 129
1,7-Diethoxy-		153	Picrate, m.p. 225–226° (dec.); mono-N-oxide, m.p. 207–209°	103(a), 123
1,8-Dimethoxy-	Yellow	158	Picrate, red, m.p. 209°; mono-N-oxide, m.p. 227–229°	90, 123
1-Methoxy-8-ethoxy-	Yellow	188	Picrate, red, m.p. 219°; methosulfate, red, m.p. 197° (dec.)	90, 129

Table continued

TABLE VII (*continued*)

Substituents	Appearance	M.p. (°C.)	Derivatives, etc.	Ref.
1-Ethoxy-8-methoxy-	Yellow	139	Picrate, red, m.p. 218°	90
1,8-Diethoxy-	Yellow	135	Picrate, red, m.p. 189°	90
1,9-Dihydroxy-	Orange-red plates or orange needles	295	Diacetyl, m.p. 257–258°	98, 122
1,9-Dimethoxy-	Yellow needles	259–260	Picrate, m.p. 259–260°; methosulfate, violet, m.p. > 300°	98, 103, 129
1,9-Diethoxy-		174	Picrate, m.p. 253–254°; mono-N-oxide, m.p. 218–222°	103(a), 123
2,3-Dihydroxy-	Reddish-yellow needles		Diacetyl, yellowish plates, m.p. 230°	43–45, 104, 105
2,3-Dimethoxy-		265–275	5,6,7,8-Tetrahydro-, yellow needles, m.p. 119–120°	42, 45
2,3-Dihydroxy-1-methyl-	Brick-red needles			1
2,3-Dihydroxy-7-methyl-	Yellow-brown leaflets	265	Diacetyl, yellow needles, m.p. 160°	44
2,3-Dihydroxy-1-chloro-	Red needles		Conc. $H_2SO_4 \rightarrow$ dirty-green $\xrightarrow{H_2O}$ red-brown	64, 106
2,3-Dihydroxy-1,4-dichloro-	Red-brown	Chars 310	Conc. $H_2SO_4 \rightarrow$ dichroic soln. $\xrightarrow{H_2O}$ red	107
2,7-Dimethoxy-	Red		Mono-N-oxide, dec. 233–235°	102, 123
2,7-Diethoxy-			Conc. mineral acid $\rightarrow$ blue-violet $\xrightarrow{H_2O}$ red-violet; 5-oxide, m.p. 225° (dec.)	89, 102, 108
2,8-Dihydroxy-	Yellow leaflets		Conc. $H_2SO_4 \rightarrow$ yellow-red $\xrightarrow{H_2O}$ yellow; diacetyl, m.p. 224°	95
2,8-Dimethoxy-	Brownish	163		16

B. 3-Hydroxyaposafranone

3-Hydroxyaposafranone, 3-hydroxy-10-phenyl-2(10)-phenazinone (XXIV), is the N-phenyl derivative of the desmotropic form of 2,3-dihydroxyphenazine and has also been called "benzeneindone hydrate." It separates from benzene or ethanol as brownish-yellow crystals which, when heated, give off a brownish-red vapor at 230° and melt at about 280°. It dissolves in concentrated sulfuric acid with an orange-red coloration; and its salts are hydrolyzed by water.[22]

It is obtained by the condensation of 2,5-dihydroxyquinone (XX) with 2-aminodiphenylamine[1,28]; and this type of reaction has been used to prepare analogous compounds.[1] It is also formed by the action

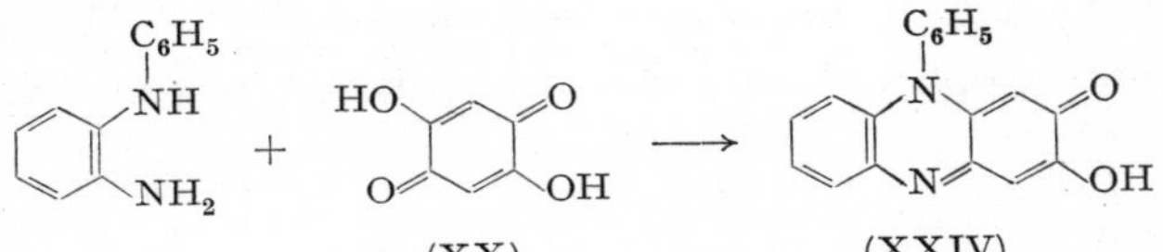

of dilute acids on 2-amino-3-anilino-10-phenylphenazinium salts (XXV) at 160–170° under pressure[23,46,47] and of hot alcoholic potassium hydroxide on aposafranone (IX).[24]

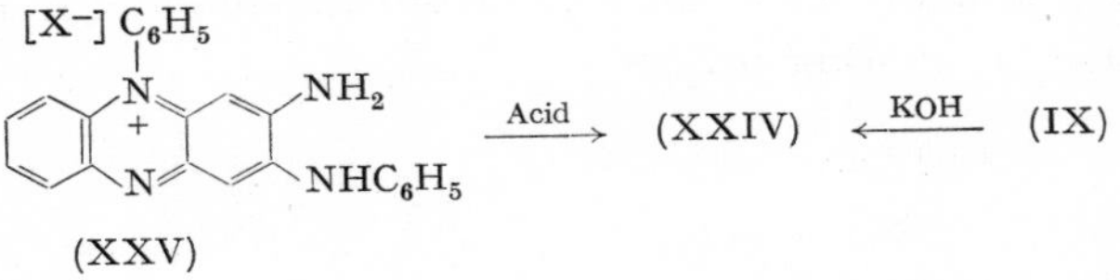

When the compound is treated with methyl iodide and potassium hydroxide in methanol, the hydroxyl group depicted in formula **XXIV** is said to be methylated.[27]

Homologs,[1,48] 10-alkyl analogs[1] and other derivatives[48] are also known. See also reference 129.

C. Phenosafranol

Phenosafranol, 8-hydroxyaposafranone, 8-hydroxy-10-phenyl-2(10)-phenazinone (XXVII), is precipitated from its carmine-red solution in alkali by the addition of acid as yellow needles, which do not melt on heating. It is very difficultly soluble in water, ethanol and acetic acid and difficultly soluble in ether; in concentrated sulfuric acid, it gives a brownish-red solution. Its absorption spectra in acid and alkaline solutions have been recorded.[49]

It was first prepared by Nietzki and Otto[50] by elimination of ammonia from phenosafranine (**XXVI**) by boiling with alcoholic

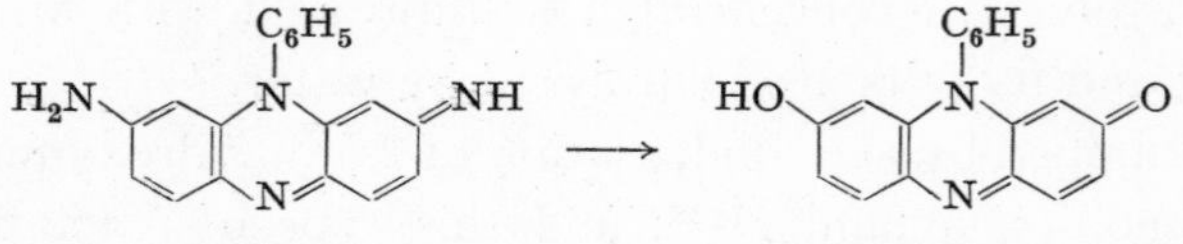

(XXVI)   (XXVII)

potassium hydroxide for some days. Jaubert[21,49,51] obtained it by heating p-nitrosophenol with 3-hydroxydiphenylamine (**XXVIII**) in

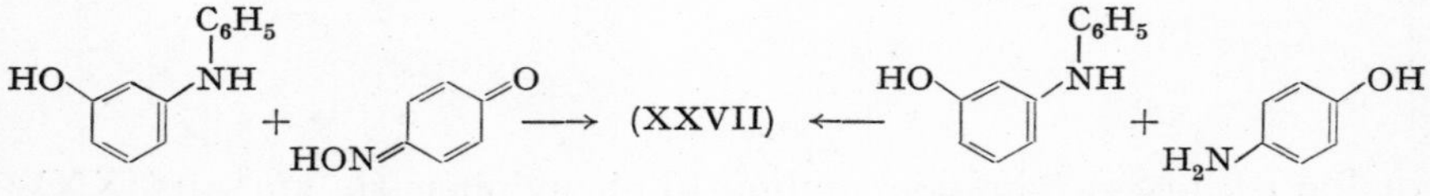

(XXVIII)   (XXVIII)

the presence of sodium hydroxide solution and by oxidation of a mixture of p-aminophenol and 3-hydroxydiphenylamine. It has also been obtained in another way.[23]

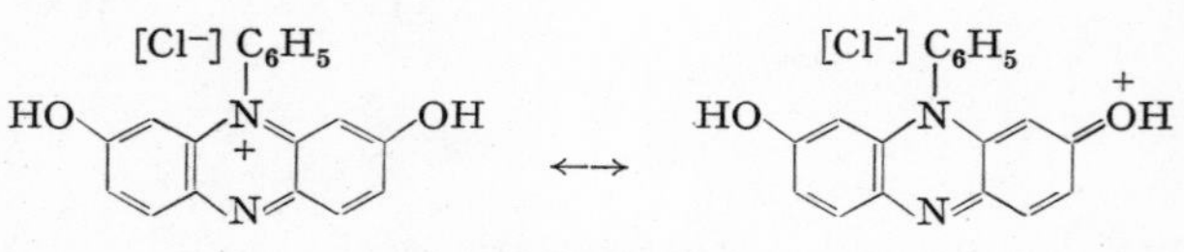

(XXIX)

Phenosafranol is a weak base, the chloride of which (**XXIX**), prepared in alcoholic solution, forms glistening blue leaflets, hydrolyzed by water; it forms only a *mono*acetyl derivative, m.p. 271° (dec.).[51] When it is treated with alkyl halides in the presence of alcoholic potassium hydroxide, it yields crystalline monoalkyl ethers, which are insoluble in alkali[23,52] By treatment of the monomethyl ether with methyl sulfate in nitrobenzene solution at 150°, followed by reaction with potassium bromide, 2,8-dimethoxy-10-phenylphenazinium bromide is formed, the solution of which on treatment with silver oxide yields an alkaline solution of the corresponding hydroxide, which readily undergoes hydrolysis of one of the methoxyl groups.[53]

When phenosafranol is heated with sulfur in high-boiling organic solvents, sulfur dyes are produced which, in a sodium sulfide bath, give violet shades on cotton. The use of copper in the presence of sulfur gives redder shades. Various derivatives (such as dichlorophenosafranol) and analogs of phenosafranol (for example, ethosafranol) are known, some of which have been used in the preparation of sulfur dyes, regarding the structure of which very little seems to be known.[38, 54-62] Phenosafranol-3-sulfonic acid is a betaine that was prepared by Jaubert,[38] although he assigned to it an incorrect structure; it has been assigned *The Ring Index* Number 2822.

4. Derivatives Containing
Three or More Oxygen Atoms

A. 3-Hydroxyphenosafranol

This compound, known also as 3,8-dihydroxyaposafranone and 3,8-dihydroxy-10-phenyl-2(10)-phenazinone (**XXXI**), forms brownish-yellow needles, m.p. above 280°, and dissolves in dilute sodium hydroxide solution to give a reddish-yellow solution. It is obtained from Induline 3B (**XXX**) by heating with dilute sulfuric acid at 230–250° under pressure,[27] or, similarly, at 180–185°, from 3-anilinophenosafranol (**XXXII**).[63]

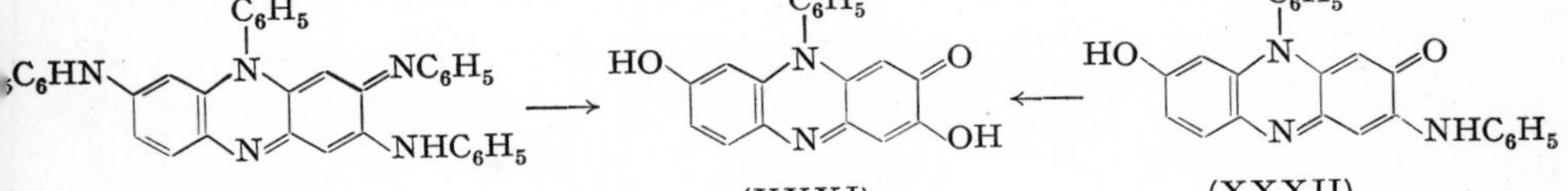

C_6H_5HN C_6H_5 NC_6H_5 NHC_6H_5
(XXX)

(XXXI)

(XXXII)

B. Derivatives Containing More than Three
Oxygen Atoms

Such derivatives as **XXXIII**, **XXXIV** and **XXXV** have been obtained from rhodizonic acid and similar substances, by condensation with o-diamines.[64-69] Supposed *p*-quinonoid compounds containing only two oxygen atoms have been described,[70] but in view of the recent work of Badger and Pettit (see Chapter XII:2,C and XVIII:3,A) the constitution of these compounds cannot be regarded as certain.

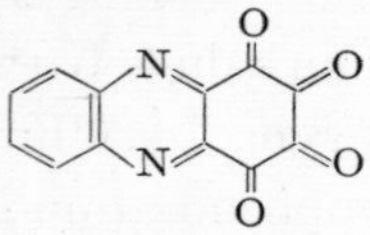

(XXXIII) 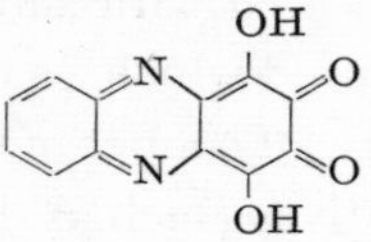   (XXXIV) 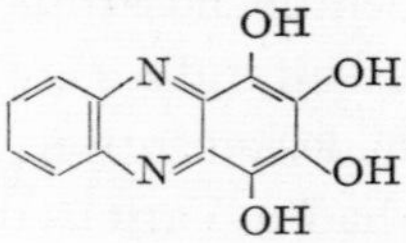   (XXXV)

5. Compounds Containing Hydroxy or Keto Groups and Amino Residues

A. Aminohydroxyphenazines

Table VIII lists the more important known aminohydroxyphenazines and their ethers; and it will be noted that these are all derived from 2-phenazinol. Similar, but more complex, derivatives are mentioned in references 71–75. Some of the aminohydroxyphenazinesulfonic acids have found application in the preparation of sulfur dyes,[59, 61, 72, 76] as for example Thionine Brilliant Claret 2R (Sulfogene Bordeaux B) (C. I. 1012), which is made by heating a mixture of 8-amino-2-phenazinol with aqueous sodium sulfide and sulfur at 140–150° and finally at 170°.

3-Amino-2-phenazinol $(10^{-7}\ M)$, 2-phenazinol, pyocyanine and 1-phenazinol $(10^{-5}\ M)$ are effective catalysts for the titanous chloride-iodine reaction.[77–79] It has also been reported that as little as one part in 100,000 of 2,3-diaminophenazine or 3-amino-2-phenazinol catalyzes the reductive cleavage by colloidal silver of azo dyes in hydrochloric acid solution.[80]

B. Phenosafraninone

Phenosafraninone, 8-amino-10-phenyl-2(10)-phenazinone (XXXVI), is an intermediate between phenosafranine and phenosafranol and separates from methanol as bluish-green, glistening prisms, which dissolve in water to give a red solution with a brownish-yellow fluorescence. Its solution in concentrated sulfuric acid is dirty-green by reflected light and violet by transmitted light.[52]

TABLE VIII. Aminohydroxy Derivatives of Phenazine

Substituents	Appearance	M.p. (°C.)	Derivatives, etc.	Ref.
2-Hydroxy-1-amino-	Red-violet		Acetyl, yellow needles, m.p. 229°	11
2-Methoxy-1-amino-		102	Acetyl, yellow needles, m.p. 202°	11
2-Hydroxy-3-amino-	Orange	> 300	Conc. $H_2SO_4 \rightarrow$ brown-red color $\xrightarrow{H_2O}$ no change; N-acetyl, red-brown needles, m.p. > 340°; diacetyl, colorless needles, m.p. 230° (approx.); phthalimido, m.p. > 300°	104, 109, 110
2-Hydroxy-3-anilino-	Brownish-red needles	Dec. > 200 without melting	Conc. $H_2SO_4 \rightarrow$ dirty-green color $\xrightarrow{H_2O}$ red $\xrightarrow{alkali}$ yellow	111
2-Hydroxy-3-amino-7- (or 8)-methyl-	Orange-yellow		N-Acetyl, red, dec. 250°	109
2-Hydroxy-3-amino-7- (or 8)-chloro-	Yellow		Conc. $H_2SO_4 \rightarrow$ brown $\xrightarrow{H_2O}$ red	112
2-Hydroxy-3-amino-7- (or 8)-bromo-	Yellow-brown			112
2-Hydroxy-3-amino-7- (or 8)-carboxylic acid		> 360		112
2-Methoxy-3-amino-7- dimethyl-amino-	Brown-red needles	258	Conc. $H_2SO_4 \rightarrow$ dichroic soln. $\xrightarrow{H_2O}$ blue $\rightarrow$ violet $\rightarrow$ red	113

(Table continued)

TABLE VIII (*continued*)

Substituents	Appearance	M.p. (°C.)	Derivatives, etc.	Ref.
2-Methoxy-4-amino-	Reddish needles	174–175	Hydrochloride, blue, m.p. 220–223°; acetyl, yellow needles, m.p. 190–191°; toluene-*p*-sulfonyl, yellow plates, m.p. 201–202°	114
2-Methoxy-4-amino-8-chloro-	Red needles	187–190	Hydrochloride, m.p. 203–205°; acetyl, yellow needles, m.p. 199–202°	114
2-Hydroxy-7-amino-	Brown-red plates		Conc. H_2SO_4 → dichroic soln. $\xrightarrow{H_2O}$ yellow → violet-red; *N*-acetyl, brown plates; diacetyl, yellow leaflets, m.p. 249°	95
2-Hydroxy-8-amino-	Yellow needles	268 or > 360	Conc. H_2SO_4 → red-brown or violet color; diacetyl, yellow, m.p 258° or 275°	61, 76, 95, 115, 116
2-Methoxy-8-amino-	Red-yellow needles	216–217		117
2-Hydroxy-8-amino-7-methyl-	Red needles	> 360	Conc. H_2SO_4 → blue-violet $\xrightarrow{H_2O}$ brown-red $\xrightarrow{alkali}$ orange; diacetyl, yellow leaflets, m.p. 291°	116, 118
2-Hydroxy-8-amino-7-chloro-	Red-brown needles	> 360	Diacetyl, yellow needles, m.p. 207°	116
2-Hydroxy-8-amino-7-methyl-3-chloro-		> 360	Diacetyl, yellow needles, m.p. 274°	116
2-Hydroxy-8-amino-1,3-dichloro-				60
2-Hydroxy-8-amino-3-sulfonic acid				61, 76

It is obtained from phenosafranine chloride by heating with aqueous sodium acetate under pressure at 150°,[52] and in low yield, from phenosafranol, by heating with ammonia at 180°.[21] Another method of preparation consists in the oxidation of a mixture of p-phenylene-diamine and 3-hydroxydiphenylamine.[21]

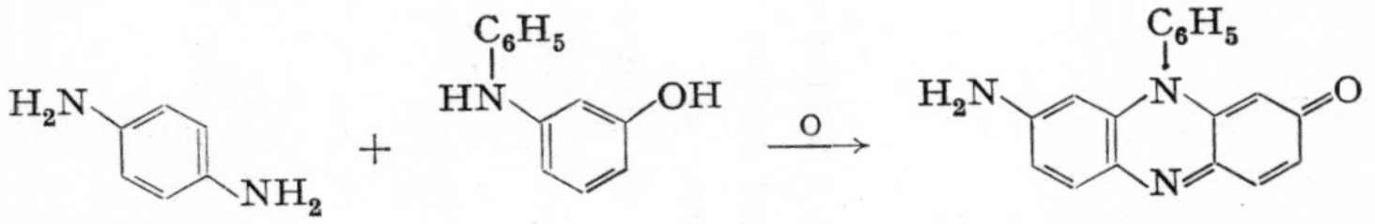

(XXXVI)

The primary amino group of this compound can be diazotized (deamination then leads to aposafranone)[21] or condensed with aldehydes, with elimination of water[52]; and the replacement by OH can be brought about by hydrolysis with 75% sulfuric acid or with alcoholic potassium hydroxide.[21] (Compare the stability of 8-chloro-10-phenyl-2(10)- phenazinone.) It forms a *mono*acetyl derivative.

In contrast to phenosafraninone, analogous compounds (**XXXVIII**) in which an alkyl radical replaces the phenyl group are easily obtained by the condensation of m-toluylenediamines alkylated on the amino group that stands p- to the methyl group (**XXXVII**) with p-nitroso-phenols (or with p-aminophenols in the presence of an oxidizing agent)[39]. These compounds, as well as phenosafraninone itself, have been used in the manufacture of various sulfur dyes; for example, when phenosafran-

(XXXVII)   (XXXVIII)

inone is heated with sulfur at 190–200°, it yields the leuco-base of a dye that colors cotton reddish-violet.[56, 58, 61, 81–84] This can be purified by dissolving in sodium sulfide solution, and precipitating by a current of air. Examples of these dyes are: Thion Violet B (*C. I.* 1008), Thion Purple 2B (*C. I.* 1009), Thion Violet 3R (*C. I.* 1010) and Immedial Maroon B (*C. I.* 1012). N-Dimethylphenosafraninone is also known.[21]

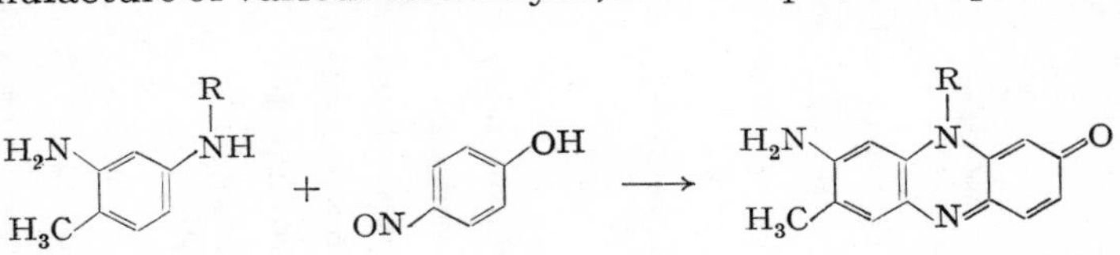

TABLE IX. Amino-Derivatives of Aposafranone (10-Phenyl-2(10)-phenazinone)

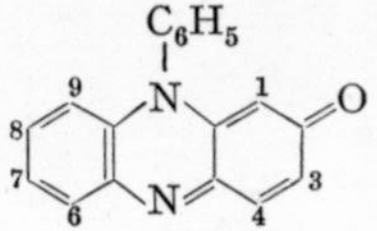

Substituents	Appearance	M.p. (°C.)	Color with conc. H_2SO_4 followed by dilution	Derivatives, etc.	Ref.
3-Amino-	Dark red needles with green iridescence		Dichroic → orange → yellow		33, 34, 40
3-Anilino-	Red or brown needles	256	Green → pink		22–24, 27, 46, 47, 111
4-Amino-	Black-brown needles	310–315 (dec.)	Yellow-green → red	N-Acetyl, greenish-black crystals with blue reflex	119, 120
8-Amino-	Bluish-green, iridescent prisms		Dichroic (green and violet)	N-Acetyl, red needles, m.p. > 280°	21, 23, 52
8-Dimethylamino-	Brownish-red		Dichroic		21
8-Anilino-	Bronzy crystals		Violet-blue → red		23
8-Methoxy-3-amino-	Brown plates				55
8-Ethoxy-3-amino-	Brown plates	ca. 250	Reddish-brown → green → red-yellow		55
8-Hydroxy-3-anilino-	Red needles or prisms with blue iridescence	> 285	Green → violet-red		23, 27, 63
3-Hydroxy-8-amino-	Green plates with metallic reflex	270–280	Greenish-brown		22, 24, 27

C. Other Amino Derivatives of Aposafranone

These require little mention beyond reference to Table IX. 3-Anilinoaposafranone was at first erroneously called "benzeneindone" and on distillation with zinc dust gives phenazine; when it is boiled with 75% sulfuric acid, it yields 3-hydroxyaposafranone (XXIV).[22,24] 3-Anilinophenosafranol (XL) has been synthesized from XXXIX as shown below.[63]

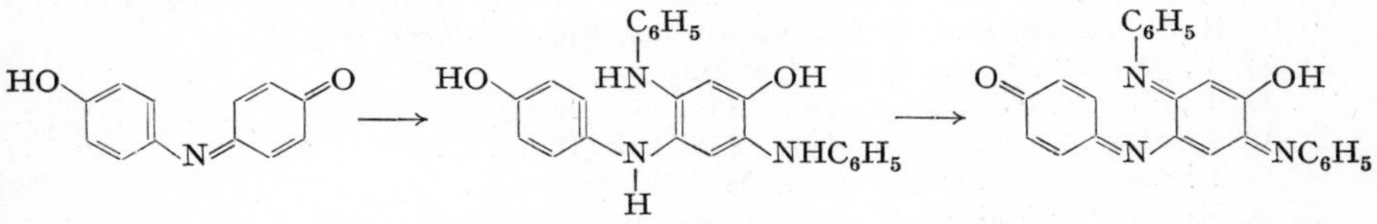

(XXXIX)

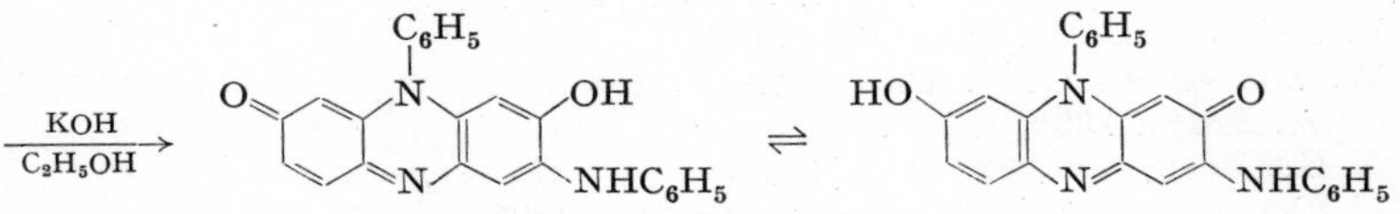

(XL)

D. Thio-Analog of Phenosafraninone

This compound is 8-amino-2-mercapto-10-phenylphenazinium hydroxide, and has been prepared by Watson and Dutt[131] from phenosafranine by diazotization, and then reaction with potassium xanthate followed by boiling with sodium hydroxide.

References

1. F. Kehrmann, *Ann.*, **290**, 247 (1896).
2. G. F. Jaubert, *Ber.*, **29**, 414 (1896).
3. G. M. Badger, R. S. Pearce and R. Pettit, *J. Chem. Soc.*, **1951**, 3204.
4. F. Wrede and E. Strack, *Z. physiol. Chem.*, **177**, 177 (1928); *Chem. Abstracts*, **22**, 3891 (1928).
5. A. R. Surrey, *Org. Syntheses*, **26**, 86 (1946).
6. V. Meló, *Boll. sci. facoltà chim. ind. Bologna*, **7**, 68 (1949); through *Chem. Abstracts*, **44**, 9450 (1950).
7. B. Hegedüs, *Helv. Chim. Acta*, **33**, 766 (1950).
8. A. Albert and H. Duewell, *J. Soc. Chem. Ind., London*, **66**, 11 (1947).
9. F. Wrede and E. Strack, *Ber.*, **62B**, 2051 (1929).
10. D. L. Vivian, *J. Am. Chem. Soc.*, **71**, 1139 (1949).
11. B. Hegedüs, *Jubilee Vol. Emil Barell*, **1946**, 388; *Chem. Abstracts*, **41**, 6262 (1947).

12. F. Kehrmann and F. Cherpillod, *Helv. Chim. Acta*, **7**, 973 (1924).
13. F. Kehrmann (with F. Cherpillod), *Helv. Chim. Acta*, **7**, 471 (1924).
14. F. Kehrmann and C. Mermod, *Helv. Chim. Acta*, **10**, 62 (1927).
15. D. L. Vivian, *J. Am. Chem. Soc.*, **73**, 457 (1951).
16. M. L. Tomlinson, *J. Chem. Soc.*, **1939**, 158.
17. H. C. Waterman and D. L. Vivian, *J. Org. Chem.*, **14**, 289 (1949).
18. W. John, *Angew. Chem.*, **A59**, 188 (1947).
19. W. John, W. Emte and E. Maue, *Reichsamt Wirtschaftsausbau, Chem. Ber.*, Prüf. Nr. 15 (PB-52014), 353 (1942); through *Chem. Abstracts*, **41**, 6391 (1947).
20(a). R. Suhrmann and H. H. Perkampus, *Naturwissenschaften*, **38**, 382 (1951)
20(b). R. Suhrmann and H. H. Perkampus, *Angew. Chem.*, **64**, 423 (1952).
21. G. F. Jaubert, *Ber.*, **28**, 270 (1895).
22. O. Fischer and E. Hepp, *Ann.*, **266**, 249 (1891).
23. O. Fischer and E. Hepp, *Ann.*, **286**, 187 (1895).
24. O. Fischer and E. Hepp, *Ber.*, **28**, 2283 (1895).
25. F. Kehrmann and W. Shaposhnikov, *Ber.*, **30**, 2620 (1897).
26. F. Kehrmann and H. Bürgin, *Ber.*, **29**, 1819 (1896).
27. O. Fischer and E. Hepp, *Ber.*, **29**, 361 (1896).
28. F. Kehrmann, *Ber.*, **28**, 1709 (1895).
29. W. Shaposhnikov, *J. Russ. Phys. Chem. Soc.*, **29**, 535 (1897); through *Chem. Zentr.*, **1898**, I, 722.
30. A. G. Green, *Ber.*, **32**, 3155 (1899).
31. H. Decker and A. Würsch, *Ber.*, **39**, 2653 (1906).
32. O. Fischer and E. Hepp, *Ber.*, **30**, 1827 (1897).
33. O. Fischer and E. Hepp, *Ber.*, **38**, 3435 (1905).
34. O. Fischer and E. Hepp, *Ber.*, **33**, 1485 (1900).
35. O. Fischer and E. Hepp, *Z. f. Farben- und Textilchemie*, **1**, 457; through *Chem. Zentr.*, **1902**, II, 902.
36. O. Fischer and E. Hepp, *Ber.*, **36**, 1807 (1903).
37. F. Kehrmann and H. de Gottrau, *Ber.*, **38**, 2574 (1905).
38. G. F. Jaubert, *Ber.*, **31**, 1178 (1898).
39. Ger. Pat. 189,078; *Chem. Zentr.*, **1907**, II, 1717; *Frdl.*, **8**, 514 (1905–07).
40. F. Kehrmann and R. Schwarzenbach, *Ber.*, **41**, 472 (1908).
41. F. Kehrmann and W. Aebi, *Ber.*, **32**, 932 (1899).
42. F. E. King, N. G. Clark and P. M. H. Davis, *J. Chem. Soc.*, **1949**, 3012.
43. O. Fischer and E. Hepp, *Ber.*, **23**, 841 (1890).
44. R. Nietzki and G. Hasterlik, *Ber.*, **24**, 1337 (1891).
45. P. Z. Slack and R. Slack, *Nature*, **160**, 437 (1947).
46. O. Fischer and O. Heiler, *Ber.*, **26**, 378 (1893).
47. O. Fischer and A. Dischinger, *Ber.*, **29**, 1602 (1896).
48. F. Kehrmann and J. Messinger, *Ber.*, **24**, 584 (1891).
49. K. Balls, J. T. Hewitt and S. H. Newman, *J. Chem. Soc.*, **101**, 1840 (1912).
50. R. Nietzki and R. Otto, *Ber.*, **21**, 1590 (1888).
51. J. T. Hewitt, S. H. Newman and T. F. Winmill, *J. Chem. Soc.*, **95**, 577(1909).
52. O. Fischer and E. Hepp, *Ber.*, **30**, 391 (1897).
53. F. Kehrmann (with X. Vogt), *Ann.*, **372**, 352 (1910).
54. G. F. Jaubert, *Bull. soc. chim. France*, (3), **21**, 186 (1899).
55. O. Fischer and F. Römer, *Ber.*, **40**, 3406 (1907).
56. Ger. Pat. 171,177; *Chem. Zentr.*, **1906**, II, 648; *Frdl.*, **8**, 783 (1905–07).
57. Ger. Pat. 168,982; *Chem. Zentr.*, **1907**, I, 779; *Frdl.*, **8**, 782 (1905–07).
58. Ger. Pat. 179,021; *Chem. Zentr.*, **1907**, I, 779; *Frdl.*, **8**, 786 (1905–07).

59. Ger. Pat. 174,331; *Chem. Zentr.*, **1906**, II, 1542; *Frdl.*, **8**, 788 (1905–07).
60. Ger. Pat. 181,327; *Chem. Zentr.*, **1907**, I, 1716; *Frdl.*, **8**, 792 (1905–07).
61. Ger. Pat. 126,175; *Chem. Zentr.*, **1901**, II, 1107; *Frdl.*, **6**, 680 (1900–02).
62. G. F. Jaubert, *Compt. rend.*, **121**, 947 (1895).
63. G. Heller, *Ann.*, **392**, 16 (1912).
64. F. Kehrmann, *Ber.*, **23**, 2446 (1890).
65. R. Nietzki and F. Kehrmann, *Ber.*, **20**, 322 (1887).
66. R. Nietzki and F. Kehrmann, *Ber.*, **20**, 3150 (1887).
67. R. Nietzki and A. W. Schmidt, *Ber.*, **21**, 1227 (1888).
68. O. Böters, *Ber.*, **35**, 1502 (1902).
69. F. Kehrmann and A. Duret, *Ber.*, **31**, 2437 (1898).
70. J. Leicester, *Ber.*, **23**, 2793 (1890).
71. F. Fichter and J. Schwab, *Ber.*, **39**, 3339 (1906).
72. Ger. Pat. 210,702; *Chem. Zentr.*, **1909**, II, 244; *Frdl.*, **9**, 277 (1908–10).
73. Ger. Pat. 187,868; *Chem. Zentr.*, **1907**, II, 1667; *Frdl.*, **8**, 793 (1905-07).
74. R. Nietzki and H. Kaufmann, *Ber.*, **24**, 3824 (1891).
75. A. S. Wheeler and R. W. Bost, *J. Am. Chem. Soc.*, **50**, 2000, (1928).
76. Ger. Pat. 120,561; *Chem. Zentr.*, **1901**, I, 1130; *Frdl.*, **6**, 679 (1900–02).
77. C. E. Johnson (Jr.) and S. Winstein, *J. Am. Chem. Soc.*, **73**, 2601 (1951).
78. C. E. Johnson (Jr.) and S. Winstein, *J. Am. Chem. Soc.*, **74**, 755, (1952).
79. P. A. Shaffer, *Cold Springs Harbor Symposia on Quantitative Biology*, **7**, 50 (1939).
80. U. S. Pat. 2,270,118; *Chem. Abstracts*, **36**, 3112, (1942).
81. Ger. Pat. 181,125; *Chem. Zentr.*, **1907**, I, 1715.
82. Ger. Pat. 168,516; *Chem. Zentr.*, **1906**, I, 1811; *Frdl.*, **8**, 775 (1905–07).
83. Ger. Pat. 177,493; *Chem. Zentr.*, **1906**, II, 1798; *Frdl.*, **8**, 777 (1905–07).
84. Ger. Pat. 179,960; *Chem. Zentr.*, **1907**, I, 1370; *Frdl.*, **8**, 778 (1905–07).
85. L. Michaelis, E. S. Hill and M. P. Schubert, *Biochem. Z.*, **255**, 66 (1932).
86. S. Maffei, *Gazz. chim. ital.*, **76**, 239 (1946); through *Chem. Abstracts*, **42**, 911 (1948).
87. G. R. Clemo and H. McIlwain, *J. Chem. Soc.*, **1938**, 479.
88. F. Wrede and E. Strack, *Z. physiol. Chem.*, **181**, 58 (1929); *Chem. Zentr.*, **1929**, II, 50.
89. I. J. Pachter and M. C. Kloetzel, *J. Am. Chem. Soc.*, **74**, 971 (1952).
90. S. B. Serebryanyĭ, *Zhur. Obshcheĭ Khim.* (*J. Gen. Chem.*), **20**, 1629 (1950); through *Chem. Abstracts*, **45**, 2009 (1951) and **46**, 10182 (1952).
91. H. McCombie, H. A. Scarborough and W. A. Waters, *J. Chem. Soc.*, **1928**, 353.
92. H. E. Ungnade and K. T. Zilch, *J. Org. Chem.*, **15**, 1108 (1950).
93. D. L. Vivian, G. Y. Greenberg and J. L. Hartwell, *J. Org. Chem.*, **16**, 1 (1951).
94. Ger. Pat. 368,169; *Chem. Zentr.*, **1923**, II, 1187.
95. F. Kehrmann and E. Haenny, *Helv. Chim. Acta*, **8**, 676 (1925).
96. S. Maffei, *Gazz. chim. ital.*, **80**, 651 (1950); through *Chem. Abstracts*, **45**, 9063 (1951).
97. G. R. Clemo and A. F. Daglish, *Nature*, **160**, 752 (1947).
98. G. R. Clemo and A. F. Daglish, *J. Chem. Soc.*, **1950**, 1481.
99. G. R. Clemo and A. F. Daglish, *J. Chem. Soc.*, **1948**, 2318.
100. S. B. Serebryanyĭ, V. P. Chernetskiĭ and A. I. Kiprianov, *Doklady Akad. Nauk S.S.S.R.*, **70**, 645 (1950); through *Chem. Abstracts*, **45**, 4249 (1951).
101. I. J. Pachter and M. C. Kloetzel, *J. Am. Chem. Soc.*, **73**, 4958 (1951).
102. B. K. Malaviya and S. Dutt, *Proc. Acad. Sci. United Provinces Agra Oudh, India*, **4**, 319 (1935); through *Chem. Abstracts*, **30**, 1056 (1936).

103 (a). S. B. Serebryanyĭ and V. P. Chernetskiĭ, *Zhur. Obshcheĭ Khim.* (*J. Gen. Chem.*), **21**, 2033 (1951); through *Chem. Abstracts*, **46**, 6654 (1952).

103 (b). A. I. Kiprianov, S. B. Serebryanyĭ and V. P. Chernetskiĭ, *Doklady Akad. Nauk S.S.S.R.*, **69**, 651 (1949); through *Chem. Abstracts*, **46**, 4010 (1952).

104. F. Ullmann and F. Mauthner, *Ber.*, **35**, 4302 (1902).

105. U. S. Pat. 2,292,808; *Chem. Abstracts*, **37**, 892 (1943).

106. F. Kehrmann, *Ber.*, **28**, 353 (1895).

107. F. Kehrmann (with C. Buffat), *Ber.*, **56B**, 2390 (1923).

108. R. Neu, *Ber.*, **72B**, 1505 (1939).

109. F. Kehrmann and D. Kissine, *Ber.*, **47**, 3100 (1914).

110. A. C. Sircar and S. C. Sen, *J. Indian Chem. Soc.*, **11**, 363 (1934); *Chem. Abstracts*, **28**, 6151 (1934).

111. F. Kehrmann and M. Cordone, *Ber.*, **46**, 3009 (1913).

112. F. Ullmann and F. Mauthner, *Ber.*, **36**, 4026 (1903).

113. F. Kehrmann, *Ber.*, **50**, 554 (1917).

114. R. C. Elderfield, W. J. Gensler and O. Birstein, *J. Org. Chem.*, **11**, 812 (1946).

115. R. Nietzki and C. Simon, *Ber.*, **28**, 2973 (1895).

116. F. Ullmann and J. Gnaedinger, *Ber.*, **45**, 3437 (1912).

117. O. Fischer, *Ber.*, **29**, 1873 (1896).

118. Ger. Pat. 208,109; *Chem. Zentr.*, **1909**, I, 1626; *Frdl.*, **9**, 460 (1908–10).

119. F. Kehrmann and O. Kramer, *Ber.*, **33**, 3074 (1900).

120. F. Kehrmann and A. Maslenikov, *Ber.*, **45**, 2891 (1912).

121. I. Yoshioka and Y. Kidani, *J. Pharm. Soc. Japan*, **72**, 847 (1952); through *Chem. Abstracts*, **47**, 3320 (1953).

122. S. B. Serebryanyĭ, *Zhur. Obshcheĭ Khim.* (*J. Gen. Chem.*), **22**, 702 (1952); through *Chem. Abstracts*, **47**, 5408 (1953).

123. V. P. Chernetskiĭ and A. I. Kiprianov, *Zhur. Obshcheĭ Khim.* (*J. Gen. Chem.*), **22**, 1876 (1952); through *Chem. Abstracts*, **47**, 6953 (1953).

124. H. H. Perkampus and R. Suhrmann, *Angew. Chem.*, **65**, 328 (1953).

125. W. S. Moos and J. W. Rowen, *Arch. Biochem. Biophys.*, **43**, 88 (1953).

126. I. Yoshioka, *J. Pharm. Soc. Japan*, **72**, 1128 (1952); through *Chem. Abstracts*, **47**, 6426 (1953).

127. I. Yoshioka and Y. Kidani, *J. Pharm. Soc. Japan*, **72**, 1301 (1952); through *Chem. Abstracts*, **47**, 10542 (1953).

128. I. Yoshioka, *J. Pharm. Soc. Japan*, **73**, 23 (1953); through *Chem. Abstracts*, **47**, 10542 (1953).

129. S. B. Serebryanyĭ, *Zhur. Obshcheĭ Khim.*, **22**, 2203 (1952); through *Chem. Abstracts*, **48**, 680 (1954).

130. D. L. Vivian, J. L. Hartwell and H. C. Waterman, *J. Org. Chem.*, **19**, 1136 (1954).

131. E. R. Watson and S. Dutt, *J. Chem. Soc.*, **121**, 1939 (1922).

CHAPTER VI

Amino Derivatives of Phenazine

1. Introduction

The introduction of auxochromic amino groups into the phenazine nucleus results in the formation of coloring matters to which the name eurhodines has been applied.[1,2] These are very weak dyes of very little technical importance.

It should be noted that, although Kehrmann's spectroscopic studies indicated that all the salts (except those formed in most strongly acid solution) of the mono- and di-aminophenazines possess p-quinonoid structures, the location of the protons added on in the formation of these salts is not known. (See Chapter VII:1,C(2).)

2. Monoamino Derivatives

With the exception of the hydroxyamino phenazines, which are given in Table VIII in Chapter V, very few monoamino phenazines are known.

A. 1-Aminophenazine

This compound (II), first prepared by Kehrmann and Prunier[3,4] in 1924, separates from benzene as red needles, m.p. 175–176°,[5,6] and on sublimation forms red-violet crystals, m.p. 179–181°.[7] It is insoluble in water, but readily soluble in ether and ethanol, giving dark red solutions. It dissolves in concentrated sulfuric acid, giving a lemon-yellow solution which on dilution becomes successively green and blue and, on basification, red. An alcoholic solution of the base becomes blue on the addition of acetic acid. At a molar dilution of 300, the base has pK_a 2.6.[6] The redox potential against a normal hydrogen electrode is —0.176 v.[5]

This compound was originally prepared by treatment of the mono-perchlorate of 1,3-diaminophenazine with acetic anhydride, and de-amination of the resulting 1-acetamido-3-aminophenazine (I) *via* the

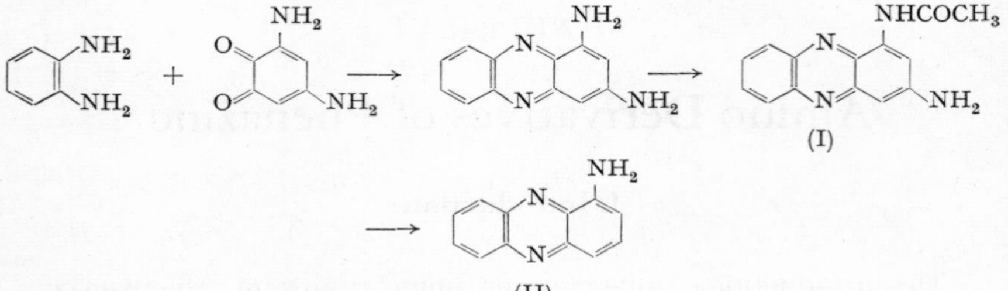

diazo compound.[3,4] However, the synthesis was long, the yield obtained low and Albert and Duewell[5] found a better preparative method in the action of stannous chloride on 1'-amino-2,6-dinitrodiphenylamine-4-carboxylic acid (III) in a sealed tube at 153° for five hours that yielded a mixture of the 1-amino- (14%) and 1-hydroxy- (20%) compounds, which are readily separated by using alkali.

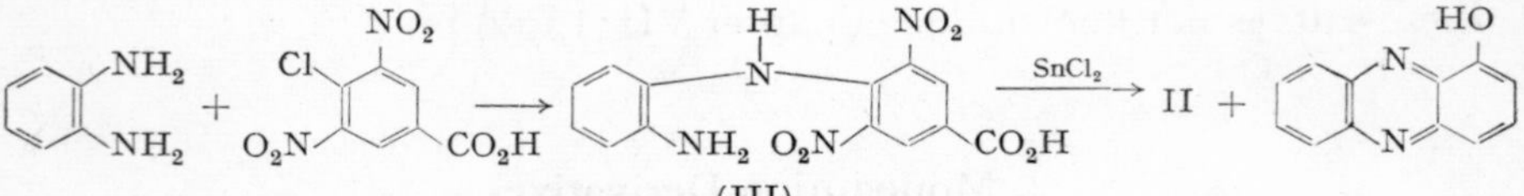

A good preparative method appears to be that of Hegedüs,[7] who obtained 1-aminophenazine in 69% yield by hydrogenating 2,2',6-trinitrodiphenylamine (IV) in the presence of palladium charcoal and oxidizing the crude product with ferric chloride. The same general

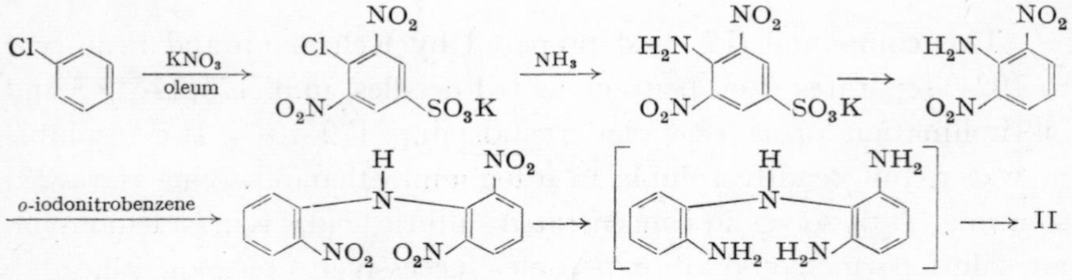

method had already been used by Elderfield, Gensler and Birstein[8] to prepare a number of derivatives of 1-aminophenazine, including

1-amino-3-chlorophenazine, which forms red needles, m.p. 202–204°, and which yields an acetyl derivative, crystallizing as yellow needles, m.p. 196–197°. See also reference 102.

B. 2-Aminophenazine

This compound (VI) was first prepared by Fischer and Hepp[9] in 1889 by distilling 2,3-diaminophenazine with zinc dust. It separates from ethanol, benzene or xylene as red needles with a bronze luster and sublimes readily. Different authors have recorded melting points ranging from 265° to 290–291°, of which a recently quoted value is 279°.[6] It is almost insoluble in water; but dilute solutions of the base in ethanol are orange, with an orange-red fluorescence,[9,10] and solutions in ether show a yellow fluorescence.[11] It dissolves in concentrated sulfuric acid to give a brown solution which, on dilution, becomes first green, then red and, on basification, orange-yellow.[9,10] At a molar dilution of 120 and 12,000 the base has a pK_a value of 3.46 and 4.75, respectively.[6] It shows absorption maxima at 472 and 265 mμ.[11–13]

Various methods[14–19] for the preparation of this compound have been described, among which may be mentioned the reduction by stannous chloride and hydrochloric acid in ethanol of 2'-amino-4,6-

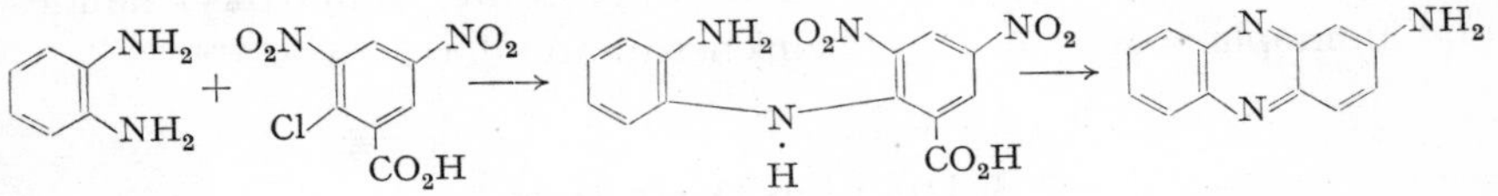

(V)   (VI)

dinitrodiphenylamine-2-carboxylic acid (V)[10] and the formation in 68% yield of 2-acetamidophenazine (VII) by condensation of 4-acetamido-*o*-quinone with *o*-phenylenediamine.[20]

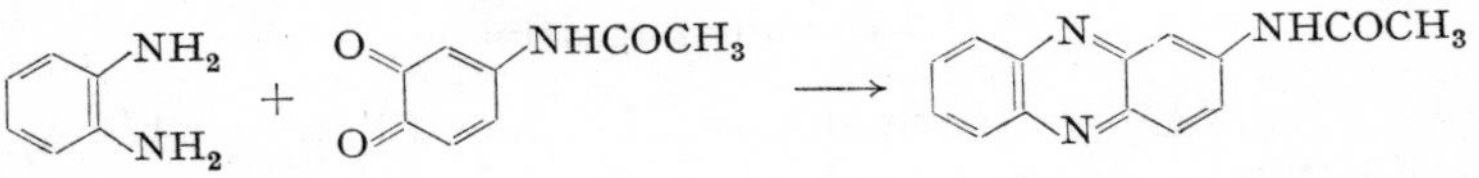

(VII)

2-Aminophenazine can be diazotized and the product reduced by ethanol to phenazine[9]; but conversion to 2-phenazinol is not possible by this route, although the latter compound can be obtained by the action of 15% hydrochloric acid on the amino compound at 180° in a sealed tube.[20] 2-Aminophenazine couples with benzenediazonium chloride under conditions in which neither 3-amino-2-phenazinol nor 2,3-diaminophenazine do so.[21]

7-Methyl-2-dimethylaminophenazine separates from ethanol as dark red plates or needles with a bronze luster.[22] 2-Amino-3,8-dimethylphenazine (VIII), which separates from benzene-light petroleum as orange needles, m.p. 248–249° (dec.), reacts with p-toluidine in the presence of its hydrochloride, at 150–160°, to yield the corresponding 2-toluidino compound (IX), which is formed in low yield by the action of hydrogen peroxide in the presence of ferrous ions on p-toluidine.[23] Other derivatives of 2-aminophenazine are described in references 24 and 25.

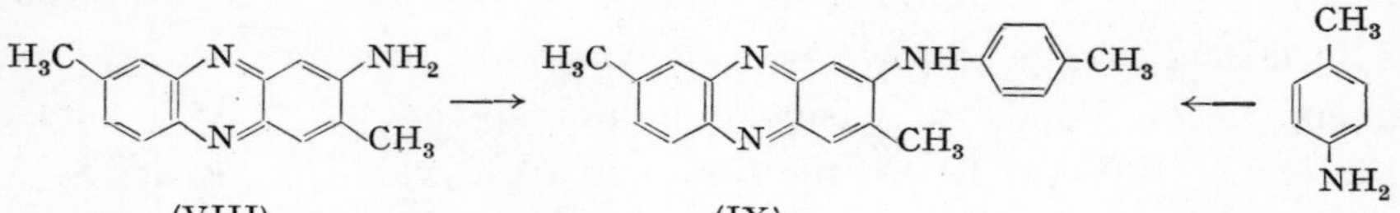

(VIII)   (IX)

Phenazine derivatives containing the side chain $-NX(CH_2)_n NR^1R^2$ (where $X = H$ or alkyl, R^1 and R^2 are alkyl and $n = 0$, 1 or 2) have been prepared by interaction of the appropriate aminoalkyl halides and aminophenazines or their benzenesulfonyl derivatives.[8, 26, 27]

3. Diamino Derivatives

The more important known di- and poly-amino derivatives of phenazine are listed in Table X. More complex compounds are described in references 28–30 and 103.

A. 1,3-Diaminophenazine

First prepared by Kehrmann and Prunier (Chapter VI;2,A), this compound (XI) separates from benzene as red crystals with a coppery luster, m.p. 284–285° (corr.),[5] which are slightly soluble in cold water, but soluble in hot water with a cherry-red color. It is readily soluble in ethanol and hot benzene and gives a dark olive-green solution in acetic acid. In a molar dilution of 240, the base has pK_a 5.64.[6] It is

TABLE X. Diamino and Polyamino Derivatives of Phenazine

Substituents	Appearance	M.p. (°C.)	Color with conc. H_2SO_4, followed by dilution	Derivatives, remarks	Ref.
1,3-Diamino-	Red, with coppery luster	284–285 (corr.)	Yellow-brown → magenta → green		3, 4, 5, 6
2,3-Diamino-	Yellow leaflets	dec.	Green → orange-red	Diacetyl, yellow needles, m.p. 270° (approx.); mono-hydrochloride, ruby-red cryst.	9, 12, 31–35 89–93, 104, 105; also Chapter I:12
2,3-Dianilino-	Orange-yellow	218–219	Violet → violet-red		94
2,3-Diamino-7-chloro-	Yellow-brown needles	> 360			95
2,3-Diamino-7-bromo-	Yellow-brown needles	> 360			95
2,7-Diamino-	Dark red	> 320	Green → blue-violet → orange	Triacetyl, yellow prisms, m.p. > 320°	6, 12, 38, 39
2,7-Diamino-3-methyl-	Bronze plates or needles				38
2,8-Diamino-	Dark yellow needles	280 (dec.)	Green → blue → violet → red	Diacetyl, yellow needles, m.p. 330° (approx.)	12, 13, 40
2,8-Diamino-3-methyl-	Green			Hydrochloride, red needles or prisms	22
2-Amino-8-dimethyl-amino-					47

Table continued

TABLE (*continued*)

Substituents	Appearance	M.p. (°C.)	Color with conc. H$_2$SO$_4$, followed by dilution	Derivatives, remarks	Refs.
2-Amino-8-dimethyl-amino-1,3-dimethyl-	Brown-red needles	241–242			96
2-Amino-8-dimethyl-amino-1,4-dimethyl-	Yellow needles	215–216			96
2-Amino-8-dimethyl-amino-3,4-dimethyl-	Yellow needles	265 (dec.)			96
2-Amino-8-dimethyl-amino-3-methyl-	Orange-red needles (hydrate); Blood-red (anhydrous)		See "Neutral red"		47, 50
2-Amino-8-dimethyl-amino-4-methyl-	Needles with copper luster		Green $\rightarrow$ blue $\rightarrow$ red		97
2-Amino-8-dimethyl-amino-3-chloro-					98
2-Amino-8-dimethyl-amino-4-nitro-	Red-brown needles		Blue $\rightarrow$ red		106
2,8-Bisdimethylamino-					44
2,8-Bisbenzylamino-			Ochre $\rightarrow$ green $\rightarrow$ violet $\rightarrow$ red		99
1,4,7-Triamino-	Brown needles	dec. > 100	Yellow $\rightarrow$ violet $\rightarrow$ red $\rightarrow$ yellow	Triacetyl, yellow	100
2,3,7,8-Tetramino-	Brown		Yellow $\rightarrow$ blue $\rightarrow$ violet $\rightarrow$ red $\rightarrow$ yellow	Tetracetyl, orange-yellow	101

obtained in 45% yield by the stannous chloride reduction of 2'-amino-2,4,6-trinitrodiphenylamine (X).[5]

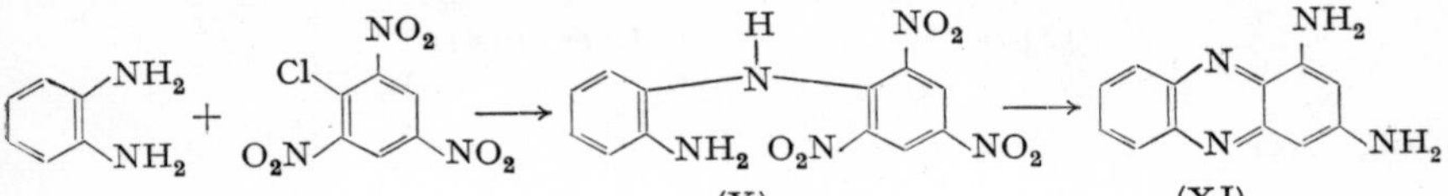

(X) (XI)

B. 2,3-Diaminophenazine

This compound (XIII) sublimes to give yellow leaflets that decompose on heating without showing a definite melting point and in benzene forms solutions with a yellowish-green fluorescence.[9] At a molar dilution of 130, the base has pK_a 4.74.[6] The absorption curve has maxima at 265, 285 and 454 mμ.[13]

It is readily prepared by the oxidation of o-phenylenediamine (see Chapter I:12). When the oxidation is carried out by ferric chloride in acid solution, 3-amino-2-phenazinol is formed as a by-product (it is the main product in strongly acid solution); and the diaminophenazine is obtained in high yield.[31] But by using iodine (2 atoms per mole of o-phenylenediamine) in ethanol as the oxidizing agent, almost quantitative yields are obtained.[32, 33] If the oxidation is carried out by using silver oxide or lead oxide in ether in the cold, the primary oxidation product is light yellow in color and is very unstable; it contains o-quinonediimine (XII) and on warming with hydrochloric acid yields 2,3-diaminophenazine (XIII) and 2,2'-diaminoazobenzene.[34]

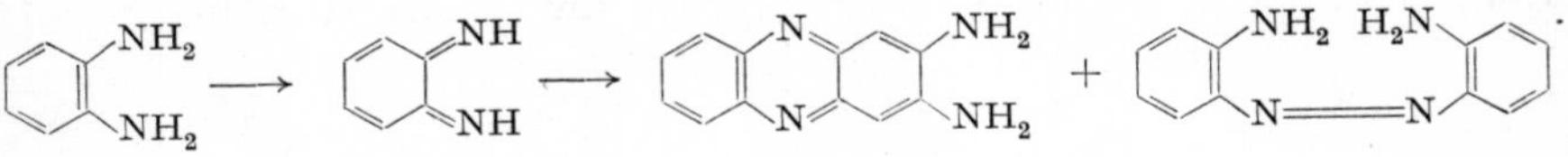

(XII) (XIII)

Distillation of the diaminophenazine with zinc dust yields 2-aminophenazine.[9] The fact that the two amino groups are in positions ortho to one another is shown by the formation, with benzil, of a quinoxaline $C_{26}H_{16}N_4$, which separates from toluene as red-brown plates with a metallic luster.[35] (See Chapter XVIII:2.) The action of concentrated hydrochloric acid at 200° yields 2,3-phenazinediol,[35] the structure of which has been proved independently (Chapter V:3,A). In agreement

with structure XIII is the formation of an analogous product (XIV) by
the oxidation of 2,3-diamino-4-methylbenzoic acid.[36]

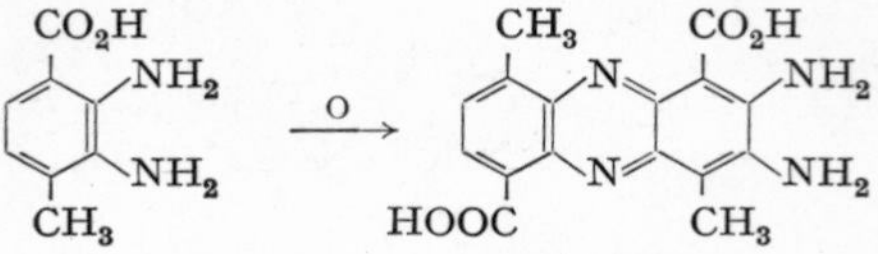

(XIV)

A solution of 2,3-diaminophenazine gives yellow or orange precipitates with bismuth, lead and cadmium, and red precipitates with
mercuric and cupric salts, the two latter being very sensitive ($1:10^5$
for Hg^{++} and 1.6×10^6 for Cu^{++}). This reaction is not shown by
2,7-diaminophenazine, phenosafranine and certain other phenazine
derivatives; its use has been suggested as an analytical method.[37]

C. 2,7-Diaminophenazine

2,7-Diaminophenazine (XVI) separates from ethanol as dark red
plates with a metallic luster, unchanged at 320°, insoluble in cold
benzene, sparingly soluble in water, ether and chloroform and moderately soluble in ethanol and acetone. Solutions of the base in organic
solvents are yellow to orange with yellow to orange fluorescence. At a
molar dilution of 8,000 and 160 it has pK_a values of 4.63 and 3.9,
respectively.[6] The absorption curve shows maxima at 285 and 506 mμ.[12]

It has been prepared by the reduction of 2,3′,4-trinitrodiphenyl-
amine (XV) with sodium sulfide[38] and (in low yield) by reduction of

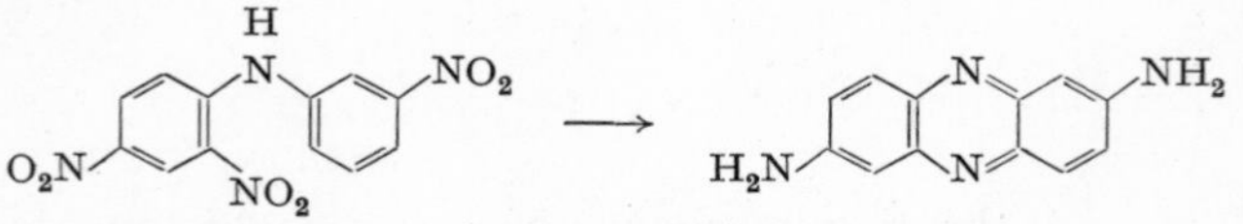

(XV)   (XVI)

2,2′,4,4′-tetranitrodiphenyl ether (XVII).[12] It seems unlikely that a

(XVII)

compound of melting point 138°, obtained by the action of sunlight on a solution of *m*-phenylenediamine in dilute hydrochloric acid and formulated as **XVI** does in fact possess this structure.[39]

D. 2,8-Diaminophenazine

This compound (**XIX**) is slightly soluble in cold water and readily soluble in ethanol and ether, giving yellow solutions with strong fluorescence. The absorption spectrum shows bands at 265 and 447 mμ.[13] Its salts dye silk and cotton, mordanted with tannic acid, red.

It was prepared in 1890 by Nietzki and Ernst by oxidation of 2,4,4′-triaminodiphenylamine (**XVIII**); and it is also formed by the joint oxidation of *m*- and *p*-phenylenediamines.[40]

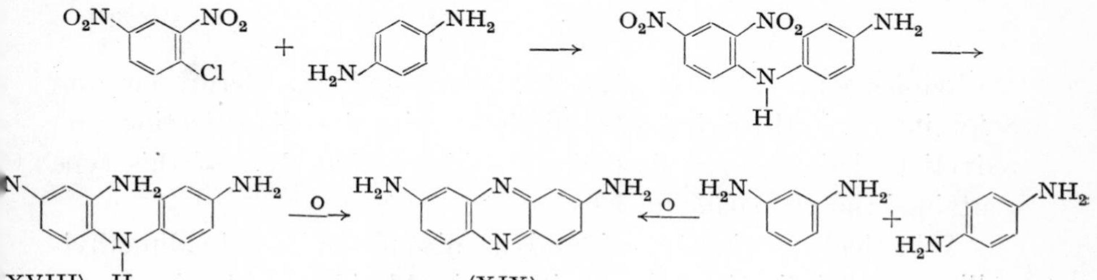

It has been deaminated to phenazine.[40] The action of methyl sulfate on its diacetyl derivative has been investigated.[41]

A compound prepared by Karrer[42] and originally formulated by him as 2,8-bisdimethylaminophenazine was shown to be a safranine (**XX**)[43]; but Karrer[44] subsequently prepared the true 2,8-bisdimethyl-aminophenazine, by cyclization of an acetylamino derivative of Bindschedler's Green, although full details were not given.

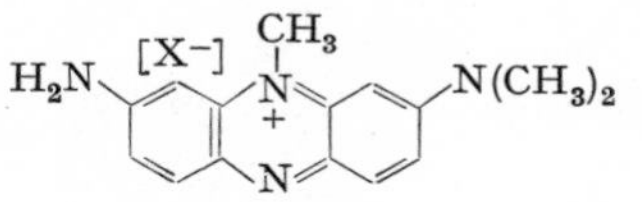

(XX)

A diaminophenazine has found application in electroplating with nickel,[45] and another in the preparation of sulfur dyes.[46]

E. Neutral Red

Neutral Red is also known as Toluylene Red, *C. I.* 825. The joint oxidation of *m-* and *p*-phenylenediamines mentioned above is the simplest case of a remarkable reaction first used in 1879 by Witt[47-51] and proceeds by way of an indamine intermediate. Thus, when *p*-phenylenediamine is oxidized with ferric chloride in the presence of 2,4-diaminotoluene, the "simplest toluylene blue" (XXI) (which is, in fact, violet) arises; and when this is boiled with dilute hydrochloric acid in the presence of air, the "simplest toluylene red," $C_{13}H_{12}N_4.HCl$, is produced. The latter is, in fact, the hydrochloride of 2,8-diamino-3-

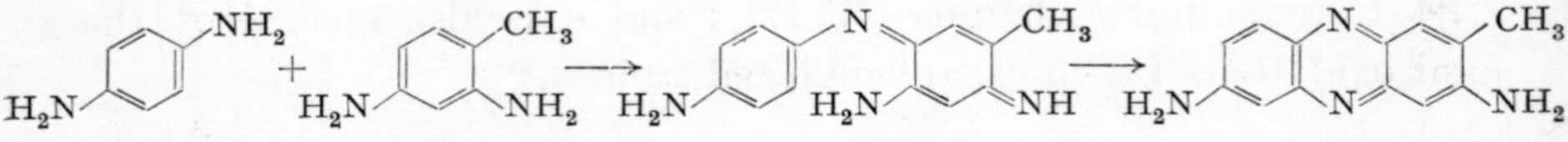

(XXI)

(XXII)

methylphenazine (XXII) and was converted by Bernthsen and Schweitzer[22] in 1886 into 2-methylphenazine by diazotization and reduction. This was the first direct evidence that dyes of this type contained the phenazine nucleus.

Witt had previously oxidized a mixture of *p*-aminodimethyl-aniline and 2,4-diaminotoluene with ferric chloride or potassium ferri-cyanide and obtained toluylene red, which is 2-amino-8-dimethyl-amino-3-methylphenazine (XXIV). The reaction probably proceeds through a nitroso compound; and Witt showed that the indamine XXIII (toluylene blue) was easily formed by the condensation of

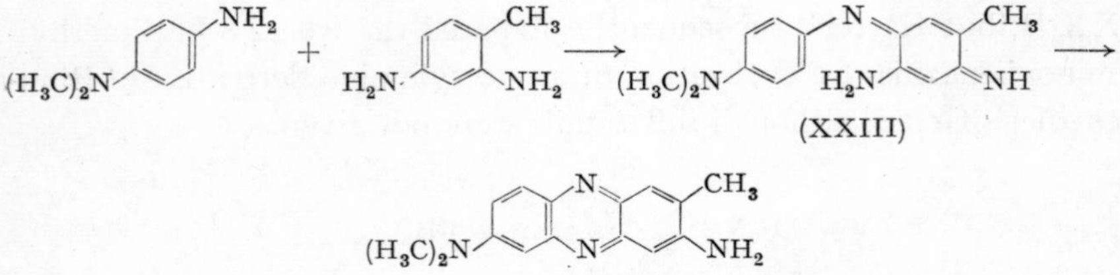

(XXIII)

(XXIV)

p-nitrosodimethylaniline hydrochloride with 2,4-diaminotoluene in warm, aqueous solution. (*N N'*-Dichloroquinonediimine can also be used instead of a nitroso compound). He also showed that *p*-nitrosodimethylaniline does not react with 4,6-diamino-*m*-xylene to yield an eurhodine.[2] When boiled in aqueous solution the toluylene blue dismutates into toluylene red and the leuco-base (reduced indamine).[24] Deamination of toluylene red yields 2-dimethylamino-7-methyl-phenazine.[22] The dyestuff was introduced commercially under the name "neutral red"; it dyes cotton mordanted with tannic acid bluish-red, although it is not now of commercial importance. It has, however, some action as a photographic desensitizer[52] and has been used in a very sensitive test for the presence of nitrous acid in water (a blue color being produced in acid solution[53, 54]) and as a catalyst in the Diels-Alder reaction.[55]

Neutral red has been used as an adsorption indicator in the argentometric determination of halide ions.[56] It has also been found that the sensitivity of titanium oxalate developers to changes in bromide ion concentration is greatly diminished by the addition of neutral red.[57] The partition of the dye between water and isobutanol has been studied[58(a)]; and its R_f value recorded.[58(b)]

The dissociation constant for neutral red has been found to be $3.2 \times 10^{-7}/25°$ [59]; in methanol and water, respectively, pK_1 values of 8.2 and 7.4 have been recorded.[60] A solution in 5.5 *N*HCl is blue, but becomes red on addition of water; at pH 6.8 to 8.0 it becomes orange-yellow.[61] In the pH range 1.6–3.9 (corresponding to the form BH^+) a single absorption maximum at 540 mμ is present, and likewise in the range 8.03–11.28 (corresponding to the free base, B) a single maximum at 460 mμ is present. At pH 6.49, however, the two maxima are present with equal optical density. From these results (in buffered 50% ethanol) it has been calculated that $pK_a = 6.77$.[62, 63] Use of the light absorption has been made in the estimation of neutral red.[64–66] It is a sensitive indicator, which gives a sharp color change not only in aqueous solution, but also in methanol and ethanol, and gives only a low "salt error".[67, 68] It has also been employed in Schönberg's rancidity test for lard and butter,[69–72] and as an indicator of hydrolysis and synthesis within the living cell.[73] The change in color of the fluorescence at pH 6.8 makes possible the use of neutral red as a neutralization indicator in strongly colored solutions.[67]

When a solution of neutral red is reduced, it becomes colorless and is then stable in an atmosphere of nitrogen or hydrogen at pH 8.2; but at pH 2.7 it slowly becomes yellow with a green fluorescence. At pH 5.3 a rapid development of the green fluorescence occurs. Reoxidation of the solution obtained at pH 2.7 or 8.2 gives a solution that is nearly the same as the original; but the solution at pH 5.3 retains its fluorescence.[74] Neutral red has been used in distinguishing certain bacteria. For example, at 37°, *Escherichia coli* causes the ruby-red bouillon agar medium to change to canary yellow with a strong fluorescence, while *Salmonella typhosa* causes no color change or fluorescence. The change is probably due to reduction.[75] The redox potential of neutral red at pH 7 is —0.34 volt and at pH 5 it is —0.20 volt. At pH 7 or more alkaline solutions, neutral red is likely to precipitate itself colloidally from solution and it should therefore be used as a redox indicator only in acid solution.[67] Neutral red produces well-formed waves in polarographic curves even in concentrations of 10^{-7} M in buffered solution; this is due to a catalytic effect.[76]

Neutral red has been used as a dye in many physical and biochemical investigations; but one of its more important applications is as a weak histological stain, particularly for embryological tissues, in conjunction with Janus green.[77] It has been claimed that, at pH 9.0, virulent *Mycobacterium tuberculosis* var. *hominis* or *bovis* immediately stains deep red, while avirulent forms stain yellow.[78] It has been much used for staining living protozoa, as a vital stain for nuclei in tissues and of fresh blood and for staining fresh gonorrheal pus.[79-81] The chief drawback is the toxicity of certain batches that have been on the market, due to impurities present in the dye. It seems that these impurities can be eliminated more readily if the dye is prepared as the hydriodide rather than as the hydrochloride. However, it also seems that neutral red itself may be toxic, may influence cell division and may have a photodynamic action (see Chapter XI:3,C). Neutral red has been used by various workers on gastric excretion. It has been found that, in cases of gastric ulcer, the time taken by neutral red, after intravenous injection, to appear in the gastric contents, is shorter than in a normal subject. In cases of chronic gastritis, gastric carcinoma and pernicious anemia, however, the time is longer than normal.[63,82-87]

Neutral red forms a lake with palladous cyanide.[88]

For compounds of the neutral red type produced in color photography see Chapter VII:2,1.

Neutral Violet (*C. I.* 826) is the hydrochloride of base **XXV**: it is more bluish than neutral red, giving a violet-red color, but is otherwise similar in properties. From measurements of its absorption spectrum, it has been calculated that $pK_a = 7.31$ (in buffered 50% ethanol).[62, 63]

(XXV)

References

1. G. P. Jaubert, *Ber.*, **29**, 414 (1896).
2. O. N. Witt, *Ber.*, **21**, 2418 (1888).
3. F. Kehrmann (with P. Prunier), *Helv. Chim. Acta*, **7**, 472 (1924).
4. F. Kehrmann and P. Prunier, *Helv. Chim. Acta*, **7**, 984 (1924).
5. A. Albert and H. Duewell, *J. Soc. Chem. Ind., London*, **66**, 11 (1947).
6. A. Albert, R. Goldacre and J. Phillips, *J. Chem. Soc.*, **1948**, 2240.
7. B. Hegedüs, *Helv. Chim. Acta*, **33**, 766 (1950).
8. R. C. Elderfield, W. J. Gensler and O. Birstein, *J. Org. Chem.*, **11**, 812 (1946).
9. O. Fischer and E. Hepp, *Ber.*, **22**, 355 (1889).
10. F. Ullmann (with G. Engi), *Ann.*, **366**, 82 (1909).
11. F. Kehrmann, E. Havas and E. Grandmougin, *Ber.*, **47**, 1881 (1914).
12. K. Matsumura, *J. Am. Chem. Soc.*, **52**, 3199 (1930).
13. F. Kehrmann and M. Sandoz, *Helv. Chim. Acta*, **3**, 104 (1920).
14. O. Fischer, *Ber.*, **29**, 1873 (1896).
15. R. Nietzki, *Ber.*, **28**, 2969 (1895).
16. J. T. Hewitt, S. H. Newman and T. F. Winmill, *J. Chem. Soc.*, **95**, 577 (1909).
17. A. Wohl and M. Lange, *Ber.*, **43**, 2186 (1910).
18. F. Kehrmann and E. Havas, *Ber.*, **46**, 341 (1913).
19. I. J. Pachter and M. C. Kloetzel, *J. Am. Chem. Soc.*, **74**, 971 (1952).
20. F. Kehrmann and C. Mermod, *Helv. Chim. Acta*, **10**, 62 (1927).
21. S. Maffei, *Gazz. chim. ital.*, **76**, 239 (1946); through *Chem. Abstracts*, **42**, 911 (1948).
22. A. Bernthsen and H. Schweitzer, *Ann.*, **236**, 332 (1886).
23. D. G. H. Daniels, F. T. Naylor and B. C. Saunders, *J. Chem. Soc.*, **1951**, 3433.
24. A. Korczynski, *Bull. soc. chim. France, Mém.*, (4) **35**, 1186 (1924).
25. A. S. Wheeler and L. F. P. Cutlar, *J. Am. Chem. Soc.*, **49**, 2819 (1927).
26. Ger. Pat. 488,945; *Frdl.*, **16**, 2696 (1927–29); *Chem. Abstracts*, **24**, 2242 (1930).
27. Brit. Pat. 267,169; *Chem. Zentr.*, **1929**, I, 1965; see also U.S. Pat., 1,879,540; *Chem. Abstracts*, **27**, 1094 (1933).
28. E. R. Watson and S. Dutt, *J. Chem. Soc.*, **121**, 1939 (1922).
29. R. Nietzki and J. Slaboszewicz, *Ber.*, **34**, 3727 (1901).
30. A. S. Wheeler and R. W. Bost, *J. Am. Chem. Soc.*, **50**, 2000 (1928).

31. F. Ullmann and F. Mauthner, *Ber.*, **35**, 4302 (1902).
32. E. Knoevenagel, *J. prakt. Chem.*, (2), **89**, 1 (1914).
33. M. M. Richter, *Ber.*, **44**, 3466 (1911).
34. R. Willstätter and A. Pfannenstiel, *Ber.*, **38**, 2348 (1905).
35. O. Fischer and E. Hepp, *Ber.*, **23**, 841 (1890).
36. F. Kehrmann, *Ber.*, **22**, 1983 (1889).
37. T. Pavolini, *Industria Chimica*, **8**, 692 (1933); through *Chem. Abstracts*, **27**, 5270 (1933).
38. Ger.Pat. 148,113; *Chem. Zentr.*, **1904**, I, 414; *Frdl.*, **7**, 341 (1902–04).
39. B. K. Malaviya and S. Dutt, *Proc. Acad. Sci. United Provinces Agra Oudh, India*, **4**, 319 (1935); through *Chem. Abstracts*, **30**, 1056 (1936).
40. R. Nietzki and O. Ernst, *Ber.*, **23**, 1852 (1890).
41. F. Kehrmann and M. Ramm, *Ber.*, **51**, 385 (1918).
42. P. Karrer, *Ber.*, **49**, 1643 (1916).
43. F. Kehrmann and G. Falconnier, *Ber.*, **50**, 421 (1917).
44. P. Karrer, *Ber.*, **50**, 420 (1917).
45. U.S. Pat. 2,291,590; *Chem. Abstracts*, **37**, 568 (1943).
46. Ger. Pat. 147,990; *Chem. Zentr.*, **1904**, I, 236; *Frdl.*, **7**, 554 (1902–04).
47. Ger. Pat. 15,272; *Ber.*, **14**, 2434 (1881); *Frdl.*, **1**, 274 (1877–87).
48. Ger. Pat. 19,224; *Ber.*, **15**, 2645 (1882).
49. Ger. Pat. 59,063; *Ber.*, **24**, *Ref.*, 929 (1891).
50. O. N. Witt, *Ber.*, **12**, 931 (1879).
51. E. Noelting, *Ber.*, **49**, 1751 (1916).
52. E. Stenger and H. Stammreich, *Z. wiss. Phot.*, **23**, 11 (1924); through *Chem. Zentr.*, **1924**, II, 908.
53. A. Zlatarov, *Z. anal. Chem.*, **62**, 384 (1923).
54. H. Stooff and M. Horn, *Wasser u. Gas*, **14**, 175 (1924); through *Chem. Abstracts*, **18**, 873 (1924).
55. W. Flaig, *Reichsamt Wirtschaftsausbau, Chem. Ber.*, Prüf. Nr. 093 (PB. 52020), 1073 (1942); through *Chem. Abstracts*, **41**, 6189 (1947).
56. G. Mannelli, *Ann. chim. (Rome)*, **40**, 163 (1950); through *Chem. Abstracts*, **45**, 10123 (1951).
57. J. Rzymkowski, *Phot. Korr.*, **85**, 93 (1950); through *Chem. Abstracts*, **45**, 3741 (1952).
58(a) R. Collander, *Acta Chem. Scand.*, **4**, 1085 (1950); *Chem. Abstracts*, **45**, 3690 (1951).
58(b) M. Lederer, *Science*, **112**, 504 (1950).
59. I. Tachi, *Mem. Coll. Agr., Kyoto Imp. Univ.*, **1938**, No. 42 Chem. Ser. No. 22; through *Chem. Abstracts*, **32**, 5685 (1938).
60. I. M. Kolthoff and L. S. Guss, *J. Am. Chem. Soc.*, **60**, 2516 (1938).
61. A. Meretoja, *Suomen Kemistilehti*, **21B**, 24 (1948); through *Chem. Abstracts*, **43**, 3307 (1949).
62. S. Woislawski, *J. Am. Chem. Soc.*, **75**, 5201 (1953).
63. S. Woislawski, *Proc. Soc. Exptl. Biol. Med.*, **79**, 390 (1952).
64. W. R. Brode, *J. Am. Chem. Soc.*, **46**, 581 (1924).
65. J. Stauff, *Z. physik Chem.*, **A191**, 69 (1942); through *Chem. Abstracts*, **37**, 4286 (1943).
66. W. C. Holmes and A. R. Peterson, *Stain Tech.*, **5**, 91 (1930); through *Chem. Abstracts*, **24**, 4314 (1930).
67. O. Tomïcek, *Chemical Indicators*, Butterworths, London, 1951.
68. I. M. Kolthoff, *Pharm. Weekblad;* through *Chem. Zentr.*, **1921**, IV, 452.
69. G. Knaysi, *J. Bact.*, **42**, 587 (1941); *Chem. Abstracts*, **36**, 512 (1942).

70. G. Knaysi, *J. Dairy Sci.*, **25**, 585 (1942); through *Chem. Abstracts*, **36**, 5270 (1942).
71. F. Schönberg, *Z. Fleisch- u. Milchhyg.*, **53**, 61 (1943); through *Chem. Abstracts*, **38**, 3375 (1944).
72. F. Schönberg, *Z. Fleisch- u. Milchhyg.*, **54**, 221 (1944); through *Chem. Abstracts*, **41**, 6638 (1947).
73. V. Koehring, *J. Morphol. Physiol.*, **49**, 45 (1930); through *Chem. Abstracts*, **25**, 1543 (1931).
74. W. M. Clark and M. E. Perkins, *J. Am. Chem. Soc.*, **54**, 1228 (1932).
75. E. M. Chamot and C. M. Sherwood, *J. Am. Chem. Soc.*, **39**, 1755 (1917).
76. V. Vojiř, *Coll. Czech. Chem. Communs.*, **18**, 629 (1953).
77. H. S. Faris, *Anat. Rec.*, **27**, 241 (1924).
78. L. de Andrade, *Mem. inst. Oswaldo Cruz*, **49**, 7 (1951); through *Chem. Abstracts*, **46**, 5124 (1952).
79. S. Skraup, *Ber.*, **49**, 2142 (1916).
80. J. R. Baker, *Nature*, **168**, 1089 (1951).
81. A. J. Dalton and M. D. Felix, *Nature*, **170**, 541 (1952).
82. E. M. Robertson, *Glasgow Med. J.*, **25**, 158 (1945); through *Chem. Abstracts*, **39**, 4673 (1945).
83. A. Winkelstein and J. M. Marcus, *J. Am. Med. Assoc.*, **85**, 1397 (1925).
84. R. Kolm, S. A. Komarov and H. Shay, *Rev. Can. Biol.*, **8**, 262 (1949); through *Chem. Abstracts*, **44**, 3069 (1950).
85. L. E. Edwards, R. Kolm, S. A. Komarov and H. Shay, *Rev. Can. Biol.*, **8**, 280 (1949); through *Chem. Abstracts*, **44**, 3070 (1950).
86. S. Sevitt and R. P. Jepson, *J. Clin. Path.*, **1**, 217 (1948).
87. V. G. Khlystov, *Terapevt. Arkh.*, **23**, No. 4, 16 (1951); through *Chem. Abstracts*, **46**, 598 (1952).
88. F. Feigl and G. B. Heisig, *J. Am. Chem. Soc.*, **73**, 5631 (1951).
89. O. Fischer and E. Hepp, *Ber.*, **23**, 2789 (1890).
90. O. Fischer and J. Trost, *Ber.*, **26**, 3083 (1893).
91. F. Ullman and R. Heisler, *Ber.*, **42**, 4263 (1909).
92. F. Kehrmann and B. Mascioni, *Ber.*, **28**, 345 (1895).
93. T. Zincke and P. Schwarz, *Ann.*, **307**, 28 (1899).
94. F. Kehrmann and M. Cordone, *Ber.*, **46**, 3009 (1913).
95. F. Ullmann and F. Mauthner, *Ber.*, **36**, 4026 (1903).
96. E. Noelting and G. Thesmar, *Ber.*, **35**, 628 (1902).
97. R. Nietzki and E. Rehe, *Ber.*, **25**, 3005 (1892).
98. P. Cohn and A. Fischer, *Monatsh.*, **21**, 267 (1900); through *J. Chem. Soc.*, *Abstracts*, **78**, (i), 458 (1900).
99. R. Meldola and J. H. Coste, *J. Chem. Soc.*, **55**, 590 (1889).
100. E. Müller, *Ber.*, **22**, 856 (1889).
101. R. Nietzki and E. Müller, *Ber.*, **22**, 440 (1889).
102. L. Birkofer and A. Widmann, *Chem. Ber.*, **86**, 1295 (1953).
103. J. Alfthan, *Ber.*, **53**, 78 (1920).
104. M. Battegay and W. Kern, *Bull. soc. chim. France, Mém.*, (4), **41**, 34 (1927).
105. E. Gebauer-Fülnegg and E. Riesz, *Monatsh.*, **49**, 31 (1928).
106. A. Korczynski and Piasecki, *Anzeiger Akad. Wiss. Krakau*, **1917**, 176, through *Chem. Zentr.*, **1921**, I, 866.

CHAPTER VII

The Safranines

1. General Account of the Preparation and Structure of the Safranines

A. Historical

The dyestuffs of this group (the aposafranines and the safranines) are amino derivatives of the phenazinium salts, to which they stand in the same relation as the eurhodines to the azines, the corresponding hydroxy derivatives being termed safranols.[1] The discovery of the safranines appears to be due to Greville Williams in 1859[2] and these dyes were in commercial use shortly after that date. Phenosafranine was first obtained in the pure state by Witt,[3] who exhibited it in Paris in 1878 and who recognized the analogy between the eurhodines and the safranines in 1888.[4, 5] The phenazine nature of phenosafranine was first realized in 1886 through the work of Bernthsen[6] and of Witt.[7] Aposafranine (the name of which implies that it is obtained from phenosafranine by removal of an amino group) was discovered by Nietzki[8] in the same year by boiling phenosafranine with sodium nitrite in alcoholic sulfuric acid solution.

B. Preparation

(*1*) The original method for preparing safranine consisted in heating a mixture of aminoazotoluene and toluidine with an oxidizing agent such as arsenic acid or potassium dichromate, although Witt[9] observed that the presence of the oxidizing agent is unnecessary and that safranine can be obtained by simply heating aminoazotoluene with toluidine hydrochloride. He also found that 2,5-diaminotoluene was invariably formed during the reaction and concluded that safranine was the product of the mutual oxidation of this (formed by reduction of part of the aminoazo compound) and o-toluidine, the dehydrogenation being accomplished by the action of the aminoazo compound. Indeed, the most important method of preparation of safranines is the joint oxidation of a mixture of 1 mole of a p-diamine and 2 moles of an aromatic monoamine.[3,10,11] This led to the discovery of other dyes, by varying the mono- and di-amines used, and, in particular, of phenosafranine, which is derived from p-phenylenediamine and aniline. Manganese dioxide or potassium dichromate in hot, neutral solution, or potassium chlorate in the presence of magnesium chloride,[12] may be used as oxidizing agent; and the process may be carried out *in situ* on the fabric.

When potassium dichromate is added to a cold solution of the diamine and monoamine mixture, an intense blue, green or violet color is produced immediately, due to the formation of an "indamine" (a derivative of p-quinonediimine), for example, as shown in Equation (1).

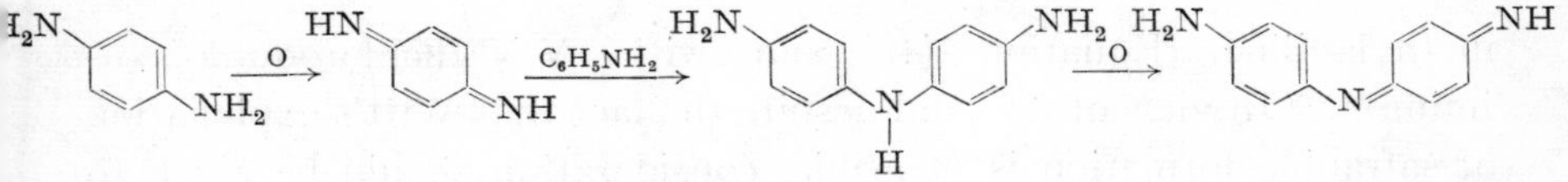

(1)

Indamine

On further oxidation (sometimes warming is necessary) the indamine unites with a second molecule of the same (or a different) monoamine to give a phenazine derivative containing two symmetrically placed amino residues. Various more detailed schemes have been put forward; but the exact mechanism of safranine formation is not completely understood, although the last step may proceed through the interme-

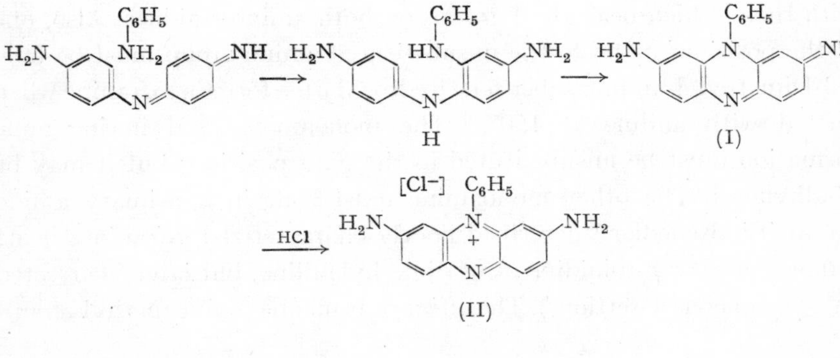

(2)

diate shown in Equation (2).[13-15] In 1883, Nietzki[16] discovered an analogous process for the formation of safranines, in the mutual oxidation of 1 mole of 4,4'-diaminodiphenylamine and 1 mole of a primary monoamine, as shown in Equation (3). A small amount of phenosafranine (together with indulines) is also formed by the inter-

$$
\begin{array}{c}
C_6H_5 \\
\end{array}
$$

$$H_2N \underset{\overset{|}{N} \atop \overset{|}{H}}{\overset{NH_2}{\bigcirc}} NH_2 \quad \overset{O}{\longrightarrow} \quad (I) \tag{3}$$

action of p-nitrosoaniline (1 mole) and aniline hydrochloride (2 moles) in neutral solution; and a similar reaction occurs with p-nitrosodi-

$$(H_3C)_2N\!\!-\!\!NO \;+\; NH_2 \;\longrightarrow\; (H_3C)_2N\!\!-\!\!=NH \;\longrightarrow\; [X^-] \; (H_3C)_2N\!\!-\!\!\overset{C_6H_5}{\underset{+}{N}}\!\!-\!\!NH$$

methylaniline (Equation (4)) and with N,N'-dichloroquinonediimine.[17-19] In view of this and despite the fact that Witt's explanation of safranine formation is plausible, consideration should be given to the alternative mechanism of indamine formation shown in Equation (5).

$$H_2N\!\!-\!\!\underset{\overset{\|}{N}\atop NC_6H_5}{N} \;+\; NH_2 \;\longrightarrow\; H_2N\!\!-\!\!=NH \;+\; C_6H_5NH_2 \tag{5}$$

Safranine formation results when p-diamines alkylated on one amino group (for example, p-aminodimethylaniline) are used, but not with those which bear alkyl groups on both amino residues. Also, one of the positions ortho to the unsubstituted amino group must be free. 2,3-Dimethyl-4-aminoazobenzene hydrochloride forms a safranine when heated with aniline at 150°.[20] The monoamine used in indamine formation must be unsubstituted in the para position; but it may be N-alkylated. The other monoamine must contain a primary amino group (Bindschedler[21] described poorly characterized safranines using 2 moles of o- or p-toluidine or of dimethylaniline, but later[22] corrected these erroneous assertions). The effect of from one to five methyl groups in various positions of the second amine molecule has been investigated, with some apparently contradictory results. Thus, whereas 2,6-xylidine and mesidine fail to form safranines with indamines the reaction suceeds with 2,3,4,5,6-pentamethylaniline.[14, 23, 24]

Commercial safranine (*C. I.* 841) is made by treating a crude mixture of aniline and *o*-toluidine with hydrochloric acid and a concentrated solution of sodium nitrite, forming a mixture of aminoazotoluene, aminoazobenzene, aniline and *o*-toluidine. Instead, however, of heating the crude mixture directly, it is usual to reduce the aminoazo compounds *in situ* with tin, zinc or iron; and the resultant mixture of mono- and di-amines is then oxidized with chromic acid or manganese dioxide to a mixture of pheno- and tolu-safranines, the shade varying according to the proportions of the different products present.[25, 26]

(2) Safranines are also formed by the oxidation of 2-arylamino-*p*-phenylenediamines (which may contain sulfonic acid groups[27]) in the presence of secondary or tertiary aromatic amines with free *p*-positions,

as shown in Equation (6). In place of the first component, a 4-amino-2-phenylaminoazobenzene may be used.[28, 29]

(3) Safranines can also be obtained (in a modification of *(1)*) from *N*-monoaryl-*m*-phenylenediamines by the action of *p*-nitrosoamines (or the corresponding *p*-diamines under oxidizing conditions) as shown in Equation (7). The components are mixed in cold solution to form the indamine, which is then cyclized by warming. Instead of the nitrosoamine, *N*,*N'*-dichloroquinonediimine or a *p*-aminoazo compound may

be employed (Equations (8) and (9)).[30–34] The use of a 4-aminodiphenylamine under oxidizing conditions leads to the production of an induline,[35] and sulfonic acid derivatives of safranines have been synthesized from N-monoaryl-m-phenylenediamines containing sulfonic acid groups.[36]

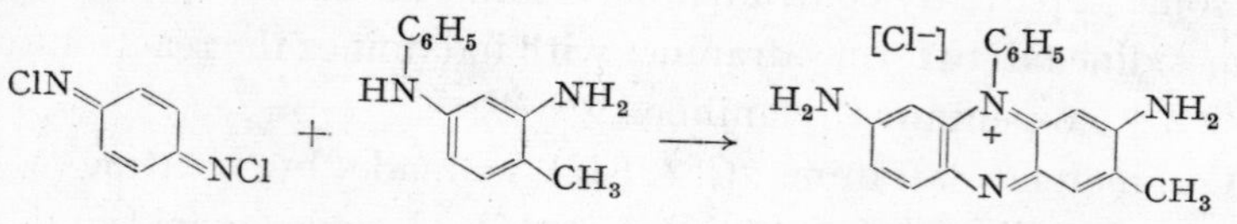

$$(8)$$

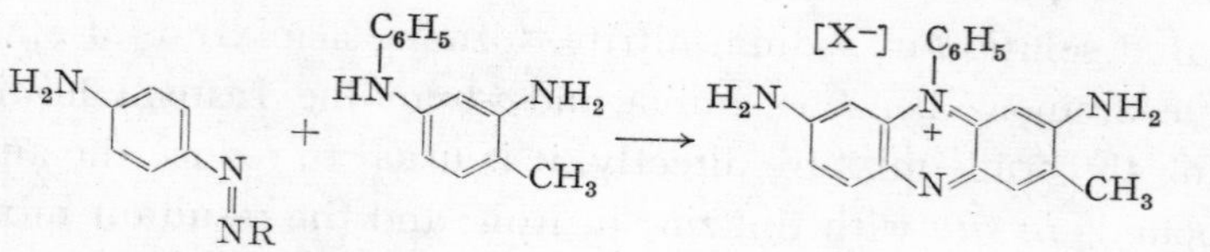

$$(9)$$

C. Structure

Since the papers[37,38] in which the suggestion was made that the acid residue of the phenazinium salts is free (that is, ionic) scarcely require mention here, the structure of the safranines may be discussed under two headings only.

(1) Symmetrical Arrangement of the Amino Residues in Phenosafranine. One problem that caused controversy among the earlier investigators is whether the amino groups are arranged symmetrically or unsymmetrically in the safranine molecule. Thus, the formation of phenosafranine by the mutual oxidation of 1 mole of 4,4′-diaminodiphenylamine with 1 mole of aniline might occur to give either the "symmetrical" II or the "unsymmetrical" III. After a long dispute, the symmetrical formulation was finally established; Nietzki's[16] claim to

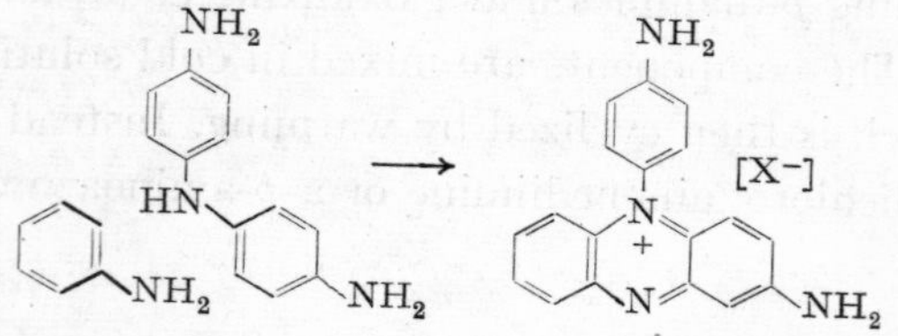

(III)

have isolated two isomeric diethylsafranines, which implied the unsymmetrical structure, was disproved by Körner and Schraube.[39] Likewise, Barbier and Sisley's[40,41] claim to have proved the existence of two isomeric safranines (symmetrical and unsymmetrical) and that the commercial dye consisted of a mixture of these was discredited by the work of Hewitt, Newman and Winmill[42] and Havas and Bernhard.[43]

Evidence in favor of the "symmetrical" formulation was found by Jaubert[44] in 1895 in the formation of safranine-like dyestuffs by the mutual oxidation of p-phenylenediamine and an N-monoalkylated m-diamine; for example, equation (10). Since in these dyestuffs an

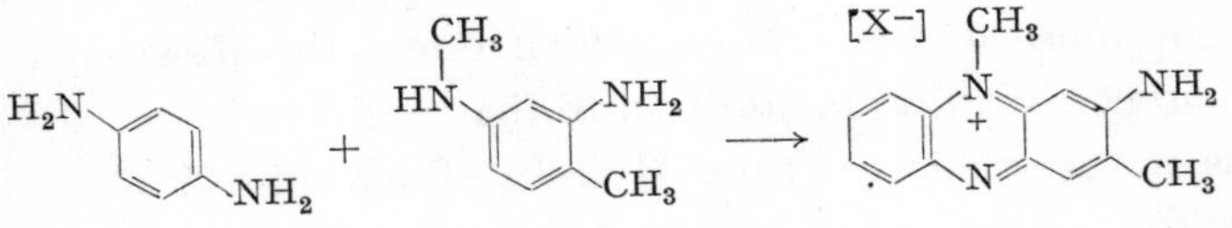

alkyl and not an aryl group is linked to the phenazine system, it is obvious that an unsymmetrical formulation analogous to III is impossible in this case. Moreover, in 1896, Nietzki[45] showed that the condensation of *(a)* 3-aminodiphenylamine with 4-aminodiphenylamine and *(b)* sym-diphenyl-m-phenylenediamine with p-phenylenediamine yielded the same phenylphenosafranine (Equations (11) and (12)). Also, the

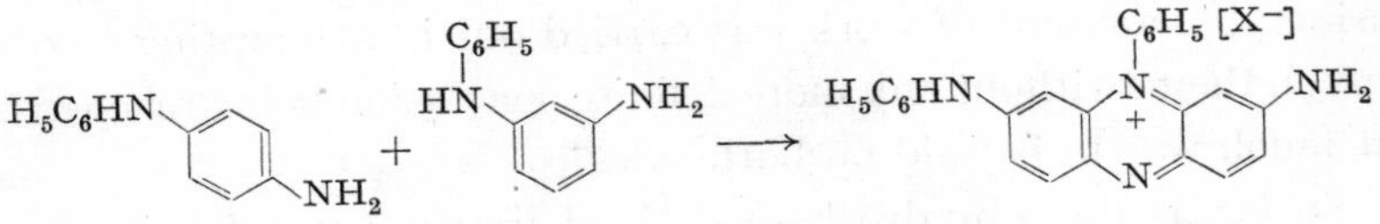

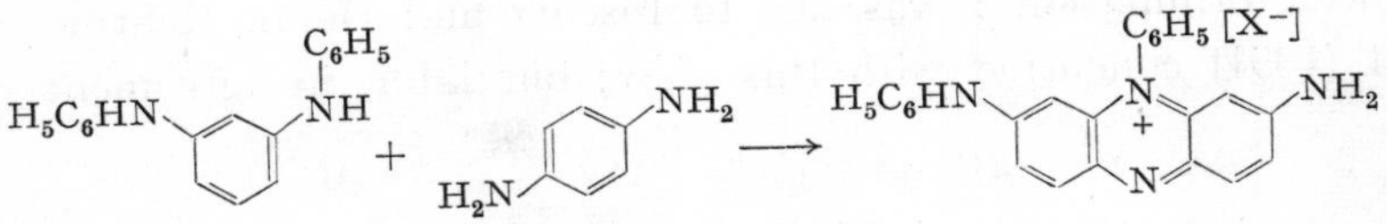

condensation of p-nitrosophenol with m-hydroxydiphenylamine yields a product **(IV)** that appears to be identical with one obtained from

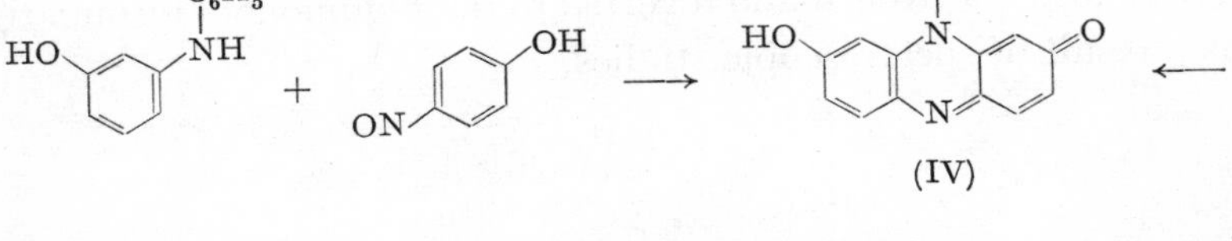

phenosafranine.[42,46,47] A good deal of other evidence also supports the "symmetrical" structure.[48-53]

(2)   *The o- and p-Quinonoid Formulations.* As mentioned in Chapter II:1,C., much early work was concerned with deciding between the "symmetrical" (bridged-ring) and "unsymmetrical" (o-quinonoid) structures for the phenazine nucleus; but now we can regard the nucleus as being symmetrical, due to resonance involving (mainly) the two (equivalent) o-quinonoid forms. In the case of the phenazinium dyestuffs, however, the matter is further complicated by the presence of one or more amino groups, which offers the possibility of a *p*-quinonoid constitution in addition to the o-quinonoid one. To-day it is obvious enough that structures II and V differ appreciably only in the

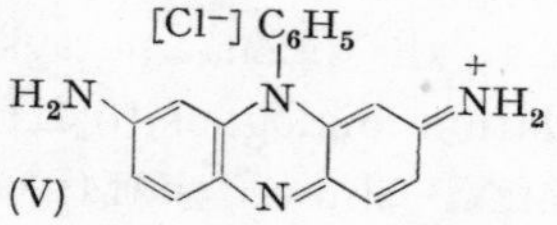

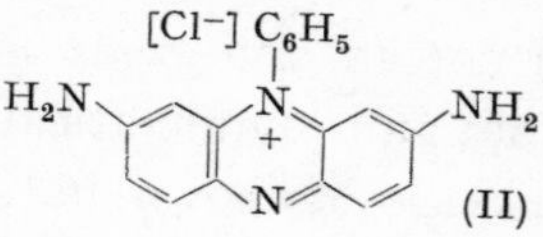

distribution of valency electrons and that, in fact, one must expect a resonance hybrid. But to the pioneer investigators in the safranine field, these two structures were regarded as being desmotropic; and a considerable amount of work was carried out in attempting to decide between them, without any more definite conclusion being reached than that much was to be said on both sides!

So far as the anhydro base derived from phenosafranine is concerned, formulation I was due to Fischer and Hepp. Kehrmann at first (1891) concurred with this view; but later, in agreement with

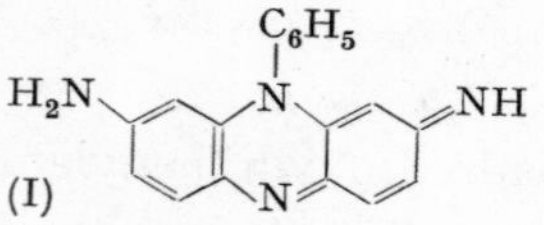

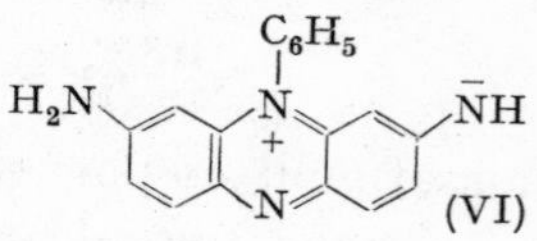

Nietzki,[45] favored a structure the modern equivalent of which is VI. Still later, however, Kehrmann reverted to the *p*-quinonoid formulation (I), as a result of spectroscopic studies.

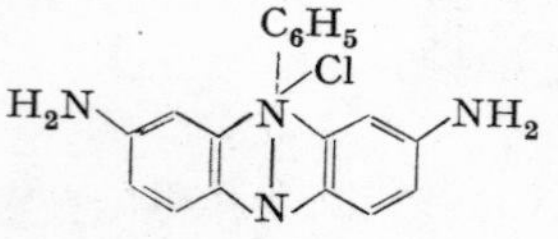

(VII)

So far as the phenosafranine salts are concerned, the original formulation was the bridged-ring structure (VII); but the alternative o-quinonoid structure (II) was soon suggested by Kehrmann and the p-quinonoid (V) by Jaubert and by Fischer and Hepp. Finally, Kehrmann came to believe that the salts must be partly o- and partly p-quinonoid in nature.

It was thought that a decision between structures II and V for phenosafranine could be arrived at by a consideration of the behavior of the dye with nitrous acid, since V contains only one amino group, whereas II contains two. Actually, one amino group is readily removed by diazotization in the ordinary way (the red solution changing to blue) followed by reduction with ethanol, yielding aposafranine, while the second amino group is considerably more resistant. Kehrmann, however, by diazotization in concentrated sulfuric acid solution, followed by reduction with ethanol, succeeded in removing the second amino group, thus obtaining 5-phenylphenazinium chloride (VIII), which cannot have a p-quinonoid structure.[47, 54–56] This was taken by Kehrmann as evidence in favor of the o-quinonoid structure for phenosafranine and aposafranine (IX).

The introduction of one or two amino groups into the 5-phenyl-phenazinium salts by ammonia in the presence of air, mentioned in Chapter II:2,D, was further used by Kehrmann in evidence for the o-quinonoid structure. Moreover, when it was found that syntheses for the production of the amino-free phenazinium compounds (which can only be o-quinonoid) by appropriate variations yielded amino-containing compounds which proved by their properties to be very similar to safranine, the o-quinonoid formulation was thought to be further upheld. Still the p-quinonoid structure remained necessary to explain the fact that, although in phenosafranine one cannot differentiate between the two amino groups, yet, if one is attacked, the other ceases to function as an amino group (except in concentrated sulfuric acid solution). Thus, Balls, Hewitt and Newman[57] found that phenosafranine reacts with only 1 mole of an aldehyde. Also, N,N'-tetramethylpheno- safranine iodide combines with only 1 mole of methyl iodide, so the product was believed to be p-quinonoid, otherwise there would be no reason why a second mole of methyl iodide should not react. Further- more, N-methylphenosafranine chloride when heated with acetic anhydride under pressure at 160° forms only a *mono*acetyl derivative.[58]

Moreover, Kehrmann[59-61] obtained much evidence in favor of the p-quinonoid formulation by the use of absorption spectra, although, by present day standards, the measurements are to be regarded only as qualitative. A wide range of phenazine and phenazinium derivatives was used in these investigations, in each case the absorption spectrum being measured in solutions of varying concentrations of sulfuric acid (from 0–100% and also in oleum). By increasing the concentration of the acid, striking color changes are produced, and the results show that (with few exceptions) the number of color changes produced increases with the number of amino groups present in the molecule, which is explained by assuming that salt formation takes place progressively, each transformation of a basic group into a salt group causing a color change. These color changes are not sudden, due to the presence of mixtures of mono-, di-, etc. salts. Very slight basic properties are shown by all basic groups except the first, to which the normal color is due; all other salts are obtained only in strongly acid solution.

$[X^-] \ C_6H_5 \qquad\qquad 2 \ [X^-] \ C_6H_5$

Yellow　　　　　　Red-brown

(X)　　　　　　　(XI)

Phenazine and the 5-phenylphenazinium derivatives give two series of salts, *(1)* yellow, *(2)* red-brown, which can be only *o*-quinonoid (X and XI). In the case of 4-amino-10-phenylphenazinium derivatives, derived from the anhydro-base XII, we obtain three series of salts, *(1)* blue-green, *(2)* yellow, *(3)* red-brown, the latter two corresponding to the amino-free compound in spectra and, hence, also in structure. These are therefore satisfactorily represented by the *o*-quinonoid structures XIII, XIV and XV, respectively. It is clear that the introduction of an $-NH_3^+$ group into the phenazine nucleus would not be expected to produce any marked effect in the absorption spectrum, while the introduction of an $-NH_2$ group would be expected to do so. It therefore seems that we are justified in assuming that the second and third salts do have the additional hydrogen nuclei attached to the nitrogen atoms indicated in formulas XIV and XV.

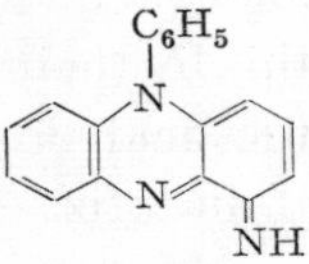

(XII)	Blue-green (XIII)	Yellow (XIV)	Red-brown (XV)

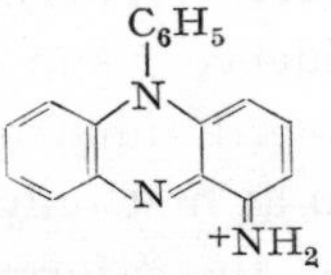

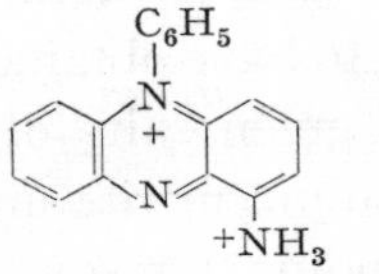

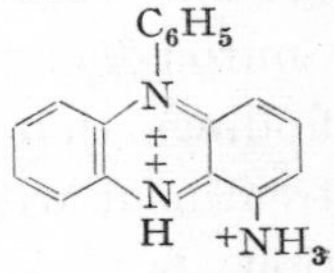

In the case of aposafranine, derived from the anhydro-base XVI, the colors obtained are *(1)* blue-red, *(2)* green, *(3)* red-brown. The almost complete identity in the behavior of the triacid (red-brown) salts XV and XX leaves no doubt as to their *o*-quinonoid nature. However, the mono- and di-acid salts differ in color, and hence in structure, from those of the 1-amino compound. Kehrmann regarded the monoacid salts as being *p*-quinonoid (XVII) and the diacid salts as being a mixture of (mainly) the *p*- (XVIII), with a little of the *o*-

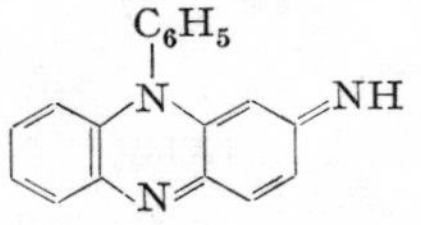

Red (XVI)	Blue-red (XVII)

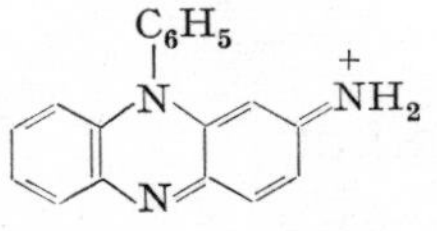

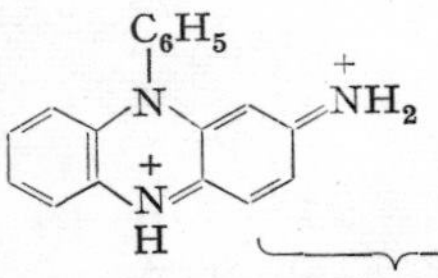

Blue Green (XVIII)	Yellow (XIX)	Red-brown (XX)

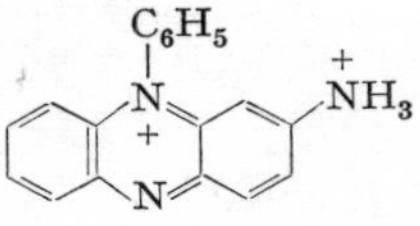

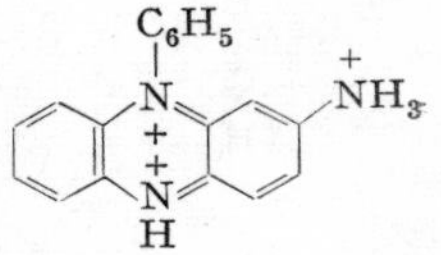

(XIX), quinonoid forms. It seems likely that we are justified in assuming that the third salt does have the additional hydrogen nucleus attached as in formula XX; but the position of attachment of the protons in the first and second salts is less certain. Only the triacid salts are true primary amines and therefore capable of being diazotized.

In the case of phenosafranine (anhydro-base, XXI), the spectroscopic data indicate that the mono- (red) and di- (blue) acid salts are p- and the tetra- (red-brown) is o-quinonoid. Kehrmann regarded the triacid salt (green) as being mainly p- (blue) mixed with a little o- (yellow) quinonoid form (structures XXII–XXVII). Grandmougin and Smirous[62] claimed to have obtained evidence in support of this by their findings that the green salts of phenosafranine in sulfuric acid on treatment with sodium nitrite undergo at first only partial diazotization; but, on standing for some days, the p-form was supposed to rearrange slowly into the o-form, and then to be tetrazotized, so that on treatment with ethanol the free 5-phenylphenazinium salt was formed.

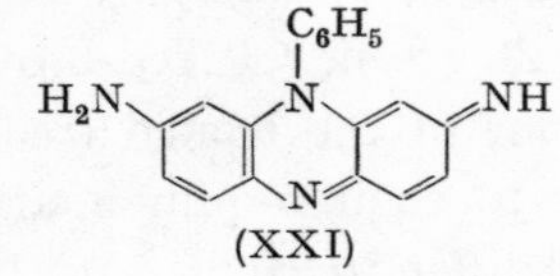

(XXI)
Yellow-red

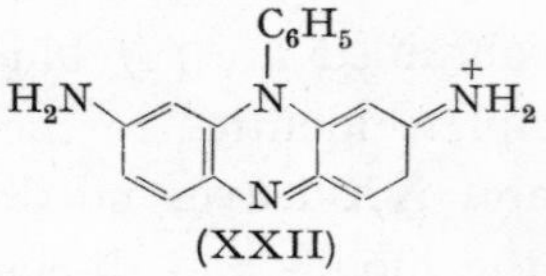

(XXII)
Red

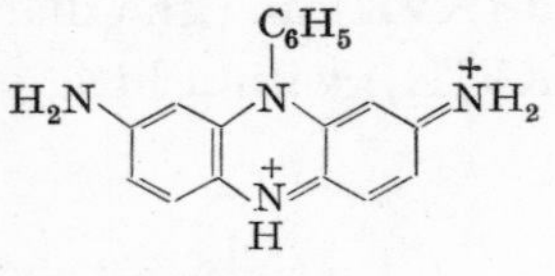

(XXIII)

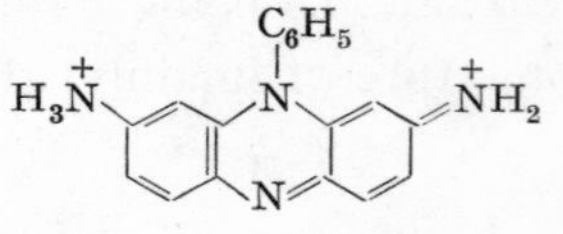

(XXIV)

Blue

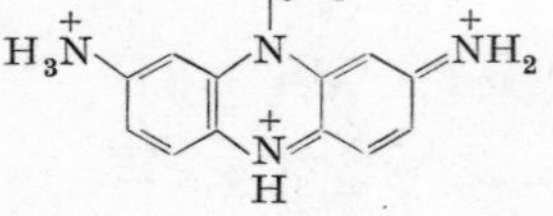

(XXV)
Blue

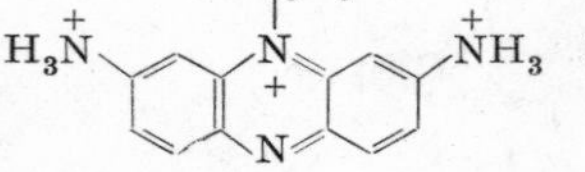

(XXVI)
Yellow

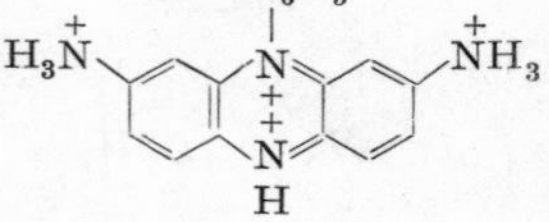

(XXVII)
Red-brown

Green

References 63–84 provide further information on this subject, of which the first gives a useful summary.

Although, as shown above, the usually obtained salts of the safranine type are essentially *p*-quinonoid in structure, we have, in general, throughout this book named (and also often formulated) these compounds as being *o*-quinonoid, to be in keeping with the nomenclature of *Chemical Abstracts*, that is, to regard these as being amino derivatives of phenylphenazinium salts, etc. This has also the advantage of showing the relationships to the aminophenazines and to the parent phenazinium system.

2. Detailed Account of Certain Safranines

A. Aposafranine

Aposafranine, 2-amino-10-phenylphenazinium salts, is shown in formula XVII. The chloride[55] separates from dilute ethanol as prisms with a weak greenish reflex and the bromide[85] from ethanol as dark red prisms with a green iridiscence. The salts dye wool and silk red[47]; but aposafranine is of no practical importance as a dye. The anhydro-base (XVI)[55] is precipitated from aqueous solutions of the salts by addition of potassium hydroxide, and separates from methylal as crystalline crusts with a dark green reflex, which are fairly readily soluble in benzene and ether to give yellowish-red solutions[60] and are soluble in water. The base in the dry state is stable at 100°, but undergoes decomposition on being heated in benzene solution. Acetyl[47,56] and benzoyl[86] derivatives have been described.

Barbier and Sisley[41,87] prepared aposafranine by heating *p*-amino-azobenzene hydrochloride with aniline hydrochloride in water saturated with aniline at 160–170° under pressure, small amounts of 2,3-dianilino-5-phenylphenazinium chloride (see Chapter VIII:3,C) also being produced. They suggested the mechanism illustrated in Equation (13), which does not appear to be very acceptable (compare a mechanism

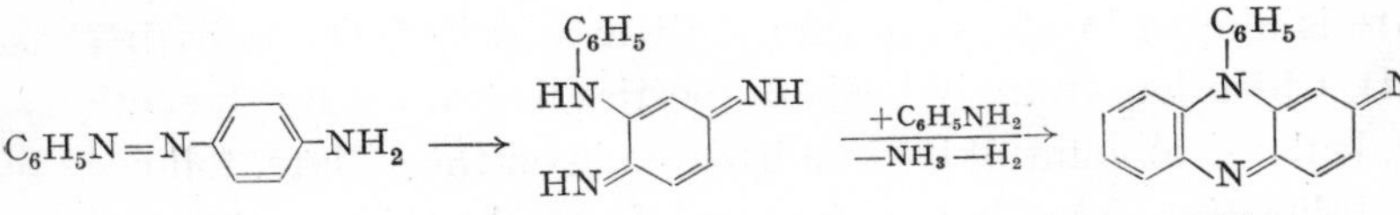

$$C_6H_5N{=}N{-}\!\!\bigcirc\!\!{-}NH_2 \longrightarrow \underset{HN}{\overset{\overset{\displaystyle C_6H_5}{\overset{|}{HN}}}{\bigcirc}}\!\!{NH} \quad \xrightarrow[-NH_3\,-H_2]{+C_6H_5NH_2} \quad \underset{(XVI)}{\overset{\overset{\displaystyle C_6H_5}{\overset{|}{N}}}{\bigcirc\!\!\bigcirc}}\!\!{NH} \quad (13)$$

suggested for induline formation by Fischer and Hepp, mentioned in Chapter VIII:2,B). We have found no record in the literature of other workers repeating this preparation; but, assuming the experimental results to be correct, further study of the mechanism involved seems desirable.

Aposafranine has also been obtained in various other ways mentioned in the following chapters: II:2,D; IV:2; VII:1,C(2); VII:2,C and VIII:3,B. For the deamination of aposafranine to the 5-phenyl-phenazinium salts, and the re-formation of aposafranine from the latter, see Chapter II:2,D. Although the action of ammonia or primary or secondary bases on N-acetylaposafranine leads to substitution in position 8, aposafranine itself apparently reacts in position 3. Thus, the action of alcoholic methylamine solution on aposafranine chloride at 100° results in the formation of 2-amino-3-methylamino-10-phenyl-phenazinium chloride, according to Fischer and Giesen,[88] although definite proof of the orientation of this compound appears to be lacking. See, however, also Chapters VII:2,E and VIII:3,B. The action of sulfites or bisulfites on aposafranines, followed by oxidation, leads to the production of sulfonic acid derivatives, in which, it has been suggested, the sulfonic acid group is present in position 8.[89] The action of aniline on aposafranine is discussed in Chapter VIII:3,C. For the hydrolysis to aposafranine, see Chapter V:2,C.

Homologs and various derivatives, including N-dialkyl derivatives of aposafranine are also known.[41, 54, 56, 87, 90-92]

B. Phenosafranine

Phenosafranine, 2,8-diamino-10-phenylphenazinium salts (*C.I.* 840) are derived from the cation XXII. The chloride, which is hygroscopic, becomes anhydrous at 130° and forms green needles, difficultly soluble in cold water, but readily soluble in hot water.[16, 22,40,41,93] The electrical conductivity of aqueous solutions has been measured.[41, 44,94,95] The nitrate is almost insoluble in dilute nitric acid.[16, 22] The anhydro-base (XXI), which has strongly basic properties, is formed by the action of the calculated amount of barium hydroxide on the sulfate, followed by recrystallization from hot water, and forms lustrous, golden plates, easily soluble in ethanol, difficultly soluble in water and almost insoluble in ether.[47] According to Kehrmann, Havas and Grandmougin,[96] when a solution of phenosafranine is treated with alkali in the presence of ether, the two red layers show different absorption spectra, the aqueous layer containing the quaternary base and the ethereal layer the anhydro-base. When, however, N,N'-tetraethylphenosafranine is treated with dilute alkali, only an ether-soluble base is formed. The spectrum of indamine closely resembles that of safranine; but, when treated with water, it does not show appreciable hydration to give a quaternary base. The absorption spectrum of phenosafranine and some of its homologs in solutions of varying acidity has been measured; within the pH range 0.7–11.4, no significant change in optical density occurs, so that the pK_a value of safranine cannot be calculated from the spectrum, as has been done for neutral red.[57, 59, 60, 97–104] The absorption has also been calculated by the molecular orbital method.[105, 106] A maximum occurs at 525 mμ with $\varepsilon_{max} = 24,550$; alkylation of the amino groups results in increased basicity and a shift of the absorption maximum towards longer wavelengths (to 590 mμ in the case of the tetraethyl compound).[103] For a discussion of the light absorption of phenosafranine, as well as of various other phenazine, acridine, oxazine and thiazine dyestuffs, see references 107 and 108. Phenosafranine changes from blue to red in solution at pH 0.3–1.0; and can be used as a neutralization indicator in basic, non-aqueous solutions.[109] The fluorescence of safranine in various solvents has also been investigated.[110–111] A strong fluorescence is shown in alcoholic solution; but the aqueous solutions are almost non-fluorescent.

The hydrolytic deamination of phenosafranine has been mentioned in Chapter V:3,C. A leuco compound is formed by gentle reduction of phenosafranine with zinc dust or stannous chloride in acid solution (although not by sulfur dioxide[112]); and this is reoxidized by air to the dyestuff.[47] When phenosafranine chloride is heated with sodium acetate and acetic anhydride, a diacetyl derivative is formed.[16]

For the determination of safranine in solution, a method suitable for low concentrations has been devised that depends on the fact that safranine picrate is nearly insoluble in water but readily soluble in chloroform. An aqueous solution of the dye is titrated with picric acid solution in the presence of chloroform until the aqueous solution loses its red color.[113]

Phenosafranine dyes cotton, mordanted with tannin and tartar emetic, red. It was formerly much employed in calico printing and in the dyeing of paper, straw, etc., but has now been replaced by Safranine T. Safranine-aniline oil has been used for staining bacteria and fungi; thus, although the tubercle bacillus is only very weakly and diffusely stained, the leprosy bacillus is very intensely colored.[114, 115] The interaction of phenosafranine with suramin (Bayer 205) in aqueous solution gives rise to a colored complex; use has been made of this fact for staining suramin present in animal cells.[116] The metachromasy (the phenomenon of a single dyestuff staining different histological elements in different shades) of phenosafranine has been studied by Michaelis[117, 118]; but this effect is much less marked than in the case of toluidine blue. Pigments for printing inks and cosmetics have been prepared by the treatment of safranine with zirconia.[119] Phenosafranine is also of importance as a photographic desensitizer[120, 121]; its action towards X-rays differs from that towards visible light.[122]

A 0.001 M solution of safranine in potassium sulfate solution has been found to give a photopotential of 24 mv.[123] Thin films of phenosafranine show photoconductivity.[124, 125] Phenosafranine has been used as an adsorption indicator in halide titrations using silver nitrate.[126–129] The elution chromatography of phenosafranine, using silver bromide as the adsorption medium and aqueous pyridine as the developer has been studied.[130] Safranine has been used for detecting colorless organic compounds on silicic acid columns.[131] It is adsorbed to a large extent on colloidal arsenic trisulfide.[132] Phenosafranine has also been employed as an indicator in oxidation-reduction titrations; it is, however, not fully reversible in alkaline media and should, therefore, be used only in acid solution.[109, 133] Its redox potential at 30° at pH 7 is —0.25 to —0.26 volt and at pH 6.5, —0.234 volt .[109, 134–137] For studies of the polarography and anisotropy of phenosafranine, see references 138–139 and 140, respectively. It has an inhibitory effect on the autoxidation of linseed oil.[141] An alkaline solution of safranine at 60–65° is reduced (decolorized) by glucose, and this provides a method for the estimation of the sugar in urine.[142–145]

C. Isomers of Aposafranine and Phenosafranine

A number of isomers of aposafranine and phenosafranine, differing from these compounds only in the position of the amino group(s) in the phenazine nucleus, are known, mainly through the work of Kehrmann and his collaborators (see Table XI), and have been referred to as isoaposafranines and isophenosafranines, respectively. The alleged 5,10-dihydro-1,3-dinitro-5-phenylphenazine of Kehrmann and Messinger (Chapter III:2,C) when reduced with stannous chloride and hydrochloric acid yields a leuco-isophenosafranine, which affords 2,4-diamino-10-phenylphenazinium salts (**XXIX**) on atmospheric oxidation.[146] Since, however, the leuco compound decomposes very readily into ammonia and aposafranine under slightly alkaline conditions, it is preferable to convert 2′-anilino-2,4,6-trinitrodiphenylamine (**XXVIII**) into isophenosafranine (**XXIX**) directly in one operation by treatment with the theoretical amount of stannous chloride in alcoholic hydrogen chloride solution.[147] This product (a photographic desensitizer) has been converted into 4-amino-10-phenylphenazinium salts (isoaposafranine) (**XXXI**) by acetylation to the 4-acetamido-2-amino compound (**XXX**),

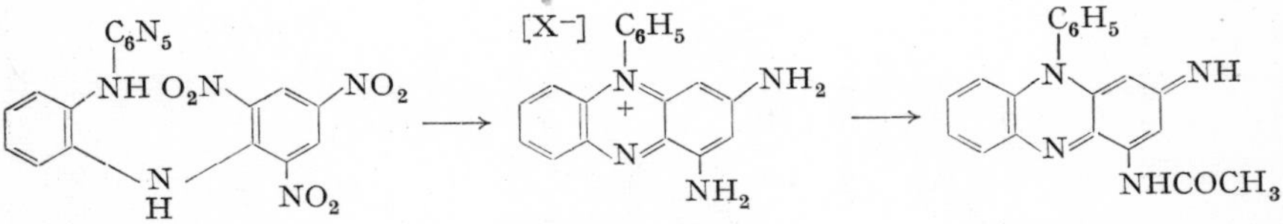

(XXVIII)   (XXIX)   (XXX)

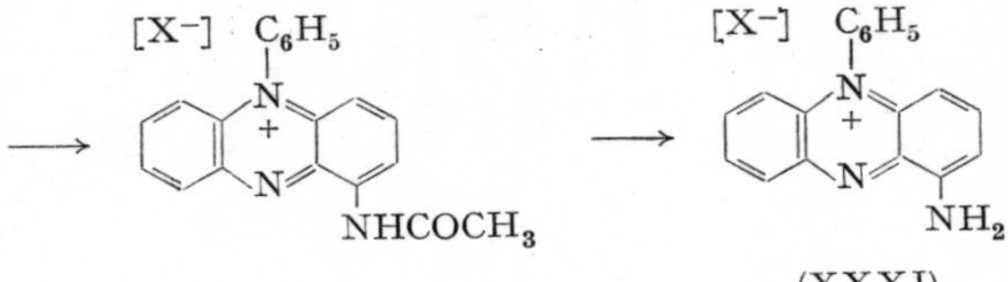

(XXXI)

followed by deamination and hydrolysis.[148] A number of patents[149–151] describe azine dyestuffs produced from compounds such as **XXXII** by the action of alkaline reagents. In some cases a dihydrophenazine structure (**XXXIII**) is attributed to these compounds, although it seems more likely that the dyes would, in fact, be phenazinium salts

TABLE XI. Amino-10-phenylphenazinium Derivatives

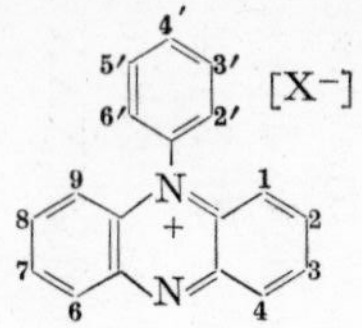

Substituents	Appearance (of chloride unless otherwise stated)	Colors of soln. in decreasing concn. of H_2SO_4, beginning with 100% or oleum	Ref.
2-Amino-	Prisms with greenish reflex	Red-brown, green, blue-red	See VII:2,A
3-Amino-	Almost black	Olive-green, green, violet (alkaline)	237
4-Amino-	Bromide, black-green lustrous crystals	Green-yellow, red-yellow, green, blue (alkaline)	59, 148
2-Amino-3-methyl-	Brownish needles	Yellow-green, green, red	33, 91
2-Amino-3,7-dimethyl-	Dark brown needles	Yellow-brown, green, violet, pink	34, 91
2-Amino-3,4′-dimethyl-	Green powder		92
2,3-Diamino-	Perchlorate, orange needles	Brown-red, olive-green, red-brown, orange	238
2,4-Diamino-	Greenish-black needles or prisms	Red-brown, yellow, red, yellow-green	59, 146–148, 239
2,7-Diamino-	Black-violet	Red-brown, green, red, blue-green, violet-blue (neutral)	59, 237
2,8-Diamino-	Green needles	Red-brown, green, blue, red	See VII:2,B
2,4′-Diamino-		Red-brown, green, red	43, 59
3,4′-Diamino-		Red-brown, green, violet	60
2,8-Diamino-3-methyl-	Yellow-green	Green	33
2,8-Diamino-3,7-dimethyl-	Yellow needles		34
2,4′,8-Triamino-			43, 240, 241
2,4,4′,8-Tetramino-	Red-brown, lustrous	Green, violet, red	242

(XXXIV). (Compare also, Chapter III:2,C.) The above-mentioned example (XXXIV)[149] dyes wool a fast yellowish-brown color.

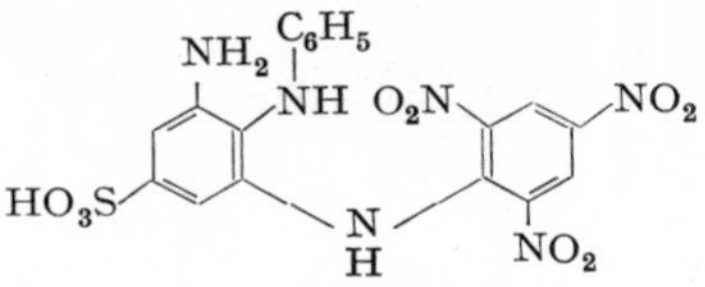

(XXXII)

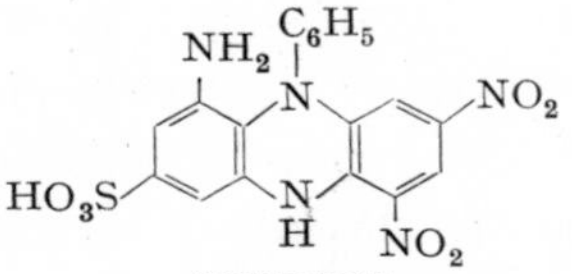

(XXXIII)

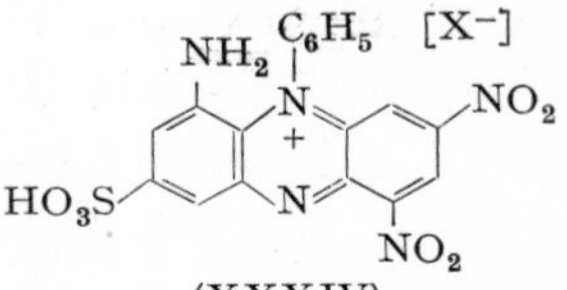

(XXXIV)

D. Homologs of Phenosafranine

Commercial safranine (Safranine T, O, G, etc., *C. I.* 841) consists of a mixture of tolusafranines prepared as described in Chapter VII:I,B and dyes tannin-mordanted cotton in brilliant red shades that are fast to washing and slightly faster to light than the dyeings from pheno-safranine. The substitution of alkyl or aryl groups into phenosafranine results in the color becoming bluer. Safranine T is an important nuclear stain used in histology and cytology, and stains chromatin. In bacterio-logy it is used as a counter stain, while in botany it is valuable in bringing out lignified and cutinized tissues in vascular plants; it also stains protein.[152] Safranine T has been used with Niagara blue in a differential staining method for distinguishing damaged from whole starch granules.[153] It has also been used for staining the flocculated mass of the precipitin reaction.[154] The redox potential of safranine T at pH 7 is —0.289 volt.[109]

E. N-Alkylated Safranines

The oxidation of a mixture of *p*-aminodimethylaniline and aniline yields Fuchsia or Methylene Violet (*C. I.* 842) (XXXV), which gives violet shades.[16, 21, 22, 39] The tetraethylsafranine (XXXVI) is known as Heliotrope B, Iris Violet or Amethyst Violet (*C. I.* 847) and has been used as a microscopic stain[152]; it dyes silk or mordanted cotton violet with a red fluorescence, but its fastness is not good.[16] It also has

(XXXV)   (XXXVI)

properties of a photographic desensitizer. Tannin Heliotrope or Giroflé (*C. I.* 852) is a reddish-violet dye of good fastness, formed by the action of *p*-nitrosodimethylaniline hydrochloride on a mixture of the hydrochlorides of *m*- and *p*-xylidines. Other *N*-alkylated safranines are *C. I.* 839, 843, 844, 848, 850, 851 and 854. Schweitzer[155] claimed to have obtained two isomeric products: *(a)* from *p*-aminoethylaniline (1 mole) and aniline (2 moles) and *(b)* from equimolecular amounts of *p*-phenylenediamine, ethylaniline and aniline. There seems, however, little to distinguish these alleged isomers; and they probably both consisted, essentially, of 2-amino-8-ethylamino-10-phenylphenazinium chloride. A patent[156] claims that *N*-substituted phenosafranine derivatives are obtained from *N*-substituted aposafranines by the action of primary or secondary amines in the presence of air; but proof of the position of entry of the attacking group seems to be lacking (compare Chapter VII:2,A).

Compounds of this type have also been obtained by treatment of safranines containing free NH_2 groups with alkylating agents.[157]

As in the case of crystal violet, when *N,N'*-tetraethylphenosafranine is treated with concentrated alkali, an ethyl group is eliminated, giving triethylphenosafranine.[96]

Most commercial safranine dyes are mixtures of the nominal compound with various other derivatives.[158,159] In the case of methylene violet, spectrophotometric methods have been found unsatisfactory for assay; the use of nitrogen analyses has been recommended. Chromatographic analysis on alumina of the purest methylene violet obtainable commercially has been found to give two main fractions that are violet (eluted with ethanol), and smaller red (eluted with chloroform) and blue (eluted with acetone) fractions and others. The first of these is pure methylene violet, with an absorption maximum at 250–255 mμ, while the second shows a maximum at 235–240 mμ and appears to be an oxidation product of unknown constitution. The latter has also been isolated from the urine of animals treated with methylene violet.

See also reference 11, 14, 58 and 160–163.

F. Azosafranine Dyes

Blue azo dyes with basic properties can be prepared from phenosafranine and its homologs by diazotization and coupling with various aromatic amines and phenols such as 2-naphthol.[33, 164–178] These are known under various trade names such as Janus Blue G, Indoine Blue, Naphthindone BB, an example being *C. I.* 135 (**XXXVII**). Diazine Green or Janus Green, *C. I.* 133, has structure **XXXVIII**, and is used in vital staining techniques (see Chapter XI:I). Its absorption spectrum shows a maximum at 606 mμ, $\varepsilon_{max} = 27,700$.[103] These materials are

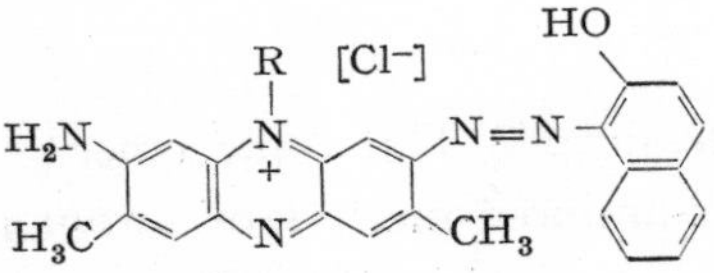

$R = C_6H_5$ or $C_6H_4CH_3$

(XXXVII)

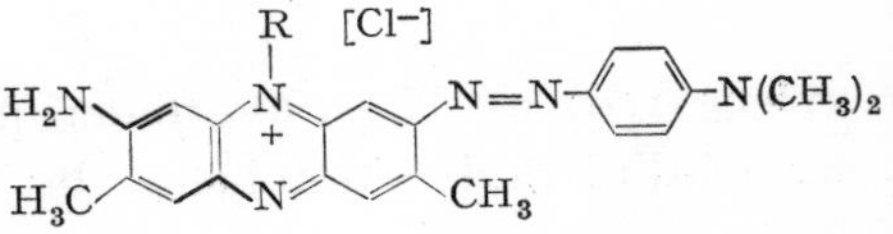

$R = C_6H_5$ or $C_6H_4CH_3$

(XXXVIII)

used for dyeing tannin-mordanted cotton and also for calico printing; on the fabric, the dye can be reduced to the safranine and the colorless amine, so that red patterns can be produced on a blue background.[179, 180] A material of structure **XXXIX**, which dyes chrome leather in bright greenish-black shades, is formed by coupling the diazotized diethyl analog of methylene violet with 2,2′-(phenylimino)diethanol.[181] Dyes

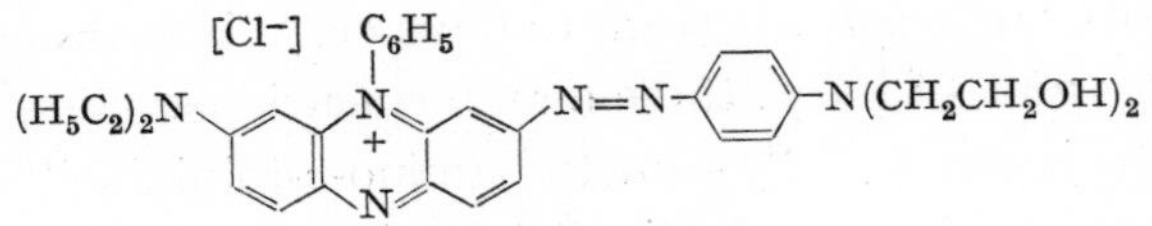

(XXXIX)

are also obtained by reaction of diazotized safranines with β-diketones[182] and pyrazolones.[183]

G. 5-Alkylphenazinium Salts

Salts such as ethosafranine (Formula XXII with C_2H_5 instead of C_6H_5) require little special mention. They have been prepared in analogous ways to the safranines essentially as in Chapter VII;1,B(3) from N-monoalkyl-m-phenylenediamines,[92, 161, 184–190] but also by the addition of alkyl halides to diaminophenazines.[191, 192] Thus, the action of p-nitrosodimethylaniline on 2-amino-4-dimethylaminotoluene in a reaction involving the splitting off of a methyl group yields the same dye (XL) as does the action of methyl chloride on 2,8-diamino-3-methylphenazine

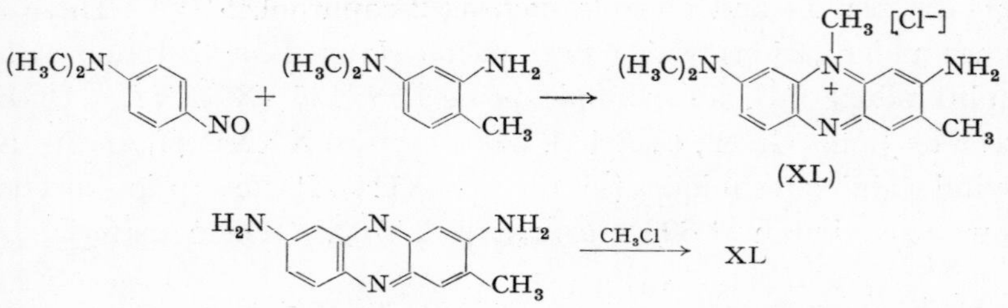

(toluylene red) at 170–190° under pressure.[193] The replacement of 2-amino-4-dimethylaminotoluene by 2-amino-4-methylaminotoluene gives the same product.[194] Compare also Equation (14). Compounds

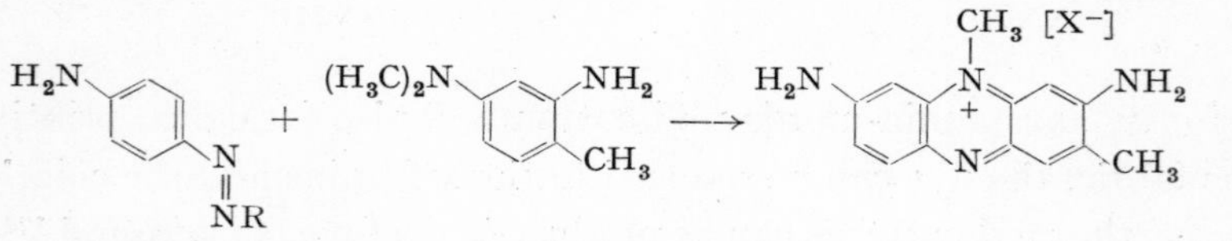

(14)

such as XL are known as Azine Scarlets; and a number of these were prepared by Cohen and Crabtree[194] to determine the effect of ring and amino group substituents on the color of the dyes. Unfortunately a number of errors or misprints seem to have crept into the paper of the latter authors; and, of these, three may be mentioned here. At the foot of page 2060, instead of "p-dimethylamino-o-toluidine" one should read "6-dimethylamino-m-toluidine" (see also Chapter XIV:5,D) and in the last paragraph of page 2066, instead of "m-aminodimethyl-p-toluidine" one should read "o-aminodimethyl-p-toluidine." Again, the compound obtained by Karrer by the oxidation of a mixture of m-

aminodimethylaniline and *p*-aminodimethylaniline and at first thought
to be 2,8-bis(dimethylamino)phenazine (**XLII**) was later shown to be
of the safranine type (**XLI**), although Karrer subsequently reported
briefly the preparation of the true **XLII** by a quite different method.
(See also Chapter VI:3,D.) On page 2064 of their paper, Cohen and
Crabtree make the erroneous statement that this compound (**XLII**)
is "formed by oxidizing a mixture of dimethyl-*p*-phenylenediamine and
dimethyl-*m*-phenylenediamine with potassium dichromate solution in
the presence of hydrochloric acid." However, these errors do not
seriously detract from the general conclusions drawn, namely, that the
substitution of methyl or other radicals for hydrogen in the amino
group of a 2,8-diamino-10-methylphenazinium salt produces a change
in tint from scarlet to magenta, or, in other words, a displacement of
tint towards the blue end of the spectrum. The heavier the radical,
the bluer becomes the shade; and the absence of radicals in the nucleus
enhances the blueness of the shade.

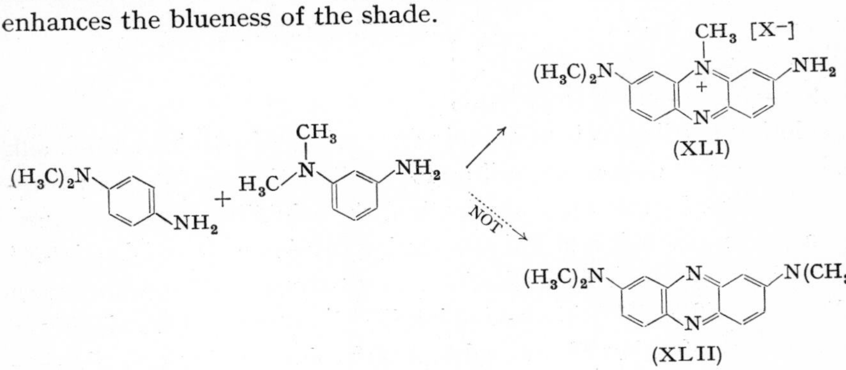

(XLI)

(XLII)

Azine Scarlet G, *C. I.* 838 (**XLIII**) and Fast Neutral Violet, *C. I.*
839 (**XLIV**) are examples of this class.

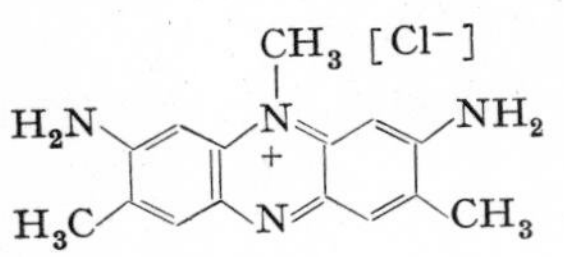

(XLIII)

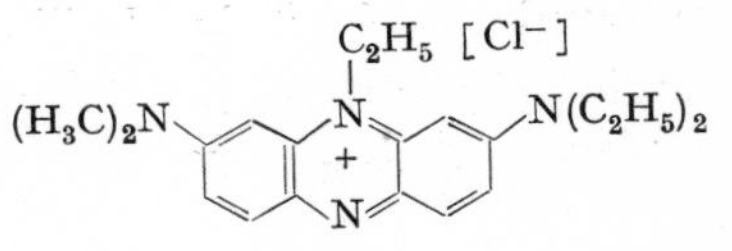

(XLIV)

Various 1,3-diamino-5-alkylphenazinium salts have recently been
shown to possess photographic desensitizing properties.[195]

H. Miscellaneous

Safranine sulfonic acids have generally been obtained by synthesis from aromatic mono- or di-amines containing sulfonic acid groups rather than by sulfonation of the safranines.[27, 196-197] The treatment of aposafranines with warm sulfite solution, followed by oxidation of the resulting leuco compounds in air has also been used for the preparation of similar compounds.[89] Moreover, it is claimed that the sulfonic acid groups of the resulting products can be exchanged by amino residues by treatment with ammonia or primary amines to yield safranines.[198] Although the majority of these compounds contain the sulfonic acid group in either the phenazine or the phenyl nuclei, dyes containing the solubilizing group in a sidechain have also been prepared.[199-200] Thus, compound XLV dyes wool a reddish blue. Compounds containing a phosphate group in a sidechain have also been recommended for use

$$CH_2CH_2OSO_3H$$

$$(H_3C)_2N\diagdown\diagup N_{\diagdown}\diagup\diagdown NHCH_2CH_2O\bar{S}O_3$$

$$N$$

(XLV)

in coloring textiles such as organic derivatives of cellulose, wool, silk and mordanted cotton, as well as for antihalation backing of photographic films. In the latter application, the solubility of the dyestuffs in water renders their removal easy during development and fixation.[201]

Other dyes have been obtained by treatment of safranines with sulfur or sulfides,[202] with o-diamines[203, 204] or with aldehydes.[205-208] Mercurated safranines[209] and salts of safranines with pyrogallol-4,6-dicarboxylic acid[210] of therapeutic interest have been prepared. A compound obtained by the action of iodine on aniline at high temperatures has been formulated as a safranine derivative.[211] The structure of a compound obtained by boiling 2'-chloro-4-hydroxyazobenzene-3-carboxylic acid with aniline is uncertain, although this is probably a phenazinium compound.[212]

I. Phenazine Derivatives in Color Photography

A recent series of patents by General Aniline and Film Corporation[213-234] claim a new type of color development process for obtaining a phenazine or phenazinium dyestuff that is more stable than the normal azomethine or quinoneimine dyestuff obtained by color development. (For recent reviews on such processes, see references 235 and 236.) It is stated that complete subtractive dye images may be obtained with a single color development by the use of a multi-layer film. Each silver halide emulsion layer is sensitized to one of the primary colors and contains a non-diffusing color former (color coupler) capable of reacting with the oxidation product of the developer to yield an azine dye image complementary in color to the exposing light. Various modifications have been described, and may be divided roughly into two groups.

In the first group, the color former may be a phenol containing a sulfonamido group in the *m*-position to the hydroxyl group, or a *m*-diamine of type XLVI, where Z is a group more electronegative than

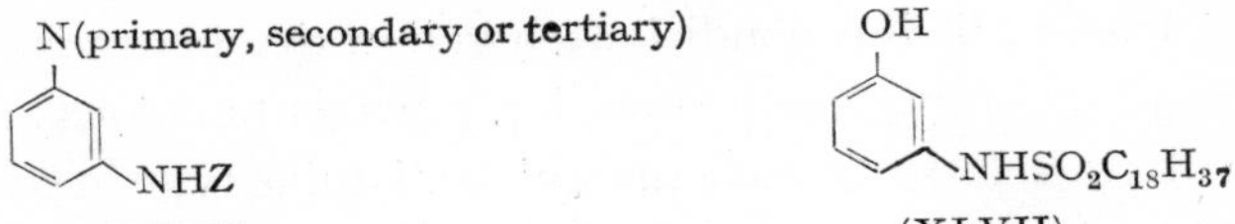

N(primary, secondary or tertiary)

NHZ

(XLVI)

OH

NHSO$_2$C$_{18}$H$_{37}$

(XLVII)

hydrogen (such as acyl, aryl or SO$_2$C$_6$H$_5$). The developer is a *p*-dialkyl-aminoaniline, and its oxidation product, produced during the development of the silver image, couples with the color former. Thus, if compound XLVII is added to the silver emulsion, which is exposed and then developed with *p*-diethylaminoaniline, an image of silver plus a purple quinoneimine is produced. On treatment with sodium hydroxide, the latter is converted into a brown phenazine dye, after which the silver image may be removed, and the film fixed, leaving a bluish-magenta image when viewed by transmitted light. Likewise, from compounds of type XLVI we obtain:

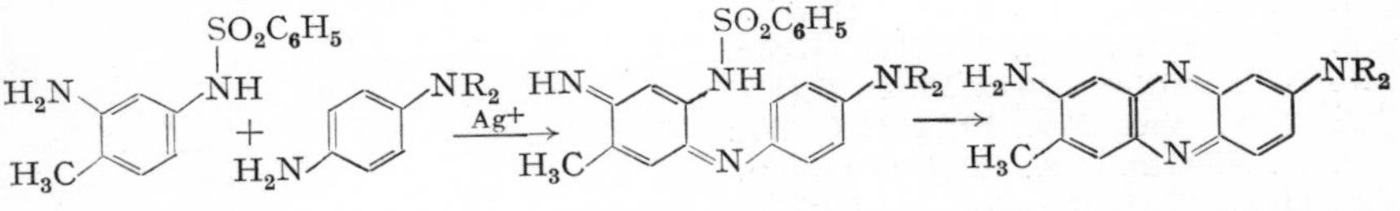

(If Z = C$_6$H$_5$, a phenazinium compound, rather than a phenazine, will result.) By varying the color formers, different colored images may be produced. The compounds may also have substituents, such as alkyl chains, that render them non-diffusing, and groups (for example SO_3H or CO_2H) that will increase their solubility to facilitate dispersion in the emulsion.

In the second group (the one apparently favored for commercial development) the developer is an *o*-diamine, frequently a derivative of 2,4-diaminoaniline of type XLVIII and the color coupler may be a

(XLVIII)   (XLIX)

primary aromatic amine, a phenol or a keto-methylene compound. (In the latter case, the product will be a quinoxaline instead of a phenazine.) Under alkaline conditions, a yellow dye image is produced; but by using 8-quinolinol as the coupler, a magenta color is produced. By the use of a developer of the *o*-phenylenediamine type in conjunction with a naphthol or 4-hydroxy-7,8-benzoquinoline as coupler, a bluish image is formed. Developers of type XLIX, where X is SO_3H or CO_2H, have also been recommended. These reactions are essentially like the formation of benzo[*a*]phenazine by the oxidation of a mixture of *o*-phenylenediamine and 2-naphthol with ferricyanide, although a phenazinium compound generally results unless R = H (see Chapter XII:3,B(11)).

References

1. G. P. Jaubert, *Ber.*, **29**, 414 (1896).
2. Brit. Pat. 1,090 (1859); through *C I.*, p. 210.
3. O. N. Witt, *J. Soc. Chem. Ind., London*, **1**, 255 (1882).
4. O. N. Witt, *Ber.*, **21**, 719 (1888).
5. O. N. Witt, *Ber.*, **21**, 2418 (1888).
6. A. Bernthsen, *Ber.*, **19**, 2690 (1886).
7. O. N. Witt, *Ber.*, **19**, 3121 (1886).
8. R. Nietzki, *Ber.*, **19**, 3017 (1886).
9. O. N. Witt, *Ber.*, **10**, 873 (1877).
10. P. Barbier and L. Vignon, *Bull. soc. chim. France, Mém.*, **48**, 338 (1887); through *J. Chem. Soc., Abstracts*, **54**, (ii), 688 (1888).
11. Ger. Pat. 88,954; *Frdl.*, **4**, 404 (1894–97).
12. K. A. Hofmann, F. Quoos and O. Schneider, *Ber.*, **47**, 1991 (1914).

13. H. T. Bucherer, *Ber.*, **40**, 3412 (1907).
14. D. Hardin, *Ber.*, **33**, 1212 (1900).
15. A. G. Green, *J. Chem. Soc.*, **103**, 925 (1913).
16. R. Nietzki, *Ber.*, **16**, 464 (1883).
17. O. Fischer and E. Hepp, *Ber.*, **21**, 2617 (1888).
18. A. Cobenzl, *Oesterr. Chem. Zeit.*, **28**, 25 (1925); through *Chem. Zentr.*, **1925,** I, 1737.
19. Ger. Pat. 90,256; *Frdl.*, **4**, 406 (1894-97); *Chem. Zentr.*, **1897**, I, 839.
20. K. Menton, *Ann.*, **263**, 316 (1891).
21. R. Bindschedler, *Ber.*, **13**, 207 (1880).
22. R. Bindschedler, *Ber.*, **16**, 864 (1883).
23. R. Nietzki, *Ber.*, **19**, 3163 (1886).
24. M. Andresen, *Ber.*, **19**, 2212 (1886).
25. A. W. Hofmann and A. Geyger, *Ber.*, **5**, 526 (1872).
26. Thorpe's *Dictionary of Applied Chemistry*, 4th ed., Longmans, Green, London, 1937, Vol. I, p. 576.
27. Ger. Pat. 212,472; *Frdl.*, **9**, 271 (1908–10); *Chem. Abstracts*, **3**, 2874 (1909); *Chem. Zentr.*, **1909**, II, 772.
28. Ger. Pat. 84,442; *Ber.*, **29**, *Ref.*, 61, (1896).
29. Ger. Pat. 84,504; *Ber.*, **29**, *Ref.*, 60, (1896).
30. Ger. Pat. 81,963; *Frdl.*, **4**, 412 (1894–97); *Ber.*, **28**, *Ref.*, 819 (1895).
31. Ger. Pat. 84,992; *Ber.*, **29**, *Ref.*, 205 (1896).
32. Ger. Pat. 87,975; *Ber.*, **29**, *Ref.*, 819 (1896).
33. W. Shaposhnikov and N. Orlov, *J. Russ. Phys. Chem. Soc.*, **42**, 512 (1910); through *Chem. Zentr.*, **1910**, II, 481.
34. N. Orlov, *J. Russ. Phys. Chem. Soc.*, **42**, 939 (1910); through *Chem. Zentr.*, **1910**, II, 1761.
35. U.S. Pat. 1,878,531; *Chem. Abstracts*, **27**, 1197 (1933).
36. Ger. Pat. 499,966; *Chem. Abstracts*, **23**, 3583 (1929); *Frdl.*, **17**, 936 (1930).
37. H. E. Fierz and H. Koechlin, *Helv. Chim. Acta*, **1**, 210 (1918).
38. F. Kehrmann, *Helv. Chim. Acta*, **5**, 69 (1922).
39. G. Körner and K. Schraube, *Chem. Zeit.*, **17**, 305 (1893).
40. P. Barbier and P. Sisley, *Bull. soc. chim. France, Mém.*, (3) **33**, 1190 (1905); through *J. Chem. Soc.*, *Abstracts*, **90**, (i), 51 (1906).
41. P. Barbier and P. Sisley, *Ann. chim. phys.*, (8) **13**, 96 (1908).
42. J. T. Hewitt, S. H. Newman and T. F. Winmill, *J. Chem. Soc.*, **95**, 577 (1909).
43. E. Havas and R. Bernhard, *Ber.*, **46**, 2723 (1913).
44. G. F. Jaubert, *Ber.*, **28**, 1578 (1895).
45. R. Nietzki, *Ber.*, **29**, 1442 (1896).
46. G. F. Jaubert, *Ber.*, **28**, 270 (1895).
47. R. Nietzki and R. Otto, *Ber.*, **21**, 1590 (1888).
48. A. Bernthsen, *Ber.*, **20**, 179 (4887).
49. C. Ris, *Ber.*, **27**, 3318 (1894).
50. G. F. Jaubert, *Ber.*, **28**, 508 (1895).
51. R. Nietzki, *Ber.*, **28**, 1354 (1895).
52. R. Nietzki, *Ber.*, **29**, 2771 (1896).
53. F. Kehrmann, *Ann.*, **290**, 247 (1896).
54. F. Kehrmann, *Ber.*, **29**, 2316 (1896).
55. O. Fischer and E. Hepp, *Ann.*, **286**, 187 (1895).
56. W. Shaposhnikov, *J. Russ. Phys. Chem. Soc.*, **29**, 535 (1897); through *Chem. Zentr.*, **1898**, I, 722.
57. K. Balls, J. T. Hewitt and S. H. Newman, *J. Chem. Soc.*, **101**, 1840 (1912).

58. O. Fischer and E. Hepp, *Ber.*, **30**, 391 (1897).
59. F. Kehrmann, E. Havas and E. Grandmougin, *Ber.*, **46**, 2802 (1913).
60. F. Kehrmann, E. Havas and E. Grandmougin, *Ber.*, **47**, 1881 (1914).
61. F. Kehrmann, R. Speitel and E. Grandmougin, *Ber.*, **47**, 3205 (1914).
62. E. Grandmougin and K. Smirous, *Ber.*, **46**, 3425 (1913).
63. Beilstein, *Handbuch der organischen Chemie*, 4th ed., Vol. 25, Springer, Berlin, 1936, p. 331.
64. A. G. Green, *Ber.*, **32**, 3155 (1899).
65. E. Havas, *Ber.*, **47**, 994 (1914).
66. G. F. Jaubert, *Bull. soc. chim. France, Mém.* (3), **23**, 178 (1900).
67. J. Landauer, *Ber.*, **11**, 1772 (1878).
68. W. Dilthey, *J. prakt. Chem.*, (2), **109**, 273 (1925).
69. A. Burawoy, *Ber.*, **63**, 3155 (1930).
70. A. Burawoy, *Ber.*, **64**, 462 (1931).
71. O. Fischer, *Ber.*, **29**, 1870 (1896).
72. F. Kehrmann and J. Messinger, *Ber.*, **24**, 2167 (1891).
73. F. Kehrmann, *Ber.*, **31**, 977 (1898).
74. F. Kehrmann, *Ber.*, **41**, 2340 (1908).
75. F. Kehrmann, *Ber.*, **46**, 3036 (1913).
76. F. Kehrmann, *Ann.*, **414**, 131 (1918).
77. F. Kehrmann and M. Sandoz, *Helv. Chim. Acta*, **1**, 270 (1918).
78. F. Kehrmann and M. Sandoz, *Helv. Chim. Acta*, **3**, 104 (1920).
79. F. Kehrmann and M. Sandoz, *Helv. Chim. Acta*, **4**, 31 (1921).
80. F. Kehrmann, *Helv. Chim. Acta*, **4**, 527 (1921).
81. F. Kehrmann, *Helv. Chim. Acta*, **5**, 158 (1922).
82. F. Kehrmann and M. Sandoz, *Helv. Chim. Acta*, **5**, 895 (1922).
83. F. Kehrmann, *Helv. Chim. Acta*, **7**, 964 (1924).
84. F. Kehrmann, E. Havas and E. Grandmougin, *Ber.*, **46**, 2131 (1913).
85. O. Fischer and E. Hepp, *Ber.*, **33**, 1485 (1900).
86. O. Fischer and E. Hepp, *Ber.*, **28**, 2283 (1895).
87. P. Barbier and P. Sisley, *Bull. soc. chim. France, Mém.*, (4), **1**, 468 (1907).
88. O. Fischer and C. Giesen, *Ber.*, **30**, 2489 (1897).
89. Ger. Pat. 102,458; *Chem. Zentr.*, **1899**, II, 504; *Frdl.*, **5**, 361 (1897–1900).
90. F. Kehrmann and W. Shaposhnikov, *Ber.*, **30**, 2620 (1897).
91. F. Kehrmann and A. Wetter, *Ber.*, **31**, 966 (1898).
92. G. F. Jaubert, *Ber.*, **31**, 1178 (1898).
93. P. Barbier and P. Sisley, *Bull. soc. chim. France, Mém.*, (3), **35**, 858 (1906).
94. A. Miolati, *Ber.*, **28**, 1696 (1895).
95. A. Hantzsch and G. Osswald, *Ber.*, **33**, 278 (1900).
96. F. Kehrmann, E. Havas and E. Grandmougin, *Ber.*, **46**, 2131 (1913).
97. G. Rossi and A. Basini, *Ann. chim. applicata*, **16**, 299 (1926); through *Chem. Abstracts*, **21**, 353 (1927).
98. H. J. Conn, *Stain Tech.*, **4**, 65 (1929); through *Chem. Abstracts*, **23**, 4717 (1929).
99. H. Lunelund, *Öfvers. Finsk. Vetensk. Soc. Förh.*, **59**, No. 21, 21 (1916–1917); through *Chem. Zentr.*, **1921**, III, 810.
100. W. C. Holmes, *J. Am. Chem. Soc.*, **46**, 2118 (1924).
101. H. W. Meyer and W. D. Treadwell, *Helv. Chim. Acta*, **35**, 1460 (1952).
102. S. Woislawski, *J. Am. Chem. Soc.*, **75**, 5201 (1953).
103. S. Brenner, *Biochem. et Biophys. Acta*, **11**, 480 (1953).
104. E. V. Cowdry, *Contributions to Embryology*, Carnegie Institution of Washington, **8**, 1918, p. 39.

105. H. Kuhn, *Helv. Chim. Acta*, **34**, 2371 (1951).
106. M. J. S. Dewar, *J. Chem. Soc.*, **1950**, 2329.
107. M. J. S. Dewar, *The Electronic Theory of Organic Chemistry*, Oxford University Press, 1949, p. 308.
108. G. N. Lewis, *J. Am. Chem. Soc.*, **67**, 770 (1945).
109. O. Tomiček, *Chemical Indicators*, Butterworths, London, 1951.
110. G. Lépine, *Ann. Phys.*, (9), **4**, 207 (1915).
111. N. R. Tawde and N. Ramanathan, *Proc. Phys. Soc.*, **65B**, 33 (1952).
112. H. Weil, K. Dürrschnabel and P. Landauer, *Ber.*, **44**, 3173 (1911).
113. A. Castiglioni, *Z. anal. Chem.*, **97**, 334 (1934).
114. V. Babeş, *Bull. sect. sci. acad. roumaine*, **5**, 211 (1918); through *Chem. Zentr.*, **1921**, II, 1.
115. E. J. Moore, *Science*, **77**, 23 (1933).
116. N. Janscó and A. Janscó-Gabor, *Nature*, **170**, 567 (1952).
117. L. Michaelis and S. Granick, *J. Am. Chem. Soc.*, **67**, 1212 (1945).
118. L. Michaelis, *Cold Spring Harbor Symposia on Quantitative Biology*, **12**, 131 (1947).
119. W. B. Blumenthal, *Am. Dyestuff Reptr.*, **37**, 285 (1948); through *Chem. Abstracts*, **42**, 5229 (1948).
120. A. Hübl, *Z. wiss. Phot.*, **24**, 133 (1926); through *Chem. Zentr.*, **1926**, II, 968.
121. G. Kögel and A. Steigmann, *Kolloid Z.*, **39**,52 (1926); through *Chem. Zentr.*, **1926**, II, 1231.
122. K. S. Bogomolov and Y. S. Moshkovskiï, *Zhur. Priklad. Khim. (J. Applied Chem.)*, **22**, 831 (1949); through *Chem. Abstracts*, **45**, 831 (1949).
123. H. T. Nga, *J. chim. phys.*, **32**, 564 (1935); through *Chem. Abstracts*, **30**, 2116 (1936).
124. A. T. Vartanyan, *J. Phys. Chem. (U.S.S.R.)*, **20**, 1065 (1946); through *Chem. Abstracts*, **41**, 2988 (1947).
125. A. T. Vartanyan, *Izvest. Akad. Nauk S.S.S.R., Ser. Fiz.*, **16**, 169 (1952); through *Chem. Abstracts*, **46**, 10860 (1952).
126. A. J. Berry, *Analyst*, **57**, 511 (1932).
127. A. J. Berry, *Analyst*, **61**, 315 (1936).
128. H. R. Fleck, R. F. G. Holness and A. M. Ward, *Analyst*, **60**, 32 (1935).
129. T. Sotgie-Rovelli, *Boll. chim. farm.*, **74**, 265 (1935); through *Chem. Abstracts*, **29**, 7213 (1935).
130. T. H. James and W. Vanselow, *J. Am. Chem. Soc.*, **73**, 5617 (1951).
131. A. L. Le Rosen, R. T. Moravek and J. K. Carlton, *Anal. Chem.*, **24**, 1335 (1952).
132. C. Cohn, *Compt. rend.*, **223**, 1022 (1946).
133. C. Cuschniv, *Rev. facultad cien. quim. (Univ. nacl. La Plata)*, **22**, 25 (1947); through *Chem. Abstracts*, **45**, 3283 (1951).
134. R. D. Stiehler, T. Chen and W. M. Clark, *J. Am. Chem. Soc.*, **55**, 891 (1933).
135. R. D. Stiehler and W. M. Clark, *J. Am. Chem. Soc.*, **55**, 4097 (1933).
136. E. Vellinger, *Arch. phys. biol.*, **7**, 113 (1929); through *Chem. Abstracts*, **24**, 2939 (1930).
137. J. S. C. Wessels and E. Havinga, *Rec. trav. chim.*, **71**, 809 (1952).
138. R. Brdička, *Coll. Czechoslov. Chem. Communs.*, **12**, 522 (1947); through *Chem. Abstracts*, **42**, 5355 (1948).
139. J. van Cakenberghe, *Bull. soc. chim. Belges*, **60**, 3 (1951); through *Chem. Abstracts*, **45**, 9392 (1951).
140. P. P. Feofilov, *Bull. acad. sci. U.R.S.S., Sér. phys.*, **9**, 317 (1945); through *Chem. Abstracts*, **40**, 4296 (1946).

141. M. Rac, *Kem. Vjestnik (Zagreb)*, **15—16,** 67 (1941–2); through *Chem. Abstracts,* **40,** 4895 (1946).
142. Crismer, *Vierteljahrssch. u. d. Fortschr. a. d. Geb. d. Chem. d. Nahrungs- u. Genussmittel,* **4,** 195; through *Chem. Zentr.,* **1890,** I, 299.
143. K. A. Hasselbalch and J. Lindhard, *Biochem. Z.,* **27,** 273 (1910); through *Chem. Zentr.,* **1910,** II, 1331.
144. N. Wender, *Biochem. Z.,* **28,** 523 (1910); through *Chem. Zentr.,* **1910,** II, 1838.
145. K. A. Hasselbalch and J. Lindhard, *Biochem. Z.,* **29,** 416 (1910); through *Chem. Zentr.,* **1911,** I, 97.
146. F. Kehrmann, *Ber.,* **32,** 2601 (1899).
147. F. Kehrmann and O. Kramer, *Ber.,* **33,** 3074 (1900).
148. F. Kehrmann and A. Maslenikov, *Ber.,* **44,** 2628 (1911).
149. Brit. Pat. 348,902; *Chem. Zentr.,* **1931,** II, 2065.
150. Brit. Pat. 511,193; *Chem. Zentr.,* **1940,** I, 2716.
151. Ger. Pat. 728,376; *Chem. Zentr.,* **1943,** I, 1938.
152. H. J. Conn, *Biological Stains,* 5th ed., Biotech Publication, Geneva, N. Y., 1946.
153. F. Baker and P. N. Hobson, *J. Soc. Sci. Food and Agric.,* **3,** 608 (1952).
154. I. Yamaguchi, *Japan Med. J.* **2,** 70 (1949); through *Chem. Abstracts,* **46,** 7208 (1952).
155. W. Schweitzer, *Ber.,* **19,** 150 (1886).
156. Ger. Pat. 102, 362; *Frdl.,* **5,** 360 (1899–1900).
157. Ger. Pat. 87,175; *Frdl.,* **4,** 407 (1894–97).
158. E. Stotz, H. J. Conn, F. Knapp and A. J. Emery (Jr.), *Stain Technol.,* **25,** 57 (1950); through *Chem. Abstracts,* **44,** 5417 (1950).
159. F. Hawking, W. E. Ormerod, J. P. Thurston and W. A. F. Webber, *Brit. J. Pharmacol.,* **7,** 494 (1952).
160. P. Barbier and L. Vignon, *Bull. soc. chim. France, Mém.,* (2), **48,** 636 (1887).
161. F. Kehrmann and W. Shaposhnikov, *Ber.,* **30,** 1565 (1897).
162. Ger. Pat. 59,063, *Frdl.,* **3,** 396 (1890–94).
163. R. Meldola and J. H. Coste, *J. Chem. Soc.,* **55,** 590 (1889).
164. Ger. Pat. 38,310; *Frdl.,* **1,** 541 (1877–87).
165. Ger. Pat. 61,692; *Frdl.,* **3,** 794 (1890–94).
166. Ger. Pat. 78,875; *Frdl.,* **4,** 803 (1894–97).
167. Ger. Pat. 85,932; *Frdl.,* **4,** 804 (1894–97).
168. Ger. Pat. 83,312; *Frdl.,* **4,** 805 (1894–97).
169. Ger. Pat. 95,668; *Frdl.,* **4,** 805 (1894–97).
170. Ger. Pat. 85,690; *Frdl.,* **4,** 806 (1894–97).
171. Ger. Pat. 91,721; *Frdl.,* **4,** 807 (1894–97).
172. Ger. Pat. 92,015; *Frdl.,* **4,** 808 (1894–97).
173. Ger. Pat. 95,483; *Frdl.,* **5,** 535 (1897–1900).
174. Ger. Pat. 99,574; *Frdl.,* **5,** 536 (1897–1900).
175. Ger. Pat. 104,906; *Frdl.,* **5,** 537 (1897–1900).
176. Ger. Pat. 105,433; *Frdl.,* **5,** 538 (1897–1900).
177. Ger. Pat. 108,497; *Frdl.,* **5,** 540 (1897–1900).
178. Ger. Pat. 128,618; *Frdl.,* **6,** 943 (1900–02).
179. Ger. Pat. 88,547; *Frdl.,* **4,** 817 (1894–97).
180. Ger. Pat. 89,590; *Frdl.,* **4,** 817 (1894–97).
181. U. S. Pat. 2,554,443; *Chem. Abstracts,* **46,** 2305 (1952).
182. Ger. Pat. 490,114; *Frdl.,* **16,** 1026 (1927–29).
183. Ger. Pat. 245,322; *Chem. Zentr.,* **1912,** I, 1409.
184. Ger. Pat. 69,188; *Frdl.,* **3,** 387 (1890–94); *Ber.,* **26,** *Ref.,* 733 (1893).

185. Ger. Pat. 80,758; *Ber.*, **28**, *Ref.*, 637 (1895).
186. Ger. Pat. 85,231; *Ber.*, **29**, *Ref.*, 317 (1896).
187. Ger. Pat. 86,608; *Ber.*, **29**, *Ref.*, 469 (1896).
188. Ger. Pat. 89,659; *Ber.*, **29**, *Ref.*, 1191 (1896).
189. Ger. Pat. 282,346; *Frdl.*, **12**, 235 (1914–16); *Chem. Zentr.*, **1915**, I, 586.
190. Ger. Pat. 287,271; *Frdl.*, **12**, 236 (1914–16); *Chem. Zentr.*, **1915**, II, 773.
191. F. Ullman and P. Wenner, *Ann.*, **327**, 120 (1903).
192. F. Kehrmann and M. Ramm, *Ber.*, **51**, 385 (1918).
193. Ger. Pat. 101,487; *Frdl.*, **5**, 370 (1897–1900).
194. J. B. Cohen and H. G. Crabtree, *J. Chem. Soc.*, **119**, 2055 (1921).
195. U. S. Pat. 2,400,872; Brit. Pat. 563,691; *Chem. Abstracts*, **40**, 5458 (1946).
196. Ger. Pat. 243,491; *Chem. Zentr.*, **1912**, I, 699.
197. U. S. Pat. 1,934,727; *Chem. Abstracts*, **28**, 910 (1934).
198. Ger. Pat. 103,687; *Frdl.*, **5**, 363 (1897–1900).
199. Brit. Pat. 181,750; *Chem. Zentr.*, **1923**, II, 191.
200. Brit. Pat. 182,031; *Chem. Zentr.*, **1922**, IV, 1171.
201. U. S. Pat. 2,238,487; *Chem. Abstracts*, **35**, 4967 (1941).
202. Ger. Pat. 177,709; *Frdl.*, **8**, 785 (1905–07); *Chem. Zentr.*, **1906**, II, 1798.
203. Ger. Pat. 50,467; *Frdl.*, **2**, 212 (1887–90).
204. Ger. Pat. 86,971; *Frdl.*, **4**, 407 (1894–97).
205. Ger. Pat. 94,238; *Frdl.*, **4**, 410 (1894–97); *Chem. Zentr.*, **1898**, I, 357.
206. Ger. Pat. 94,855; *Frdl.*, **4**, 412 (1894–97).
207. Ger. Pat. 105,862; *Frdl.*, **5**, 192 (1897–1900).
208. R. N. Sen and B. Sett, *J. Am. Chem. Soc.*, **46**, 111 (1924).
209. Ger. Pat. 286,097; *Frdl.*, **12**, 860 (1914–16); *Chem. Zentr.*, **1915**, II, 569.
210. Ger. Pat. 285,500; *Frdl.*, **12**, 890 (1914–16); *Chem. Zentr.*, **1915**, II, 374.
211. H. H. Hodgson and E. Marsden, *J. Chem. Soc.*, **1937**, 1365.
212. J. T. Hewitt and H. E. Stevenson, *J. Chem. Soc.*, **69**, 1257 (1896).
213. W. A. Schmidt, V. Tulagin, J. A. Sprung, R. C. Gunther, R. F. Coles and D. E. Sargent, *Ind. Eng. Chem.*, **45**, 1726 (1953).
214. U. S. Pat. 2,414,491; *Chem. Abstracts*, **41**, 3387 (1947).
215. U. S. Pat. 2,486,440; *Chem. Abstracts*, **45**, 488 (1951).
216. U. S. Pat. 2,498,466; *Chem. Abstracts*, **45**, 2347 (1951).
217. U. S. Pat. 2,522,802; *Chem. Abstracts*, **45**, 4156 (1951).
218. U. S. Pat. 2,524,725; *Chem. Abstracts*, **45**, 3272 (1951).
219. U. S. Pat. 2,524,741; *Chem. Abstracts*, **45**, 3272 (1951).
220. U. S. Pat. 2,525,502; *Chem. Abstracts*, **45**, 3272 (1951).
221. U. S. Pat. 2,525,503; *Chem. Abstracts*, **45**, 3272 (1951).
222. U. S. Pat. 2,527,379; *Chem. Abstracts*, **45**, 487 (1951).
223. U. S. Pat. 2,536,010; *Chem. Abstracts*, **45**, 5551 (1951).
224. U. S. Pat. 2,537,460; *Chem. Abstracts*, **45**, 3276 (1951).
225. U. S. Pat. 2,543,338; *Chem. Abstracts*, **45**, 6520 (1951).
226. U. S. Pat. 2,555,127; *Chem. Abstracts*, **45**, 10110 (1951).
227. U. S. Pat. 2,570,116; *Chem. Abstracts*, **46**, 2938 (1952).
228. U. S. Pat. 2,591,642; *Chem. Abstracts*, **46**, 6023 (1952).
229. U. S. Pat. 2,594,917; *Chem. Abstracts*, **46**, 6980 (1952).
230. U. S. Pat. 2,596,926; *Chem. Abstracts*, **46**, 8555 (1952).
231. U. S. Pat. 2,611,785; *Chem. Abstracts*, **47**, 6292 (1953).
232. U. S. Pat. 2,623,823; *Chem. Abstracts*, **47**, 6294 (1953).
233. U. S. Pat. 2,627,461; *Chem. Abstracts*, **47**, 6291 (1953).
234. Brit. Pat., 633,760; 633,823; 640,122; 644,863; 646,490 and 662,419.
235. O. W. Wahl, *Angew. Chem.*, **64**, 259 (1952).

236. K. M. Hornsby, *Brit. J. Phot.*, **97**, 331 (1950).
237. F. Kehrmann and J. R. y Punti, *Ber.*, **44**, 2622 (1911).
238. E. Hoehn, *Helv. Chim. Acta*, **8**, 275 (1925).
239. F. Kehrmann and P. Prunier, *Helv. Chim. Acta*, **7**, 984 (1924).
240. A. Beretta, *Gazz. chim. ital.*, **55**, 711 (1925); through *Chem. Abstracts*, **20**, 1084, (1926); and *Chem. Zentr.*, **1926**, I, 949.
241. Ger. Pat. 222,418; *Chem. Zentr.*, **1910**, II, 122; *Frdl.*, **10**, 312 (1910–12).
242. A. Beretta, *Ann. chim. applicata*, **16**, 211 (1926); through *Chem. Abstracts*, **20**, 3238 (1926), and *Chem. Zentr.*, **1926**, II, 1464.

CHAPTER VIII

The Indulines and Nigrosines

1. Introduction

Following the suggestion of Caro,[1] the coloring matters obtained by heating aminoazo compounds, such as p-aminoazobenzene, with amines, such as aniline, and their hydrochlorides are called indulines, whereas the greyer products obtained from nitrobenzene or nitrophenols, which contain varying proportions of fluorindines, are called nigrosines. The indulines are N-phenylphenazinium compounds which carry aminophenyl- (or iminophenyl-) groups in the benzene rings of the phenazine nucleus, and are therefore closely related to the safranines. But these two groups of dyestuffs are readily differentiated by their behavior towards concentrated sulfuric acid, in which the simple safranines dissolve with a greenish color, while the indulines give violet to blue colors, which do not undergo striking color changes on dilution as do the safranines.[2] (2-Anilino-10-phenylphenazinium chloride gives a green solution in concentrated sulfuric acid.)

2. General Account of the Structure and Formation of the Indulines

A. The "Induline Melt"

Dyes of the induline class have been known since the early days of aniline dyestuff manufacture. Originally they were prepared by heating aniline or its hydrochloride with various compounds having an oxidizing action, such as nitrobenzene, azobenzene,[3] cupric oxide,[4] etc.; but the usual method for their production is the so-called "aminoazobenzene melt" or "induline melt." This process was invented by Dale and Caro[5] in 1863 and consists in heating p-aminoazobenzene with aniline and aniline hydrochloride. It leads to a mixture of products that are not easy to separate; but the relative proportions of the various constituents formed can be altered by varying the experimental conditions.[6] The classical work of Otto Fischer and E. Hepp, published between 1887[7] and 1902, and summarized in a final paper,[8] resulted in the isolation of the following compounds from the "induline melt":

(*1*) *p*-Phenylenediamine.

(*2*) 4,4'-Diaminodiphenylamine.

(*3*) Azophenine (I).

(*4*) 2,8-Diamino-3-anilino-10-phenylphenazinium chloride (II).

(*5*) 8-Amino-2,3-dianilino-10-phenylphenazinium chloride (Indamine Blue) (III).

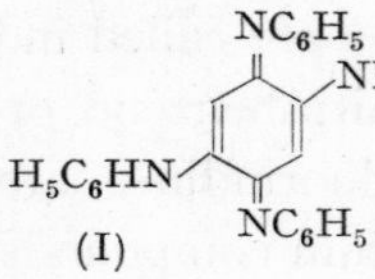

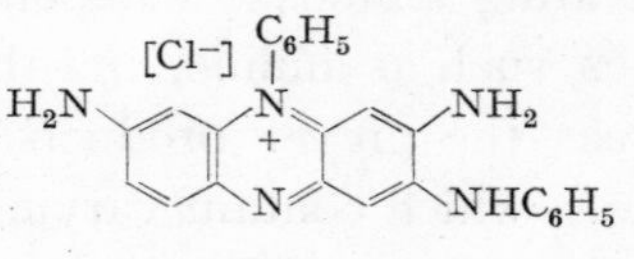

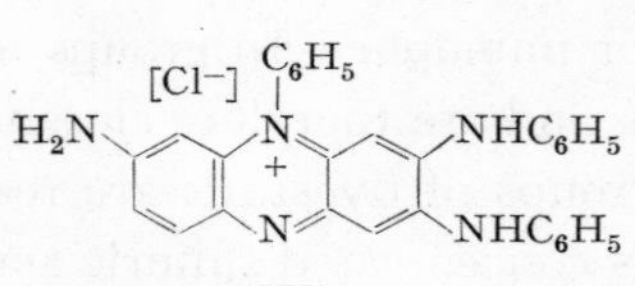

(*6*) 2,3,8-Trianilino-10-phenylphenazinium chloride (Induline 3B) (IV).

(*7*) 2,3,7,8-Tetraanilino-10-phenylphenazinium chloride (Induline 6B) (V).

(*8*) 5,12-Diphenylfluorindine in small amounts (see Chapter XVIII:3,B).

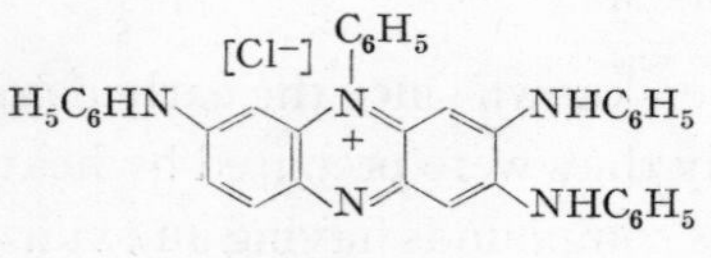

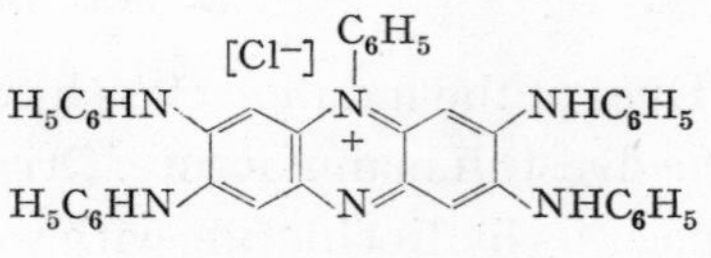

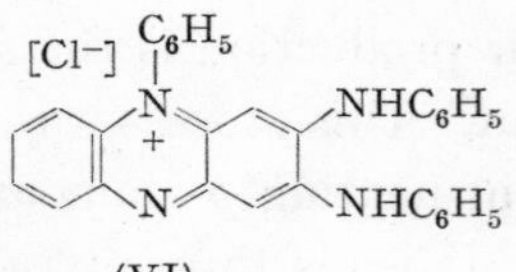

The reaction between p-aminoazobenzene hydrochloride and aniline hydrochloride in aqueous aniline at 160–170° in an autoclave, on the other hand, gives rise to aposafranine, together with small amounts of 2,3-dianilino-5-phenylphenazinium chloride (VI)[9] (but see Chapter VII:2,A). Some indulines have also been prepared by appropriate adaptations of the standard safranine syntheses described in Chapter VII:1,B.

B. Mechanism of the "Induline Melt"

According to Meyer-Jacobson,[10] the first reaction occurring in the "aminoazobenzene melt" process is one between aminoazobenzene and aniline leading to the reduction of the former to p-phenylenediamine, which is then oxidized to p-quinonediimine, which in its turn reacts with aniline or p-phenylenediamine to form indulines. It should be noted that indulines are formed by oxidation of mixtures of p-phenyl-

$$C_6H_5N{=}N{-}\underset{}{\bigcirc}{-}NH_2 \xrightarrow{C_6H_5NH_2} H_2N{-}\underset{}{\bigcirc}{-}NH_2 \xrightarrow{O} HN{=}\underset{}{\bigcirc}{=}NH$$

$$\xrightarrow{C_6H_5NH_2} HN{=}\underset{}{\bigcirc}{=}NC_6H_5$$

$$(VII)$$

enediamine and aniline.[11] Green,[12] however, following the work of Willstätter and Moore,[13] assumes the primary formation of N-phenylquinonediimine (VII), by oxidation of aniline, a reaction which, it has been suggested, occurs *via* the radical $C_6H_5N{<}$:[14]

$$C_6H_5NH_2 \xrightarrow{O} C_6H_5N{<} \longrightarrow (VII)$$

N-Phenylquinonediimine is a very reactive substance and rapidly polymerizes or reacts with aniline. Green points out that the subsequent reactions depend on the pH of the solution. Under strongly acidic conditions, polymerization occurs in a linear manner, yielding, finally, emeraldine and nigraniline (see Chapter IX:2); while, under neutral or only weakly acidic conditions, a reaction occurs, with the ultimate formation of indulines and nigrosines. In the latter reaction, the first step is the addition of aniline to phenylquinonediimine, followed by oxidation of the product by the aminoazobenzene (Equation (1)). A repetition of these reactions then yields VIII, which by further reaction

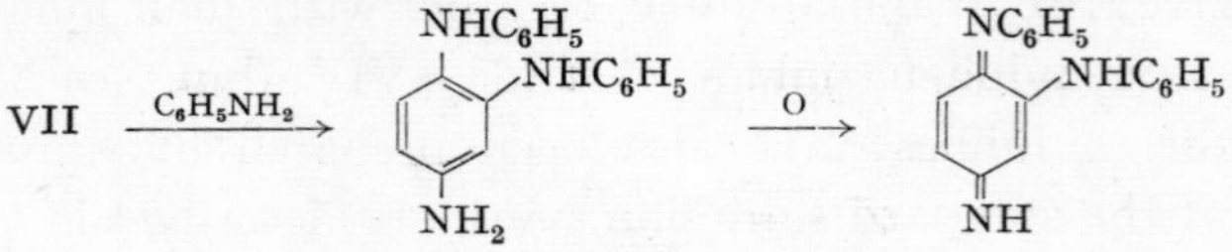

$$VII \xrightarrow{C_6H_5NH_2} \quad \text{(structure)} \quad \xrightarrow{O} \quad \text{(structure)} \tag{1}$$

with aniline gives azophenine (Equation (2)). The direct introduction

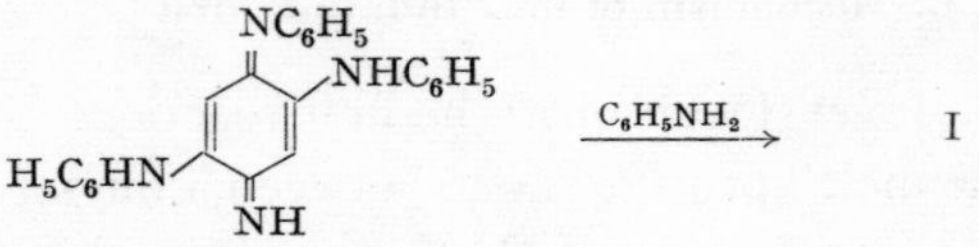

$$\text{(VIII structure)} \xrightarrow{C_6H_5NH_2} \quad I \tag{2}$$

(VIII)

of amino groups into the nucleus of quinones and quinonoid compounds is a well-known reaction; for example, p-quinone gives dianilino-p-quinone and its anils. Also, Goldschmidt and Wurzschmitt[14] showed that, under weakly acidic conditions, the oxidation of aniline yields a trimolecular polymer of phenylquinonediimine (IX), which, by the

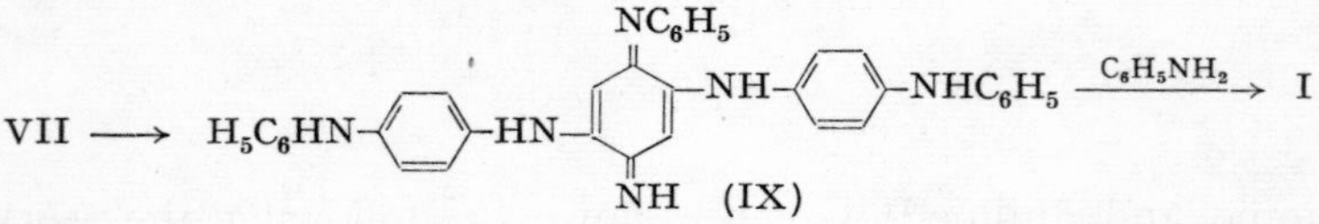

$$VII \longrightarrow \quad \text{(IX structure)} \xrightarrow{C_6H_5NH_2} \quad I \tag{3}$$

(IX)

action of aniline, can be converted into azophenine (Equation (3)). Compound VIII or its tautomer (X) and azophenine constitute the intermediate stages in the formation of indulines and nigrosines, in which the role of the oxidizing agent is fulfilled by the aminoazobenzene and nitrobenzene, respectively (Equations (4), (5) and (6)). The further

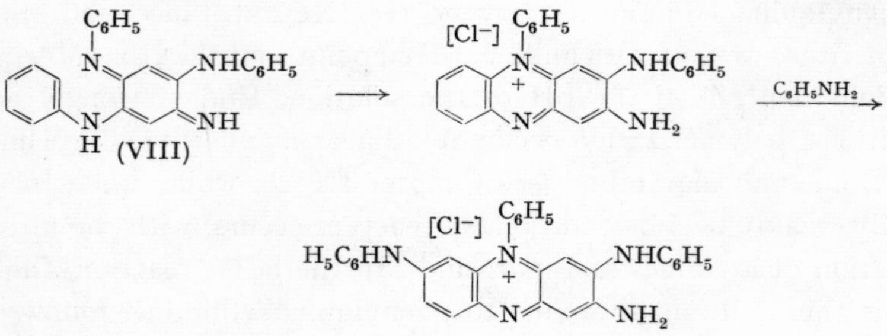

$$\text{(VIII structure)} \longrightarrow \text{(structure [Cl}^-\text{])} \xrightarrow{C_6H_5NH_2}$$

$$\text{(structure [Cl}^-\text{])} \tag{4}$$

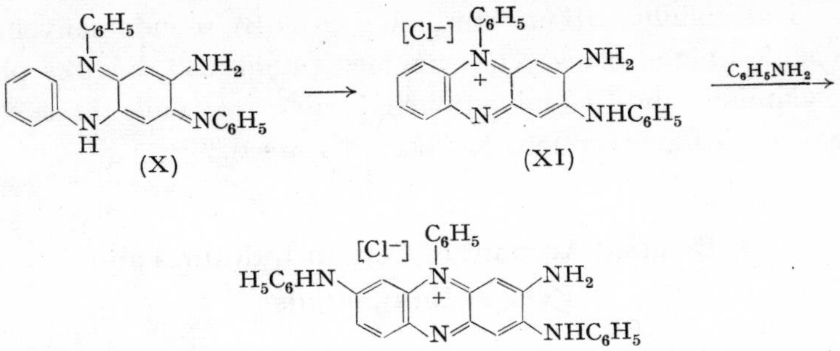

$$(5)$$

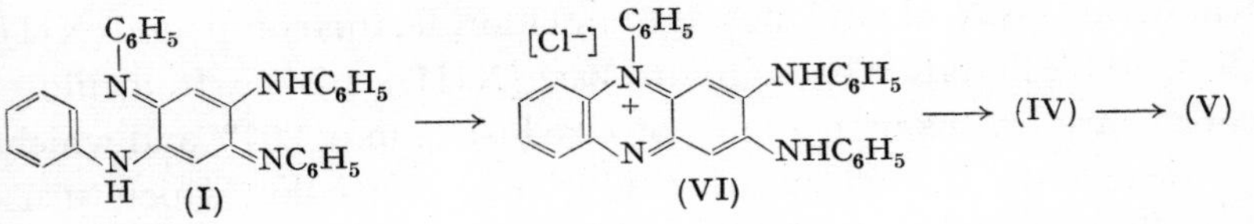

$$(6)$$

introduction of the anilino residues into the phenazine ring is an example of a type of reaction mentioned above. (Compare the conversion of 5-phenylphenazinium chloride into aposafranine, Chapter II:2,D.)

An explanation of the role of the aminoazobenzene offered in 1892 by Fischer and Hepp[15] in which a migration is involved (Equation (7))

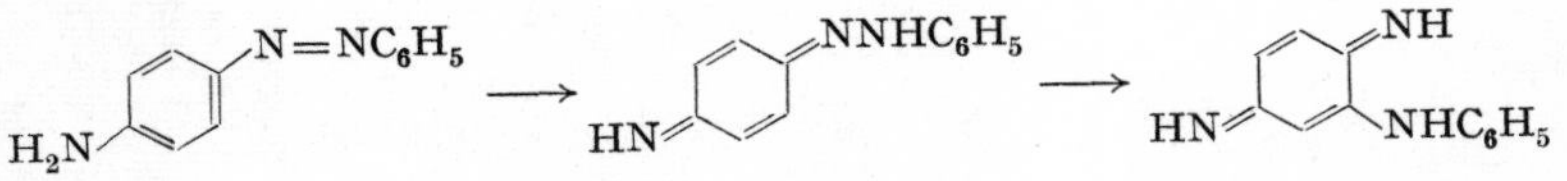

$$(7)$$

appears to have received little support. More accurate knowledge of the mechanism of this complicated process is still lacking.

Indulines are also formed by heating aminoazo compounds in the presence of mono- or di-hydric phenols or aromatic quinones.[9,16,17] Oxygen-free indulines result when a solution of azobenzene in phenol, saturated with hydrogen chloride, is heated at 180–200°, the phenol presumably not being directly involved in the reaction.[18] Induline formation from aniline is also brought about by hydroxylamine, hydrazine, phenylhydrazine and hydrazobenzene, probably via the radical $C_6H_5N\!\!<$.[19] It is also interesting to note that the action of peroxidase in the presence of dilute hydrogen peroxide at pH 4.5 on aniline yields induline 3B (and probably also 6B), pseudomauveine and ungreenable aniline black. The enzyme system also oxidizes phenyl-hydroxylamine and *p*-aminodiphenylamine to emeraldine.[20] The mechanism of these reactions has been discussed.[21]

3. Detailed Account of Certain Indulines and Related Compounds

A. 2-Anilino-10-phenylphenazinium Chloride

Known also as *N*-phenylaposafranine chloride, this compound (XII) is readily soluble in water. The anhydro-base (XIII) separates from dilute ethanol as dark prisms with a faint bronze luster, m.p. 201°, and which are soluble in concentrated sulfuric acid with a green color, which turns violet on dilution with water.[22] The compound is obtained by the action of aniline on the ferric chloride double salt of 5-phenylphenazinium chloride followed by atmospheric oxidation,[23] or on 2-chloro-10-phenyl-phenazinium chloride,[22] and also by the deamination of pseudo-mauveine (XIV).[24] For the 8-chloro-derivative, see references 25 and 26.

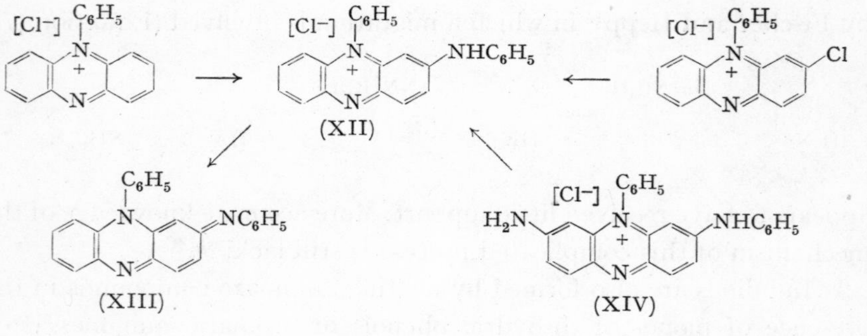

B. 2-Amino-3-anilino-10-phenylphenazinium Chloride

This compound, also known as 3-anilinoaposafranine chloride (XI), separates from ethanol as green needles with a metallic luster, which are difficultly soluble in water, but readily soluble in ethanol with a red color that turns violet-red on addition of hydrochloric acid. The anhydro-base separates from ethanol or benzene as red rhombic plates, m.p. either

189–190°[27, 28] or 203–204°,[29, 30] depending on the temperature at which crystallization sets in; it is insoluble in water.[31]

The compound is obtained by oxidation of 2-aminodiphenylamine in alcoholic hydrogen chloride solution with ferric chloride,[27, 29, 31, 32] also (besides small amounts of 2,3-dianilino-10-phenylphenazinium chloride (VI)) by heating aposafranine chloride with aniline at water-bath temperature[2, 28, 33, 34] (although recent attempts by Barry and Belton[27(b)] to repeat the latter reaction did not lead to the successful isolation of the product), and by other methods.[35, 36] When it is boiled first with zinc dust and acetic acid, then with lead dioxide, it yields aposafranine.[33] For derivatives, see references 37 and 38. For the action of acids on the compound, see Chapter V:3,B.

C. 2,3-Dianilino-10-phenylphenazinium Chloride

This compound (VI) separates from ethanol as green prisms. The anhydro-base separates from benzene-methanol as violet tablets with a bluish iridiscence, m.p. 235–237°,[39] is readily soluble in benzene, but is difficultly soluble in methanol. This base gives a brown-red solution in ethanol, and red in acetic acid. Its blue-violet solution in concentrated hydrochloric or sulfuric acid becomes magenta on dilution.[39-41] As mentioned in the preceding paragraph, it is obtained as a by-product in the formation of 2-amino-3-anilino-10-phenylphenazinium chloride by the action of aniline on aposafranine chloride; but at 150–160° it is formed as the main product.[34] Prolonged heating of azophenine hydrochloride with concentrated hydrochloric acid at 160° brings about an oxidation, with the formation of VI (See Equation (6)).[2, 40, 41] It is also obtained (besides N-phenylaposafranine) by the action of aniline on the ferric chloride double compound of 5-phenyl-phenazinium chloride, a reaction that has been cited in favor of the quinonoid nature of the phenazinium compounds[23, 42] As a structural

(XV)

proof, the synthesis by the condensation of 4,5-dianilino-*o*-quinone (XV) with 2-aminodiphenylamine hydrochloride in hot alcoholic solution is important.[39] For an analog, see reference 43.

D. 2,8-Dianilino-10-phenylphenazinium Chloride

This compound gives, in concentrated sulfuric acid, a green solution which becomes blue on dilution. The anhydro-base separates from benzene as yellow needles, m.p. 256–257°. The compound is produced in small amounts by the action of aniline and aniline hydrochloride on *N*-phenylaposafranine at 180°, and is also formed by the condensation of *N*,*N'*-diphenyl-*m*-phenylenediamine with *N*-nitrosodiphenylamine.[24, 34(b)]

E. 2,8-Diamino-3-anilino-10-phenylphenazinium Chloride

This compound is also known as 3-anilinophenosafranine chloride (II). The anhydro-base separates from pyridine as green prisms, m.p. 158° (dec.).[36] The salts are reddish-violet and are readily soluble in water; sulfuric acid yields a blue-violet solution. The compound is formed in the earlier stages of the "aminoazobenzene melt" and has been isolated from such a melt which has been heated to only 125–130° for thirty minutes, but, even then, only in small amounts.[8, 44, 45] When it is diazotized and boiled with ethanol it yields 2-amino-3-anilino-10-phenylphenazinium chloride (XI).[36]

F. 2-Amino-7,8-dianilino-10-phenylphenazinium Chloride

Also known as Indamine Blue (*C. I.* 859), this compound (III), although easily soluble in water, is almost completely precipitated from its neutral solution by the addition of a small amount of hydrochloric acid; it dyes mordanted cotton bluish-violet. The anhydro-base separates from ethanol or benzene as greenish prisms, m.p. 150–152°, is sparingly soluble in benzene, and gives a blue solution in concentrated sulfuric acid.[40] The chloride can be isolated when the "induline melt" is carried out with a large proportion of aniline hydrochloride for a limited period at 115–140°.[40, 46, 47] It can also be obtained by heating azophenine with p-phenylenediamine hydrochloride and aniline in ethanol at 140°,[34(b), 48] or by heating 3 moles of p-quinonedianil with 1 mole of p-phenylenediamine hydrochloride and an excess of aniline at 150°.[34(b)]

Deamination of indamine blue *via* the diazo reaction leads to 2,3-dianilino-10-phenylphenazinium chloride (VI).[40] The action of ammonia and ammonium chloride on the base at 130–140°, followed by acidification with hydrochloric acid, results in its transformation into 2,8-diamino-3-anilino-10-phenylphenazinium chloride (II).[36] When indamine blue is heated with dilute sulfuric acid at 230–250°, 3-hydroxyphenosafranol is formed (see Chapter V:4,A).[2] The base forms a benzylidene derivative, m.p. 261–262°.[34(b)]

G. 2,3,8-Trianilino-10-phenylphenazinium Chloride

This compound, also known as Induline 3B (IV), forms glistening brown leaflets that are soluble in hot ethanol.[6] The anhydro-base separates from benzene in almost black plates with a greenish reflex, m.p. 242°, soluble in benzene with a reddish-violet color and in concentrated sulfuric acid with a blue-violet color.[2, 3, 6, 19, 49] As mentioned above, it occurs in the "induline melt." It is also produced (together with induline 6B) by boiling indamine blue with aniline[3] and can be prepared in good yield by heating 4-anilinoazobenzene with aniline and aniline hydrochloride in ethanol at 150–160°.[3] Its structure was proved by synthesis by Kehrmann.[49] 4,5-Dianilino-o-quinone was condensed with 2-amino-5-chlorodiphenylamine and the resulting 2,3-dianilino-8-chloro-10-phenylphenazinium salt (XVI) was condensed with aniline to give Induline 3B. Treatment of the latter with aniline in the presence of mercuric oxide yielded induline 6B (V).[49]

(XVI)

H. 2,3,7,8-Tetraanilino-10-phenylphenazinium Chloride

Also known as Induline 6B, this compound (V) forms lustrous green crystals that are very difficultly soluble in ethanol, giving a greenish-blue color. The acetate separates from acetic acid in characteristic plates with a coppery-bronze luster. The anhydro-base separates from aniline as green needles or from xylene as plates with a greenish reflex, m.p. 286–288°.[2, 3, 6, 19] This compound is the final product of the "induline melt," but is best prepared by heating a mixture of azobenzene, aniline, aniline hydrochloride and nitrobenzene for eight hours at 170°.[3, 19] It is also obtained from phenosafranine chloride, pseudomauveine, indamine blue or 2,8-dianilino-10-phenylphenazinium chloride by heating with aniline.[2, 3] Kehrmann synthesized induline 6B by condensing 4,5-dianilino-o-quinone with 4,6-dianilino-m-phenylenediamine to form an amino derivative of Induline 3B (XVII), which on further treatment with aniline and aniline hydrochloride afforded Induline 6B.[50–52]

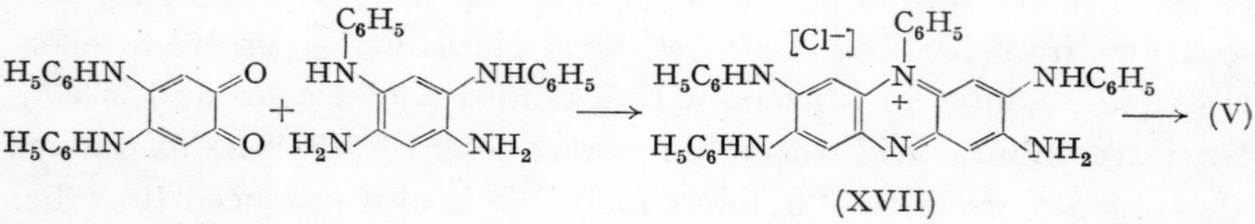

(XVII)

I. 1-Amino-2,4,8-trianilino(or 4-amino-1,3,8-trianilino)-
10-phenylphenazinium Chloride

The anhydro-base separates from benzene as glistening bronze prisms, m.p. 235°.[31]

J. Indazine

The condensation of p-nitrosodimethylaniline hydrochloride with N,N'-diphenyl-m-phenylenediamine (prepared by heating resorcinol with aniline hydrochloride in the presence of zinc chloride) yields a dye known commercially as Indazine.[53] Fischer and Hepp[34(b), 40] described the product (XVIII) as separating from benzene as prisms with a bronze luster, containing benzene, m.p. 218–220°, and giving in concentrated sulfuric acid a green solution that became violet on dilution.

However, the commercial product (*C. I.* 849) contains this indazine, together with the derived compound XIX formed by further reaction

$$H_5C_6HN \underset{}{\overset{C_6H_5}{\longrightarrow}} NH \quad + \quad ON \longrightarrow N(CH_3)_2 \quad \longrightarrow \quad H_5C_6HN \overset{[Cl^-]\; C_6H_5}{\underset{N}{\overset{N^+}{\longrightarrow}}} N(CH_3)_2$$

(XVIII)

with *p*-aminodimethylaniline (formed from *p*-nitrosodimethylaniline during the reaction).

$$(H_3C)_2N \longrightarrow HN \underset{}{\overset{[Cl^-]\; C_6H_5}{\overset{N^+}{\longrightarrow}}} H_5C_6HN \longrightarrow N(CH_3)_2$$

(XIX)

It dyes mordanted cotton bright indigo blue of good fastness. The sulfonation of indazine has been described.[54]

K. Mauveine

The discovery[55-60] of the dye known as Mauveine (*C. I.* 846), mauve or rosolane arose from an attempt of W. H. Perkin, a pupil of Hofmann, in 1856, at the age of eighteen, to synthesize quinine by the oxidation of allyltoluidine (at that time the only available information on the constitution of the alkaloid was its empirical formula, and the oxidation of allyltoluidine could, theoretically, yields a product of the required empirical formula!). Although the original aim of the work was not achieved, Perkin was led to investigate the oxidation of impure aniline (containing toluidines) sulfate with chromic acid in cold aqueous solution, and from the resulting resinous mass (despite strong discouragement from Hofmann, who, like most chemists of his day, believed in the liberal use of charcoal, and the abandonment of resinous or colored products) he isolated, in 5% yield, the violet dyestuff that became known as mauveine. Moreover, without any previous experience of industrial chemistry, he set up a factory, and this, the first synthetic dyestuff to be manufactured, was in commercial use in 1857, although it was extremely costly at first. It dyes silk reddish-violet and cotton, mordanted with tannin and tartar emetic, a rather bluer shade. Later it was displaced by other synthetic dyes and its manufacture was abandoned. One of its last uses was for the manufacture of the lake used for printing the British lilac penny postage stamps of the Queen Victoria issue. An account of the discovery and development of the dye is to be found in an obituary notice to Perkin, written by Meldola,[61] and in a lecture on the growth of the coal-tar industry by Caro.[62]

Perkin prepared many salts of mauveine in the crystalline form, and by their analysis deduced the composition $C_{27}H_{24}N_4$ for the free base, which dissolves in concentrated sulfuric acid to give a green solution that becomes first blue, then reddish-violet on dilution.

When aniline free from toluidine is used in the mauveine process, a similar but more soluble dye, pseudomauveine, to which Perkin assigned the composition $C_{24}H_{20}N_4$, is produced. Fischer and Hepp synthesized the latter by treating (a) p-nitrosodiphenylamine with

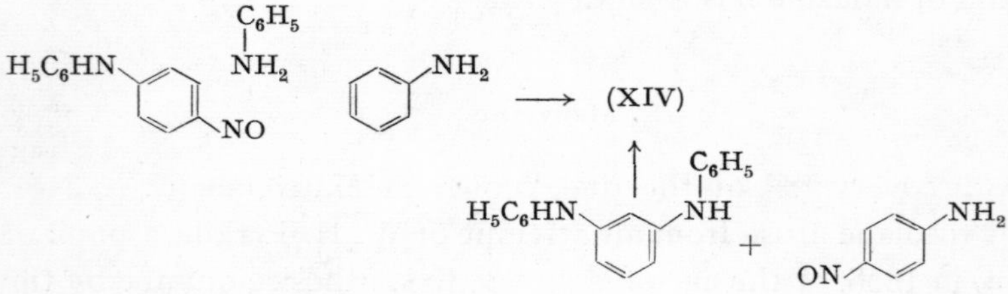

$$\tag{8}$$

aniline and (b) N,N'-diphenyl-m-phenylenediamine with p-nitroso-aniline (Equation (8)).[45,63,64] Nietzki[65] obtained the same product by treating (a) N,N'-diphenyl-m-phenylenediamine with p-phenylene-

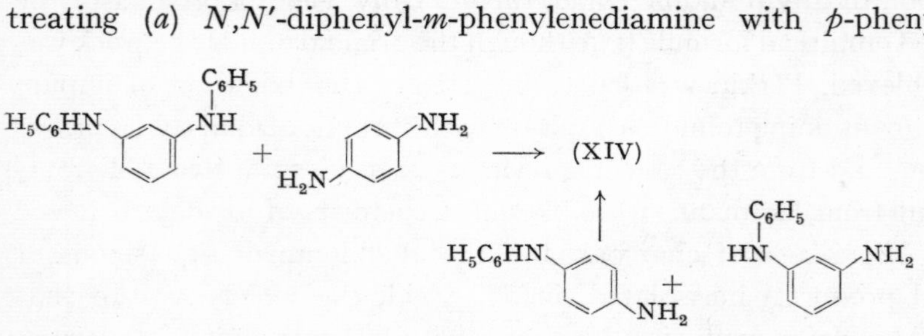

$$\tag{9}$$

diamine and (b) m-aminodiphenylamine with p-aminodiphenylamine (Equation (9)). These syntheses show the structure of pseudomauveine to be XIV (2-amino-8-anilino-10-phenylphenazinium chloride) and hence suggest for mauveine the formulation XX. It is claimed that XXI (*C. I.* 845), intermediate between mauveine and pseudomauveine, can be obtained by oxidizing a mixture of *p*-aminodiphenylamine, *o*-toluidine and aniline hydrochlorides.[66, 67]

$$H_5C_6HN \underset{H_3C}{\overset{[Cl^-]}{\bigg|}} \underset{N}{\overset{C_6H_5}{\underset{+}{N}}} \overset{NH_2}{\underset{CH_3}{\bigg|}}$$

(XX)

$$H_5C_6HN \overset{[Cl^-]}{\underset{N}{\overset{C_6H_5}{\underset{+}{N}}}} \overset{NH_2}{\underset{CH_3}{\bigg|}}$$

(XXI)

Pseudomauveine chloride forms bronzy crystals, is fairly readily soluble in water and is extremely soluble in ethanol.[60] The anhydro-base, $C_{24}H_{18}N_4$, separates from benzene as glittering, bronze crystals, m.p. 246°, and forms a carbonate.[45, 63] *N*-Alkylated pseudomauveines are also known.[53]

L. Various Commercial Induline Dyestuffs

The indulines are usually encountered in the form of the chlorides, which are insoluble in water, and difficultly soluble in ethanol (spirit-soluble indulines). The free bases are soluble in oils and fats. The commercial products are not usually homogeneous, but consist of a mixture of the induline chlorides in varying proportion, 3-anilinopheno-safranine preponderating in the redder grades, whereas the higher indulines preponderate in the bluer shades. "Induline spirit-soluble" (*C. I.* 860) consists of a mixture of indulines 3B and 6B. Aromatic amines other than aniline are also used in the preparation of indulines (for example, diphenylamine, naphthylamines and benzidine).[30, 68, 69] Sulfonation yields water-soluble acids known under such names as "Induline water-soluble," "Solid Blue," "Fast Blue," etc. (*C. I.* 861)[54, 70, 71] and which are used for dyeing silk, leather and paper. When the spirit-soluble indulines are heated with *p*-phenylenediamine, the water-soluble "Para Blue" (*C. I.* 862), probably (XXII), is formed.[72, 73] Heating with the methyl or ethyl ether of *p*-aminophenol has also been recommended for increasing the solubility of indulines in the lower

alcohols.[74] The spirit-soluble indulines are mainly used in the preparation of spirit lacquers, varnishes and printing inks,[75, 76] and in calico

$$[Cl^-] \quad \overset{C_6H_5}{\underset{|}{N}}$$

$$H_2N-\langle\ \rangle-HN \overset{\displaystyle N^+}{\underset{\displaystyle N}{\bigcirc}} \overset{NHC_6H_5}{\underset{NH-\langle\ \rangle-NH_2}{}}$$

(XXII)

printing the dyestuff, dissolved in acetin, is known as "Acetin Blue,"
"Printing Blue," etc. The free bases are also used to color wax polishes,
etc.[77] Indulines and nigrosines have been used in the counter staining
of bulk tissue and in the negative staining of bacteria.[78–82]

Indulines have also been prepared by heating leuco (dihydro)
safranines with primary aromatic amines.[83]

M. The Nigrosines

Nigrosines are prepared by heating the hydrochlorides of aniline
or other similar amines with nitrobenzene or nitrophenols or polynitro
compounds and a little iron at 180–200° [69, 84–86] They may be related to
the indulines or to aniline black in structure, and are usually greyish-
blue. These spirit-soluble nigrosines (C. I. 864) can be converted into
water-soluble nigrosines (C. I. 865) by sulfonation or by condensation
with p-phenylenediamine.[70, 84–86] The nigrosines are marketed in large
amounts because of their cheapness, and are used as either free bases
or hydrochlorides for the coloring of waxes, shoe polish, leather,
plastics, typewriter ribbons and spirit lacquers. The use of water-
soluble carboxylic acids has been recommended for deodorizing indulines and nigrosines.[87, 88]

References

1. *Colour Index*, p. 214.
2. O. Fischer and E. Hepp, *Ber.*, **29**, 361 (1896).
3. O. Fischer and E. Hepp, *Ann.*, **266**, 249 (1891).
4. A. Steopoe, *Bull. chim. soc. Românŏ, Stiinte*, **27**, 11 (1924); through *Chem. Abstracts*, **21**, 1795 (1927).
5. Brit. Pat. 3,307 (1863); through *C. I.*, p. 215.
6. O. N. Witt and E. G. P. Thomas, *J. Chem. Soc.*, **43**, 112 (1883).

7. O. Fischer and E. Hepp, *Ber.*, **20**, 2479 (1887).
8. O. Fischer and E. Hepp, *Z. f. Farben- u. Textilchemie*, **1**, 457; through *Chem. Zentr.*, **1902**, II, 902.
9. P. Barbier and P. Sisley, *Ann. chim. phys.*, (8), **13**, 96 (1908).
10. Meyer-Jacobson, *Lehrbuch der organischen Chemie*, de Gruyter, Berlin, 1923, Vol. 2, part 3, p. 1412.
11. K. A. Hofmann, F. Quoos and O. Schneider, *Ber.*, **47**, 1991 (1914).
12. A. G. Green, *J. Chem. Soc.*, **103**, 925 (1913).
13. R. Willstätter and C. W. Moore, *Ber.*, **40**, 2665 (1907).
14. S. Goldschmidt and B. Wurzschmitt, *Ber.*, **55**, 3220 (1922).
15. O. Fischer and E. Hepp, *Ber.*, **25**, 2731 (1892).
16. Ger. Pat. 18,360; *Frdl.*, **1**, 291 (1877–87).
17. P. Barbier and P. Sisley, *Bull. soc. chim. France, Mém.*, (3), **35**, 1279 (1906).
18. R. Pummerer and M. Dally, *Ber.*, **59**, 2175 (1926).
19. K. A. Hofmann, F. Hartmann and F. Kroll, *Ber.*, **57B**, 945 (1924).
20. P. J. G. Mann and B. C. Saunders, *Proc. Roy. Soc., London*, **119 B**, 47 (1935).
21. D. G. H. Daniels and B. C. Saunders, *J. Chem. Soc.*, **1951**, 2112.
22. O. Fischer and E. Hepp, *Ber.*, **30**, 1827 (1897).
23. F. Kehrmann and W. Shaposhnikov, *Ber.*, **30**, 2620 (1897).
24. F. Kehrmann, *Ber.*, **50**, 554 (1917).
25. O. Fischer and E. Hepp, *Ber.*, **31**, 299 (1898).
26. K. Balls, J. T. Hewitt and S. H. Newman, *J. Chem. Soc.*, **101**, 1840 (1912).
27(a). F. Kehrmann and J. Messinger, *J. prakt. Chem.*, (2), **46**, 565, (1892); through *J. Chem. Soc., Abstracts*, **64**, (i), 199 (1893).
27(b). V. C. Barry and J. G. Belton, *Proc. Roy. Irish Acad.*, **55 B**, 149 (1953).
28. F. Kehrmann, *Ber.*, **28**, 1709 (1895).
29. O. Fischer and A. Dischinger, *Ber.*, **29**, 1602 (1896).
30. Ger. Pat. 62,974; *Frdl.*, **3**, 311 (1890–94).
31. O. Fischer and O. Heiler, *Ber.*, **26**, 378 (1893).
32. M. Schöpff, *Ber.*, **23**, 1839 (1890).
33. O. Fischer and E. Hepp, *Ber.*, **28**, 2283 (1895).
34(a). O. Fischer and E. Hepp, *Ber.*, **26**, 1655 (1893).
34(b). O. Fischer and E. Hepp, *Ann.*, **286**, 187 (1895).
35. F. Kehrmann and B. Mascioni, *Ber.*, **28**, 345 (1895).
36. O. Fischer and E. Hepp, *Ber.*, **33**, 1498 (1900).
37. F. Kehrmann and B. Guggenheim, *Ber.*, **34**, 1217 (1901).
38(a). O. Ernst, *Ber.*, **23**, 3423 (1890).
38(b). V. C. Barry, J. G. Belton, J. F. Chambers, M. L. Conalty, R. Kelly and D. Twomey, *Proc. Roy. Irish Acad.*, **55 B**, 157 (1953).
39. F. Kehrmann and M. Cordone, *Ber.*, **46**, 3009 (1913).
40. O. Fischer and E. Hepp, *Ann.*, **262**, 237 (1891).
41. O. Fischer and E. Hepp, *Ann.*, **256**, 233 (1890).
42. W. Shaposhnikov, *J. Russ. Phys. Chem. Soc.*, **29**, 535 (1897); through *Chem. Zentr.*, **1898**, I, 722.
43. J. T. Hewitt and H. E. Stevenson, *Ber.*, **31**, 1785 (1898).
44. O. Fischer and E. Hepp, *Ber.*, **23**, 838 (1890).
45. O. Fischer and E. Hepp, *Ann.*, **272**, 306 (1892).
46. Ger. Pat. 50,534; *Frdl.*, **2**, 195 (1887–90); *Ber.*, **23**, *Ref.*, 221 (1890).
47. Ger. Pat. 54,657; *Frdl.*, **3**, 313 (1890–94), and **2**, 200 (1887–90); *Ber.*, **24**, *Ref.*, 382 (1891).
48. P. Barbier and P. Sisley, *Bull. soc. chim. France, Mém.*, (4), **4**, 148 (1908).
49. F. Kehrmann (with W. Klopfenstein), *Ber.*, **56**, 2394 (1923).

50. F. Kehrmann, *Helv. Chim. Acta*, **7**, 471 (1924).
51. F. Kehrmann and L. Stanoyévitch, *Helv. Chim. Acta*, **8**, 661 (1925).
52. F. Kehrmann and L. Stanoyévitch, *Helv. Chim. Acta*, **8**, 663 (1925).
53. Ger. Pat. 47,549; *Ber.*, **22**, *Ref.*, 463 (1889).
54. F. Kehrmann and A. Herzbaum, *Ber.*, **50**, 873 (1917).
55. Brit. Pat. 1,984 (1856); through *C. I.*, p. 211.
56. W. H. Perkin, *Jahresber.*, **1859**, 756.
57. W. H. Perkin, *Jahresber.*, **1863**, 420.
58. W. H. Perkin, *J. Chem. Soc.*, **14**, 230 (1862).
59. W. H. Perkin, *J. Chem. Soc.*, **22**, 25 (1869).
60. W. H. Perkin, *J. Chem. Soc.*, **35**, 717 (1879).
61. R. Meldola, *J. Chem. Soc.*, **93**, 2214 (1908).
62. H. Caro, *Ber.*, **25**, *Ref.*, 955 (1892).
63. O. Fischer and E. Hepp, *Ber.*, **21**, 2617 (1888).
64. O. Fischer and E. Hepp, *Ber.*, **26**, 1194 (1893).
65. R. Nietzki, *Ber.*, **29**, 1442 (1896).
66. A. Cobenzl, *Oesterr. Chem. Ztg.*, **28**, 25 (1925); through *Chem. Zentr.*, **1925**, I, 1737.
67. Ger. Pat. 49,853; *Frdl.*, **2**, 161 (1887–90).
68. Ger. Pat. 57,346; *Frdl.*, **3**, 313 (1890–94).
69. Fr. Pat. 809,057; *Chem. Zentr.*, **1937**, I, 5057.
70. J. B. Lal, and S. N. Kapur, *Dept. Ind. Com., United Provinces, Bull.*, No. 34 (1942); through *Chem. Abstracts*, **39**, 5079 (1945).
71. Ger. Pat. 17,340; *Frdl.*, **1**, 291 (1877–87).
72. Ger. Pat. 50,819; *Frdl.*, **2**, 198 (1887–90); *Ber.*, **23**, *Ref.*, 310 (1890).
73. Ger. Pat. 60,426; *Frdl.*, **3**, 309 (1890–94).
74. U. S. Pat. 2,045,069; *Chem. Zentr.*, **1937**, I, 200.
75. U. S. Pat. 2,392,376; *Chem. Abstracts*, **40**, 2319 (1946).
76. U. S. Pat. 2,392,657; *Chem. Abstracts*, **40**, 2319 (1946).
77. Thorpe, *Dictionary of Applied Chemistry*, 4th ed., Longmans, Green, London, 1943, Vol. 6, p. 467.
78. J. E. Lynch, *Z. wiss. Mikroskop*, **46**, 465 (1930).
79. R. W. Aimley, *Stain Tech.*, **10**, 53 (1935).
80. W. Dorner, *Lait*, **6**, 8 (1926); through *Chem. Abstracts*, **21**, 2010 (1927).
81. E. Pfitzer, *Ber. deut. bot. Ges.*, **1**, 44 (1883).
82. R. J. Bean, *Stain Tech.*, **2**, 56 (1927); through *Chem. Abstracts*, **21**, 2143 (1927).
83. Fr. Pat. 701,622; *Chem. Zentr.*, **1932**, I, 456.
84. Ger. Pat. 79,983; *Frdl.*, **4**, 448 (1894–97).
85. Ger. Pat. 84,293; *Frdl.*, **4**, 449 (1894–97).
86. Ger. Pat. 84,294; *Frdl.*, **4**, 451 (1894–97).
87. Brit. Pat. 498,751; *Chem. Abstracts*, **33**, 4432 (1939).
88. U. S. Pat. 2,328,759; *Chem. Abstracts*, **38**, 1125 (1944).

CHAPTER IX

Aniline Black

1. Introduction

Fritzsche[1,2] in 1840 noticed that the oxidation of aniline salts with chromic acid led to the formation of dark green and blue-black substances. Later, Perkin, in 1856, obtained a dark colored precipitate by the oxidation of aniline (containing toluidine) sulfate with chromic acid, from which he extracted mauveine (see Chapter VIII:3,K). The formation of this "aniline black" on cotton fiber was first described in 1860; and the first successful process for so doing was patented by Lightfoot[3] in 1863. Aniline Black (C. I. 870) is a very insoluble and very stable black powder, not readily attacked by acids, alkalis or oxidizing or reducing agents. Nietzki[4] in 1878 ascribed to it the composition $C_{30}H_{25}N_5$, but a more recent formula is $C_{54}H_{43}N_9$.[5] It is formed by the action of numerous oxidizing agents on aniline (chromic acid, chromates, persulfates or chlorates,[6] in the presence of salts of copper, cerium, tungsten or vanadium as oxygen carriers), and can also be produced by electrolytic or atmospheric oxidation. Other primary aromatic amines on oxidation also afford similar products, some of which are of commercial importance[7]; thus, the oxidation of p-phenylenediamine yields Paramine Brown (C. I. 875), which is used to dye furs.

2. Structure

As mentioned in Chapter VIII:2,B, in the discussion of the mechanism of the formation of indulines, N-phenylquinonediimine (I) is regarded as a precursor not only of the indulines and nigrosines but also of emeraldine and nigraniline, which are, in turn, precursors of aniline black. With regard to the mode of formation of N-phenyl-

quinonediimine from aniline, Goldschmidt and Wurzschmitt[8,9] suggested the intermediate formation of free $C_6H_5N{<}$ radicals, which would
presumably mean that the reaction would be unimolecular with respect
to aniline. However, it must be remembered that all the oxidation
experiments carried out by these authors used lead dioxide in ether.
Piccard and Montmollin[10] have studied the rate of formation of aniline
black from aniline colorimetrically, using potassium dichromate and
sulfuric acid and found the reaction to be bimolecular with respect to
aniline, and autocatalytic. Oxalic acid has been found to increase the
rate of formation of aniline black; and industrial use has been made of
this.[11,12] The primary oxidation product of aniline by hydrogen peroxide
and Caro's acid is believed to be aniline oxide or phenylhydroxylamine,
which then gives rise to mono- and bi-molecular products; but polymerization does not occur.[13] However, Mann and Saunders[14] have
shown that the action of the enzyme peroxidase in the presence of
dilute hydrogen peroxide at pH 4.5 oxidizes aniline to 2,5-dianilino-N-
phenylquinonediimine, pseudomauveine, induline and ungreenable
aniline black, presumably by way of N-phenylquinonediimine. Recently, the mechanism of the formation of the latter in this reaction was
discussed.[15]

Green[16] in 1913 pointed out that, under strongly acidic conditions,
the N-phenylquinonediimine polymerizes in a linear manner to yield,

$$H_5C_6N{=}\langle\rangle{=}NH$$

(I)

$$\downarrow$$

$$H_5C_6N{=}\langle\rangle{=}N{-}\langle\rangle{-}NH{-}\langle\rangle{-}NH_2$$

(II)

$$\downarrow$$

$$H_5C_6N{=}\langle\rangle{=}N{-}\langle\rangle{-}N{=}\langle\rangle{=}NH$$

(III)

$$\downarrow$$

$$H_5C_6HN{-}\langle\rangle{-}NH{-}\langle\rangle{-}N{=}\langle\rangle{=}N{-}\langle\rangle{-}N{=}\langle\rangle{=}N{-}\langle\rangle{-}N{=}\langle\rangle{=}NH$$

(IV)

finally, emeraldine and nigraniline, whereas, under neutral or only weakly acidic conditions, a reaction leading to the formation of indulines and nigrosines occurs. Earlier ideas on the structure of aniline black are due to Willstätter,[17-19] who suggested its formation via the polymerization of N-phenylquinonediimine (I). The blue dimerization product (II) was isolated in the crystalline form, and was oxidized to the red diquinonoid III. This polymerization process may then be repeated to give a product containing eight aniline residues (IV) and this compound may then be oxidized further, with the formation of further quinonoid structures, and so on. A product of type IV can exist in various states of oxidation, which differ from one another in the number of benzenoid and quinonoid rings in the chain, so that a series of compounds can be obtained from the oxidation of aniline that are related to each other in this way. They are called (in decreasing states of oxidation): perinigraniline, nigraniline, emeraldine and protoemeraldine. The reduced compound in which all the rings are benzenoid and none quinonoid is leucoemeraldine. The number of quinonoid groups present was determined by measuring the volume of nitrogen evolved on treatment with phenylhydrazine carbamate.[20, 21] The existence of chains of this type in these compounds is fairly well established, because on vigorous oxidation and hydrolysis, they are broken down with the formation of p-benzoquinone, in which the o-positions remain unattacked. The physical properties of these substances do not lend themselves to molecular weight determination, so it is not known whether the compounds are correctly represented by formulas with eight aniline residues (such as IV) or whether linear polymerization proceeds further.

With the exception of the leuco forms (which are not formed by the oxidation of aniline), all these compounds are deeply colored, and Willstätter supposed that they constituted aniline black. Bucherer,[22, 23] however, pointed out that this is unlikely in view of the fact that the above compounds are indamines and therefore unstable, whereas aniline black formed commercially on the fiber (the so-called "ungreenable black") is a very stable substance, and suggested a phenazine structure for the latter. But the most important contribution to our knowledge of the structure of aniline black is due to Green.

Green and Woodhead[24, 25] drew attention to the fact that a sharp distinction must be drawn between emeraldine, nigraniline, etc., which are purely oxidation products of aniline, and "ungreenable aniline black," which is the condensation product of these with aniline, and that only the latter, and not the former, can be properly regarded as true aniline black. The important experiments of Willstätter, in fact, referred only to the former class of compounds; and his view that "ungreenable black" is a compound of the same type as emeraldine and nigraniline is incorrect. Green and Woodhead made the valuable discovery that, whereas the emeraldine and nigraniline bases are readily soluble in 80% acetic acid or 60% formic acid, the higher condensation products are insoluble; by using this observation, they showed that Willstätter's products consisted mainly of the former type. Willstätter, however, did not agree with these observations.[26]

These workers also showed that "ungreenable black" produced on the fiber is not reduced at all by sulfur dioxide; and that more powerful reducing agents such as dithionite convert it into a brownish leuco compound that is rapidly reoxidized by air to the original aniline black, apparently without passing through any lower stage of oxidation. On the other hand, emeraldine and nigraniline readily give on reduction the almost colorless leucoemeraldine, which is only slowly oxidized by air. If Willstätter's views were correct, vigorous reduction should lead to the same product in both cases. They also showed that leucoemeraldine is not reduced further by boiling titanous chloride solution, thus showing that it is not a monoquinonoid compound as Willstätter thought.

In 1913, Green and Wolff[5,27] suggested that aniline black is a phenazine compound, related to nigraniline in the same way as safranine is related to the simplest blue indamine, because the conversion of emeraldine or nigraniline into aniline black by oxidation (for example, by chromic acid) occurs only in the presence of free aniline. They showed that "ungreenable black" dyes are also obtained when emeraldine or nigraniline is oxidized on the fiber in the presence of other primary aromatic amines, but not with dimethylaniline. Thus, the end-products of the aniline black formation arise through a reaction other than that which leads to the intermediate (emeraldine and nigraniline) and in which the amino group of the aniline takes part.

The latter reaction, like safranine formation, occurs under neutral or only weakly acidic conditions. The increase in weight of nigraniline when treated with various amines, and also the amount of amine used up, were measured. By using halogen-containing amines such as p-bromoaniline a further check was obtained by a halogen estimation on the resulting aniline black. The results of a considerable number of experiments showed that the maximum number of amine residues taken up by nigraniline (assumed to be made up of eight aniline residues) was three; and that the end-product obtained in the case of aniline itself was identical with "ungreenable aniline black." Green therefore suggested structure VI for aniline black, representing its formation from nigraniline (V) as shown below. To-day, structure VI requires modification to

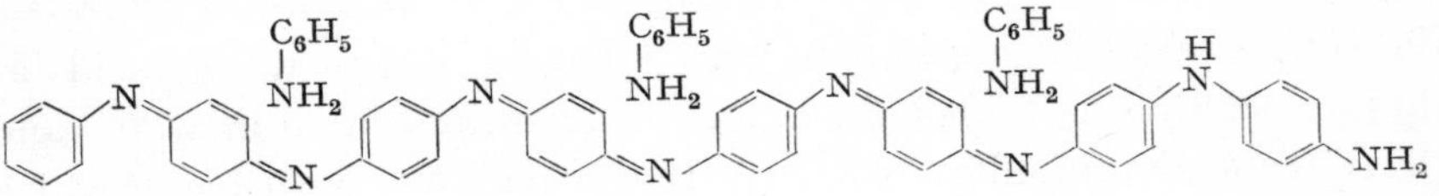

(V)

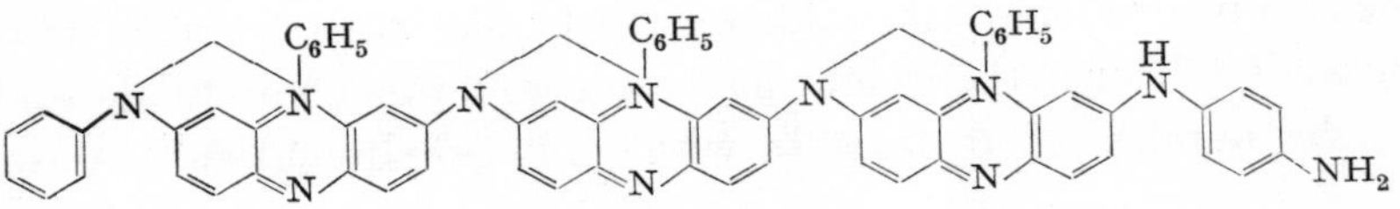

(VI)

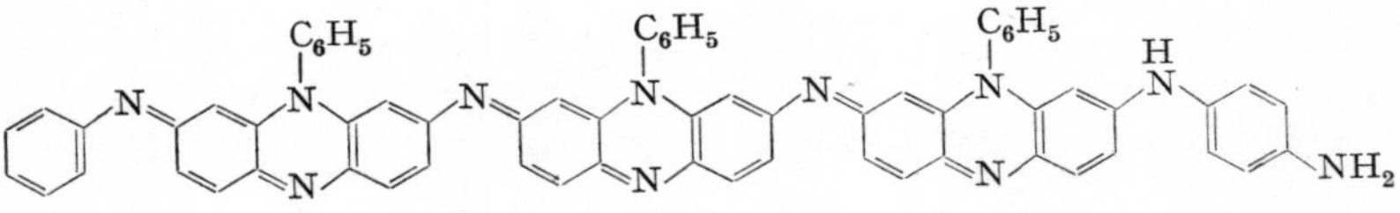

(VII)

VII, which structure is to be found in reference 28 (1920), although, in suggesting the same modification in 1935, Mann and Saunders[14] stated: "This formula for aniline black has not previously been put forward." Alternatively, one could consider the bonds uniting two nitrogen atoms in VI as being electrovalent, the phenazinium nitrogen atoms being positively charged.[29] Perhaps one may have a resonance hybrid of this structure and VII.

According to Green and Johnson,[30, 31] the oxidation of aniline black with lead dioxide and sulfuric acid affords a yield of quinone corresponding to that required on the assumption of the above structure, the mono- and di-substituted benzene nuclei (but not the trisubstituted ones) being oxidized to quinone. Their value for the amount of sodium nitrite absorbed in the presence of mineral acid corresponds to the presence of one primary amino group in a molecule the size of VII. However, in the absence of further evidence, the length of the chains in the aniline black molecule must be regarded as being unknown.

Since Green's work, little of importance on the structure of aniline black has been published, with the exception of three papers by the Russian Joffe and his collaborators[32–34] which, unfortunately, we have been able to read in the form of abstracts only, and which claim to disprove a considerable part of Green's work. In attempting to repeat the condensation of nigraniline with sulfanilic and metanilic acids as the amine, they obtained products that were insoluble in water and that did not contain sulfur. Secondly, they carried out experiments which appeared to show that the reaction between nigraniline and aniline hydrochloride involves simply a mutual oxidation-reduction, both being converted into emeraldine, which may then be reoxidized to nigraniline. Hence the weight increase goes on indefinitely, depending on the number of treatments with aniline hydrochloride. Without

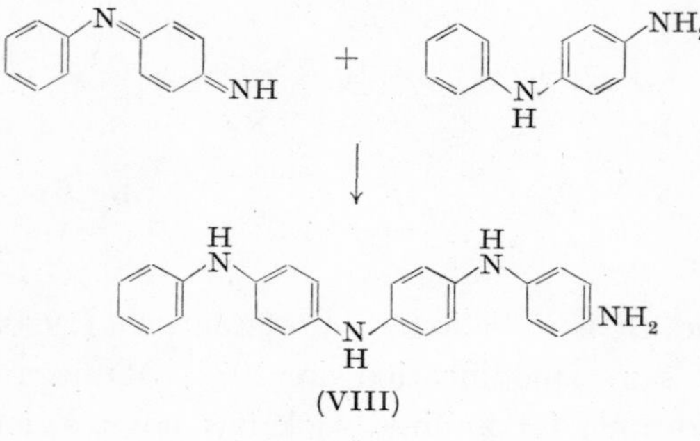

(VIII)

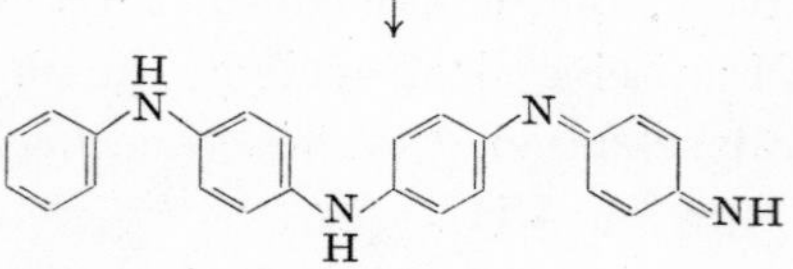

(IX)

knowing the exact conditions used in these experiments, one cannot fairly judge to what extent they conflict with the earlier results. Thirdly, the Russian workers showed that, whereas the reaction between 4-aminodiphenylamine and 1 mole of ferric chloride gives IX, the action of a little ferric chloride yields VIII, without the formation of IX. From this they concluded that IX is formed not by direct polymerization of N-phenylquinonediimine, but by oxidation of VIII, which is formed by the action of 4-aminodiphenylamine on N-phenylquinonediimine. However, this scarcely seems a valid argument for, in absence of sufficient ferric chloride for complete oxidation, it would appear possible that IX might be reduced to VIII by 4-aminodiphenylamine.

Apart from the oxidation to quinone, little degradative work on aniline black has been described. By reduction with hydriodic acid or stannous chloride and hydrochloric acid, Nietzki obtained p-phenylenediamine and 4,4'-diaminodiphenylamine. But it seems that the degradation of aniline black to phenazine or one of its simpler derivatives has not yet been achieved; and, in fact, the phenazine structure still rests on probable assumptions, rather than on definite experimental proof. It is interesting to note that a phenazinium structure has recently been suggested for the resinous products formed by the action of nitrous acid on primary aromatic amines.[35(a)]

3. Manufacture and Technical Importance

In the preparation of aniline black in substance, aniline is first oxidized for forty hours at 0–5° with sodium chlorate in hydrochloric acid solution containing vanadium chloride. The resulting green salt is basified with ammonia, yielding the violet-blue base emeraldine, which is then further oxidized with hydrogen peroxide in the presence of ammonia, giving the dark blue base, nigraniline. Finally, this is treated with aniline hydrochloride in the presence of chromic acid, and the precipitate is basified with ammonia, yielding "ungreenable aniline black" as a black powder.

Except as a pigment, aniline black is not sold in the finished state but is always produced upon the fiber (that is, it is an ingrain dye). In one method of dyeing (essentially that of Lightfoot), the fiber is impregnated with a solution of aniline hydrochloride containing the oxidizing agent (sodium chlorate) and a salt of vanadium; the black is then developed by a process known as "ageing," which consists in subjecting the impregnated fiber to the action of air at a moderately high temperature, thus converting the emeraldine first into nigraniline, then into "ungreenable black." In another process, the fiber is dyed in a bath containing ammonium chloride, sodium dichromate and a mixture of sulfuric and hydrochloric acids. Many patents and technical papers have been published on dyeing with aniline black, of which very few need to be mentioned here.[35(b), 36-43] The function of various metallic and organic catalysts that are used is not fully understood.[11, 12, 39, 40]

Well-dyed aniline black is one of the most fast and intense blacks that can be produced. For this reason, and because of its cheapness, it is still one of the most important dyestuffs, especially for the dyeing of cotton, although for the latter purpose it has, in recent years, been superseded to some extent by sulfur black dyes. The fact that the formation of aniline black is accelerated by ultraviolet irradiation of aniline hydrochloride solutions containing suitable oxidizing agents and catalysts has been used to produce a photographic image[41] and suggests a free radical reaction. The electrometric titration curves of aniline black and analogous materials have suggested their possible use as acid absorbers, like ion-exchangers.[42, 43] The action of high-frequency vibrations on aniline black has been studied.[44]

References

1. J. Fritzsche, *J. prakt. Chem.*, **20**, 453 (1840).
2. J. Fritzsche, *J. prakt. Chem.*, **28**, 198 (1843).
3. Brit. Pat. 151 (1863); through *C. I.*, p. 217.
4. R. Nietzki, *Ber.*, **11**, 1093 (1878).
5. A. G. Green and S. Wolff, *Ber.*, **46**, 33 (1913).
6. K. A. Hofmann, F. Quoos and O. Schneider, *Ber.*, **47**, 1991 (1914).
7. Brit. Pat. 306,632; *Chem. Abstracts*, **23**, 5330 (1929); *Frdl.*, **16**, 1665 (1927–29).
8. S. Goldschmidt and B. Wurzschmitt, *Ber.*, **55**, 3220 (1922).
9. S. Goldschmidt and B. Wurzschmitt, *Ber.*, **55**, 3216 (1922).
10. J. Piccard and F. de Montmollin, *Helv. Chim. Acta*, **6**, 1021 (1923).
11. J. Piccard, *Helv. Chim. Acta*, **6**, 1029 (1923).
12. E. Justin-Mueller, *Rev. gén. des mat. color.*, **28**, 126; through *Chem. Zentr.*, 1924, II, 1411.
13. E. Bamberger and F. Tschirner, *Ber.*, **32**, 1675 (1899).
14. P. J. G. Mann and B. C. Saunders, *Proc. Roy. Soc. London*, **119 B**, 47 (1935).

15. D. G. H. Daniels and B. C. Saunders, *J. Chem. Soc.*, **1951**, 2112.
16. A. G. Green, *J. Chem. Soc.*, **103**, 925 (1913).
17. R. Willstätter and C. W. Moore, *Ber.*, **40**, 2665 (1907).
18. R. Willstätter and S. Dorogi, *Ber.*, **42**, 2147 (1909).
19. R. Willstätter and S. Dorogi, *Ber.*, **42**, 4118 (1909).
20. R. Willstätter and C. Cramer, *Ber.*, **43**, 2976 (1910).
21. A. G. Green and S. Wolff, *Ber.*, **44**, 2570 (1911).
22. H. T. Bucherer, *Ber.*, **40**, 3412 (1907).
23. H. T. Bucherer, *Ber.*, **42**, 2931 (1909).
24. A. G. Green and A. E. Woodhead, *J. Chem. Soc.*, **97**, 2388 (1910).
25. A. G. Green and A. E. Woodhead, *J. Chem. Soc.*, **101**, 1117 (1912).
26. R. Willstätter and C. Cramer, *Ber.*, **44**, 2162 (1911).
27. A. G. Green and S. Wolff, *Proc. Chem. Soc.*, **28**, 250 (1912).
28. Meyer-Jacobson, *Lehrbuch der organischen Chemie*, de Gruyter, Berlin, 1923, Vol. 2, part 3, p. 1415.
29. L. F. Fieser and M. Fieser, *Organic Chemistry*, Heath, Boston, 1944, p. 840.
30. A. G. Green and W. Johnson, *Ber.*, **46**, 3769 (1913).
31. A. G. Green and W. Johnson, *Proc. Chem. Soc.*, **29**, 276 (1913).
32. I. S. Joffe and R. M. Metrikina, *J. Russ. Phys. Chem. Soc.*, **62**, 1101 (1930); through *Chem. Abstracts*, **25**, 2707 (1931).
33. I. S. Joffe and R. M. Metrikina, *J. Russ. Phys. Chem. Soc.*, **62**, 1115 (1930); through *Chem. Abstracts*, **25**, 2707 (1931).
34. I. S. Joffe and V. Y. Soloveĭchik, *J. Gen. Chem. U.S.S.R.*, **9**, 129 (1939); through *Chem. Abstracts*, **33**, 6268 (1939).
35(a). H. Gies and E. Pfeil, *Ann.*, **578**, 11 (1952).
35(b). H. Sunder and L. A. Lantz, *Bull. soc. ind. Mulhouse*, **102**, 106 (1936); through *Chem. Abstracts*, **30**, 4010 (1936).
36. E. K. Zil'berkveit and L. A. Vasil'ev, *J. Applied Chem. U.S.S.R.*, **9**, 2231 (1936); through *Chem. Abstracts*, **31**, 5166 (1937).
37. Russ. Pat. 27,372; *Chem. Abstracts*, **27**, 2312 (1933).
38. Russ. Pat. 29,163; *Chem. Abstracts* **27**, 4097 (1933).
39. E. Justin-Mueller, *Tiba*, **14**, 753 (1936); through *Chem. Abstracts*, **31**, 867 (1937).
40. G. V. Zotov, *Khlopchatobumazhnaya Prom.*, **10**, No. 1–2, 49 (1940); through *Chem. Abstracts*, **36**, 5654 (1942).
41. H. Freytag, *Melliand. Textilber.*, **13**, 144 (1932); through *Chem. Abstracts*, **27**, 1834 (1933).
42. E. H. Shaw (Jr.), *Proc. S. Dakota Acad. Sci.*, **22**, 82 (1942); through *Chem. Abstracts*, **39**, 4278 (1945).
43. H. P. Schmitt and E. H. Shaw (Jr.), *Proc. S. Dakota Acad. Sci.*, **24**, 116 (1944); through *Chem. Abstracts*, **39**, 5011 (1945).
44. L. I. Belen'kiĭ, *Khlopchatobumazhnaya Prom.*, **10**, No. 1–2, 58 (1940); through *Chem. Abstracts*, **37**, 777 (1943).

CHAPTER X

The Bacterial Pigments

1. Pyocyanine

A. Historical

Pseudomonas aeruginosa (Bacillus pyocyaneus) is a common parasite of the human skin, especially common in sweaty places such as the armpits, where its presence can be recognized by the blue color of the sweat. It is found also in blue pus; and the green color of certain samples of wool has been traced to this organism.[1] It has been known for a long time that the organism can be grown on such media as agar-peptone, bouillon, milk and potatoes, with the production of the characteristic blue pigment, pyocyanine. In 1860, Fordos[2,3] added ammonia to a culture and was then able to extract the pigment with chloroform; he showed that the coloring matter was basic. The method of extraction was improved by Gessard,[4-8] who shook the chloroform solution with dilute mineral acid and obtained a red aqueous solution of the salt from which the blue base could be extracted with chloroform after basification. Pyocyanine picrate was first prepared in 1888 by Ledderhose,[9] who suggested for the base the empirical formula $C_{14}H_{14}ON_2$.

Little more became known about the chemical nature of the pigment until 1923, when McCombie and Scarborough,[10] failing to obtain the base in a pure state, prepared and analyzed a series of different salts, from which they deduced that pyocyanine had the empirical formula $C_{26}H_{28}O_3N_4$ (perhaps minus 1 or 2 H_2O). They also determined the molecular weight of the base in chloroform solution and obtained a value agreeing fairly well with this molecular formula. In the following year, Wrede and Strack[11] advanced the formula $C_{26}H_{24}O_2N_4$, but later[12(a)] modified this to $C_{26}H_{20}O_2N_4$, which is double the now-accepted molecular formula.

There has recently been isolated from fermentations a bacterium for which the name *Cyanococcus chromospirans* has been suggested and which also yields pyocyanine.[12(b)]

B. Physical Properties of Pyocyanine and Its Salts

Pyocyanine, $C_{13}H_{10}ON_2$, separates from water as dark blue needles, m.p. 133°,[13] obtained anhydrous over phosphoric oxide *in vacuo* at 50°.[14] It can be kept without decomposition for several weeks in a vacuum desiccator in the dark; but on longer standing it decomposes to 1-phenazinol.[13] It is soluble in hot water, dilute alcohol, chloroform, acetone and ethyl acetate, but insoluble in ether, benzene, xylene, carbon tetrachloride, light petroleum and carbon disulfide.[10] The absorption spectrum of pyocyanine has been recorded.[15] The dipole moment in dioxan solution is approximately 7.0 D.[16]

Numerous salts have been described. The perchlorate, $C_{13}H_{10}ON_2 \cdot HClO_4$, separates from hot aqueous perchloric acid as dark red needles, m.p. 221–223° (dec.).[10, 12(a)] The picrate separates from methanol as dark red, almost black leaflets with a violet sheen, m.p. 194–5° (dec.).[10, 11] The molecular susceptibility of the semiquinone perchlorate is 48.8 $\times$ 10^{-5}.[17]

C. Preparation

Various methods for the culture of *Pseudomonas aeruginosa* to obtain the best yield of pyocyanine have been recommended. Thus, McCombie and Scarborough[10] grew the organism on a peptone-agar medium for 4–6 days at 37°. Wrede and Strack[11] found that a good yield could be obtained at pH 7.4 on bouillon made from horse flesh or (better) human placenta, with 1% of peptone and 0.5% of sodium chloride; but later[14] they cultivated the organism on Ragitbouillon at pH 7.8, obtaining from 10 liters of the culture fluid about 300 mg. of the decahydrate. In old cultures, the dye separated as the leuco compound, which readily turned blue on exposure to air. They isolated the pyocyanine in the manner of the earlier workers, but purified it by conversion, in chloroform solution, into the picrate, which was recrystallized from ethanol and then treated with hydrogen chloride, giving the crystalline hydrochloride, from which the base was regenerated. From a chloroform solution, either by evaporation, or by addition of light petroleum, the base was precipitated and was then recrystallized from water.

Elema and Sanders[18] obtained yields of 260 mg./l. on peptone containing gelatin at pH 7.2 after fifteen days at 25° and observed that aeration of the cultures was important to obtain the highest yield of pyocyanine, the latter being greatly reduced by the addition of nitrate. The ions Mg, SO_4, K, PO_4 and Fe have been found by Burton, Campbell and Eagles[19] to be essential for the formation of the pigment. The same authors[20, 21] found that hydrolyzed casein with glycerol and salts gave a yield of pyocyanine equal to that obtained on peptone-glycerol-agar, and that the monoaminomonocarboxylic acids were the source of nitrogen essential to pyocyanine formation. No pigment is produced in a medium containing sufficient glucose ($> 1\%$) to establish and maintain an acid reaction.[22] See also references 23 and 24.

To prepare considerable quantities of pyocyanine by biosynthesis is tedious and laborious. However, a convenient chemical synthesis is now available that gives an overall yield of 16% from pyrogallol-1-methyl ether (see Chapter X:1,D).[13]

D. Structure

Pyocyanine, the first phenazine compound discovered in nature, is a deep blue basic compound that forms dark red salts; its structure was elucidated largely through the work of Wrede and Strack. It forms a nitrosamine (brown crystals decomposing explosively at about 190°) that is only weakly basic[14]; but it seems likely that the formation of this compound involves a preliminary reduction. Thus, pyocyanine is reduced by glucose or sodium dithionite in alkaline solution[11] or by sodium amalgam in acid or alkaline solution[25] to give a colorless product (leucopyocyanine), which readily absorbs oxygen from the air, reforming pyocyanine.[11] In the presence of platinum, it takes up 2 atomic proportions of hydrogen, again giving the oily leucopyocyanine (dihydropyocyanine), which is soluble in alkali and which yields a benzoyl derivative that separates from chloroform as greenish crystals, m.p. 150°, and has the composition $C_{13}H_{11}ON_2$ (C_7H_5O).[12(a)]

When pyocyanine is allowed to stand in dilute alkaline solution in the presence of air for a few hours, the color changes to wine-red (the same change is produced immediately on boiling). The coloring matter cannot then be extracted with chloroform; but after the addition of acetic acid, concentration leads to the deposition of yellow needles, and addition of mineral acid changes the color back to wine-red again.[11, 26] This yellow compound, which is designated hemipyocyanine, has the formula $C_{12}H_8ON_2$[25] and is also obtained by dry heating of pyocyanine[11]; it can be recrystallized from aqueous methanol or sublimed in a vacuum, forming bright yellow crystals, m.p. 158°.[25] It forms a monoacetyl derivative, separating from aqueous methanol as greenish-yellow needles containing water of crystallization, melting anhydrous at 120°, and a monobenzoyl derivative, separating from aqueous pyridine as green needles, m.p. 173°; these can be obtained by direct acetylation or benzoylation of pyocyanine itself under alkaline conditions.[11, 12(a)]

In the absence of oxygen, pyocyanine is not completely converted into hemipyocyanine by alkali, part forming leucopyocyanine.[25] The oxidation can also be effected by hydrogen peroxide in alkaline solution,[12(a)] when formic acid is also formed (Equation (1)).

$$\text{Pyocyanine} \xrightarrow[\text{NaOH}]{\text{H}_2\text{O}_2} \text{Hemipyocyanine} + \text{Formic acid} \tag{1}$$
$$C_{13}H_{10}ON_2 \qquad\qquad C_{12}H_8ON_2 \qquad\qquad CH_2O_2$$

The first glimpse into the nature of the nucleus of the pigment was provided by the isolation, by Wrede and Strack, of a fair yield of phenazine by zinc dust distillation of hemipyocyanine,[14] which they then showed, by synthesis, to be 1-phenazinol (I).[25, 27] Pyrogallol-1-methyl ether was oxidized by lead dioxide in benzene and, after filtration, the resulting solution of 3-methoxy-o-quinone was treated with one of o-phenylenediamine in acetic acid and benzene, yielding 1-methoxyphenazine. The latter, on demethylation with hydrobromic

(I)

acid, gave 1-phenazinol, identical with hemipyocyanine. When this is heated with methyl sulfate for ten minutes at 100°, it gives a methosulfate which, on treatment with sodium hydroxide, is transformed into a blue product that Wrede and Strack showed to be identical with pyocyanine.[12(a), 13, 27] Later, the pigment was also synthesized by McIlwain[28] in 45% yield by exposing an aqueous solution of phenazine methosulfate to sunlight for one day.

In 1929, Wrede and Strack[12, 27] suggested the alternative structures II and III for pyocyanine, although these are quite inadmissible in the light of present-day valency concepts. They favored the bi-

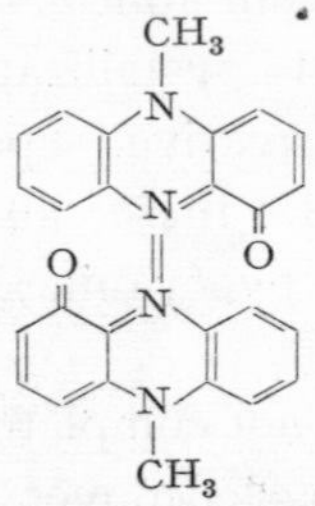

(II) 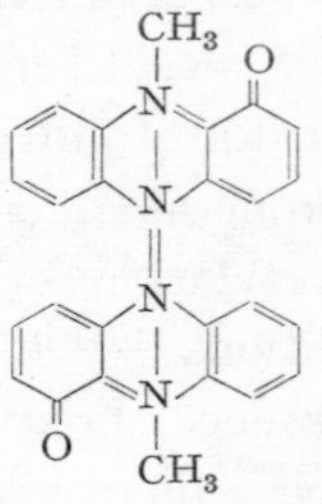   (III)

molecular formulation because of the molecular weight values[10] and to explain the oxidative demethylation of pyocyanine in alkaline solution to 1-phenazinol. However, Michaelis[29] pointed out that there is no need to assume the bimolecular structure and that pyocyanine is better represented as IV, which is now accepted as correct. The con-

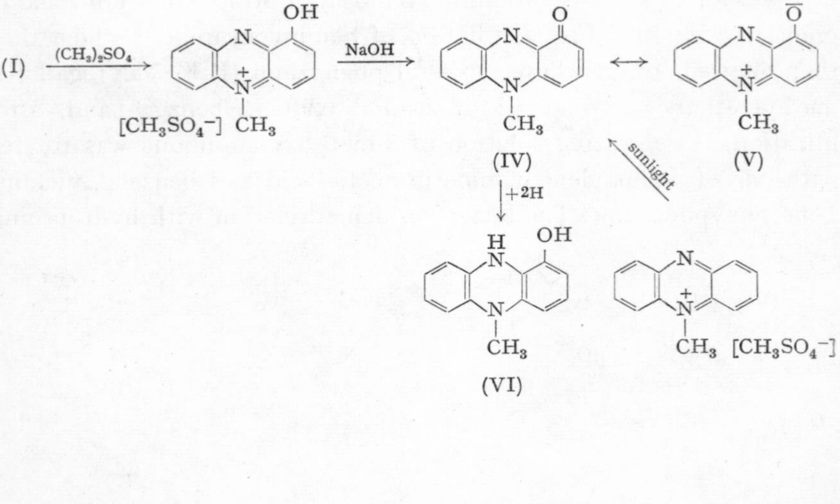

(IV)

(V)

(VI)

version of pyocyanine into 1-phenazinol recalls the demethylation of methylene blue in alkaline solution; and other examples of oxidative demethylation occur in the phenazine series (Chapters II:2,B and III:2,F). On this formulation, the reduction product, leucopyocyanine, is represented as VI which, being phenolic, is alkali-soluble.

The above work does not establish the relative positions of the N-methyl group and the oxygen atom in the pyocyanine molecule. However, this point was settled by Hillemann,[30] who treated leuco-pyocyanine (VI) with oxalyl chloride in chloroform solution in the presence of pyridine, and obtained a cyclic product of structure VII, which separated from a mixture of pyridine and light petroleum as

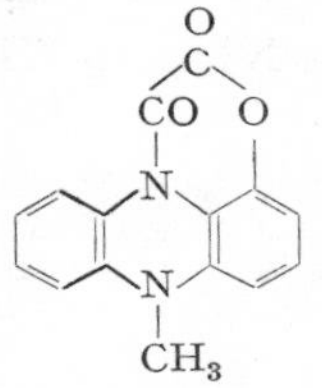

(VII)

brown needles, sintering at 209°, m.p. 218–220° (dec.) in a sealed capillary. This supports structure VI for leucopyocyanine and hence IV for pyocyanine itself. In the case of the latter compound, there is the possibility of resonance involving also the dipolar, phenol-betaine structure V and the physical properties, especially the dipole moment,[16] suggest that this latter form makes a substantial contribution to the resonance hybrid. Dipole association may well explain the molecular weight values determined by freezing point depression in organic solvents.

Reduction of pyocyanine to the colorless leuco compound VI, the dissociation constant of which (pK $=9.5$) is compatible with that of an ordinary phenolic hydroxyl group, occurs in acid solution by two

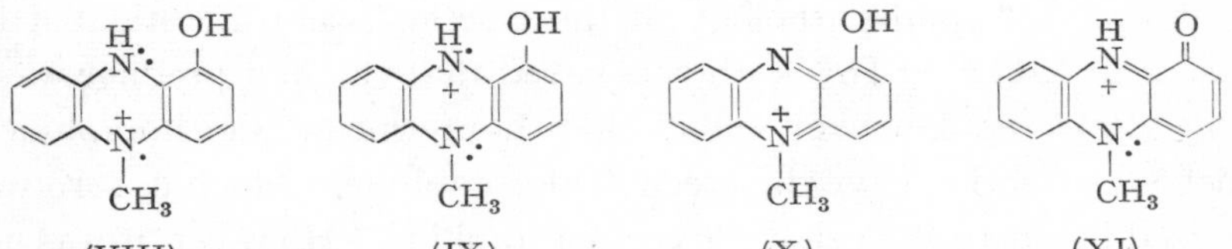

(VIII)   (IX)   (X)   (XI)

one-electron steps, the intermediate being a semiquinone, which is an ion-radical. This has already been discussed in Chapter III:2,B. The semiquinone can be represented as a resonance hybrid of structures VIII and IX; it arises from the reduced form by ejection of one electron. Further oxidation leads to the ejection of a second electron, giving X, which is the red cation present in solutions of pyocyanine in acid solution; when this solution is made alkaline, it becomes blue, a proton being ejected, giving pyocyanine (IV). The dissociation constant involved in the latter process is $pK = 5.0$; and the color change indicates a change in structure, which indicates that in acid solution the structure is essentially X rather than the tautomeric form XI.[31]

Pushkareva and Postovskiĭ have suggested for the intermediate stage one of the formulations XII and XIII (see Chapter III:2,D):[32]

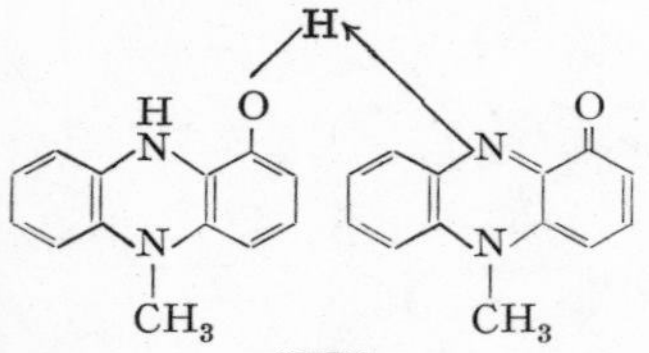

(XII) 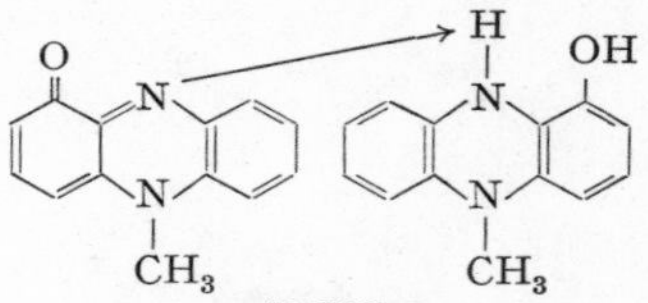   (XIII)

The antibiotic and physiological importance is discussed in Chapter XI.

2. Chlororaphine

A. Historical

In 1894, Guignard and Sauvageau isolated from worms a microorganism *(Bacillus chlororaphis* or *Pseudomonaschlororaphis)* that gave green ("chlororaphine") or yellow ("oxychlororaphine") crystals in culture fluids. The same organism was also isolated from spring and well waters from France and the conditions for its growth, as well as the morphology and pathology of the bacillus, were investigated by Lasseur in 1911.[33, 34] This author believed that the first product was a water-soluble yellow compound that he termed "xanthoraphine," which on reduction gave the green "chlororaphine," which in turn was oxidized by air to the yellow "oxychlororaphine." However, it was not until 1930, when the first work of Kögl and his collaborators was published,[35] that anything definite was known about the structure of the pigment produced. It was then shown that the so-called "xanthoraphine" was, in fact, identical with "oxychlororaphine".[36]

B. Physical Properties

(*1*) Chlororaphine forms green crystals; in the absence of oxygen, it melts with blackening at 225° and sublimes at 210° (in the presence of air, it gives a yellow sublimate). It is almost insoluble in water, carbon disulfide, chloroform, light petroleum, benzene, toluene and alkalis, sparingly soluble in methanol and ethanol, but readily soluble in acetone, phenol, aniline and acids. Solutions in organic solvents are yellow or brown; but addition of hydrochloric acid to a solution in acetone changes the color from yellow to emerald green. In 25% hydrochloric acid solution, it shows absorption maxima at 712, 641.5, 586 and 536 mμ.[36]

(*2*) Oxychlororaphine separates from acetone as yellow needles, m.p. 236.8°, which sublime in the absence of oxygen giving yellow crystals, m.p. 241°. It is insoluble in light petroleum, sparingly soluble in water, methanol, ethanol and ether, but moderately soluble in chloroform, aniline and acetic acid.[35]

C. preparation

Oxychlororaphine can be obtained by culture of *Bacillus chlororaphis* at 25° on a synthetic medium containing 2.5% of glycerol and 0.7% of asparagine as sole carbon sources, although various sugars and derived alcohols can be used in place of glycerol and the asparagine may be replaced by certain other nitrogenous compounds. The pigment is not formed at 35–37°,[37] although if the organism is first passed through the mouse the pigment can then be produced at this higher temperature. Both chlororaphine and oxychlororaphine may be present together, but can be separated by fractional crystallization from acetone, in which the latter is less soluble.[35] Four types of the organism have been described, and these give varying yields of the pigment.[38]

Chlororaphine and oxychlororaphine have also been isolated from old cultures of *Bacillus pyocyaneus*.[39, 40] Although the pigment can be obtained synthetically the yield is very low. See also references 41 and 42.

D. Structure

For oxychlororaphine, Lasseur found the formula $C_{14}H_{11}ON_3$ or $C_{15}H_{10}ON_4$; but reinvestigation by Kögl and Postowsky[35] established the composition $C_{13}H_9ON_3$. The latter authors were unable to acetylate oxychlororaphine, but found the substance to be weakly basic. On heating with 33% potassium hydroxide, 1 mole of ammonia per mole of oxychlororaphine was split off, forming an acid $C_{13}H_8O_2N_2$, m.p. 237°, which gave phenazine when distilled with soda-lime at 400°. They therefore concluded that oxychlororaphine was either phenazine-1- or 2-carboxamide, and proved it to be the former (XV) by synthesis. A mixture of nitrobenzene and anthranilic acid was heated with sodium hydroxide at 145–160°, giving phenazine-1-carboxylic acid (XIV) (see Chapter IV:6,A.). By the action of thionyl chloride, this was converted

(XIV)   (XV)

into the corresponding acid chloride, which, when treated with ammonia, gave phenazine-1-carboxamide (XV), which separated from methanol as lustrous, bright yellow needles, m.p. 241°, identical with oxychlororaphine. Clemo and McIlwain[43] have also synthesized this acid by oxidation of 1-methylphenazine.

Reduction of the synthetic phenazine-1-carboxamide with zinc dust in the presence of water gave a green crystalline product, identical with chlororaphine, and which Kögl believed to be a molecular compound of phenazine-1-carboxamide with its dihydro derivative, that is, a phenazhydrin $C_{26}H_{20}O_2N_6$. Reduction of phenazine-1-carboxamide with zinc dust and acetic acid gave the dihydro derivative,[35] which separated from chloroform as yellow leaflets, m.p. 197° (in nitrogen), turning green on exposure to the air for a few hours, and which gave a

brilliant orange fluorescence in ultraviolet radiation, whereas chlororaphine does not fluoresce.[44] Kögl and his collaborators suggested

H   CONH$_2$ CONH$_2$
N   N

N   N
H   H H
(XVI)   (XVII)

that the yellow compound was not 5,10-dihydrophenazine-1-carbox-
amide (XVI), but had structure XVII. When a solution of this was
mixed with one of phenazine-1-carboxamide in acetic acid, grass-green

⎡   CONH$_2$ CONH$_2$⎤ ⎡ H CONH$_2$ CONH$_2$⎤
│ N   N   │ │ N   N   │
│   │ │   │
│ N   N   │ │ N   N   │
⎣H H (XVIII)   ⎦ ⎣ H   (XIX)   ⎦

needles of chlororaphine were obtained. They therefore represented
chlororaphine as a phenazhydrin (XVIII) and carried out active-
hydrogen determinations in an effort to confirm this structure. Thus,
phenazine contains no active hydrogen, 5,10-dihydrophenazine contains two and phenazine-1-carboxamide contains one atom of active
hydrogen, per molecule. If chlororaphine had structure XIX, the
complex molecule should contain four atoms of active hydrogen but,
if XVIII, then only three. They actually found a value of three, which
they took as evidence in favor of XVIII. However, structure XVII is
very unlikely for dihydrochlororaphine, and Clemo and McIlwain[45]
suggested that the active-hydrogen values could be explained in terms
of structure XIX for chlororaphine, on the assumption of hydrogen-
bonding preventing one of the hydrogen atoms from being active (XX).
Unfortunately active-hydrogen values for the analogous product
derived from phenazine-2-carboxamide are not available. Birkofer[46]
has recently shown 5,10-dihydrophenazine-1-carboxamide to give only
two active hydrogen atoms, although the corresponding methyl ester
surprisingly gives two also. This hydrogen bonding could also account
for the stability to oxidation—thus, dihydrophenazine-2-carboxamide
is oxidized at room temperature, under conditions that leave chloro-

raphine unchanged. Moreover, this idea has recently received further support by the spectroscopic studies of Birkofer,[46] who has shown that, whereas phenazine, 1-methylphenazine and 1-phenazylcarbinol all form colorless dihydro derivatives, phenazine-1-carboxylic acid and its amide and esters form orange dihydro derivatives. Moreover, all these compounds yield both mono- and di-acetyl derivatives; but the absorption spectra of the products derived from the first group differ from those of the second (the non-hydrogenated phenazines all agree in spectral characteristics), and are against a structure such as XVII. Birkofer believes that these results are explicable in terms of structure XX for the dihydro compound. The monoacetyl derivative of 5,10-dihydrophenazine-1-carboxamide was shown to be acetylated in the 10-position by the formation of the cyclic product XXa, which could be further acetylated in position 5. Methyl-5,10-dihydrophenazine-1-carboxylate, when treated with alcoholic potassium hydroxide in the

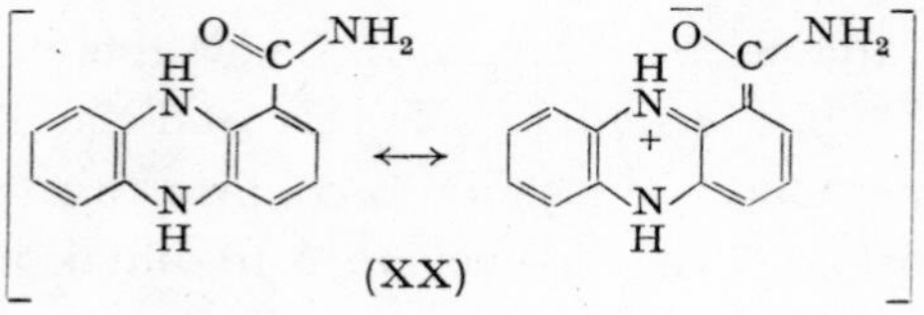

(XX)

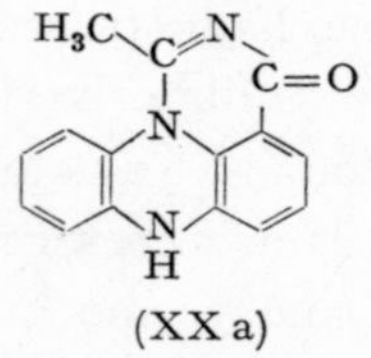

(XXa)   (XXb)

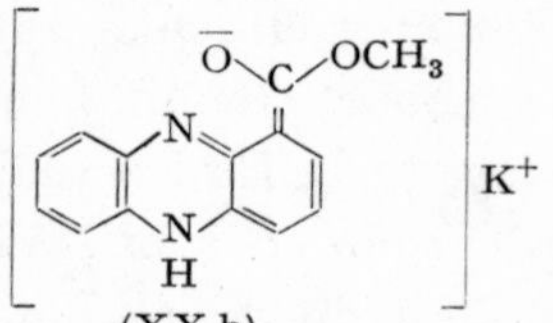

absence of oxygen, yields the interesting deep green salt XXb reminiscent of the intensely yellow sodium salt derived from glutaconic ester. Phenazine-2-carboxamide also forms an orange dihydro derivative (XXI). In spite of the above result, however, Dufraisse, Etienne and

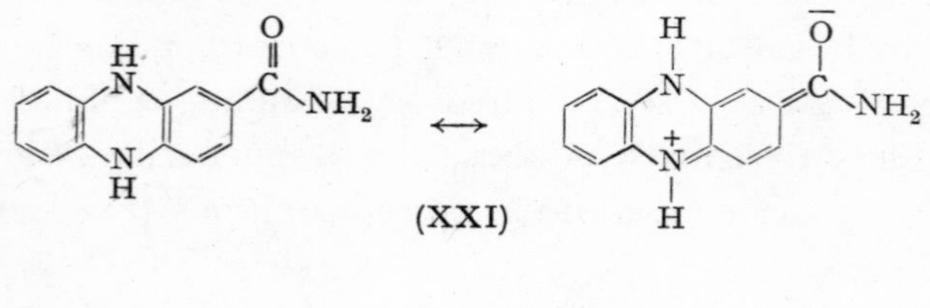

(XXI)

Toromanoff[47] have recently suggested that chlororaphine is a molecular compound of phenazine-1-carboxamide and its dihydro derivative in the ratio 3:1, confirmed by iodine titration.

The above refers to the structure of chlororaphine in the crystalline state. Solutions in organic solvents are yellow or brown, due to dissociation, as in the case of phenazhydrin, but yield grass-green crystals. Also, the yellow solution in acetone precipitates green crystals when diluted with water. Addition of hydrochloric acid to the acetone solution, on the other hand, changes the color to emerald green, due to the formation of a semiquinonoid salt. Thus Elema[48] showed that in acid solution (pH 1) phenazine-1-carboxamide undergoes reversible reduction by two one-electron steps, the initially slightly yellow solution becoming intensely emerald (semiquinone, XXII) and finally orange-yellow

(dihydro compound). In the pH range 4–10, however, a normal two-electron one-step process occurs, and no green color is produced at 50% reduction, although green crystals (presumably of the phenazhydrin) may be deposited. Elema therefore concluded that the semiquinone does not exist in aqueous solution at pH > 4; but Cattaneo, Sartori and Morellini,[42] from polarographic studies, detected its existence throughout pH 1.75–10.85, although to a lesser extent in the higher range.

E. Biosynthesis of Chlororaphine

Kögl, Tönnis and Groenewegen[36] found that the addition of phenazine-1-carboxylic acid to the medium in which *Bacillus chlororaphis* was growing increased the yield of phenazine-1-carboxamide isolated, although benzoic and nicotinic acids were not converted into the corresponding amides. In the case of the addition of picolinic acid, 51% was recovered unchanged and only 3% converted into the amide, although the yield of phenazine-1-carboxamide was considerably increased. Addition of pyrocatechol and pyrocatechol-3-carboxylic acid also increased the yield of phenazine-1-carboxamide.

3. Iodinin

A. Historical

The organism *Chromobacterium iodinum* was first isolated from milk by Davis,[49] and the name was proposed because of a violet, copper-glinting pigment occurring outside the organism at the later stages of its growth. The pigment was isolated in a pure state by Clemo and McIlwain[50] in 1938; and the name iodinin proposed by McIlwain in 1943.[51]

B. Physical Properties

Iodinin, $C_{12}H_8O_4N_2$, separates from chloroform as purple crystals with a coppery glint, m.p. 236°, that decompose with vigorous gas evolution and are insoluble in water. In chloroform solution, it shows an absorption maximum at 530 mμ.[50,52] The infrared absorption has also been recorded.[53]

C. Preparation

The bacteria were grown on a solid beer-wort-agar medium, which was incubated at 30° for 5 days and then kept at room temperature for 7–9 days, during which a deep purple layer of coppery luster developed. The pigment was removed from the surface of the medium by washing with water, and was then extracted with chloroform. The crystals that separated on concentration of the extract were recrystallized from chloroform. The homogeneity of the product was indicated by the failure to change its melting point by repeated recrystallization, and by its adsorption on alumina, which gave a single, sharp, narrow band. The average yield was 1 g./m.² of medium.[50]

D. Structure

Analytical data indicate the empirical formula $C_{12}H_8O_4N_2$ for iodinin; but its solubility in camphor is too low to permit the determination of the molecular weight by Rast's method. It is not basic, being insoluble in acids except concentrated sulfuric acid; but it is phenolic in properties, being soluble in sodium hydroxide solution, giving a brilliant blue solution that deposits green crystals of the sodium salt. Under the microscope, the deposit is seen to dissolve transitorily in water to a rich blue solution, which almost immediately, due to hydrolysis, deposits purple crystals of the original pigment.

Alkaline solutions of the pigment are reduced by dithionite, the color changing through red to yellow; the last stage only is reversible by air or persulfate oxidation. The pigment and its reduction product are precipitated from the alkaline solutions by excess of bicarbonate or sulfur dioxide. The reduction product is best obtained by hydrogenation in alcoholic solution in the presence of platinum and separates after filtration and concentration of the solution as golden plates, melting on rapid heating in a sealed tube at 260° and having the composition $C_{12}H_{10}O_2N_2$. This product is unstable and on recrystallization from ethanol or ethyl acetate yields a different compound, $C_{12}H_8O_2N_2$, forming yellow prisms, m.p. 273–274°.

The pigment was shown to be a phenazine derivative by zinc dust distillation of its reduction product, when phenazine itself was obtained. The facile dehydrogenation of the reduction product suggests the 5,10-dihydrophenazine nature of the first-formed compound. The product is still phenolic; it gives a green coloration with ferric chloride in alcoholic solution and forms a diacetyl derivative that separates from ethanol as light yellow needles, m.p. 234°.

The above results, together with the fact that iodinin liberates iodine from potassium iodide in acetic acid solution, suggest that iodinin might be a dihydroxyphenazinedi-N-oxide, although up to 1938, when this work was carried out, phenazinedi-N-oxides were still unknown (certain mono-N-oxides had been synthesized by Wohl's method). Clemo and McIlwain, however, converted 1-phenazinol into its di-N-oxide by the action of hydrogen peroxide in acetic acid, and the product showed great similarity to the natural pigment. Later,

McIlwain[51] demonstrated the reconversion of the reduction product $C_{12}H_8O_2N_2$ (a dihydroxyphenazine) into iodinin by reaction with perbenzoic acid in benzene solution. Moreover, the phenazinedi-*N*-oxides liberate iodine from acidified potassium iodide solution. They therefore concluded that iodinin was probably 1,2-phenazinediol-5,10-dioxide. The evidence that the hydroxyl groups are in the 1,2-positions will not be discussed here, as this formulation was disproved by Hegedüs,[54] who synthesized 1,2-phenazinediol, its dimethyl ether and diacetate and showed them to differ from the analogous products obtained from the pigment. Independent syntheses of 1,2-dimethoxy-phenazine were reported by Slack and Slack[55] and by Clemo and Daglish,[56] the melting point recorded in each case being 138–139°, whereas the product of Hegedüs definitely melts at 145°, an anomaly that remains unexplained.[53] The action of diazomethane in a mixture of ether and methanol on the phenazinediol derived from iodinin yields a dimethyl ether that separates from benzene as yellow needles, m.p. 245–246°.[53, 57] Clemo and Daglish also showed this to differ from 1,4-dimethoxyphenazine, synthesized by Slack and Slack.[55] King, Clark and Davis[58] also synthesized 1,4-dimethoxyphenazine and demethylated it by aluminum chloride to the dihydroxy compound, the properties of which differed from those of the product obtained from iodinin. When Clemo and Daglish[59] synthesized 1,3-dihydroxy-phenazine and found this also to be different from the naturally derived product, it became clear that the two hydroxyl groups could not be present in the same benzene ring. They[53, 57] therefore condensed 3-methoxy-*o*-quinone with 2,3-diaminoanisole to give a mixture of 1,6- and 1,9-dimethoxyphenazines (**XXIII** and **XXIV**, respectively), which were separated chromatographically on alumina, and one of which

proved identical with the dimethoxyphenazine derived from iodinin. In view of the work of Flett,[60] which showed that infrared absorption spectra differentiated between the isomeric dihydroxyanthraquinones, it was hoped that the same method might distinguish between the 1,6- and 1,9-dihydroxyphenazines (obtained by demethylation of the synthetic methyl ethers); but this proved not to be the case.

After many unsuccessful attempts to prepare either 1,6- or 1,9-dimethoxyphenazine by an unambiguous synthesis, the former isomer was eventually obtained by condensing 3-bromo-2-nitroanisole with 2-amino-3-nitroanisole to give 3,6′-dimethoxy-2,2′-dinitrodiphenylamine (XXV), which was hydrogenated in ethanol in the presence of platinum to the diamino compound, which underwent cyclization on oxidation with ferric chloride. The resulting 1,6-dimethoxyphenazine was identical with the product derived from the pigment.

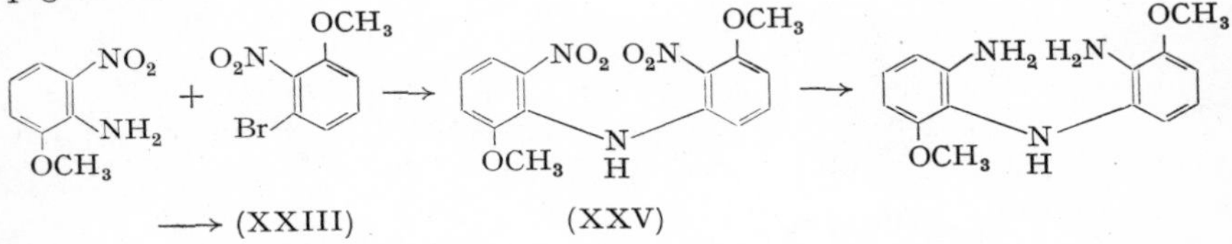

Thus, iodinin is 1,6-phenazinediol-5,10-dioxide (XXVI) and this

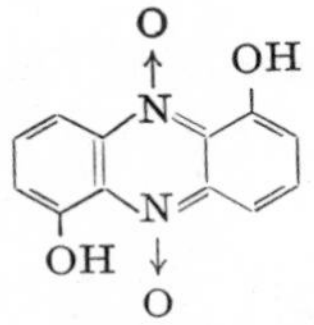

synthesis, considered in conjunction with McIlwain's reconversion of the dihydroxyphenazine to iodinin, constitutes a complete synthesis of the latter. Another synthesis has been described by Serebryanyĭ, Chernetskiĭ and Kiprianov,[52, 61] who obtained 1,6-diethoxyphenazine (XXVII) by boiling a toluene solution of o-nitrophenetole and o-ethoxyaniline in the presence of potassium hydroxide (a similar synthesis was later reported by Pachter and Kloetzel[62] and by Yoshioka and Kidani[63]). This was dealkylated by treatment with hydrobromic acid at 130–140°, to 1,6-phenazinediol (XXVIII), which was purified through the diacetyl derivative (m.p. 240–241°), and which separated from benzene as

golden yellow plates, m.p. 280–281° (sealed tube). Treatment of this
with perbenzoic acid in benzene afforded a product identical with

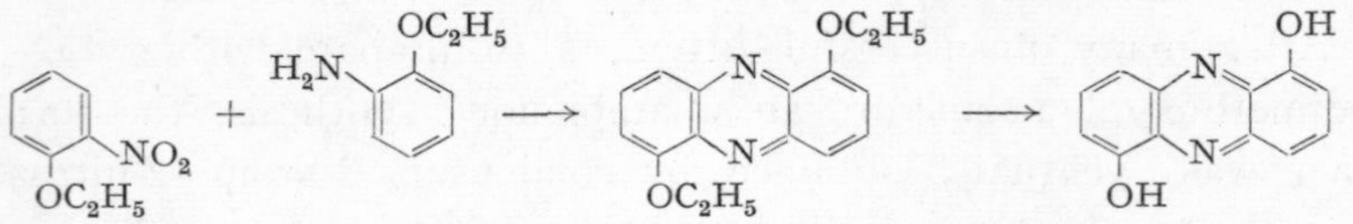

(XXVII)   (XXVIII)

iodinin. The synthesis of a mixture of 1,7- and 1,9-dimethoxyphenazines
by condensation of *m*-anisidine with *o*-nitroanisole and of a mixture
of the 1,6- and 1,9- compounds from 3-methoxy-*o*-quinone and 3-
methoxy-*o*-phenylenediamine is also reported.[64, 65] See also reference 66.

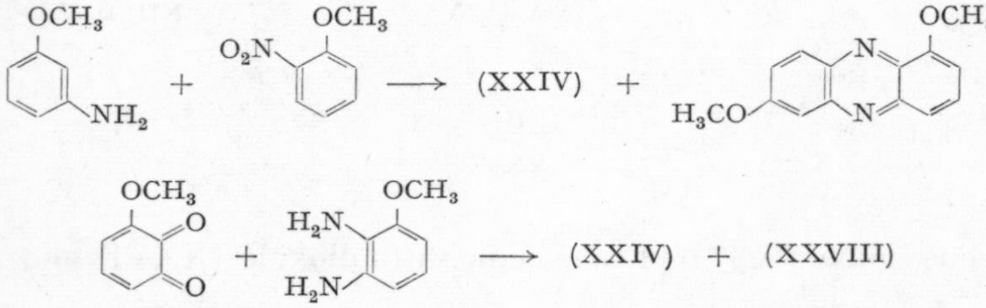

An interesting, although purely speculative, scheme for the
biogenetic formation of iodinin from an unstable phenazine peroxide
(XXIX) has been suggested.[67]

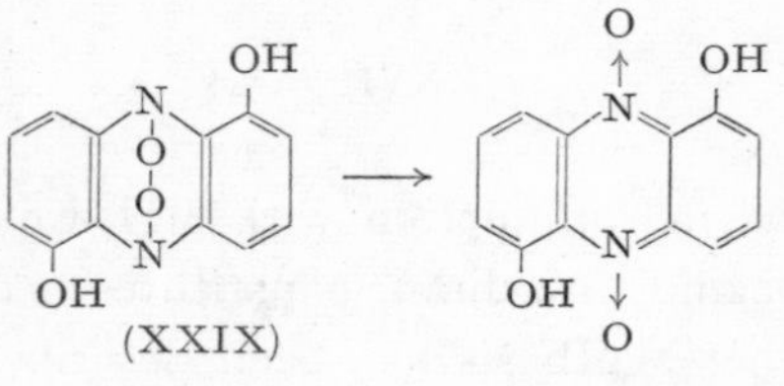

(XXIX)

References

1. H. R. Seddon, *Dept. Agr., N. S. Wales, Sci. Bull.*, No. 54, 96 (1937); through
   Chem. Abstracts, **32**, 4269 (1938).
2. Fordos, *Compt. rend.*, **51**, 215 (1860).
3. Fordos, *Compt. rend.*, **56**, 1128 (1863).
4. C. Gessard, *Ann. inst. Pasteur*, **4**, 88 (1890).
5. C. Gessard, *Ann. inst. Pasteur*, **5**, 737 (1891).
6. C. Gessard, *Ann. inst. Pasteur*, **6**, 801 (1892).

7. C. Gessard, *Ann. inst. Pasteur*, **15**, 817 (1901).
8. C. Gessard, *Ann. inst. Pasteur*, **16**, 313 (1902).
9. Ledderhose, *Deut. Zeit. Chirurgie*, **28**, 201 (1888).
10. H. McCombie and H. A. Scarborough, *J. Chem. Soc.*, **123**, 3279 (1923).
11. F. Wrede and E. Strack, *Z. physiol. Chem.*, **140**, 1 (1924); *Chem. Zentr.*, **1924**, II, 2664.
12(a). F. Wrede and E. Strack, *Z. physiol. Chem.*, **181**, 58 (1929); *Chem. Zentr.*, **1929**, II, 50, and *Chem. Abstracts*, **23**, 2717 (1929).
12(b). G. Farber, *Sbornik Ceskoslov. Akad. Zemedelske*, **23**, 355 (1951); through *Chem. Abstracts*, **45**, 9605 (1951).
13. A. R. Surrey, *Org. Syntheses*, **26**, 86 (1946).
14. F. Wrede and E. Strack, *Z. physiol. Chem.*, **142**, 103 (1925); *Chem. Zentr.*, **1925**, I, 2013.
15. O. Ehrismann and W. Noethling, *Biochem. Z.*, **284**, 376 (1936).
16. K. A. Jensen and C. H. Holten, *Acta Chem. Scand.*, **3**, 1446 (1949); *Chem. Abstracts*, **44**, 10409 (1950).
17. H. Katz, *Z. Physik*, **87**, 238 (1933).
18. B. Elema and A. C. Sanders, *Rec. trav. chim.*, **50**, 796 (1931).
19. M. O. Burton, J. J. R. Campbell and B. A. Eagles, *Can. J. Research*, **26 C**, 15 (1948).
20. M. O. Burton, B. A. Eagles and J. J. R. Campbell, *Can. J. Research*, **25 C**, 121 (1947).
21. J. V. King, J. J. R. Campbell and B. A. Eagles, *Can. J. Research*, **26 C**, 514 (1948).
22. G. Young, *J. Bact.*, **54**, 109 (1947).
23. A. Grosser and W. Friderich, *Z. Naturforsch.*, **3 b**, 425 (1948); through *Chem. Abstracts*, **43**, 8435 (1949).
24(a). R. Schoental, *Brit. J. Exptl. Path.*, **22**, 137 (1941).
24(b). H. Katagiri, T. Shibutani and M. Kurachi, *Bull. Inst. Chem. Research, Kyoto Univ.*, **25**, 71 (1951); through *Chem. Abstracts*, **46**, 4607 (1952).
24(c). W. S. Moos, *J. Bact.*, **62**, 767 (1951).
24(d). E. E. Hays, I. C. Wells, P. A. Katyman, C. K. Cain, F. A. Jacob, S. A. Thayer, E. A. Doisy, W. L. Gaby, E. C. Roberts, R. D. Muir, C. J. Carroll, L. R. Jones and N. J. Wade, *J. Biol. Chem.*, **159**, 725 (1945).
25. F. Wrede and E. Strack, *Z. physiol. Chem.*, **177**, 177 (1928); *Chem. Zentr.*, **1928**, II, 2027; *Chem. Abstracts*, **22**, 3891 (1928).
26. F. Wrede, *Deut. med. Wochschr.*, **50**, 1649 (1924); through *Chem. Zentr.*, **1925**, I, 678.
27. F. Wrede and E. Strack, *Ber.*, **62 B**, 2051 (1929).
28. H. McIlwain, *J. Chem. Soc.*, **1937**, 1704.
29. L. Michaelis, *J. Biol. Chem.*, **92**, 211 (1931).
30. H. Hillemann, *Ber.*, **71 B**, 46 (1938).
31. L. Michaelis, in *The Enzymes*, edited by J. B. Sumner and K. Myrbäck, Academic Press, New York, 1951. Vol. 2, Part 1, p. 27.
32. Z. V. Pushkareva and I. Y. Postovskiĭ, *J. Gen. Chem. U.S.S.R.*, **8**, 158 (1938); through *Chem. Zentr.*, **1939**, I, 4328, and *Chem. Abstracts*, **32**, 5405 (1938).
33. A. P. Lasseur, Thèses Faculté des Sciences de l'Université de Nancy (1911); through *Centr. Bakt. Parasitenk.*, *Abt. I*, **53**, *Ref.*, 49 (1912).
34. P. Lasseur and F. Girardet, *Contribution à l'étude des pigments microbiens*, Nancy, 1914.
35. F. Kögl and J. J. Postowsky, *Ann.*, **480**, 280 (1930).
36. F. Kögl, B. Tönnis and H. J. Groenewegen, *Ann.*, **497**, 265 (1932).

37. L. Mercier and P. Lasseur, *Compt. rend.*, **152**, 1415 (1911).
38. P. Lasseur and A. Dupaix-Lasseur, *Trav. lab. microbiol. faculté pharm. Nancy*, **9**, 35 (1936); through *Chem. Abstracts*, **31**, 1844 (1937).
39. L. Birkofer, *Chem. Ber.*, **80**, 212 (1947).
40. L. Birkofer and A. Birkofer, *Klin. Wochschr.*, **26**, 528 (1948); *Chem. Abstracts*, **44**, 8400 (1950).
41. P. Lasseur, *Trav. lab. microbiol. faculté pharm. Nancy*, **7**, 31 (1934); through *Chem. Abstracts*, **30**, 1413 (1936).
42. C. Cattaneo, G. Sartori and M. Morellini, *Gazz. chim. ital.*, **77**, 381 (1947); through *Chem. Abstracts*, **42**, 3018 (1948).
43. G. R. Clemo and H. McIlwain, *J. Chem. Soc.*, **1934**, 1991.
44. C. Dhéré, *Compt. rend. soc. biol.*, **115**, 1461 (1934); *Chem. Abstracts*, **28**, 4438 (1934).
45. G. R. Clemo and H. McIlwain, *J. Chem. Soc.*, **1935**, 738.
46(a). L. Birkofer, *Chem. Ber.*, **85**, 1023 (1952).
46(b). L. Birkofer, *Angew. Chem.*, **64**, 111 (1952).
46(c). L. Birkofer, *Angew. Chem.*, **63**, 486 (1951).
47. C. Dufraisse, A. Etienne and E. Toromanoff, *Compt. rend.*, **235**, 920 (1952).
48. B. Elema, *Rec. trav. chim.*, **52**, 569 (1933).
49. J. G. Davis, *Zentr. Bakt., Parasitenk., Abt. II*, **100**, 273 (1939); through *Chem. Abstracts*, **33**, 6383 (1939).
50. G. R. Clemo and H. McIlwain, *J. Chem. Soc.*, **1938**, 479.
51. H. McIlwain, *J. Chem. Soc.*, **1943**, 322.
52. S. B. Serebryanyĭ, V. P. Chernetskiĭ and A. I. Kiprianov, *Doklady Akad. Nauk S.S.S.R.*, **70**, 645 (1950); through *Chem. Abstracts*, **45**, 4249 (1951).
53. G. R. Clemo and A. F. Daglish, *J. Chem. Soc.*, **1950**, 1481.
54. B. Hegedüs, *Jubilee Vol. Emil Barell*, **1946**, 388; *Chem. Abstracts*, **41**, 6262 (1947).
55. P. Z. Slack and R. Slack, *Nature*, **160**, 437 (1947).
56. G. R. Clemo and A. F. Daglish, *Nature*, **160**, 752 (1947).
57. G. R. Clemo and A. F. Daglish, *Nature*, **162**, 776 (1948).
58. F. E. King, N. G. Clark and P. M. H. Davis, *J. Chem. Soc.*, **1949**, 3012.
59. G. R. Clemo and A. F. Daglish, *J. Chem. Soc.*, **1948**, 2318.
60. M. St. C. Flett, *J. Chem. Soc.*, **1948**, 1441.
61. S. B. Serebryanyĭ, *Zhur. Obshcheĭ Khim. (J. Gen. Chem.)*, **22**, 702 (1952); through *Chem. Abstracts*, **47**, 5408 (1953).
62. I. J. Pachter and M. C. Kloetzel, *J. Am. Chem. Soc.*, **73**, 4958 (1951).
63. I. Yoshioka and Y. Kidani, *J. Pharm. Soc. Japan*, **72**, 847 (1952); through *Chem. Abstracts*, **47**, 3320 (1953).
64. A. I. Kiprianov, S. B. Serebryanyĭ and V. P. Chernetskiĭ, *Doklady Akad. Nauk S.S.S.R.*, **69**, 651 (1949); through *Chem. Abstracts*, **46**, 4010 (1952).
65. S. B. Serebryanyĭ and V. P. Chernetskiĭ, *Zhur. Obshcheĭ Khim. (J. Gen. Chem.)*, **21**, 2033 (1951); through *Chem. Abstracts*, **46**, 6654 (1952).
66. I. Yoshioka and Y. Kidani, *J. Pharm. Soc. Japan*, **72**, 1301 (1952); through *Chem. Abstracts*, **47**, 10542 (1953).
67. B. Witkop and H. M. Kissmanm *J. Am. Chem. Soc.*, **75**, 1975 (1953).

CHAPTER XI

The Biological Properties of Phenazine and Its Derivatives

1. Introduction

Biological interest in phenazine compounds has extended throughout the period in which their chemistry has been developed, and has given much impetus to chemical studies. Their first biological application was that of safranines in staining. This application has been maintained; phenazine compounds still find important application in staining techniques, those of greatest current interest being the relative specific coloration of subcellular particles, including mitochondria, by Janus green and neutral red. It has been found that the more basic is the dye, the lower is the concentration necessary to stain mitochondria supravitally; and hence it has been suggested that the more basic dyes (as cations) penetrate the cells more readily.[1,2] (See also Chapter VI:3,E and Chapter VII:2,B,D and E.)

Natural occurence of phenazine compounds has been recorded only among bacteria; the blue pus of wounds was noted early though only later was the coloration realized as being due to a bacterial product, and only relatively recently has the product been characterized as a phenazine derivative. This subject also continues to develop.

The function first ascribed to naturally occurring phenazine compounds was that of respiratory catalysts. Pyocyanine certainly has such an action both in bacterial culture and in separated enzyme systems. Pyocyanine was also observed quite early to be antibacterial and the possibility of such a function extending to other phenazine compounds was noted during the recent interest in antibiotic agents.

After this observation, it was natural that attempts should be made to apply the antibiotic properties of phenazine derivatives, and several such examinations have recently been made. These were not, however, the first attempt to inhibit microorganisms with phenazine compounds, for, following limited successes with methylene blue, phenazine as well as acridine compounds were examined in experimental chemotherapy.

2. Natural Occurrence of Phenazines

Pseudomonas aeruginosa is one of the oldest known examples of a microorganism producing substances antagonistic to other bacteria.[3] Emmerich and Löw[4] in 1899 drew attention to the fact that old cultures of this organism were highly bactericidal to a number of other Gram-positive and Gram-negative bacteria and noticed that such cultures, when concentrated *in vacuo*, had the interesting property of causing quick and complete lysis of thick suspensions of *Vibrio comma* and *Bacillus anthracis*. They ascribed this effect to the action of an enzyme they termed "pyocyanase" and a preparation of this name appears to have been sold in Germany until 1936 or later, although its efficacy is very doubtful.[5] Recent investigations by Hettche[6–8] and Schoental[9] into the nature of pyocyanase have made it clear that the antibacterial activity of old cultures of *Pseudomonas aeruginosa* is due to the presence of several different substances, none of which is of enzymatic nature. The blue pigment pyocyanine and its yellow degradation product 1-phenazinol are bactericidal. Five other compounds have been isolated; and the structures of three of these determined.[10] It has recently become clear that oxychlororaphine is also an essential constituent of pyocyanase.[11(a)] Pyocyanine, like many basic dyes, is not only strongly bactericidal, but is also toxic and therefore not promising for therapeutic use. The concentrations of pyocyanine found on human burns are capable of causing toxic effects on skin *in vitro*.[11(b)]

Cultures of *Pseudomonas aeruginosa* incubated for longer than about ten days turn brownish-yellow and, from these, 1-phenazinol can be isolated.[9,12,13] The latter compound is also formed when alkaline solutions of pyocyanine are allowed to stand in air. Although it is less toxic than pyocyanine, its antibacterial activity is lower, and it is of low solubility.

The natural occurrence of chlororaphine and iodinin, both of which have bacteriostatic action, has been mentioned in Chapter X.

3. Biochemical and Biological Effects of Phenazines

A. Phenazines with Separated Enzyme and Cell-Free Systems

Phenazine derivatives, in common with many other basic substances, have been known for some time to combine with proteins, including enzymes. Thus, interaction between safranine and proteolytic enzymes was studied by Marston.[14-16] Complexes are also formed *in vitro* with heparin and these do not possess heparin activity.[17,18]

Interaction between phenazines and biological systems has most commonly been shown not by separating such a complex (though such may well exist) but by observing changed behavior of the system on addition of the phenazine. Of this category are an interesting series of interactions with various dehydrogenases. Pyocyanine is the substance most fully studied from this point of view. Pyocyanine inhibits succinic dehydrogenase from heart muscle,[19] but accelerates aerobic oxidation of their respective substrates by malic, lactic, hexosemonophosphoric, phosphohexonic and α-hydroxyglutaric dehydrogenases.[20-22] This acceleration is due to reduction of the phenazine by the enzyme-substrate system and its reoxidation by oxygen. This is the most clearly understood of the biological actions of phenazine derivatives. Their ability to do this depends on the reversibility of their oxidation and reduction at values of pH and E_h (oxidation-reduction potential) encountered biologically.[23] (For general accounts, see references 24 and 25.)

Many aspects of such activities remain, however, to be understood. This appears when one considers the specificity of the dehydrogenases already named for different hydrogen carriers. Phenazines are outstanding as carriers for the α-hydroxyglutaric dehydrogenase, many other substances of similar E_h being relatively inactive. Among phenazines, the N-ethyl quaternary salts were most active, and the corresponding methyl compounds slightly less so; but N-methyl-2-

phenazinone was almost inactive. These quaternary salts are also active with the hexosemonophosphate and phosphohexonic systems; but the natural alloxazine carrier is more effective. With malic or lactic dehydrogenases, the phenazine compound studied, pyocyanine, was not markedly more active than other carriers.

From this it would appear that the carriers enter into a sufficiently close relationship with at least certain of the dehydrogenase proteins for structural factors to become important in their action. There is a very large difference in the effectiveness of 1- and 2-phenazinol derivatives in coupling with α-hydroxyglutaric dehydrogenase.[21]

Other enzymes, like succinic dehydrogenase, are inhibited by phenazine derivatives. This occurs in carboxylase with 5-methylphenazinium chloride, but not with phenosafranine or pyocyanine,[19, 20] and occurs also in cozymase-degrading enzyme with a variety of phenazines.[26, 27] On the other hand, pyocyanine inhibits the bacterial diamine oxidases.[28]

There are relatively few reports of separated enzyme systems causing changes in phenazines other than their reversible oxidation and reduction. Indophenoloxidase preparations from heart muscle have, however, been found to convert 5-methylphenazinium chloride to a substance with the properties of N-methyl-2-phenazinone.[20]

See also references 29–35.

B. Phenazines and the Metabolism of Cells and Tissues

McIlwain[27] has shown that phenazine derivatives may be actively absorbed by animal tissues, reaching there concentrations 50–300 times those of the surrounding medium. Processes dependent on the metabolism of the tissue are involved in this, in addition to any staining or direct combination with tissue constituents.

Many effects in intact tissues parallel those in simple systems sufficiently for the latter to be regarded as the basis of the former. Thus, pyocyanine is acting as a carrier in increasing 20-fold the oxygen uptake of bacterial suspensions,[36–40] and this is probably a way in which the pigment can be of functional value to the organism that produces it. Increase in respiration with phenazine dyes has also been observed in systems including animal tissue.[41, 42] This increase in respiration is dependent on the presence of glucose; but pyocyanine can partly overcome the inhibition of oxygen uptake caused by the presence of, for example, sodium fluoride or azide.[43-47]

Other aspects of the action of pyocyanine and other phenazine derivatives on tissue metabolism indicate more complex effects. Concomitantly with the increased respiration with glucose as substrate, the formation of lactic acid may under different circumstances increase or decrease.[48, 49] The decrease is understandable through the effect described above of pyocyanine in relation to lactic dehydrogenase. The increase must have some other explanation.

The ability to increase aerobic acid formation by certain tissues is an outstanding property of several other phenazines. This was first recognized in phenosafranine with cerebral cortex, embryonic and carcinomatous tissues[50, 51] and was attributed to interference with cell catalysts such as cozymase. Similar properties were indeed found in compounds more closely related to cozymase and also in neutral red and Janus green. In searching for a basis for this, these substances as well as phenosafranine were found to inhibit an enzymatic breakdown of cozymase. Quantitative correlation existed between the concentrations of inhibitors active on cozymase degradation and an aerobic formation of lactic acid.[27]

Phenazines also inhibit the phosphorylation normally associated with respiration in cerebral[52] and kidney[53] preparations.

Phenazines may themselves undergo chemical change, other than reversible oxidation and reduction, during their interaction with tissues. Thus, N-methylphenazinium salts were probably converted into the N-methyl-2-phenazinone by tissue slices in oxygen.[54]

C. Phenazines and Whole Organisms

Phenazine derivatives affect the growth and viability of a wide range of microorganisms. Pyocyanine as carrier can accelerate the growth of *Pseudomonas aeruginosa*. It and the other naturally occurring phenazine pigments can also inhibit the growth of a variety of microorganisms.

Inhibition by pyocyanine of the growth of the following organisms has been recorded: *Vibrio comma, V. metchnikovii, Micrococcus pyogenes* var. *aureus (Staphylococcus aureus), M. hemolyticus, M. lysodeikticus, Bacillus anthracis, B. subtilis, Corynebacterium diphtheriae, Escherichia coli, Mycobacterium smegmatis, Brucella abortus, B. suis* and *Sarcina lutea*,[5,11,55,56] as well as amebas and paramecia.[57] The development of resistance to pyocyanine has also been noted[58]; and the effect on the antibiotic action of pyocyanine of sulfhydryl compounds (for example, cysteine) which cause reduction has been studied.[59–61]

1-Phenazinol exhibits bactericidal action towards *Vibrio comma* and *Micrococcus pyogenes* var. *aureus* and inhibits the growth of many bacteria, including anaerobes.[9,11,12,62,63] Its tuberculostatic activity is increased in the presence of cupric ions[64]; and its use in *Brucella abortus* infections and bovine mastitis has been discussed.[12]

Chlororaphine inhibits the growth of *Streptococci*[65]; and oxychloro-raphine is bacteriostatic to *Bacillus anthracis* in concentrations of $2 \times 10^{-5}\ M$,[11] but phenazine-2-carboxamide is inactive, although it shows higher activity against *Mycobacterium tuberculosis* typ. *gallinaceus*.[66] Iodinin inhibits the growth of some pathogenic bacteria.[67–71] Thus, it completely inhibits the growth of streptococci in concentrations of 1.5 to $2 \times 10^{-6}\ M$. The inhibition is relatively little influenced by extracts of many natural materials but is antagonized by certain naphthaquinone and anthraquinone derivatives. It is also effective against micrococci; and at the highest concentrations which can be obtained readily $(4 \times 10^{-5}\ M)$ it shows a certain tuberculostatic activity. It seems that, when organisms overcome inhibition due to iodinin, the N-oxide is destroyed, probably by reduction.

The inhibitory action of phenazine and a number of its synthetic derivatives against a variety of different organisms has been investigated; but, on the whole, the results have not been very promising except in a few cases. Phenazine differs from certain bacteriostatic aminoacridines and di- and tri-phenylmethane dyes in that, unlike the latter, it does not form apparently stable semiquinones in aqueous solution in the pH region around 7; it has been suggested that this might be related to its comparative lack of bacteriostatic activity.[72] Of fifty compounds (mostly dyes) tested by Martin[73] for antibacterial power against *Micrococcus pyogenes* var. *aureus*, it was found that the oxazine and thiazine nuclei conferred greater power than did the azine nucleus. (See also reference 74.) Neutral red was one of the first phenazines to be investigated from this point of view. It has for long been used in vital staining, but affects cell division and is toxic, the effects being stronger in light than in the dark (photodynamic action).[75-80] The toxic effects of neutral red, safranine and Janus green have been studied.[81] Safranine has been found to prevent the growth of Gram-positive bacteria,[82] to kill bacterial spores[83] and to show some promise in the chemotherapy of brucillosis, although it is very toxic.[84] It has also been found to be an efficient photosensitizing dye on certain Gram-negative organisms.[85] Anti-*Micrococcus* bacteriophage is reversibly inactivated by safranine.[86] In dilutions of about 10^5, safranine is harmless to fish and other aquatic animals.[87] Methylene violet has been found to be bacteriostatic to selected strains of *Vibrio comma*,[88] to hemolytic streptococci and to *Micrococcus pyogenes* var. *aureus*. Of ten phenazine derivatives tested by Schales, Schales and Friedman,[89] the highest activity against *M. pyogenes* var. *aureus* was exhibited by 1,4-dichloro-2,3-phenazinediol, but none inhibited the growth of *Escherichia coli* in concentrations of about $5 \times 10^{-4} M$. See also references 90 and 91. Phenazine itself has no antimalarial or analgesic value[92]; but its metho- and etho- salts are mildly active against bacteria *in vitro*, and the 5,10-dioxide inhibits the growth of streptococci in concentrations of the order of 4×10^{-5} to $10^{-4} M$.[71] See also reference 63. A series of compounds of structures (I), where $R=H$, Me, MeO or Cl, $R'=H$ or Me and $n=2$ or 3, have been tested against

$$R'-CH-(CH_2)_n-NEt_2$$

(I)

malarial parasites in ducklings and chicks,[93] but had only low activities. Janus green B and another safranine azoderivative have been reported to be effective against the influenza virus in mice[94]; and various other compounds, including mercurated safranine and neutral red derivatives, have been claimed to be of therapeutic value.[95-97]

The azine dyes were found, in 1930, to have a very slight therapeutic effect against tuberculosis[98] and a study in 1948 by Iland[70] showed phenazine-5,10-dioxide in concentrations of $5 \times 10^{-6}\ M$ to inhibit the growth of *Mycobacterium tuberculosis* for eight days. Of the other derivatives tested by the latter worker, iodinin ($10^{-5}\ M$) was the next most effective, followed by 1,2,3,4-tetrahydrophenazine-5,10-dioxide ($2 \times 10^{-4}\ M$), phenazine-5-oxide ($10^{-4}\ M$) and 1,2,3,4-tetrahydrophenazine ($5 \times 10^{-4}\ M$). Neutral red also has an effect.[99, 100] Barry and his collaborators[101–105] noticed that the antitubercular action of 2-aminodiphenylamine was increased when an aqueous solution of a salt was kept for some weeks with occasional warming, due to the formation of a 2-amino-3-anilino-10-phenylphenazinium salt (II). The product was tested against a number of bacteria, and, of those tested, it was most effective against *Mycobacterium tuberculosis*, which it

(II)

inhibited at a dilution of 2×10^7 in broth or 3×10^6 in the presence of human serum. It was also very effective against *Mycobacterium smegmatis* and *Corynebacterium diptheriae*, but less active against *Micrococcus pyogenes* var. *aureus*, *Streptococcus faecalis*, *Str. pyogenes*, *Str. mitis*, *Vibrio 10*, *Salmonella typhosa* and *Escherichia coli* (in descending order). They also prepared similar dyes from certain substituted 2-aminodiphenylamines; but the products were less active. A small-scale preliminary clinical trial has shown II to be comparable with streptomycin in the treatment of renal tuberculosis.[106] It has also shown promise in the treatment of leprosy.[107] Activity in the case of 2,3-diaminophenazine ($2.5 \times 10^{-4}\ M$) has also been reported.[108] Carl and Marquardt[109] also found that 2-amino-3-anilino-10-phenylphenazinium chloride was active in concentrations of $10^{-7}\ M$, and reported a direct relationship between the bacteriostatic activities of most of the active antitubercular drugs and their abilities to form copper complexes. Sorkin and Roth[64] have recently reported that 1-phenazinol has tuberculostatic activity, which is increased in the presence of cupric ions (M/5000), so that it is then effective in concentrations of M/20,000. Birkofer has reported high activity against *M. tuberculosis* typ. *gallinaceus* in the case of phenazine-1-carboxyhydrazide and phenazine-1-carboxaldehyde thiosemicarbazone and somewhat lower activity with phenazine-1-carboxylic acid.[66, 110] Smith and Emmart[111] found that the tubercle bacillus when grown on Kirchner's medium produced a fluorescent substance resembling riboflavin and that this increased progressively with growth. 2,4-Diamino-5,10-dihydro-7,8-dimethyl-10-ribitylphenazine inhibited growth and possibly riboflavin production.[112] This latter compound has also been found to inhibit completely the utilization of riboflavin by *Lactobacillus casei*.[113] A solution of induline (0.5%) or nigrosulfine (1%) is stated to retard somewhat the development of experimental tuberculosis in rabbits[114]; and positive results against cases of tuberculosis in animals have been reported for safranine and Induline 3B.[115] A study of the adsorption of indulines on the waxy surface of the tubercle bacillus has suggested that the dye is selectively adsorbed and slows down or stops growth.[116] For a review of the chemotherapy of tuberculosis see reference 117.

Neutral red was found to be inactive and methylene violet slightly active when tested for chemotherapeutic activity against infections of *Plasmodium berghei*.[118]

In the flocculation test for syphilis, Janus green has both a sensitizing and indicator action, the dye being taken up by the precipitate, leaving a clear solution.[119] The effect of dyes on the tobacco mosaic virus has been studied. The safranines generally inactivate the virus, with formation of precipitates.[120] Neutral red has been found to be inhibitory to virus tumor tissue from the roots of *Rumex acetosa*.[121(a)] Janus green has a neutralizing effect against foot and mouth disease *in vitro*.[121(b)]

In whole organisms, the effect of phenazines may be preferentially exerted on certain organs or tissues. Thus in frogs and axolotls, over-development and then failure of the nervous systems are observed with pyocyanine.[122, 123] Accelerated development has been recorded also in chick embryos,[124] and an acceleration of respiration in sea urchin embryos.[125–129] Similar effects have been observed with grasshopper embryos,[130] with *Hydromedusae*[131] and with starfish eggs.[132] It would appear that growth is to some extent normally limited and controlled by the rate of respiration, which pyocyanine can increase. 1-Methoxyphenazine does not display the activity of pyocyanine.[133] Neutral red and the safranines have an activating effect upon *Clupea pallasii* sperms[134]; and the former increases the pendulum-like movement of the diatom *Nitzschia closterium*, which occurs in salt springs in Germany.[135]

Compounds of the phenosafranine series were filaricidal when tested upon cotton rats infected with *Litomosoides carinii*.[136] The compounds killed the adult worms, but did not affect the microfilariae *in vivo*. Methylene violet was the most active compound of the series investigated. It was administered intravenously to about fifty patients infected with filariasis in Gambia; but had no filaricidal action upon the microfilariae or adult worms of *Wuchereria bancrofti, Acanthocheilonema perstans*, or *Onchocerca volvulus*. The doses given, which were comparable with those effective in cotton rats, were generally well tolerated, the limiting untoward effect being the production of albuminuria. However, some of the patients showed a curious toxic effect upon the development of the finger nails three weeks after the end of the treatment. Failure to act is probably due to a difference in susceptibility between the human worms and those of the cotton rats. The failure of methylene violet to kill the parasite in dogs infected with *Paragonimus* has also been recorded.[137]

The fungistatic action of neutral red, phenosafranine and certain other dyes against *Alternaria tenuis* and *Fusarium solani* has been investigated; no parallelism between these activities and redox potentials was found.[138] Neutral red also has an inhibitory effect on the growth of seedlings.[139]

Phenazine has been found to be toxic to the clothes moth, the southern beet webworm, the Hawaiian beet webworm, the rice weevil, termites and the larva of the codling moth; but under orchard conditions, this compound burned foliage severely.[140-142] It has also been reported to be somewhat effective against the European corn borer of corn plants,[143] and against the pea aphid.[144] Of a number of heterocyclic compounds tested against the young larvae of *Cochliomyia americana* (screw worms), dihydrophenazine was the most toxic.[145] 1-Phenazinol has insecticidal properties.[146]

Neutral red has been found to have an inhibitory effect on the growth of carcinoma in mice.[147-149] Dibenzo[a,h]phenazine also produces retardation of growth of tumors in mice; but the effect is less on chemically induced sarcomata than on spontaneous or transplanted tumors.[150] On the other hand, painting the skin of mice that had been tieated with benzopyrene with a 1% alcoholic solution of pyocyanine has been found to increase the incidence of cancer.[151] Neutral red and dibenzo[a,h]phenazine have been reported as non-carcinogenic[152(a)]; rosinduline 2G, neutral red and safranine T did not increase the life of mice bearing ascites tumors.[152(b)] The action of pyocyanine, phenosafranine, neutral red and 5-methylphenazinium iodide on the metabolism of normal and tumor tissues has been studied by Dickens.[54] Pyocyanine causes a great increase in respiration and inhibits aerobic glucolysis of tumors. Phenosafranine causes an enormous increase in aerobic glucolysis. Several compounds closely related to pyocyanine (including 5-methylphenazinium chloride) affect the metabolism in the same manner. Pyocyanine does not restore the defective carbohydrate oxidation of tumors and cannot be regarded as transforming tumor metabolism to normal function.

Neutral red has a mutagenic action on *Escherichia coli*,[153] and pyocyanine prevents the mitotic action of colchicine.[154] Other cytological effects of phenazine dyes have also been observed.[155, 156]

Finally, one can say that, although the biological effects of many phenazine derivatives have been investigated, up to the present no such compound has proved to be of very great medical value. The following facts are, however, worthy of mention. In experimental animals, pyocyanine has been found to bring about some depression of reflex activity (frogs), to cause temporary excitation (mice) and to be a powerful vasoconstrictor. It has little effect on the blood pressure, on muscle and on respiratory movement.[157] Neutral red has been found to act as an anticonvulsant in children and in experimental animals.[158] In experiments in which fresh sections of excised lung tissue were used in microscopic studies of the reaction to drugs of rabbit pulmonary arteries, Janus green was found to produce contraction of the arteries.[159] The injection of safranine has been found to result in kidney damage in dogs,[35, 160] and methylene violet caused kidney lesions in monkeys.

Neutral red and neutral violet have a direct cytotoxic effect on the mammalian heart.[161]

References

1(a). E. V. Cowdry, *Textbook of Histology*, 3rd ed., Kimpton, London, 1944.
1(b). R. D. Lillie, *Histopathologic Technik*, Blakiston, Philadelphia, 1952.
2. S. Brenner, *Biochim. et Biophys. Acta*, **11**, 480 (1953).
3. C. Bouchard, *Compt. rend.*, **108**, 713 (1889).
4. R. Emmerich and O. Löw, *Zeit Hyg.*, **31**, 1 (1899); through *J. Chem. Soc. Abstracts*, **78**, (ii), 159 (1900).
5. H. Kramer, *Z. Immunitäts.*, **84**, 505 (1935); through *Chem. Abstracts*, **29,** 8047 (1935).
6. H. O. Hettche, *Arch. Hyg. u. Bakteriol.*, **107**, 337 (1932); through *Chem. Zentr.*, **1932**, II, 234.
7. H. O. Hettche, *Klin. Wochschr.*, **12**, 1804 (1933); through *Chem. Abstracts*, **28**, 2028 (1934).
8. H. O. Hettche, *Z. Immunitäts*, **83**, 499 (1934); through *Chem. Abstracts*, **29**, 7379 (1935).
9. R. Schoental, *Brit. J. Exptl. Path.*, **22**, 137 (1941).
10. I. C. Wells, *J. Biol. Chem.*, **196**, 331 (1952).
11(a). L. Birkofer and A. Birkofer, *Klin. Wochschr.*, **26**, 528 (1948).
11(b). C. N. D. Cruickshank and E. J. L. Lowbury, *Brit. J. Exptl. Path.*, **34,** 583 (1953).
12. J. Zweig, *Vet. J.*, **102**, No. 3, 55 (1946); *Expt. Sta. Record*, **95**, 242 (1946); *Chem. Abstracts*, **42**, 5950 (1948).
13. W. S. Moos and J. W. Rowen, *Arch. Biochem. Biophys.*, **43**, 88 (1953).
14. H. R. Marston, *Biochem. J.*, **17**, 851 (1923).
15. A. A. Epstein and N. Rosenthal (with E. H. Maechling and V. de Beck), *Am. J. Physiol.*, **71**, 316 (1925).
16. H. R. Jacobs and H. T. Ricketts, *Proc. Soc. Exptl. Biol. Med.*, **35,** 473 (1936).
17. T. J. Haley and F. Stolarsky, *J. Am. Pharm. Assoc.*, **39**, 76 (1950); through *Chem. Abstracts*, **44**, 4204 (1950).
18. T. J. Haley and F. Stolarsky, *Proc. Soc. Exptl. Biol. Med.*, **73**, 103 (1950).
19. H. Weil-Malherbe, *Biochem. J.*, **31**, 299 (1937).
20. F. Dickens and H. McIlwain, *Biochem. J.*, **32**, 1615 (1938).
21. H. Weil-Malherbe, *Biochem. J.*, **31**, 2080 (1937).
22. D. E. Green, L. H. Stickland and H. L. A. Tarr, *Biochem. J.*, **28**, 1812 (1934).
23. W. A. Waters, *Trans. Faraday Soc.*, **39**, 140 (1943).
24. M. Dixon in *Perspectives in Biochemistry*, edited by J. Needham and D. E. Green, Cambridge University Press, 1938, p. 114; and D. E. Green, p. 175.
25. L. Michaelis in *Currents in Biochemical Research*, edited by D. E. Green, Interscience, New York–London, 1946, p. 207.
26. H. McIlwain, *Biochem. J.*, **46**, 612 (1950).
27. H. McIlwain and I. Grinyer, *Biochem. J.*, **46**, 620 (1950).
28. C. A. Owen (Jr.), A. G. Karlson and E. A. Zeller, *J. Bact.*, **62**, 53 (1951).
29. W. Franke (with D. Siewerdt-Kibat), *Z. physiol. Chem.*, **281**, 162 (1944).
30. L. Michaelis and C. V. Smythe, *J. Biol. Chem.*, **113**, 717 (1936).
31. K. Hardebeck, *Arch. exptl. Path. Pharmakol.*, **211**, 57 (1950); through *Chem. Abstracts*, **45**, 3886 (1951).

32. G. Pacheco and A. Trejos, *Brasil-Med.*, **59,** 169 (1945); through *Chem. Abstracts*, **45,** 693 (1951).
33. F. G. Fischer and H. Eysenbach, *Ann.*, **530,** 99 (1937).
34(a). W. Seubert and F. Lynen, *J. Am. Chem. Soc.*, **75,** 2787 (1953).
34(b). F. Lynen and S. Ochoa, *Biochim. et Biophys. Acta*, **12,** 299 (1953).
35. A. M. Ginzler, *Proc. Soc. Exptl. Biol. Med.*, **61,** 231 (1946).
36. E. A. H. Friedheim, *J. Exptl. Med.*, **54,** 207 (1931).
37. E. A. H. Friedheim, *Naturwissenschaften*, **20,** 171 (1932).
38. E. A. H. Friedheim, *Biochem. J.*, **28,** 173 (1934).
39. A. A. Stheeman, *Biochem. Z.*, **191,** 320 (1927); through *Chem. Abstracts*, **22,** 2589 (1928).
40. G. B. Reed and E. M. Boyd, *Can. J. Research*, **8,** 173 (1933).
41. J. Runnström and L. Michaelis, *J. Gen. Physiol.*, **18,** 717 (1935).
42. J. F. Fazekas, H. Colyer, S. Nesin and H. E. Himwich, *Proc. Soc. Exptl. Biol. Med.*, **42,** 446 (1939).
43. O. Ehrismann, *Z. Hyg. Infektionskrankh.*, **116,** 209 (1934); through *Chem. Abstracts*, **28,** 5489 (1934).
44. Å. Lennerstrand, *Biochem. Z.*, **287,** 172 (1936).
45. Å. Lennerstrand, *Naturwissenschaften*, **25,** 347 (1937).
46. Å. Lennerstrand, *Naturwissenschaften*, **26,** 45 (1938).
47. H. C. Lichstein and M. H. Soule, *J. Bact.*, **47,** 239 (1944).
48. L. Young, *J. Biol. Chem.*, **120,** 659 (1937).
49. R. H. De Meio, M. Kissin and E. S. G. Barron, *J. Biol. Chem.*, **107,** 579 (1934).
50. F. Dickens, *Nature*, **135,** 762 (1935).
51. F. Dickens, *Biochem. J.*, **30,** 1233 (1936).
52. E. M. Case and H. McIlwain, *Biochem. J.*, **48,** 1 (1951).
53. J. D. Judah and H. G. Williams-Ashman, *Biochem. J.*, **48,** 33 (1951).
55. F. Dickens, *Biochem. J.*, **30,** 1064 (1936).
55. S. A. Waksman and H. B. Woodruff, *J. Bact.*, **44,** 373 (1942).
56. N. P. Brazil, *Arch. Uruguay med. cirugia y especial Montevideo*, **25,** 627 (1944).
57. A. A. Imshenetskiĭ, *Mikrobiologiya*, **16,** 3 (1947); through *Chem. Abstracts*, **42,** 8879 (1948).
58. J. W. Klimek, C. J. Cavallito and J. H. Bailey, *J. Bact.*, **55,** 139 (1948).
59. C. J. Cavallito, J. H. Bailey, T. H. Haskell, J. R. McCormick and W. F. Warner, *J. Bact.*, **50,** 61 (1945).
60. C. J. Cavallito, *J. Biol. Chem.*, **164,** 29 (1946).
61. J. H. Bailey and C. J. Cavallito, *J. Bact.*, **55,** 175 (1948).
62. G. Young, *J. Bact.*, **54,** 109 (1947).
63. K. Kraft, *Pharmazie*, **5,** 257 (1950); through *Chem. Abstracts*, **44,** 10,800 (1950).
64(a). E. Sorkin and W. Roth, *Helv. Chim. Acta*, **34,** 427 (1951).
64(b). H. Erlenmeyer, J. Bäumler and W. Roth, *Helv. Chim. Acta*, **36,** 941 (1953).
65. H. McIlwain, *Nature*, **148,** 628 (1941).
66. L. Birkofer, *Angew. Chem.*, **64,** 111 (1952).
67. H. McIlwain, *Biochem. J.*, **37,** 265 (1943).
68. S. Wiedling, *Acta Path. Microbiol. Scand.*, **22,** 379 (1945); *Chem. Abstracts*, **40,** 3794 and 7303 (1946).
69. A. R. Frisk, *Acta Med. Scand.*, **125,** 487 (1946); *Chem. Abstracts*, **41,** 1011 (1947).
70. C. N. Iland, *Nature*, **161,** 1010 (1948).

71. H. McIlwain, *J. Chem. Soc.*, **1943**, 322.
72. R. C. Kaye and H. I. Stonehill, *J. Chem. Soc.*, **1952**, 3240.
73. G. J. Martin, *Am. J. Pharm.*, **119**, 432 (1947), through *Chem. Abstracts*, **42**, 2641 (1948).
74. R. C. Clapp, J. P. English, C. E. Fellows, J. Forsythe, R. E. Grotz and R. G. Shepherd, *J. Am. Chem. Soc.*, **74**, 1994 (1952).
75. G. Politzer, *Biochem. Z.*, **151**, 43 (1924); through *Chem. Zentr.*, **1924**, II, 2280.
76. A. Passow, *Arch. Augenheilk.*, **94**, 1; *Ber. ges. Physiol. exptl. Pharmakol.*, **27**, 210 (1924); through *Chem. Zentr.*, **1925**, I, 104.
77. P. Metzner, *Biochem. Z.*, **148**, 498 (1924); through *Chem. Zentr.*, **1924**, II, 1105.
78. G. Politzer, *Zellen u. Gewebelehre*, **1**, 644 (1924); *Ber. ges. Physiol. exptl. Pharmakol.*, **31**, 22; through *Chem. Abstracts*, **20**, 1872 (1926).
79. G. Bohn, *Compt. rend. soc. biol.*, **135**, 919 (1941).
80. M. R. Lewis, *Anat. Record*, **91**, 199 (1945).
81. T. J. Haley and F. Stolarsky, *Stanford Medical Bulletin*, **9**, 96 (1951).
82. E. Oesterlin, *Zentr. Bakt. Parasitenk.*, *I*, **94**, 313; through *Chem. Zentr.*, **1925**, I, 2313.
83. G. Salvioli, *Sperimentale*, **76**, 169 (1922); through *Chem. Zentr.*, **1923**, III, 255.
84. V. G. Drobot'ko, B. E. Aïzenman, M. O. Shvaĭger, R. G. Fel'dshteĭn and P. S. Chernysheva, *Zhur. Mikrobiol. Epidemiol. Immunobiol.*, **1945**, No. 7–8, 69; through *Chem. Abstracts*, **40**, 7396 (1946).
85. T. T'ung, *Proc. Soc. Exptl. Biol. Med.*, **39**, 415 (1938).
86(a). A. P. Krueger and D. M. Baldwin, *J. Infectious Diseases*, **57**, 207 (1935).
86(b). A. R. Bourke, M. L. Robbins and P. K. Smith, *J. Immunol.*, **69**, 75 (1952); *Chem. Abstracts*, **46**, 9654 (1952).
87. O. Haempel, *Z. Nahr. Genussm.*, **50**, 423 (1925); through *Chem. Abstracts*, **20**, 1291 (1926), and *Chem. Zentr.*, **1926**, I, 2501.
88. G. Panja and S. K. Ghosh, *Indian J. Med. Research*, **31**, 5 (1943).
89. O. Schales, S. S. Schales and D. A. Friedman, *Arch. Biochem.*, **6**, 329 (1945).
90. C. H. Browning, J. B. Cohen and R. Gulbransen, *J. Path. Bact.*, **23**, 124 (1919).
91. C. H. Browning, J. B. Cohen, R. Gaunt and R. Gulbransen, *Proc. Roy. Soc. London*, **93 B**, 329 (1922).
92. C. J. Carr, D. L. Vivian and J. C. Krantz (Jr.), *J. Pharmacol.*, **77**, 215 (1943); *Chem. Abstracts*, **37**, 2813 (1943).
93. R. G. Jones and H. A. Shonle, *J. Am. Chem. Soc.*, **68**, 2246 (1946).
94. M. S. Fleisher, *J. Immunol*, **62**, 245 (1949); *Chem. Abstracts*, **43**, 7589 (1949).
95. I. M. Levine, *Abstracts of Theses, Univ. Chicago, Science Series*, **4**, 105 (1925–6); through *Chem. Abstracts*, **22**, 3655 (1928).
96. Ger. Pat. 286,097; *Chem. Zentr.*, **1915**, II, 569.
97. Ger. Pat. 407,486; Swiss Pat. 103,102, 103,380, 103,381; *Chem. Zentr.*, **1925**, I, 1247.
98. G. Meissner and E. Hesse, *Arch. exptl. Path. Pharmakol.*, **147**, 339 (1930); through *Chem. Abstracts*, **24**, 5066 (1930).
99. H. J. Corper and M. I. Cohn, *Am. J. Clin. Path.*, **16**, 621 (1946); through *Chem. Abstracts*, **41**, 497 (1947).
100. R. J. Dubos and E. Suter, *Am. Rev. Tuberc.*, **60**, 384 (1949); through *Chem. Abstracts*, **44**, 2071 (1950).
101. V. C. Barry, J. G. Belton, M. L. Conalty and D. Twomey, *Nature*, **162**, 622 (1948).

102. V. C. Barry and J. G. Belton, *Proc. Roy. Irish Acad.*, **55 B**, 149 (1953); *Chem. Abstracts*, **48**, 1377 (1954).

103. V. C. Barry, J. G. Belton, J. F. Chambers, M. L. Conalty, R. Kelly and D. Twomey, *Proc. Roy. Irish Acad.*, **55 B**, 157 (1953); *Chem. Abstracts*, **48**, 1378 (1954).

104. V. C. Barry, *Irish J. Med. Sci.*, No. 310, 453 (1951).

105. M. L. Conalty, *Tubercle*, **32**, 263 (1951)

106. T. J. D. Lane, *Irish J. Med. Sci.*, No. 309, 393 (1951).

107. J. Barnes, see *Studies in the Chemotherapy of Tuberculosis*, by V. C. Barry, *Royal Institute of Chemistry Lectures*, 1952, No. 2.

108. P. P. Koelzer and J. Giessen, *Ärztl. Forschg.*, **3**, 241 (1949); through A. Lembke and E. Krüger-Thiemer, *Literaturstudien zum Tuberkuloseproblem unter besonderer Berücksichtigung antituberkulöser Stoffe*, Ergänzungsheft zum Band 149, *Zentr. Bakteriol. Parasitenk.*, *Abt. I/Ref.* (1952), p. 194.

109. E. Carl and P. Marquardt, *Z. Naturforsch.*, **46b**, 280 (1949); through *Chem. Abstracts*, **44**, 3158 (1950).

110(a). L. Birkofer and A. Birkofer, *Naturwissenschaften*, **36**, 92 (1949).

110(b). L. Birkofer and A. Widmann, *Chem. Ber.*, **86**, 1295 (1953).

111. M. I. Smith and E. W. Emmart, *J. Immunol.*, **61**, 259 (1949); *Chem. Abstracts*, **43**, 5084 (1949).

112(a). H. Pope and D. T. Smith, *Am. Rev. Tuberc.*, **62**, 34 (1950).

112(b). D. W. Wooley, *Bull. Tulane Med. Faculty*, **6**, 71 (1946–47); through *Chem. Abstracts*, **46**, 3127 (1952).

113. H. P. Sarett, *J. Biol. Chem.*, **162**, 87 (1946).

114. F. L. Shpanir, E. D. Chertkova and L. I. Serebrennikova, *Problemy Tuberk.*, 1940, No. 10, 3; through *Chem. Abstracts*, **39**, 1223 (1945).

115. N. Rist, *Bibliotheca Tuberculosa* (Suppl. zur *Schweiz. Z. Tuberk.*), Fasc. 1, 55 (1948); through A. Lembke and E. Krüger-Thiemer, *Literaturstudien zum Tuberkuloseproblem unter besonderer Berücksichtigung antituberkulöser Stoffe*, Ergänzungsheft zum Band 149, *Zentr. Bakteriol. Parasitenk.*, *Abt. I/ Ref.* (1952), p. 194.

116. B. B. Kudryavtzev, *Compt. rend. acad. sci. (U.R.S.S.)*, **33**, 292 (1941).

117. F. Mietzsch, *Angew. Chem.*, **63**, 250 (1951).

118. J. P. Thurston, *Brit. J. Pharmacol*, **8**, 162 (1953).

119. F. M. Berger, *Brit. J. Exptl. Path,.* **24**, 252 (1943).

120. V. L. Ryzhkov, V. A. Smirnova and O. S. Goroskaya, *Biokhimiya*, **15**, 222 (1950); through *Chem. Abstracts*, **44**, 10062 (1950).

121(a). L. G. Nickell, *Botan. Gaz.*, **112**, 290 (1951).

121(b). G. Ciaccio and N. Ercoli, *Boll. ist. sieroterap. milan*, **30**, 533 (1951); through *Chem. Abstracts*, **46**, 6261 (1952).

122. P. Citterio, *Rend. ist. lombardo sci., Classe sci. mat. nat.*, **75**, 142 (1941–42); through *Chem. Abstracts*, **38**, 5980 (1944).

123. S. Ranzi, R. Arosio, P. Citterio, P. Menotti and F. Semenza, *Experientia*, **2**, 315 (1946); through *Chem. Abstracts*, **40**, 7418 (1946).

124. C. Soresina, *Tumori*, **12**, 306 (1938); through *Chem. Abstracts*, **34**, 7381 (1940).

125. P. E. Lindahl and L. O. Öhman, *Biol. Zentr.*, **58**, 179 (1938); through *Chem. Abstracts*, **32**, 4671 (1938).

126. A. R. Moore, H. S. Bliss and E. H. Anderson, *J. Cellular Comp. Physiol.*, **25**, 27 (1945); through *Chem. Abstracts*, **39**, 4158 (1945).

127. J. Runnström and D. Thörnblom, *Naturwissenschaften*, **24**, 447 (1936).

128. R. Deotto, *Boll. soc. ital. biol. sper.*, **14**, 327 (1939); through *Chem. Abstracts*, **34**, 4812 (1940).

129. J. Runnström, *Biol. Bull.*, **68**, 327, through *Chem. Abstracts*, **29**, 4458 (1935).
130. L. D. Carlson and J. H. Bodine, *J. Cellular Comp. Physiol.*, **14**, 159 (1939); through *Chem. Abstracts*, **34**, 529 (1940).
131. R. Deotto, *Pub. staz. zool. Napoli*, **17**, 206 (1939); through *Chem. Abstracts*, **34**, 1404 (1940).
132. E. S. G. Barron and L. A. Hoffman, *J. Gen. Physiol.*, **13**, 483 (1930).
133. G. Steensholt, *Acta Physiol. Scand.*, **11**, 318 (1946).
134. M. Kôshi and Y. Ogawa, *Igaku to Seibutsugaku (Med. and Biol.)*, **19**, 72 (1951); through *Chem. Abstracts*, **45**, 9755 (1951).
135. K. Peteler, *Ber. oberhess. Ges. Natur- u. Heilkunde Giessen, Naturw. Abt.*, **19**, 122 (1939–40); through *Chem. Abstracts*, **45**, 224 (1951).
136. F. Hawking, W. E. Ormerod, J. P. Thurston and W. A. F. Webber, *Brit. J. Pharmacol.*, **7**, 494 (1952).
137. H. W. Brown and K. L. Hussey, *J. Parasitol.*, **33**, 33 (1947); *Chem. Abstracts*, **41**, 4236 (1947).
138. G. B. Marini-Bettòlo and G. Borzini, *Ist. botan. univ. lab. crittogam, Pavia, Atti*, [5], **3**, 261 (1947); *Chem. Abstracts*, **43**, 8435 (1949).
139. E. Gilles, *Bull. mens, soc. linnéenne Lyon*, **15**, 77 (1946); through *Chem. Abstracts*, **43**, 1084 (1949).
140. L. E. Smith, *Ind. Eng. Chem.*, **34**, 499 (1942).
141. U. S. Pat. 2,110,614; *Chem. Abstracts*, **32**, 3546 (1938).
142(a). M. C. Swingle, J. B. Gahan and A. M. Phillips, *U. S. Dept. Agr., Bur. Entomol. Plant Quarantine*, E-730 (1947); through *Chem. Abstracts*, **42**, 1691 (1948).
142(b). V. Prey, F. Beran and H. Böhm, *Mitt. chem. Forsch.-Inst. Wirtschaft österr.*, **6**, 28 (1952); through *Chem. Abstracts*, **46**, 8802 (1952).
142(c). J. G. Horsfall and S. Rich, *Contribs. Boyce Thompson Inst.*, **16**, 313 (1951); through *Chem. Abstracts*, **46**, 11543 (1952).
143. D. D. Questel, R. V. Connin and S. I. Gertler, *U. S. Dept. Agr., Bur. Entomol. Plant Quarantine*, E-785 (1949); through *Chem. Abstracts*, **43**, 9936 (1949).
144. J. E. Dudley (Jr.), T. E. Bronson and F. H. Harries, *U. S. Dept. Agr., Bur. Entomol. Plant Quarantine*, E-651 (1945); through *Chem. Abstracts*, **39**, 3111 (1945).
145. L. E. Smith and R. Melvin, *J. Econ. Entomol.*, **36**, 475 (1943); through *Chem. Abstracts*, **38**, 208 (1944).
146. G. T. Bottger and A. P. Yerington, *U. S. Dept. Agr., Bur. Entomol. Plant Quarantine*, E-744 (1948); through *Chem. Abstracts*, **43**, 1896 (1949).
147. J. F. Riley, *Cancer Research*, **8**, 183 (1948); through *Chem. Abstracts*, **43**, 1856 (1949).
148. L. Karczag, *Biochem. Z.*, **230**, 411 (1931).
149. H. M. Dyer, *An. Index of Tumor Chemotherapy*, Federal Security Agency, U.S. Public Health Service, 1949.
150. A. Haddow, *J. Path. Bact.*, **47**, 567 and 581 (1938).
151. W. Beltrami, *Tumori*, **14**, 41 (1940); through *Chem. Abstracts*, **34**, 7001 (1940).
152(a). J. L. Hartwell, *Survey of compounds which have been tested for carcinogenic activity*, Federal Security Agency, 1941.
152(b). H. Lettré, *Z. Krebsforsch.*, **57**, 1 (1950); through *Chem. Abstracts*, **46**, 4680 (1952).
153. M. Demerec, G. Bertani and J. Flint, *Am. Naturalist*, **85**, 119 (1951).
154. H. Lettré, *Naturwissenschaften*, **39**, 483 (1952).

155. E. Battaglia, *Caryologia*, **2**, 223 (1950); through *Chem. Abstracts*, **45**, 2065 (1951).
156. G. Freudenberg-Dumur, *Ber. oberhess. Ges. Natur.-u. Heilkunde Giessen, Naturw. Abt.*, **24**, 124 (1949); through *Chem. Abstracts*, **45**, 1652 (1951).
157. N. S. Kharchenko, E. O. Ryabushko and O. I. Petukhova, *Vrachebnoe Delo*, **27**, 19 (1947); through *Chem. Abstracts*, **42**, 4675 (1948).
158. S. Cobb, M. E. Cohen and J. Ney, *Trans. Am. Neurol. Assoc.*, **62**, 139 (1936); through *Chem. Abstracts*, **31**, 4722 (1937).
159. A. J. Gilbert, *J. Pharmacol.*, **62**, 228 (1938); *Chem. Abstracts*, **32**, 3023 (1938).
160. C. J. Díaz, R. Picatoste, H. Castro-Mendoza and M. M. Pleguezuelo, *Rev. Clín. españ.*, **35**, 377 (1949); through *Chem. Abstracts*, **44**, 10160 (1950).
161. J. L. Leitch and T. J. Haley, *J. Pharmacol. Exptl. Therap.*, **104**, 416 (1952).

PART II

Condensed Phenazine Systems

By D. G. I. FELTON

CHAPTER XII

Monobenzophenazines

1. Introduction

There are two positions in the phenazine molecule to which an additional benzene ring may be fused, giving benzo[a]phenazine (I) and benzo[b]phenazine (II), which are ciphered as shown in the appended formulas.

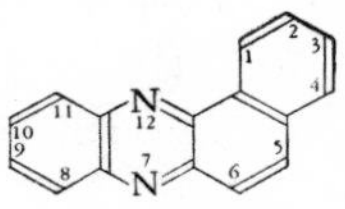

(I) 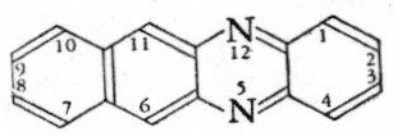   (II)

Since the representatives of the latter compound are so few in number, we may disregard the logical order and deal with this ring system first.

2. Benzo[b]phenazine
(5,12-Diazanaphthacene, II, R. I. 2666)

A. Benzo[b]phenazine

This compound, which forms intensely red plates, m.p. 233° (with blackening), from benzene or chloroform, is obtained by the oxidation of 5,12-dihydrobenzo[b]phenazine (III) (Section XII:2,B) by means of potassium dichromate in acetic acid.[1] This change may be reversed by means of stannous chloride or alcoholic ammonium sulfide. The azine (II) reacts with benzenesulfinic acid to give a sulfone (see Chapter IV:4), and with aniline to give an anilinobenzo[b]phenazine (bluish-black powder, m.p. ca. 155°), neither of which have been orientated, but which on analogy with the phenazine series are formulated as 2-derivatives. These reactions indicate the strongly quinonoid character of benzo[*b*]phenazine, as indeed does the color of the azine. The latter reaction is a typical addition of an amine to a quinone, followed by oxidation.

B. Hydrogenated Derivatives

(*1*)   *5,12-Dihydrobenzo[b]phenazine* (III).   This compound forms a difficultly soluble, yellow, crystalline powder, which does not melt below 300°. It is obtained by the fusion together at 180° of 2,3-di-hydroxynaphthalene and *o*-phenylenediamine.[1]

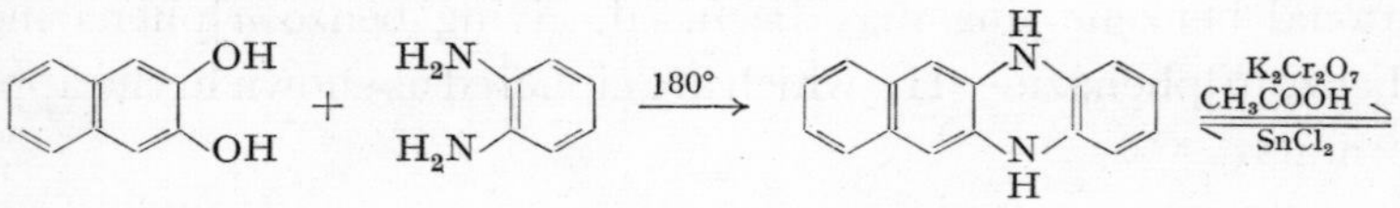

(III)

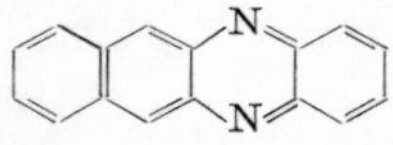

(II)

Oxidation of (III) by dichromate in acetic acid gives benzo[*b*]-phenazine (Section XII:2,A) from which follows the structure of the latter compound. The dihydroazine (III) behaves normally and forms a nitrosamine. The greater stability of 5,12-dihydrobenzo[*b*]phenazine over 5,10-dihydrophenazine (Chapter III:1,A) is noteworthy and has been commented upon.[2]

(*2*)   *trans-6,6a,7,8,9,10,10a,11-Octahydrobenzo[b]phenazine* (IV).

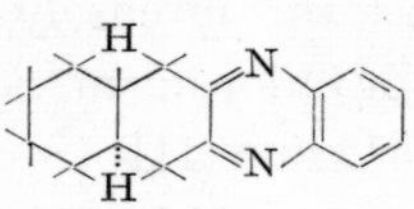

(IV)

When *trans*-2-decalone is oxidized with selenium dioxide, *trans*-2,3-diketodecalin is formed, and this, upon reaction with *o*-phenylene-diamine in acetic acid, affords another representative (IV) of the benzo[*b*]phenazine series, as glistening plates, m.p. 177–178.[3,4]

C. Benzo[b]phenazine-6,11-quinone (V, R = H)

This compound is said to be obtained when 2-(2′-nitroanilino)-1,4-naphthoquinone, formed by heating 1,4-naphthoquinone with 2-nitroaniline in acetic acid, is heated in a sealed tube with alcoholic ammonium sulfide.[5] It forms green leaflets from alcohol, in which solvent its solutions are brown with a weak green fluorescence. The 2-methyl homolog (V, R = CH₃), obtained similarly from 1,4-naphthoquinone and 3-nitro-4-aminotoluene,[5] forms steely blue leaflets with a green reflex from alcohol and its solutions show a faint green fluorescence also. In view of the color of the compounds and of the reductive nature of the preparation, it is possible that these compounds belong to the azhydrin series. However, a recent paper[2] has disproved the claim, made simultaneously with the above work,[5] to have prepared 5,12-dihydro-5,7,12,14-tetrazapentacene-6,13-quinone (VI) by a similar reduction of 2,5-di-(2′-nitroanilino)-1,4-benzoquinone. It has been shown that the nitro groups upon reduction react with the quinone oxygen atoms to yield 5,12-dihydro-5,7,12,14-tetrazapentacene (VII). If the same mechanism is operative in the reaction under consideration here, the product should be 5-hydroxybenzo[a]phenazine (VIII) (Chapter XIII:2,A), and in view of the lack of physical data and the unreliable nature of the earlier analytical evidence, the structure (V) must be treated with reserve.

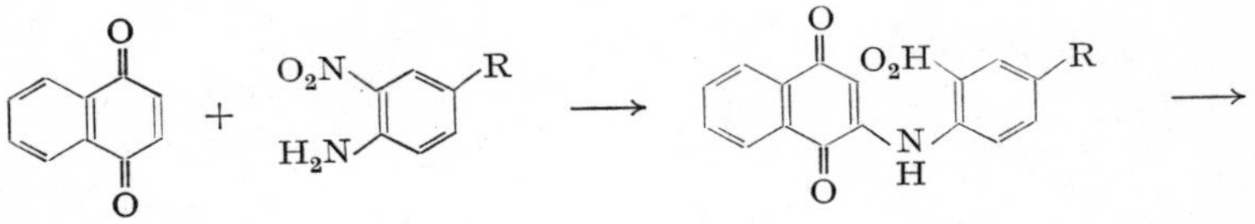

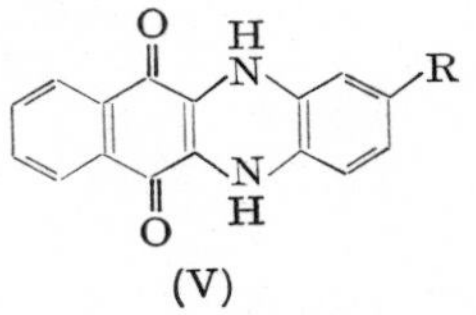

(V)   or   (VIII)

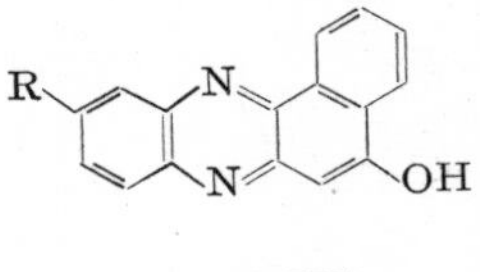

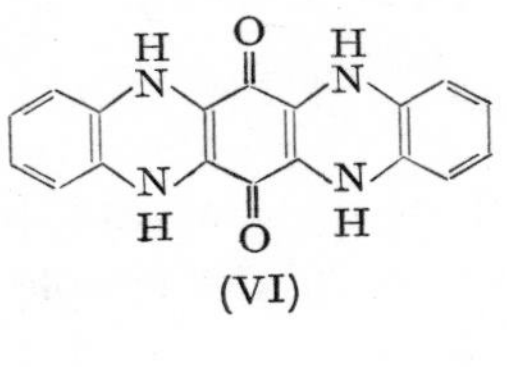

(VI) 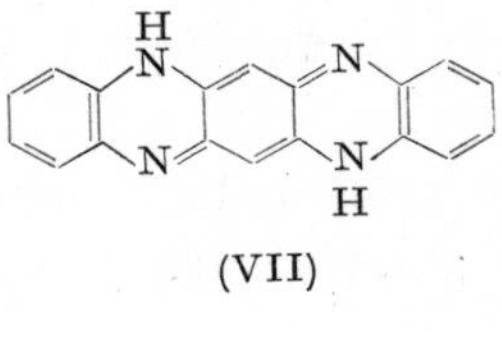   (VII)

D. Halogen Derivatives of Benzo[b]phenazine

By the condensation of o-phenylenediamine with 2,3-diketo-1,1,4,4-tetrachloro-1,2,3,4-tetrahydronaphthalene, Zincke and Fries[128] obtained 6,11-dichlorobenzo[b]phenazine, loss of chlorine occurring to give the aromatic structure (IIa). The product forms red needles with a bluish luster, m.p. 265°, which give a dark brown solution in concentrated sulfuric acid, becoming green on the addition of a little water. Further dilution reprecipitates the extremely weak base.

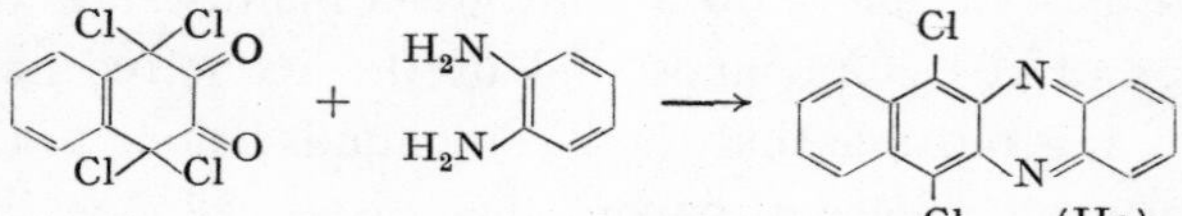

The only other halogen derivative of this series is 8-bromo-6-chloro-11-methylbenzo[b]phenazine (IIb), which was obtained as red needles, charring at 270° after preliminary darkening, by the condensation of o-phenylenediamine and 6-bromo-4-chloro-1-methyl-2,3-naphthoquinone.[129] The product is identical with that obtained by Fries and Hempelmann[130] from o-phenylenediamine and 6-bromo-1,4,4-trichloro-2,3-diketo-1-methyl-1,2,3,4-tetrahydronaphthalene, this reaction proceeding in ethanol to the aromatic system by loss of the extra halogen atoms, as noted in the earlier reaction quoted.

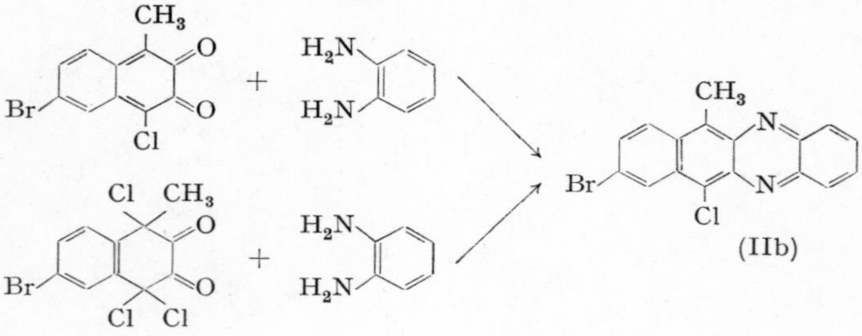

3. Benzo[a]phenazine (I, R. I. 2670)

A. General

In the case of the benzo[a]phenazine series, we are dealing with almost as great a variety of compounds as in the simple phenazine series, among which are a number of important dyestuffs. It is clearly impracticable, and would be unnecessarily repetitive, if they were dealt with as fully; but there are facets in their chemistry that are due solely to the presence of the additional benzene ring. This is nowhere more clearly reflected than in the methods of preparation available. A number of these methods have already been dealt with in Chapter I, but for the sake of completeness they are repeated here. Just as in the case of substituted phenazines, there are possibilities of isomerism in some of the condensations.

B. General Methods of Preparation of Benzo[a]phenazines

(1) The simplest and most widely applicable method is the condensation of an o-phenylenediamine with a 1,2-naphthoquinone, usually in acetic acid solution.[6-9] Since 1,2-naphthoquinones are, in general, more easy to prepare than 1,2-benzoquinones, this method is of greater utility for the preparation of condensed phenazines.

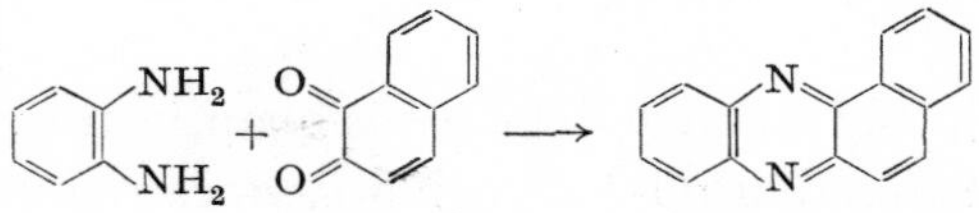

(I)

This method was used very widely by Kehrmann and his pupils for the synthesis of substituted (acetamido- or amino-) benzo[a]-phenazines (see Chapter XIII).

(2) A method closely related to (1) is the condensation of a 1,2-diaminonaphthalene with a 1,2-benzoquinone,[10-12] for example:

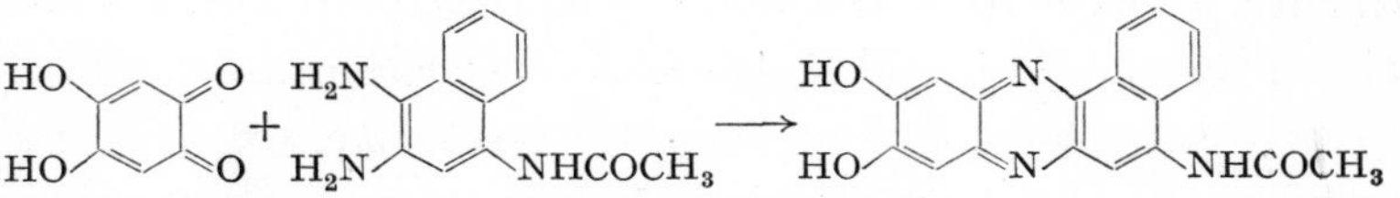

(3) Another variant of method (1) is the condensation of a 1-nitroso-2-naphthol (1,2-naphthoquinone-1-monoxime) with an o-phenylenediamine.[13]

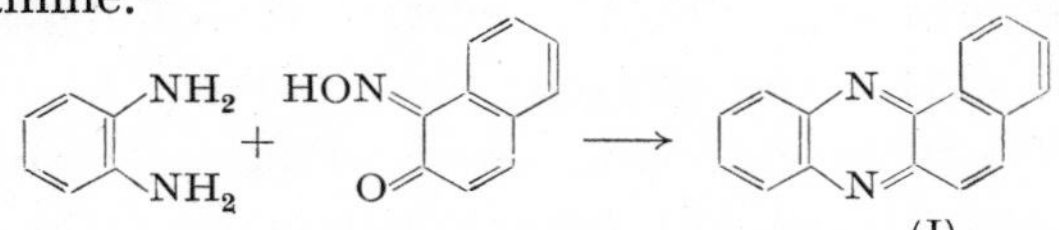

(I)

(*4*)   An alternative to method (*3*) employs a 2-nitroso-1-naphthol and an *o*-phenylenediamine.[14]

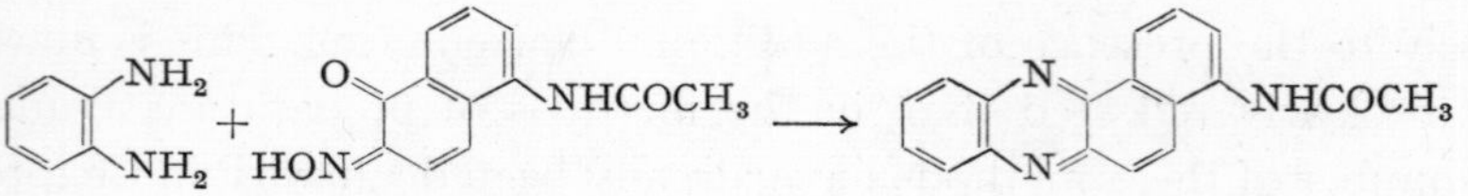

(*5*)   A reaction due to Witt, which is capable of many possibilities, is the formation of benzo[*a*]phenazines when the azo-derivative, formed by coupling with a naphthyl-2-arylamine, is boiled with dilute acid.[7,15–18]

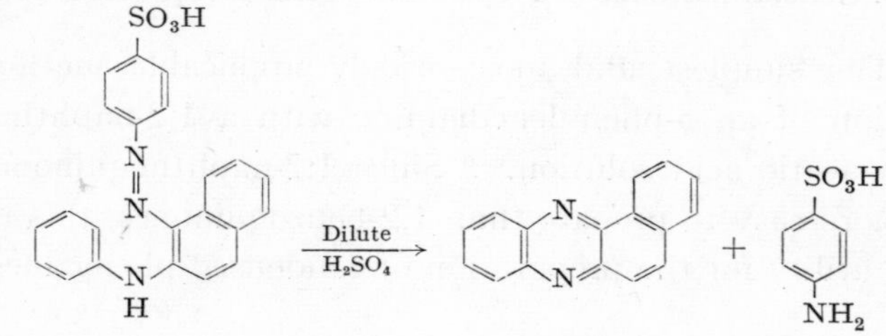

The yield in the reaction depicted is quantitative. This reaction is only applicable to naphthyl-2-arylamines, since the azo group will be attached at position 4 in a naphthyl-1-arylamine. In place of dilute acid, benzoyl chloride has been employed, best at room temperature,[19] but appears to offer no advantages.

A reaction that is so closely related that it must be included under this heading is that studied by Bucherer and coworkers.[20,21] They found that treatment of a naphthalene azo dye, Orange II (IX, *C. I.* 151), with phenylhydrazine-sodium bisulfite mixture led to a modified Bucherer reaction[22] to yield X. The action of concentrated hydrochloric acid upon this yielded an aminobenzo[*a*]phenazine, which at first was thought to be the 10-derivative (XII),[20] derived from a semidine rearrangement product (XI, R = H). Later, however, 10-amino-benzo[*a*]phenazine was synthesized unequivocally[21] by condensing diazotized sulfanilic acid with 2-(4′-acetamidophenyl)-naphthylamine-1-sulfonic acid (XIII) and treating this product (XI, R = Ac) with 80% sulfuric acid at 70°, when cyclization to 10-aminobenzo[*a*]-phenazine (XII) occurred. This was different from the product from

Orange II, and so it was concluded that the intermediate product (X) must have undergone an *o*-semidine rearrangement to (XIV), which upon ring closure gave 8-aminobenzo[*a*]phenazine (XV). The reaction does not appear to be of general use for the preparation of benzo[*a*]-phenazines.

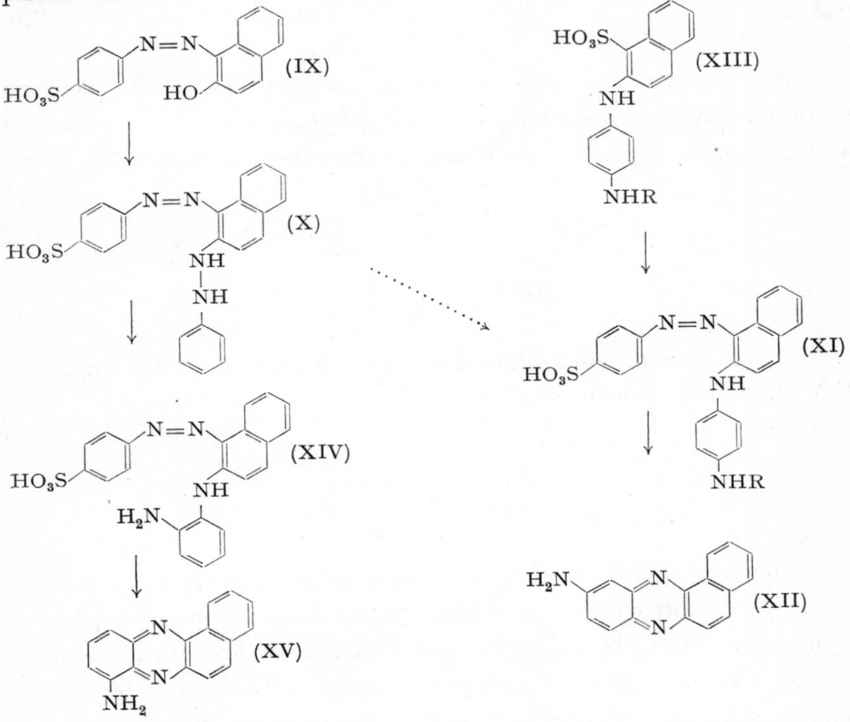

(6)   A method related to method (5) is the formation of benzo[*a*]-phenazines by the action of cold, alcoholic hydrochloric acid on 1-nitrosonaphthyl-2-arylamines.[23]

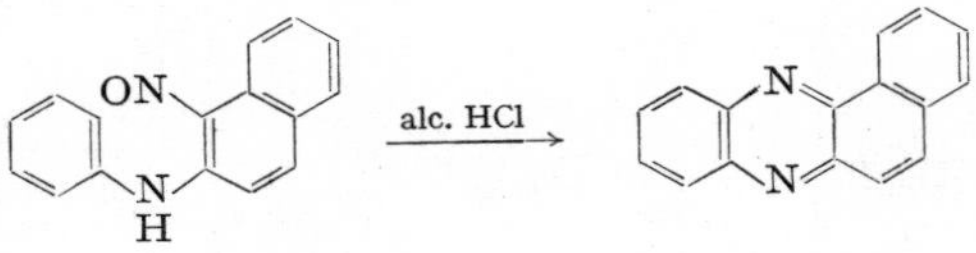

(7)   An extension of this method, applicable only to benzo[*a*]-phenazines substituted with alkylamino groups, was found by Kehr-

mann, who condensed 4-ethylamino-1-nitrosonaphthalene with a
m-diamine in acetic acid in the presence of hydrochloric acid.[24,25]

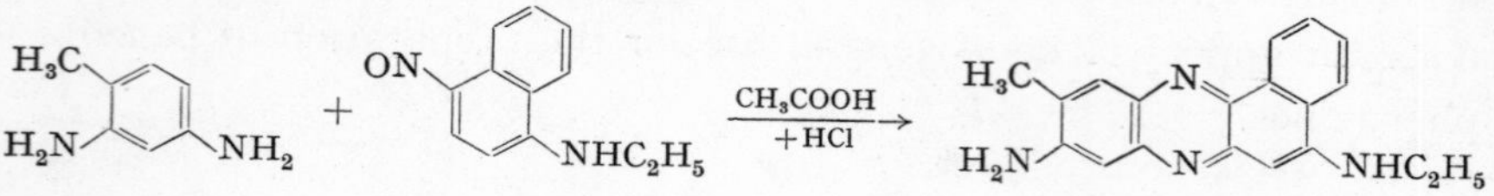

(*8*) Alternatively the nitroso group may be in the benzene
portion, for Witt showed that *p*-nitrosodialkylaminobenzenes condensed
with 2-naphthylamine in acetic acid in the presence of acid.[26]

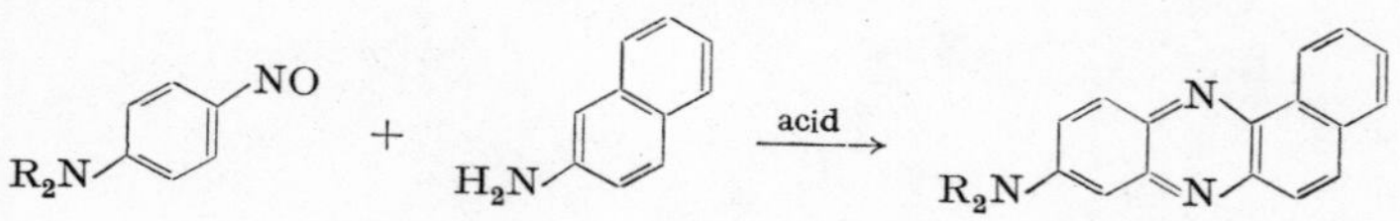

In place of *p*-nitrosoaniline derivatives, Nietzki and Otto employed
N,N'-dichloroquinonediimine.[27]

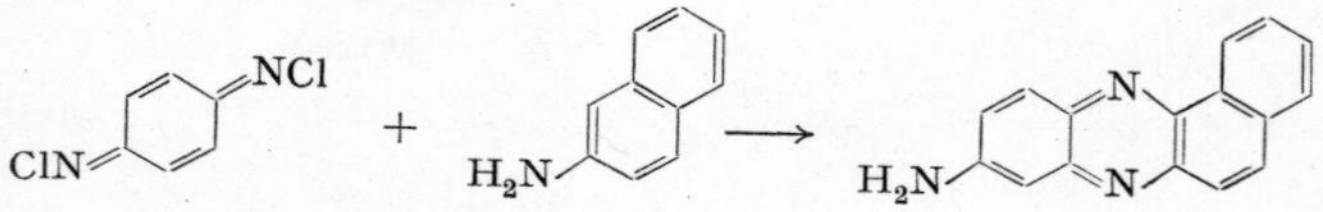

When the amino substituent is unalkylated, as in the last example,
it may be diazotized and on boiling the diazonium solution in alcohol
it yields the parent benzo[*a*]phenazine nucleus by loss of nitrogen.[27]

(*9*) An extension of Crippa's synthesis (Chapter I:6) to the
benzo[*a*]phenazine series has recently been reported.[28] Cyclohexanone
condenses with 1-benzeneazo-2-naphthylamine in hot methanolic
hydrochloric acid solution to give 8,9,10,11-tetrahydrobenzo[*a*]-
phenazine (XVI), (colorless needles, m.p. 102°), which may be dehydrogenated by means of iodine in acetic acid to I.

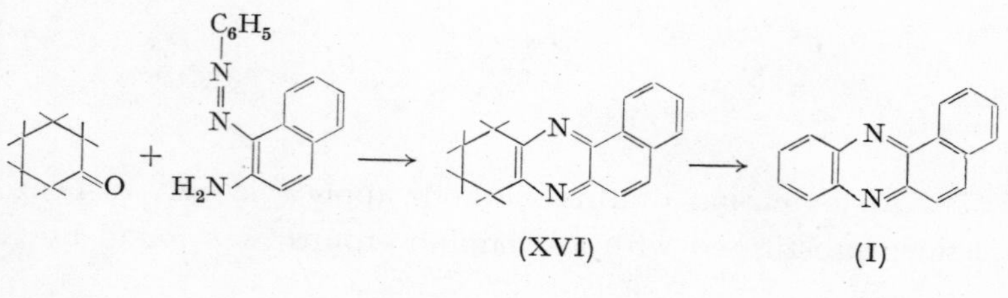

(XVI)   (I)

(10) Wohl and Aue's synthesis (Chapter I:8), the reaction between an aromatic amine and an aromatic nitro compound, is applicable to the benzo[a]phenazine series. Thus 2-naphthylamine and nitrobenzene react together in the presence of dry sodium hydroxide at 115–140° to yield a mono N-oxide of benzo[a]phenazine[29] together with benzo[a]phenazine itself. The modified Wohl-Aue synthesis, due to Soule,[30] has been shown to be applicable to the benzo[a]phenazine series also.[31] Recently, interest in this method has reawakened and the structure of the N-oxide has been proved[31] (Section XII:3,E(1)). Owing to the oxidative effect of alkali upon 2-nitroaniline, the method cannot be extended to yield aminobenzo[a]phenazines in the same way. However, using zinc chloride as a condensing agent, Wohl and Lange[32] showed that an aminobenzo[a]phenazine was formed from 2-nitro-aniline and 1-naphthylamine. At first sight this would appear to be a related reaction, but the nature of the product, namely 5-aminobenzo-[a]phenazine (XVII), shows that the amino group of 1-naphthylamine is not involved directly in the reaction. An incorrect interpretation of this reaction is given on page 39 of the volume in this series entitled *Six Membered Heterocyclic Nitrogen Compounds with Four Condensed*

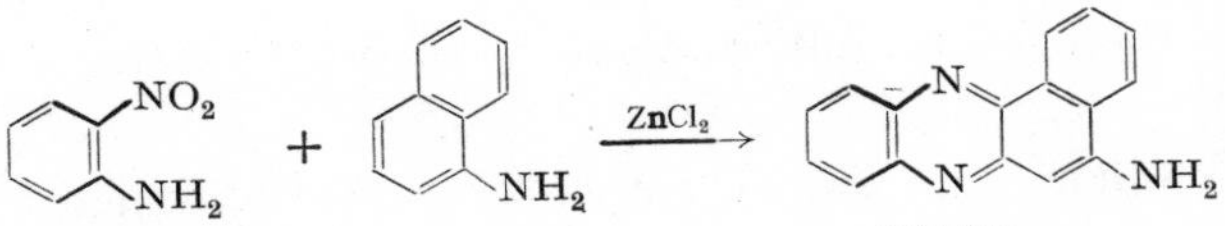

(XVII)

Rings, by C. F. H. Allen and associates. We wish, with Dr. Allen's agreement, to call attention to and correct the error, here.

(11) Methods that yield the benzo[a]phenazine nucleus but that are probably not of great preparative importance include the pyrolysis

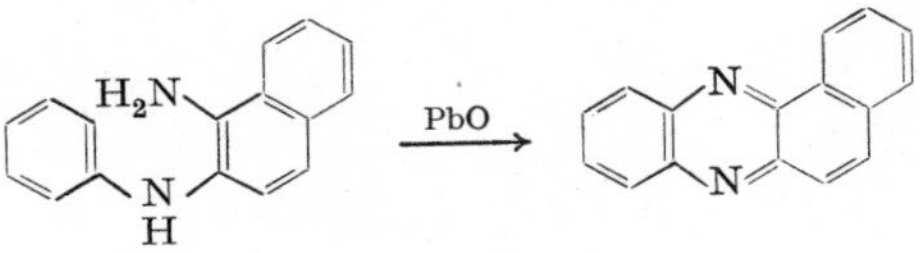

of 2-arylamino-1-naphthylamines over litharge,[33] or *via* the intermediate formed by the action of carbon disulfide in alcoholic alkali upon the diamine,[33] and the zinc dust distillation of hydroxy-7-phenyl-benzo[a]phenazinium salts (for example, rosindone (Chapter XIV: 2,C(1))) in an atmosphere of hydrogen,[34] or of 5-hydroxybenzo[a]-phenazine.[35] Benzo[a]phenazine has also been reported as the product from the oxidation of an equimolar mixture of o-phenylenediamine and 2-naphthol by alkaline potassium ferricyanide.[7]

Other general methods, which are applicable only to the synthesis of substituted benzo[a]phenazines, are included herein for the sake of completeness.

(12)   4-Benzeneazo-1-naphthylamine hydrochloride will condense with o-phenylenediamines in alcoholic solution under pressure to yield 5-aminobenzo[a]phenazines.[25,35,36]

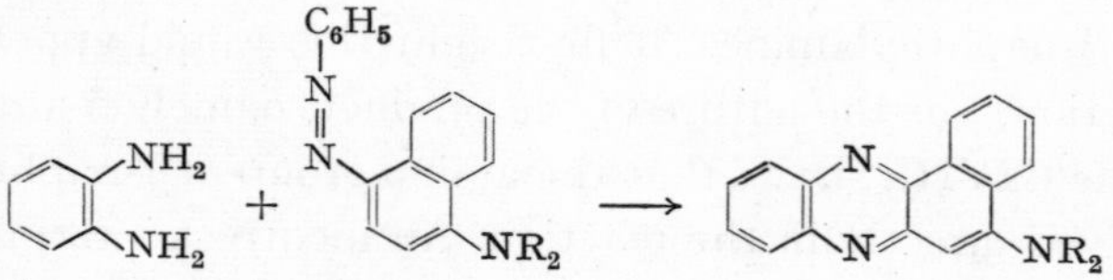

Assuming the first step to be the normal addition of an amine to a quinonoid structure (derivable from the 4-azo derivative), this method is then somewhat analogous to Witt's reaction (Section XII:3,B(5)).

(13)   Similar aminobenzo[a]phenazines are obtained by heating o-aminoazo compounds of the benzene series with 1-naphthylamine hydrochloride alone at 140° or in phenol at 130°. The reaction does not occur with 2-naphthylamines. The o-aminoazo compound is apparently reduced by part of the naphthylamine to an o-diamine, which then condenses with the naphthylamine[37,38] (compare with the Wohl-Lange

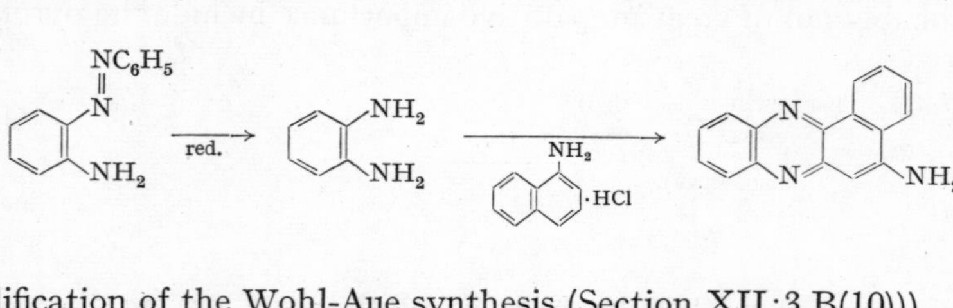

modification of the Wohl-Aue synthesis (Section XII:3,B(10))).

(14)   2,4-Diaminobenzeneazo compounds (chrysoidines) behave

somewhat similarly and react with 2-naphthol on melting together to give aminobenzo[a]phenazines.[39,40]

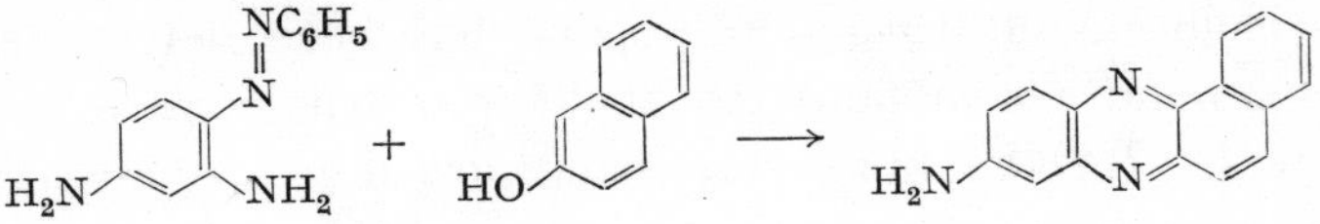

(15) Diaminobenzo[a]phenazines are formed when picryl-1- or -2-naphthylamines are reduced by stannous chloride in concentrated hydrochloric acid.[41]

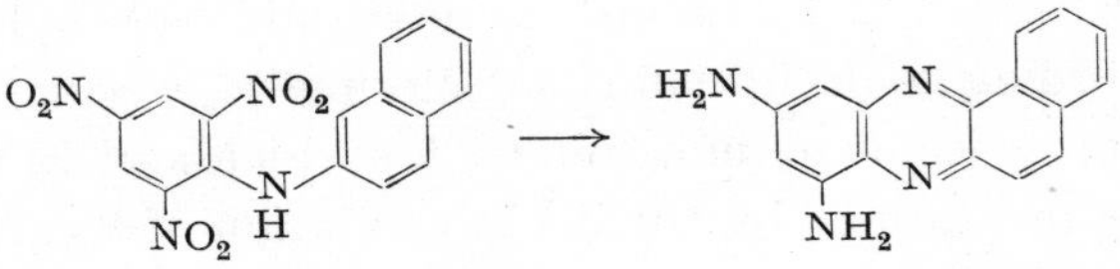

(16) Just as hydroxy-1,2-benzoquinones react with 1,2-naph-thylenediamines (Method 2), 2-hydroxy-1,4-naphthoquinones and o-phenylenediamine yield hydroxybenzo[a]phenazines,[42] and 2-hy-

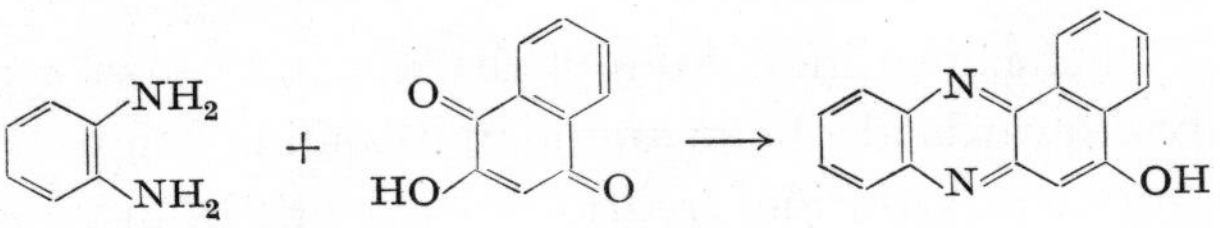

droxy-1,4-naphthoquinone-4-imines and o-phenylenediamine yield aminobenzo[a]phenazines.[42]

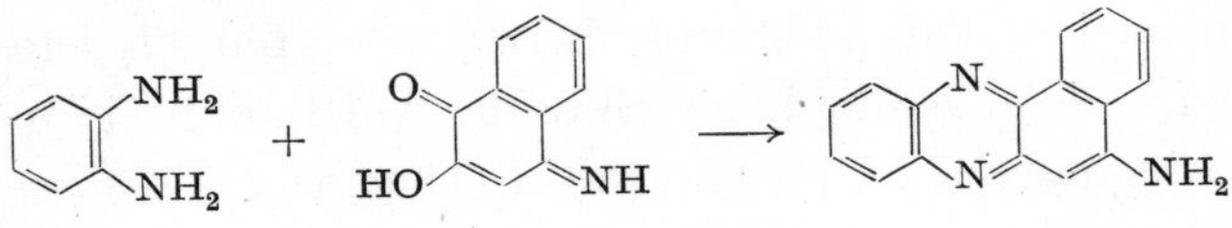

C. Benzo[a]phenazine (1,2-Benzophenazine, I)

(1) This compound forms colorless prisms, m.p. 142°, from ethanol,[23] though it has also been reported as lemon-yellow prisms, m.p. 142.5°, from benzene.[7,28] It may be readily sublimed at 200° and is sparingly soluble in cold benzene, ethanol and ether. It gives a brownish-red coloration with concentrated sulfuric acid, which on

dilution becomes lemon yellow. On further dilution, the base is deposited, showing the ease of hydrolysis of the salts. Two series of salts are said to be formed.[7] The ultraviolet absorption spectrum of an ethanolic solution of benzo[a]phenazine has been determined.[43] It shows a general resemblance to the carbocyclic analog, benz[a]-anthracene (R. I. 2805), but certain bands are of greater intensity and at longer wavelengths than in the case of the hydrocarbon.

(2) It is obtained by many methods of preparation (Section XII:3,B), the two methods which appear to be the most satisfactory being that due to Witt (XII:3,B(5)), which gives a quantitative yield, and the condensation of 1,2-naphthoquinone and o-phenylenediamine, modified according to Kehrmann and Mermod[44] by conducting it in ether in the presence of sodium sulfate, for which a yield of 88% was claimed. It is also formed by the decarboxylation of 8-carboxybenzo-[a]phenazine, by distillation with calcium oxide,[45] and by distillation of the 6-carboxy isomer also.[13]

D. Reactions of Benzo[a]phenazine

Benzo[a]phenazine differs from phenazine and benzo[b]phenazine in being stable towards alcoholic ammonium sulfide below 160°.[46] It is reduced by stannous chloride, hydriodic acid or sodium amalgam in acetic and hydrochloric acids to a violet hydrochloride said to be a dihydrochloride of the phenazhydrin type,[7,46] which is hydrolyzed by boiling water to a brownish-yellow base, easily reoxidized by air to benzo[a]phenazine. This is now probably to be reinterpreted as the formation of a violet semiquinone chloride, which on basification may yield an easily reoxidized phenazhydrin. The magnetic susceptibility of a related perchlorate has been studied by Katz[47] and has been shown to be paramagnetic, confirming the semiquinone nature of this salt. It possesses a molecular magnetic susceptibility of 102.7×10^{-5} c.g.s. units, equivalent to ca. 8 Weiss magnetons (one unpaired electron is equivalent to 8.6 Weiss magnetons).

Strenuous attempts have been made to reduce benzo[a]phenazine to the 7,12-dihydro compound, but when using sodium in methanol or isoamyl alcohol, ammonium sulfide, alkaline sodium sulfide or lithium aluminum hydride no reduction has been observed.[48] However, hydrogenation over Raney nickel catalyst or palladized charcoal yields 1,2,3,4-tetrahydrobenzo[a]phenazine as pale yellow needles, m.p. 125°, from benzene. The structure of this compound is indicated by the close similarity of its ultraviolet absorption spectrum to that of phenazine[48] (for a mention of another tetrahydro derivative of benzo[a]phenazine, see Section XII:3,B(9)).

Bromine in acetic acid does not react with benzo[a]phenazine, but fuming nitric acid produces an uncharacterized, crystalline nitro derivative.[7] The azine can be sulfonated[7,50] with extreme difficulty (35% oleum at 100° for 12 hours), giving a monosulfonic acid (orange-red needles, m.p. above 290°), which has been converted by fusion with potassium hydroxide to the corresponding yellow hydroxy compound. This is said to be different from 5-hydroxybenzo[a]phenazine on the basis of color reactions. Likewise the corresponding cyano compound (m.p. 236–237°; compare 5-cyanobenzo[a]phenazine, yellow needles, m.p. 247° [49]) is obtained from the sulfonic acid and potassium cyanide, and this is hydrolyzed with difficulty to the high-melting acid, white needles from water[50] (cf. 5-carboxybenzo[a]phenazine, deep yellow prisms, m.p. 305° [49] and 6-carboxybenzo[a]phenazine, yellow needles, m.p. 275–278° [13]). The position of these substituents has not been determined.

Oxidation of benzo[a]phenazine by means of chromic acid in acetic acid-acetic anhydride at 100° affords benzo[a]phenazine-5,6-quinone (XVIII) in good yield [51,52] (see Section XII:3,F).

(I)   (XVIII)

Benzo[a]phenazine is mono-N-alkylated by heating it under pressure at 130° in methanolic or ethereal solution with alkyl iodides, though the reaction does not proceed to completion.[53] Methyl benzo-[a]phenazinium iodide forms brownish-red needles, which are difficultly soluble in water or ethanol to give a yellow solution with a greenish-yellow fluorescence. The corresponding ethiodide, which forms almost black needles, m.p. *ca.* 150° (dec.), is perhaps a semiquinone (see Chapter III:2). Just as in the simple phenazinium series, these alkyl benzo[*a*]phenazinium salts are attacked by alcoholic ammonia in the presence of air, the amino group entering position 5.[54] On analogy with the behavior of the simple phenazinium salts and with benzo[*a*]- phenazinium compounds of known structure, the alkyl group is located at position 7, in agreement with steric considerations. A detailed study of alkyl- and arylbenzo[*a*]phenazinium compounds is deferred to Section XII:4.

E. Benzo[*a*]phenazine N-Oxides

(*1*)   The first *N*-oxide of benzo[*a*]phenazine to be described was the monoöxide obtained by Wohl and Aue in their original paper.[29] The compound was described as green crystals, yellow when powdered, m.p. 182°, but the position of the oxygen atom was not determined. Maffei has recently studied the formation of *N*-oxides in a number of azines, among them benzo[*a*]phenazine.[55] This, with hydrogen peroxide in acetic acid at 50° for 24 hours, yielded a monoöxide, m.p. 181°, which Maffei stated was identical with the product obtained by Wohl and Aue. Phenazine itself under identical conditions yielded a di-*N*-oxide, but further treatment of the benzo[*a*]phenazine *N*-oxide with hydrogen peroxide failed to yield a dioxide. Maffei made the reasonable assumption that steric hindrance was responsible for the failure to form a dioxide and that, consequently, the oxide obtained was benzo[*a*]- phenazine-7-oxide (XIX). But the identity of this product with that of Wohl and Aue, claimed by Maffei, implies that the mechanism advanced by Wohl and Aue, which should yield benzo[*a*]phenazine-12- oxide (XX), must be incorrect.

More recently, the question has been reopened by Pachter and Kloetzel,[31] who showed that, contrary to Maffei's claim, the two mono-*N*-oxides, although similar in melting point, showed a depression on mixing. They further pointed out that, while XIX may not form a dioxide, owing to steric hindrance, XX most certainly should. In fact, under drastic conditions (30% hydrogen peroxide at 75°), they

were able to isolate the dioxide (XXI) in 6% yield from the monoöxide
(XIX). But on the other hand there was no difficulty in obtaining the
dioxide (XXI) from the monoöxide (XX) formed by either the Wohl-
Aue[29] or the Soule[30] procedure. They made the interesting observation
that the highest yield of XXI from XX was obtained at room temperature with hydrogen peroxide in acetic acid. At higher temperatures
(50°), the dioxide was partially *reduced* by hydrogen peroxide to the
monoöxide (XIX), the mixture being separated chromatographically.
The dioxide (XXI) is an orange substance, m.p. 191° (dec.).[31] Maffei and

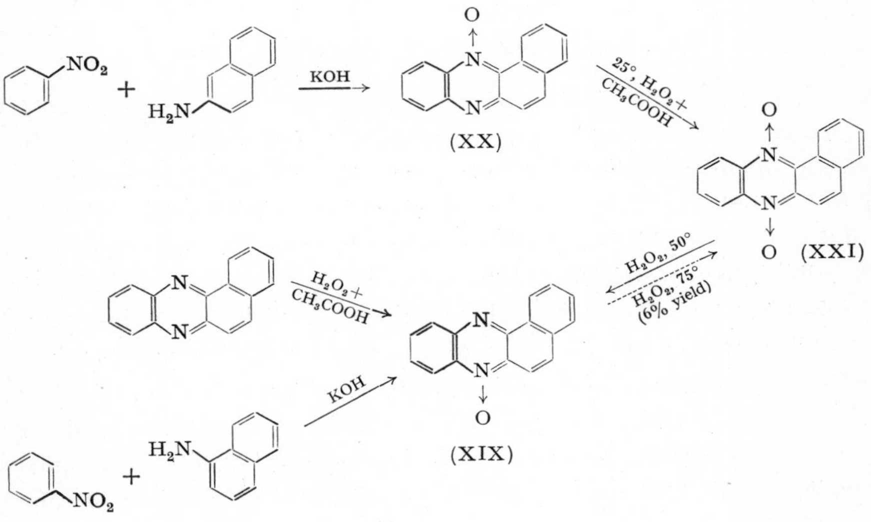

his co-workers[131] have since agreed with Pachter and Kloetzel and have
provided further proof in that the Wohl-Aue reaction between nitrobenzene and 1-naphthylamine yields the 7-oxide (XIX), identical with
that obtained by the hydrogen peroxide oxidation of benzo[a]-
phenazine.

(2)   Mention should be made here of 5,6-dihydrobenzo[a]oxiro-
[c]phenazine (XXII, *R. I.* 2861) obtained by Zincke[56] by the action of
o-phenylenediamine upon 3,4-dihydroxy-1,2-diketotetralin. This forms
small yellowish needles, m.p. 186–187°, from benzene. It possesses
many of the typical properties of oxirane compounds, for example
cold mineral acid opens the oxirane ring to yield 6-hydroxybenzo[a]-

phenazine (XXIII), while aniline in alcoholic solution yields an unstable hydroxyanilino compound, readily losing aniline on boiling with acids to form XXIII. Distillation of XXII with zinc dust yields benzo-[a]phenazine.

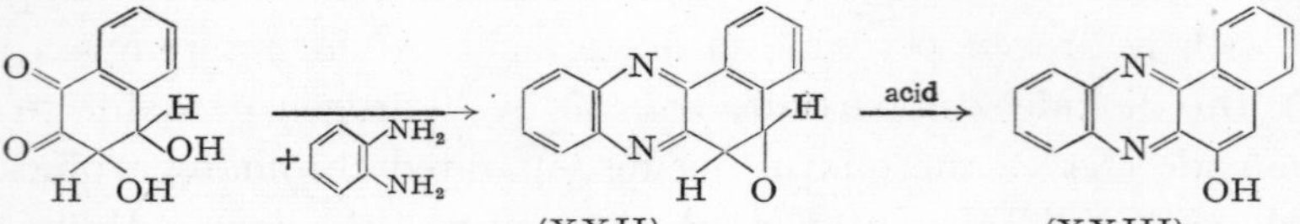

(XXII)   (XXIII)

F. Benzo[a]phenazine-5,6-quinone (XVIII)

This compound forms golden yellow needles, m.p. 265° (dec.).[51] It is most readily prepared by the oxidation of benzo[a]phenazine by means of chromic acid in a mixture of acetic acid and acetic anhydride at 100°.[51,52] It had been earlier obtained by the nitric acid oxidation of 5-hydroxy-6-chlorobenzo[a]phenazine,[57] or the bromo analog,[58] of 5,6-dihydroxybenzo[a]phenazine or a dihydro derivative of this[59] or of 5-chloro-6-hydroxybenzo[a]phenazine.[60] It yields an oxime, m.p. 219°.[51,59] Reduction with any of the usual reducing agents yields 5,6-dihydroxybenzo[a]phenazine[51,59,61] (see Chapter XIII:3,A). The 5,6-quinone system may be condensed with a second molecule of o-diamine to produce members of the naphtho[1,2-b,3,4-b']-diquinoxaline series[59,127] (R. I. 3580), for example (XXIV) (see Chapter XVIII:7).

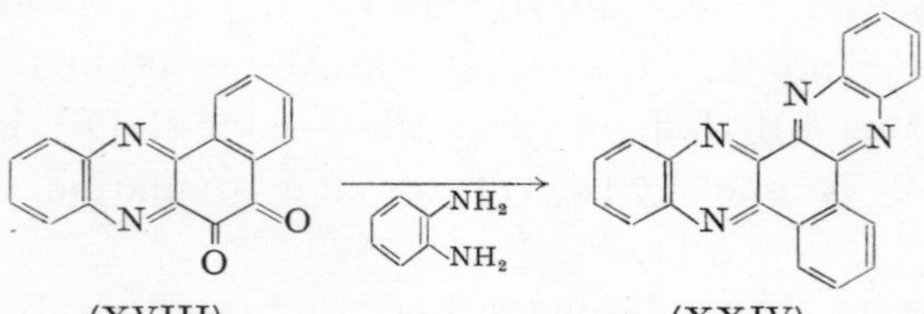

(XVIII)   (XXIV)

When XVIII is boiled with concentrated aqueous alkali, a benzilic acid type of reaction occurs to yield 11-carboxy-11-hydroxy-11-indeno[1,2-b]quinoxaline (XXV, R. I. 2517), which forms needles, m.p. 223–224°, from water.[51] Among the other products of the reaction

are found 3-hydroxy-2-(2'-carboxyphenyl)-quinoxaline (XXVI), silvery
prisms, m.p. 237°, and 11-keto-11-indeno[1,2-*b*]quinoxaline (XXVII),
yellow prisms, m.p. 187°. When XVIII is fused with alkali,
it yields 2-(2'-carboxyphenyl)-quinoxaline (XXVIII) (felted needles,
m.p. 275° (dec.), from dilute ethanol) which on distillation is decarboxylated to 2-phenylquinoxaline (XXIX), fine needles, m.p. 78°,
from petrol.[52]

(For a somewhat similar reaction see Chapter XIV:2,C(1).)

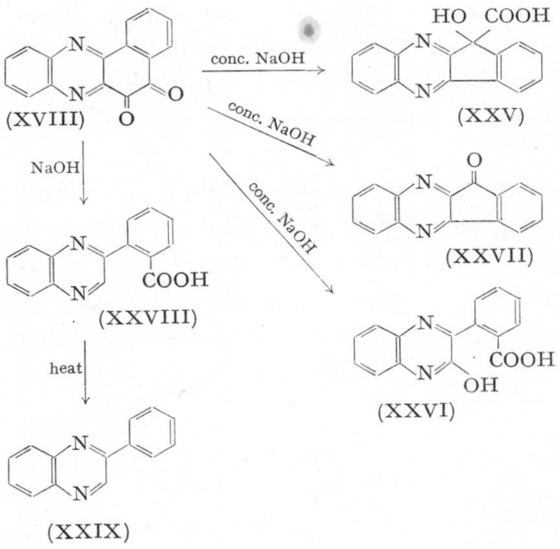

G. Homologs of Benzo[*a*]phenazine

Homologs of benzo[*a*]phenazine may be obtained by many of the
general methods, using appropriately substituted starting materials.
Owing to the unsymmetrical nature of the basic nucleus, ambiguity
may sometimes arise. Thus Witt oxidized a mixture of 2-naphthol and
toluene-3,4-diamine with potassium ferricyanide and obtained a product
of m.p. 179.8°.[62] In order to show the orientation unambiguously, he
then took 4'-toluidino-2-naphthylamine, reacted this with diazotized
sulfanilic acid and decomposed the 1-azo derivative[112] with boiling

dilute sulfuric acid to obtain 10-methylbenzo[a]phenazine (XXX), which formed lustrous lemon-yellow plates, m.p. 169°, from ethanol.[39, 63]

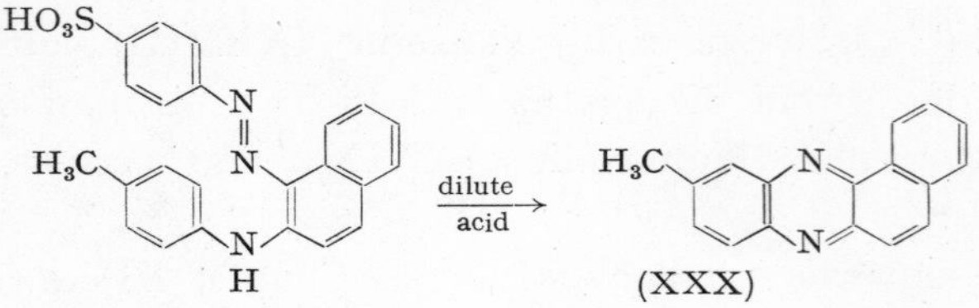

The isomer, m.p. 179.8°, was accordingly 9-methylbenzo[a]-phenazine. Witt showed that the product, m.p. 139–142°, obtained by Hinsberg[6] by the condensation of 1,2-naphthoquinone and toluene-3,4-diamine, was an equimolar mixture of the 9- and 10-methyl compounds.

A third methylbenzo[a]phenazine, (yellow needles, m.p. 208.5°) was obtained by application of the Wohl-Aue reaction to the condensation of 2-naphthylamine and 3-nitrotoluene.[29] Two products are possible, the 8- or 10-methyl homologs, so that in this case it appears that anionoid attack by the 2-naphthylamine anion has taken place at the 2-position of the nitrotoluene to yield the vic-derivative, which then

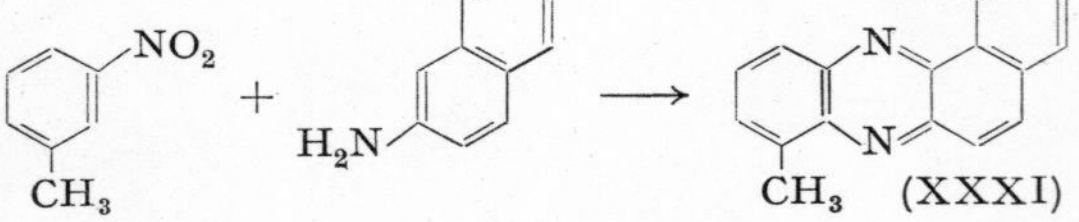

undergoes ring closure to XXXI. The alkyl and aryl derivatives of benzo[a]phenazine are listed in Table XII.

H. Nitro, Chloro and Bromo Derivatives

(1) *Nitro Derivatives.* As stated earlier (XII:3,D), nitration of benzo[a]phenazine is extremely difficult and the nitro derivative obtained has not been characterized.[7] Since the amino compounds, which are of some commercial importance, are more readily prepared by some of the general methods given above, the study of nitrobenzo-[a]phenazines has been neglected. 6-Nitrobenzo[a]phenazine was

TABLE XII. Alkyl, Aralkyl and Aryl Derivatives of Benzo[a]phenazine

Substituent and position	Color and crystalline form	M.p. (°C.)	Remarks	Ref.
5-Methyl-	Flat, yellow needles	174		109
6-Methyl-	Needles	139–141		110
8-Methyl-	Yellow needles	208.5	Sublimes at 240°/13 mm.	29
9-Methyl-	Pale straw-colored needles	179.8		62
10-Methyl-	Lustrous lemon-yellow plates	169	Cherry-red color with conc. H_2SO_4, SO_4^{--}; orange needles	39, 63, 111
1,5,6-Trimethyl-	Yellow needles	142	Red color with HCl	113
5-Benzyl-	Yellow needles	195.5–196		109, 114
5-(4'-Chlorobenzyl)-	Yellow plates	243–244		114
5-Diphenylmethyl-	Feathery yellow needles	263–264		115
5-Carboxymethyl-	Small, pale yellow plates	168–172		109
5-Dicarbethoxymethyl-	Very pale yellow needles	164–165		109
5,6-Diphenyl-	Yellow needles	274–275		116
5-Phenyl-6-(4'-tolyl)-		283–284		117

prepared by direct condensation of 3-nitro-1,2-naphthoquinone with
o-phenylenediamine.[8] It forms greenish-yellow prisms, m.p. 221–222°,
from a mixture of phenol and acetic acid, and gives a carmine-red
coloration with concentrated sulfuric acid. On progressive dilution, this
color first changes to yellow and then the azine is reprecipitated.
Reduction of the nitro compound with alcoholic ammonium sulfide
affords the corresponding amino compound.

(2)   *Chloro- and Bromo-Derivatives.* The benzo[a]phenazine system
is resistant to the action of halogens,[7] and consequently members
bearing halogen substituents are prepared by condensation of suitably
substituted compounds,[57] for example:

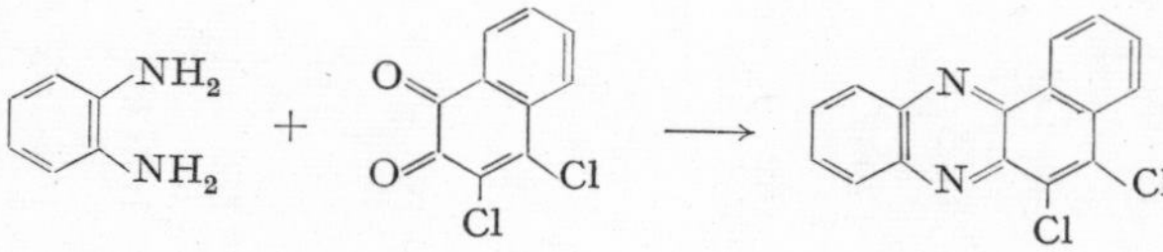

Instead of a halogenated 1,2-naphthoquinone, a 1,4-naphtho-
quinone bearing at least one halogen in the 2- or 3-position may be
used, when a 5-hydroxybenzo[a]phenazine results that may or may
not be halogenated, depending upon the extent of substitution in the
parent quinone.[57,58]

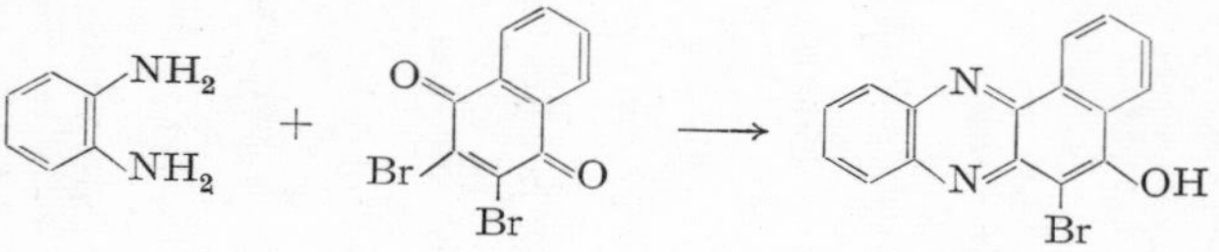

When the quinone component is 2-chloro-3-hydroxy-1,4-naphtho-
quinone, the product (**XXXII**) retains the halogen atom in preference
to the hydroxyl group.[57,119]

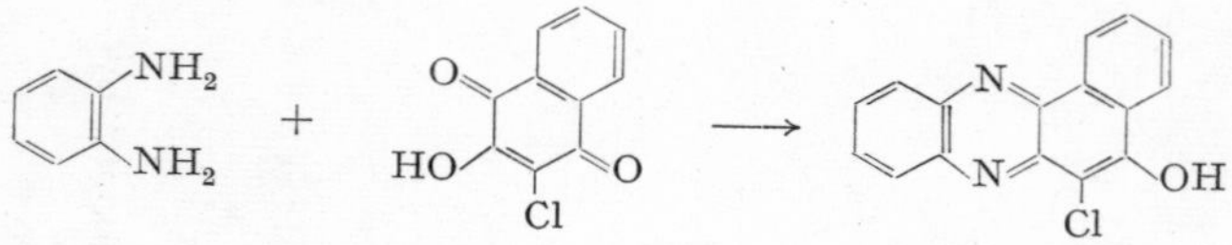

(**XXXII**)

However, with the corresponding 2-hydroxy-3-iodo-1,4-naphtho-
quinone and o-phenylenediamine, the products were 2,3-diaminophen-

azine and 5-hydroxybenzo[a]phenazine,[64] due to the reductive removal of iodine with the simultaneous oxidation of o-phenylenediamine.

There is an isolated instance of a chlorobenzo[a]phenazine (the 9-chloro compound (XXXIV)) arising from the pyrolysis of the corresponding 9-chloro-7-ethylbenzo[a]phenazinium chloride (XXXIII).[65]

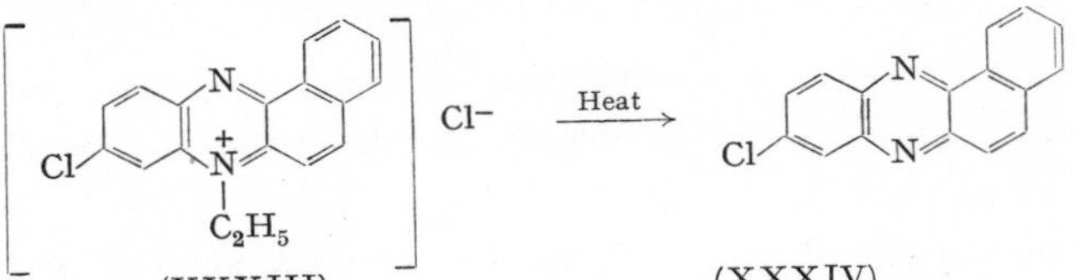

(XXXIII)   (XXXIV)

The halogen atoms are inert to the action of warm alkali,[57] but the halohydroxy compounds behave as typical phenols and form sodium salts. Both 5-chloro-6-hydroxy- and 6-chloro (or bromo)-5-hydroxy-benzo[a]phenazines are oxidized by concentrated nitric acid to benzo-[a]phenazine-5,6-quinone[57,58,60] (XVIII). For the reactions of these chlorohydroxy compounds with o-diamines,[127] see Chapter XVIII:7.

The bromine atom in 6-bromo-5-hydroxybenzo[a]phenazine (XXXV) is somewhat more reactive. It may be removed by treatment with phenol and sulfuric acid, yielding 5-hydroxybenzo[a]phenazine, and reacts with aniline in ethanolic solution under reflux to yield 6-anilino-5-hydroxybenzo[a]phenazine[58] (XXXVI; crimson plates, m.p. 210–220°; diacetyl derivative, yellow crystals, m.p. 226°). Com-

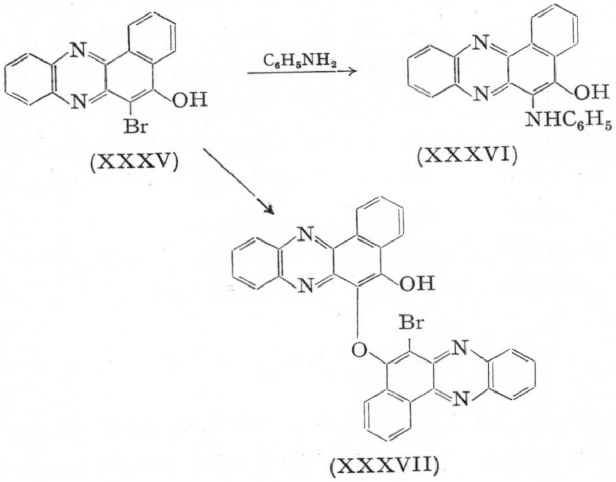

(XXXV)   (XXXVI)

(XXXVII)

pound (XXXV) will also undergo self-condensation on heating in nitrobenzene to yield 5-hydroxy-6'-bromodi-5',6-benzo[a]phenazine ether (XXXVII), as brownish-violet needles, m.p. 300°,[58] which may yield further condensed heterocyclic systems by reactions involving the two remaining functional groups.

These halohydroxybenzo[a]phenazines will react with a second molecule of 2,3-dichloro-1,4-naphthoquinone in the presence of sodium acetate and copper to give yellow dyes, which may be used either as pigments or as vats.[66]

The principal halogen and halohydroxyderivatives of benzo[a]-phenazine are listed in Table XIII.

I. Hydroxy and Amino Derivatives

These commercially important substances, the eurhodols and eurhodines, respectively, are dealt with in Chapter XIII.

J. Sulfonic Acids

There are a number of patent specifications dealing with the preparation of sulfonic acids of the benzo[a]phenazine series. They may be prepared by condensation of 1,2-diaminobenzene derivatives with suitably sulfonated 1,2-naphthoquinones, for example, 1,2-naphtho-quinone-3,8-disulfonic acid or its amino derivatives.[67] The 8-sulfonyl group is more readily replaceable by hydroxyl by means of potassium hydroxide at 180°,[67-70] when yellow to red dyes for wool are obtained. The resulting 1-hydroxy-6-sulfonylbenzo[a]phenazines may be brominated by bromine or chlorinated by sulfuryl chloride in nitrobenzene, giving a dye with a vivid golden-yellow shade,[71] or by sulfur dichloride, when a brown sulfur-containing dye for cotton results.[72] Alternatively the product from the alkali melt of the sulfonic acid may be coupled with diazotized sulfanilic or naphthionic acid etc.[73] (See also references 13, 16 and 50.)

K. Miscellaneous

(1) A number of benzo[a]phenazines bearing 4'-arsonoanilino groups in the 5-position and solubilized with 1-sulfonyl groups have

TABLE XIIIa. Carboxylic Acid Derivatives of Benzo[a]phenazine

Substituent	Color and crystalline form	M.p. (°C.)	Remarks	Ref.
4,6-Dibromo-2-carboxy-	Yellow needles*			132
5-Carboxy-	Deep yellow prisms	305		49
6-Carboxy-	Yellow needles	275–278		13
8-Carboxy-	Yellow needles	255	Orange-red color with conc. H_2SO_4	45
9(or 10)-Carboxy-	Yellow needles	366	Ethyl ester: yellow needles, m.p. 205°. Hydrazide: yellow needles, dec. 270–320°. Acid inhibits *M. tuberculosis* at 1×10^{-4} g./ml. Hydrazide inhibits *M. tuberculosis* at 3×10^{-5} g./ml.	133
9(or 10)-β-Carboxyethyl-	Yellow needles	212	Violet color with conc. H_2SO_4. Inhibits *M. tuberculosis* at 1×10^{-4} g./ml.	133
11-Carboxy-	Yellow needles	256	Inhibits *M. tuberculosis* at 1×10^{-4} g./ml.	133
x-Carboxy-	Pale yellow needles	236–237		50

TABLE XIII. Halogen and Halohydroxy Derivatives of Benzo[a]phenazine

Substituents	Physical properties	M.p. (°C.)	Derivatives, etc.	Ref.
9-Chloro-	Yellow needles	191	Cherry-red color with H_2SO_4	65
5,6-Dichloro-	Fine yellow needles	202		57
6-Chloro-5-hydroxy-	Brownish-red needles, bronze luster	dec. 280	Na salt, yellowish-red plates; acetyl deriv., m.p. 230–232°	57, 119, 127
6-Chloro-5-methoxy-		177–178		127
6-Chloro-5-hydroxy-10-methyl-	Needles		H_2SO_4, intense green; acetyl deriv., m.p. > 220°	124
5-Chloro-6-hydroxy-	Lemon-yellow needles	199–200	Na salt, deep red	60
1,2,6-Trichloro-3,4,5-trihydroxy-	Greenish-red plates, bronze luster	> 250	Triacetyl deriv., yellowish prisms, m.p. > 250°	57
5-Bromo-	Yellow needles	186		118
3,5,6-Tribromo-	Yellow needles	250		118
3,4,6-Tribromo-	Yellow needles	271		118
6-Bromo-5-hydroxy-	Red lustrous flakes	dec. 230	Na salt, golden lustrous flakes; acetyl deriv. silky yellow needles, m.p. 221°	58
6-Bromo-5-ethoxy-	Yellow needles	173		58

been prepared for chemotherapeutic evaluation. They were very toxic, however, and showed no trypanocidal properties.[74]

(2)   A product crystallizing in greenish needles from a large volume of xylene was obtained by Leeman and Grandmougin by the action of 2-naphthylamine on 2,2',4,4',6,6'-hexanitroazobenzene and formulated by these workers as 7,7'-dihydro-9,11,9',11'-tetranitro-12,12'-bisbenzo[a]phenazine (XXXVIII).[75]

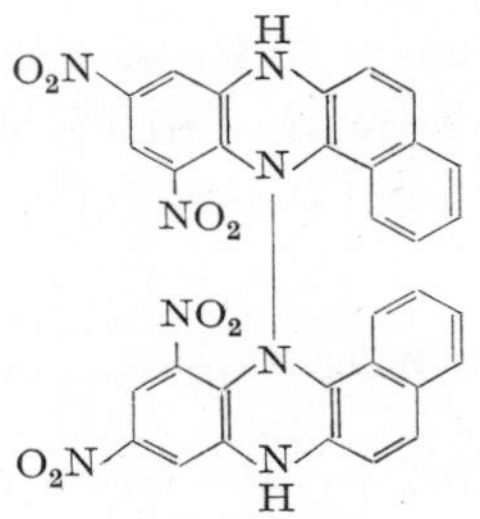

(XXXVIII)

On steric considerations, this structure is highly improbable and the compound may be a phenazyl or phenazhydrin, especially in view of the corresponding intensely colored (blue-violet) derivatives in the simple phenazine series (Chapter III:2,D).

4. Benzo[a]phenazinium Salts

A. Introduction

Two series of mono-substituted benzo[a]phenazinium salts are possible: those in which the substituent is attached at position 7 and those in which it is bound to the 12-position. The former series is the "normal" one (the so-called "naphthophenazonium" series of Kehrmann), while the latter is the "iso" ("isonaphthophenazonium") series. The position of the substituent group modifies the properties of the series, for example, color, fluorescence etc., and also the position of entering groups.

When the substituent is an alkyl or aralkyl group, it may be introduced directly into the benzo[a]phenazine nucleus. Then, owing to steric difficulties, only the "normal," that is 7-alkylbenzo[a]phenazinium series, is obtained. For aryl substituents it is necessary and, for alkyl substituents, generally more convenient, to introduce the substituent indirectly, for example, by using components bearing the required substituent in a condensation reaction. Then two isomers are possible, for example, 7- or 12-phenylbenzo[a]phenazinium salts, and in general both are obtained, though in variable proportions.

General methods for the preparation of benzo[a]phenazinium salts have largely been designed for the preparation of hydroxy and amino derivatives (rosindones and rosindulines, respectively). These series of compounds, which are of considerable commercial importance as dyestuffs, are dealt with in Chapter XIV.

B. 7-Methylbenzo[a]phenazinium Salts

These may be prepared by alkylation of benzo[a]phenazine by heating it with methyl iodide in methanol or ether at 130° under pressure,[53] although the reaction does not go to completion. The iodide forms brownish-red needles which, while insoluble in non-polar solvents, dissolve with difficulty in water or alcohol to give yellow solutions with a greenish-yellow fluorescence. Evaporation of an alcoholic solution leads to the loss of methyl iodide. The chloride forms brownish-yellow needles and the nitrate brownish-red prisms. Other salts have been described.[53,120]

Just as in the simple phenazinium compounds, these quaternary systems are easily attacked by reagents such as alkali and ammonia. Thus, treatment of the iodide with moist silver oxide, which was originally thought to yield the hydroxide, in fact leads to the formation of the 5-hydroxy derivative (7-methyl-5(7)-benzo[a]phenazinone or "methylrosindone"), which forms red leaflets with a metallic luster, m.p. 257–9°, and which gives reddish-yellow solutions in ether or ethanol, with a brick-red fluorescence. Alcoholic alkalis give the same result.[53] (Chapter XIV:2,B(1)). 7-Methylbenzo[a]phenazinium chloride and alcoholic ammonia yield the 5-amino derivative ("methylrosinduline"), the anhydro-base of which forms prisms with a bronze luster, decomposing at about 140° and giving a green solution in concentrated sulfuric acid. Various salts of this have been described.[54]

Substituted 7-methylbenzo[a]phenazinium compounds may be prepared by the condensation of an appropriately substituted 1,2-naphthoquinone component, for example, 4-acetamido-1,2-naphtho-quinone, with a 2-methylaminoaniline, for example the 5-nitro derivative.[76] This yielded a mixture of the 7- and 12-methyl derivatives (XXXIX) and (XL).

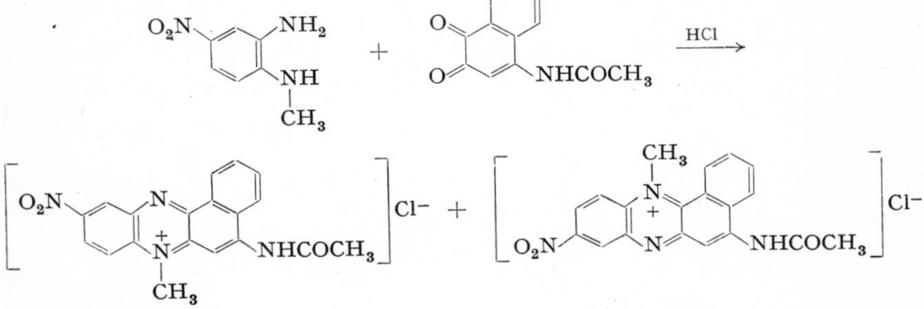

(XXXIX)   (XL)

On boiling with ethanol, the 12-methyl group was very readily lost as methyl chloride and the corresponding 5-acetamido-9-nitrobenzo[a]phenazine was obtained. The 7-methyl group was more stable under these conditions, but, when the parent 5-amino-10-nitro-7-methyl-benzo[a]phenazinium chloride was acetylated, methyl chloride was expelled and 5-acetamido-10-nitrobenzo[a]phenazine resulted.

C. 7-Ethylbenzo[a]phenazinium Salts

The iodide, formed by heating benzo[a]phenazine with ethyl iodide under pressure at 145°, forms almost black needles, m.p. about 150° (dec.). The color may be adventitious, but the possibility of a semiquinone should be borne in mind. 7-Ethylbenzo[a]phenazinium salts have also been obtained by deamination of 9-amino-7-ethylbenzo-[a]phenazinium sulfate.[126] The ferrichloride, m.p. 205°, an ochre-colored crystalline solid, is decomposed by sodium carbonate and the iron-free solution so obtained reacts with ammonia and amines to give 5-amino derivatives ("ethylrosindulines") and with alkalis to form the corresponding rosindone (Chapter XIV:2,B(1) and 4,F), cinnabar-red leaflets that become amorphous at 100° and melt at 192–193° on rapid heating.[53,126] Salts of the 7-n-propyl homolog have also been described.[121]

D. 7-Phenylbenzo[a]phenazinium Salts (XLII)

(1) *Preparation and Properties.* These have to be prepared by indirect means. The system was first obtained by Kehrmann,[77-79] by the deamination of 5-amino-7-phenylbenzo[a]phenazinium chloride (rosinduline chloride, XLI) by diazotization and treatment of the diazonium salt solution with ethanol.

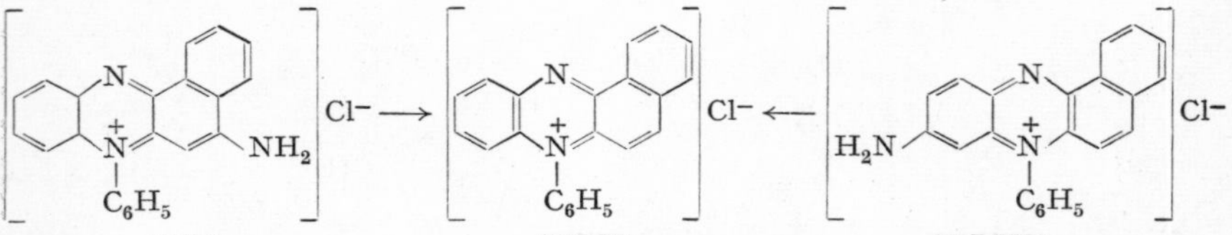

The product was isolated as the ferrichloride, which crystallizes from acetic acid as lustrous crystals, m.p. 202°, with a greenish metallic glance but which appear red by transmitted light; it gives yellowish-red aqueous solutions with a light yellow fluorescence.

Very soon after its discovery, Fischer and Hepp reported its preparation in the same manner from 9-amino-7-phenylbenzo[a]-phenazinium chloride (XLIII, isorosinduline chloride) (see also reference 79) and confirmed Kehrmann's preparation from rosinduline chloride.[80] Numerous salts were described.[79,81,122,123] Kehrmann and Helwig[82] showed that the chloride was also produced by the condensation of 1,2-naphthoquinone with 2-aminodiphenylamine. Here the condensation may occur to give two products, XLII and 12-phenyl-benzo[a]phenazinium chloride (XLIV). In fact, XLII is formed to the extent of only 2% at the most, the major product being XLIV.

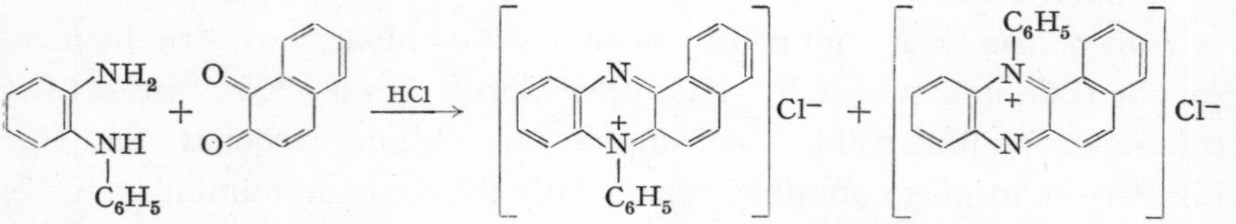

The spectra of 7-phenylbenzo[a]phenazinium salts have been recorded,[83-85] though the results are not of present-day accuracy.

(2) *Reactions*. 7-Phenylbenzo[a]phenazinium salts undergo the same type of reactions as do the simple *N*-arylated phenazinium compounds. Thus on standing with an alcoholic solution of ammonia or an amine, amino derivatives, for example 5-amino-7-phenylbenzo-[a]phenazinium (rosinduline) compounds, are formed.[78,80,81] Likewise, solution in alkali yields the corresponding 5-hydroxy (rosindone) derivatives.[78,81] The mechanism of these reactions may be regarded from two viewpoints: Kehrmann considered the reaction to be the addition of an amine to an *o*-quinonoid system; a second molecule of the quinone then oxidized the substituted dihydroquinone, being reduced to the dihydro state itself. The hydrogen was finally passed along by the aerial oxidation of the unsubstituted dihydroquinone back to the quinonoid state. An alternative explanation is that of direct anionoid attack, which may be expected to occur at either the 5- or 9-positions, both of which are meta to the arylated nitrogen atom.

(XLV)   (XLVI)

Kehrmann[86] pointed out that very unequal amounts of the two possible isomers were formed and that the 5-amino derivative was predominant. He used this as an argument in favor of some degree of fixation of the *o*-quinonoid double bonds, as in XLV. This view has been sustained by Fieser and Fieser,[87] who have cited redox potential evidence to show that the 1,2-naphthoquinone system will be stabilized to the extent of *ca*. 240 mv., relative to the alternative 1,2-benzoquinone arrangement. Later, Kehrmann[88] studied the position of attack of aniline upon substituted 7-phenylbenzo[a]phenazinium salts. He found that the 10-nitro derivative (XLVII) was attacked in the naphthalene residue to yield the 5-anilino derivative (XLVIII), but that the 10-amino compound (XLIX) yielded 10-amino-9-anilino-7-phenylbenzo-[a]phenazinium salts (L); and therefore he postulated the shift in *o*-quinonoid double bonds as shown.

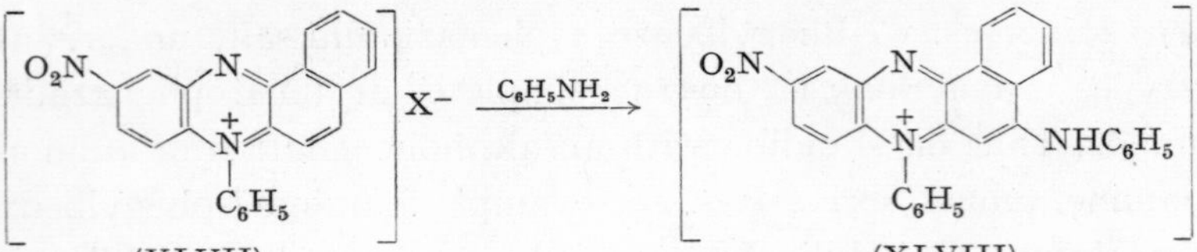

(XLVII) — $\xrightarrow{C_6H_5NH_2}$ — (XLVIII)

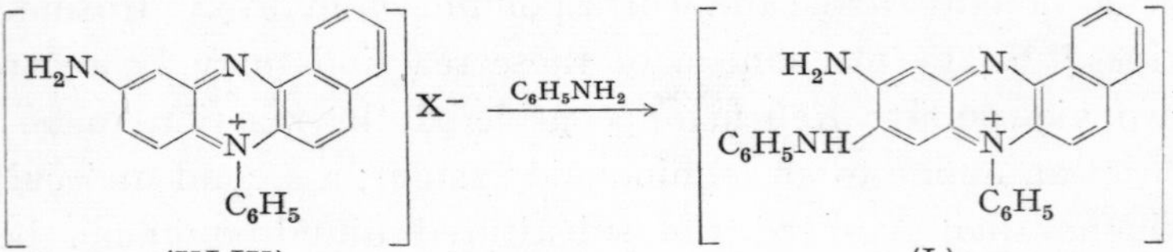

(XLIX) — $\xrightarrow{C_6H_5NH_2}$ — (L)

This evidence is the antithesis of what might be expected in the case of direct anionoid attack, but is quite in harmony with the "addition with simultaneous oxidation" theory originally put forward by Kehrmann, since an anionoid group, for example amino, is known to exert a stabilizing influence upon quinones, while a cationoid group, say nitro, exerts an opposite effect (see reference 87, p. 755). Thus the presence of an amino group in the benzene ring will stabilize an *o*-benzoquinonoid arrangement of double bonds, as in XLIX. However, it seems that an electronic effect due to the positive charge is also operative, since positions 9 and 10 are not equivalent in case of substitution, although they are equivalent positions in the quinone system. A similar case exists in the 12-phenylbenzo[*a*]phenazinium series, where the 5-position is not substituted in this manner (see Section XII:4,E(2)).

As an alternative to anionoid attack in the case of hydroxyl substitution, we have the analogy of pseudo-base formation in the simple pyridine to pyridone transformation. A theory resembling this in all but the fine detail of electronic shifts was canvassed by Hantzsch and Osswald.[89] A reason for the position taken up by the migrating hydroxyl group is adumbrated in Chapter XV:2,B.

(*3*) *Homologs.* The only homolog, which is otherwise unsubstituted, is the 10-methyl derivative described by Orlov,[90] who prepared it by successive deamination of 5,9-diamino-10-methyl-7-phenylbenzo-[*a*]phenazinium chloride. It was isolated as the ferrichloride, m.p. 205°, which with ammonia re-formed the 5-amino compound.

(4) Nitro Compounds. 7-Phenylbenzo[a]phenazinium nitrate is nitrated by nitric acid at 0° in excellent yield to a mixture of the 1- and 4-nitro-7-phenylbenzo[a]phenazinium nitrates, separated by solution in cold alcohol.[91] The orientation of these derivatives follows from the reduction to the corresponding amines, orientated by combining appropriately substituted components (see Chapter XIV). Other nitro compounds of the 7-phenylbenzo[a]phenazinium series must be prepared by indirect methods, for example, condensation of 2-amino-4-nitrodiphenylamine with 4-amino-1,2-naphthoquinone, followed by deamination of the resulting 5-amino-10-nitro-7-phenylbenzo[a]-phenazinium chloride[92] (LI, R = H). It is interesting in this connection to note that condensation of the same nitroaminodiphenylamine with 1,2-naphthoquinone itself leads to the formation in good yield of 9-nitro-12-phenylbenzo[a]phenazinium chloride (LII, R = H), a member of the so-called "iso" series.[93] When the 4-acetamido-1,2-naphthoquinone is used, both (LI, R = Ac) and (LII, R = NHAc) are obtained.[76]

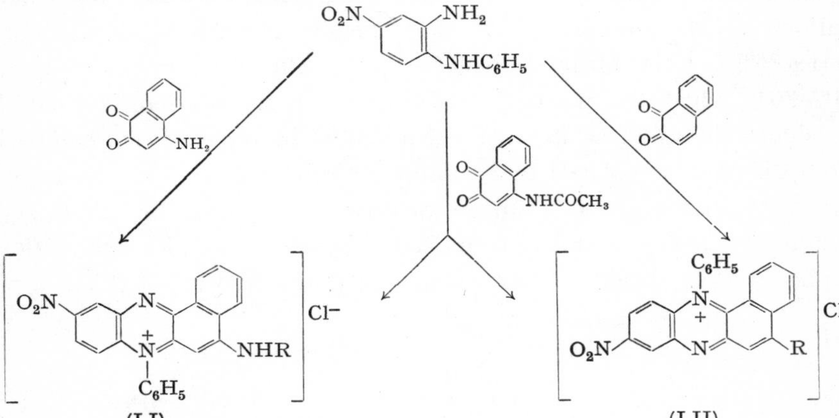

(LI)   (LII)

Compounds of the 7-phenylbenzo[a]phenazinium series with nitro groups in the 7-phenyl group may be obtained by a typical condensation reaction.[94]

(5) Sulfonic Acids. A fairly general rule of dyestuff chemistry is that sulfonation of a dye improves its solubility in water and renders it more substantive to fibers. In the case of dyes of the phenazinium

type, among others related to these, sulfonation does not give acid
products since the basic phenazinium center present leads to the
formation of betaines.[95] In the case of the simple 7-phenylbenzo[a]-
phenazinium series, the sulfonic acids are unimportant. They may be
prepared by a typical condensation reaction, for example between
2-aminodiphenylamine and 4-sulfonyl-1,2-naphthoquinone,[77,96] which
yields both 7- and 12-phenylbenzo[a]phenazinium-5-sulfonic acid
betaines, (LIII) and (LIV), separated by fractional crystallization from
acetic acid. The formulation for LIII given in *The Ring Index* (*R. I.* 3185)

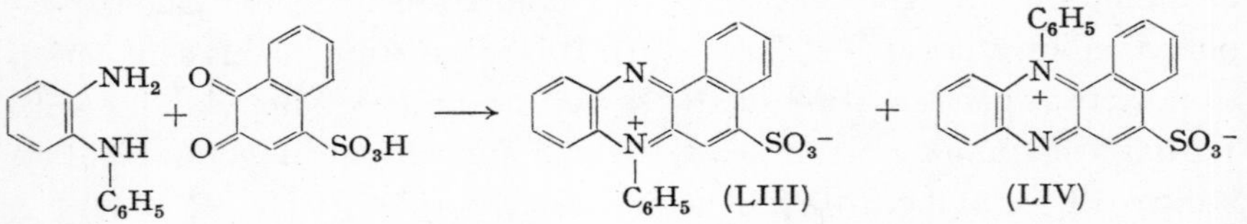

and the designation 7-phenyl-7,5(7)-epoxythiobenzo[a]phenazine-
14,14-dioxide has nothing to recommend it; the same condemnation
applies to *The Ring Index* structures 3393, 3405, and 3415 for other
sulfonic acid betaines of 7- and 12-phenylbenzo[a]phenazinium
series.[77,97,98] LIII forms brownish-yellow, glittering crystals, m.p.
302–304°, which are sparingly soluble in water. Its solutions in ethanol
are light yellow and exhibit a greenish-yellow fluorescence. The sulfonyl
group is readily replaced by an amino or substituted amino group by
means of ammonia or an amine in the presence of air, and by a hydroxy
group by means of alkali. Similarly, benzene sulfinic acid yields
7-phenyl-5-phenylsulfonylbenzo[a]phenazinium hydroxide (LV), m.p.

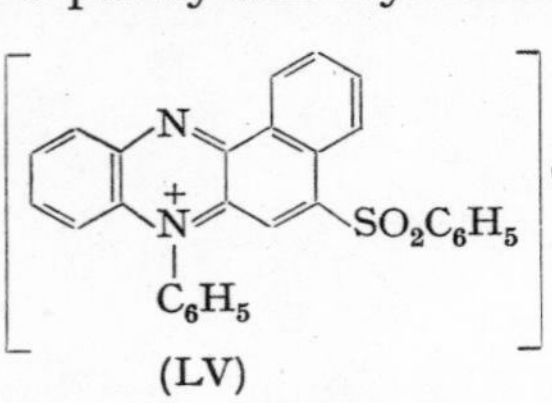

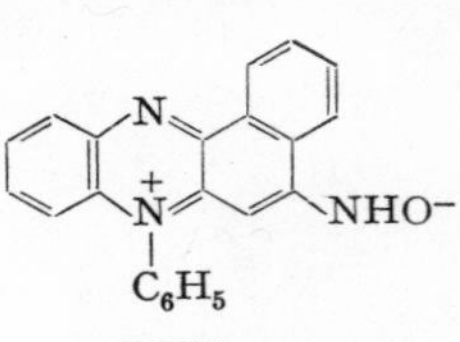

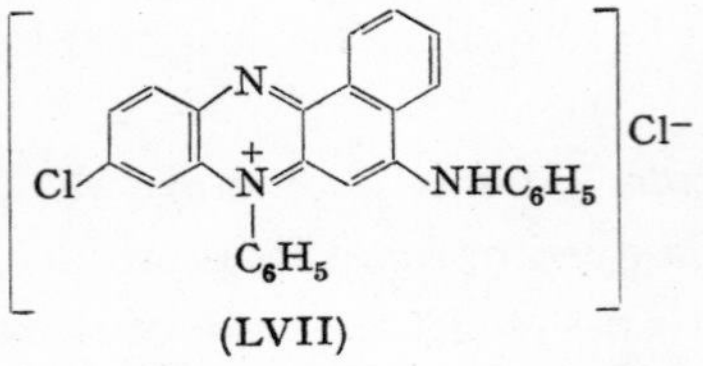

287°, while hydroxylamine behaves like a substituted amine and yields a hydroxylamino betaine[96] (LVI), to which *The Ring Index* has assigned a further unacceptable structure (*R. I.* 3186).

Disulfonic acids have also been described.[97]

(*6*)   *Chloro Compounds.*   7-Phenylbenzo[*a*]phenazinium salts are apparently unattacked by halogens. Chloro compounds may be prepared by the usual condensation procedures from suitably chlorinated components, for example, 4-anilino-1,2-naphthoquinone and 2-amino-5-chlorodiphenylamine yield 5-anilino-9-chloro-7-phenylbenzo-[*a*]phenazinium chloride (LVII).[99] The same diamine, and 1,2-naphthoquinone itself, yield 10-chloro-12-phenylbenzo[*a*]phenazinium chloride.[99] An alternative route to some of the chloro compounds is the replacement of certain hydroxyl groups by means of phosphorus pentachloride in phosphoryl chloride[100–104] (see also reference 65). The hydroxyl groups which may be replaced are those para to the unarylated nitrogen atom, that is, in the 5- and 9-positions (rosindones and isorosindones). This has a possible bearing upon the structures to be written for these compounds. For a discussion of this, see Chapter XIV:2,C(1).

As a corollary to the ease of preparation of chloro-7-phenyl-benzo[*a*]phenazinium salts by the direct replacement of hydroxyl groups by chlorine, chlorine atoms are relatively reactive and are replaceable by amines or hydroxyl groups when they occupy positions 5 or 9.[99,101,103] Thus 6-acetamido-5-chloro-7-phenylbenzo[*a*]phenazinium chloride (LVIII) reacts with aniline in the cold to yield the 5-anilino

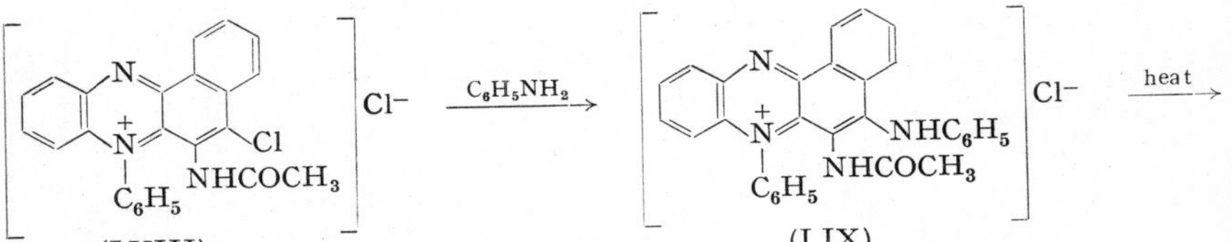

(LVIII)   (LIX)

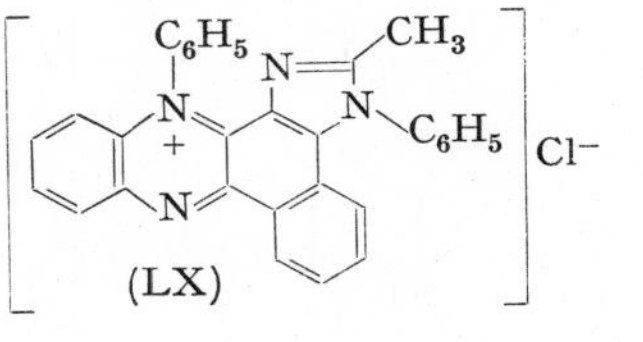

(LX)

derivative (LIX), as iridescent needles giving a dark magenta-colored solution. This readily undergoes ring closure on heating to the imidazole derivative[100] (LX, *R. I.* 3038).

A 5-chloro group is more reactive in this respect than is a 9-chloro atom. Thus, whereas 5-chloro-7-phenylbenzo[a]phenazinium chloride and aniline yield exclusively the 5-anilino derivative, 9-chloro-7-phenylbenzo[a]phenazinium chloride (LXI) undergoes both replacement of the chloro atom by aniline to give 9-anilino-7-phenylbenzo-[a]phenazinium chloride (LXII) and also the typical oxidative addition of aniline to yield some of the anhydro-base of 5-anilino-9-chloro-7-phenylbenzo[a]phenazinium hydroxide (LXIII).

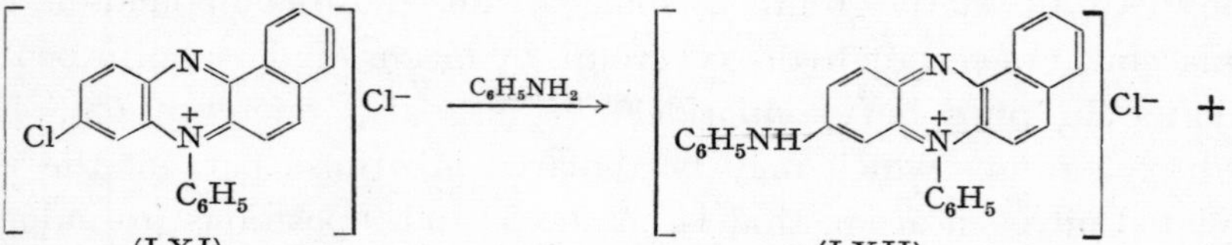

(LXI)   (LXII)

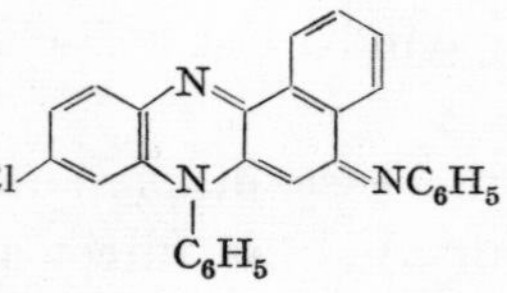

(LXIII)

The proportion of LXIII is small when the reaction is carried out in ethanol, but predominant when the reaction medium is water.[102] Similarly 5-anilino-9-chloro-7-phenylbenzo[a]phenazinium chloride

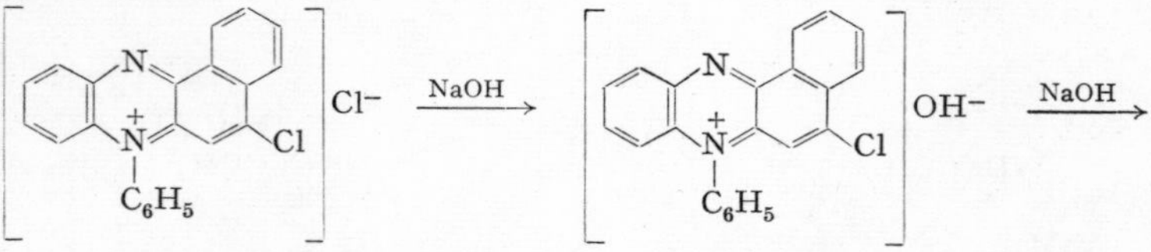

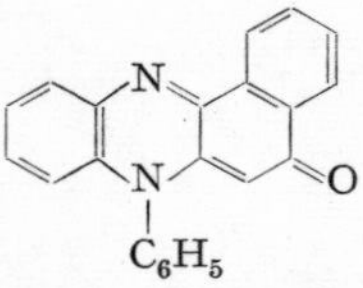

(LXIV)

and related 7-aryl compounds do not react with aromatic amines at room temperature (contrast the behavior of (LVIII)), but only at 150°.[99]

The 5-chloro atom is reactive towards alkalis also and readily regenerates the hydroxy compound.[104] This has been followed by means of conductivity measurements that show the reaction leads to an unionized compound[89] (LXIV).

The 9-chloro compounds are not so readily hydrolyzed. 9-Chloro-7-phenylbenzo[a]phenazinium chloride with water under pressure at 200–250° yields isorosindone (LXV) and also 9-chloro-7-phenyl-5(7)-benzo[a]phenazinone (LXVI, 9-chlororosindone).[102]

(LXV)   (LXVI)

This difference in reactivity of 5- and 9-chloro compounds is in agreement with the behavior to be expected from the effect of substituents upon redox potentials of quinonoid compounds. The chlorine substituent exerts a destabilizing influence of ca. +240 mv., approximately the difference between the 1,2-benzo- and 1,2-naphthoquinonoid forms. Hence the 5-chloro group does not destabilize the 1,2-naphthoquinonoid structure sufficiently to make it transform into a benzoquinonoid arrangement of bonds. Consequently reaction with an amine proceeds solely by replacement to yield a 5-amino compound, the amino group stabilizing the 1,2-naphthoquinonoid arrangement by ca. —180 to —250 mv. In contradistinction to this, a 9-chloro group destabilizes the 1,2-benzoquinonoid arrangement relative to the 1,2-naphthoquinonoid by +480 mv., so that an amine will add on to the 1,2-naphthoquinone system of double bonds in preference to replacing the chlorine atom, the latter process providing only partial stabilization, i.e., from +300 to +230 mv., while the former process increases still further the stabilization of the 1,2-naphthoquinone system.

The hydroxyl group is similar in effect to the amino or substituted amino group, although not to such a marked degree.

(7) *Thio Derivatives.* These are relatively unimportant. Fischer and Hepp[102] showed that 5-chloro-7-phenylbenzo[a]phenazinium chloride and potassium hydrosulfide in ethanol yielded 7-phenyl-5(7)-benzo[a]phenazinthione (LXVII) as dark blue plates from pyridine.

(LXVII)   (LXVIII)

This is a remarkable stable compound that withstands boiling with dilute acids and is hydrolyzed to rosindone (LXIV) only by dilute sulfuric acid under pressure at 170–180°. It reacts with hydroxylamine to yield the anhydro-betaine (LVI) of 5-hydroxylamino-7-phenyl-benzo[a]phenazinium hydroxide[125]; *cf.* rosindone. It is probably better formulated as the betaine (LXVIII). The corresponding 5-ethylthio-ether has also been described.[102]

E. 12-Phenylbenzo[a]phenazinium Salts (XLIV)

(1) *Preparation and Properties.* These are similar in some respects to the 7-phenyl derivatives already described (Section XII: 4,D). Thus they must be prepared by indirect means and in fact are generally obtained along with the 7-phenyl derivatives in condensation reactions. They are less important than the corresponding 7-phenyl series since they are not parents of commercially valuable dyestuffs such as rosinduline.

Like the isomeric 7-phenyl compound, this system was first obtained by Kehrmann[78] by condensation of 2-aminodiphenylamine with 1,2-naphthoquinone, in which reaction the 7-phenyl isomer is only formed in, at most, 2% yield,[82] and also by deamination of 5-amino-12-phenylbenzo[a]phenazinium chloride[78] (LXIX) or of 3-amino-12-phenylbenzo[a]phenazinium chloride (LXX).[105]

12-Phenylbenzo[a]phenazinium chloride was isolated as the ferrichloride,[78,82] which crystallizes from ethanol as orange-yellow, lustrous leaflets, m.p. 200.5°. It is easily soluble in water, giving orange-yellow solutions which, in contradistinction to the 7-phenyl isomer, do not exhibit fluorescence. With concentrated sulfuric acid it yields a

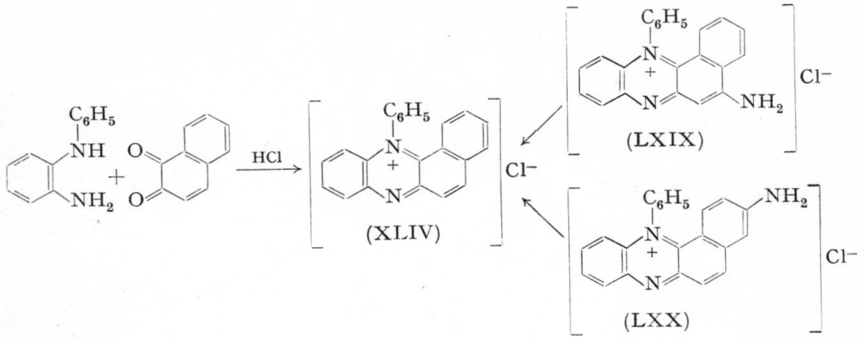

reddish-violet color, again without fluorescence. The absorption spectra of 12-phenylbenzo[a]phenazinium mono- and di-salts have been recorded[106,107] though by modern standards the accuracy is probably not high. The spectra resemble those of the corresponding salts of the 7-phenyl compound quite closely.

(2) *Reactions.* Like the 7-phenyl isomer, 12-phenylbenzo[a]-phenazinium salts react with amines, the amino group entering at a position meta to the arylated nitrogen atom, that is, position 10.[82] The considerations of partial bond fixation into either benzoquinonoid or naphthoquinonoid forms do not arise here because the corresponding position in the naphthalenic portion is not available for reaction; doubtless the same effect is operative, nonetheless.

(3) *Nitro Derivatives.* Direct nitration of 12-phenylbenzo[a]-phenazinium nitrate, by means of concentrated nitric acid at 0°, gives a mixture of two nitro compounds, separated by fractional crystallization from ethanol.[108] The less soluble isomer forms yellow glistening needles and on reduction gives an amine, identified as 2-amino-12-phenylbenzo[a]phenazinium chloride, thereby demonstrating that the nitro group occupied position 2 (LXXI). The major product was too soluble to be purified satisfactorily, but in a similar fashion the nitro group was shown to occupy position 4, forming 4-nitro-12-phenyl-benzo[a]phenazinium nitrate (LXXII).

The 9-nitro derivative has been prepared by deamination of

aminonitro-12-phenylbenzo[a]phenazinium salts or by condensation of suitably substituted components.[93] It yields a bright red, crystalline nitrate and a bright red ferrichloride.

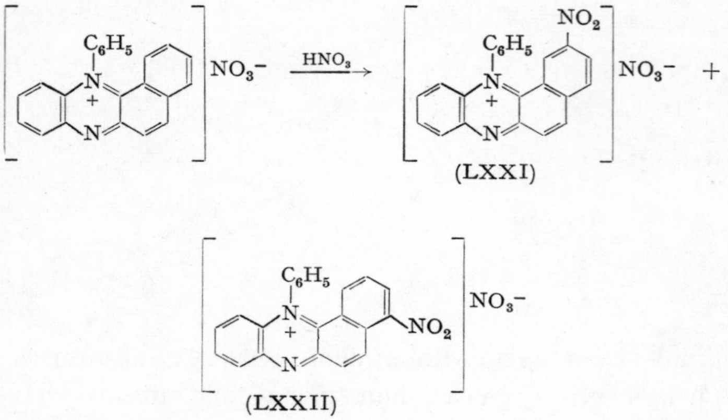

(LXXI)

(LXXII)

(*4*) *Chloro Compounds.* Chloro derivatives do not appear to have been prepared from hydroxy compounds in this series, in contrast to the 7-phenyl series, but are obtained, for example, by condensing 2-amino-5-chlorodiphenylamine and 1,2-naphthoquinone, which yield 10-chloro-12-phenylbenzo[a]phenazinium salts[99] (LXXIII). This structure follows from the fact that reaction with dimethylamine yields the same amino compound (LXXIV) as is obtained from 12-phenylbenzo-[a]phenazinium chloride and dimethylamine.

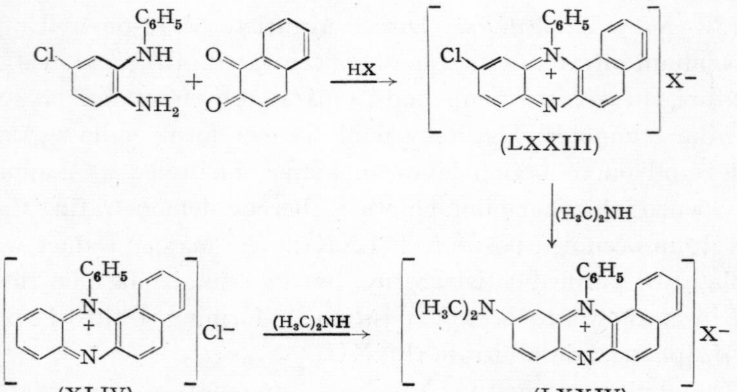

(LXXIII)

(H₃C)₂NH

(XLIV)   (LXXIV)

It is noteworthy that the chlorine atom is in a "reactive" position, but the fact that it reacts with water only on prolonged boiling[99] is a further indication of the lack of activity to be associated with a "reactive" chlorine atom in the benzoquinonoid moiety.

(5) *Sulfonic Acids.* These, like the 7-phenyl isomers, exist as betaines. They are prepared by condensation reactions between suitably substituted components, for example 4-sulfonyl-1,2-naphthoquinone and 2-aminodiphenylamine, and are separated from their 7-phenyl isomers by fractional crystallization.[77] In the example cited the products are LIII and LIV. These behave differently in their reactions with amines. LIII exchanges the sulfonyl group for an amino group, since it is in a reactive position, and this exchange will lead to stabilization (lower redox potential). With LIV, however, the sulfonyl group is not in a reactive position, while the only reactive position, position 10, is unsubstituted so that treatment of LIV with an amine leads to introduction of the amino group to yield 10-dimethylamino-12-phenyl-benzo[a]phenazinium-5-sulfonic acid betaine (LXXV), as dark violet, coppery needles, insoluble in water.[96]

(LIV)   (LXXV)

F. Conclusion

The chemistry of the 7- and 12-phenylbenzo[a]phenazinium salts can largely be explained and predicted by a consideration of two factors.

(*1*) Reagents usually classed as anionoid, that is amines or alkalis, react with these quaternary compounds at positions meta to the arylated nitrogen. They may do so either by direct anionoid attack or by addition to the quinonoid system with simultaneous oxidation of the dihydro compound produced by a second molecule of the quaternary salt, which in turn is oxidized by the air. The consensus of facts appears to favor the latter explanation. When such a reactive position is already occupied, ejection of the occupying group may occur; this is governed by (*2*).

(2)   The reactivity of an atom or group at one or other of these reactive positions is governed by the relative effects the substituent and substituting groups have upon the redox potential of a quinonoid system, the net result being that which tends to produce a more stable quinonoid system, that is, one with a lower redox potential.

References

1. O. Hinsberg, *Ann.*, **319**, 257 (1901).
2. G. M. Badger and R. Pettit, *J. Chem. Soc.*, **1951**, 3211.
3. K. Ganapati, *J. Indian Chem. Soc.*, **15**, 407 (1938).
4. K. Ganapati, *Current Sci.*, **6**, 448 (1938); *Chem. Abstracts*, **32**, 4973 (1938).
5. J. Leicester, *Ber.*, **23**, 2793 (1890).
6. O. Hinsberg, *Ann.*, **237**, 327 (1887).
7. O. N. Witt, *Ber.*, **20**, 571 (1887).
8. R. Zärtling, *Ber.*, **23**, 175 (1890).
9. W. Autenrieth and O. Hinsberg, *Ber.*, **25**, 492 (1892).
10. R. Nietzki and G. Hasterlik, *Ber.*, **24**, 1337 (1891).
11. F. Kehrmann and J. A. Schedler, *Helv. Chim. Acta*, **8**, 3 (1925).
12. F. Kehrmann and I. Safar, *Helv. Chim. Acta*, **8**, 668 (1925).
13. F. Ullmann and R. Heisler, *Ber.*, **42**, 4263 (1909).
14. L. S. Efros, A. E. Poraï-Koshits and B. A. Poraï-Koshits, *J. Gen. Chem. (U.S.S.R.)*, **17**, 1801 (1947); *Chem. Abstracts*, **42**, 5869 (1948).
15. T. Zincke and A. T. Lawson, *Ber.*, **20**, 1167 (1887).
16. R. Lesser, *Ber.*, **27**, 2363 (1894).
17. G. R. Levi and M. Faldino, *Gazz. chim. ital.*, **54**, 818 (1924); *Chem. Zentr.*, **1925**, I, 657.
18. Ger. Pat. 82,240; *Frdl.*, **4**, 392 (1894–1897).
19. F. Krollpfeiffer, G. Wolf and H. Walbrecht, *Ber.*, **67B**, 908 (1934).
20. H. T. Bucherer and F. Stickel, *J. prakt. Chem.*, **110**, 309 (1925).
21. H. T. Bucherer and M. Rauch, *J. prakt. Chem.*, **132**, 227 (1931).
22. N. L. Drake, "The Bucherer Reaction," Chapter 5 in *Organic Reactions*, Vol. I, Wiley, New York, 1942.
23. O. Fischer and E. Hepp, *Ber.*, **20**, 2471 (1887).
24. F. Kehrmann, *Ber.*, **50**, 554 (1917).
25. J. B. Cohen and H. G. Crabtree, *J. Chem. Soc.*, **119**, 2055 (1921).
26. O. N. Witt, *Ber.*, **21**, 719 (1888).
27. R. Nietzki and R. Otto, *Ber.*, **21**, 1598 (1888).
28. S. Maffei and S. Pietra, *Boll. Sci. Bologna*, **8**, 104 (1950); *Chem. Abstracts*, **46**, 120 (1952).
29. A. Wohl and W. Aue, *Ber.*, **34**, 2442 (1901).
30. U. S. Pat. 2,332,179; *Chem. Abstracts*, **38**, 1534 (1944).
31. I. J. Pachter and M. C. Kloetzel, *J. Am. Chem. Soc.*, **73**, 4958 (1951).
32. A. Wohl and M. Lange, *Ber.*, **43**, 2180 (1910).
33. O. Fischer, *Ber.*, **26**, 187 (1893).
34. O. Fischer and E. Hepp, *Ann.*, **256**, 233 (1890).
35. O. Fischer and E. Hepp, *Ber.*, **23**, 841 (1890).
36. K. Eicker, *Ber.*, **23**, 3803 (1890).
37. O. N. Witt, *Ber.*, **18**, 1119 (1885).

38. O. N. Witt, *Ber.*, **19**, 441 (1886).
39. F. Ullmann and J. S. Ankersmit, *Ber.*, **38**, 1811 (1905).
40. Ger. Pat. 157,861; *Frdl.*, **8**, 517 (1906–1907).
41. F. Kehrmann and J. Riera y Punti, *Ber.*, **44**, 2618 (1911).
42. F. Kehrmann, *Ber.*, **23**, 2446 (1890).
43. G. M. Badger, R. S. Pearce and R. Pettit, *J. Chem. Soc.*, **1951**, 3199.
44. F. Kehrmann and C. Mermod, *Helv. Chim. Acta*, **10**, 62 (1927).
45. R. Huisgen and G. Sorge, *Ann.*, **566**, 162 (1950).
46. O. Hinsberg and H. Garfunkel, *Ann.*, **292**, 258 (1896).
47. H. Katz, *Z. Physik*, **87**, 238 (1933).
48. G. M. Badger, J. H. Seidler and B. Thomson, *J. Chem. Soc.*, **1951**, 3207.
49. W. Bradley and R. Robinson, *J. Chem. Soc.*, **1934**, 1484.
50. R. Brunner and O. N. Witt, *Ber.*, **20**, 2660 (1887).
51. O. Fischer, *Ber.*, **36**, 3622 (1903).
52. O. Fischer and E. Schindler, *Ber.*, **39**, 2238 (1906).
53. O. Fischer and E. Franck, *Ber.*, **26**, 179 (1893).
54. O. Fischer and E. Hepp, *Ber.*, **30**, 391 (1897).
55. S. Maffei, *Gazz. chim. ital.*, **76**, 239 (1946); *Chem. Abstracts*, **42**, 911 (1948).
56. T. Zincke, *Ber.*, **26**, 613 (1893).
57. T. Zincke and M. Schmidt, *Ann.*, **286**, 27 (1895).
58. S. Lindenbaum, *Ber.*, **34**, 1050 (1901).
59. T. Zincke and P. Wiegand, *Ann.*, **286**, 58 (1895).
60. T. Zincke, *Ann.*, **295**, 1 (1897).
61. G. M. Badger, R. S. Pearce and R. Pettit, *J. Chem. Soc.*, **1951**, 3204.
62. O. N. Witt, *Ber.*, **19**, 914 (1886).
63. O. N. Witt, *Ber.*, **20**, 577 (1887).
64. F. Kehrmann and B. Mascioni, *Ber.*, **28**, 345 (1895).
65. O. Fischer and E. Hepp, *Ber.*, **31**, 2477 (1898).
66. Ger. Pat. 365,902; *Chem. Zentr.*, **1923**, II, 1186.
67. Ger. Pat. 492,161; *Chem. Abstracts*, **27**, 1195 (1933).
68. U. S. Pat. 1,873,938; *Chem. Abstracts*, **26**, 6154 (1932).
69. Fr. Pat. 668,078; *Chem. Abstracts*, **24**, 1520 (1930).
70. Brit. Pat. 322,209; *Chem. Abstracts*, **24**, 2891 (1930).
71. Fr. Pat. 584,401; *Chem. Zentr.*, **1925**, I, 2665.
72. Brit. Pat. 217,936; *Chem. Zentr.*, **1924**, II, 2791.
73. Brit. Pat. 253,488; *Chem. Abstracts*, **21**, 2564 (1927).
74. E. A. H. Friedheim, *Compt. rend. soc. phys. hist. nat. Genève*, **55**, 73 (1938), in *Arch. sci. phys. nat.*, **20**, July–Aug. (1938); *Chem. Abstracts*, **33**, 8787 (1939).
75. H. Leeman and E. Grandmougin, *Ber.*, **41**, 1295 (1908).
76. F. Kehrmann and H. Jacob, *Ber.*, **31**, 3087 (1898).
77. F. Kehrmann and E. Locher, *Ber.*, **29**, 2072 (1896).
78. F. Kehrmann, *Ber.*, **29**, 2316 (1896).
79. F. Kehrmann and W. Shaposhnikov, *Ber.*, **29**, 2967 (1896).
80. O. Fischer and E. Hepp, *Ber.*, **29**, 2752 (1896).
81. F. Kehrmann and W. Shaposhnikov, *Ber.*, **30**, 2620 (1897).
82. F. Kehrmann and W. Helwig, *Ber.*, **30**, 2629 (1897).
83. F. Kehrmann and P. Nüesch, *Ber.*, **34**, 3099 (1901).
84. F. Kehrmann, R. Speitel and E. Grandmougin, *Ber.*, **47**, 3205 (1914).
85. F. Kehrmann and M. Sandoz, *Helv. Chim. Acta*, **6**, 982 (1923).
86. F. Kehrmann, *Ber.*, **31**, 977 (1898).
87. L. F. Fieser and M. Fieser, *Organic Chemistry*, 2nd ed., Heath, Boston, 1950, p. 890.

88. F. Kehrmann, *Ber.*, **33**, 395 (1900).
89. A. Hantzsch and G. Osswald, *Ber.*, **33**, 278 (1900).
90. N. Orlov, *J. Russ. Phys. Chem. Soc.*, **42**, 522, (1910); *Chem. Zentr.*, **1910**, II, 481.
91. F. Kehrmann and P. Filatov, *Ber.*, **32**, 2627 (1899).
92. F. Kehrmann and O. Feder, *Ber.*, **30**, 2637 (1897).
93. F. Kehrmann and A. Levy, *Ber.*, **31**, 3097 (1898).
94. F. Kehrmann, F. Rademacher and O. Feder, *Ber.*, **31**, 3076 (1898).
95. F. Kehrmann and A. Herzbaum, *Ber.*, **50**, 873 (1917).
96. F. Kehrmann and C. Locher, *Ber.*, **31**, 2428 (1898).
97. Ger. Pat. 99,609; *Chem. Zentr.*, **1899**, I, 462; *Frdl.*, **5**, 366 (1897–1900).
98. Ger. Pat. 72,343; *Frdl.*, **3**, 346 (1890–1894).
99. F. Kehrmann and W. Hiby, *Ber.*, **34**, 1085 (1901).
100. F. Kehrmann and G. Barche, *Ber.*, **33**, 3067 (1900).
101. O. Fischer and E. Hepp, *Ber.*, **31**, 299 (1898).
102. O. Fischer and E. Hepp, *Ber.*, **33**, 1485 (1900).
103. O. Fischer, *Ber.*, **34**, 940 (1901).
104. O. Fischer and E. Hepp, *Ber.*, **30**, 1827 (1897).
105. F. Kehrmann and M. Ravinson, *Ber.*, **32**, 927 (1899).
106. F. Kehrmann, R. Speitel and E. Grandmougin, *Ber.*, **47**, 3363 (1914).
107. F. Kehrmann and M. Sandoz, *Helv. Chim. Acta*, **8**, 250 (1925).
108. F. Kehrmann and G. Steiner, *Ber.*, **33**, 3276 (1900).
109. L. F. Fieser and C. K. Bradsher, *J. Am. Chem. Soc.*, **61**, 417 (1939).
110. F. Weygand and K. Schröder, *Ber.*, **74B**, 1844 (1941).
111. O. Fischer and H. Fritzweiler, *Ber.*, **27**, 2777 (1894).
112. Ger. Pat. 38,425; *Frdl.*, **1**, 418 (1877–1887).
113. L. Westenberg and J. P. Wibaut, *Rec. trav. chim.*, **50**, 188 (1931); *Chem. Abstracts*, **25**, 2714 (1931).
114. L. F. Fieser and M. Fieser, *J. Am. Chem. Soc.*, **61**, 596 (1939).
115. L. F. Fieser and J. L. Hartwell, *J. Am. Chem. Soc.*, **57**, 1484 (1935).
116. L. I. Smith and H. H. Hoehn, *J. Am. Chem. Soc.*, **61**, 2619 (1939).
117. L. I. Smith and H. H. Hoehn, *J. Am. Chem. Soc.*, **63**, 1175 (1941).
118. K. Fries and K. Schimmelschmidt, *Ann.*, **484**, 245 (1930).
119. F. Kehrmann (with C. Buffat), *Ber.*, **56B**, 2390 (1923).
120. K. Yamada and K. Oiwa, *J. Soc. Chem. Ind. Japan*, **39**, Suppl. binding, 208 (1936); *Chem. Abstracts*, **30**, 6567 (1936).
121. K. Yamada and N. Hasebe, *J. Soc. Chem. Ind. Japan*, **41**, Suppl. binding, 290 (1938); *Chem. Abstracts*, **33**, 1740 (1939).
122. K. Yamada and K. Oiwa, *J. Soc. Chem. Ind. Japan*, **39**, Suppl. binding, 207 (1936); *Chem. Abstracts*, **30**, 6567 (1936).
123. K. Yamada, T. Noguchi and K. Oiwa, *Bull. Chem. Soc. Japan*, **11**, 225 (1936); *Chem. Abstracts*, **30**, 5993 (1936).
124. S. C. Hooker, *J. Chem. Soc.*, **63**, 1376 (1893).
125. O. Fischer and K. Arntz, *Ber.*, **39**, 3807 (1906).
126. W. G. Shaposhnikov, *J. Russ. Phys. Chem. Soc.*, **30**, 546 (1898); *Chem. Zentr.*, **1898**, II, 919.
127. G. M. Badger and R. Pettit, *J. Chem. Soc.*, **1952**, 1877.
128. T. Zincke and K. Fries, *Ann.*, **334**, 342 (1904).
129. K. Fries and J. Empson, *Ber.*, **42**, 3375 (1909).
130. K. Fries and E. Hempelmann, *Ber.*, **42**, 3381 (1909).
131. S. Maffei, S. Pietra and A. M. Rivolta, *Ann. chim. (Rome)*, **42**, 519 (1952).
132. T. Zincke and B. Francke, *Ann.*, **293**, 136 (1896).
133. L. Birkofer and A. Widmann, *Chem. Ber.*, **86**, 1295 (1953).

CHAPTER XIII

Hydroxy and Amino Derivatives of Benzo[a]phenazines

1. Introduction

Hydroxy and amino derivatives of benzo[a]phenazine are worthy of separate consideration since substitution of these auxochromic groups in the benzo[a]phenazine molecule leads to the development of useful dyeing properties. The two series of derivatives are known under the general designations of "eurhodols" and "eurhodines", respectively. The corresponding names for the related classes of hydroxy- and amino-benzo[a]phenazinium derivatives (Chapter XIV) are "rosindones" and "rosindulines," respectively. Halohydroxy derivatives of benzo[a]phenazine are described in Chapter XII.

2. Monohydroxybenzo[a]phenazines

The hydroxybenzo[a]phenazines may be prepared by a number of the general methods discussed earlier (Chapter XII:3,B), for example, by the condensation of an o-diamine with a hydroxy- or polyhydroxy-quinone. Several of the hydroxybenzo[a]phenazines are capable of tautomerism, like their simpler analogs of the phenazine series (Chapter V) and may exist in either hydroxy or keto forms (lactim-lactam tautomerism).

The simpler monohydroxy and monoalkoxy derivatives are listed later in Table XIV.

A. 5-Hydroxybenzo[a]phenazine

5-Hydroxybenzo[a]phenazine (5-7H-benzo[a]phenazinone, (Ia or b) forms yellowish-red needles, for which no melting point has been recorded,[1-3] and may be sublimed. It forms an acetyl derivative, yellowish needles, m.p. 217°, which is readily hydrolyzed by alkalis.[4] It was prepared by heating the corresponding amino compound under pressure at 180–200° with concentrated hydrochloric acid[1] or by diazotization of the amino group and conversion to the phenol[5]; Eicker[3] showed that the corresponding 5-ethylamino compound suffered the same hydrolysis. A more direct method of preparation is that due to Kehrmann, who condensed 2-hydroxy-1,4-naphthoquinone with o-phenylenediamine[2] or with 2-benzamidoaniline in aqueous acetic acid[6] (Chapter XII:3,B(16)).

It has also been obtained, accidently, from the reaction of o-phenylenediamine with 2-hydroxy-3-iodo-1,4-naphthoquinone,[7] owing to the reductive removal of the iodine atom accompanied by simultaneous oxidation of part of the o-diamine to 2,3-diaminophenazine (Chapter XII:3,H(2)), and also by the removal of bromine from 6-bromo-5-hydroxybenzo[a]phenazine by treatment with phenol and concentrated sulfuric acid[8] (Chapter XII:3,H(2)).

5-Hydroxybenzo[a]phenazine retains the weakly basic properties of the benzo[a]phenazine series, and, with strong acids, forms yellowish-red salts that are hydrolyzed by water. Moreover, because of the presence of a phenolic group, it is soluble in dilute alkali, giving a blood-red solution from which, on addition of concentrated sodium hydroxide solution, the sodium salt is precipitated as gold metallic-lustered leaflets,[2,6] a very characteristic property. Zinc dust distillation of 5-hydroxybenzo[a]phenazine yields the parent heterocyclic system.[1]

The tautomerism of 5-hydroxybenzo[a]phenazine has been discussed by Kehrmann.[10,11] The hydroxy formulation is favored by the preparation from the amino compound by diazotization and by the solubility in alkalis, while the keto formulation follows from the preparation from 2-hydroxy-1,4-naphthoquinone. That the compound is a system in tautomeric equilibrium follows from observations of Kehrmann and Messinger,[12] who took the sodium salt described above and heated it under reflux with methanolic methyl iodide. The product was crystallized from ethanolic hydrochloric acid by the addition of water, when 5-methoxybenzo[a]phenazine (II) separated as long light yellow needles (from ethanol), m.p. 176–177° (a later value is 180° [13]) that were insoluble in alkalis and gave an intense yellow coloration in concentrated sulfuric acid. Treatment of the mother liquors from the first crystallization with ammonia precipitated 7-methyl-5(7)-benzo-[a]phenazinone (III) as vermilion needles with a green reflex from ethanol-benzene. These melted at 257–259° and were sparingly soluble in organic solvents, giving a yellowish-red color with a strong brick-red fluorescence. This product was identical with that formed in the condensation between 2-methylaminoaniline and 2-hydroxy-1,4-naphthoquinone. It gave a dichroic solution in concentrated sulfuric acid, thin layers being dirty-green while thick layers appeared purplish-red.

B. 5-Hydroxy-10-methylbenzo[a]phenazine

This compound (IV), or 10-methyl-5(7)-benzo[a]phenazinone, was the original eurhodol prepared by Witt in his pioneering research.[14,15] He heated a mixture of the corresponding eurhodine (Section XIII:5,C) with dilute hydrochloric acid in a sealed tube at 180° and obtained the eurhodol as a glittering yellow powder consisting of minute, dichroic crystals with yellow and red faces, which did not melt below 265°.[16] When Witt attempted to remove the amino group by diazotization with ethyl nitrite and acid and decomposition in ethanol, he obtained the ethoxy compound (m.p. 175°) instead of the parent heterocyclic system.[15,99]

The compound IV has also been obtained by the condensation of 3,4-diaminotoluene with 2-hydroxy-1,4-naphthoquinone.[2,16,17] The hydroxyl group may be replaced by anilino by heating with a mixture of aniline and aniline hydrochloride[9] (see Section XIII:5,G). Other homologs of 5-hydroxybenzo[a]phenazine are listed in Table XIV. A number of them were prepared during the classic research of Hooker on the constitution of lapachol.

C. 6-Hydroxybenzo[a]phenazine (V)

This crystallizes from ethanol in lemon-yellow needles, m.p. 199°, which dissolve in dilute alkali to give a red solution from which concentrated sodium hydroxide solution precipitates the sodium salt as flesh-colored needles. It was first prepared by Zincke by the opening of the oxide ring of 5,6-dihydrobenzo[a]oxiro[c]phenazine (Chapter XII:3,E(2)) by means of alcoholic hydrochloric acid.[4] Later, it was prepared by the acid hydrolysis of the corresponding 6-amino compound under pressure at 140°.[18]

(IV)   (V)   (VI)

Theoretically, compound V is capable of tautomerism to 6(12H)-benzo[a]phenazinone (VI). However the 12-aza atom is sterically hindered and therefore unlikely to be methylated. Moreover hydrogen bonding between the hydroxyl group and the 7-aza atom will stabilize the hydroxy form. Indeed, methylation by means of methyl iodide and methanolic sodium hydroxide yields only one compound, fine yellow needles (from benzene) m.p. 158°.[4] Zincke stated that the compound was similar to 7-methyl-5(7H)-benzo[a]phenazinone (III) and formulated it as an N-methyl compound; but clearly the properties are better in accord with the formulation as 6-methoxybenzo[a]phenazine, showing that the eurhodol reacts as V.

D. 9-Hydroxybenzo[a]phenazine (VII)

This compound has been obtained by the condensation of 1,2-diaminonaphthalene with 2-hydroxy-1,4-benzoquinone[19, 20] and by the acid hydrolysis of the corresponding 9-amino compound, which may be independently orientated and from which the formulation of the hydroxy compound is deduced.[21] It crystallizes from ethanol in brick-red needles, which decompose without melting at 290°, and it dissolves in concentrated sulfuric acid with a magenta color, which becomes lemon-yellow on dilution. With acetic anhydride, it yields an acetyl derivative as pale yellow needles, m.p. 216.5°, from benzene.

Since the 9-hydroxy group is environed relative to the azine ring in a similar manner to the 5-hydroxyl group, the compound should be capable of tautomerism. In fact, after methylation with methyl sulfate, the alkali-insoluble fraction yields the N-methyl compound (VIII) as dark-red crystals from benzene, the properties of which closely resemble those of the related N-phenyl compound (Chapter XIV:2,C(12)). Thus it gives a dirty blue color with concentrated sulfuric acid and its ethereal solution exhibits a definite green fluorescence.

HO—⟨VII⟩ $(CH_3)_2SO_4$ →   O=⟨VIII⟩ CH_3

(VII)   (VIII) CH_3

E. Miscellaneous

A 9- or 10-methyl substituted 3,6-disulfonic acid of 1-hydroxybenzo[a]phenazine has been described.[105] 2-Hydroxybenzo[a]phenazine is obtained from 7-hydroxy-1,2-naphthoquinone and o-phenylenediamine[23] or from 2,7-dihydroxy-1-nitrosonaphthalene and o-phenylenediamine.[24] It forms yellow leaflets, m.p. 285°, from ethanol and gives a yellowish-green coloration with concentrated sulfuric acid, changing on dilution through brown to red. The acetyl derivative forms brownish-yellow needles, m.p. 207°, from ethanol, while methyl sulfate and alkali affords the 2-methoxy derivative as brownish-yellow lustrous needles, m.p. 168°, a solution of which in benzene exhibits a green fluorescence. 4-Hydroxybenzo[a]phenazine has been obtained by the alkaline fusion of the corresponding sulfonic acid[22] but has not been characterized. An unorientated hydroxybenzo[a]phenazine, obtained by the alkaline fusion of a sulfonic acid produced by the sulfonation of benzo[a]phenazine, which is described[25] as yellow and giving a green coloration with sulfuric acid which changes to red on dilution, may be identical with 2-hydroxybenzo[a]phenazine. An unorientated ethoxybenzo[a]phenazine, fine yellow needles, m.p. 186–187°, obtained from 1,2-naphthoquinone and 3,4-diaminophenetole, may be either the 9- or the 10-ethoxy compound.[26]

F. Eurhodol Dyestuffs

The alkaline fusion of sulfonic acids of the benzo[a]phenazine series has been applied to the commercial production of eurhodol dyes.[27] The sulfonic acid group replaced is generally in the 1-position. The 1,6-disulfonic acid, on heating under pressure at 180° with potassium hydroxide, yields 1-hydroxybenzo[a]phenazine-6-sulfonic acid,[28-30] which gives fast yellow to red shades on wool. These eurhodol dyes may be modified by halogenation, treatment with sulfuryl chloride or bromide giving dyes of brighter golden-yellow shades which dye cotton from a vat,[31] while sulfur monochloride yields sulfur-containing brown dyes.[32]

Alternatively, the simple eurhodols may be elaborated, for example, by coupling with diazotized sulfanilic acid, to give monazo derivatives,[33,107] or a eurhodol component may be united with a naphtholsulfonic acid by coupling with a tetrazotized bianisidine and the disazo derivative further modified by incorporation of copper giving a dye that yields on cotton and regenerated cellulose[34-36] blue-gray tones which are of excellent fastness. A modification of the basic eurhodol dyes from 5-hydroxybenzo[a]phenazine (I) may be brought about by causing them to react in the presence of solvents such as nitrobenzene, with 1,4-quinones, for example, 1,4-benzoquinone,[37,38] or, in the presence of anhydrous sodium acetate also, with chlorinated 1,4-quinones such as 2,3-dichloro-1,4-naphthoquinones,[39,40] chloranil[41] and other chlorinated 1,4-quinones,[42,43] the products, presumably ethers, giving green to yellow dyeings on cotton.

TABLE XIV. Monohydroxybenzo[a]phenazines and Derivatives

Substituents	Physical characteristics	M.p. (°C.)	Derivatives, etc.	Ref.
2-Hydroxy-	Yellow leaflets	285	Ac-, 207°; MeO-, 168°	23, 24
3-Hydroxy-	Brown ppt.		MeO-, 160–161°	87
4-Hydroxy-			K salt, green crystals	22
5-Hydroxy-	Yellowish-red needles		MeO-, 180°; EtO-, 158.5°; Ac-, 217°	1, 2, 3, 4, 12, 13
6-Hydroxy-	Lemon-yellow needles	199	MeO-, 158°	4, 18
9-Hydroxy-	Brownish needles	dec. 290	Ac-, 216.5°; EtO-, 186–187°	19, 20, 21, 26
5-Hydroxy-6-methyl-				88
5-Hydroxy-10-methyl-	Yellow(red) dichroic micro-crystals	> 265	EtO-, 175°	2, 14, 15, 16, 17, 99
5-Hydroxy-1,2,3,4-tetrahydro-	Yellow needles	> 300		89
5-Hydroxy-6-(3'-methyl-2'-butenyl)-	Dark-red prisms or scales with dark-green reflex	161.5–162.5		90
5-Hydroxy-6-(3'-methyl-2'-butenyl)-9(or 10)-methyl-	Dark-red prisms	153.5–154.5		16, 90
5-Hydroxy-6-(3'-methyl-3'-hydroxybutyl-9(or 10)-methyl-	Reddish-brown needles	183.5–184.5		16
5-Hydroxy-6-(2'-methyl-1'-propenyl)-	Amber prisms	226–227		91

3. Dihydroxybenzo[a]phenazines

A. 5,6-Dihydroxybenzo[a]phenazine (IX)

This compound forms striking violet-blue needles of indefinite m.p. (*ca.* 270°) with decomposition.[44-46] It is obtained by the reduction of the corresponding quinone (Chapter XII:3,F) by means of a wide variety of reducing agents, even phenylhydrazine in chloroform, and is readily reoxidized to the quinone by nitric acid[44] and, on standing, by air.[46] It forms a diacetyl derivative, pale yellow blades, m.p. 214–216° from acetic anhydride.[44,46] This is very unstable and readily undergoes hydrolysis.[46] The dimethoxy compound, obtained by methylation with methyl sulfate and alkali, crystallizes from acetic acid in canary-yellow needles, m.p. 160–161°. Its ultraviolet absorption spectrum in ethanol has been recorded.[46] The 5,6-methylenedioxy compound, pale yellow crystals, m.p. 228°, is obtained by the action of diazomethane in ether upon the corresponding quinone,[110] and the 5:6-diphenylmethylene-dioxy derivative, m.p. 238°, is likewise formed by the action of diazo-diphenylmethane.[111]

Like the closely related 5-hydroxybenzo[a]phenazine, compound IX is capable of tautomerism to 6-hydroxy-5(7H)-benzo[a]phen-azinone (X).

This tautomerism has recently been invoked by Badger and his coworkers[46] to explain the deep-blue color observed in aqueous alcoholic solutions of compound IX, and the unusual color of the solid compound. In anhydrous dioxan, it exhibits an ultraviolet absorption spectrum closely related to that of the dimethoxy compound, but this changes on dilution with water when the initial reddish-brown color of the solution becomes dark blue. The dark blue solution, presumably due to structure X, rapidly fades, owing to aerial oxidation to the quinone, the lactam form being readily oxidized. Because of this ease of oxida-tion, spectrophotometric measurements could be made only in the presence of a little hydrazine (1%) as a reducing agent. A similar lactam-lactim tautomerism has been used to explain the violet-blue color of certain products obtained by the photoaddition of aromatic aldehydes to benzo[a]phenazine-5,6-quinone and the thermochromasy of these derivatives.[110]

A dihydro derivative of compound IX, X, namely, 6,6a-dihydro-6-hydroxy-5(7H)-benzo[a]phenazinone (XII), was described as formed by the action of o-phenylenediamine upon 1a,7a-dihydroöxiro[b]-naphthalene-2,7-quinone (XI), together with compound IX and naphtho[1,2-b,3,4-b']diquinoxaline (XIII, R. I. 3580).[44] The dihydro compound (XII) forms brownish-red needles from ethanol and, on heating, loses hydrogen, becoming blue owing to formation of compound IX. Other derivatives of type (XII) have been described.[92-94] 5,6-

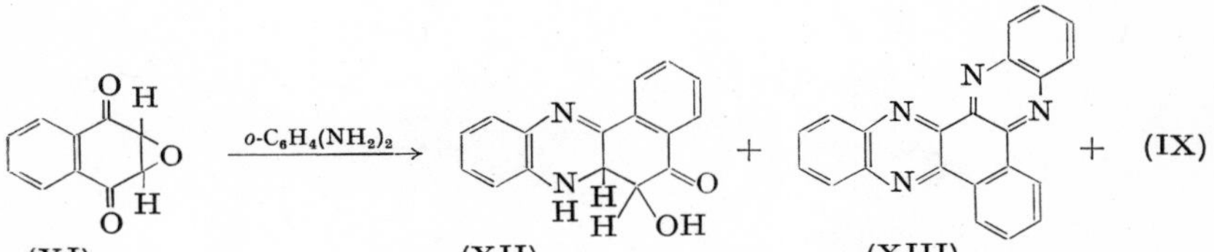

Dihydroxybenzo[a]phenazine (IX) reacts with o-phenylenediamine to yield XIII,[106] spontaneous oxidation occurring during the reaction.

B. 9,10-Dihydroxybenzo[a]phenazine (XIV)

This is obtained from 1,2-diaminonaphthalene and 2,5-dihydroxy-1,4-benzoquinone (Chapter XII:3,B(2)). It crystallizes from nitrobenzene in orange-yellow crystals, which melt with decomposition at ca. 300°, dissolves in alkalis giving a yellow solution and exhibits a carmine coloration in concentrated sulfuric acid.[47,48] It yields a diacetyl derivative as pale yellow needles, m.p. 217–218°.[48]

The importance of this dihydroxy compound stems from its use as an intermediate in the synthesis of benzofluorindines (Chapter XVIII:6,A). Thus it condenses with o-phenylenediamine in boiling benzoic acid to give 7,14- or 9,16-dihydrobenzo[a]quinoxalo[2,3-i]-phenazine (XV or XVI, respectively; R. I. 3577), which forms greenish metallic lustrous crystals from nitrobenzene, and which in ethanol or benzene, in which solvents it is only sparingly soluble, exhibits a fiery red fluorescence.[48]

It also condenses with 1,2-diaminonaphthalene in boiling benzoic acid to yield either 7,16-dihydro-7,9,16,18-tetrazadibenzo[a,n]pentacene (R. I. 3754) or 9,18-dihydro-7,9,16,18-tetrazadibenzo[a,l]pentacene (no R. I. enumeration), as a violet powder, forming a dark green crystalline chloride.[48] The base is readily oxidized by air to the fully aromatic system, which may be reduced to the dihydro form by stannous chloride[104] (see Chapter XVIII:14).

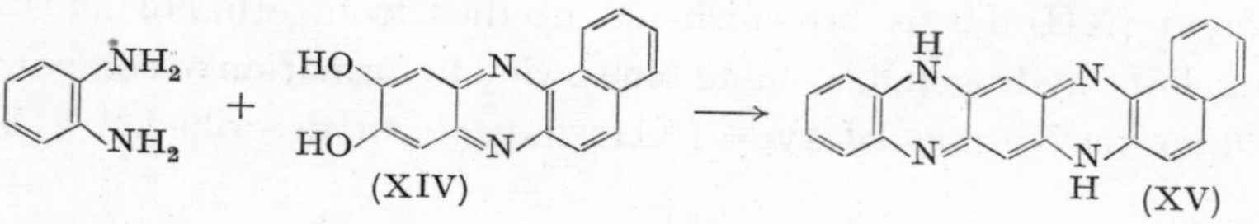

(XIV)   (XV)   or

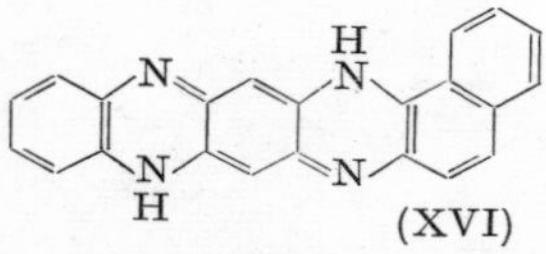

(XVI) 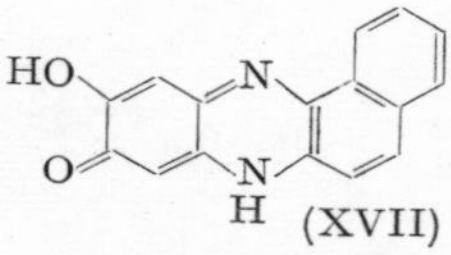   (XVII)

From the formulas XV and XVI it would appear that compound XIV reacts in a lactam form, e.g. XVII. There is no experimental evidence on this point, but the high melting point and brownish color of the parent substance would appear to support this suggestion, which would favor structure XV as the correct formulation of the product. On the other hand, the diacetyl derivative is readily hydrolyzed by dilute alkali, a point that indicates it is an O-diacetyl compound derived from structure XIV.

9,10-Dihydroxybenzo[a]phenazine (XIV) is an intermediate in the synthesis of other heterocyclic derivatives of phenazine; thus it reacts with 2-aminophenol in boiling benzoic acid to yield 7-benzo[a]-[1,4]benzoxazino[3,2-i]phenazine (XVIII, R. I. 3573) (see Chapter XIX:37), which crystallizes from nitrobenzene in orange-red crystals, dissolving in organic solvents to give a yellow solution, which exhibits a weak green fluorescence.[49]

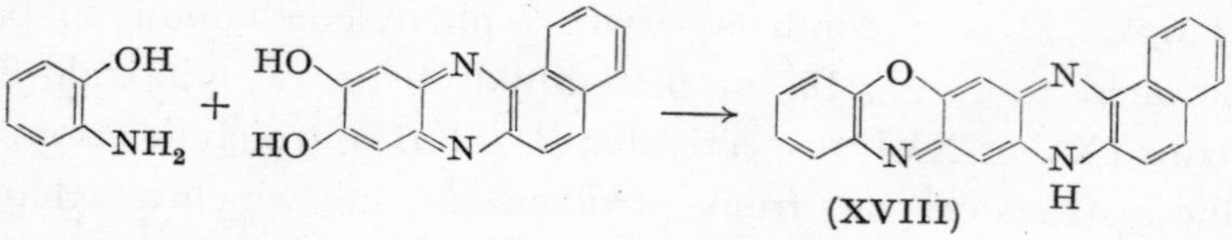

(XVIII)

4. Hydroxyaminobenzo[a]phenazines

The chemistry, such as it is, of the few derivatives of benzo[a]-phenazine that contain both hydroxy and amino groups is dominated by the behavior of the hydroxy groups and so finds its logical position here.

A. General

A general method of preparation is an extension of method *14* (Chapter XII:3,B), in which dihydroxynaphthalenes, in which one hydroxy group occupies the 2-position, are fused with 2,4-diaminoazobenzenes (chrysoidines).[50] In this manner, 9-amino-2-hydroxybenzo[a]-phenazine (XIX) has been prepared. It forms brownish-red needles, m.p. 350°, from nitrobenzene and gives an olive-green coloration with sulfuric acid, passing on progressive dilution through blue and violet to red, from which a red sulfate is precipitated. The 10-methyl homolog, m.p. >360°, is obtained when 2,4-diamino-5-methylazobenzene is employed. 9-Amino-6-hydroxybenzo[a]phenazine is obtained similarly

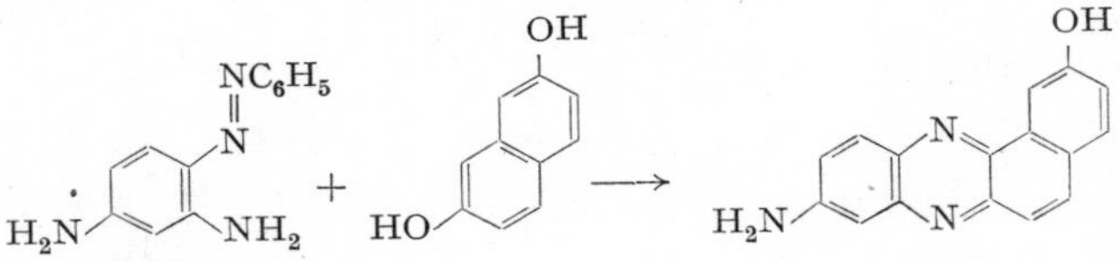

(XIX)

from 2,3-dihydroxynaphthalene and 2,4-diaminoazobenzene and forms reddish-brown needles, m.p. 263°; the 10-methyl homolog, m.p. 260°, on heating in aniline exchanges the hydroxy group for an anilino residue, the 6-anilino derivative so formed crystallizing in lustrous reddish-brown needles, m.p. 270.5°.[50]

6-Amino-5-hydroxybenzo[a]phenazine, dark-violet needles, m.p. 225° (*N*-acetyl derivative, brownish-yellow needles, m.p. 257–258°), was obtained by condensing 3-acetamido-2-hydroxy-1,4-naphthoquinone with *o*-phenylenediamine.[102]

B. 5-Acetamido-9,10-dihydroxybenzo[a]phenazine (XX)

This compound is obtained by the condensation of 4-acetamido-1,2-diaminonaphthalene with 4,5-dihydroxy-1,2-benzoquinone in 50%

acetic acid solution.[51,52] It forms straw yellow crystals (no m.p. given), which dissolve in dilute sodium hydroxide solution to give a yellow

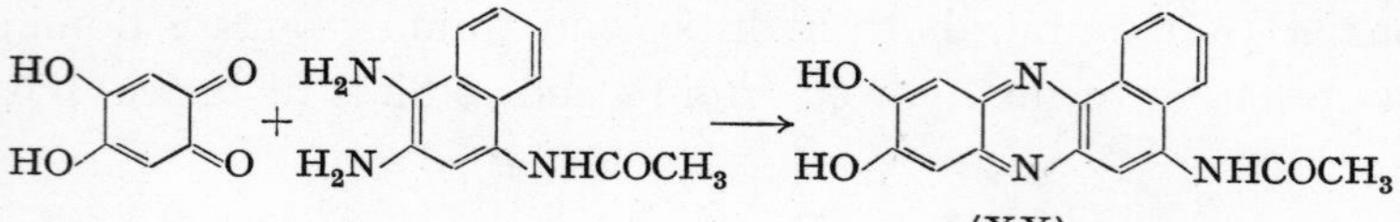

(XX)

solution, and in concentrated sulfuric acid with a magenta coloration, which becomes orange on dilution and burgundy on neutralization. It reacts with 2-aminodiphenylamine hydrochloride in boiling benzoic acid to yield either 5-acetamido-7,14-dihydro-14-phenyl- or 5-acetamido-9,16-dihydro-9-phenylbenzo[a]quinoxalo[2,3-i]phenazine (XXI or XXII, respectively; R. I. 3577), as brownish-red microscopic crystals that give a reddish-violet solution in ethanolic benzene, characterized by a greenish fluorescence, and which with concentrated

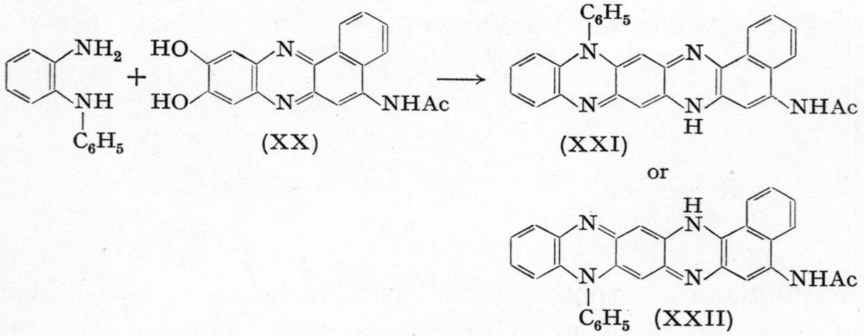

(XX)   (XXI)

or

(XXII)

sulfuric acid give a greenish-blue solution from which the dark-blue sulfate is precipitated on dilution.[49] When o-phenylenediamine replaces 2-aminodiphenylamine in the reaction, the product is 5-acetamido-7,14-(or -9,16)dihydrobenzo[a]quinoxalo[2,3-i]phenazine, which forms dark-violet crystals with a coppery luster and gives a blue chloride, which exhibits a weak red fluorescence in alcoholic solution,[104] indicating slight dissociation. Similarly, compound XX and 1-anilino-2-aminonaphthalene react together to yield either 5-acetamido-7,16-dihydro-16-phenyl-7,9,16,18-tetrazadibenzo[a,n]pentacene (XXIII, R. I. 3754) or 5-acetamido-9,18-dihydro-9-phenyl-7,9,16,18-tetrazadibenzo[a,l]pentacene (XXIV, no R. I. enumeration), which product forms violet-black microscopic needles, giving a violet solution, with a red fluorescence, in benzene or ethanol, in which solvents it is but sparingly soluble. It gives a green coloration in concentrated sulfuric acid [49]

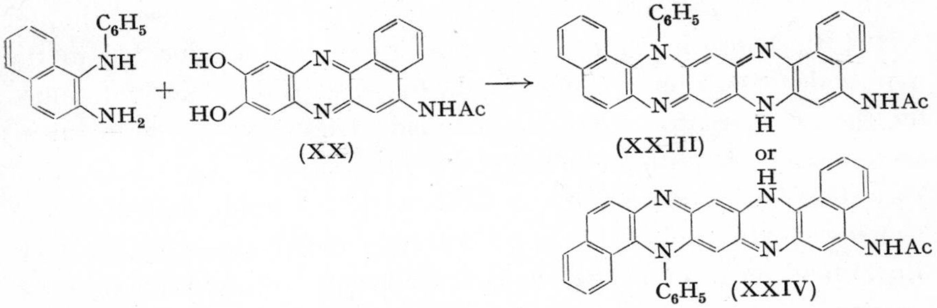

With 1,2-diaminonaphthalene, again only one product is formed. The chloride forms violet-black grains with a weak metallic reflex. The free base is a violet-blue color and readily oxidizes to the azine state in the air.[104]

With 4-acetamido-1,2-diaminonaphthalene, compound XX yields a poorly characterized reddish-brown solid (forming blue salts), which is formulated as a dihydro derivative of either 5,11-diacetamido-7,9,16,18-tetrazadibenzo[a,n]pentacene or 5,14-diacetamido-7,9,16,18-tetrazadibenzo[a,l]pentacene.[49]

It seems probable that compound XX reacts with 1,2-diamines in a lactam form (see Section XIII:3,B).

C. 5-Anilino-6-hydroxy-5,6-dihydrobenzo[a]phenazine (XXV)

This compound has already received a brief mention under another heading. It is formed by heating benzo[a]oxiro[c]phenazine (Chapter XII:3,E(2)) with aniline and crystallizes from benzene in yellow needles, m.p. 204–205°. It is unstable, however, and on boiling with acids loses aniline to yield 6-hydroxybenzo[a]phenazine[4] (Section XIII:2,C).

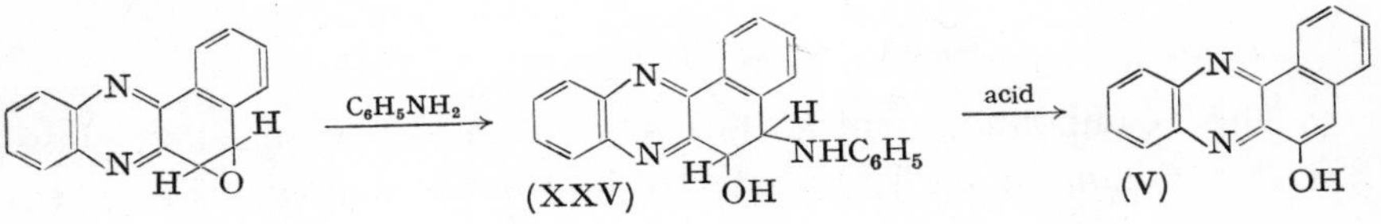

5. Monoaminobenzo[a]phenazines

A. Review of Preparative Methods

Monoaminobenzo[a]phenazines have been prepared by a variety of the general methods outlined in an earlier chapter (see Chapter XII:3,B). Those in which the amino group is to be located in the naphthalenic portion of the molecule are perhaps most easily obtained by the condensation of an o-phenylenediamine with the requisite acetamido-1,2-naphthoquinone[18,53–56] (Chapter XII:3,B(1)), or with some derivative related to this such as a 2-nitroso-1-naphthol[57] or 1-nitroso-2-naphthol[24] (1,2-naphthoquinone monoxime, Chapter XII: 3,B(3) and (4)). Other methods include the reaction between an o-phenylenediamine and a 4-benzeneazo-1-naphthylamine derivative[1,3] (Chapter XII:3,B(12)) or between a 2-aminoazobenzene compound, which yields an o-diamine *in situ*, and a 1-naphthylamine[14,15,58] (Chapter XII:3,B(13)).

When the amino group is required in the benzenoid half of the molecule, two general methods have been used: by the condensation of a 2-naphthylamine with a p-nitrosoaniline derivative,[59] or with N,N'-dichloroquinonediimine[60] (Chapter XII:3,B(8)); or by the fusion together of a 2,4-diaminoazobenzene derivative (chrysoidine) with a 2-naphthol[50] (Chapter XII:3,B(14)).

Other methods include the condensation of a 1,2-naphthoquinone with a triaminobenzene,[21] and the complicated sequence of reactions elucidated by Bucherer and his pupils.[61,62] A full account of this latter sequence has been given in Chapter XII:3,B(5), to which the reader is referred. Since the nitrobenzo[a]phenazines are inaccessible by direct nitration, the method which has proved so fruitful in simple aromatic chemistry, namely, reduction of a nitro compound to an amine, has been applied only once in this series.[63]

The monoaminobenzo[a]phenazines and their derivatives are listed later in Table XV.

B. 5-Aminobenzo[a]phenazine (XXVI)

This compound, which forms reddish-yellow needles, m.p. 294° [10,55,56] (and not 264° as stated in the original memoir[1]), was

obtained by Fischer and Hepp by heating a mixture of o-phenylenediamine and 4-benzeneazo-1-naphthylamine hydrochloride in alcohol
under pressure at 160°.[1] Kehrmann[2] described an alternative preparation from o-phenylenediamine hydrochloride and 2-hydroxy-1,4-
naphthoquinone-4-imine in alcohol under reflux and later[55,56] from
4-acetamido-1,2-naphthoquinone and o-phenylenediamine, a reaction
giving a quantitative yield of the acetamido compound (sulfur-yellow
needles, m.p. > 370°), which is readily hydrolyzed by refluxing a
solution in glacial acetic acid with a few drops of concentrated hydrochloric acid. 5-Aminobenzo[a]phenazine has also been obtained by
heating 2-nitroaniline with 1-naphthylamine in the presence of zinc
chloride[64] (Chapter XII:3,B(10)). Various salts have been described.[1]

Prolonged heating under pressure with concentrated hydrochloric
acid causes the 5-amino group to be hydrolyzed,[1] yielding 5-hydroxy-
benzo[a]phenazine (I) (Section XIII:2,A).

The structure of 5-aminobenzo[a]phenazine has been discussed by
Kehrmann[2] and Fischer and Hepp.[5] The amino formulation (XXVI) is
favored by the ability of the amino group to undergo diazotization, and
by the existence of dialkylamino derivatives,[3] while the imino form
(XXVII) was advanced by Kehrmann on analogy with the corresponding hydroxy compound and because of his original method of preparation.[2] Clearly, here too we have a system in tautomeric equilibrium.

(XXVI)   (XXVII)   (XXVIII)

C. 5-Amino-10-methylbenzo[a]phenazine (XXVIII)

This compound was the original eurhodine prepared by Witt in
his early researches[14,15,58] by heating a mixture of 2-amino-5,4'-
dimethylazobenzene with 1-naphthylamine hydrochloride alone at
140°,[58] or in phenol at 130°.[14] The base forms golden glittering crystals,
which sublime readily and which in solution in ether exhibit a striking
green fluorescence. It yields a red coloration in concentrated sulfuric
acid. Various salts have been described. It is sulfonated by means of

oleum[58] (the sulfonic acid so produced dyeing silk in orange shades) and is acetylated by means of acetic anhydride, yielding the acetamido derivative as pale yellow felted crystals. The early formula given[58] was later shown to be incorrect.[14] Like the lower homolog, the amino group of the eurhodine is replaced by hydroxyl on hydrolysis with sulfuric acid at 180°, and may be diazotized by means of alkyl nitrites. When the diazonium salt is decomposed by alcohol, however, ethers are formed.[14]

D. 5-Alkylamino- and 5-Dialkylamino Derivatives of Benzo[a]phenazine (XXIX)

A number of these were prepared by Eicker[3] by the general method of heating the hydrochlorides of 4-benzeneazo-1-naphthylamines, suitably alkylated on the free amino group, with o-diamines in alcohol under pressure at 140°.

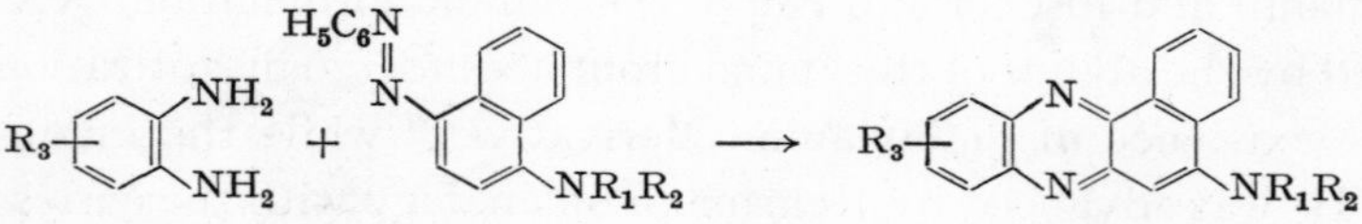

(XXIX)

These included 5-ethylamino-(XXIX; $R_1 = C_2H_5$; $R_2 = R_3 = H$), yellow needles, m.p. 169°, and 5-dimethylaminobenzo[a]phenazine (XXIX; $R_1 = R_2 = CH_3$; $R_3 = H$), yellow needles, m.p. 221°; and, when 3,4-diaminotoluene was employed, the corresponding 9- (or 10-) methyl homologs (XXIX; $R_1 = C_2H_5$; $R_2 = H$; $R_3 = CH_3$) golden-yellow leaflets, m.p. 182°, and (XXIX; $R_1 = R_2 = R_3 = CH_3$), brownish-yellow needles, m.p. 230°, were obtained. Others are described in patents.[73,108]

E. 9-Aminobenzo[a]phenazine (XXX)

This was prepared first by Nietzki and Otto by treating an alcoholic solution of 2-naphthylamine with N,N'-dichloroquinonediimine.[60] Later it was produced by heating a mixture of 2-naphthol and 2,4-diaminoazobenzene at 150° [50,65] and also by the condensation of 1,2-

naphthoquinone with 1,2,4-triaminobenzene.[21] This last reaction can, in theory, give both 9- and 10-amino derivatives, but in practice only the former was found.

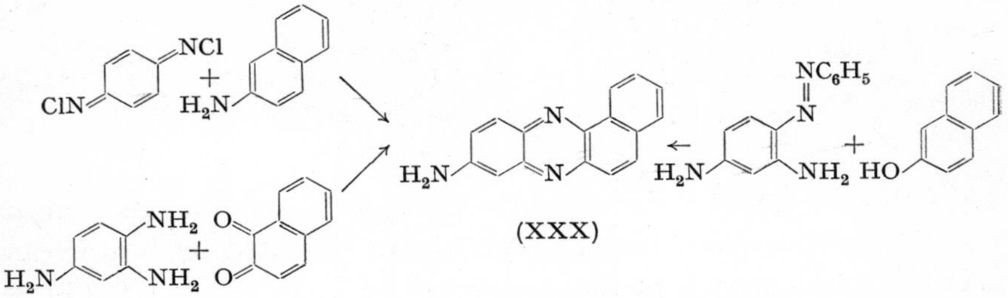

(XXX)

It crystallizes from benzene in orange-yellow needles, m.p. 267° (acetyl derivative, yellow needles, m.p. 298°).[50] Its solutions in benzene and ether are yellow, with an intense green fluorescence. Concentrated sulfuric acid gives a reddish-violet coloration, which passes on progressive dilution through olive-green to magenta.[21] Removal of the amino group by diazotization and boiling with ethanol gives benzo[a]-phenazine[60] (Chapter XII:3,C).

The 10-methyl homolog, which forms bright yellow sheaves of needles, m.p. 250°, is obtained from 2-naphthol and 2,4-diamino-5-methylazobenzene.[50] Its acetyl derivative forms yellow needles, m.p. 295°.

F. 9-Dimethylaminobenzo[a]phenazine

This compound, which forms dichroic rhombic plates, m.p. 205°, which appear red by transmitted light and red or green, depending upon the crystal face viewed, by reflected light, is obtained by heating 2-naphthylamine in acetic acid with 4-nitrosodimethylaniline hydrochloride.[59,109] Its solutions in organic solvents show a characteristic fluorescence, the maximum of which in the fluorescence spectrum changes with change in solvent and appears to show a dependence upon the dielectric constant of the solvent.[66]

G. Eurhodine Dyes

Benzo[a]phenazines carrying a 5-anilino residue and sulfonated by one or more sulfonyl groups, for example, XXXI, have been described in a patent specification[67] as formed from 1,3-dianilino-4-benzeneazonaphthalenes by heating with concentrated sulfuric acid. The products dye bluish-red shades on wool.

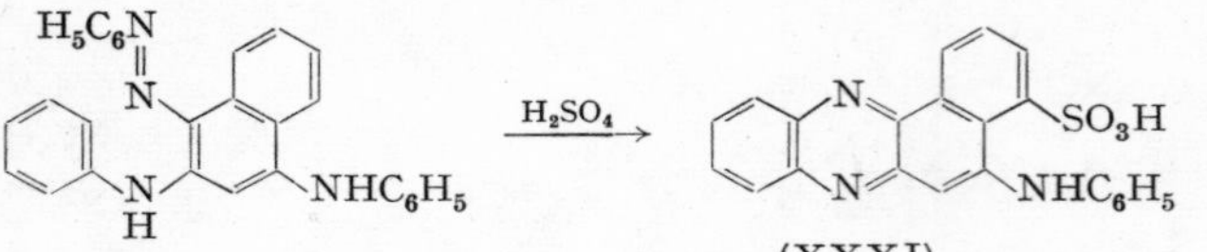

(XXXI)

Other dyes, which also give bluish-red shades on wool, are formed when sulfonic acids of the type XXXI are alkylated by heating an alkaline solution with methyl iodide under pressure at 120–130°,[68] reaction occurring with the tautomeric form (XXXII).

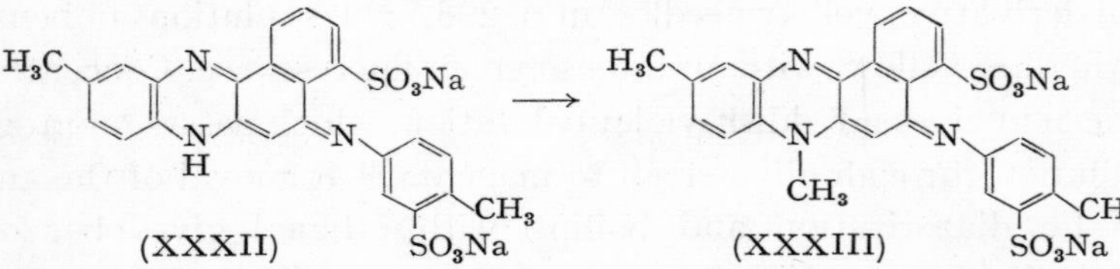

(XXXII)   (XXXIII)

Alternatively, simple eurhodines, such as 5-aminobenzo[a]-phenazine (XXVI), may be converted into phenyleurhodines by heating with a mixture of aniline and aniline hydrochloride and the product methylated by means of methyl iodide under pressure. The phenyl-eurhodine may also be prepared by a similar process applied to the corresponding eurhodol. The products of alkylation may be sulfonated later to yield coloring matters that dye wool from acid baths in bluish-red shades.[9, 69–75] The unsulfonated products give orange-red dyeings on silk or cotton mordanted with tannin.

The alkylated products, of type XXXIII, may be obtained by direct condensation reactions using suitably alkylated components.[76–80] Logically, these alkylated products belong in the benzo[a]phenazinium series of which they are anhydro-base forms. They are also considered in Chapter XIV.

The parent of many of these eurhodine dyes, 5-anilinobenzo[a]-phenazine is unknown, but the 10-methyl homolog obtained by heating 5-amino-10-methylbenzo[a]phenazine with aniline and aniline hydro-chloride, forms yellow needles, m.p. 230°.[9] (See also reference 3.)

TABLE XV. Monoaminobenzo[a]phenazines and Derivatives

Substituents	Physical characteristics	M.p. (°C.)	Derivatives, etc.	Ref.
1-Amino-		215–216	Ac-, 233–234°; Bz-, 218–219°; p-NO₂Bz-, 305–307°	81
2-Amino-	Reddish-brown needles	232	Ac-, yellow needles, 288°	53
3-Amino-	Orange leaflets, gold luster	217	Ac-, yellow needles 274°	54
4-Amino-	Reddish-brown needles	270–271	Ac-, yellow needles, 311–313°	24, 57, 101
5-Amino-	Reddish-yellow needles or plates	294	Ac-, yellow crystals, > 370°; Cl–, red needles; Tos-, yellow tablets, 274–276°; Bz-, sulfur-yellow needles, 274°	1, 2, 5, 10, 55, 56, 64, 96, 97, 100
6-Amino-	Blood-red prisms	198–199	Ac-, bright yellow needles, 240°; Bz, yellow needles, 220°	18, 63, 98
8-Amino-	Reddish-brown plates	156	Acetate, ca. 224°	61, 62
9-Amino-	Dark-yellow needles	267	Ac-, yellow needles, 298°; Cl–, red leaflets 264°; NO₃–, red-bronze needles, 243°	21, 50, 60, 65
10-Amino-	Rectangular golden crystals	302	Ac-, yellow needles, 292°	62
5-Amino-10-methyl-	Golden glittering crystals		Ac-, pale yellow crystals	2, 14, 15, 58
9-Amino-10-methyl-	Yellow sheaves of needles	250	Ac-, yellow needles, 295°	50

(Table continued)

TABLE XV (continued)

Substituents	Physical characteristics	M.p. (°C.)	Derivatives, etc.	Ref.
5-Anilino-10-methyl-	Yellow crystals	230		9
5-Anilino-9(or 10)-methyl-	Brassy-yellow needles	214		3
5-(4'-Hydroxyanilino)-	Thick orange crystals	291		95
5-Ethylamino-	Golden-yellow leaflets	169	Ac-, yellow crystals	3
5-Ethylamino-9(or 10)-methyl-	Golden-yellow leaflets	182	Ac-, straw yellow prisms	3
5-Dimethylamino-	Brownish-yellow needles	221	Cl⁻, red needles	3
5-Dimethylamino-9(or 10)-methyl-	Brownish-yellow needles	230	Cl⁻, garnet-red needles	3
5-(2'-Diethylaminoethyl)amino-			Di-Cl-, vermilion needles, 250°; picrate, deep orange blades, 220° (dec.); Tos-, pink needles, 85–90°	96
9-Dimethylamino-	Dichroic, rhombic plates	205		59, 109
5-Methylamino-10-methyl-	Yellow needles			73
5-Benzylamino-10-methyl-	Yellow crystals			108

1-Acylamido and 1-amino derivatives of benzo[a]phenazines, which carry solubilizing sulfonyl groups, are claimed to give fast, level yellow to red shades on wool.[28-30] The sulfonyl groups may be removed by heating under pressure with mineral acids and 1-aminobenzo[a]-phenazine so obtained is stated to give vivid orange dyeings on acetate rayon; its aryl derivatives have been suggested as pigment dyes.[81]

The simple eurhodines can be made to react with a 1,4-quinone, when products dyeing in green tints result.[37] Alternatively, the eurhodines may be modified by diazotization and coupling with azo dye components.[82] Sulfur-containing dyes derived from eurhodines have been described.[32]

6. Diaminobenzo[a]phenazines

A small number only of these have been described. Their methods of preparation follow the general pattern, for example, 1,5-diamino-benzo[a]phenazine is obtained by hydrolysis of its diacetyl derivative, which is in turn prepared from 4,8-diacetamido-1,2-naphthoquinone and o-phenylenediamine.[83] A touch of novelty in this series is introduced by the method in which the picryl-1- and -2-naphthylamines are reduced by stannous chloride in concentrated hydrochloric acid to yield 9,11- and 8,10-diaminobenzo[a]phenazines, respectively[84] (Chapter XII:3,B(15)). A third method that has been used consists in the condensation of a 4-nitroso-1-naphthylamine, alkylated or arylated on the amino group, with a 1,3-diamine, which may or may not be alkylated on one only of the amino groups,[85,86] but this reaction does not always afford satisfactory yields.[103]

An attempt to prepare a derivative of 5,6-diaminobenzo[a]-phenazine by condensation of o-phenylenediamine and 3-acetamido-4-methylamino-1,2-naphthoquinone led to the isolation of 2,3-dimethyl-3-benz[a]imidazo[c]phenazine (XXXIV, R. I. 3038), as orange needles, m.p. 264°, which gives a weakly green fluorescence in ethereal solution and dissolves in concentrated sulfuric acid to yield a violet-brown coloration that becomes orange and then yellow on dilution. It forms a series of stable monacidic salts.[18]

5-Anilino-9-diethylamino- and 5-anilino-10-diethylaminobenzo-

TABLE XVI. Diaminobenzo[a]phenazines and Derivatives

Substituents	Physical characteristics	M.p. (°C.)	Derivatives, etc.	Ref.
1,5-Diamino-	Yellowish-red needles		DiAc., golden-yellow needles; base shows v. weak fluorescence	83
8,10-Diamino-	Red satiny leaflets	sublimes 320 (dec.)	DiAc., yellow needles, m.p. 320° (dec.)	84
9,11-Diamino-	Dark-red crystals	sublimes 290–300 (dec.)	DiAc., yellow needles, m.p. 320 (dec.)	84
9-Amino-5-ethylamino-10-methyl-			Cl⁻, green metallic crystals, magenta in solution, with orange-yellow fluorescence	85
9-Amino-5-dimethylamino-10-methyl-			Cl⁻, black powder, giving magenta color in aq. solution	86
5-Anilino-9-diethylamino-		sinters 95; gum at 125; one sample m.p. 165	Strong yellow-green fluorescence; green coloration with conc. H₂SO₄; yellow in 4% alcoholic KOH	103
5-Anilino-10-diethylamino-		215–217		103
6-Anilino-9-amino-10-methyl-	Reddish-brown needles	270.5	Weak green fluorescence; olive-green coloration with conc. H₂SO₄	50

[a]phenazines have been prepared for chemotherapeutic evaluation as potential antitubercular drugs. Both compounds, when given orally to mice infected with tuberculosis, were inactive.[103]

(XXXIV)

The diaminobenzo[a]phenazines are listed in Table XVI.

References

1. O. Fischer and E. Hepp, *Ber.*, **23**, 841 (1890).
2. F. Kehrmann, *Ber.*, **23**, 2446 (1890).
3. K. Eicker, *Ber.*, **26**, 3803 (1890).
4. T. Zincke, *Ber.*, **26**, 613 (1893).
5. O. Fischer and E. Hepp, *Ber.*, **23**, 2787 (1890).
6. F. Kehrmann, *Ber.*, **28**, 353 (1895).
7. F. Kehrmann and B. Mascioni, *Ber.*, **28**, 345 (1895).
8. S. Lindenbaum, *Ber.*, **34**, 1050 (1901).
9. Ger. Pat. 66,361; *Frdl.*, **3**, 352 (1890–1894).
10. F. Kehrmann, *Ann.*, **290**, 247 (1896).
11. F. Kehrmann, *Ann.*, **414**, 131 (1918).
12. F. Kehrmann and J. Messinger, *Ber.*, **24**, 2167 (1891).
13. L. F. Fieser, *J. Am. Chem. Soc.*, **48**, 2922 (1926).
14. O. N. Witt, *Ber.*, **19**, 441 (1886).
15. O. N. Witt, *J. Chem. Soc.*, **49**, 391 (1886).
16. S. C. Hooker, *J. Chem. Soc.*, **63**, 1376 (1893).
17. T. Zincke, *Ber.*, **25**, 1168 (1892).
18. F. Kehrmann and F. Zimmerli, *Ber.*, **31**, 2405 (1898).
19. F. Kehrmann, *Helv. Chim. Acta*, **7**, 471 (1924).
20. F. Kehrmann and F. Cherpillod, *Helv. Chim. Acta*, **7**, 973 (1924).
21. F. Kehrmann and C. Mermod, *Helv. Chim. Acta*, **10**, 62 (1927).
22. R. Lesser, *Ber.*, **27**, 2363 (1894).
23. F. Kehrmann and R. Brunel, *Ber.*, **41**, 1832 (1908).
24. F. Ullmann and R. Heisler, *Ber.*, **42**, 4263 (1909).
25. P. Brunner and O. N. Witt, *Ber.*, **20**, 2660 (1887).
26. W. Autenreith and O. Hinsberg, *Ber.*, **25**, 492 (1892).
27. Brit. Pat. 322,209; *Chem. Abstracts*, **24**, 2891 (1930).
28. Ger. Pat. 492,161; *Chem. Abstracts*, **27**, 1195 (1933); *Frdl.*, **18**, 859 (1931).
29. U. S. Pat. 1,873,938; *Chem. Abstracts*, **26**, 6154 (1932).
30. Fr. Pat. 668,078; *Chem. Abstracts*, **24**, 1520 (1930).
31. Fr. Pat. 584,401; *Chem. Zentr.*, **1925**, I, 2665.
32. Brit. Pat. 217,936; *Chem. Zentr.*, **1924**, II, 2791.
33. Brit. Pat. 253,488; *Chem. Abstracts*, **21**, 2564 (1927).
34. Swiss Pat. 253,479; *Chem. Abstracts*, **44**, 6144 (1950).

35. Swiss Pat. 259,318–23; *Chem. Abstracts*, **44**, 6634 (1950).
36. Brit. Pat. 633,206; *Chem. Abstracts*, **44**, 7547 (1950).
37. U. S. Pat. 1,853,362; *Chem. Abstracts*, **26**, 3385 (1932).
38. U. S. Pat. 1,854,045; *Chem. Abstracts*, **26**, 3385 (1932).
39. Ger. Pat. 365,902; *Chem. Zentr.*, **1923**, II, 1186; *Frdl.*, **14**, 739 (1921–1925).
40. Ger. Pat. 368,168; *Chem. Zentr.*, **1923**, II, 1186; *Frdl.*, **14**, 739 (1921–1925).
41. Ger. Pat. 368,170; *Chem. Zentr.*, **1923**, II, 1187; *Frdl.*, **14**, 741 (1921–1925).
42. Ger. Pat. 368,171; *Chem. Zentr.*, **1923**, II, 1187; *Frdl.*, **14**, 741 (1921–1925).
43. Ger. Pat. 368,172; *Chem. Zentr.*, **1923**, II, 1187; *Frdl.*, **14**, 742 (1921–1925).
44. T. Zincke and P. Wiegand, *Ann.*, **286**, 58 (1895).
45. O. Fischer, *Ber.*, **36**, 3622 (1903).
46. G. M. Badger, R. S. Pearce and R. Pettit, *J. Chem. Soc.*, **1951**, 3204.
47. R. Nietzki and G. Hasterlik, *Ber.*, **24**, 1337 (1891).
48. F. Kehrmann and J. A. Schedler, *Helv. Chim. Acta*, **8**, 3 (1925).
49. F. Kehrmann and C. Collaud, *Helv. Chim. Acta*, **11**, 1028 (1928).
50. F. Ullmann and J. S. Ankersmit, *Ber.*, **38**, 1811 (1905).
51. F. Kehrmann and I. Safar, *Helv. Chim. Acta*, **8**, 668 (1925).
52. S. Mihaéloff, *Bull. soc. chim.*, [5], **5**, 1655 (1938).
53. F. Kehrmann and H. Wolff, *Ber.*, **33**, 1538 (1900).
54. F. Kehrmann and M. Matis, *Ber.*, **31**, 2413 (1898).
55. F. Kehrmann, *Ber.*, **27**, 3337 (1894).
56. O. N. Witt and J. Dedichen, *Ber.*, **29**, 2945 (1896).
57. L. S. Efros, A. E. Poraï-Koshits and B. A. Poraï-Koshits, *J. Gen. Chem. (U.S.S.R.)*, **17**, 1801 (1947); *Chem. Abstracts*, **42**, 5869 (1948).
58. O. N. Witt, *Ber.*, **18**, 1119 (1885).
59. O. N. Witt, *Ber.*, **21**, 719 (1888).
60. R. Nietzki and R. Otto, *Ber.*, **21**, 1598 (1888).
61. H. T. Bucherer and F. Stickel, *J. prakt. Chem.*, **110**, 309 (1925).
62. H. T. Bucherer and M. Rauch, *J. prakt. Chem.*, **132**, 227 (1931).
63. R. Zärtling, *Ber.*, **23**, 175 (1890).
64. A. Wohl and M. Lange, *Ber.*, **43**, 2186 (1910).
65. Ger. Pat. 157,861; *Frdl.*, **8**, 517 (1906–1907); *Chem. Zentr.*, **1905**, I, 483.
66. H. Ley and K. von Engelhardt, *Ber.*, **41**, 2509 (1908).
67. Ger. Pat. 82,240; *Frdl.*, **4**, 392 (1894–1897).
68. Ger. Pat. 86,109; *Frdl.*, **4**, 393 (1894–1897).
69. Ger. Pat. 71,666; *Frdl.*, **3**, 355 (1890–1894).
70. Ger. Pat. 75,017; *Frdl.*, **3**, 356 (1890–1894).
71. Ger. Pat. 78,043; *Frdl.*, **4**, 382 (1894–1897).
72. Ger. Pat. 75,929; *Frdl.*, **4**, 383 (1894–1897).
73. Ger. Pat. 77,226; *Frdl.*, **4**, 383 (1894–1897).
74. Ger. Pat. 77,228; *Frdl.*, **4**, 385 (1894–1897).
75. Ger. Pat. 79,539; *Frdl.*, **4**, 387 (1894–1897).
76. Ger. Pat. 78,222; *Frdl.*, **4**, 387 (1894–1897).
77. Ger. Pat. 79,540; *Frdl.*, **4**, 389 (1894–1897).
78. Ger. Pat. 79,960; *Frdl.*, **4**, 389 (1894–1897).
79. Ger. Pat. 79,972; *Frdl.*, **4**, 391 (1894–1897).
80. Ger. Pat. 71,665; *Frdl.*, **3**, 354 (1890–1894).
81. Ger. Pat. 495,900; *Chem. Abstracts*, **27**, 1195 (1933); *Frdl.*, **18**, 861 (1931).
82. Ger. Pat. 548,393; *Chem. Abstracts*, **27**, 1195 (1933); *Frdl.*, **18**, 862 (1931).
83. F. Kehrmann and E. Misslin, *Ber.*, **34**, 1224 (1901).
84. F. Kehrmann and J. R. y Punti, *Ber.*, **44**, 2618 (1911).
85. F. Kehrmann, *Ber.*, **50**, 554 (1917).

86. J. B. Cohen and H. G. Crabtree, *J. Chem. Soc.*, **119**, 2055 (1921).
87. H. E. French and K. Sears, *J. Am. Chem. Soc.*, **70**, 1279 (1948).
88. W. John, *Angew. Chem.*, **59A**, 188 (1947); *Chem. Abstracts*, **42**, 4498 (1948).
89. A. Skita and W. Rohrmann, *Ber.*, **63B**, 1473 (1930).
90. S. C. Hooker (with H. W. Sheppard, J. G. Walsh and G. H. Connitt), *J. Am. Chem. Soc.*, **58**, 1190 (1936).
91. S. C. Hooker, *J. Amer. Chem. Soc.*, **58**, 1168 (1936).
92. L. A. Shchukina and M. M. Shemyakin, *Zhur. Obshcheĭ Khim.*, **19**, 193 (1949); *Chem. Abstracts*, **43**, 6191 (1949).
93. Yu. B. Shvetsov and M. M. Shemyakin, *Zhur. Obshcheĭ Khim.*, **19**, 480 (1949); *Chem. Abstracts*, **43**, 7009 (1949).
94. Yu. B. Shvetsov, L. A. Shchukina and M. M. Shemyakin, *Zhur. Obshcheĭ Khim.*, **19**, 498 (1949); *Chem. Abstracts*, **43**, 7009 (1949).
95. F. Ullmann and J. Gnaedinger, *Ber.*, **45**, 3437 (1912).
96. F. E. King and R. J. S. Beer, *J. Chem. Soc.*, **1945**, 791.
97. H. G. Goldstein and G. Genton, *Helv. Chim. Acta*, **20**, 1413 (1937).
98. H. G. Goldstein and G. Genton, *Helv. Chim. Acta*, **21**, 56 (1938).
99. O. N. Witt, *Ber.*, **19**, 914 (1886).
100. F. Ullmann and W. Bruck, *Ber.*, **41**, 3932 (1908).
101. F. Kehrmann and A. Denk, *Ber.*, **33**, 3295 (1900).
102. F. Kehrmann and G. Barche, *Ber.*, **33**, 3067 (1900).
103. R. C. Clapp, J. P. English, C. E. Fellows, J. Forsythe, R. E. Grotz and R. G. Shepherd, *J. Am. Chem. Soc.*, **74**, 1994 (1952).
104. F. Kehrmann and R. Logoz, *Helv. Chim. Acta*, **10**, 339 (1927).
105. L. Hantower and E. Taüber, *Ber.*, **31**, 2156 (1898).
106. G. M. Badger and R. Pettit, *J. Chem. Soc.*, **1952**, 1877.
107. Brit. Pat. 335,896; *Chem. Zentr.*, **1931**, II, 131.
108. Ger. Pat. 75,911; *Frdl.*, **4**, 381 (1894–1897).
109. Ger. Pat. 19,224; *Frdl.*, **1**, 277 (1877–1887).
110. A. Schönberg, A. Mustafa and S. M. A. D. Zayed, *J. Am. Chem. Soc.*, **75**, 4302 (1953).
111. A. Schönberg, A. Mustafa, W. I. Awad and G. E-D. M. Moussa, *J. Am. Chem. Soc.*, **76**, 2273 (1954).

CHAPTER XIV

Hydroxy and Amino Derivatives of Benzo[*a*]phenazinum Salts

1. Introduction

The hydroxy and amino derivatives of 7- and 12-alkyl- or aryl-substituted benzo[*a*]phenazinium salts occupy an important place in the history of dyestuffs, the former being known under the generic names of rosindones and isorosindones, while the latter are the rosindulines and isorosindulines. The terminology is a rather loose use for, strictly, rosindone applies only to the anhydro-base, 7-phenyl-5(7)-benzo[*a*]phenazinone (I), derived from the 5-hydroxy-7-phenylbenzo-[*a*]phenazinium salts (II), while related compounds in which the position of the hydroxyl group and the position and nature of the *N*-substituent are varied are all grouped together as isorosindones.

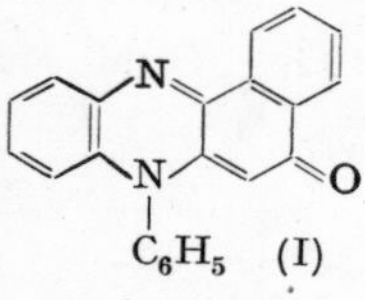

C_6H_5 (I) C_6H_5 (II) X^-

The same considerations apply to rosinduline (5-amino-7-phenyl-benzo[*a*]phenazinium) salts (III), the name isorosinduline applying to position isomers. Derivatives of structure III, in which the hydrogen atoms of the amino group are replaced by, for example, a phenyl residue, are often named by prefixing rosinduline with the name of the substituent in question. Thus structure IV is called phenylrosinduline.

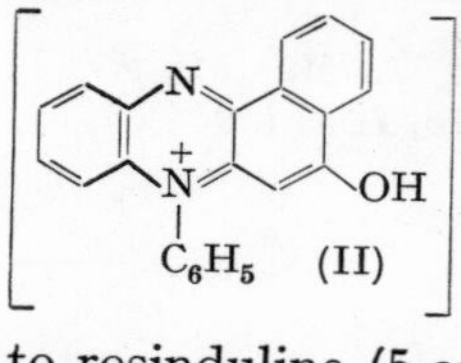

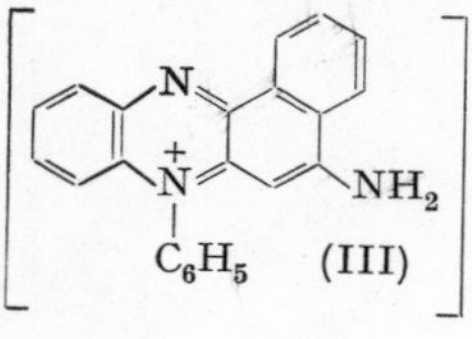

C_6H_5 (III) X^- C_6H_5 (IV) X^-

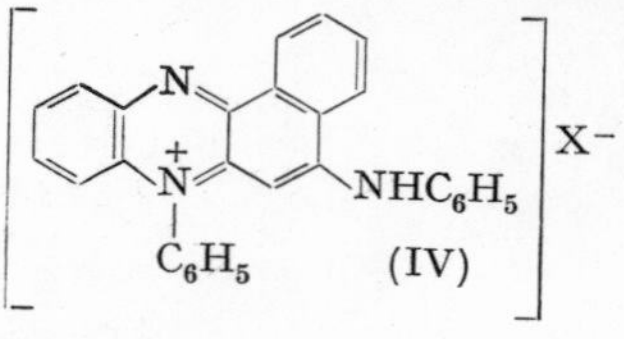

Where the nature of the N-substituent is varied, as, for example, methyl replacing phenyl in compound I, the name rosindone has been qualified by mention of the new substituent giving methylrosindone. This may on occasion lead to ambiguity, so that in this chapter the systematic chemical nomenclature will be adhered to, except where the meaning is quite clear.

2. Monohydroxybenzo[a]phenazinium Salts and Anhydro-Bases

A. General Methods of Preparation

Monohydroxy derivatives of 7- and 12-substituted benzo[a]-phenazinium salts, in which the N-substituent is alkyl, aralkyl or aryl, are all known. Methods for their preparation are determined to a high degree by the nature of the final product required. Thus 7-alkylbenzo-[a]phenazinium compounds may be prepared by direct alkylation of monohydroxybenzo[a]phenazines (Chapter XII:4,A), while 12-alkyl and 7- and 12-aryl analogs are clearly inaccessible by this means. Amino groups may be replaced by hydroxyl groups by diazotization and heating the aqueous diazonium salt solution in the normal manner; amino and substituted amino groups may also be converted to hydroxyl residues by hydrolysis, but only when they occupy certain "reactive" positions. These reactive positions are those which are attacked by alkalis and amines in the presence of air in the case of benzo[a]-phenazinium compounds (Chapter XII:4,D(2)), that is, positions 5 and 9 in the case of 7-substituted benzo[a]phenazinium compounds and position 10 in the case of the 12-isomers. The position of attack, where there is a choice, is governed by the relative redox potentials attributed to the 1,2-naphthoquinonoid and 1,2-benzoquinonoid structures concerned, as has been adumbrated earlier. Such oxidative attack by alkalis provides another means of synthesizing hydroxy derivatives. Similarly chlorine atoms at the reactive positions undergo ready alkaline hydrolysis to the corresponding hydroxy derivatives, though this method is of limited preparative value because the chloro compounds are generally themselves prepared from the hydroxy compounds. Other groups, for example hydroxylamino or sulfonic acid groups, at these reactive centers are also replaceable by hydroxyl groups on mild alkaline treatment, while sulfonic acid groups situated elsewhere may be so replaced by alkaline fusion or high temperature hydrolysis.

The most widely applicable general method remains the condensation of a suitably mono-N-substituted o-diamine with a 1,2-quinone, the two components being individually or collectively substituted in the required positions by hydroxyl or protected hydroxyl groups etc. This frequently leads to mixtures of isomers, depending on the manner in which the two components unite, with a consequent ambiguity, but the properties of the two products often permit of orientation. Examples of these general methods will be presented in the ensuing sections.

The principal members of this group of compounds are collected at the end of the chapter in Tables XVII, XVIII, XIX and XX.

B. 7-Alkyl- and -Aralkyl- and 12-Alkylmonohydroxybenzo[a]-phenazinium Salts and Anhydro-Bases

The structures of the salts are clearly derived from the parent N-alkylbenzo[a]phenazinium salts etc. by replacement of hydrogen by hydroxyl. The bases derived from these salts are shown by analysis to be, in general, anhydro-bases of the type I (see aposafranone, Chapter V:2,C).

(1)   *7-Methyl-5(7)-benzo[a]phenazinone* (V, "Methylrosindone"). This substance, which crystallizes from ethanol-benzene in cinnabarred needles with a green, metallic luster, m.p. 257–259°, was originally prepared by the condensation of 2-hydroxy-1,4-naphthoquinone and 2-methylaminoaniline in ethanolic solution.[1]

It was also obtained, together with 5-methoxybenzo[a]phenazine, by the methylation of 5-hydroxybenzo[a]phenazine[1] (VI), thereby demonstrating the tautomeric nature of the latter compound (Chapter XIII:2,A). Later it was obtained by the action of ethanolic alkalis or of moist silver oxide upon 7-methylbenzo[a]phenazinium salts[2] (VII), although it was then mistakenly thought to be the hydroxide corresponding to VII.

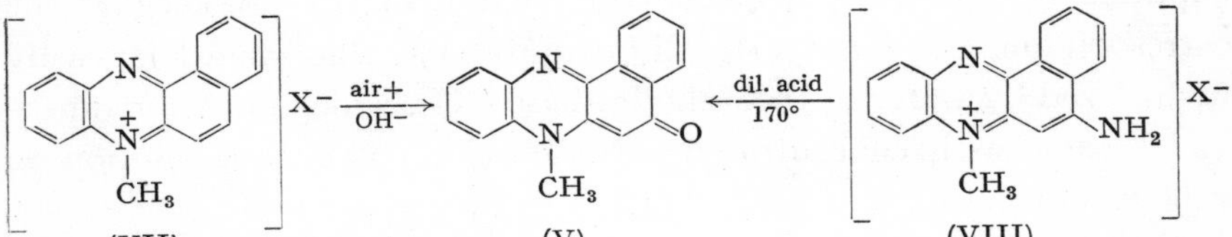

(VII)   (V)   (VIII)

It has also been obtained by the hydrolysis of the corresponding 5-amino compound ("methylrosinduline," VIII) by means of dilute sulfuric acid at 170°.[3]

7-Methyl-5(7)-benzo[a]phenazinone (V) is soluble in organic solvents, for example, ether, benzene or ethanol, giving solutions with a yellowish eosin-red color and a brick-red fluorescence.[1] This solubility would appear to discount the alternative formulation as a betaine (IX) (but see Section XIV:2 C(1)).

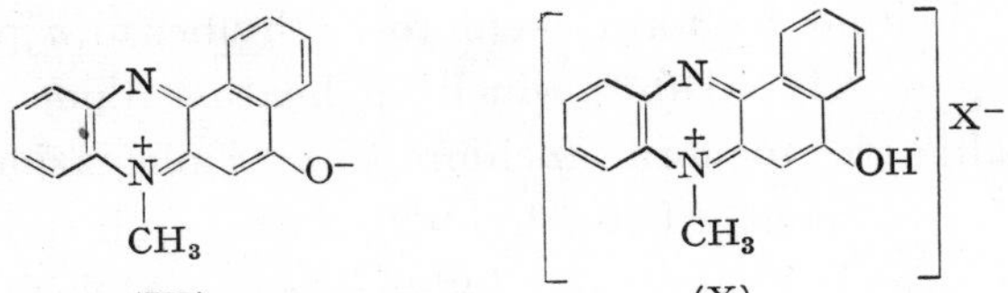

(IX)   (X)

It gives a dichroic solution in concentrated sulfuric acid, which is dirty-green in thin, and purplish-red in thick, layers and which becomes orange-red on dilution.[1,3] The salts (X) are non-fluorescent in solution[2] and form dark yellow or brown needles,[1,2] which are very readily hydrolyzed by water, showing the weak basicity of structure V. The anhydro-base reacts with bromine water, giving an unorientated bromo derivative that forms green needles, decomposing at 250° and giving a green color in concentrated sulfuric acid.[1] The 9-chloro derivative (XIV) of V has been prepared by condensing 2-hydroxy-1,4-naphthoquinone with 4-chloro-2-methylaminoaniline.[4]

The corresponding 7-ethyl[2,5,6] and 7-benzyl[5,7] compounds have been prepared (Table XVII).

(2) *7-Methyl-9(7)-benzo[a]phenazinone* (XI). This substance forms black, dendritic crystals with a metallic luster, m.p. 212–214°. The salts (XII) are obtained by heating a mixture of 2-methylamino-naphthalene and 4-nitrosophenol in ethanol in the presence of the corresponding acid.[8] They are all brownish crystalline powders, easily hydrolyzed by water to the anhydro-base (XI), which gives a reddish-violet color with concentrated sulfuric acid, passing on dilution to yellow.

The corresponding 7-ethyl homolog of XI, obtained by the inter-action of 2-ethylaminonaphthalene with 4-nitrosophenol,[8,9] forms brownish-red needles, m.p. 178°. On heating with a mixture of phosphorus pentachloride and phosphoryl chloride, the keto group is replaced by chlorine to form 9-chloro-7-ethylbenzo[a]phenazinium chloride (Chapter XII:4,D(6)), which on heating alone at 170–180° loses ethyl chloride to form 9-chlorobenzo[a]phenazine[8] (Chapter XII:3,H(2)). Treatment of 7-ethyl-9(7)-benzo[a]phenazinone with hydroxylamine yields 10-amino-7-ethyl-9(7)-benzo[a]phenazinone (hydrochloride, bluish iridescent needles),[10,11] although it was at first thought to be the oxime.

The 7-benzyl homolog has also been prepared[8] (Table XVIII).

(3) *12-Alkylmonohydroxybenzo[a]phenazinium Salts.* There are no important members of this group. The two which have been described[4] were obtained by condensation reactions, whereby both possible isomers could be produced. 10-Chloro-5-hydroxy-12-methyl-benzo[a]phenazinium chloride (XIII) was obtained as black needles, together with the isomeric 9-chloro-7-methyl-5(7)-benzo[a]phenazinone (XIV, Section XIV:2,B(1)), by the condensation of 2-hydroxy-1,4-naphthoquinone with 4-chloro-2-methylaminoaniline.

The free base from **XIII**, which forms dark-blue needles (not analyzed), is a prasindone (Chapter V:2,D), few members of which class

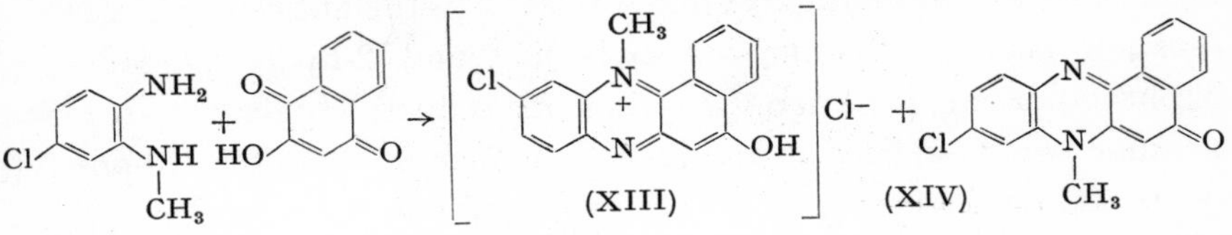

in the benzo[*a*]phenazinium series are known. It gives a yellowish-green coloration with concentrated sulfuric acid, which on dilution passes through bluish-green to magenta.

The other member of this group is the 3-sulfonic acid corresponding to compound **XIII**, which exists as a betaine.[4]

C. 7-Arylmonohydroxybenzo[*a*]phenazinium Salts and Anhydro-Bases

(*1*) *Rosindone* (7-phenyl-5(7)-benzo[*a*]phenazinone, I). Rosindone is the most important oxygenated derivative of the benzo[*a*]-

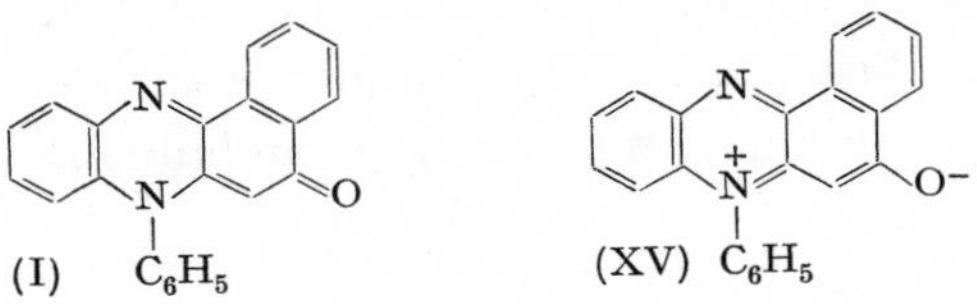

phenazinium series owing to the role it played in the elucidation of the structures of rosinduline dyes. It forms ruby-red hexagonal tablets with a green metallic luster, m.p. 261–262°, which are highly characteristic. It is insoluble in water but dissolves in ethanol to a limited extent, giving an eosin-red solution with a brick-red fluorescence.[12]

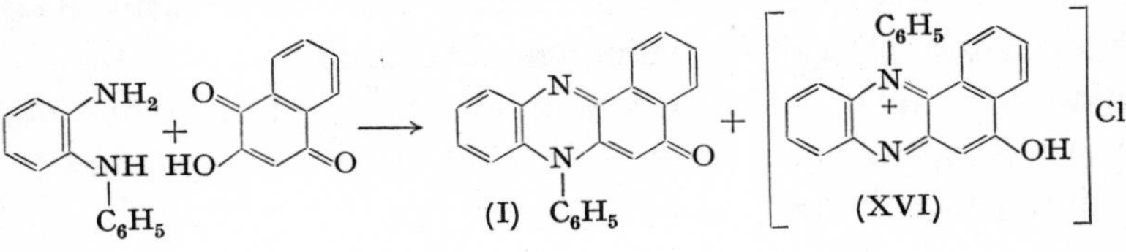

It is prepared by a variety of reactions, for example, by the condensation of 2-hydroxy-1,4-naphthoquinone with 2-aminodiphenyl-amine in cold concentrated ethanolic solution in the presence of a little acetic acid.[12] When this reaction is carried out in the presence of hydrochloric acid, the alternative isomer (XVI) is also obtained in the form of its hydrochloride.[13] Closely related to the above method is the reaction between 2-aminodiphenylamine and 2-hydroxy-3-iodo-1,4-naphthoquinone, in which the quinone is reductively deiodinated, the diamine being oxidized in the process to 2-amino-3-anilino-10-phenyl-phenazinium iodide; the deiodinated quinone then undergoes the above reaction with excess diamine giving rosindone[14] (see Chapter XIII:2,A for a comparable reaction). The second class of reaction yielding rosindone has received mention several times in earlier pages; it is the oxidative attack by alkalis in the presence of air upon 7-phenyl-benzo[a]phenazinium salts[15-17] (Chapter XII:4,D(2); compare V:2,C).

A third important method of preparation is the hydrolysis of 5-amino or substituted amino-7-phenylbenzo[a]phenazinium salts. Thus, rosinduline (5-amino-7-phenylbenzo[a]phenazinium) chloride (III, Section XIV:4,D) yields rosindone when heated to 160–180° under pressure with concentrated hydrochloric acid.[18] Similarly, phenylros-induline chloride (IV) (the 5-anilino analog of rosinduline), and other like compounds, are split by concentrated hydrochloric acid into rosindone and aniline or the corresponding amine.[18,19] Thus a sulfonic acid, obtained by sulfonation of phenylrosinduline is split by heating

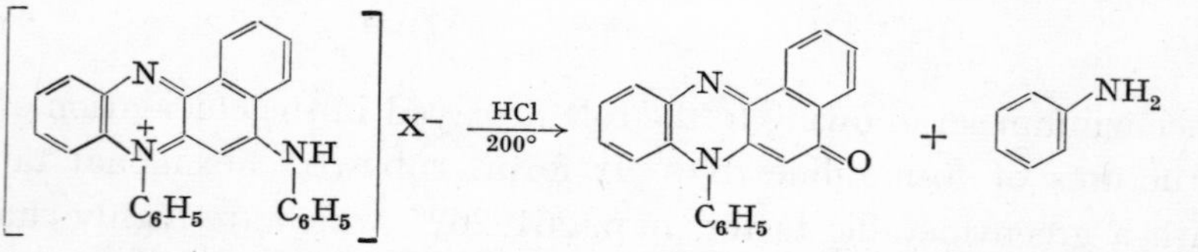

(IV)   (I)

with water under pressure at 200° into rosindone and metanilic acid (aniline-3-sulfonic acid), showing the position of entry of the sulfonic acid group.[20] This method has been adapted by Bass to the structural analysis of azine dyes[21] (see Section XIV:5,C). An alternative method of scission of a phenylrosinduline employs methylation with methyl bromide to the quaternary methobromide (XVII) of the anhydro-base form, which is then split smoothly by cold ethanolic potassium hydr-oxide into rosindone and methylaniline.[22]

Other methods of preparation of rosindone are largely of academic interest. They include: the hydrolysis of 5-chloro-7-phenylbenzo[a]-

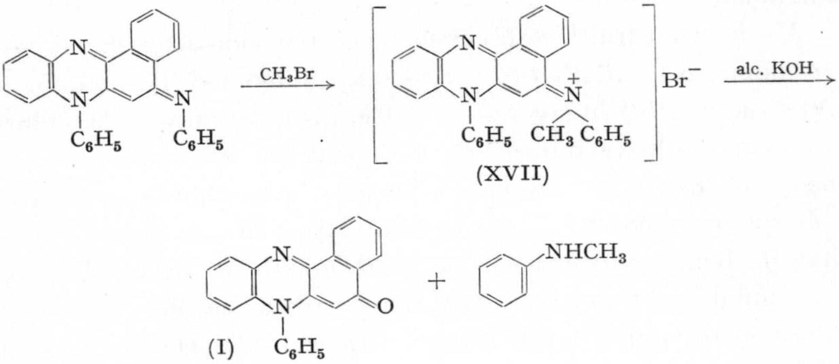

(XVII)

(I) C_6H_5

phenazinium salts by aqueous alkalis, even by sodium acetate solution[23] (Chapter XII:4,D(6)); the hydrolysis of 7-phenyl-5(7)-benzo[a]-phenazinthione (thiorosindone) by means of dilute acid under pressure at 170°[10] (Chapter XII:4,D(7)); the action of ethanolic alkali in the presence of air upon 7-phenylbenzo[a]phenazinium-5-sulfonic acid betaine[24,25] (Chapter XII:4,D(5)); and high temperature acid hydrolysis of the corresponding 5-hydroxylamino betaine.[26] Rosindone may also be prepared by melting 2,4-dinitro-1-(2'-anilino)-anilinonaphthalene (XVIII) (from 2-aminodiphenylamine and 1-chloro-2,4-dinitronaph-

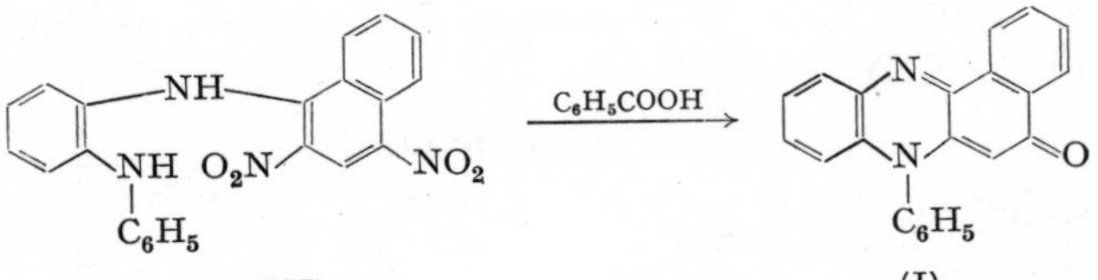

(XVIII)   (I)

thalene) with benzoic acid.[27] It is also a by-product in the formation of rosinduline by a typical induline melt[18] (see Section XIV:4,B(5)).

Rosindone is a very weakly basic substance. It dissolves in concentrated sulfuric acid to give a dark-green color that changes to orange-red on dilution; further dilution leads to the hydrolysis of the sulfate and rosindone is reprecipitated.[12] The lightening in color on combining rosindone with acids has been commented upon.[28-30] It is insoluble in aqueous alkalis and ammonia, but dissolves in ethanolic sodium hydroxide. It is a non-electrolyte, as shown by conductivity studies of the alkaline hydrolysis of 5-chloro-7-phenylbenzo[a]phenazinium chloride.[31]

A somewhat fruitless discussion occurred soon after the discovery of rosindone as to whether it possessed a *p*-quinonoid (I) or *o*-quinonoid (XV) structure.[10,16] In favor of the latter formulation was the failure to react with hydroxylamine,[24,32] the formation of 5-chloro-7-phenylbenzo[a]phenazinium chloride by means of phosphorus pentachloride in phosphoryl chloride[23] and the methylation of rosindone by methyl sulfate in boiling nitrobenzene to yield 5-methoxy-7-phenylbenzo[a]-phenazinium methosulfate as orange-yellow needles, readily decomposing to rosindone on boiling with water.[13] (The corresponding bromide reacts with alcoholic ammonia to form rosinduline.) The argument, which was inextricably involved with the structures to be attributed to the corresponding amino and substituted amino compounds, was not brought to a conclusion mutually satisfying to all parties. Today, we may regard rosindone as a mesomeric structure.

Zinc dust distillation of rosindone affords the parent heterocyclic system, benzo[a]phenazine[18] (Chapter XII:3 *et seq.*). Reductive acetylation, by means of zinc dust and acetic anhydride, yields the diacetyl derivative of leucorosindone (the 7,12-dihydro compound, XIX) which was not characterized but was oxidized by means of ferric chloride in dilute acid to 5-acetoxy-7-phenylbenzo[a]phenazinium ferrichloride[33] (XX).

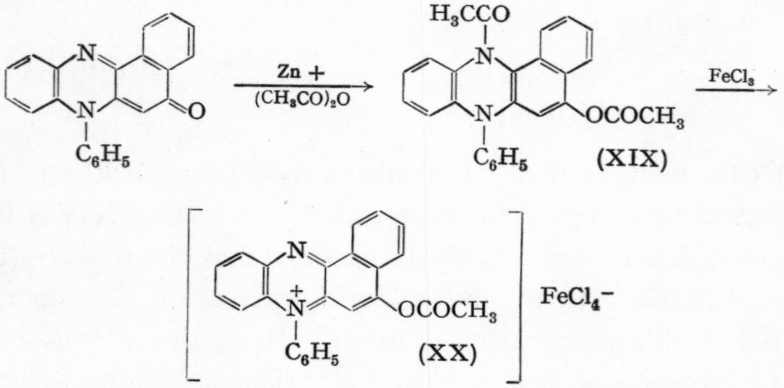

Bromination[12,20] and nitration[12,34] of rosindone have not been thoroughly studied and the positions of attack have not been determined. Reduction of the mononitro derivative (bright-red needles) affords an aminorosindone as dark-blue leaflets.[34] For the sulfonation of rosindone, see below.

The fission of arylrosindulines into an aromatic amine and rosindone has been reversed; thus rosindone, on heating with aniline and aniline hydrochloride at 120–140°, yields phenylrosinduline.[18] Phenylrosindulines substituted in the anilino group may be obtained in like manner from the corresponding aromatic amine. Since, however, these phenylrosindulines may be obtained by simple condensation processes or by the induline melt (Section XIV:4,B(5)), the above process has never achieved commercial importance.

The oxidation of rosindone by chromic acid in acetic acid at 70–80° yields isorosindonic acid (XXI) with a trace of rosindonic acid (XXII).[35] The latter substance is the sole product at higher temperatures, or after treatment of isorosindonic acid with concentrated sulfuric acid.[20,35] (See also Chapter XII:3,F.)

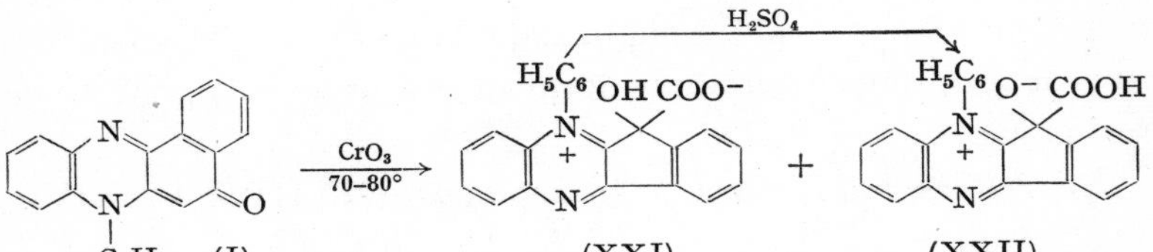

Isorosindonic acid (XXI), white prisms, m.p. 206° (effervescence; CO_2) after preliminary softening at 180°, gives a violet-red coloration with concentrated sulfuric acid, while rosindonic acid (XXII), which is a somewhat stronger acid and hence is given the above structure, forms colorless plates, m.p. 227–228°, and gives a yellow color with sulfuric acid. The names and structures allotted to isorosindonic acid (R. I. 2931) and rosindonic acid (R. I. 2879) in The Ring Index have nothing to recommend them.

While rosindone is insoluble in water and non-substantive to fibers, sulfonation leads to the formation of dyes for silk and wool. Direct sulfonation by the action of 30% oleum at 120–130° [20,36] was supplanted technically by processes involving the hydrolytic cleavage of phenylrosinduline sulfonic acids[37]; for example, Rosinduline 2G

(*C. I.* 830, position of sulfonic acid group doubtful) is obtained by the hydrolysis of phenylrosinduline trisulfonic acid (Azocarmine B or Rosinduline 2B. bluish, *C. I.* 829) by means of water or dilute acids at 160–180° under pressure,[38] while Rosinduline G (*C. I.* 831), which is the 3-sulfonic acid of rosindone, arises by the hydrolysis at 200–210° by means of water under pressure of the corresponding phenylrosinduline-3-sulfonic acid.[39] The products are isolated in the form of sodium salts and dye silk and wool from an acid bath in level orange or scarlet shades of moderate fastness to laundering. Rosinduline 2G gives a vivid fluorescence on silk fibers. It possesses considerable advantages as a redox indicator in a very negative potential range.[40]

Rosindones bearing chloro substituents in the 9-position may be obtained from the 7-phenyl-9(7)-benzo[*a*]phenazinones (isorosindones) by conversion of the latter compounds into 9-chloro-7-phenylbenzo[*a*]-phenazinium chlorides, which are then treated with alkalis in the presence of air.[10, 41] 6-Chlororosindones may be prepared by condensing 2-aminodiphenylamines, which may be further substituted by halogen with 2-chloro-3-hydroxy-1,4-naphthoquinones.[42] In the case of this latter reaction, ring closure may occur in two ways, one product being a prasindone.

(2)   *7-Phenyl-9(7)-benzo[a]phenazinones* (XXIII and XXIV).

(XXIII)   (XXIV)

The 7-phenyl-9(7)-benzo[*a*]phenazinones are often referred to as isorosindones, a practice which, unless qualified, is to be deprecated, since confusion may arise. The parent compound (XXIII) forms reddish-black crystals or needles with a bronze luster, m.p. 227–228°. It may be prepared in the form of its salts (XXV) by a variety of methods, of which the most convenient is probably the condensation of 4-nitrosophenol (1,4-benzoquinone monoxime) with 2-anilino-naphthalene in ethanol in the presence of concentrated hydrochloric acid.[9]

Other methods include the action of water under pressure at 200–250° upon 9-chloro-7-phenylbenzo[a]phenazinium chloride (Chap-

(XXV)

ter XII:4,D(6)) when, however, some 9-chloro-7-phenyl-5(7)-benzo[a]-phenazinone (9-chlororosindone) is simultaneously produced.[10] Since, however, the chloro compound is produced most readily from the isorosindone (XXIII), this method is of theoretical value. The isoros-indone chloride (XXV) may also be obtained by the hydrolysis of 9-anilino-7-phenylbenzo[a]phenazinium chloride ("phenylisorosindu-line chloride") by means of concentrated hydrochloric acid at 230–240°. This method has been adapted to the analysis of azine dyes.[21] The sulfate of (XXV) has been obtained by the deamination of 10-amino-7-phenyl-9(7)-benzo[a]phenazinone by diazotization and heating with ethanol.[26]

The salts (XXV) are readily hydrolyzed by alkalis, even by sodium acetate or sodium carbonate, when the weak anhydro-base (XXIII) is precipitated. This gives a violet coloration in concentrated sulfuric acid, which on progressive dilution passes through red to yellow.[9] The absorption spectrum of the isorosindone (XXIII) has been measured in amyl alcohol. It exhibits a main band at 547 mμ, with subsidiary bands at 507 and 589 mμ.[21]

The protracted argument as to whether the anhydro-base was to be given the structure XXIII or XXIV was ultimately inconclusive. We should today regard the compound as possessing a mesomeric structure. Cryoscopic molecular weight determinations in benzene showed it to be unassociated.[43] In favor of the betaine structure (XXIV) was the fact that it did not react with phenylmagnesium bromide.[43] It could be acetylated to 9-acetoxy-7-phenylbenzo[a]phenazinium ace-tate, which was converted to the ferrichloride. Acetylation under reductive conditions (zinc dust, acetic anhydride and sodium acetate) gave 9-acetoxy-12-acetyl-7-phenyl-7,12-dihydrobenzo[a]phenazine as colorless leaflets, m.p. 215° (slight dec.), which was oxidized by warm ferric chloride solution to the same ferrichloride as above.[33] Methylation of the anhydro-base (XXIII) could be accomplished by heating in a sealed tube at 100° with methyl iodide, when 9-methoxy-7-phenyl-benzo[a]phenazinium iodide (XXVI) was formed as green metallic needles. This lost methyl iodide, to regenerate the isorosindone (XXIII), on heating to 170° or by treatment with ethanolic potassium hydroxide.[22] The latter procedure led also to attack at position 5 to form 9-methoxy-7-phenyl-5(7)benzo[a]phenazinone (9-methoxyrosindone, XXVII) as red needles or prisms, m.p. 308° (Section XIV:3,A). Ethylation of the anhydro-base with ethyl iodide followed precisely the same course.[44]

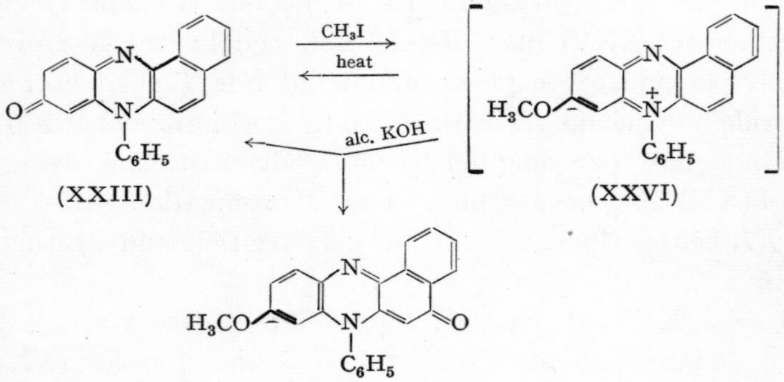

(XXIII)   (XXVI)

(XXVII)

On treatment with a mixture of phosphorus pentachloride and phosphoryl chloride, the isorosindone (XXIII) gave 9-chloro-7-phenyl-benzo[a]phenazinium chloride.[10, 22]

The reaction between the isorosindone (XXIII) and hydroxyl-amine in ethanolic potassium hydroxide solution was thought at first[10] to give the corresponding oxime (XXVIII), which would have been strong evidence in favor of the p-quinonoid, keto formulation. Later, it was shown[11, 45] that hydroxylamine reacted with N-phenylbenzo[a]-phenazinones to yield amino derivatives of the phenazinones, and the initial observation was corrected,[26] the product being described as 5-amino-7-phenyl-9(7)-benzo[a]phenazinone (XXIX). This too was incorrect and Kehrmann and Prager[46] showed the correct formulation to be 10-amino-7-phenyl-9(7)-benzo[a]phenazinone (XXX). (The reactions of this compound are discussed later in Section XIV:6,B.) Fischer and Römer[32] concurred with this view that attack occurred at position 10.

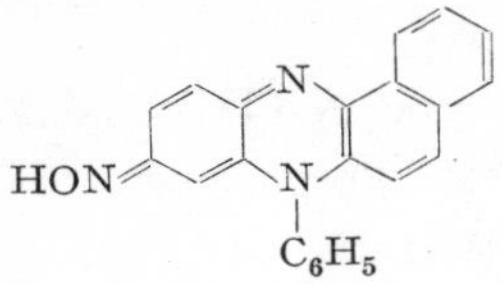

(XXVIII) 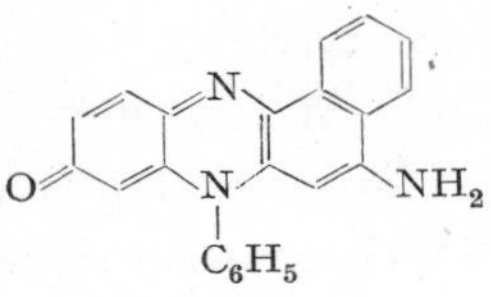   (XXIX) 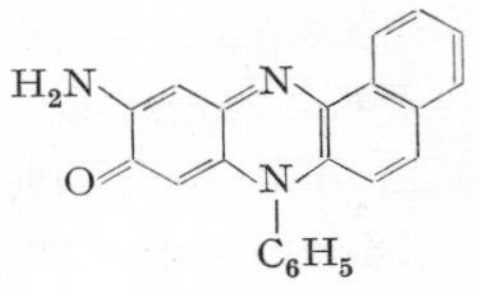   (XXX)

The isorosindone (XXIII) undergoes attack at position 5 when heated under pressure at 200° with concentrated hydrochloric acid in acetic acid,[26] or when refluxed with concentrated alcoholic potassium hydroxide.[9, 44] This may be regarded as the normal attack of benzo[a]-phenazinium derivatives at a reactive center. The product, 9-hydroxy-7-phenyl-5(7)-benzo[a]phenazinone (XXXI, 9-hydroxyrosindone) has been given the trivial name naphthosafranol, which however is objectionable owing to its use for 8-hydroxy-10(1'- or 2'-naphthyl)-2(10)-phenazinones also.[47] Hydroxybenzo[a]phenazinones are discussed in Section XIV:3.

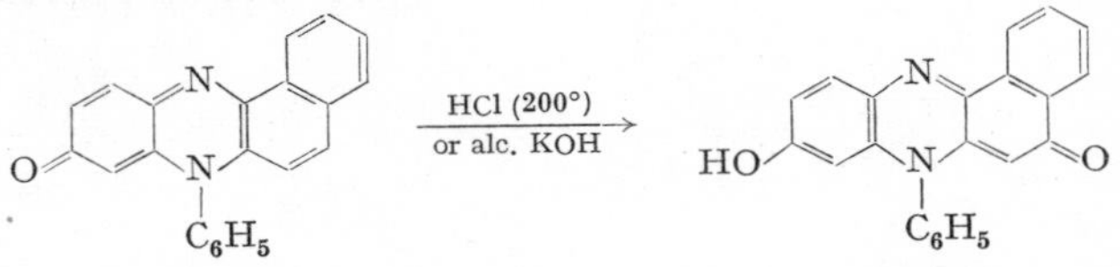

(XXIII)   (XXXI)

When either the isorosindone (XXIII) or the 10-amino derivative (XXX) is heated under pressure at 150° with o-phenylenediamine and its hydrochloride, a fluorindine derivative, 7-phenyl-7,14-dihydro-benzo[a]quinoxalo[2,3-i]phenazine (XXXII), is obtained as golden-bronze lustered plates.[32] (See Chapter XVIII:6,A.)

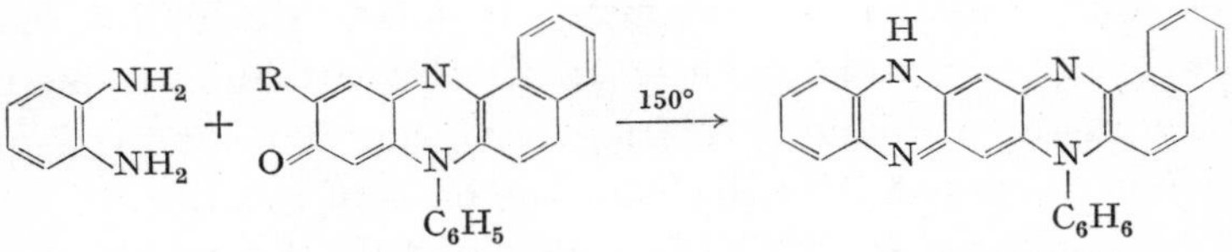

(XXIII   R=H)   (XXXII)
(XXX   R=NH₂)

Derivatives of the isorosindone (XXIII), in which the *N*-aryl group is varied,[8, 10] and the 10- and 11-methyl homologs of XXIII itself have been described.[33, 41] When position 10 is blocked by methyl, no reaction with hydroxylamine is observed.[32]

The direct sulfonation of isorosindones of type XXIII has not been described. Details have been given for the preparation of a bluish-gray dye that has been tentatively allotted the structure of 7-(4'-diethylaminophenyl)-9(7)-benzo[a]phenazinone-3-sulfonic acid.[48] There is scant evidence for the formulation as a derivative of phenazine, however, and the shade of color would appear to be conclusive evidence against it, since it is known that substituents in the 7-phenyl group do not appreciably affect the color.[49–52] It is probably an oxazine dyestuff.

The homologs of 7-phenyl-9(7)-benzo[a]phenazinone are listed in Table XIX.

(*3*) *Miscellaneous Hydroxy Derivatives of 7-Phenylbenzo[a]-phenazinium Salts.* Of the eight remaining monohydroxy derivatives of 7-phenylbenzo[a]phenazinium salts (excluding those in which the hydroxyl group is located in the 7-phenyl radical) that are possible on theoretical grounds, only two are known (XXXIII and XXXIV).

(XXXIII)   (XXXIV)

2-Hydroxy-7-phenylbenzo[a]phenazinium chloride (XXXIII) is obtained, together with the 12-phenyl isomer (Section XIV:2,D), which is the main product, by the condensation of 7-hydroxy-1,2-naphtho-quinone with 2-aminodiphenylamine. It forms steely-blue lustrous crystals and gives a violet color on treatment with aniline, due to the formation of the 5-anilino derivative,[53] showing it to be the 7-phenyl isomer. (See Section XIV:4,B(11) for the basis of this test.)

The second isomer (XXXIV) is prepared by the deamination, by diazotization and heating with ethanol, of 9-amino-10-hydroxy-7-

phenylbenzo[a]phenazinium sulfate (XXXV), itself prepared in almost quantitative yield by the condensation of 4-amino-5-hydroxy-1,2-benzoquinone with 2-anilino-1-naphthylamine hydrochloride.

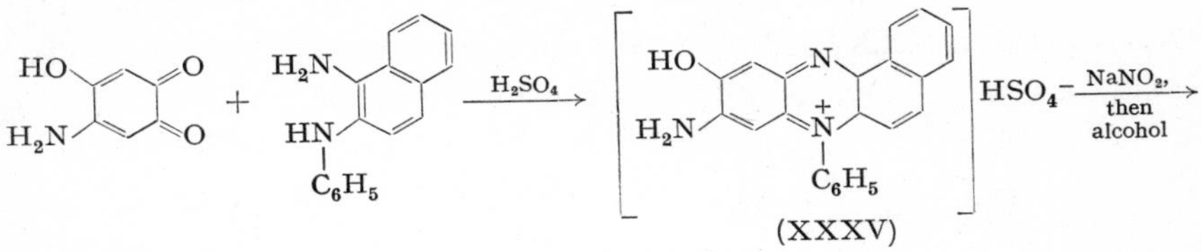

$$
\text{(XXXV)}
$$

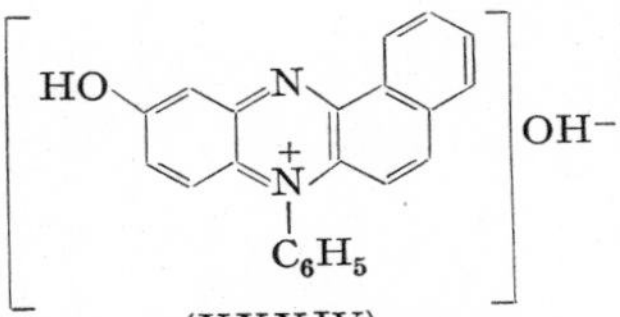

$$
\text{(XXXIV)}
$$

The quaternary hydroxide crystallizes from dilute ethanol in blue-black needles, decomposing above 300° without dehydration to the anhydro-base, which would be a prasindone[54] (Chapter V:2,D). It gives a dichroic solution in concentrated sulfuric acid (grayish-green in thin, and bluish-violet in thick, layers), which becomes orange-red on dilution.[54,55] (See Table XIX.)

D. 12-Phenylmonohydroxybenzo[a]phenazinium Salts

These isomers are relatively unimportant. They may be prepared by standard methods, examples of which have already been given. Thus they are formed by condensation of hydroxy-1,2-naphthoquinones with 2-aminodiphenylamine, when they are accompanied by the 7-phenyl isomers,[13,53,56] by deamination of aminohydroxy-12-phenylbenzo[a]-phenazinium salts by the standard procedure of diazotization and heating with ethanol,[57] or finally by hydrolysis of the corresponding amino-12-phenylbenzo[a]phenazinium salts by heating under pressure with mineral acids.[5]

Two of the corresponding bases exist in anhydro-base form. They are 12-phenyl-3(12)-benzo[a]phenazinone (XXXVI), which may be extracted from cold aqueous solutions into ether, in which it gives a blue solution, due presumably to the anhydro-base, although it has not been analyzed,[56] and 12-phenyl-10(12)-benzo[a]phenazinone (XXXVII), which forms reddish-violet lustrous leaflets, m.p. 267°, and exhibits a weak red fluorescence in ethanolic solution.[57] The remaining bases (XXXVIII and XXXIX) are quaternary hydroxides, which if they existed as anhydro-bases would be prasindones.

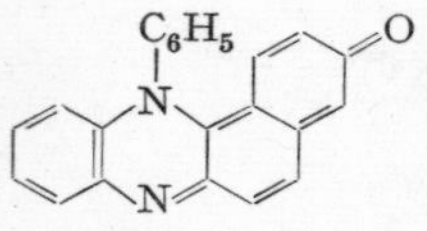

(XXXVI) 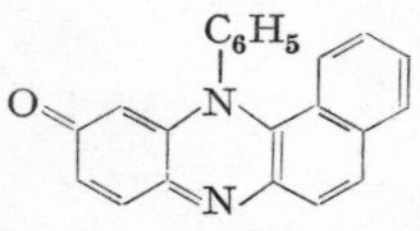   (XXXVII) 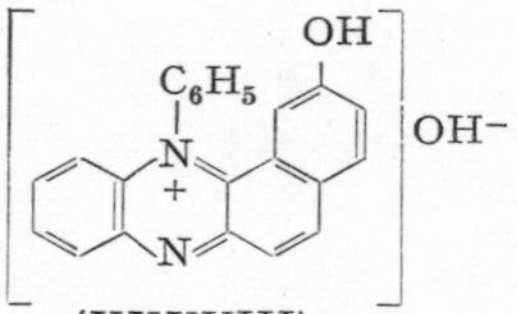   (XXXVIII)

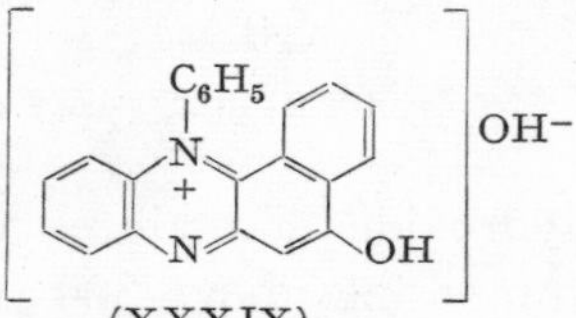

(XXXIX)

This group of substances possesses no technical importance. (See Table XX.)

3. Dihydroxybenzo[a]phenazinium
Salts and Derivatives

No examples of 7- or 12-alkyl or aralkylbenzo[a]phenazinium salts bearing two or more oxygen atoms have been prepared and only one dihydroxy-12-phenyl compound, which is unimportant.[58] A number of dihydroxy-7-phenylbenzo[a]phenazinium salts are known, however. The methods by which they may be prepared follow the general pattern sketched above: by condensation of suitably substituted 1,2-quinones with mono-N-phenyl o-diamines; by hydrolysis of diamino- or amino-hydroxy-7-phenylbenzo[a]phenazinium salts by means of acid; by the action of alkalis and air upon monohydroxy-7-phenylbenzo[a]phen-azinium salts; or by the replacement of amino groups by hydroxyl groups by diazotization and heating the aqueous solution. Members of this group are listed in Table XXI.

A. 9-Hydroxy-7-phenyl-5(7)-benzo[a]phenazinone
(XXXI, 9-Hydroxyrosindone, Naphthosafranol)

This substance is the benzo analog of phenosafranol (Chapter
V:3,C). The anhydro-base forms reddish-brown needles with a green
luster and dissolves in organic solvents, giving red solutions exhibiting a
fiery-red fluorescence that becomes more greenish on dilution. It gives
a violet-red coloration with concentrated sulfuric acid, which on dilution passes through orange to bright yellow. The presence of a phenolic
hydroxyl group is shown by its solubility in alkalis, giving a rose-red
solution with a yellow fluorescence. It is formed when 7-phenyl-9(7)-
benzo[a]phenazinone (XXIII) is heated with concentrated ethanolic
potassium hydroxide,[9, 44] or with concentrated hydrochloric acid in
acetic acid under pressure at 200°.[26] This is a further example of the
attack at the 5-position upon 7-phenylbenzo[a]phenazinium salts.
Alternatively, XXIII may first be methylated and the quaternary
iodide (XXVI) treated with ethanolic alkali to give 9-methoxyrosindone
(XXVII), bright-red needles, m.p. 308°,[22, 44, 59] which is then hydrolyzed
by heating under pressure at 170° with concentrated hydrochloric
acid.[22, 44]

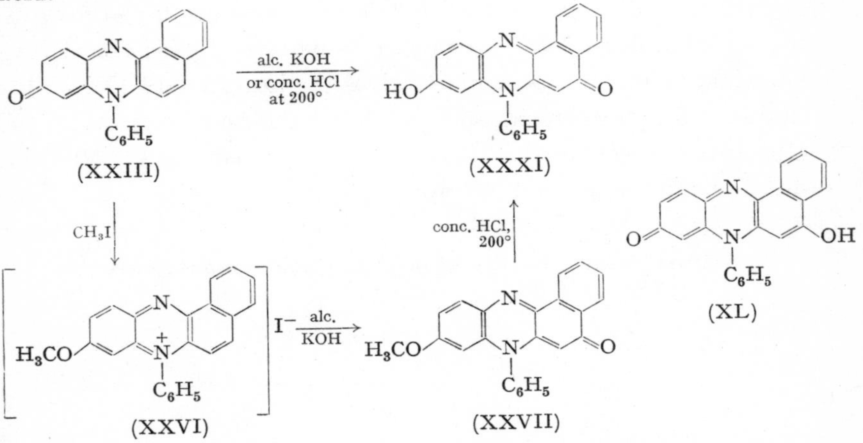

The 10-methyl homolog of XXVII (brown-red needles, m.p.
287–288°) is prepared similarly.[41]

The anhydro-base (XXXI) is also obtained by the hydrolysis of a
number of 5,9-diamino- or substituted-amino-7-phenylbenzo[a]-

phenazinium salts, for example, from 5-amino-9-dimethylamino-7-phenylbenzo[a]phenazinium chloride by the action of concentrated hydrochloric acid in acetic acid at 160–170°; or together with 9-dimethylamino-7-phenyl-5(7)-benzo[a]phenazinone by the action of ethanolic potash[60]; or from 9-amino-5-anilino-7-phenylbenzo[a]phenazinium chloride,[19] 5 9-dianilino-7-phenylbenzo[a]phenazinium chloride[34] or similar compounds by high temperature acid hydrolysis. This has proved useful in the elucidation of the structures of azine dyestuffs.[21, 34]

9-Hydroxy-7-phenyl-5(7)-benzo[a]phenazinone is given structure **XXXI** instead of the alternative isorosindone structure (**XL**) since, on treatment with methyl iodide and methanolic potassium hydroxide under pressure at 100°, it is methylated to yield 9-methoxyrosindone[44] (**XXVII**), the structure of which follows from its alternative synthesis outlined above. The 9-ethyl ether, red needles, m.p. 269°, is obtained similarly[44] (but see footnote to Section XIV:3,B). Methylation of 9-methoxyrosindone (**XXVII**) under more drastic conditions, namely, heating with methyl iodide under pressure at 150°, gives 5,9-dimethoxy-7-phenylbenzo[a]phenazinium iodide as brown crystals with a green reflex, which readily lose methyl iodide to regenerate 9-methoxyrosindone on heating at 100° [22] (compare 9-methoxy-7-phenylbenzo[a]phenazinium iodide, which similarly gives the isorosindone (**XXIII**)).

Salts of 9-hydroxyrosindone (**XXXI**) have been prepared[34] and the absorption spectrum has been recorded[21] (main band, 497 mμ; subsidiary bands, 463.5 and 532 mμ).

B. 10-Hydroxy-7-phenyl-9(7)-benzo[a]phenazinone (XLI)

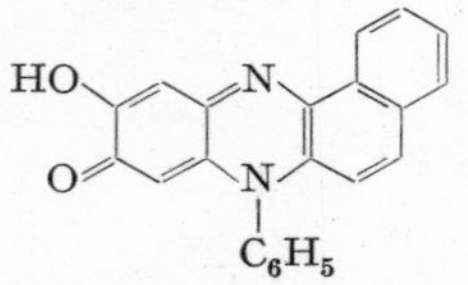

(XLI) 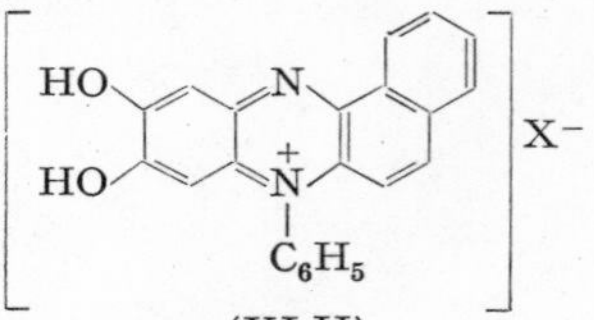   (XLII)

This substance is the anhydro-base of 9,10-dihydroxy-7-phenylbenzo[a]phenazinium salts (**XLII**). The chloride of the latter structure is obtained when 2-anilino-1-naphthylamine hydrochloride is condensed in concentrated ethanolic solution with 4,5-dihydroxy-1,2-benzoquinone.[46,61] It is also prepared by the high temperature acid hydrolysis of 10-amino-7-phenyl-9(7)-benzo[a]phenazinone[26] (XXX), the product from the reaction of hydroxylamine with 7-phenyl-9(7)-benzo[a]phenazinone (XXIII). The amino derivative (XXX) may also be hydrolyzed to the anhydro-base (XLI) in poor yield by means of ethanolic potash, the bulk of the product being the isorosindone (XXIII).

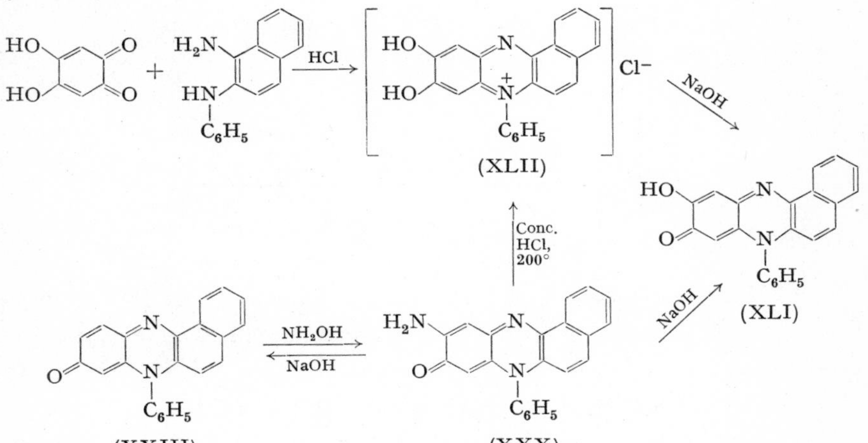

When the salts (XLII) are treated with very weak alkali, followed by dilute acetic acid, the anhydro-base (XLI) is obtained, showing its weakly basic nature. It forms bronze-lustered leaflets that decompose at about 287° [61] and give brownish-red solutions with a slight reddish fluorescence in organic solvents. With concentrated sulfuric acid, it gives a reddish-violet color, passing on dilution through red to yellow.[26]

Besides the formulation as a hydroxyisorosindone (XLI) it is possible to write a structure (XLIII) as a 9-hydroxyprasindone.

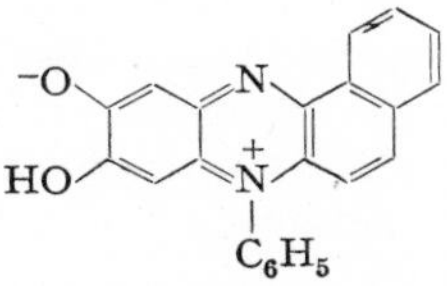

(XLIII)

However the color of the base and its solutions is not in agreement with this. Confirmatory evidence of the correctness of structure XLI follows from the result of methylation with methyl iodide and methanolic alkali, when 10-methoxy-7-phenyl-9(7)-benzo[a]phenazinone (XLIV) is obtained as red needles, m.p. about 300°. This was incorrectly formulated by Fischer[26] at the time, but, after the structure of the aminoisorosindone (XXX) was corrected,[46] an independent and unequivocal synthesis of the methyl ether from 2-anilinonaphthalene and 5-nitrosoguaiacol settled the matter.[32] The corresponding ethyl ether, red needles, m.p. 269°, is known.[26*]

(XLI)   (XLIV)

10-Hydroxy-7-phenyl-9(7)-benzo[a]phenazinone (XLI) has been reacted with 2-aminophenol in boiling benzoic acid to give 7-phenyl-7-benzo[a]-[1,4]benzoxazino[3,2-i]phenazine (R. I. 3573, XLV) as almost black microscopic crystals giving violet solutions in organic solvents and blue to bluish-green solutions in concentrated sulfuric acid, which on dilution first become pure blue and then precipitate violet-blue flocks of the sulfate.[62]

(XLI) C₆H₅   (XLV)   C₆H₅

Other heterocyclic derivatives have been prepared from XLI. Thus o-phenylenediamine hydrochloride in boiling benzoic acid reacts with

---

* There may be confusion between this compound and 9-ethoxy-7-phenyl-5 (7) benzo[a]phenazinone (Section XIV: 3,A), which is also described as red needles, m.p. 269°,[44] especially in view of the incorrect formulations that were current at the time of both papers. Thus XLI was thought by Fischer and his pupils to be identical with 9-hydroxy-7-phenyl-5(7)-benzo[a]phenazinone (naphthosafranol, XXXI). *Beilstein* (4th Edition), 23, 542, treats the ethyl ethers as different compounds.

XLI to yield 7-phenyl-7,14-dihydrobenzo[a]quinoxalo[2,3-i]phenazine (XXXII, R. I. 3577) as dark-violet needles with a bronze luster, giving reddish-violet solutions in benzene with a vermilion fluorescence.[61] With 2-aminodiphenylamine hydrochloride two products are formed: 7,14-diphenyl-7,14-dihydrobenzo[a]quinoxalo[2,3-i]phenazine (XLVI), (dark-blue needles with a green metallic luster giving a violet-red solution with a strong red fluorescence in organic solvents and a greenish-blue color in strong sulfuric acid that becomes pure blue on dilution); and an olive-green compound (giving a green color in concentrated sulfuric acid, passing to bluish-green on dilution and giving non-fluorescent solutions in organic solvents), which has been formulated as the isomer (XLVII) in which the positions of the charges are not fixed.[61] When 1,2-diaminonaphthalene is employed as o-diamine, only one of the two possible isomers (XLVIII, R. I. 3754, and XLIX, no R. I. enumeration) is obtained. It forms greenish-blue salts, reddish-violet solutions with a red fluorescence in ethanol and gives an inky black color with concentrated sulfuric acid. It has not been orientated.[61]

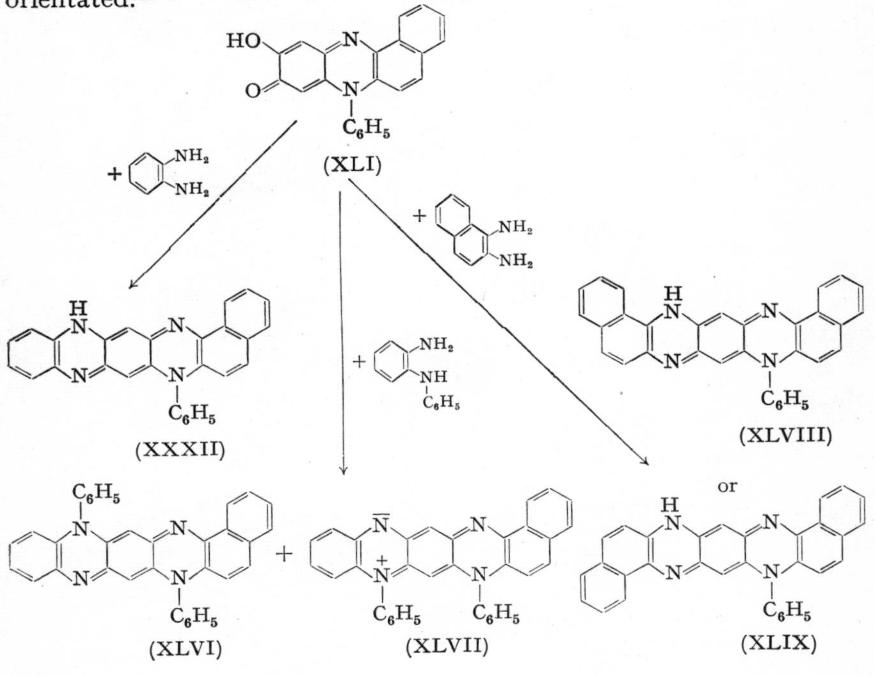

C. Miscellaneous

6-Hydroxy-7-phenyl-5(7)-benzo[a]phenazinone (L) is probably the structure to be assigned to the by-product, dark-violet needles, m.p. 212°, obtained from the mother liquors of the condensation of 1,2-naphthoquinone-4-sulfonic acid and 2-aminodiphenylamine hydrochloride.[24] It may arise from the following reaction:

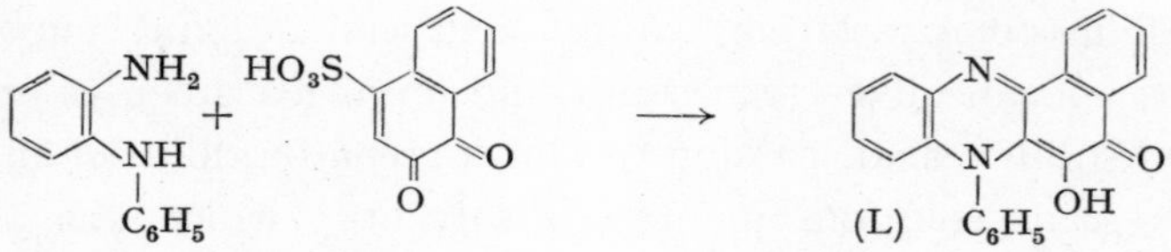

2-Hydroxy-7-phenyl-5(7)benzo[a]phenazinone (LI), yellowish-red leaflets, is obtained by high temperature (200°) hydrolysis of the corresponding rosindone-2-sulfonic acid.[34, 39] The 3-hydroxyrosindone (LII) is obtained similarly from 5-anilino-7-phenylbenzo[a]phenazinium-3-sulfonic acid betaine.[34, 39] It forms dark brownish-green prisms. 2-Hydroxy-7-phenyl-9(7)-benzo[a]phenazinone (LIII) is obtained by high temperature acid hydrolysis of 2,9-dianilino-7-phenylbenzo[a]-

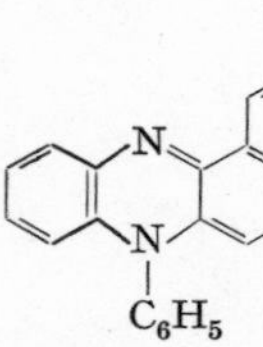

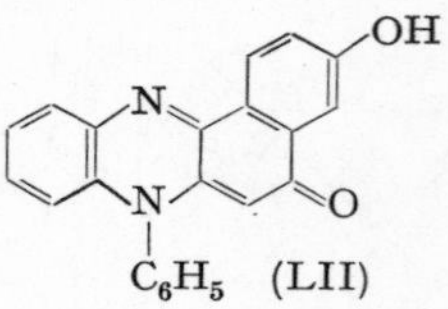

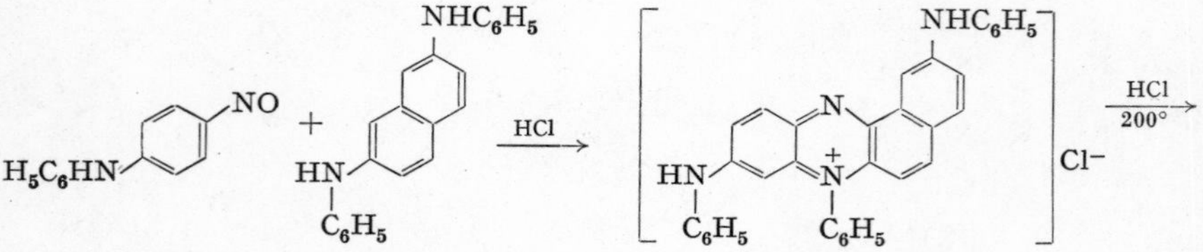

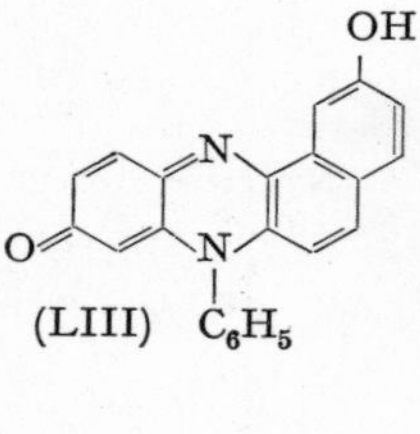

phenazinium chloride, which in turn is obtained from 4-nitrosodiphenyl-
amine and 2,7-dianilinonaphthalene,[19] or by similar acid hydrolysis of
2-anilino-7-phenyl-9(7)-benzo[a]phenazinone, obtained from p-nitrosophenol and 2,7-dianilinonaphthalene.[34]

LIII forms small bronze-colored lustrous crystals that give a deep-
blue color in caustic soda.[19]

4. Aminobenzo[a]phenazinium
Salts and Derivatives

A. General

Aminobenzo[a]phenazinium salts in which the 7- or 12-sub-
stituents are alkyl or aryl are all known. Many of them have been used
as dyestuffs and some are still of considerable importance, although the
majority of them have been superseded by dyes of greater fastness.
Certain of them, in which an amino group is para to the unsubstituted
azine nitrogen atom, form anhydro-bases of the type LIV on liberation
from their salts; the remainder give quaternary hydroxides. For the
group of substances that form anhydro-bases, there arises the question
of the structure of the salts, that is, whether they are to be given an
o-quinonoid (LV) or p-quinonoid formulation (LVI).

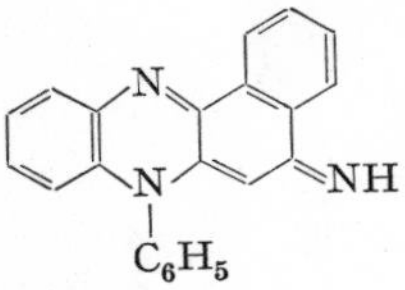

$$\text{(LIV)} \qquad\qquad \text{(LV)} \qquad\qquad \text{(LVI)}$$

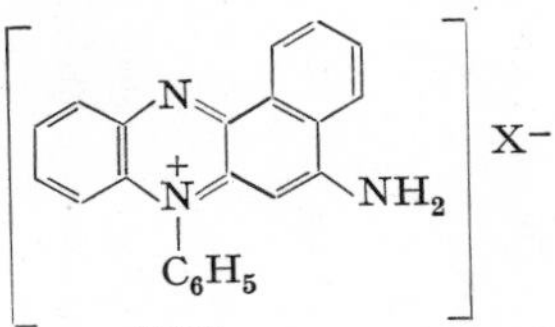

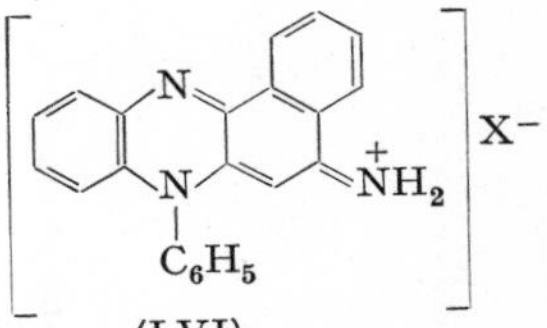

This question exercised the minds of Kehrmann and O. Fischer
to a considerable extent and will be briefly discussed later from the
viewpoint of absorption spectra (see Section XIV:4,C; also Chapter
VII:1,C(2)).

Structures LV and LVI are equivalent except for the position of
the charge, but the resonance hybrid that describes the actual state
of the molecule will undoubtedly show more affinity with one rather
than the other alternative, depending upon the relative basicities of

TABLE XVII. 7-Alkyl and -Aralkyl-5(7)-benzo[a]phenazinones

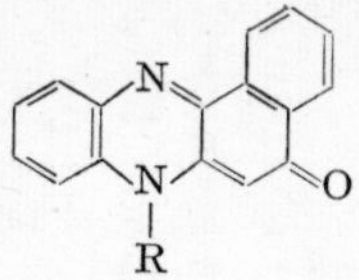

Substituent R	Other substituents	Physical characteristics	M.p. (°C.)	Color with H_2SO_4 followed by dilution	Ref.
CH_3—		Brick-red needles, green luster	257–9	Dichroic (purplish-red, dirty green), orange-red, yellow	1, 2, 3
CH_3—	9-Cl—	Garnet-red leaflets, golden luster		Mauvish-red, orange-yellow, red ppt.	4
C_2H_5—		Garnet-red prisms, green luster	192–3	Greyish-green, orange-yellow	2, 5, 6
$C_6H_5CH_2$—		Short dark-red prisms, green luster	262–4	Green	5, 7

TABLE XVIII. 7-Alkyl and -Aralkyl-9(7)benzo[a]phenazinones

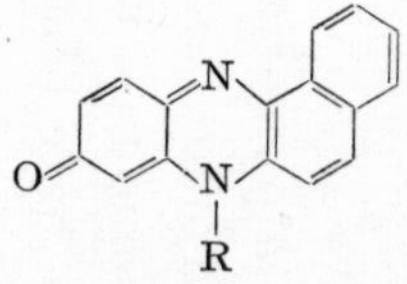

Substituent R	Physical characteristics	M.p. (°C.)	Color with H_2SO_4 followed by dilution	Ref.
CH_3—	Black crystals, metallic luster	212–4	Reddish-violet, yellow	8
C_2H_5—	Brownish-red needles	178		8, 9, 10
$C_6H_5CH_2$—	Brownish-violet needles	210	Bluish-violet	8

TABLE XIX. Monohydroxy-7-phenylbenzo[a]phenazinium Salts

Substituents	Appearance of chloride (unless otherwise stated)	Appearance of anhydro-base (where formed)	M.p. of anhydro-base (°C)	Color with H_2SO_4 followed by dilution	Ref.
2-Hydroxy-	Steel-blue lustrous crystals				53
5-Hydroxy-	SO_4^{--}, yellow leaflets	Ruby-red hexagonal tablets, green metallic luster	261–2	Dark green, orange-red, ppt.	See XIV: 2,C (1)
5-Methoxy-	Br^-, golden lustrous leaflets			Purple-red, yellow	13
5-Acetoxy-	$FeCl_4^-$, crystals			Green, red, yellow	33
5-Hydroxy-6-chloro-		Red needles with golden luster	255	Dark yellowish-green, orange, ppt.	42
5-Hydroxy-9-chloro-		Brassy lustrous needles	268	Violet-blue, brown, yellow	10
5-Hydroxy-6,9-dichloro-		Lustrous red needles with golden sheen	242–3	Dirty violet, orange-red, ppt.	42
5-Hydroxy-9-chloro-10-methyl-		Yellowish-brown needles	> 300	Dichroic (red, blue), yellowish-red, ppt.	41
5-Hydroxy-4'-nitro-		Violet-brown crystals			51
9-Hydroxy-	Green lustrous flakes	Reddish-black crystals with bronze luster	227–8	Violet, red, yellow	See XIV: 2,C (2)
9-Methoxy-	NO_3^-, leaflets with green luster				22

(Table continued)

TABLE XIX (*continued*)

Substituents	Appearance of chloride (unless otherwise stated)	Appearance of anhydro-base (where formed)	M.p. of anhydro-base (°C.)	Color with H_2SO_4 followed by dilution	Ref.
9-Ethoxy-	I−, metallic lustrous prisms				44
9-Acetoxy-	FeCl$_4$−, yellowish-brown crystals			Reddish-violet, brownish-yellow, red, orange	33
9-Acetoxy-12-acetyl-7,12-dihydro-		Base, leaflets	215 (dec.)	Yellow $\xrightarrow{stand}$ red, red fluorescence	33
9-Hydroxy-2′-methyl-	Orange-red leaflets	Dark-red needles	148	Violet, yellow	10
9-Hydroxy-10-methyl-	Bright-red needles	Reddish-brown needles, metallic luster	258	Dichroic (red, violet), yellow	33, 41
9-Methoxy-10-methyl-	I−, needles with green luster				41
9-Acetoxy-10-methyl-	Yellowish-red needles				33
9-Hydroxy-11-methyl-	Brownish-yellow prisms, metallic luster	Golden-bronze lustrous needles	220	Reddish-violet, brown, reddish-yellow	41
10-Hydroxy-	Reddish-brown crystals	Blue-black needles	> 300	Dichroic (greyish-green, bluish-violet), orange	54
10-Acetoxy-	PtCl$_6$−−, brick-red crystals			Blue-black, dark-green, orange-yellow	54

TABLE XX. Monohydroxy-12-phenylbenzo[a]phenazinium Salts

Substituents	Appearance of chloride (unless otherwise stated)	Appearance of anhydro-base (where formed)	M.p. of anhydro-base (°C.)	Color with H_2SO_4 followed by dilution	Ref.
2-Hydroxy-	Steel-blue lustrous leaflets			Dirty yellowish-green, dark red	53
2-Acetoxy-	$PtCl_6^{--}$, Scarlet-red crystals			Yellowish-green, dirty red	53
3-Hydroxy-	Reddish-brown needles with green luster	?Blue solution in ether		Violet, red, orange-yellow	56
5-Hydroxy-	Dark-red leaflets	Quaternary hydroxide, greenish-blue needles	164 (dec.)	Brownish-red, (green, purplish-red), green-ish-blue, blood-red	5, 13, 55
10-Hydroxy-	Reddish-violet leaflets with coppery luster		267	Green, brownish-red, reddish-violet (alkaline)	57

TABLE XXI. Dihydroxy-7-phenylbenzo[a]phenazinium Salts

Substituents	Appearance of chloride (unless otherwise stated)	Appearance of anhydro-base (where formed)	M.p. of anhydro-base (°C.)	Color with H_2SO_4 followed by dilution	Ref.
2,5-Dihydroxy-		Yellowish-red leaflets		Magenta	34
2,9-Dihydroxy-		Crystals with bronze luster		Violet, reddish-yellow	19
3,5-Dihydroxy-		Dark-brownish-green prisms		Reddish-violet, yellow	34
(?) 5,6-Dihydroxy-		Dark-violet needles	212		24
5,9-Dihydroxy-	Red crystals, green reflex	Reddish-brown needles, green luster		Violet-red, orange, bright-yellow	9, 19, 26, 34, 44, 60
5-Hydroxy-9-methoxy-		Needles or prisms	308	Reddish-violet, brown, yellow	22, 44, 59
5,9-Dimethoxy-	I-, brown crystals, green reflex		I-, dec. 100		22
(?) 5-Hydroxy-9-ethoxy-*		Red needles	269		44
5-Hydroxy-9-methoxy-10-methyl-		Brownish-red needles	287-8	Dichroic (reddish-violet, cherry-red), yellow	41
9,10-Dihydroxy-	Dark-red needles	Leaflets with bronze luster	dec. 260	Reddish-violet, red, yellow	10, 26, 46
9-Hydroxy-10-methoxy-		Red needles	300		26, 32
(?) 9-Hydroxy-10-ethoxy-*		Red needles	269		26

*These compounds may be identical. See footnote to Section XIV:3,B.

the two centers. However, in the section following, all the compounds mentioned will be formulated and named as salts of o-quinonoid aminobenzo[a]phenazinium hydroxides for the sake of convenience in nomenclature and in order to emphasize the relationship between this class and the other group of aminobenzo[a]phenazinium hydroxides and their salts. This does not prejudge the spectral investigations to be described later.

Although logically the whole group may be divided between mono- and di-amino derivatives, the methods of preparation, properties and uses are common to both classes and so will be dealt with together. There is such a large number of amino derivatives that we are restricting mention in the text to the most important members. Tables XXII–XXVII list the simpler members.

B. General Methods of Synthesis

The methods of synthesis available for a particular member of this series of compounds are dependent upon the position of the amino group or groups and the nature and position of the N-substituent. Some syntheses, moreover, are adapted specifically to the production of substituted amino derivatives but since these were and, in some cases, still are of commercial importance they merit generalization. As far as possible, the scope of each synthesis is indicated at the end of each subsection.

(1) The most general method is the condensation of a 1,2-naphthoquinone with a mono-N-substituted o-phenylenediamine. The N-substituent may be alkyl, aralkyl or aryl and either or both components may be substituted in the required positions with amino or substituted amino groups, which may be protected by acyl groups. Both 7- and 12-substituted benzo[a]phenazinium salts may be formed and, in practice, both are often obtained, though the proportions of the isomers vary considerably with the nature of the components. Thus 2-aminodiphenylamine condenses with 7-acetamido-1,2-naphthoquinone when both 2-acetamido-7-phenyl- (LVII) and 2-acetamido-12-phenylbenzo[a]phenazinium (LVIII) salts are formed, the latter being the major product.[63] These are converted to the bromides and the

products separated by fractional crystallization, LVII bromide being much less soluble in water. After separation the acetyl groups may be removed by hydrolysis with sulfuric acid, for example:

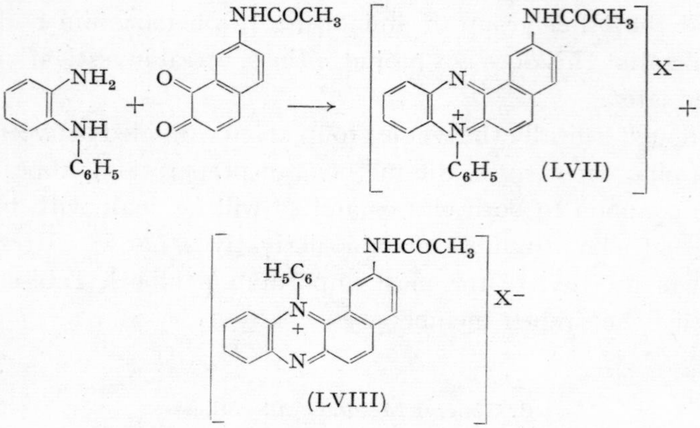

(LVII)

(LVIII)

This reaction was used widely by Kehrmann and his associates and is applicable to the synthesis of any member, provided the components are available.

(2)   A very closely similar method is the reaction of a mono-*N*-substituted diamine with a 2-hydroxy-1,4-naphthoquinone-4-imine,[12, 64] or substituted imine.[65] Insofar as one may regard the latter components as 4-amino-1,2-naphthoquinones, the method is identical with (*1*); but there is one important difference—this method gives only 5-amino-7-substituted benzo[*a*]phenazinium compounds.

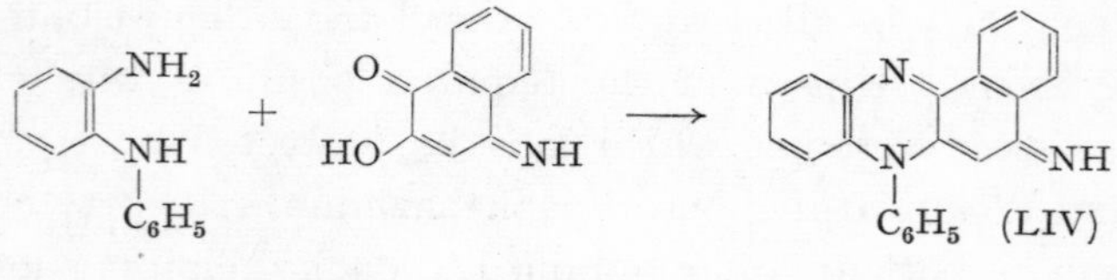

(LIV)

If a 5-amino-12-phenylbenzo[*a*]phenazinium salt is required, then a 4-acylamido-1,2-naphthoquinone must be employed and the two isomeric products separated.[5, 66]

(3)   A method of great generality and with many variants, which achieved commercial importance, consists in the condensation of a

2-substituted aminonaphthalene with a 4-nitroso aromatic amine[6, 67];
for example, 2-anilinonaphthalene condenses with 4-nitrosodimethyl-
aniline hydrochloride on gently heating a mixture in acetic acid, to
yield 9-dimethylamino-7-phenylbenzo [a]phenazinium chloride[68] (LIX),
known as Neutral Blue (*C. I.* 832; Section XIV:4,G). This reaction is
also the basis of the preparation of other important azine dyes such as
Basle Blue, Azine Green, etc. It may be extended to embrace 1,3-di-
anilinonaphthalenes, which react with substituted 4-nitrosoanilines to
give 5-anilino-9-alkyl(or aryl)amino-7-phenylbenzo [a]phenazinium salts
(LX), which are members of the Wool Fast Blue series.[69–72]

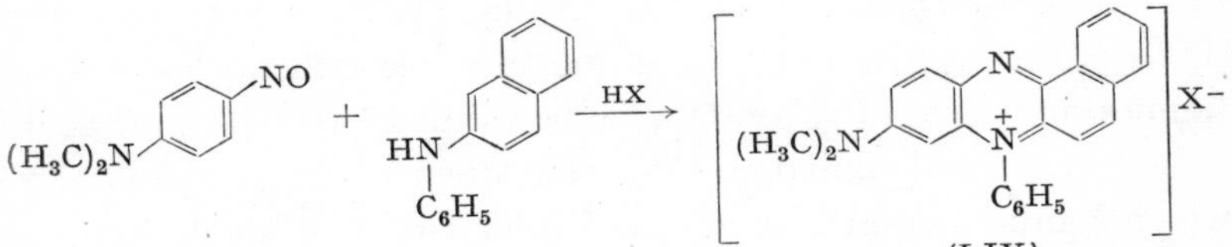

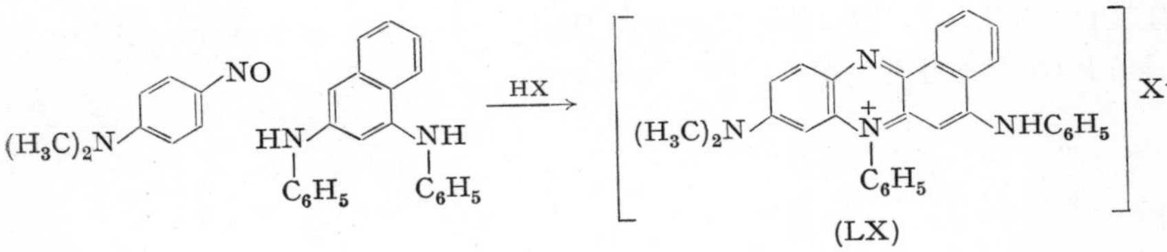

The nature of the two components may be interchanged; for
example, 4-nitroso-1-anilinonaphthalene will condense with 1,3-di-
anilinobenzene to give 5,9-dianilino-7-phenylbenzo [a]phenazinium
salts (LXI)[34] (see also reference 73).

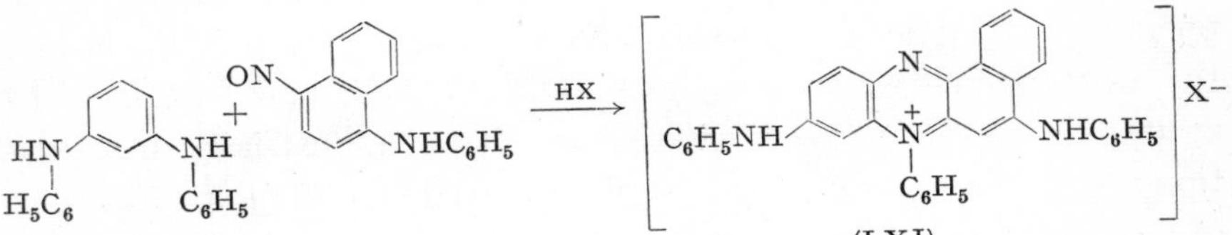

In place of a component bearing a nitroso group, a substance
bearing another nitrogenous group in a comparable state of oxidation
may be employed, for example, an azo compound. 1,3-Dianilino-

naphthalene condenses with azobenzene to give 5-anilino-7-phenyl-benzo[a]phenazinium salts[70, 71, 72, 74] (phenylrosindulines, IV).

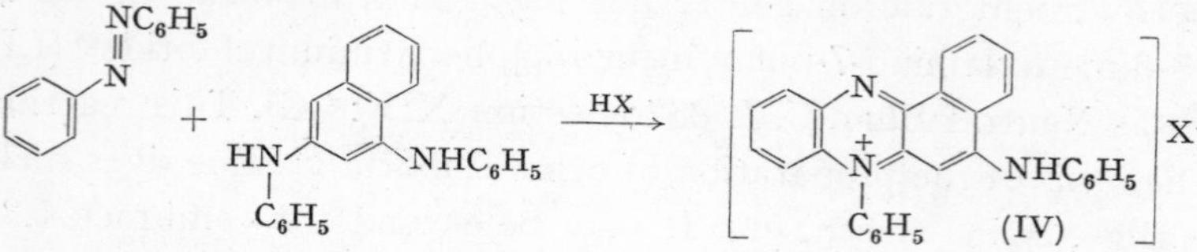

Other variations upon this include the condensation of a substituted 2-aminoazobenzene with a 1-naphthylamine in phenol at 100°.[75, 76] Instead of a 2-aminoazo grouping, a 2-nitroaniline has been used with zinc chloride as condensing agent[77] (see Wohl synthesis, Chapter XII:3,B(10)), or alternatively a mixture of a mono-N-substituted o-diamine and 1-naphthylamine may be oxidized with chromic acid.[78]

(*4*) A method similar to (*3*) is that due to Nietzki and Otto,[6, 9, 79] in which 2-anilinonaphthalene is condensed with N,N'-dichloroquinone-diimine to yield 9-amino-7-phenylbenzo[a]phenazinium chloride (LXII). When a 1,3-dianilinonaphthalene is used, a 5-anilino group is also introduced.[71]

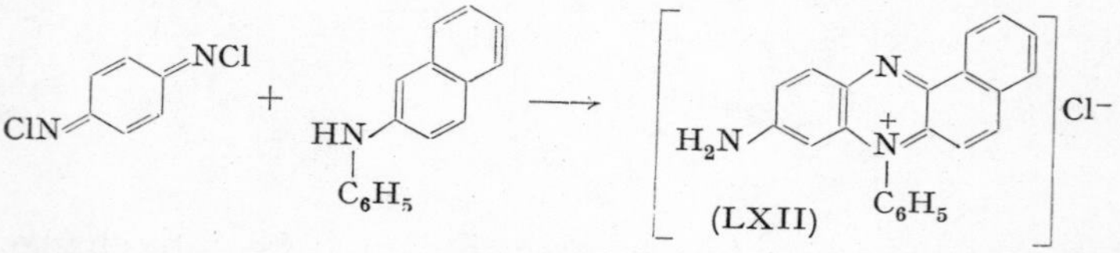

Alternatively a *m*-diamine may be condensed with 1,4-N,N'-dichloronaphthoquinonediimine.[80] Finally a mixture of a 1,3-dianilino-naphthalene and a *p*-diaminobenzene, of which one amino group must be primary, may be oxidized, when a 5,9-substituted-diamino-7-phenylbenzo[a]phenazinium salt (LXIII) results.[81] (Compare the formation of safranines by the joint oxidation of a *p*-diamine with primary aromatic amines *via* an indamine intermediate.) Industrially the oxidation may be carried out by the passage of air, preferably in the presence of a catalyst.

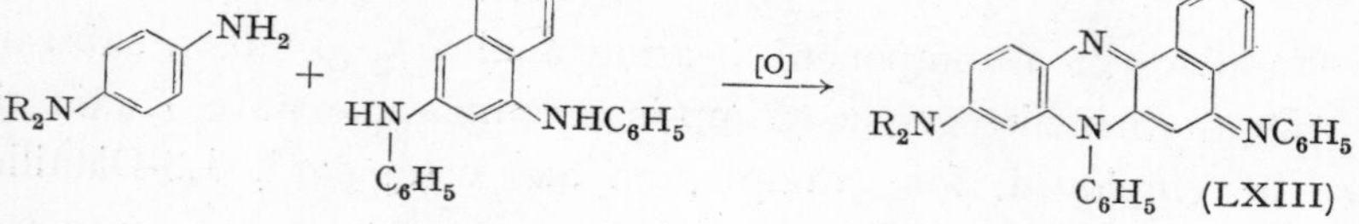

Methods (3) and (4) are applicable only to 7-substituted benzo[a]-phenazinium salts bearing amino or substituted amino groups in either the 5- or 9-positions, or both.

(5) Another widely used general method, which is of great complexity, is the reaction between an aromatic amine, for example, aniline, and a 4-nitroso-1-naphthylamine. Thus 4-nitroso-1-dimethyl-aminonaphthalene reacts with aniline and aniline hydrochloride at 70–80°, preferably in the presence of a condensing agent such as zinc chloride to yield 5-anilino-7-phenylbenzo[a]phenazinium chloride[82] (IV).

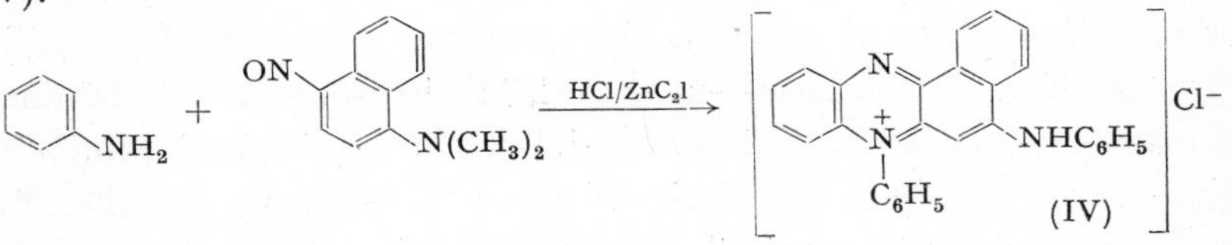

The same product is formed from 1-anilino-4-nitroso- or 1-ethyl-amino-4-nitrosonaphthalenes and aniline and aniline hydrochloride in boiling acetic acid solution.[18,83] Clearly the amino group of the naphthyl-amine has been exchanged for an aniline residue.

A development of this reaction is the reaction of an aromatic amine and its hydrochloride upon a 4-benzeneazo-1-naphthylamine, when 5-amino- or 5-substituted-amino-7-phenylbenzo[a]phenazinium salts result, depending on the conditions. Thus when 4-benzeneazo-1-naphthylamine is treated with aniline (2 moles) in ethanol at 160–170°,

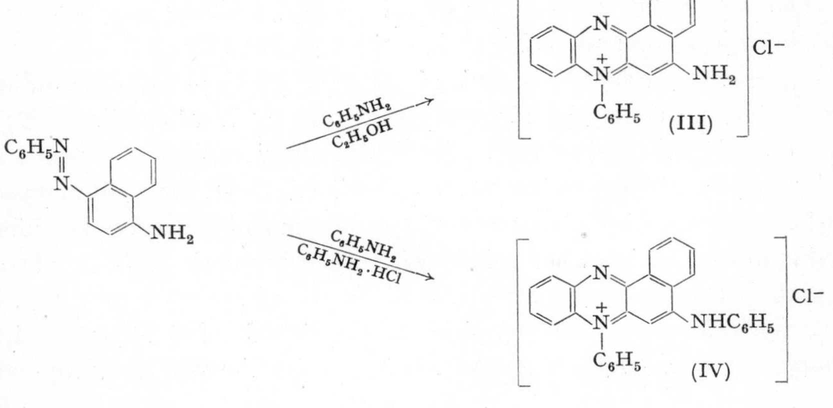

5-amino-7-phenylbenzo[a]phenazinium chloride (rosinduline chloride, III) is the main product; but when the mixture of aminoazo compound, aniline (2 moles) and aniline hydrochloride (1 mole) is heated at 160° in the absence of ethanol, the product is the 5-anilino derivative[18, 20, 84-86] (phenylrosinduline chloride, IV).

In the latter reaction, exchange of an amino group for anilino has occurred. This is a common feature of many reactions of this class and introduces complicating features. The reaction is closely allied to the "aminoazobenzene" or "induline melt" (Chapter VIII:2,A). In attempts to elucidate the mechanism of this important reaction, many new variations were discovered. Thus mixtures of aniline and aniline hydrochloride with 2-nitroso-1-naphthol,[84] 1-nitroso-2-naphthylamine,[19] 1-benzeneazo-2-naphthol,[18] 2-anilino-1,4-naphthoquinone-4-anil,[18, 84] 2-amino-1,4-naphthoquinone-4-imines[87] and even 1-nitronaphthalene[88] all give phenylrosinduline or similar compounds.

Just as azophenine plays a leading part in the probable mechanism of the induline melt, 2-anilino-1,4-naphthoquinone-1,4-dianil (LXIV) appears to be the key compound in this synthesis.[89] Fischer and Hepp[18] showed that this compound, which is an intermediate in the oxidation of 1,2,4-trianilinonaphthalene with mercuric oxide to phenylrosinduline, itself yields phenylrosinduline on oxidation. It is readily apparent that the anilinodianil (LXIV) is obtainable from all the starting materials itemized above, by reaction with aniline.[19, 20] as shown in the accompanying reaction scheme.

The multiplicity of products possible owing to exchanges between arylamino groups in the case of mixed aryl residues has been well outlined in a comprehensive review given by Lantz.[90]

(6) A new synthesis, which is probably of considerable technical importance, was developed twenty years ago by Wahl and Lantz.[90-100] It is applicable to the synthesis of phenylrosindulines and bears an obvious resemblance to the reactions outlined above. They showed that 1-halogeno-2-naphthols reacted with aromatic amines to give 1-anilino-2-naphthols, which when mixed with more aromatic amine could be oxidized by means of a stream of air in the presence of catalysts, in particular cupric oxides, to yield the cupric salt of a 2-hydroxy-1,4-naphthoquinone-1,4-anil (LXVI). This, as might be expected, will react

with a third molecule of an aromatic amine to give a phenylrosinduline, in which the three aryl residues have been introduced separately. The

hope that this might be realized in practice, so enabling phenylrosindulines of known mixed structure to be obtained, was not fulfilled, owing to the exchange reactions noted above for groups in the 5-position.

316   Condensed Phenazines

(7)   Another method, which would appear to bear some relation
to the two previous ones, involves the heating of 4-benzeneazo-1-
naphthylamines in suitable solvents, for example, phenol at 130°.[34]
Besides giving 5-amino-7-phenylbenzo[a]phenazinium salts, the reaction yields members of the 7-phenyldibenzo[a,j]phenazinium series
(LXVII, R. I. 3253; see Chapter XV:5,C).

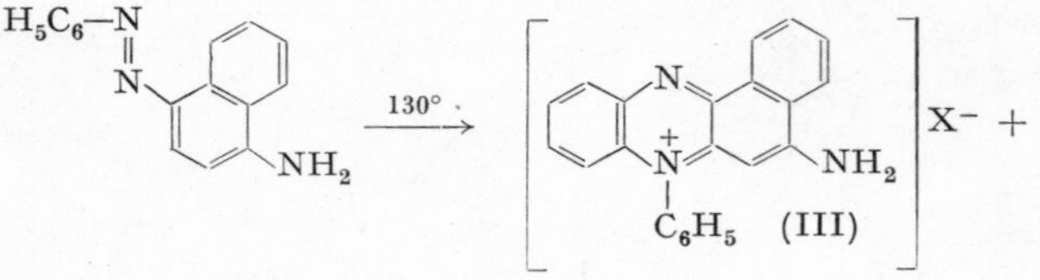

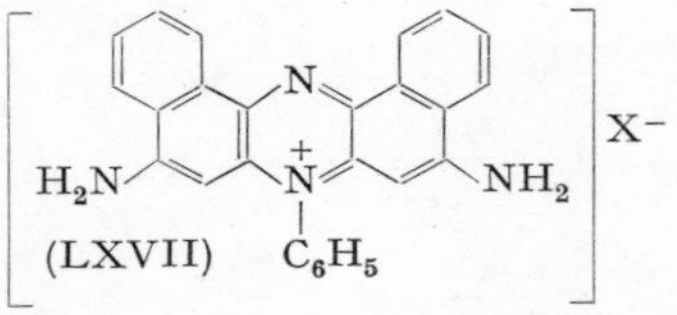

The reaction probably involves a preliminary thermal rearrangement of the aminoazo compound to a 2-anilino-1,4-naphthoquinone-
1,4-diimine, which then dimerizes, with loss of a molecule of aromatic
amine to give LXVII. The liberated aromatic amine then reacts with
a further molecule of aminoazo compound to produce the rosinduline,
according to method (5).[90]

A similar mechanism has been invoked to explain the formation of
rosinduline, phenylrosinduline and more highly indulinic products
obtained by the reaction of 4-benzeneazo-1-naphthylamine with compounds containing reactive methylene groups, for example, phenylacetic acid (Crippa synthesis).[101]

(8)   Kehrmann[27] developed a synthesis of rosinduline by the
condensation of 2,4-dinitro-1-chloronaphthalene with 2-aminodiphenyl-
amine followed by reduction with stannous chloride, when simultaneous
ring closure occurred by loss of ammonia.

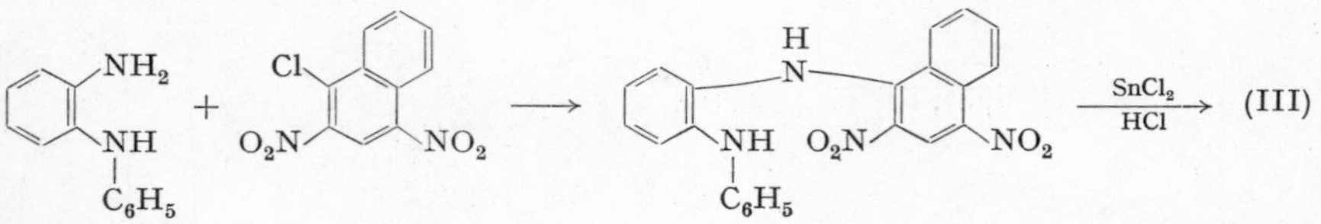

(9) Another synthesis due to Lantz[102] consists in heating a 5-substituted-aminobenzo[a]phenoxazine (LXVIII, R. I. 2614) with an aromatic amine, the product being the anhydro-base of a phenyl-rosinduline (LXV)

The foregoing nine methods and their associated variants all involve the formation of the azine ring during the synthesis. Other methods depend upon reactions of the benzo[a]phenazine or -phenazinium nucleus.

(10) 7-Alkylbenzo[a]phenazinium compounds bearing amino groups may be prepared by direct alkylation with alkyl iodides or alkyl sulfates of eurhodines.[75, 103–108]

(11) As pointed out in Chapter XII, N-substituted benzo[a]-phenazinium salts will react with ammonia or amines in the presence of air, to introduce amino or substituted amino groups. The positions attacked are the 5-[3, 6, 9, 15, 16, 109, 110] and less often 9-positions[111] with 7-alkyl or 7-aryl substituents and the 10-position in the case of a 12-substituted benzo[a]phenazinium salt[112]; the reasons for the attack at these particular positions are outlined in the earlier chapter. This reaction was used by Kehrmann and his school to enable them to decide which of the two isomers formed in condensation reactions is the 7-substituted and which is the 12-substituted benzo[a]phenazinium salt, for the 7-phenyl isomer reacts with aniline to give a rosinduline, the solution becoming violet, while the 12-phenyl isomer gives the corresponding 10-anilino derivative, which gives a dark-blue color in solution. It has been applied to determine the constitutions of the numerous isomers of rosinduline by deamination to the parent phenyl-benzo[a]phenazinium system, followed by reaction with aniline or another amine in ethanolic solution (see, for example, references 53, 113 and 114).

(*12*)   Certain groups, for example, methoxy,[13] chloro[22,23,115] or sulfonic acid groups,[24] when situated in the reactive positions, namely 5- and 9-, or 10-, may be replaced by ammonia or by primary or secondary amines. The 5-sulfonic acids may be obtained by condensation reactions from a sulfonated naphthalene component (Chapter XII:4D(5)) or else by sulfonation by means of sodium bisulfite and air.[116]

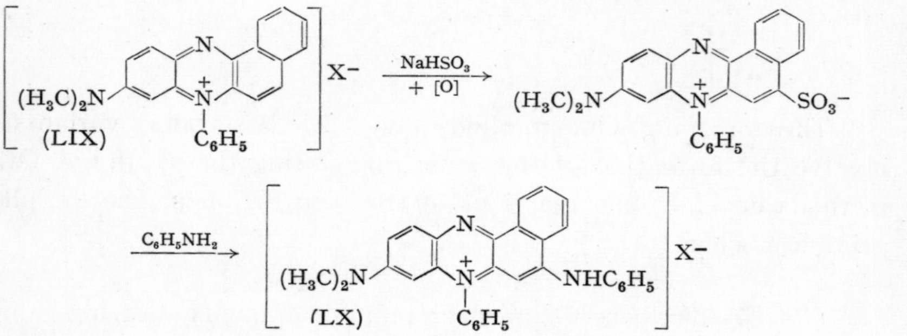

The 5-chloro compounds are generally obtained from the corresponding benzo[a]phenazinone. The oxygen atom of the latter compounds may be replaced directly by an amine; thus rosindone reacts with aniline in the presence of aniline hydrochloride to give phenylrosinduline.[18,117]

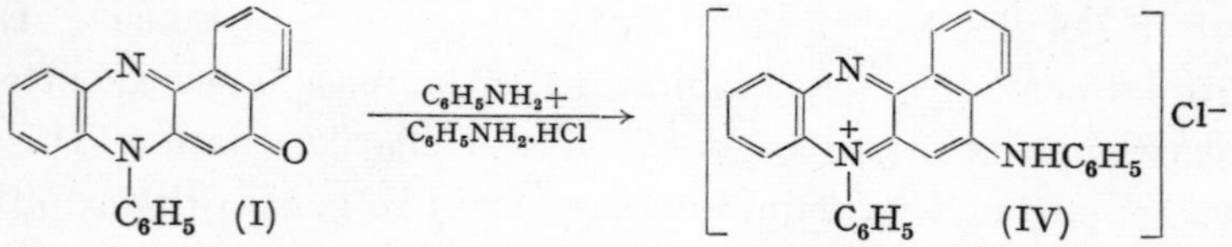

(*13*)   A relatively unimportant method is the reduction of nitrobenzo[a]phenazinium salts, which may be prepared by direct nitration[118,119] or by condensation of suitably substituted components.[57,120,121] This method is somewhat more important when diamino compounds are required.

C. General Review of Properties

The aminobenzo[a]phenazinium compounds fall into two classes: those in which the amino or substituted amino groups occupy one or other of the reactive positions (5- or 9- in the case of 7-substituted, and 10- in the case of 12-substituted benzo[a]phenazinium salts), and those in which the amino group is located elsewhere in the ring system. The latter class possesses properties that may be predicted with accuracy from a knowledge of the chemistry of aromatic amines and benzo[a]-phenazinium compounds individually. They are almost valueless as dyes and will not be considered here. A record of their chief properties is in Table XXIV.

The former class, however, includes several important groups of dyes, which are discussed more fully in succeeding sections. They possess the property of anhydro-base formation and this led to a discussion of the formulation of their salts as either o- or p-quinonoid structures (LV and LVI).[5,16,55,122] It was early noted that the colors of the salts differed considerably with the strengths of acid in which they were dissolved. Kehrmann and his associates carried out two separate investigations of these colors spectroscopically using all the known amino derivatives, the majority of which had been synthesized in Kehrmann's laboratory.[50,123–125] Their results are of low accuracy when judged by present-day standards and moreover are partly vitiated by their necessary neglect of mesomeric considerations. Translated into modern terms, their arguments run somewhat as follows.

In the case of monoaminophenylbenzo[a]phenazinium compounds, we are dealing with a system containing three basic centers of widely different basicity. The different colors observed in solutions of different strengths of acid are blended from three (or more) different ion species, the color changes being due to the assumption of protons in stepwise fashion. The parent phenylbenzo[a]phenazinium systems (for example, LXIX and LXX) are of necessity o-quinonoid, in both mono- and di-acid salt forms. The anhydro-base (LIV), moreover, must be p-quinonoid. Let us consider the effect of adding a proton to the anhydro-base form (LIV):

(LXIX)   (LXX)

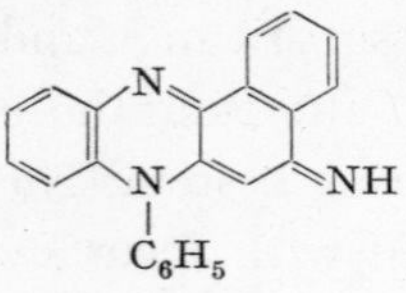

(LIV) 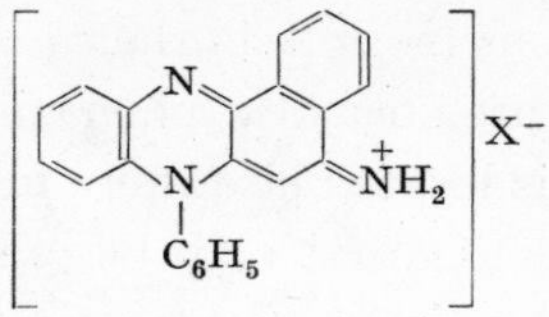   (LVI) 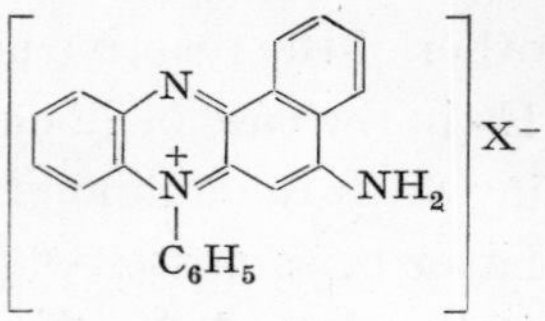   (LV)

This may add to give either an o-quinonoid (LV) or a p-quinonoid structure (LVI), both of which will differ from the anhydro-base in chromophoric properties. A second proton may now be added when two o-quinonoid (LXXI and LXXII) or a p-quinonoid (LXXIII) structures are obtained:

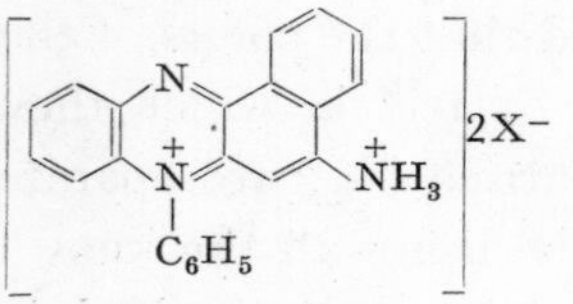

(LXXI) 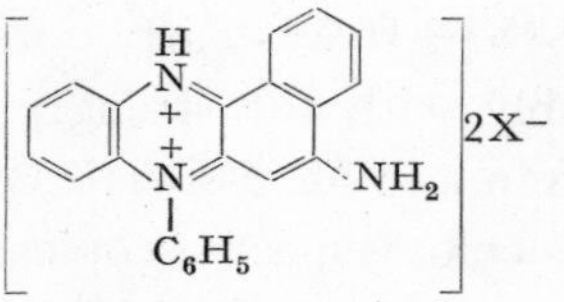   (LXXII) 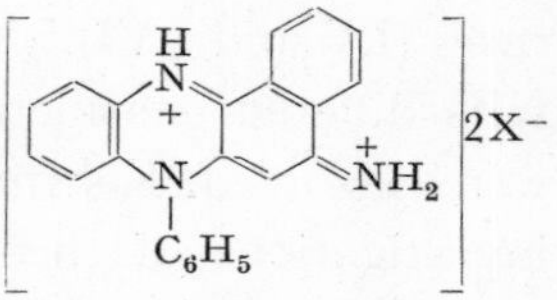   (LXXIII)

Of these, LXXI will resemble LXIX in color (Waterman-Hertjees effect, due to the involvement of the lone pair of electrons on the amino nitrogen atom in salt formation and consequent inavailability of them for excitation purposes). The remaining two structures will be different. Addition of a third proton will of necessity give the triacid salt, which will resemble LXX in color, for the same reason that LXXI resembles LXIX.

In this way a measure of the relative basicities of the three basic centers may be obtained. Kehrmann and his coworkers were thus able to show that amino derivatives, in which the amino group is situated so as to be incapable of anhydro-base formation, gave o-quinonoid structures even for the monoacidic salts, while those which gave anhydro-bases formed p-quinonoid mono- and di-acid salts, but o-quinonoid triacidic salts. Moreover, as expected, amino substituents on the N-phenyl group produced no auxochromic effect, since they are unable to conjugate with the main system.[49, 51, 52] (See also Chapter VII:1,C(2).)

Other spectroscopic evidence relevant here is the comparison made by Havas[126] between an aminophenylphenazinium compound and its benzo[a] analog.

D. Rosinduline (5-Amino-7-phenylbenzo[a]phenazinium Salts, LV)

Rosinduline chloride forms red needles with a green luster which contain water of crystallization.[12,18] Electrical conductivity measurements[31] show that it is not hydrolyzed; however, on liberation of the

(LV)   (LIV)

base, the conductivity falls to zero as the anhydro-base (LIV) is formed. This gives reddish-brown leaflets with a bronze glint, m.p. 198–199°,[9,18,85] which are insoluble in water but dissolve readily in most organic solvents, for example, ethanol, in which it gives a solution with a yellowish-red fluorescence and which rapidly absorbs carbon dioxide to form a carbonate, dark-red prisms.[18] Its salts, on the other hand, exhibit a vivid fiery-red fluorescence in dilute ethanol.[18,85] Rosinduline gives a deep reddish-violet color in oleum, a green color in concentrated sulfuric acid and a scarlet color in dilute acid.[18,124]

It is formed by the action of aqueous ethanolic ammonia upon 7-phenylbenzo[a]phenazinium salts in the presence of air[9,15,16,109] or by the replacement with ammonia of 5-methoxy[13] or 5-sulfonic acid groups.[24,25] It is best prepared by the condensation of 2-aminodiphenylamine with 2-hydroxy-1,4-naphthoquinone-4-imine[12] and is also produced by the hydrolysis of the 5-acetamido derivative (red needles, green luster, dec. about 290°), which is formed together with the 12-phenyl isomer by the condensation of 4-acetamido-1,2-naphthoquinone and the aforementioned diamine.[5,66] Fischer and Hepp[18,85] described the preparation of rosinduline by the action of ethanolic aniline under pressure upon 4-benzeneazo-1-naphthylamine hydrochloride at 160–170°. A similar reaction accounts for the production of rosinduline among the products of a Crippa reaction between 4-benzene-azo-1-naphthylamine and phenylacetic acid.[101] Kehrmann[27] devised a good method by the reduction by means of stannous chloride of 2,4-dinitro-1-(2'-anilino)anilinonaphthalene (Method (8), Section XIV:4,B), which gives a practically quantitative yield from 1-chloro-2,4-dinitro-naphthalene.

The structure of rosinduline follows from several of the syntheses. Its relationship to the parent 7-phenylbenzo[a]phenazinium series is shown by diazotization in strongly acid solution and deamination by boiling the diazonium salt with ethanol.[16,127] When rosinduline is heated under pressure at 160–180° with concentrated hydrochloric acid, the amino group is hydrolyzed with formation of rosindone.[18] The amino group of rosinduline does not react with 4,4'-di(dimethylamino)-benzhydrol.[128]

Derivatives of rosinduline bearing substituents in the 7-phenyl[51,52,64] ring and with nuclear substituents[27,49,51,111,120,121] have been described. No simple homologs have been characterized.

Rosinduline has been sulfonated, but the product is sparingly soluble in water and hence is probably a betaine.[85] Salts of rosinduline, for example, the chloride, dye cotton (mordanted with tannin) in yellowish-red shades. But the dyes have not found application.

E. Phenylrosinduline (5-Anilino-7-phenylbenzo[a]phenazinium Salts, IV)

This substance was the first member of the rosinduline group of coloring matters to be discovered. The chloride forms brownish-red prisms with a golden luster, which are rather sparingly soluble in

(IV)   (LXV)

water.[24,83] Other salts have been described. When the salts are treated with bases, the anhydro-base (LXV) is obtained; this crystallizes from ethanol in garnet-colored tablets with a green luster, or in dark-red needles. It melts at 236°,[23, 24, 83, 84] and is practically insoluble in water; it dissolves easily in benzene and ether, giving red solutions.[83] It gives a brown coloration in oleum, but becomes green on the addition of a little water.[84, 129] Solutions of the salts in water or ethanol exhibit no fluorescence.[84] The anhydro-base is a non-electrolyte.[31]

It was first prepared by adding 1-anilino (or ethylamino)-4-nitroso-naphthalene to a mixture of aniline hydrochloride (1 part) in aniline (3 parts) at 90° and heating the mixture to 120° for some hours.[83] Many methods followed closely upon the discovery that the key substance in the synthesis was 2-anilino-1,4-naphthoquinone-1,4-dianil. They are outlined under method (5) (Section XIV:4,B; see also references 20, 84, 89 and 101). A related synthesis is that due to Wahl and Lantz[90-100] (Method (6), Section XIV:4,B). Phenylrosinduline may further be prepared by a typical condensation reaction between 2-hydroxy-1,4-naphthoquinone-4-anil and 2-aminodiphenylamine,[65] which at once shows its structure. It is also obtained by reactions involving the replacement of 5-chloro[23] or 5-sulfonic acid groups[24, 25] of 7-phenyl-benzo[a]phenazinium compounds by means of aniline in ethanolic solution. Aniline will also react with rosindone at 120–140°, the anilino residue replacing the oxygen atom in the anhydro-base.[18] This last reaction has been used to prepare homologs of phenylrosinduline differing solely in the 5-amino substituent.[18, 117]

Prolonged reduction of phenylrosinduline by zinc or tin and hydrochloric acid gives aniline and naphthalene, while hydriodic acid and phosphorus gives aniline and an unidentified base $C_{22}H_{18}N_2$[83] (1,2-dianilinonaphthalene?). Oxidation of phenylrosinduline by chromic acid gives rosindonic acid[20] (XXII, Section XIV:2,C(1)). Phenylrosinduline is cleaved smoothly by heating with concentrated hydrochloric acid under pressure into aniline and rosindone.[18] This reaction may also be brought about under milder conditions by first methylating phenylrosinduline with methyl bromide at 100° and treating the 5-methylanilinium bromide with cold ethanolic alkali,[22] when rosindone and methylaniline are the products.

The reactivity of the 5-anilino group is further exemplified by the reactions in which it may be exchanged for another by heating with an excess of a different aromatic amine; for example, with o-toluidine, phenylrosinduline yields 5-o-tolylamino-7-phenylbenzo[a]phenazinium salts[19,130] (for other amines, see reference 131). It is the 5-anilino group that is attacked in nitration; for example, addition of potassium nitrate to a solution in concentrated sulfuric acid gives the 4''-nitro derivative (the double prime refers to positions in the 5-anilino phenyl group), while fuming nitric acid gives the 2'',4'',6''-trinitro derivative.[34] The position of the substituents was determined by the high temperature acid cleavage of the product and identification of the nitroanilines so formed.

Phenylrosinduline salts dye cotton, mordanted with tannin, in bordeaux-red shades,[82] but the dyeing power is not strong.[83] Sulfonation by means of concentrated sulfuric acid at 100° gives the 3''-sulfonic acid, which is split by high temperature hydrolysis into rosindone and metanilic acid.[20,84] The free acid is a betaine, insoluble in water, and scarcely dyes mordanted cotton.[132] More intensive sulfonation, using oleum, gives di- and tri-sulfonic acids. These are marketed commercially in the form of sodium salts under the names Azocarmine G (disulfonic acid) and Azocarmine B (trisulfonic acid).[18,38,84,133]

Azocarmine G (C. I. 828) dyes wool and silk in very level bluish-red shades, but leaves cotton fibers untouched. It is fast to light and acids and has been used as a substitute for archil (C. I. 1242), a natural dyestuff obtained from lichens. Azocarmine B (C. I. 829), obtained by the further sulfonation of Azocarmine G, is very level-dyeing and gives red shades on wool from an acid bath. It has been proposed as an indicator for the retention analysis by paper electrophoresis of natural protein mixtures[134] and has some use as a tissue stain, either alone or preceding a nuclear stain.[135-137]

Substituted phenylrosindulines and homologs have been described.[10,18,19,39,49,115,117,130,138-144]

F. 7-Alkyl-(or aralkyl)-5-aminobenzo[a]phenazinium Salts

These compounds may be prepared by condensation reactions,[4,145,146] by the action of ammonia upon the corresponding benzo[a]phenazinium salts[3,6] or by alkylation of eurhodines; the latter process has been the basis of a number of patents.[75, 103, 106] Sulfonic acids of such compounds have been prepared by direct sulfonation,[103, 147–149] or by starting from components already sulfonated.[107] Homologs with alkyl groups in the nucleus have also been prepared.[75–78, 106, 150, 151] Of these homologs, the most important is Induline Scarlet (*C. I.* 827), or 5-amino-7-ethyl-10-methylbenzo[a]phenazinium chloride (LXXIV).

(LXXIV)

This may be prepared by the condensation of 2-hydroxy-1,4-naphthoquinone-4-imine with 3-amino-4-ethylaminotoluene,[151] by the reaction of 4-ethylamino-3-nitrotoluene with 1-naphthylamine and its hydrochloride in the presence of zinc chloride,[77] by the reaction of 2-ethylamino- (or diethylamino-) 5-methylazobenzene-4'-sulfonic acid with 1-naphthylamine hydrochloride[76] or by the joint oxidation of a mixture of 3-amino-4-ethylaminotoluene and 1-naphthylamine with chromic acid.[78] (For related method, see reference 75.)

Induline Scarlet yields in ethanol orange-red solutions that exhibit a yellow fluorescence, and dyes cotton goods, which have been mordanted with tannin and tartar emetic, in scarlet-red shades, which are of good fastness to washing but are only moderately fast towards light. It is used in calico printing, particularly as a catalyst in discharge printing, and has been incorporated in "Rongalite special I.G.," a brand of sodium formaldehyde-sulfoxylate used in vatting.[152]

The use of Induline Scarlet in redox systems has been studied.[153]

G. 9-Amino-7-phenylbenzo[a]phenazinium Salts and Derivatives ("Isorosindulines," LXII)

This class of substance is frequently referred to as the isorosindulines, from the trivial name given to the first member of the series on its discovery. The general methods for the preparation of these substances are outlined in Sections XIV:4,B(3) and (4). We may

consider the parent substance LXII. This was prepared by Nietzki and
Otto by the interaction of 2-anilinonaphthalene with N,N'-dichloro-

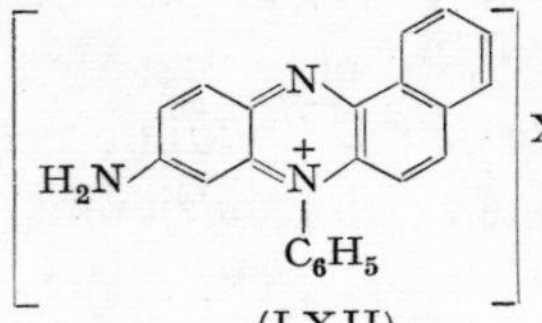

(LXII)

quinonediimine.[9,79,127] Analogs bearing substituents on the amino
group are obtained by the reaction between 2-anilinonaphthalenes and
4-nitrosoanilines, substituted on the amino group.[67,68,154]

9-Amino-7-phenylbenzo[a]phenazinium salts form brownish crystals, giving rose-red solutions that exhibit a brownish fluorescence in
organic solvents. They give blackish-violet colorations in concentrated
sulfuric acid, which on dilution become successively dirty-green, orange
and finally crimson-red.[79] In contradistinction to rosinduline, the isorosinduline (LXII) reacts with 4,4'-di(dimethylamino)benzhydrol,
giving a 9-benzhydrylamino derivative.[128] Deamination of LXII by
diazotization and heating the ethanolic solution of the diazonium salt
gives 7-phenylbenzo[a]phenazinium salts.[9,127] The isorosinduline
chloride reacts with o-phenylenediamine to give 7-phenyl-7,14-dihydro-
benzo[a]quinoxalo[2,3-i]phenazine (XXXII, R. I. 3577).[32]

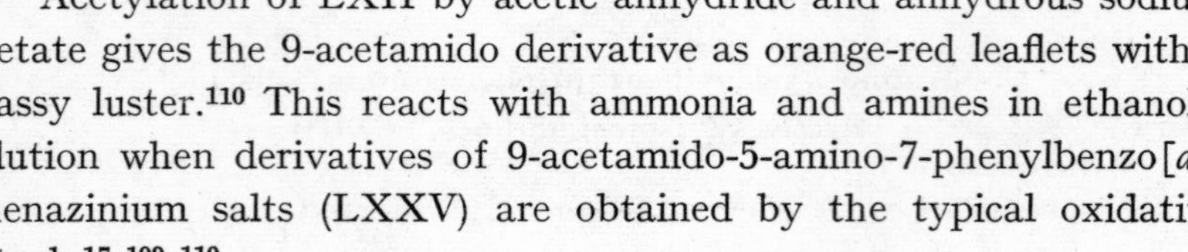

(XXXII)

Acetylation of LXII by acetic anhydride and anhydrous sodium
acetate gives the 9-acetamido derivative as orange-red leaflets with a
brassy luster.[110] This reacts with ammonia and amines in ethanolic
solution when derivatives of 9-acetamido-5-amino-7-phenylbenzo[a]-
phenazinium salts (LXXV) are obtained by the typical oxidative
attack.[17,109,110]

This reaction found some application industrially for the preparation of derivatives of 5,9-diamino-7-phenylbenzo[a]phenazinium

salts.[154-158] Alternatively, position 5 is first substituted by a sulfonic acid group, by means of sodium bisulfite and air followed by reaction

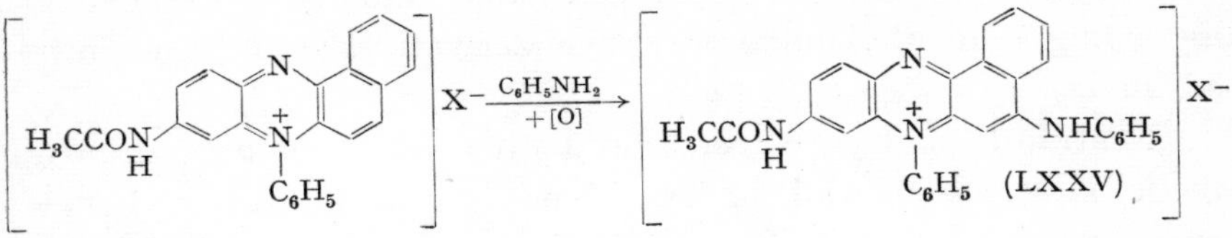

with an amine.[116,159] Reaction of these isorosindulines with amino-anthraquinones as aromatic amine yields 5-anthraquinonylamino derivatives, which after sulfonation form substances combining the vatting properties of anthraquinones with the isorosinduline structure. They dye wool from a sodium dithionite vat in blue shades.[160,161]

The amino group of the parent isorosinduline (LXII) is situated suitably for the formation of an anhydro-base. None has been recorded, however, for the unsubstituted amino compound. With one substituent on the amino group however, anhydro-bases have been noted.[9,22] When both hydrogen atoms of the amino group are substituted by alkyl residues, anhydro-base formation is naturally impossible.

The most important member of this group is 9-dimethylamino-7-phenylbenzo[a]phenazinium chloride (LIX), known commercially as Neutral Blue (C. I. 832), which was discovered in 1882 by Witt,[67,68] by the action of 4-nitrosodimethylaniline hydrochloride on 2-anilino-naphthalene. It is accompanied by 9-dimethylamino-5-(4″-dimethyl-amino)anilino-7-phenylbenzo[a]phenaziniumchloride[34] by attack of a second molecule of the nitrosoaniline at the reactive 5-position.

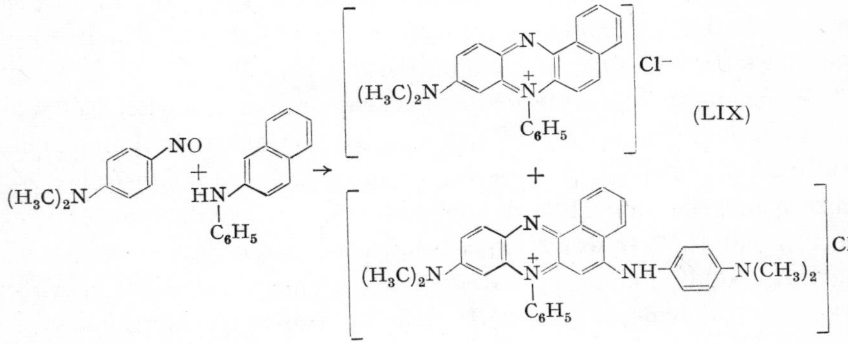

Treatment of neutral blue with sodium bisulfite gives the 5-sulfonic acid,[116] while with alkali it yields the corresponding 9-dimethylamino-rosindone[162]; analogously, treatment with amines gives the corresponding 9-dimethylaminorosinduline derivatives[155,156,157] (naphthosafranines).

Neutral blue dyes cotton, mordanted with tannin and tartar emetic, in somewhat dull shades of blue that are not fast to light or soap. Treatment with sodium sulfide gives a sulfur derivative, the sulfur atom of which may be replaced by amines giving blue basic dyes on mordanted cotton. Sulfonation of these substances gives water-soluble dyes suitable for dyeing wool from an acid bath in indigo shades of great fastness to light, washing and alkalis.[163] (See the following section on the Wool Fast Blues.)

Neutral blue and related dyes differing in the 7-aryl group have been studied as redox systems. The normal redox potential of neutral blue is 0.170 v.[153]

Amino derivatives of 12-arylbenzo[a]phenazinium salts are relatively unimportant. A list of them may be found in Table XXVI.

5. Diamino Derivatives of
7-Phenylbenzo[a]phenazinium Salts

A. 5,9-Diamino-7-phenylbenzo[a]phenazinium
Salts and Derivatives

The Wool Fast Blue Dyes

On analogy with phenosafranine (Chapter VII:2,B), the compounds of the 5,9-diamino-7-phenylbenzo[a]phenazinium series are sometimes known as naphthosafranines.

5,9-Diamino-7-phenylbenzo[a]phenazinium chloride (LXXVI) itself is relatively unimportant. It is obtained by the action of ammonia in ethanolic solution in the presence of air upon 9-acetamido-7-phenylbenzo[a]phenazinium chloride, followed by acid hydrolysis of the acetyl group.[17,110] It forms crystals with a cantharidine-green luster that are readily soluble in water, giving a cherry-red solution with an orange-yellow fluorescence.[17] It gives a bluish-green coloration with concentrated sulfuric acid, which on dilution passes through dirty-blue to rose-red.[110] Prolonged boiling with ethanolic potassium hydroxide leads to hydrolysis of the amino groups to hydroxyl, with formation of 9-hydroxyrosindone[44] (naphthosafranol, Section XIV:3,A). The compound prepared by Barbier and Sisley by the fusion of 4-aminoazobenzene and 4-benzeneazo-1-naphthylamine in phenol at 180° has been assigned structure LXXVI by the authors.[164,165]

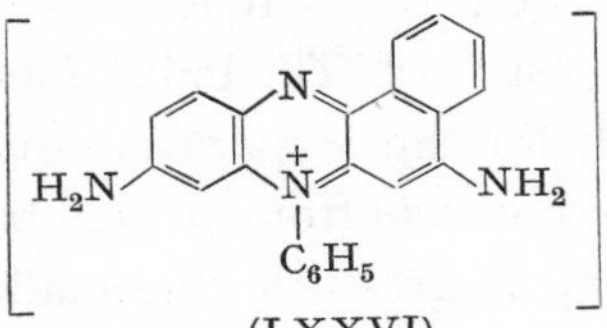

(LXXVI)

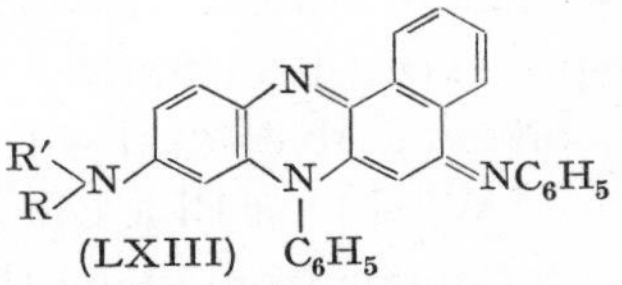

(LXIII) C_6H_5

(LXIIIa, R = C_6H_5, R' = H)

The most important members of the naphthosafranine group are the Wool Fast Blue dyes (C. I. 833), which are sulfonic acids of compounds based on (LXIII, R and R' = hydrogen, alkyl or aryl).

The simplest member (LXIII, R = R' = H) was prepared by the interaction of p-phenylenediamine hydrochloride with excess aniline at 150° on 1-nitroso-2-naphthylamine, 2-anilino-1-nitrosonaphthalene or 2-anilino-1,4-naphthoquinone-1,4-dianil,[19] from which the constitution was deduced. It is also obtained by the action of aniline and air upon an ethanolic solution of 9-amino-7-phenylbenzo[a]phenazinium salts.[9,154] 5,9-Dianilino-7-phenylbenzo[a]phenazinium anhydro-base (LXIIIa, R = C_6H_5, R' = H) is obtained by gently heating an ethanolic solution of 1-anilino-4-nitrosonaphthalene and 1,3-dianilinobenzene.[34] It is produced by the action of aniline upon 9-chlorophenylrosinduline[115] or upon isorosinduline.[9] It is also the product of heating 5,9-dianilinobenzo[a]phenoxazine salts (or the anhydro-base, LXXVII) with aniline.[102]

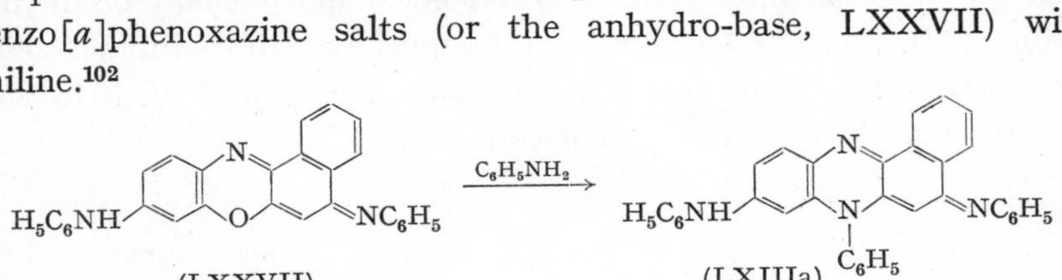

(LXXVII)

$C_6H_5NH_2 \rightarrow$

(LXIIIa) C_6H_5

The anhydro-base (LXIIIa) forms needles, m.p. 273°, giving violet-red solutions in ethanol.[102] It gives a green color in concentrated sulfuric acid.[34,115] The 2- and 3-sulfonic acids of LXIII (R = R′ = CH₃) have been prepared by reacting 4-nitrosodimethylaniline with 1,3-dianilinonaphthalene-6- and -7-sulfonic acids. They dye mordanted cotton in weak shades.[132]

Commercially, the Wool Fast Blue colors can be produced by the joint oxidation of sulfonic acids of 1,3-dianilinonaphthalene with a 1,4-diaminobenzene (or its sulfonic acid), one amino group of which must be unsubstituted. The oxidation is generally carried out by air in the presence of a cupric oxide catalyst.[166,167] The bulk of modern patents on azine dyes deal with methods for the preparation or modification of Wool Fast Blue colors, which dye wool from an acid bath in fast colors ranging from violet through blue to greenish-blue shades. As examples we may cite Wool Fast Blue BL (LXXVIII) and Indocyanine 6B, which may possess structure LXXIX. For the use of such dyes in color photography, see Chapter VII:2,1 and Section XIV:6.D.

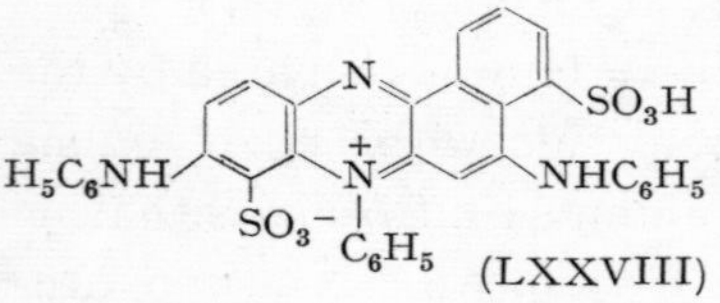

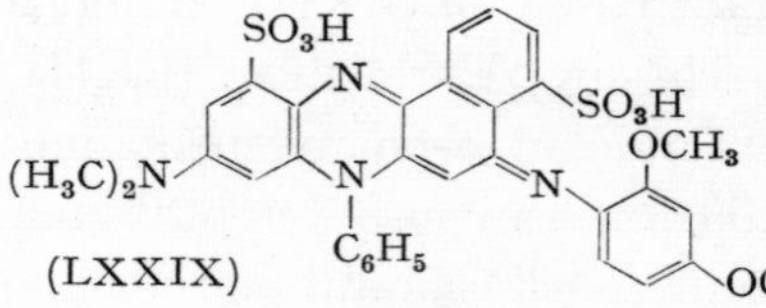

Dyes based upon LXIIIa are also produced by aerial oxidation over a cupric oxide-ammonia catalyst or by chemical oxidation of mixtures of 1,3-dianilinonaphthalene-8-sulfonic acid with 4-amino-4′-alkylamino-(or 4′-alkyl)-diphenylamine monosulfonic acids[168,169] or with a 4-aminoaniline derivative.[170] Alternatively, the dianilino-naphthalene sulfonic acid component may be condensed with a 4-nitrosodialkylaniline.[170] The naphthalene component may be further modified by using 3-arylamino-1,8-naphthosultam sulfonic acids (derivatives of 2-naphth[1,8-cd]isothiazole-1,1-dioxide, R. I. 1546); for example LXXX gives violet shades on wool.[171]

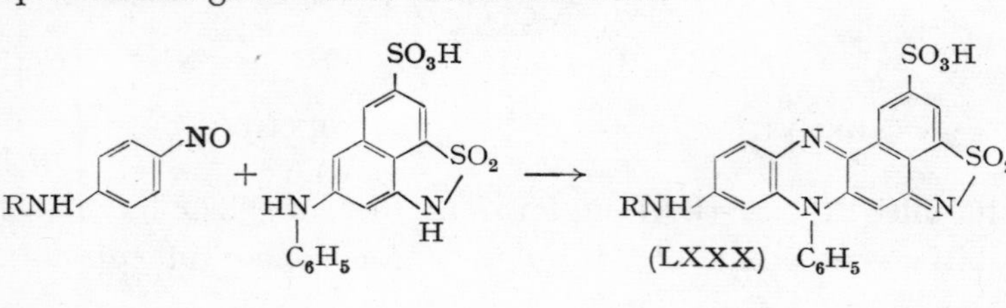

Patent claims have been made which start from 9-dialkylamino-7-phenylbenzo[a]phenazinium compounds (isorosindulines), which are sulfonated in the 5- and other positions by treatment with sodium bisulfite under oxidizing conditions.[172] Alternatively, the 5-sulfonic acids of isorosindulines may be prepared by coupling procedures from suitably sulfonated components. The products are blue dyes for woo and are also valuable intermediates, since they react with suitably substituted p-phenylenediamine sulfonic acids, of which one amino group is primary, giving dyes of the type LXXXI.[173–182] The products may be further sulfonated by means of an agent such as oleum.[176,177,180]

These dyes include the Novazol Acid Blue and Polar Blue, (Geigy)

(LXXXI)

classes of dye, which possess considerable fastness to light and alkalis and have good leveling properties. The sulfonic acid group in position 2″ of the anilino nucleus is said to be partly responsible for the good fastness.[177]

Variations in the general pattern have been made by introducing morpholino residues at position 9, in place of the alkyl- or arylamino groups. This is done in the usual way, using a 1,3-dianilinonaphthalene sulfonic acid and 4-nitrosophenyl-1-morpholine hydrochloride.[183] Alternatively, the dyes may be modified by inclusion of an alkyl sulfonic acid group, for example ethanesulfonic acid, as a substituent of the 9-amino group by treatment with 2-chloroethanesulfonic acid.[184,185] Besides use as wool colors, these dyes can be incorporated in lacquers.[186]

Dyestuffs such as Paraphenylene Violet (C. I. 858), which may possibly be aminophenylrosindulines, are obtained by heating p-phenylenediamine with 4-benzeneazo-1-naphthylamines[187–189] or by heating 1-naphthylamine with 4-aminoazobenzene and then heating the product with p-phenylenediamine in benzoic acid at 190°.[190–191] They dye cotton mordanted with tannin and tartar emetic in violet shades of moderate fastness and were also used in calico printing.

B. Other Diamino Derivatives of 7-Phenylbenzo[a]phenazinium Salts

The majority of diamino-7-phenylbenzo[a]phenazinium salts and their anilino derivatives are of little interest. They are listed in Table XXV. Two groups of dyes, however, are worthy of mention:

(1) *Basle Blue R* (2-*p*-Tolylamino-9-dimethylamino-7-*p*-tolyl-benzo[a]phenazinium chloride, *C. I.* 836, LXXXII):

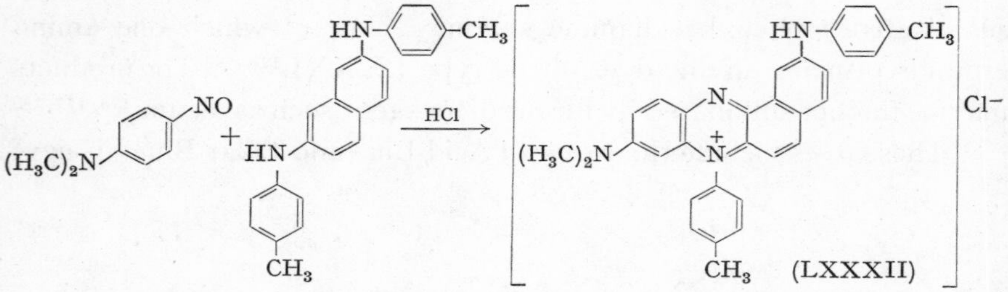

This was discovered by Annaheim[192, 193] by warming 4-nitroso-dimethylaniline with 2,7-di-*p*-tolylaminonaphthalene in alcoholic hydrochloric acid solution. The 2-anilino-7-phenyl analog was prepared by Fischer and Hepp[19] in the same way from 4-nitrosodimethylaniline and 2,7-dianilinonaphthalene. The corresponding 9-diethylamino compound is known as Basle Blue BB.

Basle Blue R gives blue shades on cotton mordanted with tannin and tartar emetic and dyes wool from an acid bath in reddish-blue colors. It may be used to some extent for topping indigo colors.

Sulfonation of Basle Blue R with 25% oleum, followed by neutralization, yields readily soluble dyes known as Basle Blue S[194] (*C. I.* 837), which dye wool and silk from an acid bath in blues of good fastness to light and soap. Basle Blue has largely been superseded.

(2) *Azine Green GB* (3-Anilino-9-dimethylamino-7-phenylbenzo-[a]phenazinium chloride, *C. I.* 834, LXXXIII). This is prepared, analogously to Basle Blue R, by the reaction between 4-nitrosodimethyl-aniline hydrochloride and 2,6-dianilinonaphthalene:[195]

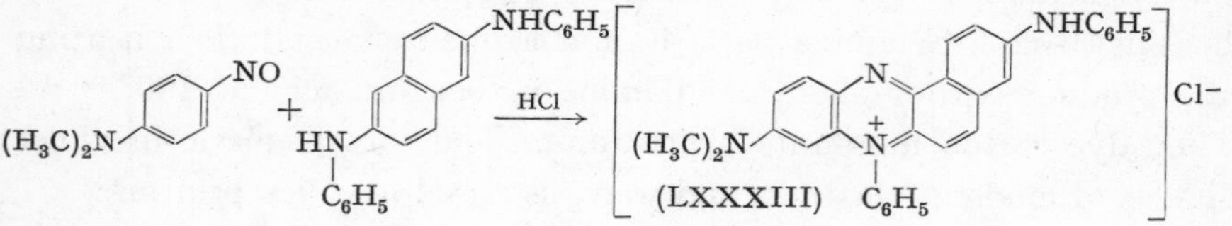

It gives a green solution in water and dyes cotton mordanted with tannin and tartar emetic in moderately fast bluish-green shades. It is still used somewhat in calico printing.

Sulfonation with 20% oleum at 50°, followed by neutralization, yields Azine Green S (C. I. 835), which is a light-fast bluish-green dye for wool.[196]

Diamino-12-phenylbenzo[a]phenazinium salts are of little intrinsic interest and are relegated to Table XXVII.

C. Analysis of Azine Dyes

Most dyes derived from the phenylbenzo[a]phenazinium series bear amino or, more often, substituted amino groups in positions 5 and 9. Bass[21] devised a method of analysis of these based on two cleavage procedures and identification of the cleavage product by spectroscopic means. The procedures were:

(1)   Heating with concentrated hydrochloric acid in a sealed tube.

(2)   Prolonged reflux with 60–70% sulfuric acid.

A third method attempted, reduction with tin and hydrochloric acid, gave no results except in very simple cases.

Procedure (1) was designed to hydrolyze both 5-and 9-amino groups to yield derivatives of 9-hydroxy-7-phenyl-5(7)-benzo[a]-phenazinone (naphthosafranol). The dyes studied by this means fell into two groups. The Wool Fast Blues and Novazol Acid Blues gave naphthosafranols, while neutral blue gave 7-phenyl-9(7)-benzo[a]-phenazinone (isorosindone). These end products could be identified by their spectral absorption maxima. But other dyes, for example, Basle Blue R and 9-dialkylamino-7-(p-substituted phenyl)-benzo[a]phen-azinium salts gave amorphous blue-black products with no characteristic properties.

Procedure (2) did not affect dyes substituted in position 9 only (neutral blue), but hydrolyzed the 5-amino and substituted amino groups to hydroxyl groups, so that a 5,9-disubstituted dye (LXXXIV) gave a 9-aminorosindone (LXXXV).

The method is of limited value, however.

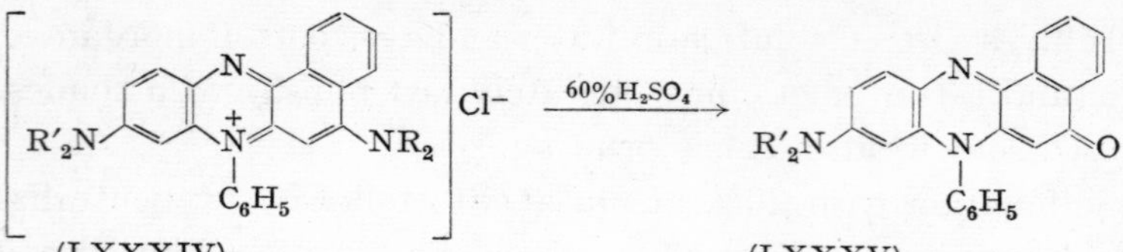

(LXXXIV)   (LXXXV)

D. Miscellaneous

There are a very small number of diamino-7-alkylbenzo[a]-phenazinium salts that are unimportant and are relegated to the tables. One point of interest, however, attaches to the paper by Cohen and Crabtree[73] on the Azine Scarlet Dyes and related substances. These workers describe a benzo[a]phenazinium derivative to which they ascribe structure LXXXVI, which was prepared by the condensation of 4-nitroso-1-naphthylamine hydrochloride with "p-dimethylamino-o-toluidine" in acetic acid solution.

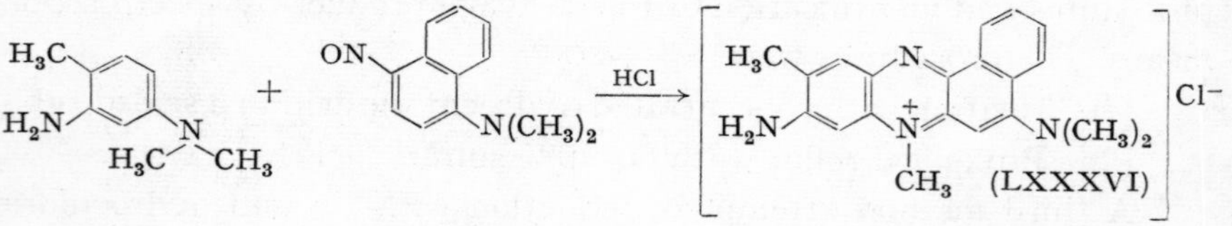

From their experimental directions, however, it is clear that "p-dimethylamino-o-toluidine," which was prepared by coupling diazotized sulfanilic acid with dimethyl-o-toluidine and splitting the azo derivative reductively, must in fact possess structure LXXXVII. This is confirmed by the same workers' identification of their product with that obtained by Bernthsen[197] by nitration of 2-acetamidotoluene, hydrolysis of the acetyl group, methylation and, finally, reduction of the nitro group.

Consequently, the product of the reaction should be formulated as 10-amino-5-dimethylamino-7,8-dimethylbenzo[a]phenazinium chloride (LXXXVIII).

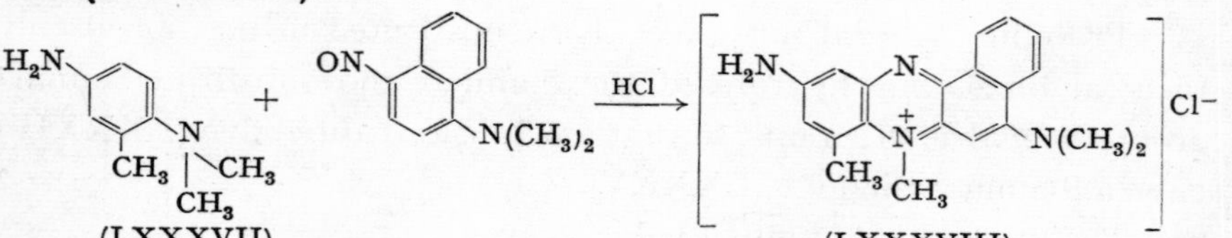

(LXXXVII)   (LXXXVIII)

TABLE XXII. Monoamino-7-alkyl- or -aralkylbenzo[a]phenazinium Salts and Derivatives

Substituents	Appearance of chloride (unless otherwise stated)	Appearance of anhydro-base (where formed)	M.p. of anhydro-base (°C.)	Color with H₂SO₄, followed by dilution	Ref.
5-Amino-7-methyl-	Dark-red needles	Prisms with bronze luster	dec. 138	Green, yellowish-red	3, 73
5-Anilino-7-methyl-	Easily soluble, dyes silk and wool bluish-red				104, 148, 149
5-Amino-9-chloro-7-methyl-	Ruby-red prisms, gold luster			Dark bluish-green, eosin-red	4, 146
5-Anilino-9-chloro-7-methyl-	Dark-red needles, gold luster			Green, red	4
5-(4″-Sulfanilino)-9-chloro-7-methyl-		Dark-red crystals, green luster			146
5-(4″-Sulfanilino)-9-chloro-7-methyl-3-sulfonic acid		Red crystals, golden luster		Yellowish-green, red ppt.	4
5-(4″-Acetamidoanilino)-9-chloro-7-methyl-3-sulfonic acid		Violet-brown crystals		Green, violet	4
5-Amino-7-methyl-10-nitro-	Green, metallic needles			Bluish-green, blue, red	120
5-Amino-7,10-dimethyl-	Red crystals				75-78, 150

(Table continued)

TABLE XXII (*continued*)

Substituents	Appearance of chloride (unless otherwise stated)	Appearance of anhydro-base (where formed)	M.p. of anhydro-base (°C.)	Color with H_2SO_4 followed by dilution	Ref.
5-Anilino-7,10-dimethyl-	Reddish-brown crystals	Crystals	210		77, 103, 145, 147
5-(3″-Sulfanilino)-7,10-dimethyl-		Yellowish-red solid			103, 147
5-(4″-Sulfanilino)-7,10-dimethyl-		Bluish-red solid			145, 147
5-Methylamino-7,10-dimethyl-	Crystals	Needles	175		75–78, 106
10-Amino-7-methyl-	Dark-violet needles			Violet, greenish-yellow, reddish-violet	120
10-Acetamido-7-methyl-	Reddish-yellow leaflets, gold luster				120
5-Amino-7-ethyl-	NO_3^-, orange crystals	Golden flakes			6
5-Amino-7-ethyl-10-methyl-	Brick-red crystals				76–78, 151, 152, 153
9-Amino-7-ethyl-	Red prisms, bronze luster			Violet, green, red	6, 9
9-Acetamido-7-ethyl-	Green prisms				6
9-Dimethylamino-7-ethyl-	$PtCl_6^-$, bluish-green crystals				6, 67, 116, 155, 159
5-Amino-7-benzyl-	Red crystals, green luster			Bluish-green	5, 7

TABLE XXIII. Diamino-7-alkyl- or -aralkylbenzo[a]phenazinium Salts and Derivatives

Substituents	Appearance of chloride (unless otherwise stated)	Appearance of anhydro-base (where formed)	M.p. of anhydro-base	Color with H_2SO_4 followed by dilution	Ref.
9,11-Diamino-7-methyl-	Dark-red needles			Dirty-red, violet-red, olive-brown	108
5,9-Diamino-7-ethyl-	Prisms with metallic luster	Yellow solution in ether			6
5-Amino-9-acetamido-7-ethyl-	Green leaflets, metallic luster				6
5-Amino-9-dimethylamino-7-ethyl-	Dyes cotton bluish-red on mordant			Bluish-green	155, 159
10-Amino-5-dimethyl-amino-7,8-dimethyl(?)*	Crimson solution				73

*See text.

TABLE XXIV. Monoamino-7-phenylbenzo[a]phenazinium Salts and Derivatives

Substituents	Appearance of chloride (unless otherwise stated)	Appearance of anhydro-base (where formed)	M.p. of anhydro-base (°C.)	Color with H_2SO_4 followed by dilution	Ref.
1-Amino-	Violet lustrous prisms			Golden-yellow, yellow, green, blue	118, 201
2-Amino-	Br^-, almost black prisms			Dirty-magenta, orange, lemon-yellow	63
2-Acetamido-	Br^-, dark-brown leaflets, bronze luster			Dirty reddish-brown, red	63
3-Amino-	Br^-, dark greyish-green needles			Blood-red, greenish-yellow	202
3-Acetamido-	Orange-red crystals			Magenta, orange-yellow	202
4-Amino-	Violet lustrous prisms			Blood-red, yellow, violet-blue	118, 221
4-Acetamido-	Brown leaflets, coppery luster			Dirty-magenta, orange-yellow	198, 221
5-Amino-	Red needles, green luster	Reddish-brown leaflets, bronze luster	198–199	Green, scarlet	See XIV: 4,D
5-Acetamido-	Red needles, green luster	Dark-red leaflets, golden luster		Violet-red, green, blood-red	5, 109, 110
5-Anilino-	Reddish-brown prisms, golden luster	Dark-red needles, green luster	236	Brown, green, red	See XIV: 4,E
5-N-Methylanilino-	Br^-, greenish-brown crystals	Dec. with alkali			22

Substituents	Appearance of chloride (unless otherwise stated)	Appearance of anhydro-base (where formed)	M.p. of anhydro-base (°C.)	Color with H_2SO_4 followed by dilution	Ref.
5-(2"-Methylanilino)-		Bronze, lustrous needles	197		19, 117, 130
5-(4"-Methylanilino)-		Bronze, lustrous needles	212–213		18, 19, 117
5-(2",4"-Dimethyl-anilino)-			177–179		117
5-(3"-Sulfanilino)-		(Hydroxide), red powder			20, 84, 132
5-(4"-Nitroanilino)-		Almost black leaflets, green luster		Green	34
5-(2",4",6"-Trinitro-anilino)-		Red leaflets or needles		Violet	34
5-(4"-Aminoanilino)-	Leaflets with bronze luster	Needles with bronze luster	247	Dull-violet	19, 24, 131
5-(4"-Acetamido-anilino)-	Greyish-brown metallic needles	Dark-brown powder			24
5-Ethylamino-		Needles with green luster	184	Green, red	18, 23
5-Methylamino-	NO_3^-, red leaflets, gold luster, dec. 257°	Leaflets or prisms, gold or green luster	180–181	Green, red	23, 24
5-Dimethylamino-				Bluish-green, red	15, 17
5-(1"-Naphthylamino)-	NO_3^-, prisms, green luster	Almost black needles, metallic luster	247	Green	18, 20, 85

(Table continued)

TABLE XXIV (*continued*)

Substituents	Appearance of chloride (unless otherwise stated)	Appearance of anhydro-base (where formed)	M.p. of anhydro-base (°C.)	Color with H_2SO_4 followed by dilution	Ref.
5-Amino-10-methyl-	Bronze crystals			Cherry-red, green, brown, rose	80
5-Anilino-9-methyl-		Dark brown crystals	224.5	Green	222
5-Anilino-4',9-dimethyl-	Brown needles, bronze luster			Green	65
5-(2"-Methylanilino)-4',9-dimethyl-	Brown needles, bronze luster			Green	223
5-(4"-Methylanilino)-4',9-dimethyl-		Blackish-red leaflets, bronze luster	260	Green, red	18, 82
5-(4"-Sulfanilino)-4',9-dimethyl-		Crystals			65
5-Amino-9-chloro-	Garnet crystals, brassy luster			Blackish-green, green, red	49
5-Anilino-9-chloro-	Dark-green prisms	Brownish-black leaflets		Green, violet	10, 115, 146
5-(4"-Methylanilino)-9-chloro-	Needles with bronze luster	Almost black leaflets	215–216	Green, brownish-red, violet-red	10, 115
5-(4"-Methylanilino)-9-chloro-4'-methyl-	Prisms with green luster	Needles, brassy luster		Yellowish-green, violet-red	49, 146
5-(3"-Amino-4"-methyl-anilino)-9-chloro-	Green, metallic crystals			magenta	115
5-(2"-Naphthylamino)-9-chloro-	Reddish-brown crystals				115
5-Amino-10-nitro-	Dark-red crystals, green luster	Dark brownish-red crystals	dec. 242	Yellowish-green, bluish-green, red	51, 111, 120, 121

Substituents	Appearance of chloride (unless otherwise stated)	Appearance of anhydro-base (where formed)	M.p. of anhydro-base (°C.)	Color with H_2SO_4 followed by dilution	Ref.
5-Acetamido-10-nitro-		Reddish-brown needles		Dirty-violet	51
5-Amino-4'-nitro-	Yellowish-red crystals			Green, red	51
6-Acetamido-	Bright-red needles, brassy luster			Reddish-violet, orange-red	114
6-Acetamido-5-chloro-	Orange-red crystals				200
9-Amino-	Crystals with bronze luster			Blackish-violet, dirty-green, orange, crimson	See XIV: 4,G
9-Acetamido-	Orange-yellow leaflets, brassy luster			Violet	17, 109, 110
9-Anilino-	Prisms, coppery-red luster	Coppery-red crystals	169–171	Blue	9, 10, 22, 154
9-(N-Methylanilino)-	I^-, bronze leaflets				22, 155, 162
9-Ethylamino-		Dark brown needles, bronze luster		Brownish-violet	154
9-Dimethylamino-	Black needles, metallic luster	Violet tablets	186	Blue	34, 67, 68
9-(4"-Methylanilino)-		(Hydroxide), greenish metallic needles			10
9-(4"-Sulfanilino)-	NO_3^-, steel-blue needles				132
9-Anilino-10-methyl-	Prisms, brassy luster	Crystals, copper luster		Blue	41

(Table continued)

TABLE XXIV (*continued*)

Substituents	Appearance of chloride (unless otherwise stated)	Appearance of anhydro-base (where formed)	M.p. of anhydro-base (°C.)	Color with H_2SO_4 followed by dilution	Ref.
9-(4''-Methylanilino)-10-methyl-	NO_3^-, bronze leaflets	Dark-blue crystals	225–226	Greenish-blue	41
9-Dimethylamino-4'-methyl-	Violet, lustrous needles				68
9-(2''-Naphthylamino)-10-methyl-	Greyish-black tablets			Deep-blue, reddish-violet	41
9-(4'',4'''-Bisdimethyl-amino)benzhydryl-amino-	Green needles, metallic luster			Blue, violet, rose	128
10-Amino-	Blackish-violet needles			Reddish-violet, yellowish-red, violet-red	111
10-Acetamido-	Brick-red needles			Dirty-violet, brick-red	111
3'-Amino-	Br^-, dark yellowish-brown crystals, green metallic luster			Violet	52
3'-Acetamido-	Br^-, crystals			Reddish-violet, golden-yellow	52
4'-Amino-	Br^-, reddish-brown crystals			Violet, golden-yellow	64
4'-Acetamido-	$FeCl_4^-$, golden-yellow leaflets			Dirty-violet, yellow	64

TABLE XXV. Diamino-7-phenylbenzo[a]phenazinium Salts and Derivatives

Substituents	Appearance of chloride (unless otherwise stated)	Appearance of anhydro-base (where formed)	M.p. of anhydro-base (°C.)	Color with H$_2$SO$_4$, followed by dilution	Ref.
2,5-Diamino-	Violet-brown needles			Green, violet-red	199
2-Acetamido-5-amino-	Dark-red needles			Greenish-blue, red	199
2-Anilino-9-amino-	Crystals with bronze luster	Bronze crystals		Yellowish-brown, green, violet	19
2,9-Dianilino-	Crystals	Blue solution in CHCl$_3$		Dirty-violet, blue	19
2-Anilino-9-dimethyl-amino-		(Hydroxide), crystals, bronze luster		Dirty-green, reddish-violet, blue	19
2-(4"-Methylanilino)-9-dimethylamino-4'-methyl-	"Basle Blue R"				See XIV: 5,B(1)
2-(4"-Methylanilino)-9-diethylamino-4'-methyl-	"Basle Blue BB"				See XIV: 5,B(1)
3-Acetamido-5-amino-	Br⁻, brick-red needles, green metallic luster			Brownish-green, green, red	202
3-Amino-5-anilino-	Crystals, green luster			Dark-green, magenta	202
3-Acetamido-5-anilino-	Dark-red prisms, golden luster	(Hydroxide), brownish-red brassy leaflets		Yellowish-green, red, ppt.	202
5,6-Dianilino-	Almost black leaflets		192	Dark-green, reddish-violet	18

(Table continued)

TABLE XXV (*continued*)

Substituents	Appearance of chloride (unless otherwise stated)	Appearance of anhydro-base (where formed)	M.p. of anhydro-base (°C.)	Color with H_2SO_4 followed by dilution	Ref.
5-Anilino-6-acetamido-	Green metallic needles				114, 200
5,9-Diamino-	Iridescent green knobs.			Bluish-green, dirty-blue, rose	17, 110, 164, 165
5-Amino-9-acetamido-	$PtCl_6{}^{--}$, reddish-brown ppt.				17, 110
5-Amino-9-dimethyl-amino-	Needles or prisms, green luster			Blue-green	60
5-Anilino-9-amino-	Prisms, green luster	Leaflets, green metallic luster	151–152 (dec.)	Green, red-violet	9, 19, 34, 59
5,9-Dianilino-	Bluish-violet crystals, coppery luster	Greenish, lustrous leaflets		Green, blue, ppt.	34, 115
5,9-Di-(4″-methyl-anilino)-	Crystals, bronze luster	Crystals, metallic green luster		Green, blue	115
5,9-Di-(4″-methyl-anilino)-4′-methyl-	Blue crystals, golden luster			Green, violet-blue	49
5-Anilino-9-ethylamino-	Crystals, bronze luster	(Hydroxide), metallic green crystals		Green	154
5-(4″-Aminoanilino)-9-dimethylamino-	Prisms, green luster	Red leaflets, green reflex		Grass-green	60
5-(4″-Dimethylamino-anilino)-9-dimethyl-amino-	Dark-violet crystals, bronze luster	Almost black, dichroic (red-green) leaflets, bronze luster	dec. 270	Green, dirty-brown, reddish-violet	19, 34

Substituents	Appearance of chloride (unless otherwise stated)	Appearance of anhydro-base (where formed)	M.p. of anhydro-base (°C.)	Color with H_2SO_4 followed by dilution	Ref.
5-Methylamino-9-anilino-	Bronze crystals	Greenish-gold crystals	225 (dec.)	Deep-green, blue	34
5,9-Diamino-10-methyl-	Yellowish-green crystals			Emerald-green, blue, violet, rose	80
5,10-Diamino-	Dark-violet needles, coppery luster			Green, yellowish-red, violet	51
5-Amino-10-acetamido-	Brown needles	Reddish-brown crystals		Green, red	51
5,10-Diacetamido-	Leaflets, yellow metallic luster	Violet needles		Dirty-violet, bright-red	51
5,10,4'-Triamino-	Blackish-violet needles	Violet-blue needles		Violet, green, bright-red, bluish-violet	51
5,3'-Diamino-	Dark-red needles			Green, red	52
5-Amino-3'-acetamido-	Red crystals, green luster			Green, red	52
5,3'-Diacetamido-	Cinnabar-red needles, green metallic luster			Reddish-violet, orange-yellow	52
5,4'-Diamino-	Prisms, green metallic luster			Green, red	64
5-Amino-4'-acetamido-	Brick-red leaflets, bronze luster			Bluish-green	64

(Table continued)

TABLE XXV (*continued*)

Substituents	Appearance of chloride (unless otherwise stated)	Appearance of anhydro-base (where formed)	M.p. of anhydro-base (°C.)	Color with H_2SO_4 followed by dilution	Ref.
5,4'-Diacetamido-	Orange-yellow leaflets, greenish-gold luster			Violet, orange	64
5,4'-Diamino-9-chloro-	Dark-brown crystals, bronze luster			Green, yellowish-red, bluish-red (alkaline)	49
5-Amino-4'-acetamido-9-chloro-	Red crystals, brassy luster			Green, red	49
5,4'-Diamino-10-nitro-	Brick-red leaflets, gold luster	(Hydroxide), red needles		Green, magenta, yellowish-red (alkaline)	51
5-Amino-4'-acetamido-10-nitro-	Dark-red crystals	(Hydroxide), yellowish-red crystals	dec. 250	Green, red	51
5,4'-Diacetamido-10-nitro-	Bright-red crystals			Violet, bright-red	51
9-Anilino-10-amino-	Crystals, green luster	Reddish-brown crystals, green luster		Greenish-blue, ultramarine-blue, violet-red	111
9-Dimethylamino-10-amino-	NO_3^-, green, metallic needles				111

TABLE XXVI. Monoamino-12-phenylbenzo[a]phenazinium Salts and Derivatives

Substituents	Appearance of chloride (unless otherwise stated)	Color with H_2SO_4 followed by dilution	Ref.
2-Amino-	Br⁻, blackish-green prisms	Brownish-red, golden-yellow, yellowish-green	63, 119
2-Acetamido-	Br⁻, brown leaflets	Yellowish-brown, orange-yellow	63
3-Amino-	Dark-violet leaflets, copper luster	Brownish-red, orange-yellow, violet	113
3-Acetamido-	Orange-yellow crystals, green luster	Magenta, yellowish-red	113
4-Amino-	Br⁻, black prisms, blue luster	Brownish-red, orange-yellow, dirty greenish-blue (alkaline)	119, 222
4-Acetamido-	Reddish-brown prisms	Dirty purplish-red, orange-red	119, 222
5-Amino-	Blue-black needles	Carmine-red, green, blue	5
5-Acetamido-	Dark brownish-red tablets, bluish luster	Violet-red, green, greenish-blue	5
5-Amino-9-nitro-	Dark-brown crystals	Yellowish-brown, green	120
6-Amino-	NO_3⁻, olive-green needles	Brownish-violet, bright yellow, yellowish-green	114

(Table continued)

TABLE XXVI (*continued*)

Substituents	Appearance of chloride (unless otherwise stated)	Color with H_2SO_4 followed by dilution	Ref.
6-Acetamido-	Almost-black crystals, metallic luster	Reddish-violet, brownish-red, golden-yellow, yellowish-green (alkaline)	114
9-Amino-	Br^-, almost-black crystals, bronze luster	Brownish-violet, dirty blue, olive-brown, reddish-violet (alkaline)	57
9-Acetamido-	Yellowish-red crystals, green luster	Violet, yellowish-red	57
10-Amino-	Violet-red needles	Brownish-violet, green, blue-green, violet-red	112
10-Anilino-	Crystals with coppery luster	Brown, green, blue	112
10-Dimethylamino-	NO_3^-, blue prisms, copper luster	Brown, green, blue	112, 115
10-(3"-Carboxy-4"-hydroxy)anilino-	Blue needles, green luster	Blue sulfonic acid with oleum	115
4'-Amino-	ClO_4^-, dark reddish-brown crystals	Dirty red, orange-yellow	224
4'-Acetamido-	ClO_4^-, orange-red needles	Dark brownish-violet, orange-yellow	224

TABLE XXXVII. Diamino-12-phenylbenzo[a]phenazinium Salts and Derivatives

Substituents	Appearance of chloride (unless otherwise stated)	Color with H_2SO_4, followed by dilution	Ref.
3,10-Diamino-	Metallic green crystals	Reddish-brown, green, blue, violet	113
3-Acetamido-10-amino-	Dark-red crystals, brassy luster	Dirty red, green, red	113
3-Amino-10-anilino-	Needles, coppery luster	Yellowish-green, bluish-green, blue	113
3-Acetamido-10-anilino-	Crystals, coppery luster	Olive-green, blue-black	113
5,9-Diamino-	Dark-violet crystals, bronze luster	Red-violet, green, cornflower-blue, red-violet (alkaline)	57
5,10-Diamino-	Greenish-blue needles, steel luster	Green, magenta, greenish-blue (alkaline)	225
5-Acetamido-10-amino-	Reddish-violet needles, metallic luster	Dirty violet, green, violet	225
5-Acetamido-10-anilino-	Dark-blue leaflets, coppery luster	Yellowish-green, blue	225
5-Acetamido-10-dimethylamino-	Blue needles	Dirty-red, green, blue	225
5,3′-Diamino-	Blue-black needles	Dark brownish-red, green, violet (alkaline)	224
5-Amino-3′-acetamido-	ClO_4^-, greenish needles	Brownish-red, green, blue (alkaline)	224
5,3′-Diacetamido-	ClO_4^-, dark brick-red, lustrous needles	Dark bluish-red, orange-yellow	224
9-Amino-10-dimethylamino-	NO_3^-, green, lustrous needles	Blue-black, greenish-blue, violet, yellowish-magenta (alkaline)	57
9-Amino-10-anilino-	Crystals, bronze luster	Greenish-brown, bluish-violet, reddish violet	57

6. Aminohydroxy Derivatives of
7- and 12-Substituted Benzo[a]phenazinium Salts

Compared with the amino derivatives and hydroxy derivatives individually, those compounds of the benzo[a]phenazinium series that contain both types of group together are of rather limited interest. They are listed in Tables XXVIII and XXIX.

A. General Methods of Preparation

The methods available for their preparation follow from the simpler examples. Thus they are formed by condensation of a suitably substituted 1,2-naphthoquinone derivative with a mono-N-substituted o-phenylenediamine, which may also bear hydroxyl or amino groups. This method is generally applicable to any isomeric possibilities.[54, 198–201] They are also obtained from diamino-7-phenylbenzo[a]phenazinium salts or their substituted amino derivatives by high temperature hydrolysis provided that one of the amino groups is in the reactive 5-position.[19, 60, 202]

As we have pointed out repeatedly (see Chapter XII:4), benzo[a]-phenazinium salts are readily attacked at certain reactive positions by ammonia or amines, or by alkalis, both reactions requiring the presence of air. For 7-phenylbenzo[a]phenazinium salts, the reactive positions are the 5-and 9-positions, with a definite preference for position 5, owing to the higher redox potential of 1,2-naphthoquinonoid structures over 1,2-benzoquinonoid arrangements. With 12-phenylbenzo[a]phenazinium salts, the reactive center is position 10 only. A number of applications of this type of reaction to the synthesis of aminohydroxy compounds is known. For example, an amino derivative of a 7-phenylbenzo[a]-phenazinium salt with alcoholic potassium hydroxide and air yields a 5-hydroxy derivative (x-aminorosindone),[22, 162, 198, 199, 201] while 9-amino-12-phenylbenzo[a]phenazinium chloride and diethylamine (which here

(LXXXIX)

reacts as a strongly basic hydroxide) yields 9-amino-12-phenyl-10(12)-benzo[a]phenazinone[57] (LXXXIX).

Alternatively, an amino-7-phenylbenzo[a]phenazinium salt such as neutral blue (LIX) may first be sulfonated by attack of sodium bisulfite at position 5 and the sulfonic acid group subsequently replaced by hydroxyl by means of alkalis,[116] the product being the anhydro-base (XC).

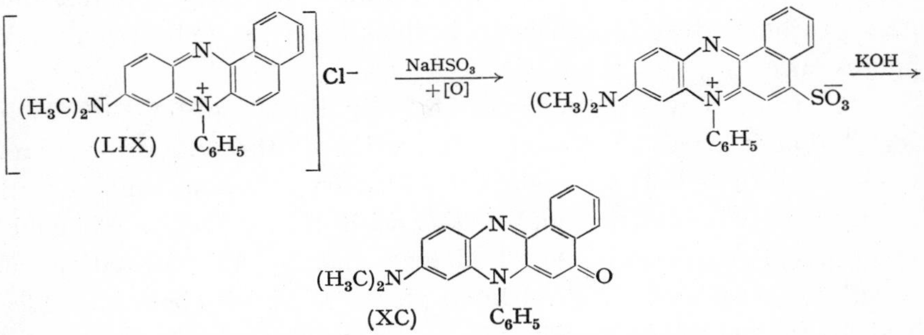

$$(H_3C)_2N \quad (LIX) \quad C_6H_5 \quad Cl^- \xrightarrow[+[O]]{NaHSO_3} (CH_3)_2N \quad C_6H_5 \quad SO_3^- \xrightarrow{KOH}$$

$$(H_3C)_2N \quad (XC) \quad C_6H_5 \quad O$$

Other methods include the attack of amines on hydroxybenzo[a]-phenazinium derivatives,[53] or on primary amino groups of amino-hydroxy derivatives.[32] Certain examples of this method provide the most interesting chemistry of this group. In attempting to show that 7-phenyl-9(7)-benzo[a]phenazinone (isorosindone) was *p*-quinonoid, Fischer and Hepp[10] reacted it with hydroxylamine and obtained what they thought was the oxime. Later work by Kehrmann and his pupils[45, 46] established that the product was 10-amino-7-phenyl-9(7)-benzo[a]phenazinone (XXX), a view with which Fischer[11, 26, 32] eventually concurred.

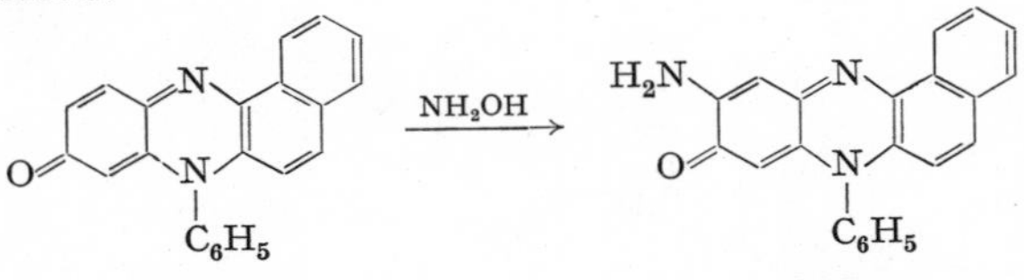

$$O \quad C_6H_5 \quad (XXIII) \xrightarrow{NH_2OH} H_2N \quad O \quad C_6H_5 \quad (XXX)$$

Another modification of a synthesis of amino derivatives is that in which 2,7-dianilinonaphthalene and 4-nitrosophenol react together in the presence of hydrochloric acid to give 2-anilino-7-phenyl-9(7)-benzo[a]phenazinone.[34]

For the use of aminohydroxybenzo[a]phenazinium dyes in color photography, see Chapter VII:2,I and Section XIV:6,D.

B. 10-Amino-7-phenyl-9(7)-benzo[a]phenazinone (XXX)

This substance, the anhydro-base of 10-amino-9-hydroxy-7-phenylbenzo[a]phenazinium salts, is obtained as shown above. It forms long metallic-looking needles, with a green luster, m.p. 242°,[54] and gives a bluish-violet color with concentrated sulfuric acid, which on dilution passes through green (purplish-red in thick layers) to red, with a weak fluorescence.

Its structure was the subject of a lively discussion.[11, 26, 32, 45, 46] On acetylation it gives an N-acetyl derivative of the anhydro-base as steel-blue leaflets.[26] The presence of a primary aromatic amino group is shown by diazotization and boiling with ethanol, when 7-phenyl-9(7)-benzo[a]phenazinone is obtained[26] and by the formation of Schiff's bases with aromatic aldehydes; for example with benzaldehyde, it yields the benzylidene derivative as brick-red crystals.[26]

On heating with hydrochloric acid and acetic acid at 180° under pressure, it yields 9,10-dihydroxy-7-phenylbenzo[a]phenazinium chloride[26, 46] (Section XIV:3,B). It reacts with aniline in the presence of aniline hydrochloride at 150° to yield 10-anilino-7-phenyl-9(7)-benzo-[a]phenazinone as bronze needles, m.p. 282–284°, giving a blue color in concentrated sulfuric acid. With o-phenylenediamine and its hydrochloride, however, reaction proceeds further to the formation of 7-phenyl-7,14-dihydrobenzo[a]quinoxalo[2,3-i]phenazine[32] (XXXII, R. I. 3577) (Chapter XVIII:6,A).

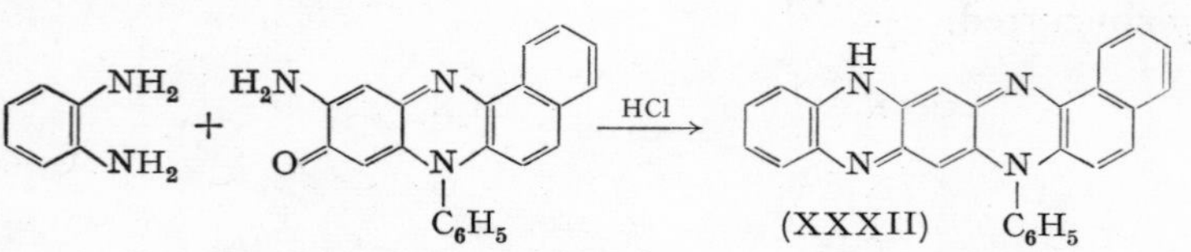

C. Dyes Derived from
Aminohydroxy-7-phenylbenzo[a]phenazinium Salts.

The Thion Violets (C. I. 1007)

On heating 1-nitronaphthalene and 4-aminophenol together at 160–170° in the presence of hydrochloric acid, a complex reaction occurs and the product obtained is said to be 5-p-hydroxyanilino-9-hydroxy-7-p-hydroxyphenylbenzo[a]phenazinium chloride.[203] It is also produced from mixtures of 1-naphthylamine and 4-aminophenol, in the presence of hydrochloric acid and small traces of 2- and 4-nitrophenols,[203] and from the fusion of 4-benzeneazo-1-naphthylamine hydrochloride and 4-aminophenol[203] or from the reaction between the same components in solvents[204, 205] or in the presence of hydrochloric acid and some 4-nitraniline at 170°.[206]

This trihydroxy derivative of phenylrosinduline is used in the preparation of sulfur-containing dyes. On heating with sodium hydroxide, sodium sulfide and sulfur at 170°, the initial yellowish-red color becomes violet. After reaction, acidification precipitates the dye.[207, 208] This type of dye is known as Thion Violet. It is used to dye cotton direct from a sodium sulfide vat in various shades of violet that are only moderately fast.

D. Color Photography and Azine Dyestuffs

It is relevant here to call attention to the recent developments in color photography and the use of diamino- and amino-hydroxybenzo-[a]phenazinium dyes as color agents for the cyan (bluish) and magenta images. For a fuller account, the reader is referred to Chapter VII:2,I (and see reference 209). One example,[210] in which the final dye is a relative (XCI) of the Wool Fast Blue colors, describes the use as color coupler of 1,3-dianilinonaphthalene-8-sulfonic acid or a derivative of this bearing a long-chain alkylamine group on the sulfonic acid and further sulfonated. This reacts with the oxidation product of a conventional primary amino aromatic developer to give a blue image.[211]

(XCI)

Another patent describes the use of aminonaphthols as color couplers, giving bluish-magenta images with a conventional p-diamine developer.[212]

TABLE XXVIII. Aminohydroxy-7-phenylbenzo[a]phenazinium Salts and Derivatives

Substituents	Appearance of chloride (unless otherwise stated)	Appearance of anhydro-base (where formed)	M.p. of anhydro-base (°C.)	Color with H_2SO_4 followed by dilution	Ref.
1-Amino-5-hydroxy-		Dark-red needles, brassy luster		Golden-yellow, red	201
1-Acetamido-5-hydroxy-		Reddish-brown leaflets, brassy luster	sublimes	Dichroic (red, greenish-brown), bright red	201
2-Acetamido-5-hydroxy-		Red leaflets	300	Dichroic (red-green), brownish-violet, rose	199
2-Anilino-9-hydroxy-		Reddish-brown crystals	325–335	Wine-red, green, brown ppt.	34
3-Acetamido-5-hydroxy-		Brick-red needles, green luster	> 310	Dirty-violet, yellow, red	202
3-Acetamido-5-methoxy-	$(CH_3SO_4^-)$, Orange crystals			Violet-red, golden-yellow	202
4-Amino-5-hydroxy-		Leaflets, bronze luster	253	Dichroic (violet-red, grey-green), brownish-green, orange, red	198
4-Acetamido-5-hydroxy-		Needles, golden luster	280	Blackish-violet	198
5-(4″-Hydroxyanilino)-9,4'-dihydroxy-	Yellowish-red solid			Bluish-violet	See XIV: 6,C
6-Amino-5-hydroxy-		Dark-blue needles, copper luster	215–216	Dirty-violet, green, red	200

Substituents	Appearance of chloride (unless otherwise stated)	Appearance of anhydro-base (where formed)	M.p. of anhydro-base (°C.)	Color with H_2SO_4 followed by dilution	Ref.
6-Acetamido-5-hydroxy-		Red needles	249–250	Dirty-red, orange-red	200
9-Amino-5-hydroxy-		Greenish lustrous prisms	270 (dec.)	Dirty-green, brown, red ppt.	19
9-Dimethylamino-5-hydroxy-		Greenish needles		Greenish-brown	60, 116
9-(N-Methylanilino)-5-hydroxy-		Lustrous green crystals	235–237	Green, violet, blue	22, 162
9-Amino-10-hydroxy-	Leaflets with bronze or green luster	Dark-brown needles	> 320	Violet, blue, reddish-violet, brownish-red	54
9-Acetamido-10-hydroxy-		Blue-black needles	342	Almost black, violet, orange-red	54
10-Amino-9-hydroxy-	Red leaflets, metallic green luster	Needles, metallic green reflex	242	Violet-blue, (green, purple-red), red	10, 11, 26, 46, 54
10-Acetamido-9-hydroxy-		Steel-blue leaflets		Bluish-violet	26
10-Benzalamino-9-hydroxy-		Red crystals		Violet	26
10-(4″-Nitrobenzal-amino)-9-hydroxy-		Red needles			26
10-Anilino-9-hydroxy-		Bronze needles	282–284	Blue, violet	32
10-Amino-9-hydroxy-2′-methyl-	Prisms, green luster			Violet, greenish-yellow	10

TABLE XXIX. Aminohydroxy-12-phenylbenzo[a]phenazinium Salts and Derivatives

Substituents	Appearance of salt	Appearance of anhydro-base (where formed)	M.p. of anhydro-base (°C.)	Color with H_2SO_4 followed by dilution	Ref.
9-Amino-10-hydroxy-		Yellowish-red leaflets	> 300	Dirty-green, blue-violet, red	57
10-Amino-5-hydroxy-	(SO_4^{--}), Dark-blue needles, violet luster	Bluish-green needles		Olive-green, blue	225
10-Dimethylamino-5-hydroxy-	(SO_4^{--}), Greenish-blue needles, coppery luster	Bright-green needles		Olive-green, bluish-green	225
10-Anilino-2-hydroxy-	(Cl^-), Crystals, metallic red luster			Dirty-green, bluish-green, dark-blue	53

With the introduction of a new type of developer, bearing a long-chain alkylsulfonamido group in the 2-position to the unsubstituted amino group of a conventional developer and further substituted, if necessary, with an alkyl or aryl substituted group in the 4-position,[213] azine formation became possible using color couplers that were already in use in certain processes. The azine color developers are unsatisfactory for developing the latent silver image alone and are used in conjunction with a conventional developer.[214] The yellow image is not a phenazine-

Blue-green (cyan) image

type dye, but both the cyan and the magenta images contain this system. The former arises from the reaction between the oxidized azine developer and a 6-amino-1-naphthol derivative[215] or an hydroxy-benzoquinoline compound[216] as color former, while the magenta dye is obtained using 1-naphthol[217] or β-quinolinol[218, 219] derivatives and the same azine-type developer. Diffusion of the color couplers in the emulsion is minimized by the incorporation of long-chain alkyl groups.[220]

References

1. F. Kehrmann and J. Messinger, *Ber.*, **24**, 2167 (1891).
2. O. Fischer and E. Franck, *Ber.*, **26**, 179 (1893).
3. O. Fischer and E. Hepp, *Ber.*, **30**, 391 (1897).
4. F. Kehrmann and H. Müller, *Ber.*, **34**, 1095 (1901).
5. F. Kehrmann, *Ann.*, **290**, 247 (1896).
6. W. G. Shaposhnikov, *J. Russ. Phys. Chem. Soc.*, **30**, 546 (1898); *Chem. Zentr.*, **1898**, II, 919.
7. M. Tichvinski, *J. Russ. Phys. Chem. Soc.*, **27**, 577 (1895).
8. O. Fischer and E. Hepp, *Ber.*, **31**, 2477 (1898).
9. O. Fischer and E. Hepp, *Ber.*, **29**, 2752 (1896).
10. O. Fischer and E. Hepp, *Ber.*, **33**, 1485 (1900).
11. O. Fischer and E. Hepp, *Ber.*, **38**, 3435 (1905).
12. F. Kehrmann and J. Messinger, *Ber.*, **24**, 584 (1891).
13. F. Kehrmann, *Ann.*, **322**, 1 (1907).
14. F. Kehrmann and B. Mascioni, *Ber.*, **28**, 345 (1895).
15. F. Kehrmann and W. Shaposhnikov, *Ber.*, **30**, 2620 (1897).
16. F. Kehrmann, *Ber.*, **29**, 2316 (1896).

17. W. Shaposhnikov, *J. Russ. Phys. Chem. Soc.*, **29**, 535 (1897); *Chem. Zentr.*, **1898**, I, 722.
18. O. Fischer and E. Hepp, *Ann.*, **256**, 233 (1890).
19. O. Fischer and E. Hepp, *Ann.*, **272**, 306 (1892).
20. O. Fischer and E. Hepp, *Ann.*, **262**, 237 (1891).
21. R. Bass, *Helv. Chim. Acta*, **16**, 403 (1933).
22. O. Fischer and E. Hepp, *Ber.*, **31**, 299 (1898).
23. O. Fischer and E. Hepp, *Ber.*, **30**, 1827 (1897).
24. F. Kehrmann and C. Locher, *Ber.*, **31**, 2428 (1898).
25. F. Kehrmann and E. Locher, *Ber.*, **29**, 2072 (1896).
26. O. Fischer and K. Arntz, *Ber.*, **39**, 3807 (1906).
27. F. Kehrmann, *Ber.*, **56B**, 2385 (1923).
28. F. Kehrmann, *Ber.*, **41**, 2340 (1908).
29. F. Kehrmann, *Ber.*, **46**, 3036 (1913).
30. F. Kehrmann, *Helv. Chim. Acta*, **7**, 964 (1924).
31. A. Hantzsch and G. Osswald, *Ber.*, **33**, 278 (1900).
32. O. Fischer and F. Römer, *Ber.*, **40**, 3406 (1907).
33. F. Kehrmann and K. L. Stern, *Ber.*, **41**, 12 (1908).
34. O. Fischer and E. Hepp, *Ann.*, **286**, 187 (1895).
35. O. Fischer, *Ber.*, **36**, 3622 (1903).
36. Ger. Pat. 55,227; *Frdl.*, **3**, 343 (1890–1894).
37. Ger. Pat. 56,843; *Frdl.*, **3**, 337 (1890–1894).
38. Ger. Pat. 67,198; *Frdl.*, **3**, 346 (1890–1894).
39. Ger. Pat. 72,343; *Frdl.*, **3**, 346 (1890–1894).
40. L. Michaelis, *J. Biol. Chem.*, **91**, 369 (1931).
41. O. Fischer, *Ber.*, **34**, 940 (1901).
42. F. Kehrmann, *Ber.*, **56B**, 2390 (1923).
43. H. Decker and A. Würsch, *Ber.*, **39**, 2653 (1906).
44. O. Fischer and E. Hepp, *Ber.*, **31**, 2482 (1898).
45. F. Kehrmann and H. de Gottrau, *Ber.*, **38**, 2574 (1905).
46. F. Kehrmann and H. Prager, *Ber.*, **40**, 1234 (1907).
47. G. F. Jaubert, *Ber.*, **31**, 1185 (1898).
48. A. Cobenzl, *Österr. Chem. Ztg.*, **28**, 25 (1925); *Chem. Zentr.*, **1925**, I, 1737; *Chem. Abstracts*, **19**, 2567 (1925).
49. F. Kehrmann and S. Krazler, *Ber.*, **34**, 1102 (1901).
50. F. Kehrmann, R. Speitel and E. Grandmougin, *Ber.*, **47**, 3205 (1914).
51. F. Kehrmann, F. Rademacher and O. Feder, *Ber.*, **31**, 3076 (1898).
52. F. Kehrmann and P. Nüesch, *Ber.*, **34**, 3099 (1901).
53. F. Kehrmann and R. Brunel, *Ber.*, **41**, 1832 (1908).
54. F. Kehrmann and R. Schwarzenbach, *Ber.*, **41**, 472 (1908).
55. F. Kehrmann, *Ann.*, **414**, 131 (1918).
56. F. Kehrmann, *Ber.*, **40**, 1960 (1907).
57. F. Kehrmann and A. Levy, *Ber.*, **31**, 3097 (1898).
58. F. Kehrmann and B. Perrot, *Helv. Chim. Acta*, **10**, 53 (1927).
59. O. Fischer and E. Hepp, *Ber.*, **36**, 1813 (1903).
60. O. Fischer and E. Hepp, *Z. Farben und Textilchem.*, **1**, 437 (1902); *Chem. Zentr.*, **1902**, II, 804.
61. F. Kehrmann and R. Logoz, *Helv. Chim. Acta*, **10**, 339 (1927).
62. F. Kehrmann and C. Collaud, *Helv. Chim. Acta*, **11**, 1028 (1928).
63. F. Kehrmann and H. Wolff, *Ber.*, **33**, 1543 (1900).
64. F. Kehrmann and E. Ott, *Ber.*, **34**, 3092 (1901).
65. Ger. Pat. 79,564; *Frdl.*, **4**, 437 (1894–1897).

66. F. Kehrmann, *Ber.*, **27**, 3348 (1894).
67. Ger. Pat. 19,244; *Frdl.*, **1**, 277 (1877–1887).
68. O. N. Witt, *Ber.*, **21**, 719 (1888).
69. Ger. Pat. 78,497; *Frdl.*, **4**, 426 (1894–1897).
70. Ger. Pat. 80,778; *Frdl.*, **4**, 429 (1894–1897).
71. Ger. Pat. 86,222; *Frdl.*, **4**, 431 (1894–1897).
72. Ger. Pat. 185,986; *Frdl.*, **8**, 526 (1905–1907).
73. J. B. Cohen and H. G. Crabtree, *J. Chem. Soc.*, **119**, 2055 (1921).
74. Ger. Pat. 79,189; *Frdl.*, **4**, 428 (1894–1897).
75. Ger. Pat. 77,226; *Frdl.*, **4**, 383 (1894–1897).
76. Ger. Pat. 78,222; *Frdl.*, **4**, 387 (1894–1897).
77. Ger. Pat. 79,960; *Frdl.*, **4**, 389 (1894–1897).
78. Ger. Pat. 88,365; *Frdl.*, **4**, 395 (1894–1897).
79. R. Nietzki and R. Otto, *Ber.*, **21**, 1598 (1888).
80. N. Orlov, *J. Russ. Phys. Chem. Soc.*, **42**, 522 (1910); *Chem. Zentr.*, **1910**, II, 481.
81. Ger. Pat. 86,224; *Frdl.*, **4**, 435 (1894–1897).
82. Ger. Pat. 50,822; *Frdl.*, **2**, 210 (1887–1890).
83. O. Fischer and E. Hepp, *Ber.*, **21**, 2617 (1888).
84. Ger. Pat. 45,370; *Frdl.*, **2**, 202 (1887–1890).
85. Ger. Pat. 71,296; *Frdl.*, **3**, 344 (1890–1894).
86. L. Paul, *Chem. Rundschau*, **1897**, 146; *Chem. Zentr.*, **1897**, I, 1168.
87. Ger. Pat. 52,922; *Frdl.*, **2**, 206 (1887–1890).
88. Ger. Pat. 67,339; *Frdl.*, **3**, 331 (1890–1894).
89. O. Fischer and E. Hepp, *Ber.*, **25**, 2731 (1892).
90. R. Lantz, *Ann. chim.*, [11], **2**, 58 (1934).
91. R. Lantz and A. Wahl, *Compt. rend.*, **182**, 705 (1926).
92. A. Wahl and R. Lantz, *Chimie et industrie*, **16**, 355 (1926); *Chem. Abstracts*, **21**, 98 (1927).
93. Ger. Pat. 365,367; *Frdl.*, **14**, 468 (1921–1925); Brit. Pat. 182,084; *Chem. Zentr.*, **1923**, II, 997.
94. Ger. Pat. 414,427; *Frdl.*, **15**, 308 (1925–1927); Brit. Pat. 191,064; *Chem. Zentr.*, **1923**, IV, 771; Brit. Pat. 206,150; *Chem. Zentr.*, **1925**, II, 1808.
95. Ger. Pat. 415,317; *Frdl.*, **15**, 309 (1925–1927); *Chem. Zentr.*, **1925**, II, 1808.
96. Ger. Pat. 415,318; *Frdl.*, **15**, 310 (1925–1927); *Chem. Zentr.*, **1925**, II, 1809.
97. Ger. Pat. 415,319; *Frdl.*, **15**, 315 (1925–1927); *Chem. Zentr.*, **1925**, II, 1810.
98. Ger. Pat. 415,320; *Frdl.*, **15**, 316 (1925–1927); *Chem. Zentr.*, **1925**, II, 1808.
99. Ger. Pat. 444,518; *Frdl.*, **15**, 317 (1925–1927); Brit. Pat. 246,482; Fr. Pat. 593,916; *Chem. Zentr.*, **1927**, I, 1747.
100. Ger. Pat. 422,119; *Frdl.*, **15**, 433 (1925–1927); Fr. Pat. 558,157; *Chem. Zentr.*, **1923**, IV, 949.
101. G. B. Crippa and R. Caracci, *Gazz. chim. ital.*, **69**, 129 (1939); *Chem. Abstracts*, **33**, 5840 (1939).
102. R. Lantz, *Ann. chim.*, [11], **2**, 101 (1934).
103. Ger. Pat. 66,361; *Frdl.*, **3**, 352 (1890–1894).
104. Ger. Pat. 71,666; *Frdl.*, **3**, 355 (1890–1894).
105. Ger. Pat. 77,228; *Frdl.*, **4**, 385 (1894–1897).
106. Ger. Pat. 79,539; *Frdl.*, **4**, 387 (1894–1897).
107. Ger. Pat. 86,109; *Frdl.*, **4**, 393 (1894–1897).
108. F. Kehrmann and J. Riera y Punti, *Ber.*, **44**, 2618 (1911).
109. F. Kehrmann, *Ber.*, **31**, 977 (1898).
110. F. Kehrmann and W. Shaposhnikov, *Ber.*, **30**, 1565 (1897).

111. F. Kehrmann, *Ber.*, **33**, 395 (1900).
112. F. Kehrmann and W. Helwig, *Ber.*, **30**, 2629 (1897).
113. F. Kehrmann and M. Ravinson, *Ber.*, **32**, 927 (1899).
114. F. Kehrmann and M. Cordone, *Ber.*, **46**, 2974 (1913).
115. F. Kehrmann and W. Hiby, *Ber.*, **34**, 1085 (1901).
116. Ger. Pat. 102,458; *Frdl.*, **5**, 361 (1897–1900); *Chem. Zentr.*, **1899**, II, 504.
117. Ger. Pat. 65,894; *Frdl.*, **3**, 338 (1890–1894).
118. F. Kehrmann and P. Filatov, *Ber.*, **32**, 2627 (1899).
119. F. Kehrmann and G. Steiner, *Ber.*, **33**, 3276 (1900).
120. F. Kehrmann and H. Jacob, *Ber.*, **31**, 3087 (1898).
121. F. Kehrmann and O. Feder, *Ber.*, **30**, 2637 (1897).
122. O. Fischer, *Ber.*, **29**, 1870 (1896).
123. F. Kehrmann, R. Speitel and E. Grandmougin, *Ber.*, **47**, 3363 (1914).
124. F. Kehrmann and M. Sandoz, *Helv. Chim. Acta*, **6**, 982 (1923).
125. F. Kehrmann and M. Sandoz, *Helv. Chim. Acta*, **8**, 250 (1925).
126. E. Havas, *Ber.*, **47**, 994 (1914).
127. F. Kehrmann and W. Shaposhnikov, *Ber.*, **29**, 2967 (1896).
128. R. Möhlau and W. Shaposhnikov, *Ber.*, **33**, 799 (1900).
129. W. Vaubel, *J. prakt. Chem.*, [2], **62**, 141 (1900); *Chem. Zentr.*, **1900**, II, 657.
130. Ger. Pat. 67,115; *Frdl.*, **3**, 345 (1890–1894).
131. O. Fischer and E. Hepp, *Ber.*, **23**, 838 (1890).
132. F. Kehrmann and A. Herzbaum, *Ber.*, **50**, 873 (1917).
133. Ger. Pat. 58,601; *Frdl.*, **3**, 329 (1890–1894).
134. T. Wieland and L. Wirth, *Angew. Chem.*, **62**, 473 (1950).
135. M. Heidenhain, *Z. wiss. Mikroskop.*, **32**, 361 (1915); *Chem. Zentr.*, **1916**, II, 424.
136. L. McGregor, *Am. J. Path.*, **5**, 545 (1929).
137. R. Volkmann and F. Strauss, *Z. wiss. Mikroskop.*, **51**, 244 (1934).
138. Ger. Pat. 58,197; *Frdl.*, **3**, 332 (1890–1894).
139. Ger. Pat. 62,191; *Frdl.*, **3**, 334 (1890–1894).
140. Ger. Pat. 62,192; *Frdl.*, **3**, 336 (1890–1894).
141. Ger. Pat. 59,180; *Frdl.*, **3**, 341 (1890–1894).
142. Ger. Pat. 64,993; *Frdl.*, **3**, 343 (1890–1894).
143. Ger. Pat. 79,953; *Frdl.*, **4**, 439 (1894–1897).
144. Ger. Pat. 85,757; *Frdl.*, **4**, 442 (1894–1897).
145. Ger. Pat. 71,665; *Frdl.*, **3**, 354 (1890–1894).
146. Ger. Pat. 116,631; *Frdl.*, **5**, 937 (1897–1900); *Chem. Zentr.*, **1901**, I, 153.
147. Ger. Pat. 75,017; *Frdl.*, **3**, 356 (1890–1894).
148. Ger. Pat. 78,043; *Frdl.*, **4**, 382 (1894–1897).
149. Ger. Pat. 75,929; *Frdl.*, **4**, 383 (1894–1897).
150. Ger. Pat. 79,540; *Frdl.*, **4**, 389 (1894–1897).
151. Ger. Pat. 79,972; *Frdl.*, **4**, 391 (1894–1897).
152. Ger. Pat. 184,381; *Frdl.*, **8**, 884 (1905–1907); *Chem. Zentr.*, **1907**, II, 565.
153. R. D. Stiehler and W. M. Clark, *J. Am. Chem. Soc.*, **55**, 4097 (1933).
154. Ger. Pat. 183,117; *Frdl.*, **8**, 523 (1905–1907); *Chem. Zentr.*, **1907**, II, 864.
155. Ger. Pat. 97,118; *Frdl.*, **5**, 355 (1897–1900); *Chem. Zentr.*, **1898**, II, 586.
156. Ger. Pat. 97,365; *Frdl.*, **5**, 357 (1897–1900); *Chem. Zentr.*, **1898**, II, 587.
157. Ger. Pat. 97,395; *Frdl.*, **5**, 358 (1897–1900); *Chem. Zentr.*, **1898**, II, 588.
158. Ger. Pat. 97,396; *Frdl.*, **5**, 358 (1897–1900); *Chem. Zentr.*, **1898**, II, 588.
159. Ger. Pat. 103,687; *Frdl.*, **5**, 363 (1897–1900); *Chem. Zentr.*, **1899**, II, 640.
160. Ger. Pat. 355,491; *Frdl.*, **14**, 774 (1921–1925); *Chem. Zentr.*, **1922**, IV, 713.
161. Ger. Pat. 357,236; *Frdl.*, **14**, 775 (1921–1925); *Chem. Zentr.*, **1922**, IV, 953.

162. Ger. Pat. 97,211; *Frdl.*, **5**, 354 (1897–1900); *Chem. Zentr.*, **1898**, II, 586.
163. Ger. Pat. 142,947; *Frdl.*, **7**, 343 (1902–1904); *Chem. Zentr.*, **1903**, II, 170.
164. P. Barbier and P. Sisley, *Ann. chim.*, [8], **13**, 96 (1908).
165. P. Barbier and P. Sisley, *Bull. soc. chim. France*, [3], **35**, 1278 (1906).
166. Ger. Pat. 206,646; *Frdl.*, **9**, 266 (1908–1910); *Chem. Zentr.*, **1909**, I, 1059.
167. U. S. Pat. 940,354; *Chem. Abstracts*, **4**, 517 (1910).
168. Ger. Pat. 611,966; *Frdl.*, **21**, 823 (1934); *Chem. Abstracts*, **29**, 6070 (1935).
169. Brit. Pat. 455,693; *Chem. Zentr.*, **1937**, I, 3071; *Chem. Abstracts*, **31**, 2019 (1937).
170. Ger. Pat. 450,922; *Frdl.*, **15**, 434 (1925–1927); *Chem. Zentr.*, **1928**, I, 260.
171. Ger. Pat. 461,382; *Frdl.*, **16**, 844 (1927–1929); *Chem. Zentr.*, **1928**, II, 397.
172. Ger. Pat. 465,581; *Frdl.*, **16**, 837 (1927–1929); see also Brit. Pat. 282,803; *Chem. Zentr.*, **1928**, I, 2010.
173 Ger. Pat. 504,331; *Frdl.*, **16**, 838 (1927–1929); *Chem. Abstracts*, **24**, 5506 (1930).
174 Ger. Pat. 528,021; *Frdl.*, **16**, 3016 (1927–1929); see Brit. Pat. 284,615; *Chem Abstracts*, **22**, 4831 (1928).
175. Ger. Pat. 528,022; *Frdl.*, **16**, 3018 (1927–1929); see Brit. Pat. 284,614; *Chem. Abstracts*, **22**, 4831 (1928).
176. Ger. Pat. 531,977; *Frdl.*, **16**, 3020 (1927–1929); see Brit. Pat. 285,486; *Chem. Abstracts*, **22**, 4832 (1928).
177. Ger. Pat. 537,939; *Frdl.*, **17**, 932 (1930); see Brit. Pat. 297,441; *Chem. Abstracts*, **23**, 2832 (1929).
178. Ger. Pat. 538,905; *Frdl.*, **17**, 933 (1930); see Brit. Pat. 300,549; *Chem. Abstracts*, **23**, 4079 (1929).
179. Fr. Pat. 573,368; *Chem. Zentr.*, **1924**, II, 2505.
180. Fr. Pat. 766,907; *Chem. Zentr.*, **1935**, I, 2606.
181. Fr. Pat. 767,104; *Chem. Zentr.*, **1935**, I, 2607.
182. Brit. Pat. 461,267; *Chem. Zentr.*, **1937**, I, 4157.
183. Brit. Pat. 384,709; *Chem. Zentr.*, **1933**, I, 2003.
184. Ger. Pat. 601,832; *Frdl.*, **21**, 819 (1934); *Chem. Abstracts*, **28**, 7549 (1934).
185. Brit. Pat. 435,479; *Chem. Abstracts*, **30**, 1581 (1936).
186. Ger. Pat. 584,387; *Frdl.*, **19**, 3133 (1932); see Brit. Pat. 385,409; *Chem. Abstracts*, **27**, 4429 (1933).
187. Ger. Pat. 45,803; *Frdl.*, **2**, 209 (1887–1890).
188. Ger. Pat. 79,410; *Frdl.*, **4**, 446 (1894–1897).
189. Ger. Pat. 83,101; *Frdl.*, **4**, 446 (1894–1897).
190. Ger. Pat. 57,346; *Frdl.*, **3**, 313 (1890–1894).
191. Ger. Pat. 69,096; *Frdl.*, **3**, 314 (1890–1894).
192. J. Annaheim, *Ber.*, **20**, 1371 (1887).
193. Ger. Pat. 40,886; *Frdl.*, **1**, 278 (1877–1887).
194. Ger. Pat. 58,363; *Frdl.*, **3**, 321 (1890–1894).
195. Ger. Pat. 54,087; *Frdl.*, **2**, 182 (1887–1890).
196. Ger. Pat. 58,576; *Frdl.*, **3**, 323 (1890–1894).
197. A. Bernthsen, *Ber.*, **25**, 3128 (1892).
198. F. Kehrmann and G. Steiner, *Ber.*, **33**, 3280 (1900).
199. F. Kehrmann and G. Steiner, *Ber.*, **33**, 3285 (1900).
200. F. Kehrmann and G. Barche, *Ber.*, **33**, 3067 (1900).
201. F. Kehrmann and E. Misslin, *Ber.*, **34**, 1224 (1901).
202. F. Kehrmann and M. Silberstein, *Ber.*, **33**, 3300 (1900).
203. Ger. Pat. 158,077; *Frdl.*, **7**, 342 (1902–1904); *Chem. Zentr.*, **1905**, I, 484.
204. Ger. Pat. 158,101; *Frdl.*, **7**, 783 (1902–1904); *Chem. Zentr.*, **1905**, I, 707.

205. Ger. Pat. 160,789; *Frdl.*, **8**, 522 (1905–1907); *Chem. Zentr.*, **1905**, II, 284.
206. Ger. Pat. 158,100; *Frdl.*, **7**, 343 (1902–1904); *Chem. Zentr.*, **1905**, I, 484.
207. Ger. Pat. 152,373; *Frdl.*, **7**, 529 (1902–1904); *Chem. Zentr.*, **1905**, I, 484.
208. Ger. Pat. 160,790; *Frdl.*, **8**, 797 (1905–1907); *Chem. Zentr.*, **1905**, II, 284.
209. W. A. Schmidt, V. Tulagin, J. A. Sprung, R. C. Gunther, R. F. Coles and D. E. Sargent, *Ind. Eng. Chem.*, **45**, 1726 (1953).
210. U. S. Pat. 2,543,338; *Chem. Abstracts*, **45**, 6520 (1951).
211. Brit. Pat. 633,760; *Brit. Abstracts*, **1950**, **BII**, 573.
212. U. S. Pat. 2,536,010; *Chem. Abstracts*, **45**, 5551 (1951).
213. U. S. Pat. 2,414,491; *Chem. Abstracts*, **41**, 3387 (1947).
214. U. S. Pat. 2,527,379; *Chem. Abstracts*, **45**, 487 (1951).
215. U. S. Pat. 2,525,503; *Chem. Abstracts*, **45**, 3272 (1951).
216. U. S. Pat. 2,525,502; *Chem. Abstracts*, **45**, 3272 (1951).
217. U. S. Pat. 2,486,440; *Chem. Abstracts*, **45**, 488 (1951).
218. U. S. Pat. 2,524,725; *Chem. Abstracts*, **45**, 3272 (1951).
219. U. S. Pat. 2,524,741; *Chem. Abstracts*, **45**, 3272 (1951).
220. U. S. Pat. 2,591,642; *Chem. Abstracts*, **46**, 6023 (1952).
221. F. Kehrmann and A. Denk, *Ber.*, **33**, 3295 (1900).
222. C. Schraube and E. Romig, *Ber.*, **26**, 575 (1893).
223. Ger. Pat. 79,954; *Frdl.*, **4**, 441 (1894–1897).
224. F. Kehrmann and L. Listwa, *Helv. Chim. Acta*, **8**, 655 (1925).
225. F. Kehrmann and W. Aebi, *Ber.*, **32**, 932 (1899).

Dibenzo- and Mononaphtho-phenazines

1. Introduction

Members of all five possible ring systems obtainable by the fusion of two benzene rings to the phenazine nucleus are known, though some of them should be regarded with caution as they are not well authenticated. Of the systems obtainable by the fusion of a naphthalene nucleus to phenazine, only two have been described. Despite the syntheses by Fieser[1,2] of both 1,2- and 3,4-phenanthrenequinones, no members of the azine systems (I and II), derivable from these by reaction with o-phenylenediamines, have been prepared.

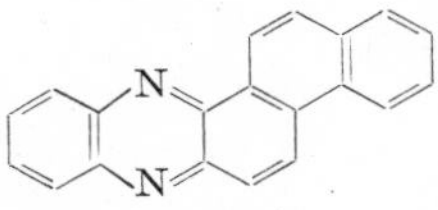

(I) 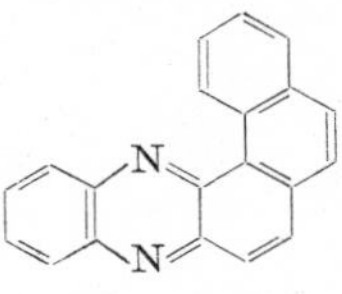   (II)

2. Dibenzo[a, c]phenazine (III)

Phenanthrophenazine, R. I. 3252

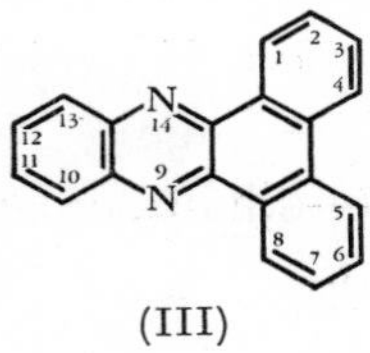

(III)

A. Preparation and Properties

The parent compound of this series was prepared originally by Hinsberg[3] by condensing 9,10-phenanthrenequinone with o-phenylenediamine. Hinsberg pointed out that this reaction provided a good, rapid test for the presence of an *o*-diamine. It was soon used also as a means of identifying substituted phenanthrenes by oxidation to the 9,10-quinone and condensation with *o*-phenylenediamine. Consequently, there are very many compounds of this series, prepared for identification purposes but of very slight intrinsic interest. Since there is very little point in cataloging these, in Table XXX we have restricted mention to alkyl and other simple derivatives.

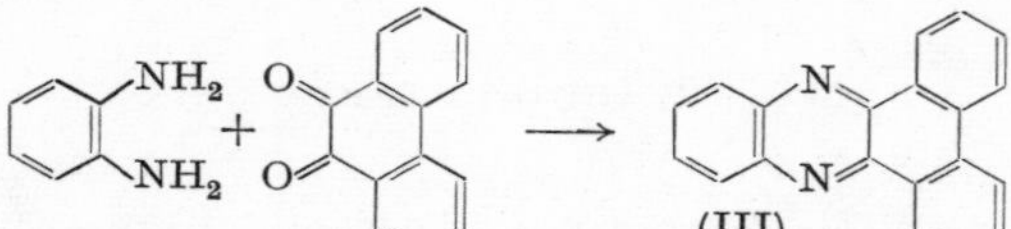

Until very recently, this reaction, since it is so satisfactory, represented the sole means of preparation of dibenzo[*a,c*]phenazines. Martynoff[4] has now shown that a good yield of dibenzo[*a,c*]phenazine can be obtained by reaction of 9-nitrophenanthrene with aniline in the presence of sodium hydroxide. This modification of the Wohl-Aue synthesis (Chapters I:(8) and XII:3,B(10)) apparently does not produce the *N*-oxide usually isolated.

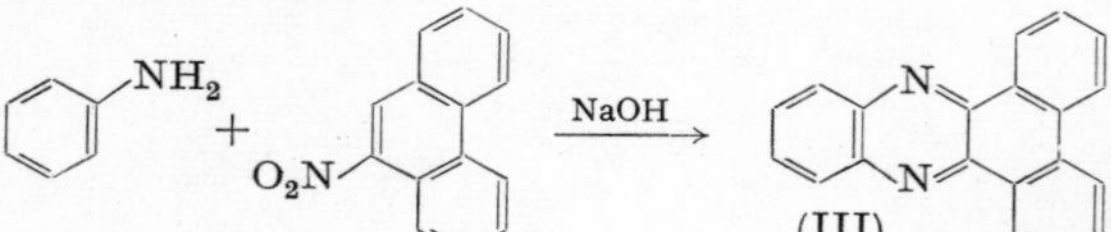

Dibenzo[*a,c*]phenazine (III) forms yellow needles, m.p. 219°, and with strong acids gives deep red salts that are readily hydrolyzed by water, showing the weak basicity of the azine system. Reduction of III with sodium amalgam and hydrochloric acid yields a violet salt, giving violet solutions in acetic acid, which is probably of a semiquinonoid nature; reduction by the same reagent in acetic anhydride,[5] however, produced 9-acetyl-9,14-dihydrodibenzo[*a,c*]phenazine (IV), a yellow substance, m.p. 252°.

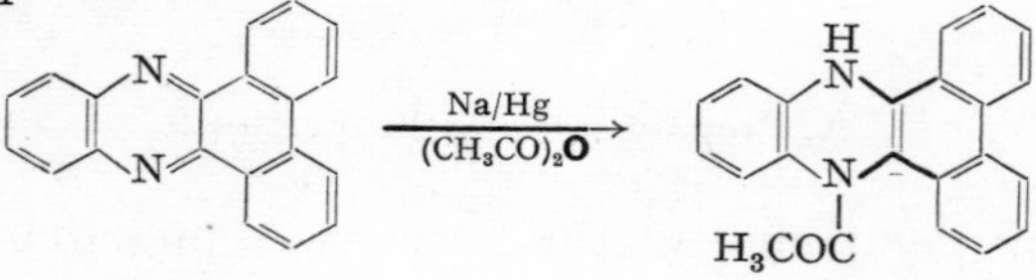

Other hydrogenated derivatives of this series were described by Einhorn and Bull,[6] who condensed 1,2-diaminocyclohexane with 9,10-phenanthrenequinone. In the course of the reaction, migration of two hydrogen atoms appears to have occurred to give 9,10,11,12,13,14-hexahydrodibenzo[a,c]phenazine (V), since the product readily forms a monoacetyl derivative (VI) with acetyl chloride in cold pyridine, and moreover readily loses two atoms of hydrogen on heating alone or with mineral acids or glacial acetic acid to give 10,11,12,13-tetrahydrodibenzo[a,c]phenazine (VII).

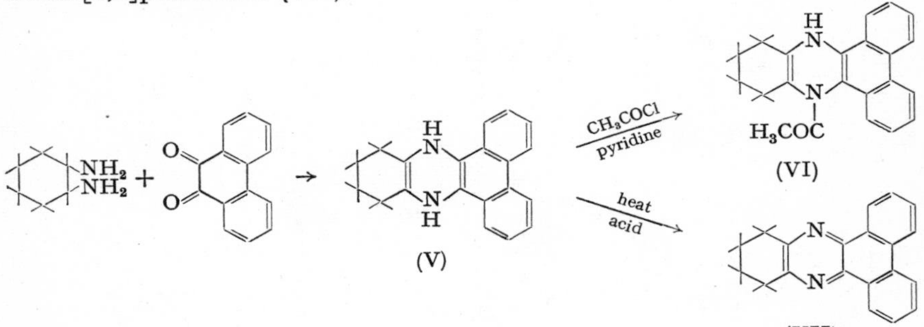

9,14-Dihydro derivatives are dealt with in the following subsection. Very little interest attaches to the hydroxy and amino derivatives of dibenzo[a,c]phenazine. They are all prepared by the condensation of the appropriately substituted components. Commercially, this group of azines has attracted little attention. Certain alkylamino derivatives bearing long aliphatic chains with terminal phosphate acid ester groups have been proposed as water-soluble dyes, suitable as antihalation backings to photographic films.[7]

B. Quaternary Derivatives

The quaternary salts of dibenzo[a,c]phenazine are of somewhat more interest. The parent 9-phenyldibenzo[a,c]phenazinium salts (VIII), known by the trivial name of flavindulines, were first described in a patent (from Badische Anilin-und-Sodafabrik[8]) in which 9,10-phenanthrenequinone in acetic acid solution was condensed with a series of mono-N-substituted o-phenylenediamines, which could be

TABLE XXX. Dibenzo[*a,c*]phenazines

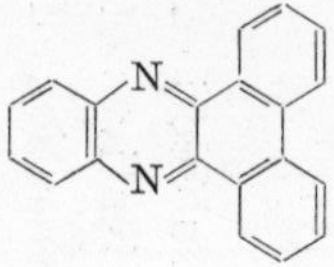

Substituents	Physical characteristics	M.p. (°C.)	Color with H_2SO_4 and other properties	Ref.
None	Yellow needles	219, 223		3, 133–135
9,14-Dihydro-			9-Acetyl deriv., pale yellow leaflets, m.p. 252°	5
1,2,3,4-Tetrahydro-	Yellow needles	190–196		136
10,11,12,13-Tetrahydro-	Pale yellow needles	202–204	Brownish-red coloration	6
9,10,11,12,13,14-Hexahydro-	Orange needles	145.5	Green; monoacetyl deriv., white crystals, m.p. 163–165°	6
9,14-Dihydro-9-phenyl-	Yellowish needles or prisms	231–232	Acetyl deriv., needles, m.p. 196–197°	5, 19
9,14-Dihydro-9,14-diphenyl-	Almost colorless prisms	243	Non-basic	18
9,14-Dihydro-9-benzyl-10-phenyl-	Colorless crystals	185	Non-basic	18
9,9a-Dihydro-9a-methyl-9-phenyl-	Yellow leaflets	176	Red salts	18
9,9a-Dihydro-9a-ethyl-9-phenyl-	Yellow prisms	172	Red salts; hydrochloride, m.p. 196°	18
9,9a-Dihydro-9a-benzyl-9-phenyl-	Yellow crystals	175–179	Red salts	18

Substituents	Physical characteristics	M.p. (°C.)	Color with H_2SO_4 and other properties	Ref.
1,4,4a,4b-Tetrahydro-2,3,4b,7-tetramethyl-	Yellow plates	137–138		137
1-Methyl-		177		138
2-Methyl-	Long pale yellow needles	186–188		138
3-Methyl-	Pale yellow needles	207–208		138
4-Methyl-	Pale yellow needles	177–178(161)		138–140
10-Methyl-	Pale yellow, very fine needles	223		141
11-Methyl-	Bright yellow crystals	212–213		3, 133, 142
1,2-Dimethyl-	Cream prisms	143–144		143
1,3-Dimethyl-	Yellow prisms	154–155		143
1,6-Dimethyl-	Slender cream needles	189		143
1,7-Dimethyl-	Pale buff needles	192–194		144–146
1,8-Dimethyl-	Cream needles	178		143
2,3-Dimethyl-	Slender yellow prisms	208–209		143, 147
2,4-Dimethyl-	Cream needles	155–156		143
2,5-Dimethyl-	Slender yellow prisms	166		143
2,6-Dimethyl-	Pale yellow needles	178–180		143
2,7-Dimethyl-	Cream needles	235		143
3,4-Dimethyl-	Pale yellow needles	203–204		143
3,5-Dimethyl-	Pale yellow needles	173–173.5		148
3,6-Dimethyl-	Cream needles	252		143

(Table continued)

TABLE XXX (*continued*)

Substituents	Physical characteristics	M.p. (°C.)	Color with H_2SO_4 and other properties	Ref.
10,11-Dimethyl-	Yellow needles	223–224	Blood-red coloration	149
10,12-Dimethyl-	Yellowish needles	206–207	Blood-red coloration	149
10,13-Dimethyl-	Yellow needles	285–286	Blood-red coloration	149
11,12-Dimethyl-	Brownish-yellow leaflets	291–292	Blood-red coloration	149
1,2,6-Trimethyl-		182–183		150
1,2,7-Trimethyl-	Cream needles	184–185		151
1,2,8-Trimethyl-	Very pale yellow	131–132		152–154
1,3,7-Trimethyl-	Slender cream needles	201–202		151
1,4,7-Trimethyl-	Cream needles	140–141		144
1,6,7-Trimethyl-	Buff needles	189–190		151
10,11,12-Trimethyl-	Orange plates	311		155
10,11,13-Trimethyl-	Yellow plates	253		155
1-Ethyl-	Slender cream needles	151		143
1-*n*-Propyl-	Pale yellow needles	144–145		143
1-Isopropyl-	Cream needles	142–143		143
2-Isopropyl-	Pale cream needles	172		143
2-Phenyl-	Yellow needles	285–287		156
2-(2'-Quinolyl)-	Yellow needles	274	Brown-red coloration	157
3-*tert.*-Butyl-	Fine pale yellow needles	232	Raspberry-red coloration	158
3-(2'-Quinolyl)-	Silky yellow needles	262	Brown-red color	157
10-Phenyl-	Yellow needles	221		159

Substituents	Physical characteristics	M.p. (°C.)	Color with H_2SO_4 and other properties	Ref.
11-tert.-Butyl-	Bright yellow needles	148.5–149.5		160–162
1-Methyl-2-ethyl-	Cream needles	108		143
1-Methyl-7-isopropyl-	Pale cream needles	163–164		144, 163
1-Methyl-8-isopropyl-	Pale yellow rods	153.5–154		164
1-Ethyl-7-isopropyl-	Very pale yellow needles	165–166		165, 166
2-Methyl-1-ethyl-	Cream needles	146–147		143
2-Methyl-8-ethyl-	Cream needles	154		146, 166
2-Methyl-8-isopropyl-	Fine cream needles	119–120		167
10-Methyl-12-tert.-butyl-	Yellow crystals	153	Red color	168
10-Methyl-12-o-tolyl-	Light brown needles	192–193	Brilliant purple color	169
10-Methyl-13-isopropyl-	Light yellow needles	181.2–181.4	Purplish-red color	170
1-Methyl-4-ethyl-7-isopropyl-	Bright yellow crystals	141–143		171
1-Methyl-7-isopropyl-β-ethyl(?)-	Yellow needles	133–134		172
10,12,13-Trimethyl-11-ethyl-		242		173
10,11,12,13-Tetraethyl-	Fine yellow needles	169–170		174
2-Hydroxy-	Brown crystals	258–259		175
3-Hydroxy-	Yellow crystals	> 340	O-Acetyl deriv., yellow needles, m.p. 223–225°; O-benzoyl deriv., leaflets, m.p. 234–236°	176

(Table continued)

TABLE XXX (continued)

Substituents	Physical characteristics	M.p. (°C.)	Color with H_2SO_4 and other properties	Ref.
4-Hydroxy-	Dark red crystals	233		177
11-Hydroxy-	Fine yellow needles	> 300	Reddish-violet color	178
11-Ethoxy-	Yellowish crystals	210	Bluish-violet color	178
1,4-Dihydroxy-	Long brown-red silky needles	288	Intense reddish-violet color	179
2,3-Dihydroxy-	Orange-yellow needles	162 (dec.)		180
10-Hydroxy-11-methoxy-	Golden-yellow needles	224	Rose-red color	181
10,11-Dimethoxy-	Yellow needles	175		181–183
10,13-Diethoxy-	Greenish-yellow needles	260		184
11-Hydroxy-12-methoxy-	Yellow crystals	239–240	Magenta color	181
11,12-Dimethoxy-	Red crystals	259–261	Violet color	185, 186
11-Methoxy-12-ethoxy-	Yellow crystals	231	Magenta color	187
11,12-Diethoxy-	Reddish needles	230	Magenta color	188
11,12-Dibutoxy-	Yellow feathery needles	190		189
2,3,4-Trihydroxy-	Dark brown crystals	255–258		175
3,4,6-Trimethoxy-	Yellow prisms	165	Deep blue color	190
10,11,12-Trimethoxy-	Pale yellow needles	180	Intense reddish-purple color	183
10,11,13-Trimethoxy-	Bright yellow needles	186	Magenta color	183
2,3,4,5-Tetramethoxy-	Orange prisms	143		191

Substituents	Physical characteristics	M.p. (°C)	Color with H_2SO_4 and other properties	Ref.
2,3,4,6-Tetramethoxy-	Pale lemon-yellow crystals	180–181		191
2,3,4,7-Tetramethoxy-	Lemon-yellow needles	176–177	Second form; orange needles, m.p. 185–186°	191
2,3,6,7-Tetramethoxy-	Golden-yellow fluffy needles	270–271		192
2-Amino-	Yellow prismatic needles	240	Dyes wool yellow from acid bath	175, 193
4-Amino-	Dull yellow needles	190, > 285	Hydrochloride, m.p. 274–275°	177, 193
11-Amino-	Yellow needles	279	Carmine-red coloration	194, 195
2,7-Diamino-	Brilliant yellow needles		Dyes wool light yellow shades	193
4,5-Diamino-			Dyes wool light yellow shades	193
11,12-Diamino-	Orange-yellow needles		Greenish-blue color becoming violet, then red on dilution	196
2,7,11-Triamino-	Yellow-brown prismatic needles	> 280	Dyes wool strong yellow shades	193
10-Acetyl-	Yellow needles	226–227		197, 198
10-Propionyl-	Long almost colorless needles	181–182		199
11-Acetyl-	Brownish leaflets	278		200
11-Carboxy-	Yellow crystals	320		201
11-Carboxy-12-hydroxy-	Yellow crystals	322	Red-violet color with $FeCl_3$	201
11-Carbomethoxy-12-methoxy-	Golden-yellow needles	283–284		201

further substituted by other amino groups to yield fast yellow to red dyes on cotton, mordanted with tannin. Hinsberg and Garfunkel[5] obtained the parent acetate from 9,10-phenanthrenequinone and 2-aminodiphenylamine hydrochloride in acetic acid, and from it prepared other salts. 9-Alkyl and 9-phenyl compounds have also been described by Yamada and coworkers.[9-13]

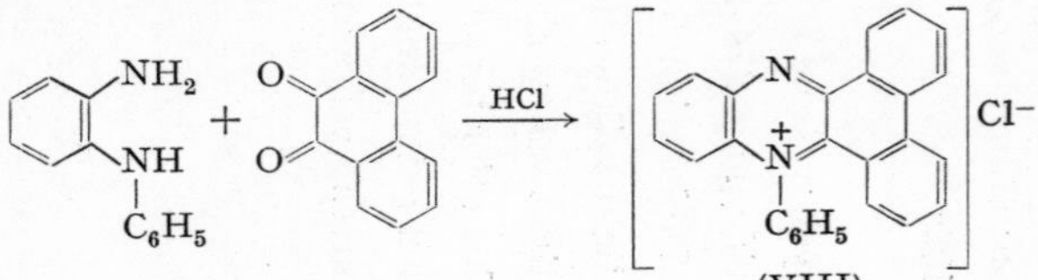

(VIII)

Hantzsch and Osswald[14] studied conductometrically the effect of one equivalent of alkali on the chloride and showed that a rearrangement of the quaternary hydroxide occurred instantaneously on formation to give a non-conducting carbinol- or pseudo-base, in contrast to the behavior of other quaternary azine systems. The position taken up in the molecule by the hydroxyl group has never been rigidly determined, but Hantzsch[15,16] suggested position 11, and wrote the pseudo base as IX or X, picturing the rearrangement as proceeding as follows:

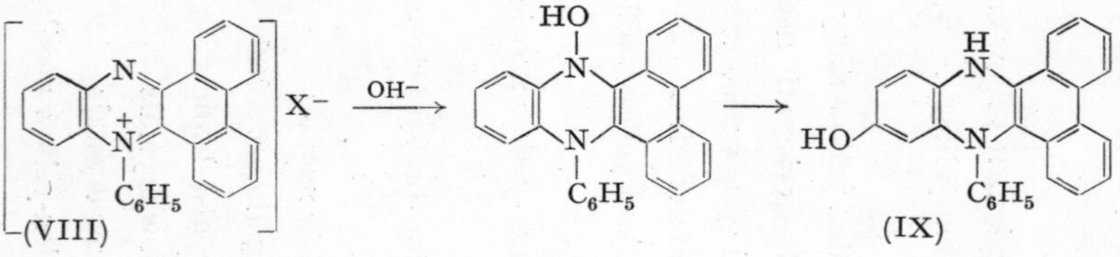

(VIII)　　　　　　　　　　　　　　　　　　　　　(IX)

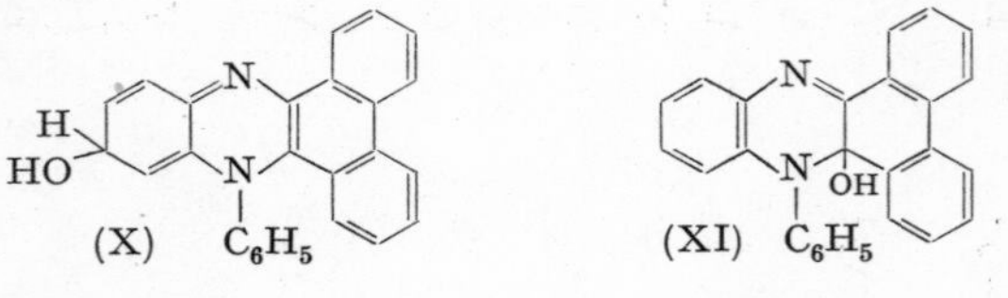

(X)　C₆H₅　　　　　　　　　　　(XI)　C₆H₅

Kehrmann[17] and Freund and Richard,[18] on the other hand, preferred to write the pseudo-base as XI. The pseudo-base readily regenerated flavinduline salts with acids, a reaction difficult to understand on the basis of Hantzsch's formulations. The alternative (XI) has the support of analogy with the pyridinium series.

Reduction of the chloride with stannous chloride in hydrochloric acid solution yields 9-phenyl-9,10-dihydrodibenzo[*a,c*]phenazine (XII), as slightly yellowish prisms, m.p. 231–232°, which readily gives an acetyl derivative (XIII), m.p. 196–197°.[5,19] This work finally disproved

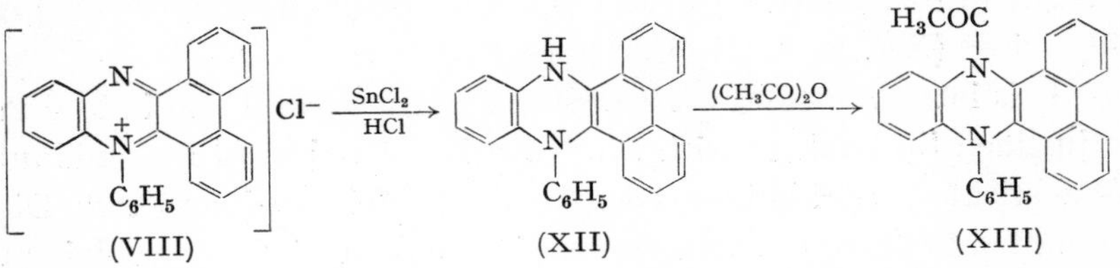
H_3COC
H
N
N
Cl⁻
$SnCl_2$
HCl
$(CH_3CO)_2O$
C_6H_5
(VIII)
(XII)
(XIII)

the theory Hinsberg[20] had held that dihydrophenazine and its benzo-analogs were tautomeric substances.

Freund and Richard[18] found that Grignard reagents reacted in a somewhat peculiar fashion with the quaternary salts (VIII). Methylmagnesium iodide reacted with VIII to form a yellow substance, m.p. 176°, which gave red salts with acids, hydrolyzed by water. The reaction with ethylmagnesium bromide was similar and gave the ethyl analog, m.p. 196°, which, too, was yellow and gave red, hydrolyzable salts. On the other hand, benzylmagnesium bromide gave a mixture of two isomers, separated by their solubilities in nitrobenzene. One was a yellow compound, m.p. 175–179°, giving red salts, while the other was colorless, m.p. 185°, and did not form salts. Prolonged heating of the yellow compound, in the case of the benzyl series, led to an isomerization to the colorless, non-basic compound. With phenylmagnesium

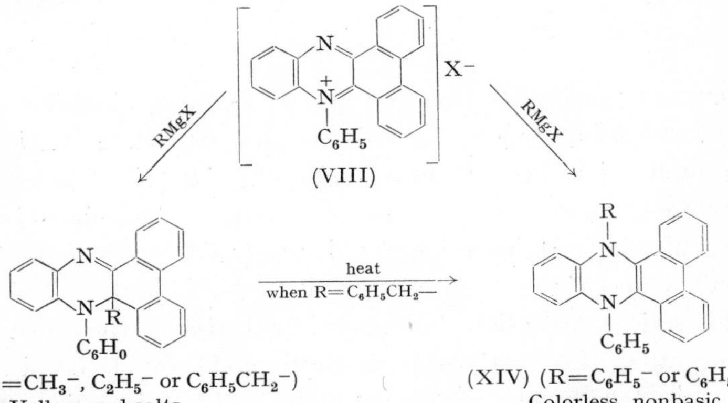
X⁻
(VIII)
RMgX
RMgX
R
heat
when $R{=}C_6H_5CH_2$—
C_6H_5

(XV) ($R{=}CH_3^-$, $C_2H_5^-$ or $C_6H_5CH_2^-$)
Yellow, red salts

(XIV) ($R{=}C_6H_5^-$ or $C_6H_5CH_2^-$)
Colorless, nonbasic

bromide only a colorless, non-basic compound, m.p. 243°, was obtained.

Freund and Richard interpreted the colorless series as 9-phenyl-14-aryl(or aralkyl)-9,14-dihydrodibenzo[a,c]phenazines (XIV, R = C₆H₅ or C₆H₅CH₂), while the yellow compounds, giving red salts, were thought to be 8a-alkyl(or aralkyl)-9-phenyl-8a,9-dihydrodibenzo[a,c]-phenazines (XV, R = CH₃, C₂H₅ or C₆H₅CH₂).

This interpretation was accepted by Hillemann[21] and indeed may be justified by analogy with the behavior of Grignard reagents upon N-substituted pyridinium compounds.[22] Meisenheimer and Ditt[23] attempted to prove the correctness of the assumptions by resolving the colorless compound in the closely similar 9-phenyltribenzo[a,c,h]-phenazinium series (see Chapter XVI:15,B), and introduced a basic center, but even so were unable to obtain crystalline bromocamphor-sulfonates.

9-Phenyldibenzo[a,c]phenazinium salts have not been studied as exhaustively as have the simple phenazinium and benzo[a]phenazinium series, but sufficient evidence has been obtained to show that they behave similarly towards amines. Kehrmann and Walty in a patent[24] showed that flavinduline chloride (VIII) reacted with piperidine in the presence of air to yield the 11-piperidino compound (XVI), which dyes silk, wool and mordanted cotton in sea-blue shades. The reaction did

(VIII)   (XVI)

not occur very easily however and, when 12-nitroflavinduline chloride (XVII) was employed,[25, 26] no reaction at all occurred. Reduction of the nitro group to yield 12-aminoflavinduline chloride (XVIII) restored the ability to react with amines to give, for example, 12-amino-11-anilino-9-phenyldibenzo[a,c]phenazinium chloride (XIX) when made to react with aniline and air.

This series of reactions is a good illustration of the effect of substitutents upon the fixation of the o-quinonoid double bonds. In the unsubstituted compounds, the 9,10-phenanthroquinonoid system is

stabilized relative to the alternative 1,2-benzoquinonoid arrangement
by about 330 mv. Substitution of a cationoid group, such as nitro, in

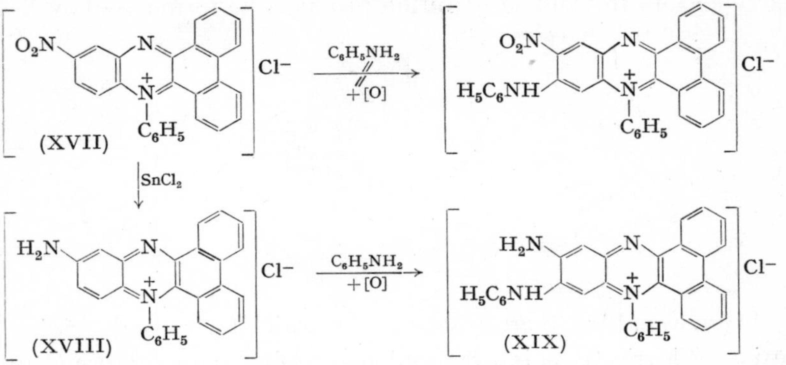

the benzenoid portion will decrease the stabilization of the 1,2-benzo-
quinonoid arrangement necessary for reaction still further. (There are
no suitable positions vacant for reaction in the phenanthrene moiety.)
When, however, an anionoid group such as amino is in the benzenoid
part of the molecule, this will stabilize the o-benzoquinonoid system
sufficiently to facilitate the oxidative addition of amines.

In the case of 12-amino-9-phenyldibenzo[a,c]phenazinium chloride
(XVIII), Kehrmann[26] showed the anilino group entered at position 11
by converting the product (XIX) into a fluorindine (9-phenyl-9,16-
dihydrodibenzo[a,c]quinoxalo[2,3-i]phenazine, XX, R. I. 3753) by
treatment with o-phenylenediamine in boiling benzoic acid.

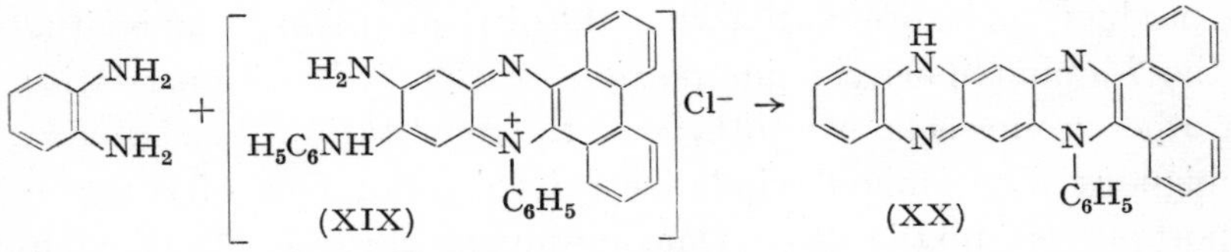

Much later, the correctness of this assumption was shown by the
synthesis of XIX from 9,10-phenanthrenequinone and 5-amino-2,4-
dianilinoaniline.[27]

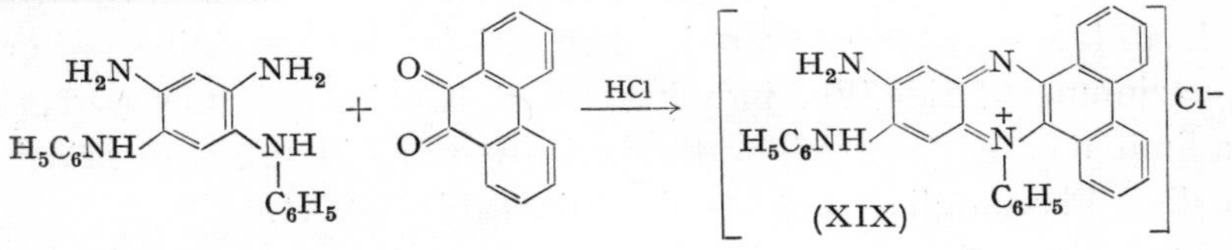

Sachs[28, 29] showed that flavinduline salts reacted with compounds containing reactive methylene groups, such as ethyl acetoacetate or desoxybenzoin to yield substitution products he formulated as **XXI**.

$$\left[\text{structure} \right] Cl^- \xrightarrow{\text{RCOCH}_2R'} \text{(XXI)}$$

(XXI)

These were blue to green substances, which formed salts giving red solutions. Clearly there is a resemblance here to the structure (**X**) that Hantzsch gave to the pseudo-base of flavinduline. The subject has not been reinvestigated since, and the structures should only be regarded as tentative.

9-Phenyldibenzo[*a,c*]phenazinium nitrate was nitrated by Kehrmann and Eichler,[30] when a nitro derivative was isolated which on reduction yielded the corresponding amino compound. The mother liquors from the crystallization of the nitro compound on reduction furnished a second amino compound. Neither product was orientated. Other nitro- and amino-flavinduline salts have been prepared by the usual condensation reactions,[26, 27, 31, 32] or by reaction between an 11-chloroflavinduline salt and an amine.[33] In condensation reactions the product can be orientated when the nitro or amino group is situated in the 2-aminodiphenylamine portion, so that its position relative to the other groups is known; otherwise the constitution of the product is ambiguous. The aminoflavinduline salts are not now of commercial importance as textile dyes. One, however, which is produced from 2-amino-9,10-phenanthrenequinone and 2-aminodiphenylamine, and to which is given the formula 2-amino-9-phenyldibenzo[*a,c*]phenazinium chloride, has been patented[34] under the name of Pinakryptol Green (*C. I.* 824a) as a photographic desensitizer. 9-Phenyldibenzo[*a,c*]-phenazinium chloride (Flavinduline O, *C. I.* 824) itself, is now used only to a limited extent as a yellow dye for leather and in discharge printing of calico. Flavinduline salts are listed in Table **XXXI**.

TABLE XXXI. 9-Phenyldibenzo[*a,c*]phenazinium Salts

Substituents	Appearance of chloride (unless otherwise stated)	Color with H₂SO₄, followed by dilution	Ref.
None	Yellow-brown prisms	Red	See text
4-Nitro(?)-	Yellow prisms	Blood-red	31, 32
7-Nitro(?)-	NO₃⁻, straw-yellow prisms	Dirty-red	30
12-Nitro-	Red-brown needles	Magenta	26
2,7-Dinitro-	Yellow prisms	Brownish-red	31, 32
11-Chloro-	Reddish-yellow crystals	Violet, red, orange-yellow	33, 202
4-Amino(?)-	Br⁻, dark green needles	Dirty-purple, lemon-yellow, olive-brown	31, 32
7-Amino(?)-(? 2-Amino)-	Dark green prisms	Cherry-red, lemon-yellow, yellowish-green	30
11-Anilino-	Dark violet needles, coppery luster	Green, blue	24, 33
11-Piperidino-	Dark blue needles, coppery luster	Magenta, orange-yellow, green, dark blue	24, 30
11-(3′-Carboxy-4′-hydroxy)anilino-	Violet, lustrous needles	Violet-red, green	33
12-Amino-	Violet-black needles	Magenta, orange-yellow, violet	26

(Table continued)

TABLE XXXI (*continued*)

Substituents	Appearance of chloride (unless otherwise stated)	Color with H_2SO_4 followed by dilution	Ref.
12-Acetamido-	Brownish-red needles, green luster	Bluish-violet, orange	26
11-Anilino-4,5-dibromo-	Dull green crystals	Blue	203
11-Anilino-2-nitro(?)-	Rectangular prisms	Dark green	203
11-Anilino-2,7-dinitro-		Green	203
2,7-Diamino-	Br⁻, blackish-green prisms, steely luster	Brownish blood-red, golden-yellow	31, 32
11,12-Diamino-	Red crystals	Blue, violet, magenta	26
12-Amino-11-anilino-	Brassy-lustered leaflets; anhydro-base, m.p. 290°	Dirty-green, blue, bluish-violet, red-violet	26, 27
12-Amino-11-methylamino-	Dark violet needles, metallic green luster	Cornflower-blue, violet, red	26
12-Amino-11-dimethylamino-	Needles, green luster	Red-violet, greenish-blue, ultra-marine-blue, violet-red	26
2,7-Diamino-11-anilino-	Bluish-black	Bluish-green	203
4,5,11-Trianilino-			203

3. Dibenzo[a, h]phenazine (XXII)

(XXII)

R. I. 3254

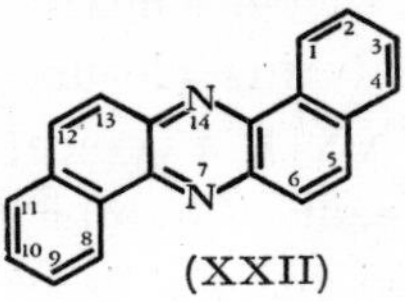

A. Methods of Preparation

The parent compound of this series (XXII) was prepared by Doer[35] in very poor yield by the zinc dust distillation of 1-nitronaphthalene. Schichuzky[36] modified this by heating 1-aminonaphthalene with litharge. Klobukowski[37] in 1877 reexamined the substance and showed that it was identical with the compound "Naphthase" prepared by Laurent[38] in 1835 by heating 1-nitronaphthalene with quicklime. Klobukowski considered the product to be 1,1'-azonaphthalene, a view with which Doer[39] hastened to concur. This was disproved by the synthesis of the azonaphthalene by Nietzki and Goll,[40] and it was O. N. Witt[41] who gave the substance its correct formula. He prepared it by the condensation of 1,2-naphthoquinone and 1,2-diaminonaphthalene in cold acetic acid solution. This reaction can also give dibenzo-[a,j]phenazine (XXIII), but it was left to Fischer and Strauss[42] to isolate this from the mother liquors of the reaction mixture.

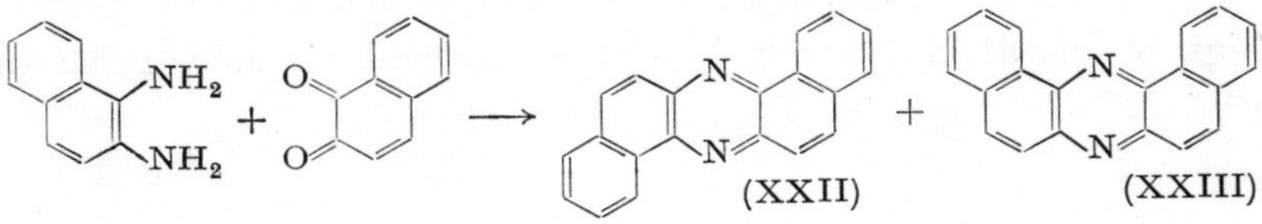

(XXII)   (XXIII)

The structure of dibenzo[a,h]phenazine follows from this evidence together with the preparation by heating 1-chloro-2-naphthylamine with quicklime, a process discovered by Cleve.[43]

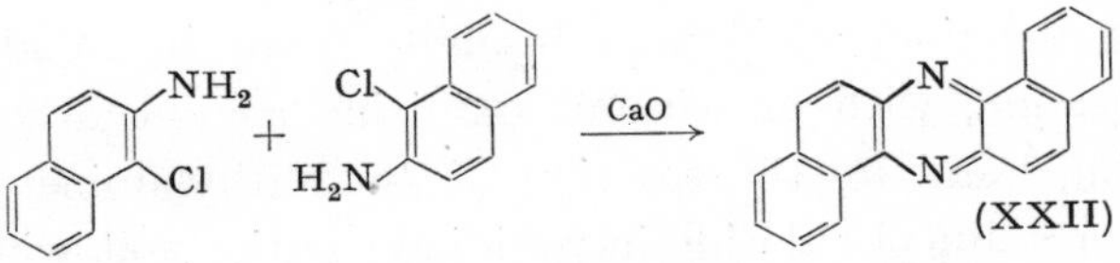

(XXII)

Many different methods of preparation have been discovered since the early days. Matthes[44] coupled benzenediazonium chloride with

2,1'-dinaphthylamine and separated the two azoamino compounds produced. One of these, 1-benzeneazo-2-(1'-naphthylamino)-naphthalene (XXIV), underwent ring closure on heating with alcoholic hydrochloric acid to yield XXII, a typical example of Witt's method of preparing benzo[a]phenazine (Chapter XII:3,B(5)). This work was repeated much later by Levi and Faldino[45] and completely confirmed.

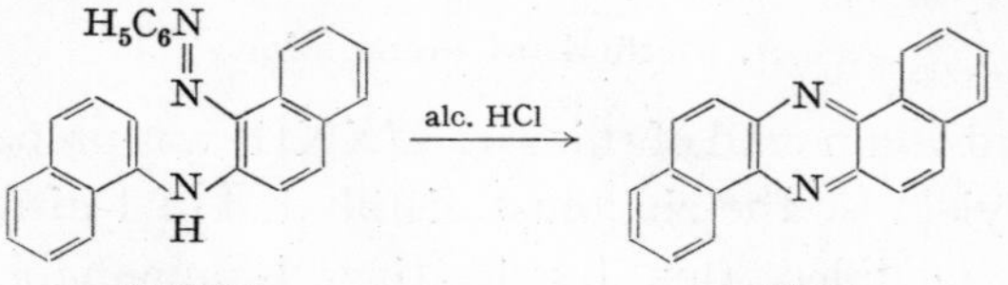

(XXIV)   (XXII)

A supposedly general method of azine formation patented by Claus and Jaeck,[46] consisting in the oxidation of primary aromatic amines by means of bleaching powder, was shown by Meigen and Normann[47] to give azo compounds as a general rule. However, in the case of 2-naphthylamine, the product of the action of sodium hypochlorite was dibenzo[a,h]phenazine (XXII), and with 2-naphthylamine-6-sulfonic acid, the corresponding 3,10-disulfonic acid (XXIIa). The latter compound was also obtained by Reitzenstein and Fitzgerald,[48] by the oxidation of 2-naphthylamine-6-sulfonic acid by potassium ferricyanide. It gives a very poor yield of the parent azine (XXII) on zinc dust distillation; fission of the sulfonyl groups does not occur even on high temperature hydrolysis with dilute sulfuric acid under pressure.[47]

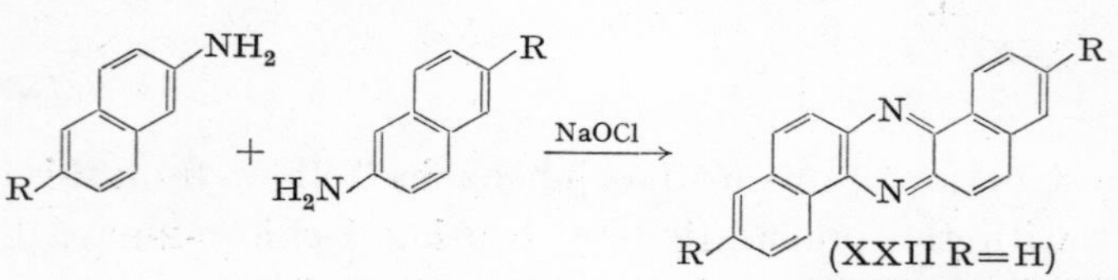

(XXII R=H)
(XXIIa R=SO$_3$H)

Similar reactions have been brought about by alkali fusion of 2-naphthylamine, with or without oxidizing agents, according to a patent claim,[49] and by the reaction of 2-naphthylamine with sulfur dichloride or sulfuryl chloride in pyridine solution following Reitzenstein and Andre.[50] These workers also obtained XXII from 2-naphthylamine by oxidation with magnesium peroxide, or a mixture of magnesium and barium peroxides, from 1-naphthylamine by heating with a mixture of calcium and barium peroxides or from 2-acetamidonaphthalene by heating it with calcium oxide. Pausacker[51] has described the formation of XXII in 28% yield by the oxidation of 2-naphthylamine with phenyl iodosoacetate and Boyland, Manson and Sims[52] have obtained XXII similarly using persulfate. Other patents describe the preparation of dibenzo[a,h]phenazines substituted by hydroxyl groups by the oxidation of hydroxy-2-naphthylamines using hypochlorites, the hydroxyl groups being suitably protected, for example, by toluene-sulfonyl residues.[53] Still other patents[54,55] describe the oxidation of 2-naphthylamines with free 1-positions and bearing other substituents, or of hydroxy-2-naphthylamines, the hydroxyl group being protected,[56] by means of a metallic oxide such as cupric oxide or manganese dioxide in an inert, high-boiling organic solvent or in aqueous solution at temperatures ranging from 100–250°.

A recent method, reminiscent of the earliest preparations, is that discovered by chance by Clemo and Dawson.[57] They were attempting the preparation of acrid[2,1,9,8-kl,mn,a]acridine (XXV, R. I. 3616) by the oxidation of 2-naphthylamine by lead oxide. Instead of the acrid-acridine, however, they isolated dibenzo[a,h]phenazine, and a small yield (2%) of a product, $C_{20}H_{14}N_2$, tentatively identified at the time as the 7,14-dihydro derivative (see below).

(XXV)   (XXII)

The dibenzophenazine (XXII) has been found[58] in commercial 2-naphthylamine and also in the so-called "pure" 2-naphthylamine used by Bonser[59] in animal experiments purporting to show that 2-naphthylamine is carcinogenic. It has also been identified as one of the many products obtained after incubation, in human urine or phosphate buffer at physiological pH, of either 1-amino-2-naphthol or 2-amino-1-naphthol.[60] This, in view of the known carcinogenic properties of XXII, has relevance in connection with the cancer-producing properties of 2-naphthylamine.

Steopoe[61] found that the dibenzophenazine (XXII) was the product of the oxidation of 1-naphthylamine using a precipitated copper oxide, with the best yield at 220–225°. At lower temperatures indulinic derivatives were formed. A similar union of two molecules has been proposed by Malaviya and Dutt[62] to explain the products obtained by exposure of 1- and 2-naphthylamines in aqueous acid solution to tropical sunlight for prolonged periods. The product from 2-naphthyl-amine was said to be dibenzo[b,i]phenazine (XXVI), while that from 1-naphthylamine was identified as XXII, although no melting point was given. This work is very unsatisfactory from other aspects (Chapter I:(9)) and the above conclusions should be treated with the greatest reserve.

(XXVI)

(XXII)

XXII is also perhaps the product, yellow needles, m.p. 278°, obtained by Pishchimuka[63] by the action of sulfur or selenium on 2-naphthylamine in the presence of organomercuric derivatives as catalysts, although according to *Chemical Abstracts*, the product is dibenzo[b,i]phenazine (XXVI). (*Chemisches Zentralblatt* does not specify the product.) Another undoubted double union reaction is that which Hauff[64] brought about by the action of dilute hydrochloric acid at 140° under pressure upon 2-naphthylsemicarbazide.

Meisenheimer and Witte[65] found that treatment of 2-nitronaphtha-lene with warm methanolic potassium hydroxide produced, among other products, one they thought to be the di-N-oxide (XXVII), since reduction of this by stannous chloride, or by means of distillation from iron powder, produced XXII. The analytical values for the dioxide are not good however and they considered their product to be a mixture of XXII and XXVII.

1,2-Naphthoquinone gives a small yield of the dibenzophenazine

(XXII) when fused with ammonium acetate according to Japp and Burton.[66] This reaction is a typically "abnormal" Leuckart reaction[67]

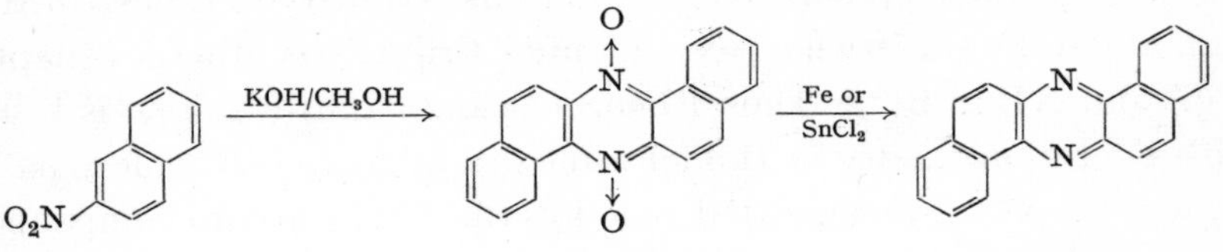

(XXVII)   (XXII)

of o-quinones. Less easily explained is the formation of XXII by the passage of dry ammonia gas into molten 2,2′-dihydroxy-1,1′-dinaphthyl, observed by Rieche, Rudolph and Seifert[68]; this is a method of limited utility however.

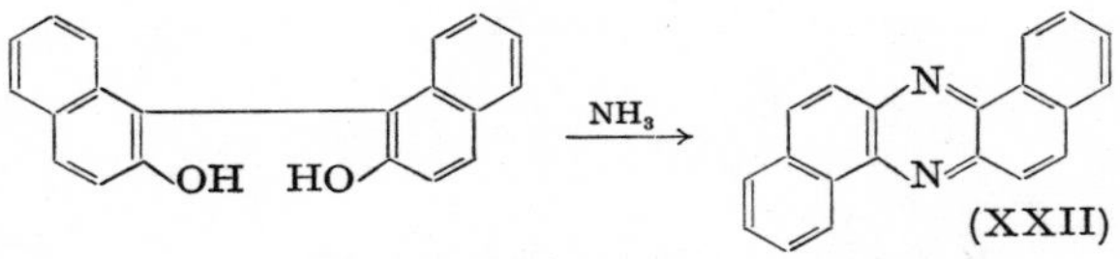

(XXII)

Lesser[69] observed the formation of 5,12-dimethyldibenzo[a,h]-phenazine (XXVIII) as a by-product in the course of the reduction of 2 benzeneazo-4-methyl-1-naphthylamine-4′-sulfonic acid. This is probably the result of dimerization of an intermediate fission product.

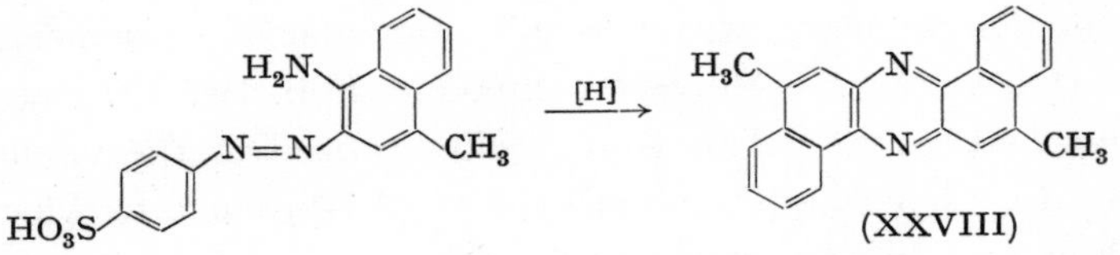

(XXVIII)

Fischer and Hepp[70] found that, when 1-nitroso-2-naphthylamine is heated with 1-naphthylamine and 1-naphthylamine hydrochloride at 100–110°, the dibenzophenazine (XXII) is the product. As will be seen later (Section XV:4,C), these workers[71] also found that, in the presence of aniline as well, the reaction took a different course to yield derivatives of dibenzo[a,j]phenazine (XXIII). The formation of XXII was aided by working at lower temperatures, preferably in boiling ethanolic solution, as described by Fischer and Junk,[72] when no trace of quaternary indulinic substances could be detected. Fischer and Albert[73] claimed that, at still lower temperatures, a red eurhodine of XXIII was formed. Clearly the reaction is very complex.

An excellent preparative method has recently been described by Maffei and Pietra,[74] who have adapted Crippa's synthesis (Chapters I:(6) and XII:3,B(9)). Thus 1-benzeneazo-2-naphthylamine is heated with 1-tetralone in dry methanol while dry hydrogen chloride is passed in, when XXII is precipitated. The intermediate dihydro compound is oxidized during the course of the reaction by a second molecule of the azo derivative. By using substituted 2-naphthylamines, the method can be extended to derivatives of XXII.

B. Properties, Reactions and Derivatives

Dibenzo[a,h]phenazine (XXII) forms yellow needles, m.p. 283–284°,[42, 44] though later values are two degrees lower. Wavelengths of absorption maxima for solutions in concentrated sulfuric acid have been recorded by Reitzenstein and Andre,[50] who used an outmoded technique. On reduction with zinc in boiling glacial acetic acid, XXII is converted to the 7,14-dihydro compound, m.p. 196–197°, according to Maffei and Pietra.[74] This is very close indeed to the value (195°) observed by Clemo and Dawson[57] for the by-product to which they attributed the dihydro structure, which now receives confirmation. Reduction with stannous chloride in hydrochloric acid gives a compound crystallizing in steel-blue needles, which is probably a semiquinonoid salt[65] (compare benzo[a]phenazine).

Oxidation of dibenzo[a,h]phenazine by means of chromic acid was studied by Fischer and Schindler,[75] and follows the course to be expected from a knowledge of the analogous benzo[a]phenazine (Chapter XII:3,D and F). Thus the initial product is dibenzo[a,h]-phenazine-5,6-quinone (XXIX), dark brownish-red needles, which reacts with o-phenylenediamine to give dibenzo[a,h]quinoxalo[2,3-c]-

phenazine (XXX, *R. I.* 3757), yellow needles, m.p. 284° (see Chapter XVIII:17).

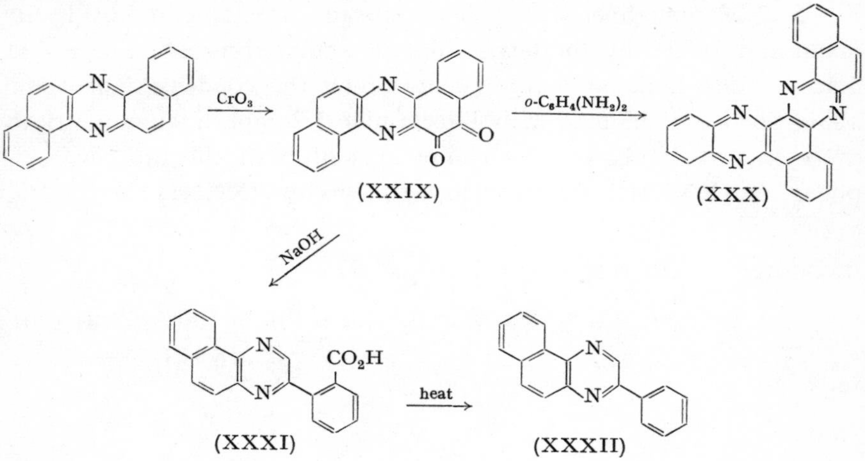

(XXIX)   (XXX)

(XXXI)   (XXXII)

On boiling **XXIX** with concentrated sodium hydroxide solution, the quinone ring is opened to give 3-2'-carboxyphenylbenzo[*f*]quinoxaline (**XXXI**), colorless needles m.p. 246°, with concomitant loss of carbon dioxide. This in turn is decarboxylated on distillation to give 3-phenylbenzo[*f*]quinoxaline (**XXXII**, *R. I.* 1907), yellowish-white needles, m.p. 163°, giving a blood-red coloration with concentrated sulfuric acid. Treatment of the quinone with phenylhydrazine leads to reduction to a blue product, readily reoxidized. This is undoubtedly the 5,6-dihydroxy compound.

The substitution reactions of dibenzo[*a,h*]phenazine have not been extensively studied. Bromination at 260°, or in the presence of a little iodine as catalyst, gives a pentabromo compound of unknown constitution, forming yellow needles,[37] m.p. > 320°. Nitration by means of a mixture of nitric and sulfuric acids yields a dinitro compound,[50, 61, 76] yellow needles, m.p. 330–332°, and Steopoe[61] isolated a mononitro derivative, m.p. 304–308°, as well; neither of these compounds has been orientated.

Reduction of the dinitro compound by sodium sulfide yielded a diamine, the amino groups of which were not converted to hydroxyl groups by heating under pressure with hydrochloric acid and hence did not occupy the 5- or 12-positions. They could be diazotized and coupled to give azo dyes for cotton fibers.[50,76]

5,12-Diaminodibenzo[*a,h*]phenazine was later prepared by Kehrmann and Safar[77] by the ferric chloride-catalyzed aerial oxidation of 4-acetamido-1,2-diaminonaphthalene, or by the condensation of the above acetamidodiamine with 4-acetamido-1,2-naphthoquinone. Both processes can, and do, give compounds of both the dibenzo[*a,h*]-phenazine (XXXIII) and dibenzo[*a,j*]phenazine (XXXIV) series.

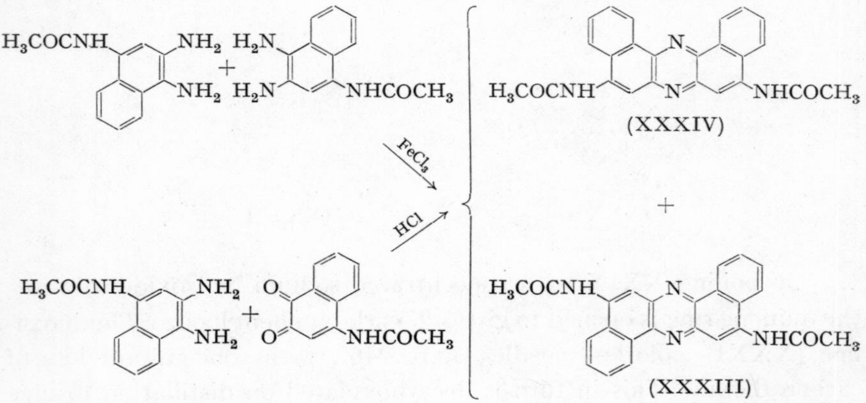

(XXXIV)

(XXXIII)

The products from the reactions could not be separated as such, but, after deacetylation by heating with 60% sulfuric acid, the resultant diamines could be fractionally crystallized from ethanol. The bulk was insoluble and was provisionally given structure (XXXIV), while the more soluble, much smaller, fraction was thought to be XXXIII. The same workers[77] also condensed 4-acetamido-1,2-diaminonaphthalene

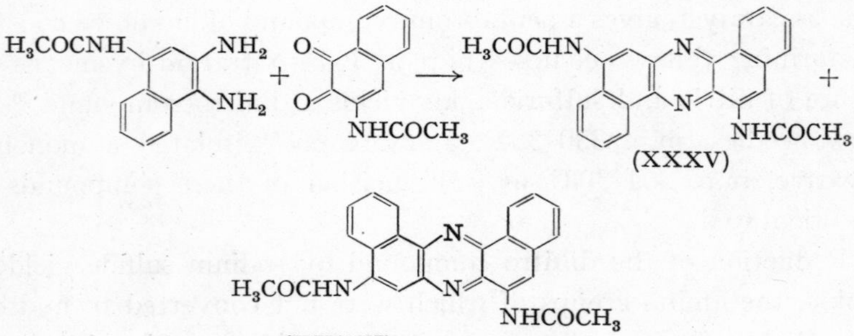

(XXXV)

(XXXVI)

TABLE XXXII. Dibenzo[a,h]phenazines

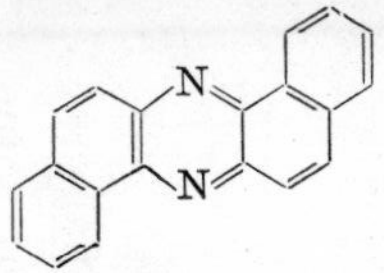

Substituents	Physical characteristics	M.p. (°C.)	Color with H$_2$SO$_4$, followed by dilution	Ref.
None	Yellow needles	283–284	Bluish-violet	See XV:3
7,14-Dihydro-	Pale yellow needles	195–197		57, 74
5,12-Dimethyl-	Golden-yellow needles	305–306	Blue, red	69
4-Nitro-	Needles	298		74
x-Nitro-		304–308		61
x,x'-Dinitro-	Yellow needles	330–332	Carmine-red	50, 61, 76
x,x'-Diamino-	Red crystals	> 300	Reddish-brown	50, 76
5,12-Diamino(?)-	Brown crystals			77, 78
6,12-Diamino(?)-	Orange needles		Dark blue, orange	77, 78
6,12-Diacetamido(?)-	Lemon-yellow crystals		Dark blue, magenta	77, 78
x,x',x'',x''',x''''-Pentabromo-	Yellow needles	> 320	Red	37
3,10-Disulfonic acid	Na salt, greenish-yellow crystals		Violet	47, 48
5,6-Quinone	Brownish-red needles	240 (dec.)	Brownish-red	75
5,6-Quinone monoxime	Yellow needles		Purplish-red	75
5,6-Dihydroxy-	Blue crystals		Easily oxidized	75
3,10-Dihydroxy-	Yellow crystals		Blue	83
5,12-Dihydroxy-	Yellow crystals		Blue	83
1,8-Dihydroxy(?)-	Orange-yellow needles	> 300	Blue	83
6,13-Dihydroxy-	Brassy-yellow crystals	375–380 (dec.)	Di-O-acetyl deriv., m.p. 322°	56
6,13-Dihydroxy-2,9-dimethoxy-	Yellowish-brown prisms	> 380		56
6,13-Dihydroxy-2,9-dibromo-	Yellow crystals	> 385		56
6,13-Dimethoxy-2,9-dibromo-	Yellow crystals	382–385		56
6,13-Dimethoxy-	Yellow lustrous leaflets	324–326		56

with 3-acetamido-1,2-naphthoquinone. Again two isomers were
produced and were separated by their solubilities in ethanol. The major
product was again the less soluble and was provisionally given the
dibenzo[a,j]phenazine structure (XXXVI), while the more soluble
substance was described as 6,12-diacetamidodibenzo[a,h]phenazine
(XXXV). Deacetylation was achieved after separation in this case.

With 2-hydroxy-1,4-naphthoquinone and 4-acetamido-1,2-di-
aminonaphthalene, again the two possible isomers (XXXVII and
XXXVIII) are produced, and after hydrolysis of the protecting acetyl
groups are separated by the difference in solubility of their hydrochlorides.[77]

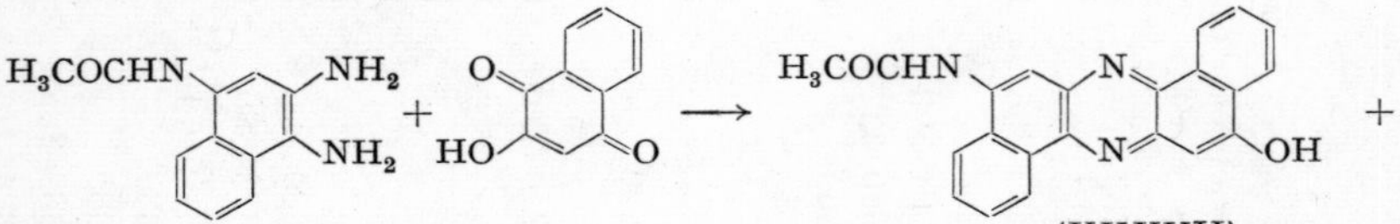

(XXXVII)

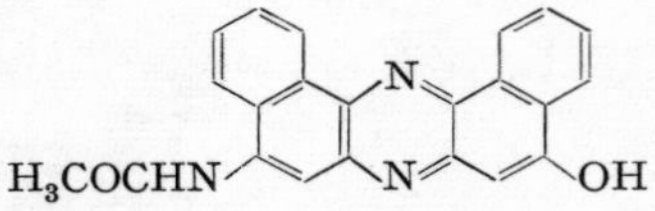

(XXXVIII)

This seems to be the point at which to call attention to a flagrant
case of plagiarism by S. Mihaéloff,[78] whose paper, published some
thirteen years after that by Kehrmann and Safar,[77] is almost word-for-
word identical to that of the latter workers; at no point is acknowl-
edgement made to the earlier paper.

Derivatives of this system are listed in Table XXXII.

C. Quaternary Salts

On treatment with methyl iodide in methanol at 160° under
pressure, dibenzo[a,h]phenazine is methylated upon one of the nitrogen

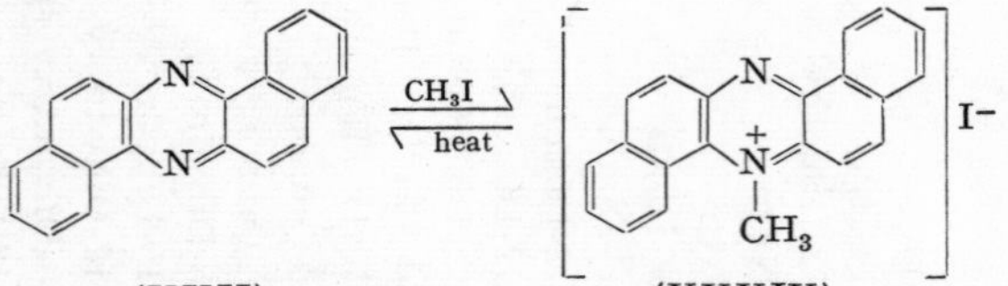

(XXII)   (XXXIX)

atoms.[72] The quaternary iodide (XXXIX) forms brown needles with a greenish luster, which give a cornflower-blue coloration in concentrated sulfuric acid solution and decompose on heating. The action of alkalis or amines upon XXXIX has not been studied.

Other quaternary derivatives of dibenzo[*a,h*]phenazine have been prepared by the usual condensation methods. Kehrmann and Sutherst[79] prepared 12-acetamido-7-phenyldibenzo[*a,h*]phenazinium chloride (XL) by condensing 4-acetamido-1,2-naphthoquinone with 2-anilino-1-naphthylamine in acetic acid solution.

(XL) (XLI)

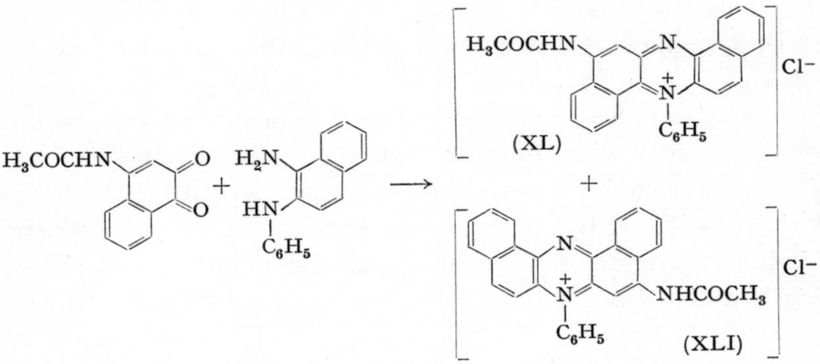

As is to be expected, XL was accompanied by 5-acetamido-7-phenyldibenzo[*a,j*]phenazinium chloride (XLI), which was the less soluble isomer and crystallized from the reaction mixture. XL on

(XLII) (XLIV) (XLIII) (XLV)

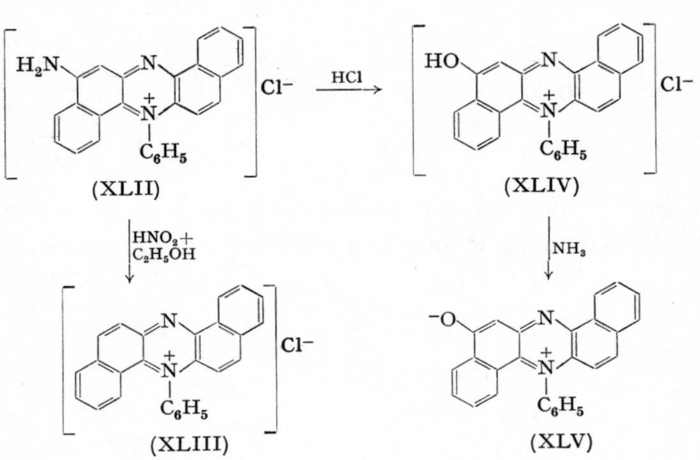

deacetylation gave the 12-amino derivative (XLII), which formed
green needles and was deaminated by diazotization and heating with
ethanol. The parent 7-phenyldibenzo[a,h]phenazinium chloride (XLIII)
so obtained was not further investigated. Heating the amino compound
(XLII) with dilute mineral acid led to hydrolysis of the amino group
and replacement by hydroxyl. 12-Hydroxy-7-phenyldibenzo[a,h]-
phenazinium chloride (XLIV), which formed chocolate needles, gave
an anhydro-base (XLV) on treatment with ammonia. This cannot
possess a phenazinone structure like aposafranone or rosindone, and
hence must be a betaine. It was the original prasindone (Chapter
V:2,D), forming bluish-green leaflets, from which the trivial name was
derived.

Much later, Kehrmann and Perrot[80] condensed 4-acetamido-1,2-
naphthoquinone with 1-anilino-4-nitro-2-naphthylamine. This time
only the 7-phenyldibenzo[a,h]phenazinium derivative (XLVI) was
obtained as shown by the color and fluorescence so characteristic of
rosinduline derivatives. The nitro group was reduced to give 5-aceta-
mido-12-amino-7-phenyldibenzo[a,h]phenazinium chloride (XLVII).

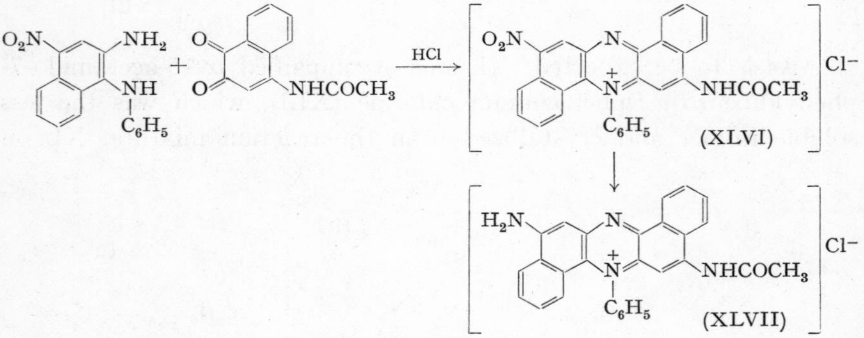

The same anilinonitronaphthylamine was condensed with 2-
hydroxy-1,4-naphthoquinone when a mixture was obtained from which

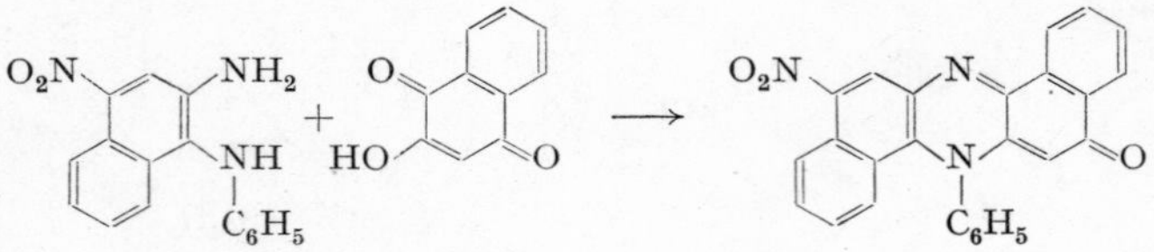

Kehrmann and Perrot[80] isolated the anhydro-base, 12-nitro-7-phenyl-5(7)-dibenzo[a,h]phenazinone (XLVIII) as a dark red powder. The alternative 7-phenyldibenzo[a,j]phenazinium compound was also formed.

Lantz[81,82] devised a novel synthesis of 7-phenyldibenzo[a,h]-phenazinium compounds substituted by anilino groups, etc., by heating the corresponding substituted dibenzo[a,h]phenoxazine (XLIX) with aniline or other aromatic amines.

The quaternary salts are listed in Table XXXIII.

D. Uses of Dibenzo[a,h]phenazines

Until comparatively recently, dibenzo[a,h]phenazines received little attention as potential sources of dyes. Within the last thirty years, however, a number of applications for them has been found. In general, these depend upon the oxidation of 2-naphthylamines substituted by various groups, such as sulfonic acid residues, to yield disulfonic acids etc. of dibenzo[a,h]phenazine,[54,55] or the oxidation of hydroxy-2-naphthyl-amines, with the hydroxyl group suitably protected.[53,56] The sulfonic acid groups may be partially or completely replaced by hydroxyl by fusion with alkali[83] or by high temperature alkaline hydrolysis[84] and the supposedly dihydroxydibenzo[a,h]phenazines may be further modified by coupling with diazotized sulfanilic or naphthionic acids, giving azo dyes of various colors, used to produce fast dyeings, printings or pigments.[85,86] Alternatively, the polyhydroxydibenzo[a,h]phenazines may be subjected to vigorous halogenation, the products dyeing cotton from a vat in golden-yellow shades when they contain four or less halogen atoms[87] and reddish shades when they contain more halogen atoms than four.[88,89] The halogenation may be carried out at high temperatures using sulfur chlorides, when incorporation of sulfur also occurs, the products dyeing cotton from a sulfide vat in various shades depending upon the extent of sulfuration.[90]

TABLE XXXIII. Quaternary Dibenzo[a,h]phenazinium Salts and Derivatives

Substituents	Appearance of chloride (unless otherwise stated)	Appearance of anhydro-base (where formed)	M.p. of anhydro-base (°C.)	Color with H_2SO_4, followed by dilution	Ref.
(a) 7-Methyl Compounds					
None	(I⁻), Brown needles, greenish luster			Cornflower-blue	72
(b) 7-Phenyl Compounds					
12-Amino-	Green needles			Violet-blue, green, brown-yellow, violet-blue	79
12-Acetamido-	Brick-red needles			Violet-blue, dark green, red	79
12-Hydroxy-	Dark brown needles	Bluish-green leaflets		Bluish-violet, bright red	79
12-Acetoxy-	(NO₃⁻, brownish-red leaflets, brassy luster)			Yellow fluorescence in ethanol	79
5-Anilino-		Needles	229	Yellowish-green	81
5-Amino-12-nitro-	Red crystals, green luster			Greenish-blue, brown, magenta	80
5-Acetamido-12-nitro-	Dark red crystals			Dark blue, red	80
5,12-Diamino-	Dark bluish-violet crystals			Bluish-green, green, magenta	80
5-Acetamido-12-amino-	Blue-black crystals			Dark blue, olive-green, bright red	80
5,12-Diacetamido-	Violet-black crystals			Dark blue, reddish-violet	80
5-Hydroxy-12-nitro-	Dark red crystals			Greenish-blue, red	80

Other procedures depend upon the condensation of 1,2-diamino-naphthalene with 2-hydroxy-1,4-naphthoquinone or with 2,3-dichloro-1,4-naphthoquinone to give a hydroxydibenzophenazine derivative. Theoretically at least, this condensation may occur in two ways. The products, (LI and LII, R = H or Cl) are then condensed further with 2,3-dichloro-1,4-naphthoquinone in nitrobenzene in the presence of

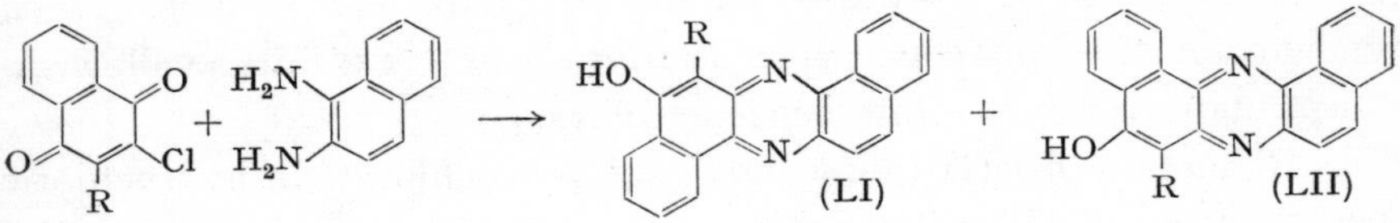

cuprous chloride and anhydrous sodium acetate to give orange-yellow, fast vat dyes for cotton.[91,92]

4. Dibenzo[a, i]phenazine (LIII)

R. I. 3250

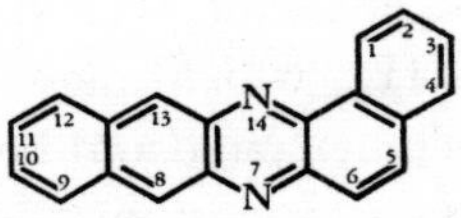

(LIII)

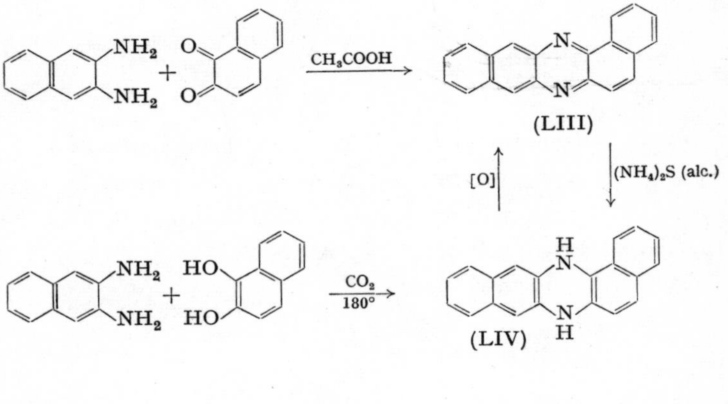

This ring system was first obtained by Fischer and Albert[73] by the condensation of 2,3-diaminonaphthalene and 1,2-naphthoquinone in cold acetic acid solution. Hinsberg[93] obtained the 7,14-dihydro compound (LIV) by an application of the Ris method (Chapter I:(1)) by heating 2,3-diaminonaphthalene with 1,2-dihydroxynaphthalene at 180° in an atmosphere of carbon dioxide. This yellow, high-melting compound (LIV), which gives a nitrosamine, was readily oxidized even by the action of air on an ethanolic solution, but best oxidized by means of potassium dichromate in acetic acid, to yield the aromatic compound (LIII), identical with that obtained by Fischer and Albert. LIII forms brownish-yellow or brownish-red needles, m.p. 247°, which give a violet coloration with concentrated sulfuric acid. It exhibits a yellowish-green fluorescence in dilute benzene solution.

Reduction of LIII by means of stannous chloride in hydrochloric acid solution yields violet needles, probably of a semiquinonoid chloride.[93] Benzo[a]phenazine reacts similarly, while benzo[b]phenazine is reduced to the N,N'-dihydro state by this reagent (Chapter XII:2,A). However, reduction of LIII by means of alcoholic ammonium sulfide proceeds to the 7,14-dihydro derivative (LIV); benzo[a]phenazine is stable towards this reagent. Dibenzo[a,i]phenazine does not react with benzenesulfinic acid, a reagent that attacks benzo[b]phenazine. Thus dibenzo[a,i]phenazine (LIII), which may be regarded as a benzo derivative of both benzo[a]phenazine and benzo[b]phenazine, exhibits the reactions of both basic ring systems. No other members of this series are known.

TABLE XXXIV.

Dibenzo[a,i]phenazines

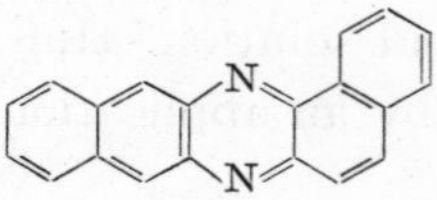

Substituents	Physical characteristics	M.p.(°C.)	Color with H_2SO_4 and other properties	Ref.
None	Brownish-yellow or brownish-red needles	247	Violet, yellow-green fluorescence in benzene	73, 93
7,14-Dihydro-	Bright yellow crystals	> 300	Red	93

5. Dibenzo[a, j]phenazine (XXIII)

R. I. 3253

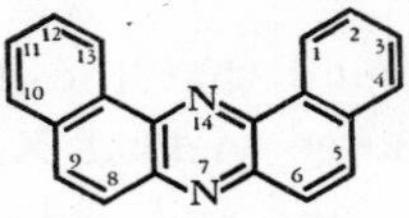

(XXIII)

A. Methods of Preparation

When 1,2-naphthoquinone and 1,2-diaminonaphthalene are condensed together in cold glacial acetic acid, both dibenzo[a,h]phenazine (XXII) and dibenzo[a,j]phenazine (XXIII) are formed, though it was many years after the preparation of the former in this way that the latter compound was isolated by Fischer and Strauss[42] from the mother liquors of the preparation (Section XV:3).

Dibenzo[a,j]phenazine was first prepared by Matthes[44] by adding a solution of benzenediazonium chloride to a hot solution of 2,2'-dinaphthylamine, the acid liberated in the coupling reaction causing the intermediate 1-benzeneazo-2,2'-dinaphthylamine to undergo a typical Witt reaction (Chapter XII:3,B(5)).

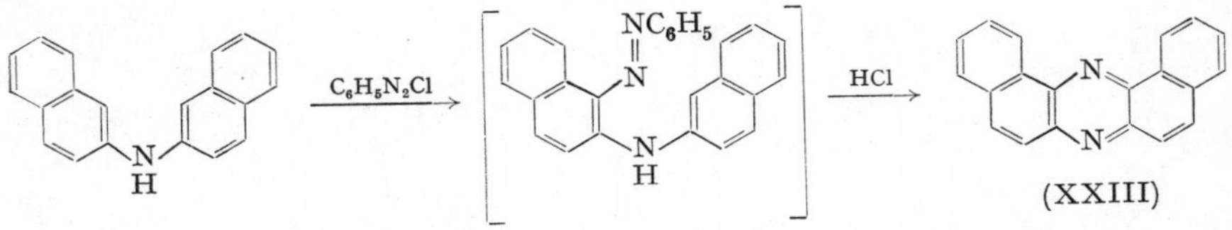

Fischer and Strauss[42] were able to obtain the intermediate azo-derivative in a pure state by using a cold pyridine solution, and showed that, on heating with acid, it underwent ring closure, confirming the correctness of the assumption. Substantially the same reaction was studied and confirmed much later by Levi and Faldino.[45]

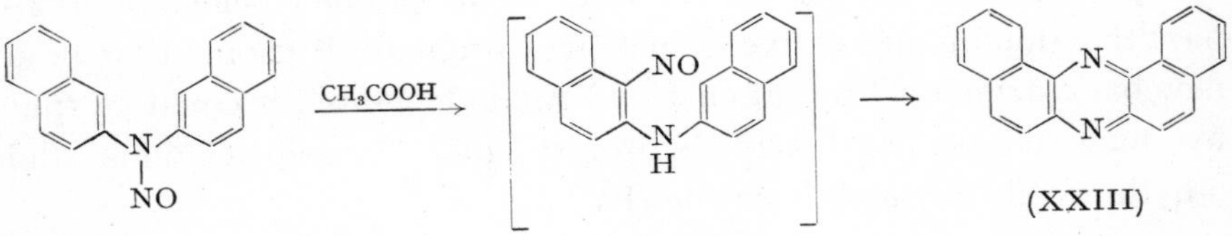

A method of preparation somewhat related to this is the action of warm acetic acid upon N-nitroso-2,2'-dinaphthylamine[72]; this presumably rearranges first to 1-nitroso-2,2'-dinaphthylamine, which then undergoes ring closure.

Fischer and Eilles[94] found that the distillation of 1-amino-2,2'-dinaphthylamine with litharge yielded XXIII, a reaction allied to those described above. Ullmann and Ankersmit[95] discovered another method, which consists in adding 1-benzeneazo-2-naphthylamine to boiling 2-naphthol, a reaction that may be extended to substitution products of XXIII.

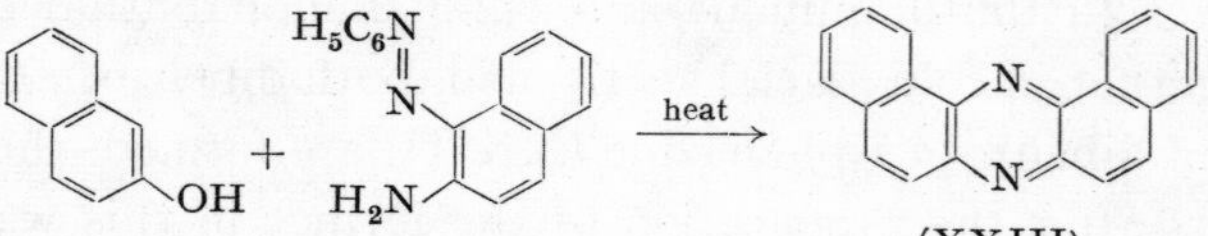

(XXIII)

Other methods, which are not of preparative importance, but which have been used to throw light on the nature of more complex derivatives include the zinc dust distillation of 5-hydroxydibenzo[a,j]-phenazine[71, 73] (LV), of 7-phenyl-5(7)-dibenzo[a,j]phenazinone[97,98] (LVI) and of 7-(1'-naphthyl)-5(7)-dibenzo[a,j]phenazinone[98] (LVII).

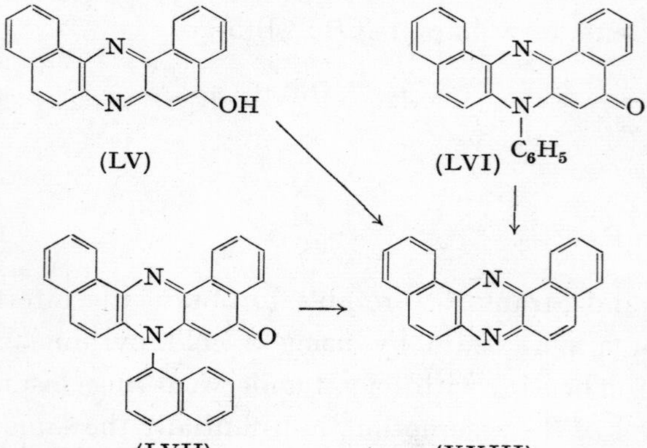

(LV)   (LVI) C_6H_5

(LVII)   (XXIII)

A very small yield of dibenzo[a,j]phenazine is obtained in the reaction between 1-nitroso-2-naphthylamine and 2-naphthylamine and its hydrochloride in ethanol, the bulk of the product being the 5-(2'-naphthylamino)- derivative, which was originally[72] thought to be a new basic azine nucleus. Fischer and Albert[73] showed it could be split by high temperature acid hydrolysis into 2-naphthylamine and 5-hydroxydibenzo[a,j]phenazine (LV).

B. Properties, Reactions and Derivatives

Dibenzo[a,j]phenazine forms yellow needles, m.p. 243°, which are soluble in ethanol and benzene giving solutions exhibiting a blue fluorescence, while solutions in acetic acid fluoresce green. It yields a dichroic solution in concentrated sulfuric acid, which is red by transmitted, and deep blue by reflected light.

Reductive acetylation[42] of XXIII gives a monoacetyl-7,14-dihydro derivative (LVIII), in which the acetyl group, on steric grounds, probably occupies position 7.

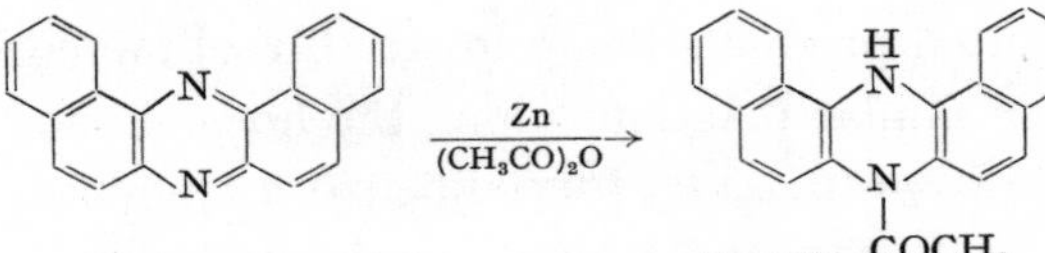

(XXIII)   (LVIII)

Oxidation of dibenzo[a,j]phenazine by chromic acid[75] proceeds similarly to the corresponding benzo[a]phenazine and dibenzo[a,h]-phenazine (Chapter XII:3,D and F and Section XV:3,B). The product is the 5,6-quinone (LIX), which readily reacts with o-phenylenediamine to give dibenzo[c,h]quinoxalo[2,3-a]phenazine (LX, R. I. 3756) as dark

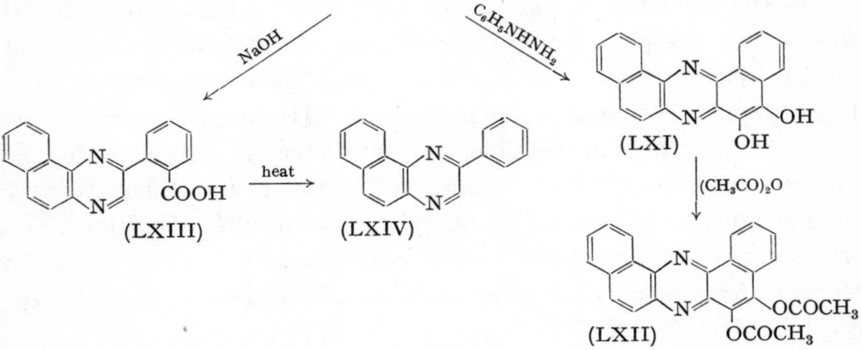

(XXIII)   (LIX)   (LX)

(LXIII)   (LXIV)   (LXI)   (LXII)

yellow needles. Reduction of the 5,6-quinone by means of phenylhydrazine in hot acetic acid gives 5,6-dihydroxydibenzo[a,j]phenazine
(LXI), which readily forms a diacetyl derivative (LXII). Treatment of
the quinone with boiling caustic soda solution leads to a ring scission
with partial decarboxylation to give 2-(2'-carboxyphenyl)benzo[f]-
quinoxaline (LXIII), yellow needles, m.p. >300°, which on distillation
loses a second molecule of carbon dioxide to yield 2-phenylbenzo[f]-
quinoxaline (LXIV, R. I. 1907), bright yellow needles, m.p. 153°, giving
a dark red color with concentrated sulfuric acid.

No substitution reactions of dibenzo[a,j]phenazines have been
studied, substituted products being invariably obtained by condensation processes or similar reactions along the lines already discussed.

The preparation of 5-hydroxydibenzo[a,j]phenazine from the
corresponding 5-(2'-naphthylamino) compound has already been
mentioned. It has also been obtained by the acid hydrolysis of the
5-anilino derivative.[71] The 2-hydroxy isomer (LXV) was obtained by
Ullmann and Ankersmit[95] by heating together at 190–240° a mixture
of 1-benzeneazo-2-naphthylamine and 2,7-dihydroxynaphthalene.

(LXV)

The only simple dihydroxy compound known is the 5,6-dihydroxy
derivative (LXI, see above).

5-Aminodibenzo[a,j]phenazine (LXVI), the simplest eurhodine of
this series, was prepared by Fischer and Albert[73] by the action of
1-naphthylamine upon 1-nitroso-2-naphthylamine. This reaction mixture also yields[72] dibenzo[a,h]phenazine (XXII), but, by working at as
low a temperature as possible, the eurhodine is obtained. In the
presence of aniline, the reaction takes yet another course and quaternary
indulinic derivatives of dibenzo[a,j]phenazine result[71] (see below). The
mechanisms of these related reactions are obviously very complicated,
since the reaction in the presence of aniline also yields 5-anilinodibenzo-
[a,j]phenazine[71] (LXVII).

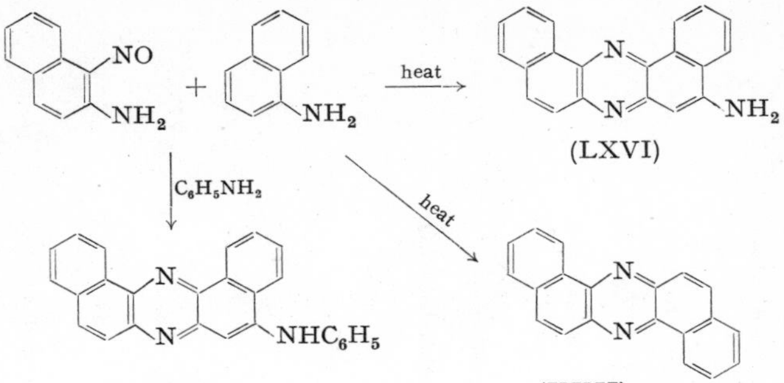

(LXVI)

(LXVII)   (XXII)

When 2-naphthylamine is substituted for 1-naphthylamine in the above reaction with 1-nitroso-2-naphthylamine, the bulk of the product is 5-(2'-naphthylamino)dibenzo[a,j]phenazine[72,73] (LXVIII). This can also be obtained[73] from LXVI by heating it with 2-naphthylamine and 2-naphthylamine hydrochloride at 180°.

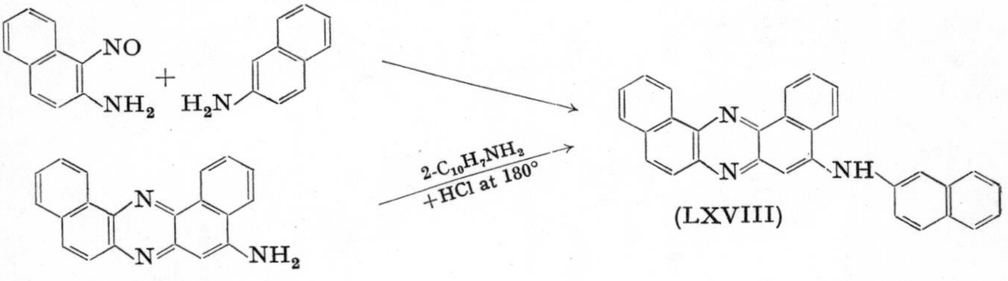

(LXVIII)

(LXVI)

5,9- and 6,9-Diamino derivatives have been obtained by Kehrmann and Safar[77] and Mihaéloff[78] by condensing 4-acetamido-1,2-diamino-naphthalene with 3- and 4-acetamido-1,2-naphthoquinones. The reactions are discussed in Section XV:3,B, to which the reader is referred. There, too, will be found the preparation of 5-acetamido-9-hydroxy-dibenzo[a,j]phenazine, prepared by the same workers.

Dyestuffs in the dibenzo[a,j]phenazine series are almost unknown. 4,10-Dihydroxydibenzo[a,j]phenazine-2,12-disulfonic acid and a simple naphtholsulfonic acid have been coupled in stepwise fashion with tetrazotized dianisidine, and the resulting bisazo dye coppered with a copper sulfate-ammonia mixture to give a blue-grey dye of good fastness for cotton and rayon.[99]

Derivatives are listed in Table XXXV.

TABLE XXXV. Dibenzo[a,j]phenazines

Substituents	Physical characteristics	M.p. (°C.)	Color with H_2SO_4, followed by dilution	Ref.
None	Yellow needles	242–243	Dichroic (deep blue-red)	See XV:5
7-Acetyl-7,14-dihydro-	Yellow prisms	228		42
5,6-Quinone	Yellowish-brown needles	300 (dec.)	Yellow or yellowish-brown	75
5,6-Quinone monoxime	Needles		Brown	75
5-Hydroxy-	Bright yellow needles	> 380	Dichroic (blue-red), red	71, 73
2-Hydroxy-	Greenish-yellow needles	301	Bluish-violet, reddish-brown, red ppt.	95
5,6-Dihydroxy-	Brown needles		Green	75
5,6-Diacetoxy-	Yellow needles	> 270 (dec.)	Green	75
5-Amino-	Bright yellow needles	325	Bluish-violet	73
5-Anilino-	Yellowish-brown needles, green luster	280		71
5-(2'-Naphthylamino)-	Orange-yellow needles	296	Greenish-blue	72, 73
5,9-Diamino-	Brick-red crystals		Violet, green, magenta	77, 78
6,9-Diamino-	Orange crystals		Violet, olive-green, violet-red	77, 78
6,9-Diacetamido-	Yellow crystals		Brownish-violet, red-brown ppt.	77, 78

C. Quaternary Derivatives

Dibenzo[*a,j*]phenazine may be *N*-methylated by heating it with a methanolic solution of methyl iodide under pressure at 160°,[72] the product being 7-methyldibenzo[*a,j*]phenazinium iodide (LXIX), which gives yellow solutions exhibiting a grass-green fluorescence in organic solvents and a dark blue coloration in concentrated sulfuric acid.

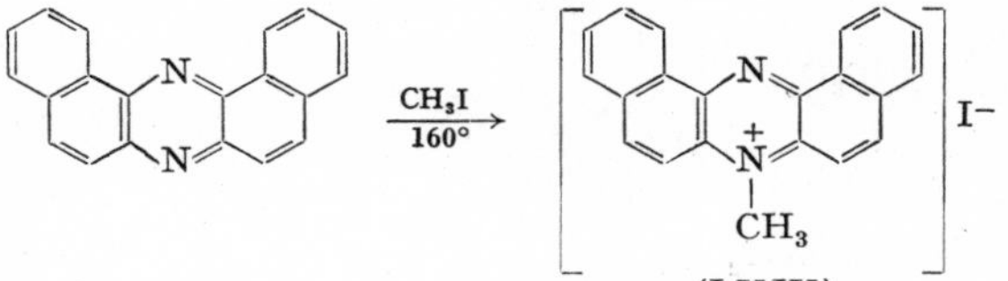

(LXIX)

The corresponding 7-phenyl salts (LXX) may be obtained by deamination of 5-amino-7-phenyldibenzo[*a,j*]phenazinium salts (LXXI), following the procedure of Kehrmann and Sutherst.[79]

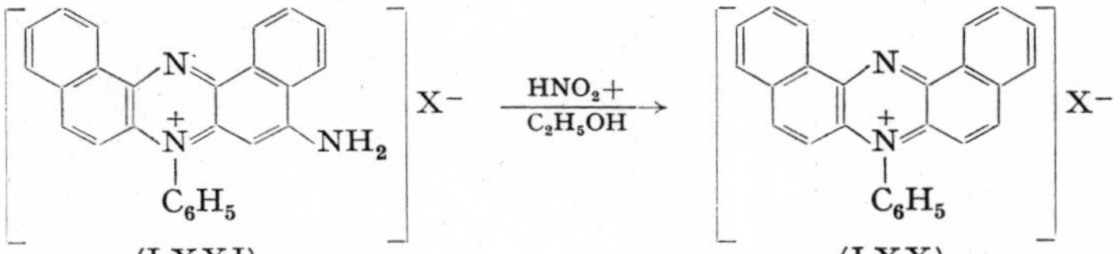

(LXXI)   (LXX)

LXXI itself may be prepared by condensing 2-anilino-1-naphthyl-amine with 4-acetamido-1,2-naphthoquinone and separating (XLI) from the isomeric 7-phenyldibenzo[*a,h*]phenazinium derivative (XL) formed simultaneously[79]; the acetyl grouping is removed after the separation.

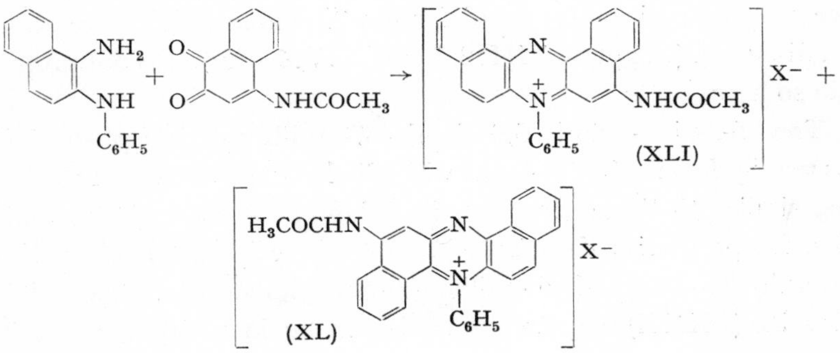

(XLI)

(XL)

In general, however, the 5-amino and substituted amino quaternary compounds are produced in a complex reaction, modeled on the simple "induline melt," which was studied by Fischer and Hepp. 4-Benzene-azo-1-naphthylamine was heated with a mixture of 1-naphthylamine hydrochloride in aniline at 150°.[71] The reaction products varied according to the precise proportions of reactants used; they are shown in the accompanying scheme.

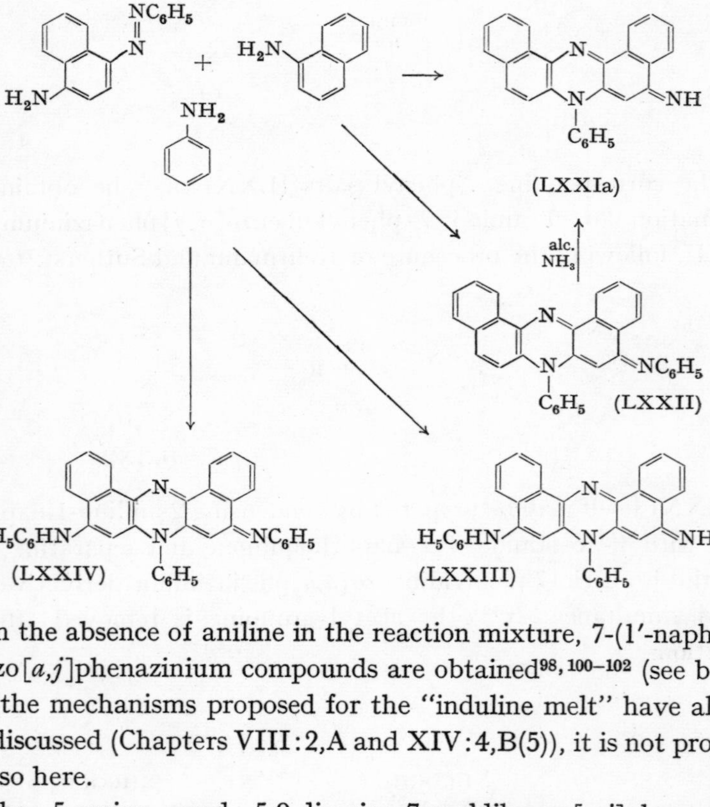

(LXXIa)

(LXXII)

(LXXIV)   (LXXIII)

In the absence of aniline in the reaction mixture, 7-(1'-naphthyl)-dibenzo[a,j]phenazinium compounds are obtained[98, 100–102] (see below). Since the mechanisms proposed for the "induline melt" have already been discussed (Chapters VIII:2,A and XIV:4,B(5)), it is not proposed to do so here.

The 5-amino- and 5,9-diamino-7-aryldibenzo[a,j]phenazinium salts readily form anhydro-bases with alkalis, the structure of the latter being similar to those of the phenazinium and benzo[a]phenazinium series. The properties of the known members are listed in Table XXXVI. The anhydro-base of 5-anilino-7-phenyldibenzo[a,j]phenazinium hydroxide (LXXII) may be obtained from the induline melt described above.[71] It has been conveniently prepared by heating 4-nitroso-1-anilinonaphthalene with 2-anilinonaphthalene in glacial acetic acid at 100°,[103] or by heating 4-nitroso-1,1'-dinaphthylamine with aniline

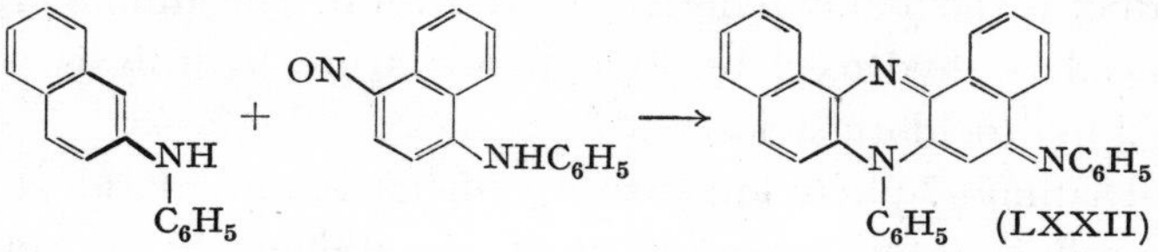

(LXXII)

and aniline hydrochloride at 120°, when a 5-(1'-naphthylamino)-7-phenylbenzo[a]phenazinium compound (LXXV) is simultaneously formed.[96]

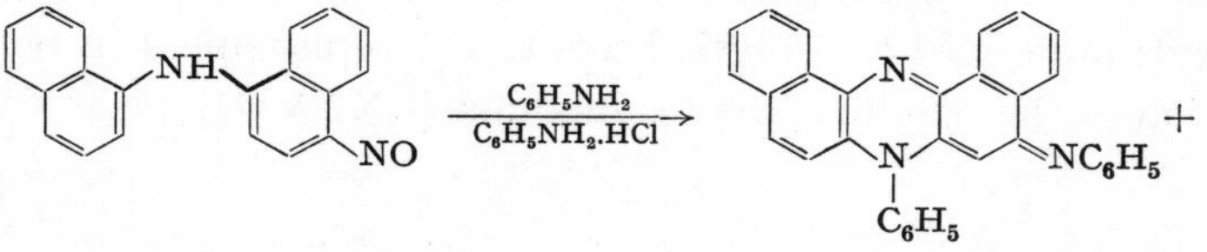

(LXXII)

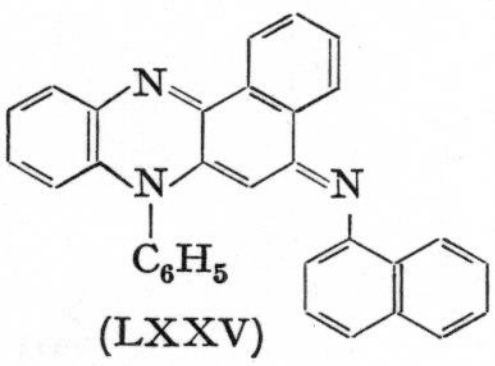

(LXXV)

The same two compounds (LXXII and LXXV) are produced when a benzeneazo group is substituted for the 4-nitroso radical.[96,97,104] The mechanism is substantially the same, as too it is when 4-(1'-naphthylazo)-1-naphthylamine is heated with aniline and aniline hydrochloride at 150–180°.[97] The products then are LXXII and phenylrosinduline (Chapter XIV:4,E). A fairly recent synthesis of LXXII, due to Lantz,[81,82] consists in refluxing a solution of 5-phenylimidodibenzo[a,j]phenoxazine (LXXVI) in aniline or other aromatic amines.

(LXXVI)   (LXXII)

5-Anilino-7-phenyldibenzo[a,j]phenazinium salts dye cotton mordanted with tannin in reddish-violet shades. Heating LXXII with alcoholic ammonia under pressure leads to an exchange of groups and the product is the 5-amino derivative (LXXIa). The anilino group may be replaced by hydroxyl by high temperature hydrolysis with concentrated hydrochloric acid.

5,9-Diamino-7-phenyldibenzo[a,j]phenazinium chloride (LXXVII) is a by-product from the synthesis of rosinduline[98, 105] (Chapter XIV: 4,D) by heating 4-benzeneazo-1-naphthylamine in phenol at 130°. When sulfonated, it is known as Naphthyl Red ($C. I.$ 856), a name Fischer and Hepp also applied to the unsulfonated compound. On high temperature acid hydrolysis, one amino group only is replaced by hydroxyl; prolonged hydrolysis leads to the replacement of both with formation of the 5,9-dihydroxy compound (LXXVIII).

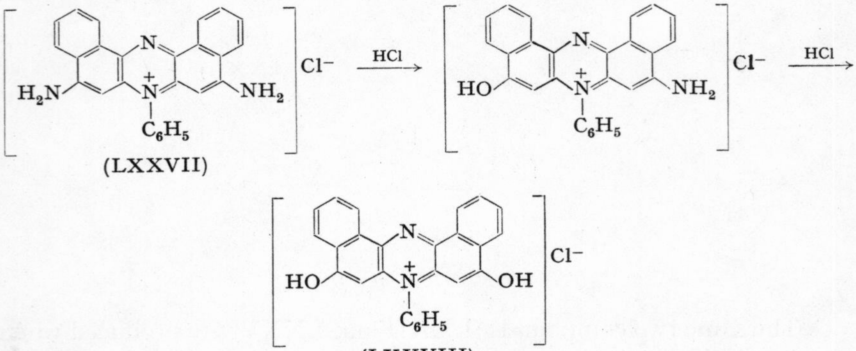

(LXXVII)

(LXXVIII)

5-Amino-9-anilino-7-phenyldibenzo[a,j]phenazinium hydroxide anhydro-base (LXXIII), known when sulfonated as Naphthyl Violet

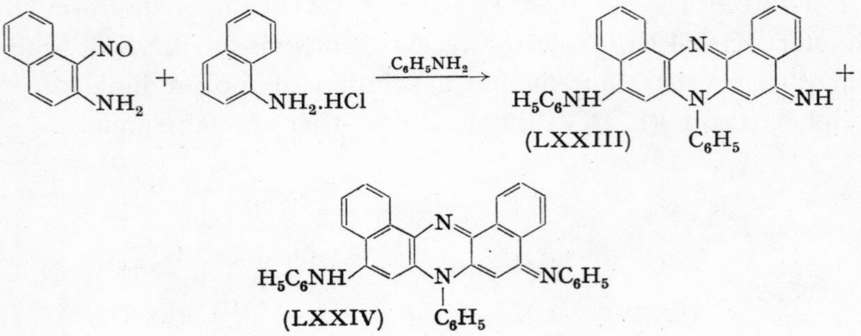

(LXXIII)

(LXXIV)

(*C. I.* 856), is another product from the induline melt of 4-benzeneazo-1-naphthylamine, 1-naphthylamine hydrochloride and aniline.[71] It is also obtained, together with the 5,9-dianilino derivative (LXXIV, Naphthyl Blue), by heating a mixture of 1-nitroso-2-naphthylamine, 1-naphthylamine hydrochloride and aniline.[71] Naphthyl violet dyes silk reddish-violet with a red fluorescence and is light-fast.

On high temperature hydrolysis of LXXIII with 50% acetic acid, the amino group is preferentially replaced by hydroxyl to yield LXXIX. More drastic treatment with concentrated hydrochloric acid at 200° under pressure yields the 5,9-dihydroxy compound (LXXVIII).

5,9 - Dianilino - 7 - phenyldibenzo [*a,j*] phenazinium hydroxide anhydro-base (LXXIV) is the final product of the induline melt discussed above,[71,96,97] especially when 1-naphthylamine hydrochloride is omitted from the mixture. It is also produced, together with the aminoanilino compound (LXXIII), by heating together 1-nitroso-2-naphthylamine, 1-naphthylamine hydrochloride and aniline[71,106] and by heating 4-benzeneazo-1-anilinonaphthalene in phenol at 120–150°.[71,107]

The structure follows from the high temperature hydrolysis first to 5 - anilino - 9 - hydroxy -7- phenyldibenzo [*a,j*] phenazinium chloride (LXXIX) and finally to the 5,9-dihydroxy compound (LXXVIII).

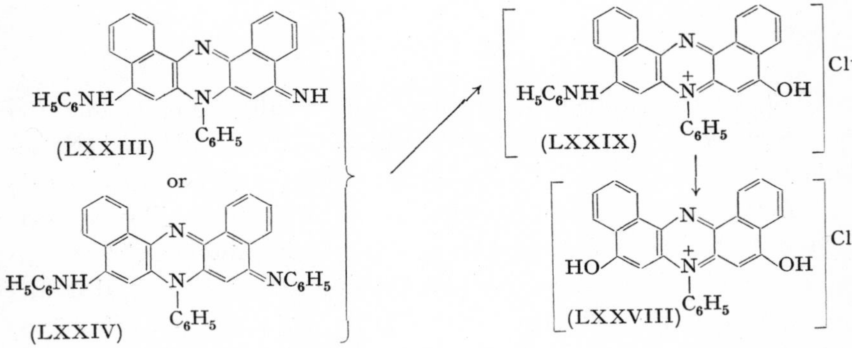

When sulfonated, LXXIV is known as Milling Blue or Naphthyl Blue (more highly sulfonated than Milling Blue, *C. I.* 856). It dyes silk and chrome-mordanted wool in blue to violet-blue shades.

5-Amino-7-ethyldibenzo[*a,j*]phenazinium salts (LXXX) have also been prepared as dyestuffs. They are obtained either by the joint oxidation of mixtures of 2-ethylamino-1-naphthylamine with 1-naph-thylamine[108] or by heating the corresponding 5-anilino compounds with

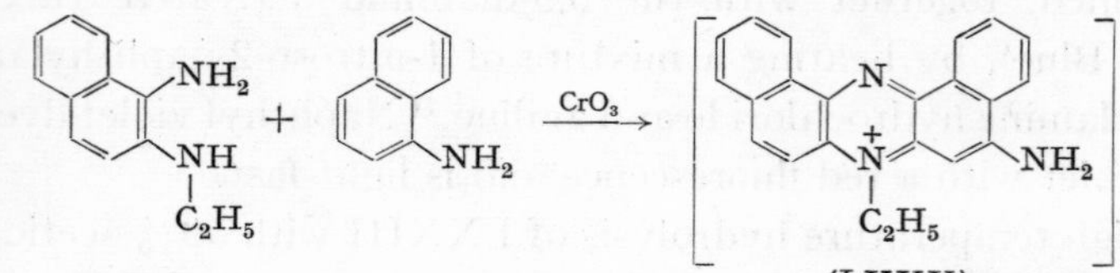

(LXXX)

ethanolic ammonia at 120–130°.[103] The anilino compound (LXXXI) is obtained from 1-anilino-4-nitrosonaphthalene and 2-ethylamino-naphthalene in acetic acid at 100°.[103]

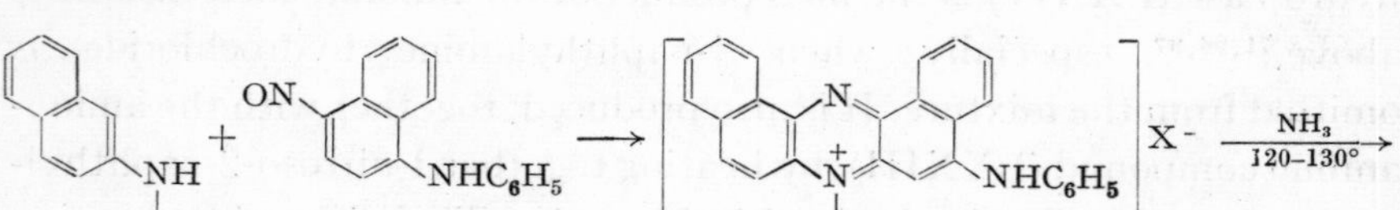

(LXXXI)

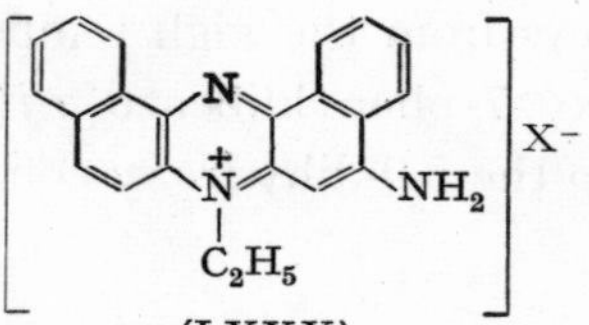

(LXXX)

7-(1'-Naphthyl)dibenzo[a,j]phenazinium salts were among the oldest coal tar dyes. Schiendl in 1868 discovered Magdala Red (Naph-thalene Red, Sudan Red, C. I. 857) by heating 4-(1'-naphthylazo)-1-naphthylamine hydrochloride with 1-naphthylamine. A very poor yield was obtained this way. It was studied by Hofmann,[100,101] who thought it was a rosaniline dye and by Julius,[109] who realized it was similar in preparation and properties to the indulines and safranines. Witt[102] improved the yield by adding 1,4-diaminonaphthalene to the reaction mixture. Fischer and Hepp[98] showed that commercial Magdala Red was a mixture of two dyes, separable by solution in benzene. One was 5-amino-7-(1'-naphthyl)dibenzo[a,j]phenazinium chloride (LXXXII), known as Rhodindine, which on hydrolysis yielded the 5-monohydroxy compound. The other constituent was 5,9-diamino-

7-(1'-naphthyl)dibenzo[a,j]phenazinium chloride (LXXXIII), Magdala Red proper, and hydrolyzed in two steps, first to the 5-amino-9-hydroxy derivative and ultimately to the 5,9-dihydroxy compound. Diazotization and deamination with ethanol of the diamino derivative yielded the monoamine (LXXXII), identical with the product isolated from the commercial dye.

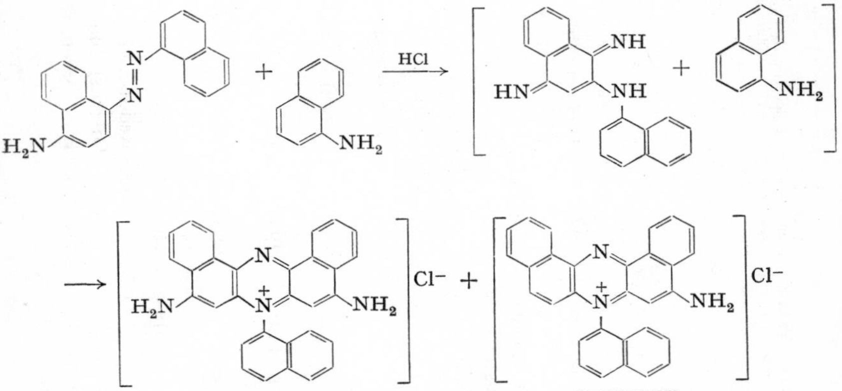

(LXXXIII)   (LXXXII)

The proportion of Magdala Red in the product was increased appreciably by Witt's modification[102] of adding 1,4-diaminonaphthalene to the melt. Magdala Red dyes silk from a soap bath in shades of delicate pink with a slight fluorescence, which is particularly fine on velvet. The absorption spectrum of Magdala Red was studied by Vogel[110] and Kalandek[111] in various solvents and substrates, but the results are of little interest.

Hodgson and Marsden[112] studied the purple dye obtained by the action of iodine (or 4-iodoaniline) upon 1-naphthylamine and proposed structure LXXXIV.

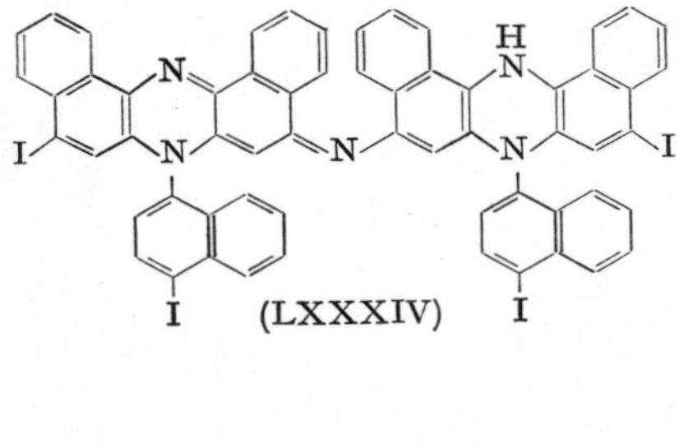

I   (LXXXIV)   I

TABLE XXXVI. Quaternary Dibenzo[a,j]phenazinium Salts and Derivatives

Substituents	Appearance of chloride (unless otherwise stated)	Appearance of anhydro-base (where formed)	M.p. of anhydro-base (°C.)	Color with H_2SO_4, followed by dilution	Ref.
(a) 7-Methyl Compounds					
None	(I⁻), Pale brown needles				72
(b) 7-Ethyl Compounds					
5-Hydroxy-	Red crystals	Golden lustrous needles	247	Dichroic (blue-red)	103
5-Amino-	Prisms, green iridescence			Blue, greenish-yellow, red	103, 108
5-Anilino-	Needles, green luster	Almost black prisms, metallic luster	254–255		103
(c) 7-Phenyl Compounds					
None	Red-brown needles, golden luster			Blue, orange-red	79
5-Chloro-	Reddish-yellow needles, green luster			Greenish-blue	114
5-Hydroxy-	Reddish-yellow crystals	Red tablets, metallic luster	295	Blue	71, 96, 97
5,9-Dihydroxy-		Leaflets	300 (dec.)		71, 97, 98
5-Hydroxy-9-methoxy-		Leaflets	> 330		71
5-Hydroxy-9-ethoxy-		Red leaflets or needles	> 340		71
5-Hydroxy-9-acetoxy-		Red needles	290–295	Reddish-violet	71
5-Hydroxy-9-benzoyloxy-		Red-brown needles		Greenish-blue	71
5-Amino-	Dark red needles, green luster	Dark violet leaflets, brassy luster	253–255	Blue, green, red	71, 79, 103

Substituents	Appearance of chloride (unless otherwise stated)	Appearance of anhydro-base (where formed)	M.p. of anhydro-base (°C.)	Color with H_2SO_4, followed by dilution	Ref.
5-Anilino-	Crystals, bronze luster	Violet leaflets, bronze luster	273	Blue	71, 81, 96, 97, 103, 104
5-Acetamido-	Brick-red needles, green luster			Violet-blue, yellowish-red	79
5,9-Diamino-	Needles, golden luster	Brown crystals, green luster		Yellow-green, rose, violet-red	98, 105
5-Amino-9-anilino-		Metallic needles, green luster		Green, blue ppt.	71
5,9-Dianilino-	Leaflets, bronze luster	Leaflets, bronze luster	338	Green, indigo blue ppt.	71, 81, 96, 97, 106, 107
5-Amino-9-hydroxy-	Needles, bronze luster	Green tablets		Dichroic (blue-red), brownish-yellow	98
5-Anilino-9-hydroxy-		Bluish-black leaflets		Blue, violet-red ppt.	71
(d) 7-(1'-Naphthyl) Compounds					
5-Hydroxy-		Matt green prisms		Bluish-green, yellow, rose	98
5,9-Dihydroxy-	Red crystals	Prisms, green luster		Blue, yellowish-red	98
5-Amino-		Reddish-brown crystals		Blue, greenish-brown, red-violet	98, 100–102
5,9-Diamino-	Green needles, metallic luster	Prisms, green luster		Yellowish-green, brownish-pink, red	98, 100–102, 109
5-Amino-9-hydroxy-		Needles, green luster		Dichroic (blue-red), violet, red	98

This is based on the isolation from the thermal decomposition at
260° of 1-naphthylamine and "αβ-dinaphthazine," yellow needles,
m.p. 280°. This would, however, imply a skeleton involving dibenzo-
[a,h]phenazine and not dibenzo[a,j]phenazine, so that the structure
must remain in doubt.

An indulinic substance, $C_{50}H_{34}N_5Cl$ (molecular formula based on
analyses for chlorine and nitrogen only), was obtained by the oxidation
of 1-naphthylamine by hydroxylamine hydrochloride or by hydrazine
at 150–160°.[113] No structure has been indicated for the product but it
could be an amino-5,9-(1',1''-dinaphthylamino)-7-(1'''-naphthyl)di-
benzo[a,j]phenazinium chloride.

The hydroxy and dihydroxy derivatives of dibenzo[a,j]phenazin-
ium salts have been mentioned in connection with the elucidation of the
structures of the dyes described above. Although they played a valuable
part in the recognition of the underlying unities, they are of little
intrinsic interest. Their properties may be predicted from a knowledge
of the corresponding rosindones. Thus they form anhydro-bases, and
these react with phosphorus pentachloride in phosphoryl chloride to
replace the oxygen atom by chlorine.[114]

Derivatives of quaternary dibenzo[a,j]phenazinium salts are
listed in Table XXXVI.

6. Dibenzo[b, i]phenazine (LXXXV)

6,13-Diazapentacene.
R. I. 3249

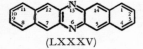

(LXXXV)

No well authenticated examples of the aromatic series corresponding to LXXXV have been described, although Malaviya and Dutt[62]
claimed to have obtained LXXXV, m.p. 240°, by exposing a solution
of 2-naphthylamine in aqueous acid to tropical sunlight for 110 days.
Their work is open to suspicion on other grounds, however. Pishchimuka[63] studied the effect of sulfur and selenium upon aromatic amines
in the presence of mercury acetamide and other organomercuric compounds that acted as catalysts and lowered the temperature required

for reaction to occur. In the case of 2-naphthylamine, this worker claimed the formation of dibenzo[b,i]phenazine, yellow needles, m.p. 278°. These properties are closely similar to those of dibenzo[a,h]phenazine, which might be expected to be formed by such a process.

The only certain representative of this ring system is 6,13-dihydro-dibenzo[b,i]phenazine (LXXXVI), prepared by Hinsberg[93] by the Ris method by heating 2,3-diaminonaphthalene with 2,3-dihydroxynaphthalene at 180° in an inert atmosphere (CO_2).

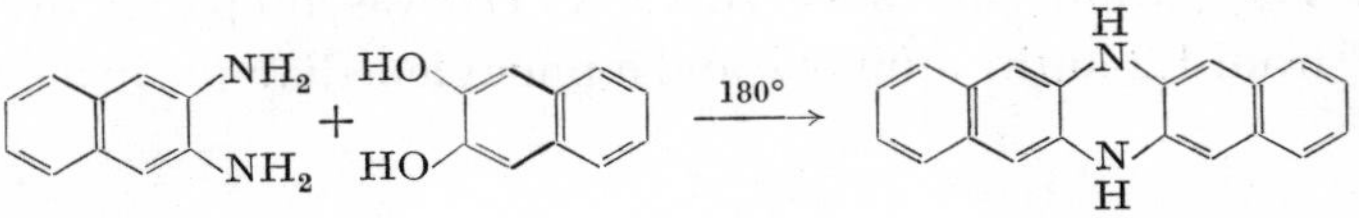

(LXXXVI)

The dihydro compound (LXXXVI) is a high-melting (> 300°), very difficultly soluble, yellow crystalline powder. Oxidation of LXXXVI to yield LXXXV was unsuccessful when potassium dichromate in acetic acid was used.

On comparing dibenzo[a,i]phenazine (LIII) and dibenzo[b,i]phenazine (LXXXV) with the corresponding benzo[a]phenazine and benzo[b]phenazine (Chapter XII), it becomes apparent that the stability of the dihydroazine is greatly increased in the case of compounds with a linear structure over those with an angular structure. Hinsberg[93] remarked upon this and recently the subject has been reconsidered from the same viewpoint by Badger and Pettit.[115]

TABLE XXXVII. Dibenzo[b,i]phenazines

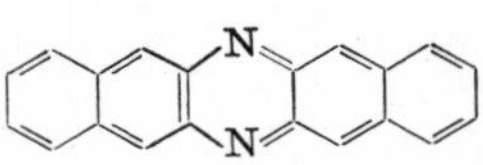

Substituents	Physical characteristics	M.p. (°C.)	Color with H_2SO_4 and other properties	Ref.
6,13-Dihydro-	Yellow microcrystals	> 300		93
None*		240		62
None*	Yellow needles	278		63

* These substances are not well authenticated. For details refer to text.

7. Naphtho[2, 3-a]phenazine (LXXXVII)

R. I. 3251

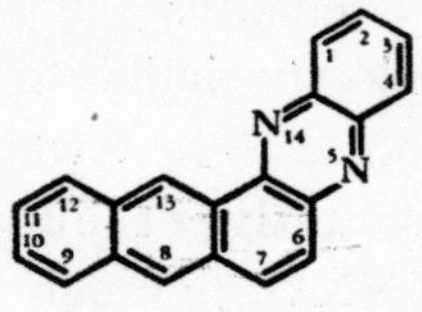

(LXXXVII)

There are only a small number of representatives of this ring system. The parent substance (LXXXVII) was prepared by Lagodzinski[116] from 1,2-anthraquinone and o-phenylenediamine in acetic acid.

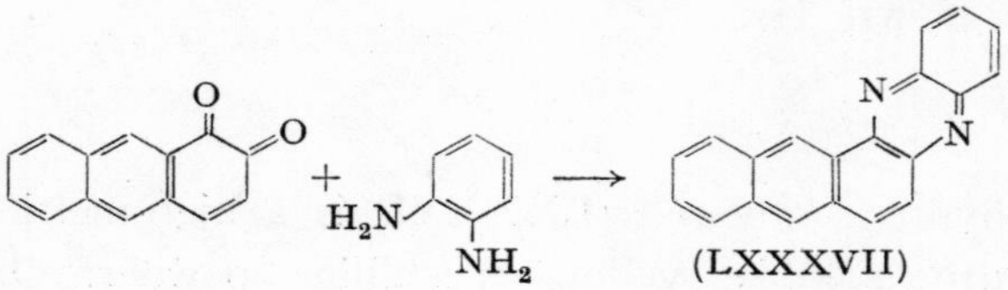

It was prepared similarly, the following year, by Dienel,[117] who agreed with Lagodzinski on its properties. It forms dark yellow platelets, m.p. 221–222°, giving a bluish-green coloration with sulfuric acid, and is only very weakly basic, its salts being readily hydrolyzed by water.

Related to this compound is 7,7'-di(naphtho[2,3-a]phenazine) (LXXXVIII), which was obtained by reducing 1,2-anthraquinone to the quinhydrone, oxidizing this with chromic acid to produce 4,4'-

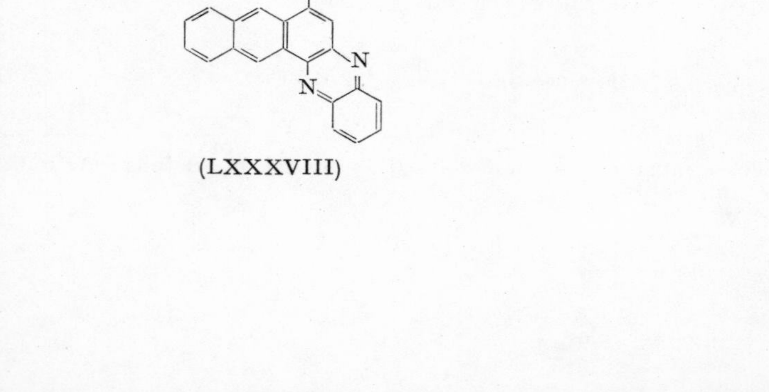

(LXXXVIII)

dianthracene-1,2,1′,2′-diquinone and treating the latter compound with o-phenylenediamine.[118] The diazine (LXXXVIII) was a high-melting solid forming greenish-yellow needles.

The interest attaching to this series depends upon the relationship to indanthrone (Chapter XVII). For this reason, Ullmann and Fodor[119] prepared the corresponding 8,13-quinone (XC). This they did by preparing 1-(2′-nitroanilino)-5,10-anthraquinone by typical Ullmann condensations either between 2-nitrochlorobenzene and 1-amino-5,10-anthraquinone or between 2-nitroaniline and 1-chloro-5,10-anthra-quinone. Ring closure to 5,14-dihydronaphtho[2,3-a]phenazine-8,13-quinone (LXXXIX) took place upon sodium sulfide reduction of the intermediate. Bradley, Leete and Stephens[120] have recently shown that the 2-(2′-nitroanilino)-5,10-anthraquinone, when reduced similarly, does not undergo ring closure.

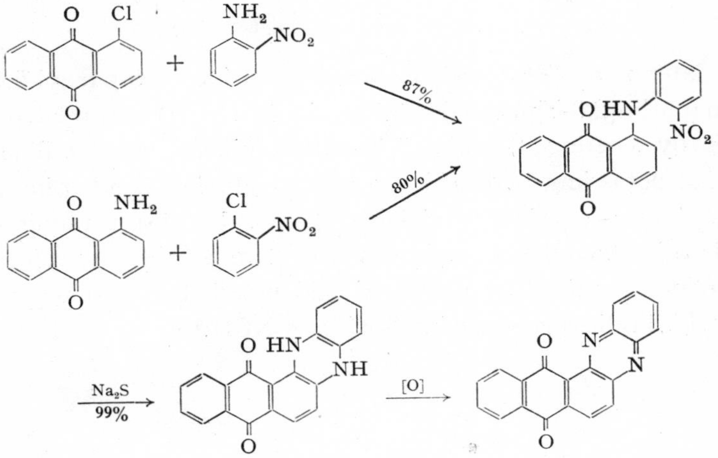

(LXXXIX)   (XC)

The compound LXXXIX was a blue substance, m.p. 310°, reminiscent of indanthrone. It was readily oxidized to the azine-quinone (XC) by lead dioxide or by mercuric oxide in boiling nitrobenzene, but better by means of concentrated nitric acid in glacial acetic acid solution. The intermediate dihydroazine-quinone (LXXXIX) gives a normal N,N′-diacetyl compound (for constitution, see Scholl and Edlbacher[121]).

Ullmann and Fodor[119] also described a homolog and a chloro derivative prepared similarly, and Ullmann and Medenwald[122] added to these. The Bayer Company, in a patent,[123] described a number of similar dihydro compounds for use as vat dyes, which were alkylated or aralkylated upon the 5-nitrogen atom. These (XCI) were prepared from the 2-amino-3-bromo-1-(4'-toluidino)-5,10-anthraquinones and various ketones by heating the mixture in acetic acid with zinc chloride. They gave red-brown vats on reduction and dyed wool in blue shades, or could be sulfonated by warming with 20% oleum to yield sulfonic acids, which were direct blue dyes for wool.

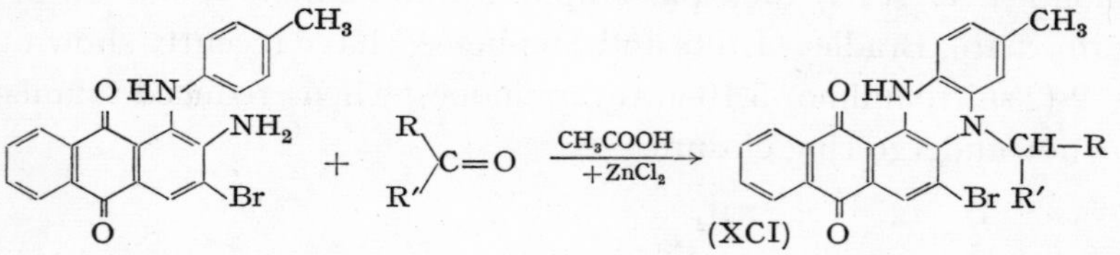

A later patent[124] described the preparation of 5-phenyl-5,14-di-hydronaphtho[2,3-a]phenazine-8,13-quinone (XCII) and related compounds by heating 2-anilino-5,10-anthraquinone with aniline and powdered potassium hydroxide or another alkaline condensing agent in the absence of air or oxidizing agents. 1-Haloanthraquinone-2-sulfonic acids have been condensed with 2-aminodiphenylamines and the products cyclized by means of acid or alkaline agents, yielding 5-phenyl-5,14-dihydro compounds of type XCII.[125]

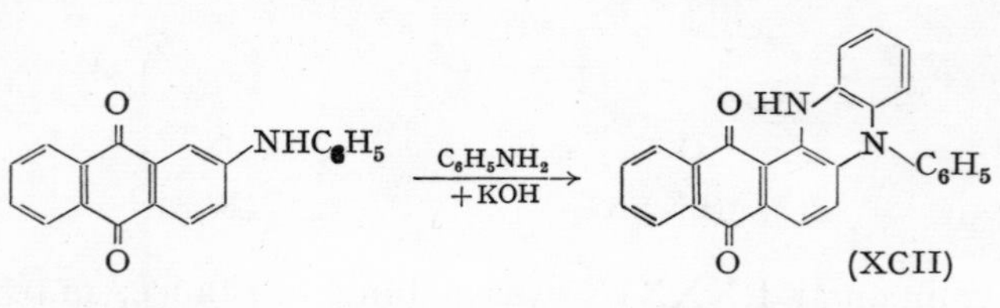

Bradley and Leete[126] have shown that this product is also obtained by the reaction of 2-chloro-5,10-anthraquinone with aniline in the presence of sodium anilide.

A somewhat related attempt to produce useful vat dyes in this series was made by Sanin,[127] who converted 1,4-diamino-5,10-anthra-quinone into the 1,4-N,N'-bischloroimino compound, which was

TABLE XXXVIII. Naphtho[2,3-a]phenazines

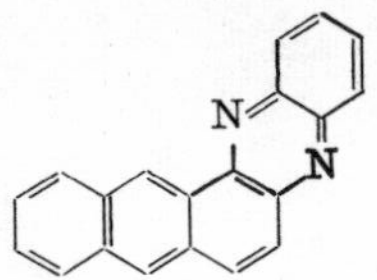

Substituents	Physical characteristics	M.p. (°C.)	Color with H_2SO_4, followed by dilution, etc.	Ref.
None	Dark yellow platelets	221–222	Bluish-green	116, 117
7,7'-Dimer	Greenish-yellow needles		Green, violet, red	118
8,13-Quinone	Yellow crystals	253	Orange-red	119
5,14-Dihydro-8,13-quinone	Blue needles, metallic luster	310 (dec.)	Green, gives blue vat	119
3-Chloro-5,14-dihydro-8,13-quinone	Violet needles, green iridescence	310–320	Olive-green	119
5,14-Diacetyl-5,14-dihydro-8,13-quinone	Yellowish-red needles	256		119
3-Methyl-5,14-dihydro-8,13-quinone	Greenish-blue needles			119
6-Bromo-3-methyl-8,13-quinone	Pale brown needles	247	Orange-red	122
6-Bromo-3-methyl-5-isopropyl-5,14-dihydro-8,13-quinone	Bluish-red needles		Greenish-blue	123
6-Bromo-3-methyl-5-(1'-phenyl-ethyl)-5,14-dihydro-8,13-quinone	Blue lustrous needles		Bluish-green	123
6-Bromo-3-methyl-5-(3'-oxindolyl)-5,14-dihydro-8,13-quinone	Blue lustrous needles		Bluish-violet	123

(Table continued)

TABLE XXXVIII (*continued*)

Substituents	Physical characteristics	M.p. (°C.)	Color with H_2SO_4, followed by dilution, etc.	Ref.
7-Anilino-5-phenyl-5,14-dihydro-8,13-quinone	Anhydro-base; hydrochloride	204–6, 280		127
5-Phenyl-5,14-dihydro-8,13-quinone	Blue needles, coppery luster	236–237	Greenish-yellow, green	124–126
5-Methyl-5,14-dihydro-8,13-quinone-2-sulfonic acid	(K salt), blue powder		Green, dyes wool greenish-blue shades	125
5-(2′-Carboxyphenyl)-5,14-dihydro-8,13-quinone	Dark-blue powder		Yellowish-green	125
5-(2′-Hydroxyethyl)-5,14-dihydro-8,13-quinone-2-sulfonic acid	Flat blue prisms		Dyes wool greenish-blue shades	125
5-Phenyl-5,14-dihydro-8,13-quinone-2-sulfonic acid	Blue powder		Dyes wool fast blue shades	125
5-(4′-Chlorophenyl)-5,14-dihydro-8,13-quinone-2-sulfonic acid	(Na salt), fine blue needles		Dyes wool greenish-blue colors	125
5-(4′-Dimethylaminophenyl)-5,14-dihydro-8,13-quinone-2-sulfonic acid	(Na salt), small blue needles		Dyes wool greenish-blue colors	125
5-(4′-Carboxyphenyl)-5,14-dihydro-8,13-quinone-2-sulfonic acid	Dark-blue powder		Dyes wool fast blue shades	125
5-(2′-Carboxyphenyl)-5,14-dihydro-8,13-quinone-2-sulfonic acid	Dark-blue powder		Dyes wool fast blue shades	125

Substituents	Physical characteristics	M.p. (°C.)	Color with H_2SO_4, followed by dilution etc.	Ref.
5-(4'-Acetamidophenyl)-5,14-dihydro-8,13-quinone-2-sulfonic acid	(Na salt), small blue crystals		Dyes wool greenish-blue colors	125
5-(3'-Carboxy-4'-hydroxyphenyl)-5,14-dihydro-8,13-quinone-7-bromo-2-sulfonic acid			Dyes wool greenish-blue shades; chroming gives a still greener color	125
5-(3'-Carboxy-4'-hydroxyphenyl)-5,14-dihydro-8,13-quinone-2-sulfonic acid	Blue ppt.		Dyes wool greenish-blue colors	125
5-(3'-Carboxy-2'-hydroxyphenyl)-5,14-dihydro-8,13-quinone-2,5'-disulfonic acid	Dark-violet powder		Blue-green color; dyes wool in violet shades after chroming	125
5-(2'-Nitrophenyl)-5,14-dihydro-8,13-quinone-4'-sulfonic acid	(Na salt), blue needles		Dyes wool blue shades	125
5-Methyl-4-carboxy-5,14-dihydro-8,13-quinone-2-sulfonic acid	Dark-blue powder		Green coloration	125
5-Cyclohexyl-5,14-dihydro-8,13-quinone-2-sulfonic acid	(Na salt), blue needles		Greenish-yellow coloration	125
5-Phenyl-5,14-dihydro-8,13-quinone-2-(o-carboxybenzoyl)-			Olive-green coloration; yields brownish-red vat	125

reacted with aniline in the presence of anhydrous sodium acetate and cupric acetate. After purification, the product (7-phenylimino-5-phenylnaphtho[2,3-a]phenazine-8,13-quinone (XCIII), compare *R. I.* 3497) formed brownish-black needles, m.p. 234–235°.

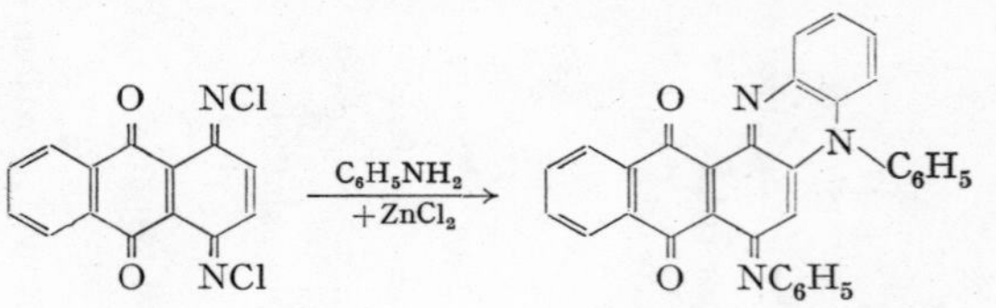

(XCIII)

Compounds of this ring system are collected in Table XXXVIII.

8. 7-Naphtho[1, 8-*ab*]phenazine

R. I. 3257 (XCIV)

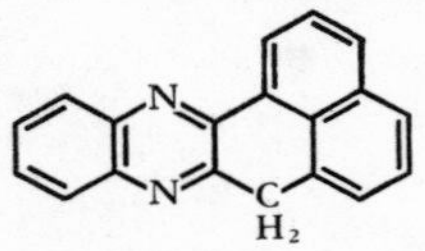

(XCIV)

A few compounds only of this series are known; the parent compound (XCIV) has not been described. The simplest member, 7-keto-7-naphtho[1,8-*ab*]phenazine (XCV), was obtained by Errara[128] by the condensation of *o*-phenylenediamine with perinaphthindan-1,2,3-trione in hot ethanol. The presence of a keto group in the molecule is confirmed by the ready formation of a phenylhydrazone. Other simple members of this class are the 4- and 5-nitro-7-keto derivatives (XCVI and XCVII), prepared similarly from *o*-phenylenediamine and 5- and 6-nitroperi-naphthindan-1,2,3-triones by Calderaro.[129, 130]

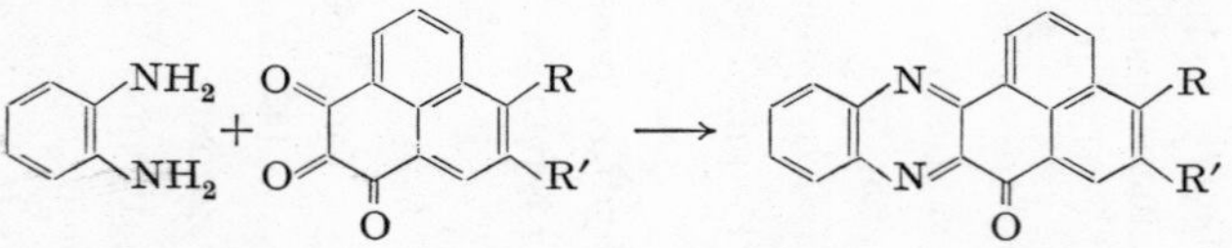

XCV   (R=R′=H)
XCVI (R=NO$_2$, R′=H)
XCVII (R=H, R′=NO$_2$)

XCVI and XCVII are the structures attributed to the products by Calderaro; but it will be apparent to the reader that condensation of the nitrotriones with o-phenylenediamine may occur in two ways, structures XCVIII and XCIX being equally feasible. These were not considered, apparently.

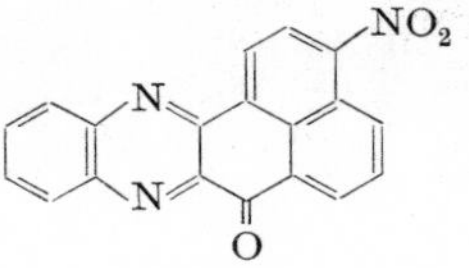

(XCVIII) 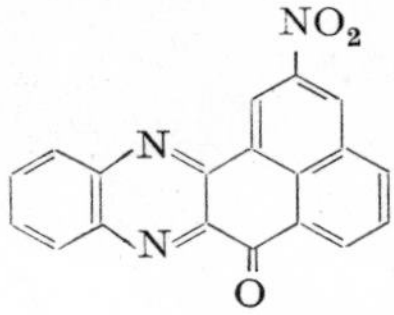   (XCIX)

In Table XXXIX, we retain the structures allotted to the compounds by the author.

TABLE XXXIX. 7-Naphtho[1,8-ab]phenazines

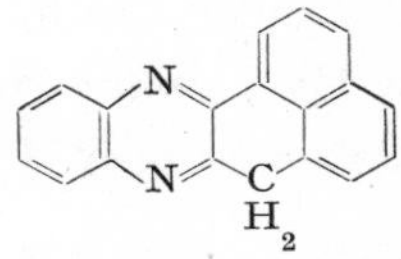

Substituents	Physical characteristics	M.p. (°C.)	Ref.
7-Keto-	Golden-yellow needles	255–256	128
7-Phenylhydrazone	Violet plates	299 (dec.)	128
7-Keto-4-nitro-(?)	Yellow needles	263–265	130
7-Keto-5-nitro-(?)	Yellow needles	276–277	129
10(or 11)-Chloro-7-keto-	Yellow needles	302	131
10(or 11)-Chloro-7-keto-4-nitro-	Yellow prisms	250° (dec.)	131
Formula (CIV)	Yellow prisms	> 320 (dec.)	131
10(or 11)-Chloro-(CIV)	Yellow needles	> 300 (dec.)	131
10(or 11)-Ethoxy-(CIV)	Rectangular prisms	> 300 (dec.)	131
Formula (CV) or (CVI)	Brown crystals		131

More recently, two patents relating to compounds of this group have been filed. The first[131] relates to the synthesis of these compounds, bearing 7-keto groups, by the chlorination by means of sulfuryl chloride at 40–70° of compounds such as perinaphthindan-1,3-dione (C) to the dichloro derivative (CI), which is then condensed with o-phenylenediamine or a chloro derivative of this or else with an o-nitroaniline, in which latter case the reaction is completed by subsequent reduction, the product being XCV or a substitution product of this.

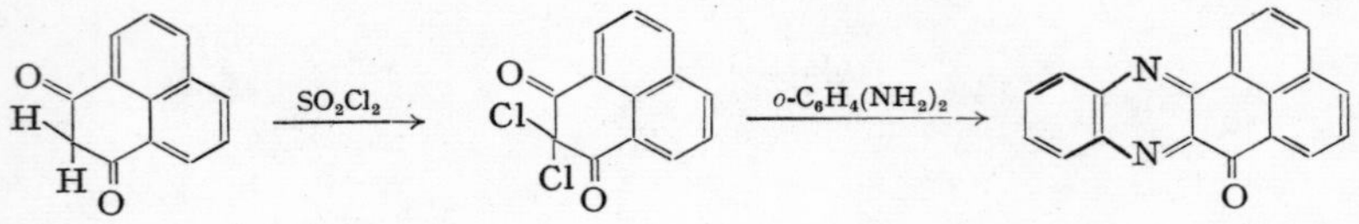

Other examples employed the dichloroperiacenaphthindandione (CII) or tetrachloronaphthaleneperidiindandione (CIII, 2,2,7,7-tetra-chloro-1,2,3,6,7,8-hexahydropyrene-1,3,6,8-tetrone) and o-phenylene-diamine, the products being 5-acenaphtho[5,6-ab]phenazin-5-one (R. I. 3542, CIV) and 8,17-dihydrodiquinoxalo[2,3-b,2',3'-i]pyren-8,17-dione (no R. I., CV), or alternatively 6,9-dihydrodiquinoxalo[2,3-a,2',3'-i]-pyren-6,9-dione (no R. I., CVI) or a mixture of CV and CVI.

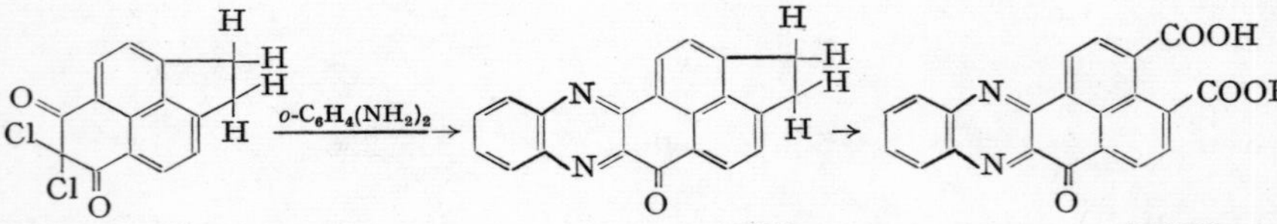

The oxidation of CIV or a substitution product of this to the 3,4-dicarboxylic acid (CVII), or its anhydride, may be carried out by heating with moderately concentrated sulfuric acid. On heating the anhydride with ammonia, a primary amine, 1,2-diamine or o-nitro-aniline, with subsequent reduction, very fast vat dyes of various colors (yellow, red, brown, green etc.) are formed whose structures are perhaps speculative[132] (see also Chapter XIX: 42).

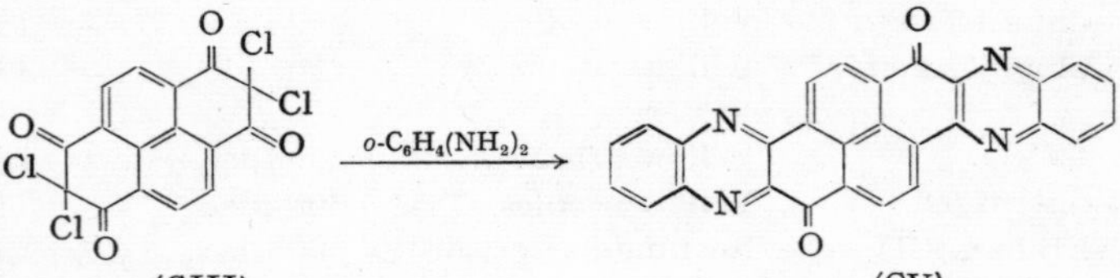

References

1. L. F. Fieser, *J. Am. Chem. Soc.*, **51**, 1896 (1929).
2. L. F. Fieser, *J. Am. Chem. Soc.*, **51**, 940 (1929).
3. O. Hinsberg, *Ann.*, **237**, 327 (1887).
4. M. Martynoff, *Compt. rend.*, **231**, 1510 (1950).
5. O. Hinsberg and H. Garfunkel, *Ann.*, **292**, 258 (1896).
6. A. Einhorn and B. S. Bull, *Ann.*, **295**, 209 (1897).
7. U. S. Pat. 2,238,487; *Chem. Abstracts*, **35**, 4967 (1941).
8. Ger. Pat. 79,570; *Frdl.*, **4**, 397 (1894–1897).
9. K. Yamada and T. Noguchi, *J. Soc. Chem. Ind. Japan*, **38**, Suppl. binding 134 (1935); *Chem. Abstracts*, **29**, 4587 (1935).
10. K. Yamada and T. Noguchi, *J. Soc. Chem. Ind. Japan*, **39**, Suppl. binding, 207 (1936); *Chem. Abstracts*, **30**, 6567 (1936).
11. K. Yamada, T. Noguchi and K. Oiwa, *Bull. Chem. Soc. Japan*, **11**, 225 (1936); *Chem. Abstracts*, **30**, 5993 (1936).
12. K. Yamada and N. Hasebe, *J. Soc. Chem. Ind. Japan*, **41**, Suppl. binding, 160 (1938); *Chem. Abstracts*, **32**, 7042 (1938).
13. K. Yamada and N. Hasebe, *J. Soc. Chem. Ind. Japan*, **41**, Suppl. binding, 290 (1938); *Chem. Abstracts*, **33**, 1740 (1939).
14. A. Hantzsch and G. Osswald, *Ber.*, **33**, 278 (1900).
15. A. Hantzsch, *Ber.*, **38**, 2143 (1905).
16. A. Hantzsch, *Ber.*, **39**, 158 (1906).
17. F. Kehrmann, *Ber.*, **38**, 2962 (1905).
18. M. Freund and L. Richard, *Ber.*, **42**, 1101 (1909).
19. O. Hinsberg, *Ber.*, **42**, 3333 (1909).
20. O. Hinsberg, *Ber.*, **38**, 2800 (1905).
21. H. Hillemann, Ber., **71B**, 42 (1938).
22. P. Karrer and A. Widmer, *Helv. Chim. Acta*, **9**, 461 (1926).
23. J. Meisenheimer and F. W. Ditt, *Ann.*, **539**, 57 (1939).
24. Ger. Pat. 97,639; *Frdl.*, **5**, 364 (1897–1900).
25. F. Kehrmann, *Ber.*, **31**, 977 (1898).
26. F. Kehrmann, *Ber.*, **33**, 395 (1900).
27. F. Kehrmann, *Ber.*, **50**, 554 (1917).
28. F. Sachs, *Ber.*, **31**, 3073 (1898).
29. F. Sachs and G. Bargellini, *Ber.*, **38**, 1742 (1905).
30. F. Kehrmann and J. Eichler, *Ber.*, **34**, 1210 (1901).
31. F. Kehrmann and Z. Kikina, *Ber.*, **32**, 2633 (1899).
32. Z. Kikina, *J. Russ. Phys. Chem. Soc.*, **32**, 170 (1900); *Chem. Zentr.*, **1900**, II, 117.
33. F. Kehrmann and W. Hiby, *Ber.*, **34**, 1085 (1901).
34. Ger. Pat. 436,161; *Chem. Zentr.*, **1927**, I, 972.
35. W. H. Doer, *Ber.*, **3**, 291 (1870).
36. Schichuzky, *Ber.*, **7**, 1454 (1874).
37. W. Klobukowski, *Ber.*, **10**, 570 (1877).
38. A. Laurent, *Ann. chim.*, [2], **59**, 376 (1835).
39. W. H. Doer, *Ber.*, **10**, 772 (1877).
40. R. Nietzki and O. Goll, *Ber.*, **18**, 297 (1885).
41. O. N. Witt, *Ber.*, **19**, 2791 (1886).
42. O. Fischer and H. Strauss, *Ber.*, **41**, 397 (1908).
43. P. T. Cleve, *Ber.*, **20**, 1989 (1887).
44. P. Matthes, *Ber.*, **23**, 1325 (1890).

45. G. R. Levi and M. Faldino, *Gazz. chim. ital.*, **54**, 818 (1924); *Chem. Zentr.*, **1925**, I, 657; *Chem. Abstracts*, **19**, 2200 (1925).
46. Ger. Pat. 78,748; *Frdl.*, **4**, 372 (1894–1897).
47. W. Meigen and W. Normann, *Ber.*, **33**, 2711 (1900).
48. F. Reitzenstein and R. Fitzgerald, *J. prakt. Chem.*, [2], **89**, 271 (1914).
49. Ger. Pat. 165,226; *Frdl.*, **8**, 518 (1905–1907); *Chem. Zentr.*, **1905**, II, 1737.
50. F. Reitzenstein and F. Andre, *J. prakt. Chem.*, [2], **87**, 97 (1913).
51. K. H. Pausacker, *J. Chem. Soc.*, **1953**, 1989.
52. E. Boyland, D. Manson and P. Sims, *J. Chem. Soc.*, **1953**, 3623.
53. Ger. Pat. 532,304; *Frdl.*, **18**, 855 (1931); *Chem. Abstracts*, **26**, 315 (1932).
54. Ger. Pat. 525,838; *Frdl.*, **18**, 856 (1931); see Brit. Pat., 339,283; *Chem. Abstracts*, **25**, 2438 (1931).
55. Ger. Pat. 531,085; *Frdl.*, **18**, 858 (1931); *Chem. Abstracts*, **25**, 5434 (1931).
56. Ger. Pat. 589,971; *Frdl.*, **20**, 499 (1933); *Chem. Abstracts*, **28**, 2374 (1934).
57. G. R. Clemo and E. C. Dawson, *J. Chem. Soc.*, **1939**, 1114.
58. R. A. M. Case and J. Pearson, *Proc. Deuxième Cong. Int. Biochem. (Paris)*, **1952**, p. 464.
59. G. M. Bonser, *J. Path. Bact.*, **55**, 1 (1943).
60. R. A. M. Case, D. B. MacDonald and J. Pearson, *British Empire Cancer Campaign, Annual Report*, **1952**, p. 41.
61. A. Steopoe, *Bul. Chim. Soc. Romana Stiinte*, **27**, 11 (1924); *Chem. Abstracts*, **21**, 1795 (1927); *Chem. Zentr.*, **1926**, I, 3524.
62. B. K. Malaviya and S. Dutt, *Proc. Acad. Sci. United Provinces Agra Oudh India*, **4**, 319 (1935); *Chem. Abstracts*, **30**, 1056 (1936); *Chem. Zentr.*, **1936**, I, 3487.
63. P. S. Pishchimuka, *J. Gen. Chem. (U.S.S.R.)*, **10**, 305 (1940); *Chem. Abstracts*, **34**, 7915 (1940); *Chem. Zentr.*, **1940**, II, 750.
64. F. Hauff, *Ann.*, **253**, 24 (1889).
65. J. Meisenheimer and K. Witte, *Ber.*, **36**, 4164 (1903).
66. F. R. Japp and C. I. Burton, *Trans. Chem. Soc.*, **51**, 98 (1887).
67. M. L. Moore, "The Leuckart Reaction," Chapter 7 in *Organic Reactions*, Vol. V, Edited by R. Adams, Wiley, New York, 1949.
68. A. Rieche, W. Rudolph and H. Seifert, *Ber.*, **73B**, 343 (1940).
69. R. Lesser, *Ann.*, **402**, 1 (1914).
70. O. Fischer and E. Hepp, *Ann.*, **255**, 144 (1889).
71. O. Fischer and E. Hepp, *Ann.*, **272**, 306 (1892).
72. O. Fischer and A. Junk, *Ber.*, **26**, 183 (1893).
73. O. Fischer and R. Albert, *Ber.*, **29**, 2086 (1896).
74. S. Maffei and S. Pietra, *Boll. Sci. Bologna*, **8**, 104 (1950); *Chem. Abstracts*, **46**, 119 (1952).
75. O. Fischer and E. Schindler, *Ber.*, **41**, 390 (1908).
76. Ger. Pat. 166,363; *Frdl.*, **8**, 518 (1905–1907); *Chem. Zentr.*, **1906**, I, 619.
77. F. Kehrmann and I. Safar, *Helv. Chim. Acta*, **8**, 668 (1925).
78. S. Mihaéloff, *Bull. soc. chim. France, Mém.*, [5], **5**, 1655 (1938).
79. F. Kehrmann and W. F. Sutherst, *Ber.*, **32**, 939 (1899).
80. F. Kehrmann and B. Perrot, *Helv. Chim. Acta*, **10**, 53 (1927).
81. R. Lantz, *Ann. chim.*, [11], **2**, 101 (1934).
82. Ger. Pat. 582,400; *Frdl.*, **19**, 1579 (1932); see *U. S. Pat.* 1,935,849; *Chem. Abstracts*, **28**, 907 (1934).
83. Ger. Pat. 394,195; *Frdl.*, **14**, 772 (1921–1925); *Chem. Zentr.*, **1924**, II, 1135.
84. Ger. Pat. 512,235; *Frdl.*, **17**, 929 (1930); see Brit. Pat. 322,209; *Chem. Abstracts*, **24**, 2891 (1930).

85. Ger. Pat. 445,403; *Frdl.*, **16**, 1044 (1925–1927); see Brit. Pat. 253,488; *Chem. Abstracts*, **21**, 2564 (1927).
86. Ger. Pat. 590,956; *Frdl.*, **20**, 1123 (1933); see Brit. Pat. 421,611; *Chem. Abstracts*, **29**, 3852 (1935).
87. Ger. Pat. 412,876; *Frdl.*, **15**, 436 (1925–1927); see Fr. Pat. 584,401; *Chem. Zentr.*, **1925**, I, 2665.
88. Ger. Pat. 481,296, *Frdl.*, **16**, 852 (1927–1929); see Brit. Pat. 291,546; *Chem. Abstracts*, **23**, 1276 (1929).
89. Ger. Pat. 484,273; *Frdl.*, **16**, 856 (1927–1929); see Brit. Pat. 315,506; *Chem. Abstracts*, **24**, 1744 (1930).
90. Ger. Pat. 417,033; *Frdl.*, **15**, 808 (1925–1927); see Brit. Pat. 217,936; *Chem. Zentr.*, **1924**, II, 2791.
91. Ger. Pat. 365,902; *Frdl.*, **14**, 739 (1921–1925); *Chem. Zentr.*, **1923**, II, 1186.
92. Ger. Pat. 368,168; *Frdl.*, **14**, 739 (1921–1925); *Chem. Zentr.*, **1923**, II, 1186.
93. O. Hinsberg, *Ann.*, **319**, 257 (1901).
94. O. Fischer, A. Fritzen and S. Eilles, *J. prakt. Chem.*, [2], **79**, 562 (1909).
95. F. Ullmann and J. S. Ankersmit, *Ber.*, **38**, 1811 (1905).
96. O. Fischer and E. Hepp, *Ann.*, **256**, 233 (1890).
97. O. Fischer and E. Hepp, *Ann.*, **262**, 237 (1891).
98. O. Fischer and E. Hepp, *Ann.*, **286**, 187 (1895).
99. Swiss Pat. 259,321; *Chem. Abstracts*, **44**, 6634 (1950).
100. A. W. Hofmann, *Ber.*, **2**, 374 (1869).
101. A. W. Hofmann, *Ber.*, **2**, 412 (1869).
102. Ger. Pat. 40,868; *Frdl.*, **1**, 276 (1877–1887).
103. O. Fischer and E. Hepp, *Ber.*, **31**, 2485 (1898).
104. Ger. Pat. 71,296; *Frdl.*, **3**, 344 (1890–1894).
105. O. Fischer and E. Hepp, *Ber.*, **26**, 2235 (1893).
106. Ger. Pat. 62,179; *Frdl.*, **3**, 349 (1890–1894).
107. Ger. Pat. 63,181; *Frdl.*, **3**, 350 (1890–1894).
108. Ger. Pat. 99,545; *Frdl.*, **5**, 368 (1897–1900); *Chem. Zentr.*, **1899**, I, 157.
109. P. Julius, *Ber.*, **19**, 1365 (1886).
110. H. W. Vogel, *Ber.*, **11**, 622 (1878).
111. S. Kalandek, *Physik. Z.*, **9**, 128 (1908); *Chem. Zentr.*, **1908**, I, 1024.
112. H. H. Hodgson and E. Marsden, *J. Chem. Soc.*, **1938**, 1181.
113. K. A. Hofmann, F. Hartmann and F. Kroll, *Ber.*, **57B**, 945 (1924).
114. O. Fischer and E. Hepp, *Ber.*, **33**, 1485 (1900).
115. G. M. Badger and R. Pettit, *J. Chem. Soc.*, **1951**, 3211.
116. K. Lagodzinski, *Ann.*, **342**, 59 (1905).
117. H. Dienel, *Ber.*, **39**, 926 (1906).
118. A. Eckert and J. Hampel, *Ber.*, **60B**, 1693 (1927).
119. F. Ullmann and O. Fodor, *Ann.*, **380**, 324 (1911).
120. W. Bradley, E. Leete and D. S. Stephens, *J. Chem. Soc.*, **1951**, 2163.
121. R. Scholl and S. Edlbacher, *Ber.*, **44**, 1727 (1911).
122. F. Ullmann and R. Medenwald, *Ber.*, **46**, 1798 (1913).
123. Ger. Pat. 252,529; *Frdl.*, **11**, 654 (1912–1914); *Chem. Zentr.*, **1912**, II, 1793.
124. Ger. Pat. 329,246; *Frdl.*, **13**, 419 (1916–1921); *Chem. Zentr.*, **1921**, II, 314.
125. Ger. Pat. 652,772; *Frdl.*, **24**, 814 (1937); see Brit. Pat. 469,016; *Chem. Abstracts*, **32**, 799 (1938).
126. W. Bradley and E. Leete, *J. Chem. Soc.*, **1951**, 2129.
127. A. A. Sanin, *J. Russ. Phys. Chem. Soc.*, **59**, 867 (1927); *Chem. Abstracts*, **22**, 3408 (1928).
128. G. Errara, *Gazz. chim. ital.*, **43**, I, 583 (1913); *Chem. Zentr.*, **1913**, II, 776.

129. E. Calderaro, *Gazz. chim. ital.*, **45**, II, 131 (1915); *Chem. Zentr.*, **1915**, II, 1104.
130. E. Calderaro, *Gazz. chim. ital.*, **46**, I, 261 (1916); *Chem. Zentr.*, **1916**, II, 573.
131. Ger. Pat. 658,203; *Frdl.*, **24**, 602 (1937); *Chem. Zentr.*, **1938**, II, 422; *Chem. Abstracts*, **32**, 4798 (1938).
132. Ger. Pat. 659,095; *Frdl.*, **24**, 973 (1937); *Chem. Zentr.*, **1938**, II, 187; *Chem. Abstracts*, **32**, 5638 (1938).
133. S. C. De and T. N. Ghosh, *J. Indian Chem. Soc.*, **7**, 357 (1930); *Chem. Abstracts*, **24**, 4781 (1930).
134. N. O. Cappel and W. C. Fernelius, *J. Org. Chem.*, **5**, 40 (1940).
135. M. Gates and W. F. Newhall, *J. Am. Chem. Soc.*, **70**, 2261 (1948).
136. A. Skita and W. Rohrmann, *Ber.*, **63B**, 1473 (1930).
137. L. F. Fieser and J. T. Dunn, *J. Am. Chem. Soc.*, **59**, 1021 (1937).
138. R. D. Haworth, *J. Chem. Soc.*, **1932**, 1125.
139. C. B. Radcliffe, I. R. Sherwood and W. F. Short, *J. Chem. Soc.*, **1931**, 2293.
140. D. Aziz and J. G. Breckenridge, *Can. J. Res.*, **28B**, 26 (1950).
141. L. Bradford, T. J. Elliott and F. M. Rowe, *J. Chem. Soc.*, **1947**, 437.
142. O. Hinsberg, *Ber.*, **17**, 318 (1884).
143. R. D. Haworth, C. R. Mavin and G. Sheldrick, *J. Chem. Soc.*, **1934**, 454.
144. R. D. Haworth, B. M. Letsky and C. R. Mavin, *J. Chem. Soc.*, **1932**, 1784.
145. L. Ruzicka and F. Balas, *Helv. Chim. Acta*, **6**, 677 (1923).
146. L. Ruzicka and F. Balas, *Helv. Chim. Acta*, **7**, 875 (1924).
147. L. F. Fieser and E. B. Hershberg, *J. Am. Chem. Soc.*, **57**, 2192 (1935).
148. E. E. Lewis and R. C. Elderfield, *J. Org. Chem.*, **5**, 290 (1940).
149. E. Noelting and G. Thesmar, *Ber.*, **35**, 628 (1902).
150. L. Ruzicka and W. J. Smith, *Chemistry & Industry*, **1938**, 1210.
151. R. D. Haworth and F. M. Bolam, *J. Chem. Soc.*, **1932**, 2248.
152. L. Ruzicka and J. R. Hosking, *Helv. Chim. Acta*, **14**, 203 (1931).
153. R. D. Haworth and C. R. Mavin, *J. Chem. Soc.*, **1932**, 2720.
154. H. Schulze, *Z. physiol. Chem.*, **238**, 35 (1936).
155. L. I. Smith and C. L. Moyle, *J. Am. Chem. Soc.*, **58**, 1 (1936).
156. M. S. Newman, *J. Org. Chem.*, **9**, 518 (1944).
157. Ng. Ph. Buü-Hoi and P. Cagniant, *Rec. trav. chim.*, **62**, 519 (1943).
158. Ng. Ph. Buü-Hoi and P. Cagniant, *Ber.*, **77B**, 118 (1944).
159. S. Sako, *Bull. Chem. Soc. Japan*, **9**, 55 (1934); *Chem. Abstracts*, **28**, 3730 (1934).
160. C. Gelzer, *Ber.*, **20**, 3252 (1887).
161. C. Gelzer, *Ber.*, **21**, 2949 (1888).
162. J. B. Shoesmith and A. Mackie, *J. Chem. Soc.*, **1929**, 476.
163. E. Bamberger and S. C. Hooker, *Ann.*, **229**, 102 (1885).
164. W. F. Short and H. Wang, *J. Chem. Soc.*, **1950**, 991.
165. L. Ruzicka and J. Meyer, *Helv. Chim. Acta*, **5**, 581 (1922).
166. R. D. Haworth, *J. Chem. Soc.*, **1932**, 2717.
167. R. M. Orcutt and M. T. Bogert, *J. Am. Chem. Soc.*, **63**, 127 (1941).
168. A. Baur-Thurgau, *Ber.*, **30**, 303 (1897).
169. M. C. Ford, W. A. Waters and H. T. Young, *J. Chem. Soc.*, **1950**, 833.
170. T. F. Doumani and K. A. Kobe, *J. Am. Chem. Soc.*, **62**, 562 (1940).
171. G. A. Nyman, *Ann. Acad. Sci. Fennicae*, **48A**, No. 6 (1937); *Chem. Abstracts*, **33**, 8193 (1939).
172. L. Ruzicka and S. Kaufmann, *Helv. Chim. Acta*, **24**, 939 (1941).
173. L. I. Smith and M. A. Kiess, *J. Am. Chem. Soc.*, **61**, 284 (1939).
174. L. I. Smith and C. O. Guss, *J. Am. Chem. Soc.*, **62**, 2635 (1940).

175. J. Schmidt and O. Spoun, *Ber.*, **55B**, 1194 (1922).
176. A. Werner, *Ann.*, **322**, 135 (1902).
177. J. Schmidt and O. Schairer, *Ber.*, **44**, 740 (1911).
178. W. Autenreith and O. Hinsberg, *Ber.*, **25**, 492 (1892).
179. K. Brass and J. Stadler, *Ber.*, **57B**, 128 (1923).
180. K. Brass, E. Ferber and J. Stadler, *Ber.*, **57B**, 121 (1923).
181. F. Pollecoff and R. Robinson, *J. Chem. Soc.*, **113**, 645 (1918).
182. I. J. Pisovchi, *Ber.*, **43**, 2137 (1910).
183. T. G. H. Jones and R. Robinson, *J. Chem. Soc.*, **111**, 903 (1917).
184. R. Nietzki and F. Rechberg, *Ber.*, **23**, 1211 (1890).
185. G. M. Robinson and R. Robinson, *J. Chem. Soc.*, **107**, 1753 (1915).
186. C. Moureu, *Compt. rend.*, **125**, 31 (1897).
187. J. Allan and R. Robinson, *J. Chem. Soc.*, **1926**, 376.
188. G. M. Robinson and R. Robinson, *J. Chem. Soc.*, **111**, 934 (1917).
189. G. K. Hughes and F. Lions, *J. Proc. Roy. Soc. N. S. Wales*, **71**, 103 (1938); *Chem. Abstracts*, **32**, 3352 (1938).
190. K. Goto and T. Arai, *Bull. Chem. Soc. Japan*, **18**, 248 (1943); *Chem. Abstracts*, **42**, 4563 (1948).
191. N. Barton, J. W. Cook and J. D. Loudon, *J. Chem. Soc.*, **1945**, 176.
192. A. Oliverio, *Rend. seminar. facoltà sci. univ. Cagliari*, **4**, 126 (1934); *Chem. Abstracts*, **31**, 4976 (1937).
193. E. R. Watson and S. Dutt, *J. Chem. Soc.*, **119**, 1211 (1921).
194. O. N. Witt, *Ber.*, **19**, 441 (1886).
195. E. Heim, *Ber.*, **21**, 2301 (1888).
196. R. Nietzki and E. Hagenbach, *Ber.*, **20**, 328 (1887).
197. J. C. E. Simpson, *J. Chem. Soc.*, **1947**, 237.
198. J. C. E. Simpson, C. M. Atkinson, K. Schofield and O. Stephenson, *J. Chem. Soc.*, **1945**, 646.
199. J. R. Keneford and J. C. E. Simpson, *J. Chem. Soc.*, **1948**, 354.
200. W. Borsche and J. Barthenheier, *Ann.*, **553**, 250 (1942).
201. C. Musante and L. Fabbrini, *Sperimentale, Sez. chim. biol.*, **3**, 33 (1952); *Chem. Abstracts*, **47**, 6888 (1953).
202. F. Ullmann and E. Cassirer, *Ber.*, **43**, 439 (1910).
203. A. C. Sircar and D. C. Roy, *J. Chem. Soc.*, **125**, 543 (1924).

CHAPTER XVI

Polybenzophenazines

There is a fairly large number of ring systems derived from phenazine by condensation of many benzo- and other cyclic residues, but with a few important exceptions they possess little or no chemistry, having been prepared originally in order to characterize o-quinones derived from the polycyclic hydrocarbon system. These and the more important members are described below in order of their *Ring Index* number.

1. 1,4-Methanobenzo[a]phenazine.
   R. I. 2994

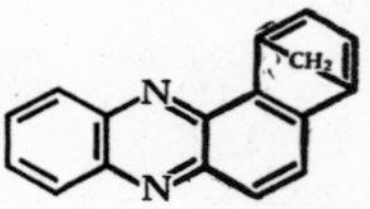

Representatives of this ring system were prepared by Smith and Hac[1] in the course of their studies of the Diels-Alder reaction between cyclopentadiene and 3,4,5,6-tetramethyl-1,2-benzoquinone. The initial product of the diene synthesis (I) reacted with o-phenylenediamine to yield 4a,4b,5,6-tetramethyl-1,4-dihydro-1,4-methanobenzo[a]phenazine (II) as white needles, m.p. 182–183°. Catalytic reduction of I

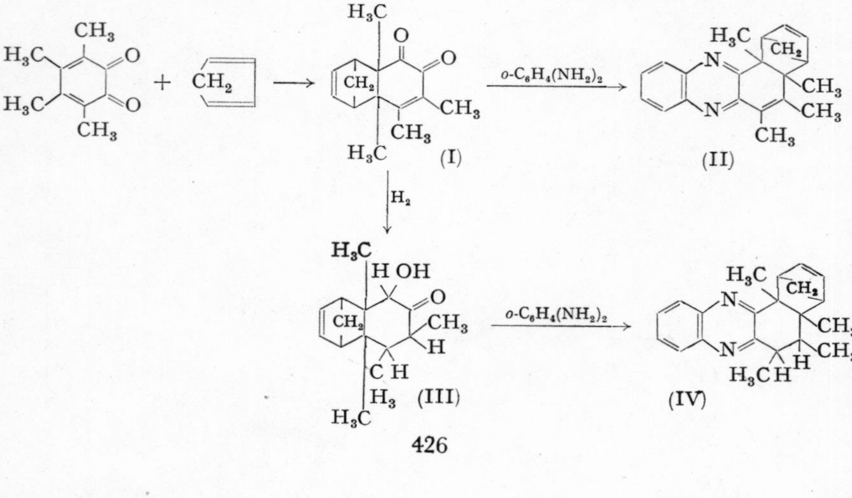

426

yielded the tetrahydro derivative (III), which also condensed with
o-phenylenediamine to yield 4a,4b,5,6-tetramethyl-1,4,5,6-tetrahydro-
1,4-methanobenzo[a]phenazine (IV) as white needles, m.p. 181–182°,
depressed to 162–165° when mixed with II.

2. 8,11-Methanobenzo[a]phenazine.
   R. I. 2995

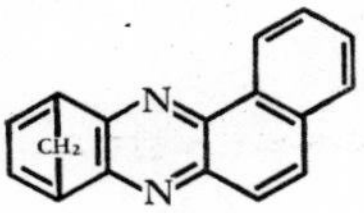

A representative of this ring systeem was prepared by Singh and
Bhaduri,[2] who condensed d-camphorquinone with 1,2-diaminonaph-
thalene. It is apparent that this condensation may occur in two directions, giving either V or VI.

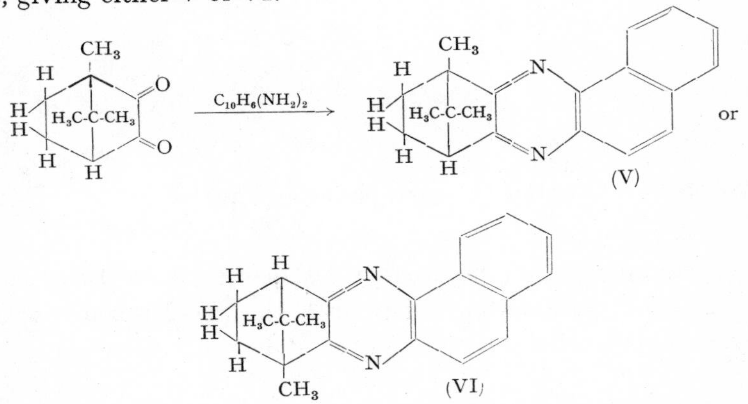

The product, d-8-(or 11-),13,13-trimethyl-8,9,10,11-tetrahydro-
8,11-methanobenzo[a]phenazine had m.p. 116–117° and the l-isomer,
prepared identically, also had m.p. 116–117°, while the dl-compound
was a colorless solid, m.p. 123–124°. These melting points are higher
than that recorded by Heckendorn,[3] who described the product he
obtained by an identical process as a colorless powder, m.p. 85–86°. This
anomaly remains unexplained.

**3. 1,4-Methanonaphtho[2,3-b]phenazine. 1,4-Methano-
   5,14-diazapentacene. R. I. 3483**

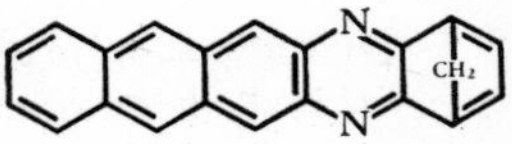

Heckendorn[3] prepared the only known representative of this
system by condensing camphorquinone with 2,3-diamino-5,10-anthra-
quinone. The product, 1,15,15-trimethyl-1,2,3,4,7,12-hexahydro-1,4-

methanonaphtho[2,3-*b*]phenazine-7,12-dione (VII), forms orange-yellow needles, m.p. 211°, which give a yellow coloration in concentrated sulfuric acid and fluorescent solutions in organic solvents.

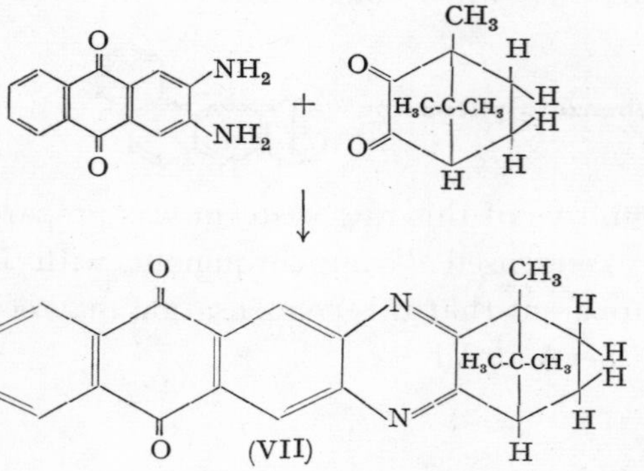

4. 1-Cyclopenta[5,6]naphtho[1,2-*b*]phenazine. R. I. 3538

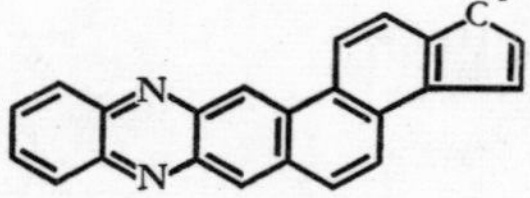

An example of this ring system (VIII) was obtained by reacting either 2,2-dibromocholestan-3-one[4] or cholestane-2,3-dione[5] with *o*-phenylenediamine. It forms colorless crystals, m.p. 184°.

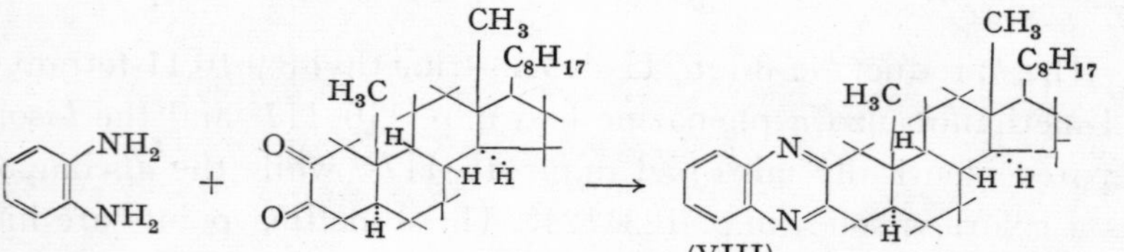

5. 1-Cyclopenta[5,6]naphtho[2,1-*a*]phenazine. (No R. I. enumeration)

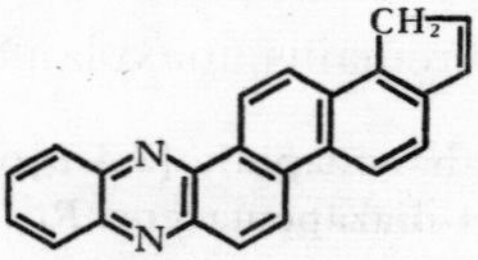

Ruzicka and his colleagues[4] prepared an example of this series by fusion together of 4,4-dibromocoprostan-3-one and *o*-phenylenediamine. The azine (IX) formed crystals, m.p. 200°. A related product, m.p.

207–$209°$, (not analyzed) was obtained[5] from o-phenylenediamine and cholestane-3,4-dione.

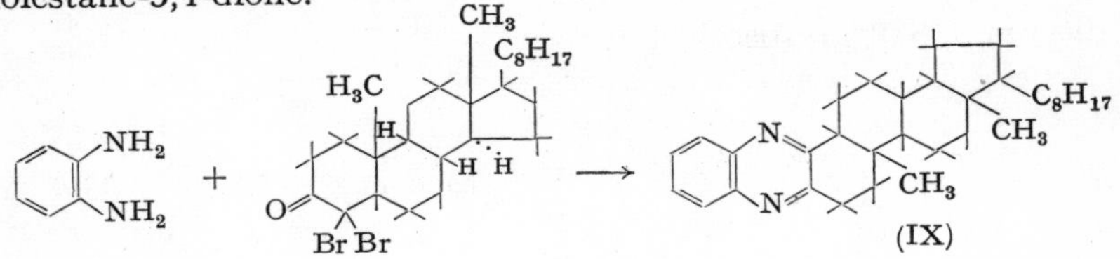

$$NH_2 \quad + \quad (Br\,Br\ ...) \longrightarrow (IX)$$

6. **5-Acenaphtho[5,6-ab]phenazine.**
   R. I. 3542

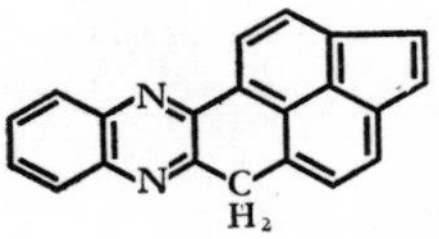

Representatives of this series of compounds have been described in a patent.[6] They are prepared by the chlorination of compounds such as periacenaphthindandione to the dichloro derivative (X), which on reaction with o-phenylenediamine, or with 2-nitroanilines followed by reduction, yields 5-keto-5-acenaphtho[5,6-ab]phenazine (XI) and its substitution products.

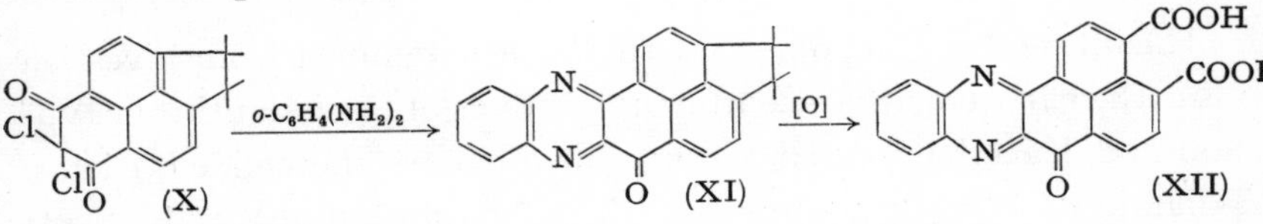

$$(X) \xrightarrow{\;o\text{-}C_6H_4(NH_2)_2\;} (XI) \xrightarrow{\;[O]\;} (XII)$$

The patent[6] also describes the oxidation of XI by moderately concentrated sulfuric acid to the dicarboxylic acid (XII), or its anhydride, which is a source of very fast vat dyes.[7] For a fuller description of these and related compounds, the reader is referred to Chapter XV: 8, to Table XXXIX in Chapter XV and to Chapter XIX: 41.

7. **4-Fluoreno[4,5-abc]phenazine.**
   R. I. 3543

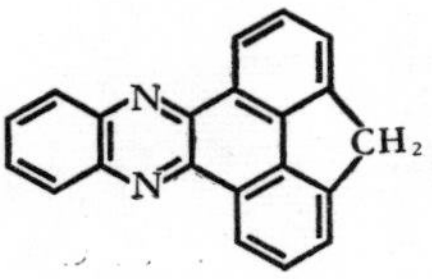

Kruber,[8] in the course of his extensive investigations of coal tar, isolated 4-cyclopenta[def]phenanthrene (XIII, *R. I.* 2570), which on oxidation gave the quinones (XIV) and (XV) among other products. These quinones condensed with o-phenylenediamine in acetic acid to yield 4-fluoreno[4,5-*abc*]phenazine (XVI) as yellow needles, m.p. 261°, and 4-keto-4-fluoreno[4,5-*abc*]phenazine (XVII) as bright yellow needles, m.p. 328°, respectively.

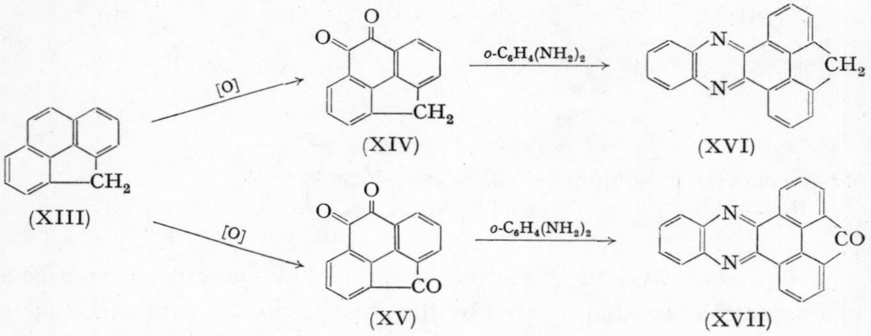

8. Benzo[*a*]naphtho[2,3-*i*]phenazine. R. I. 3593.

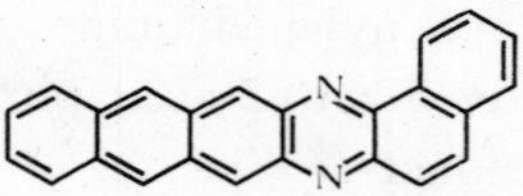

The interest in compounds of this series stemmed from investigations in the early twentieth century of vat dyes of the indanthrone type. Scholl and Kačer[9] prepared the first member by the condensation of 2,3-diamino-5,10-anthraquinone with 1,2-naphthoquinone in acetic acid. The product, 9,14-dihydrobenzo[*a*]naphtho[2,3-*i*]phenazine-9,14-dione (XVIII) formed small yellow needles melting above 320° and giving a bluish-carmine-red color in concentrated sulfuric acid. It gave an orange vat on reduction with sodium dithionite and dyed cotton in yellow shades from this.[10]

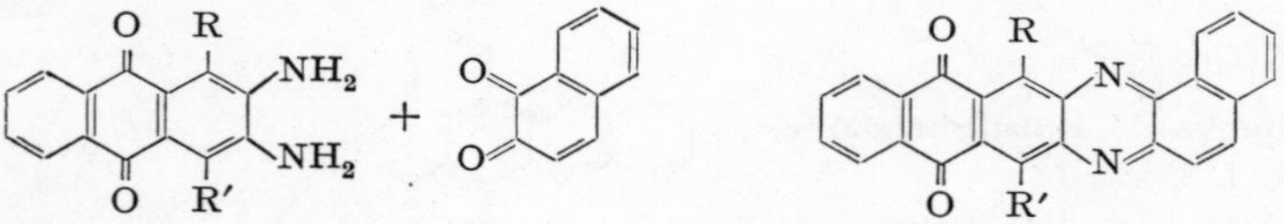

XVIII (R=R′=H)
XIX (R=NH$_2$, R′=H)
XX   (R=H, R′=NH$_2$)

A related azine (XIX or XX) was obtained by Scholl and his co-workers[11] by the condensation of 1,2,3-triamino-5,10-anthraquinone with 1,2-naphthoquinone as a dark-brown amorphous compound, m.p. 266–267°. This product, which may be formed by reaction with either the 1,2- or 2,3-amino groups, was shown to be very probably the linear isomer by the insoluble nature of the brown reduction product obtained with sodium dithionite, quite unlike a vat. There is still, however, ambiguity about the position of the amino substituent.

9. Tribenzo[a,c,i]phenazine.
   R. I. 3594

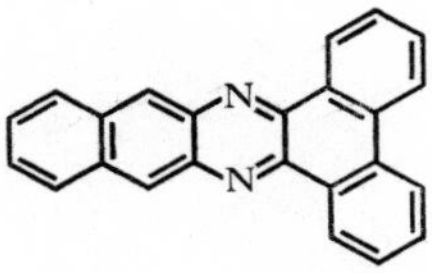

The first member of this series to be described was prepared by Schroeter[12] in the course of studies of various diaminotetralins, by the condensation of 2,3-diamino-5,6,7,8-tetrahydronaphthalene with 9,10-phenanthrenequinone. The product, 11,12,13,14-tetrahydrotribenzo-[a,c,i]phenazine (XXI) formed bright yellow, lustrous needles, m.p. 214–216°.

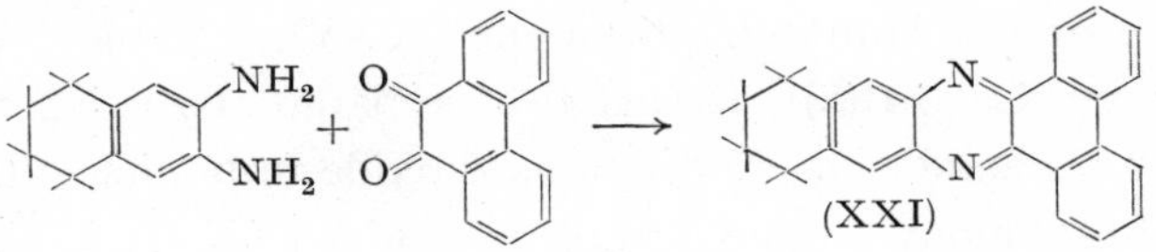

Goldstein and Streuli[13] later prepared the parent system by condensing 2,3-diaminonaphthalene with 9,10-phenanthrenequinone in ethanolic acetic acid. The product (XXII) formed fine yellow needles, m.p. 302°, which gave a violet-red color with concentrated sulfuric acid, which became brown and then yellow on progressive dilution with water.

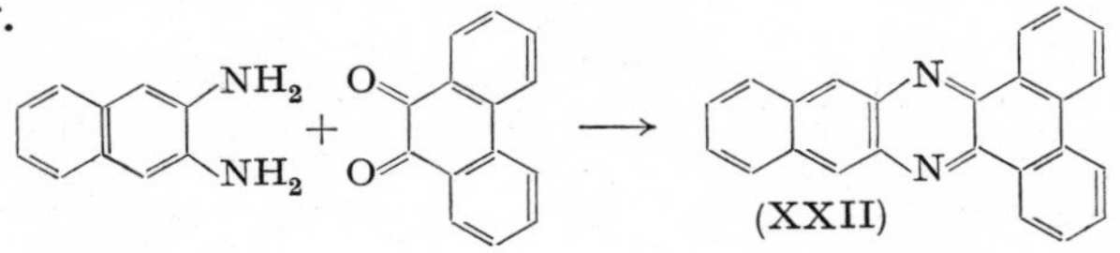

10. Benzo[a]naphtho[2,3-h]phenazine.
   R. I. 3595

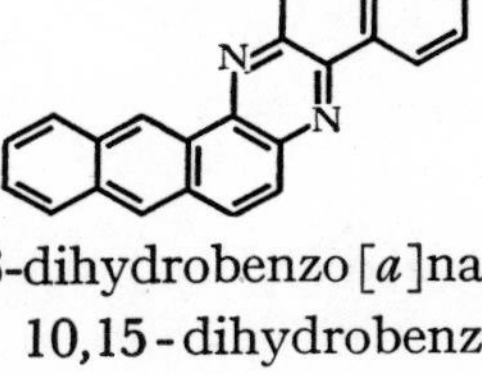

A product, which was either 8,13-dihydrobenzo[a]naphtho[2,3-h]-phenazine-,813-dione (XXIII) or 10,15-dihydrobenzo[a]naphtho-

[2,3-*j*]phenazine-10,15-dione (**XXIV**, *R. I.* 3596; see below, Section
XVI:11) was described in a patent[10] as prepared from 1,2-diamino-
5,10-anthraquinone and 1,2-naphthoquinone in glacial acetic acid.
Terres[14] repeated this work and described the product as crystallizing
from quinoline in brown needles giving a bluish-carmine coloration in
concentrated sulfuric acid and a reddish-blue insoluble vat on reduction.

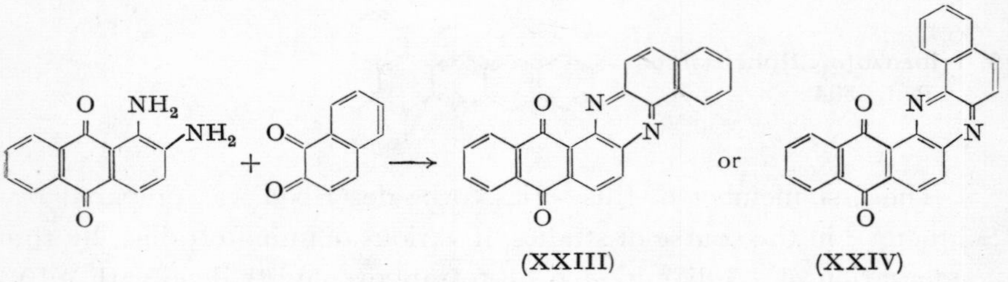

(**XXIII**)   (**XXIV**)

An unequivocal synthesis of **XXIII** was reported in a later
patent[15] by the action of 80% sulfuric acid at 100° on 1-benzeneazo-
2-(1′-anthraquinonylamino)naphthalene (**XXV**), a typical Witt reaction (Chapter XII:3,B(5)). It was also prepared according to another
patent[16] by the oxidation with mercuric oxide in boiling nitrobenzene
of 2(1′-anthraquinonylamino)-1-naphthylamine (**XXVI**), itself prepared
by reduction of **XXV** with sodium sulfide.

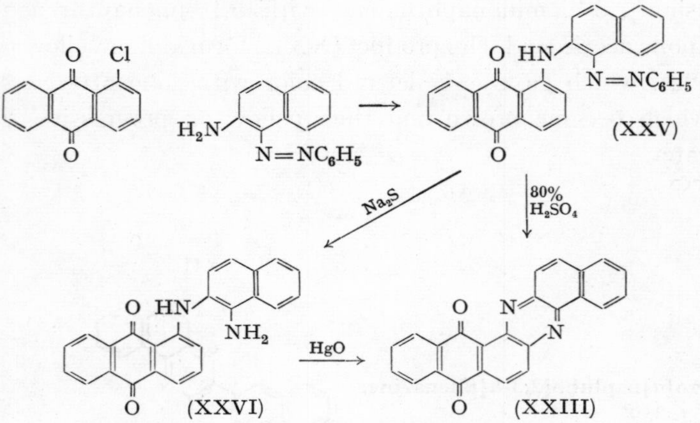

This compound (**XXIII**) of known structure forms yellow needles,
(no melting point given) and gives a reddish-violet coloration with

concentrated sulfuric acid. It dyes cotton from a blue vat in weak
yellow shades.

11. Benzo[a]naphtho [2,3-j]phenazine.
  R. I. 3596

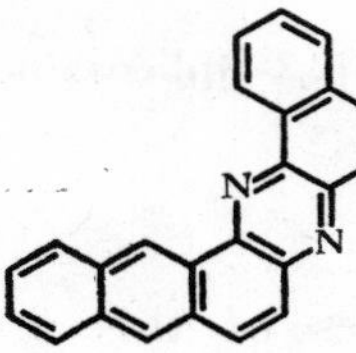

A compound (XXIV) that is possibly a member of this series has
already been described (see above, Section XVI:10). An unambiguous
synthesis of a derivative of XXIV was described in a patent.[17] 2-Amino-
3-bromo-1(1'-naphthylamino)-5,10-anthraquinone was treated with
formalin in acetic acid, when reaction occurred to yield 8-bromo-7-
methyl-7,10,15,16-tetrahydrobenzo[a]naphtho[2,3-j]phenazine-10,15-
dione (XXVII), which gave a blue solution in pyridine and an olive-
green color in concentrated sulfuric acid.

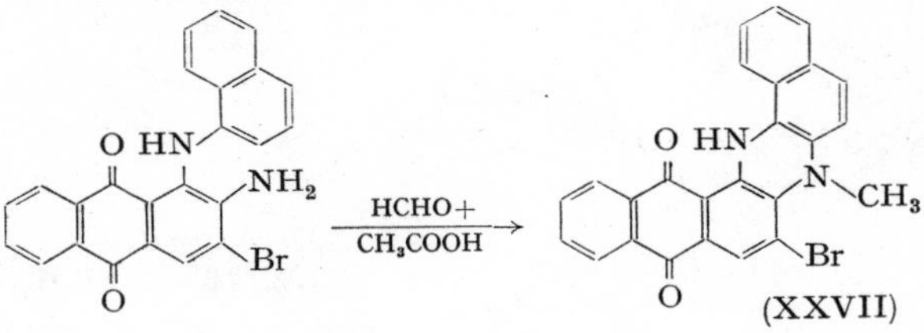

12. Benzo[a]naphtho[1,2-c]phenazine.
  R. I. 3597

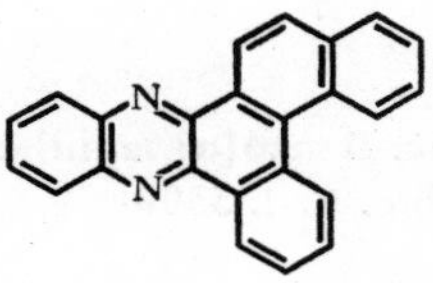

This basic ring system was prepared by Cook[18] in order to characterize the o-quinone obtained by the oxidation of benzo[c]phenan-
threne (R. I. 2807). The quinone was allowed to react with o-phenylenediamine in glacial acetic acid and the product (XXVIII) formed
canary-yellow needles, m.p. 189–190°.

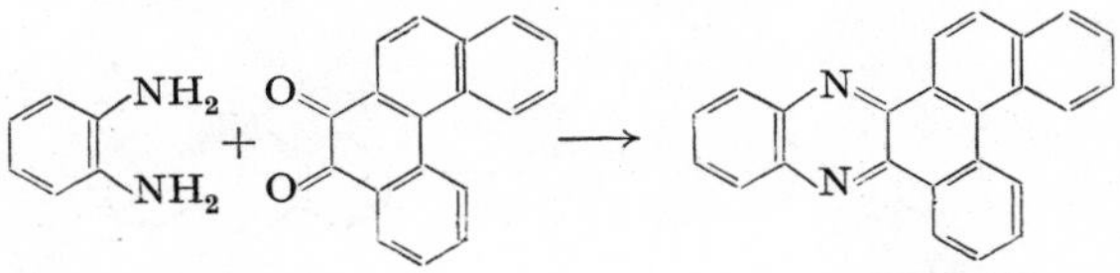

13. **Benzo[a]naphtho[2,3-c]phenazine.**
    R. I. 3598

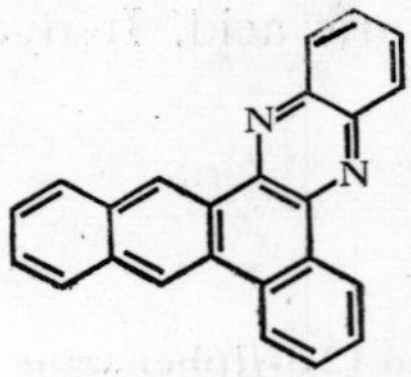

Representatives of this series of condensed phenazines were prepared by Fieser and Hershberg,[19] again merely to characterize o-quinones produced by chromic acid oxidation, in this case, of benz-[a]anthracene (R. I. 2805) derivatives. Both compounds prepared were 11,12,13,14-tetrahydrobenzo[a]naphtho[2,3-c]phenazines, further substituted at position 15. The 15-methyl derivative (XXIX) formed bright yellow crystals, m.p. 162–164°, while the 15-acetoxy compound (XXX) yielded short yellow needles, m.p. 276–278°.

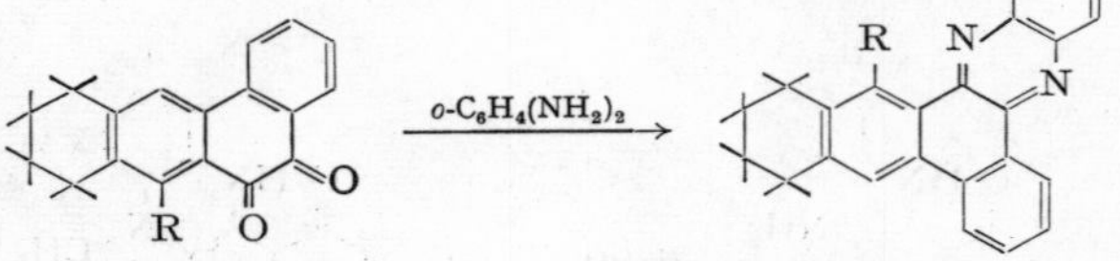

o-C$_6$H$_4$(NH$_2$)$_2$

XXIX (R=CH$_3$)
XXX (R=OCOCH$_3$)

14. **Chrysophenazine. Benzo[a]naphtho [2,1-c]phenazine. R. I. 3599**

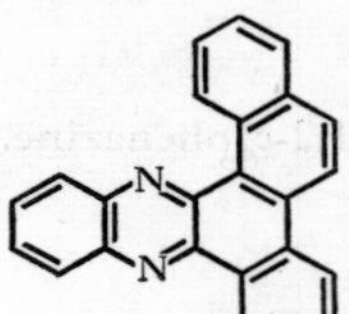

The parent substance, chrysophenazine (XXXI), itself was not described until 1938, when Newman[20] and Singh and Dutt[21] independently prepared it by the condensation of 5,6-chrysenequinone with o-phenylenediamine.

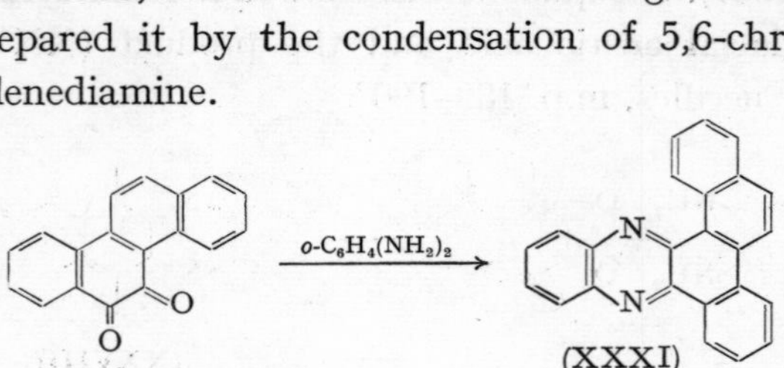

o-C$_6$H$_4$(NH$_2$)$_2$

(XXXI)

TABLE XL. Chrysophenazines (Benzo[a]naphtho [2,1-c]phenazines)

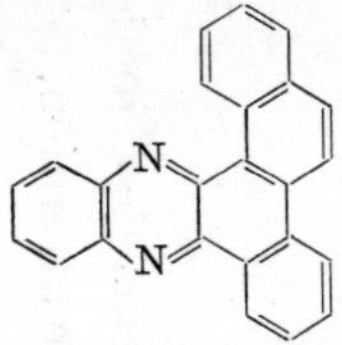

Substituents	Physical characteristics	M.p. (°C.)	Color with H_2SO_4	Ref.
None	Silky yellow needles	215–216		20, 21
5-Methyl-	Small yellow needles	220–221		20
13(or 14)-Methyl-	Lustrous yellow needles	176	Dark violet	22, 23
5-Chloro-	Yellow crystals	243	Dark violet	81
5-Bromo-	Bright yellow needles	252	Deep violet	82
5-Carboxy-	Yellow needles	> 330	Reddish-violet	82
5-Benzoyl-	Yellow needles	207	Violet-red	82
5-Nitro-	Fine yellow needles	277.6–279.6		83
5-Hydroxy-	Yellow needles	292		84
5-Ethoxy-	Yellow needles	215		84
5-Acetoxy-	Yellowish needles	252		84
5-Benzoyloxy-	Yellow needles	270		84

According to Singh and Dutt, **XXXI** exists in two modifications, yellow needles, m.p. 207–208°, and bright yellow crystals, m.p. 197°. Newman described it as forming long, silky, yellow needles, m.p. 215–216°, so that it is possible that the two forms described by the Indian workers are merely identical specimens of doubtful purity. Very much earlier the 13 (or 14)-methyl homolog had been described by Liebermann and Witt[22] and by Bamberger and Burgdorf,[23] both groups of workers preparing it from 5,6-chrysenequinone and 3,4-diaminotoluene. Since this early work, a number of other substituted chrysophenazines have been prepared. They are listed in Table XL, and were all prepared from the corresponding chrysenequinone or by some simple modification of existing chrysophenazine molecules. The chemistry of the system is unexplored.

15. Tribenzo[a,c,h]phenazine.
R. I. 3600

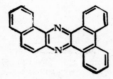

Of the many polybenzo condensed phenazine systems described in this chapter, this ring system has obtained much of the attention.

A. Nonquaternary Derivatives

The parent ring system, tribenzo[a,c,h]phenazine (**XXXII**), was synthesized by Lawson[24] in 1885 by condensing 1,2-diaminonaphthalene hydrochloride with 9,10-phenanthrenequinone in ethanolic acetic acid. It formed yellow crystals, m.p. 273°. This reaction remained the one in general use for many years.

$$\text{(XXXII)}$$

De and Ghosh[25] in 1930 claimed to have prepared **XXXII** by heating together 1,2-diaminonaphthalene and 9-amino-10-hydroxyphenanthrene at 200°. Their product, however, melted above 273° and may not be that claimed, because recently Maffei and Pietra[26] also synthesized XXXII and report it melts at 270°. This latter pair of workers applied their extension of the Crippa phenazine synthesis by fusing together at 160° 1-benzeneazo-2-naphthylamine and 9-hydroxyphenanthrene (which reacts as 9,10-dihydrophenanthrene-9-one), when they obtained XXXII in a yield of 70%.

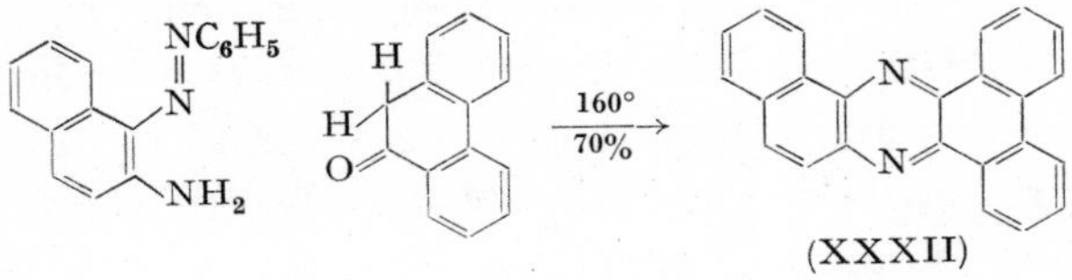

(XXXII)

12,13,14,15-Tetrahydrotribenzo[a,c,h]phenazine was prepared by Schroeter[12] by condensing 1,2-diamino-5,6,7,8-tetrahydronaphthalene with 9,10-phenanthrenequinone. Homologs of XXXII have been prepared by the normal condensation reaction.[27] The 11-sulfonic acid of XXXII was prepared by Witt[28] by condensing 9,10-phenanthrenequinone with 1,2-diaminonaphthalene-4-sulfonic acid, thereby incidently proving that Cleve's acid was 1-naphthylamine-4-sulfonic acid. The product of the condensation (XXXIII) was converted to the eurhodol, 11-hydroxytribenzo[a,c,h]phenazine (XXXIV), by fusion with potassium hydroxide.[29] This process was also the basis of a patent[30] that described the preparation of various polysulfonic acids of XXXII and the alkali fusion of these to yield other eurhodols. Where the products were insoluble, they were sulfonated.

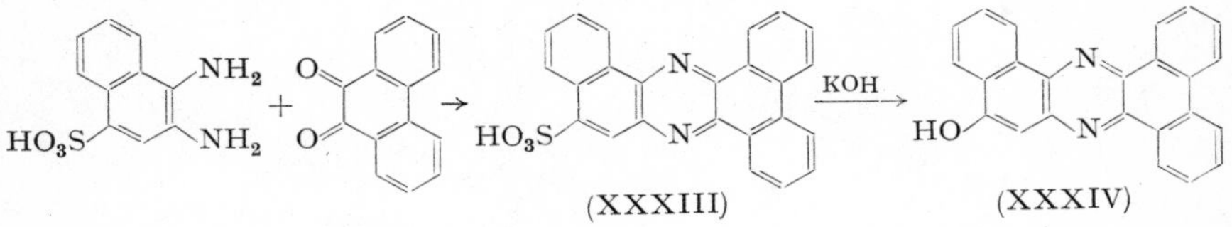

(XXXIII)   (XXXIV)

Another patent[31] described the preparation of sulfonic acids of 15-hydroxytribenzo[a,c,h]phenazine either by condensation of 9,10-phenanthrenequinone with 1,2-diamino-8-hydroxynaphthalene with subsequent sulfonation or by condensation of the quinone with sulfonic acids of the diaminohydroxynaphthalene. These eurhodol sulfonic acids were yellow dyes for wool. Other eurhodols have been described by Sircar and Dutt[32] and Poraï-Koshits and coworkers.[33,34] Sircar and Dutt have also described a wide range of substituted tribenzo[a,c,h]-phenazines, many of which were yellow to brown dyes for wool. The unsulfonated azines had to be applied from an acid bath. A recent patent[35] describes the production of a coppered azo dye, obtained by coupling tetrazotized dianisidine with a naphtholtrisulfonic acid and 12-hydroxytribenzo[a,c,h]phenazine-14-sulfonic acid. The bisazo dye is then treated with cuprammonium sulfate solution when a blue-grey copper-containing dye results.

Aminotribenzo[a,c,h]phenazines have also been prepared[32,36-39] but are unimportant.

Substitution products and derivatives of XXXII are listed in Table XLI.

B. Quaternary Salts

A number of tribenzo[a,c,h]phenazinium salts have been prepared. These are sometimes called "naphthoflavinduline" salts, an objectionable name based upon the trivial name for 9-phenyldibenzo[a,c]-phenazinium salts. Witt[40] was the first to prepare a quaternary derivative of this series by condensing 2-anilino-1-naphthylamine with 9,10-phenanthrenequinone in acetic acid and treating the product with diluted nitric acid, when the nitrate (XXXV) separated on standing in long needles. Other salts were described. Levi and Faldino[41] have likewise described 9-(1'-naphthyl)-tribenzo[a,c,h]phenazinium nitrate.

(XXXV)

Kehrmann and Walty[42] in a patent, and later Kehrmann and Eichler,[43] showed that this group of quaternary phenazinium compounds possessed the characteristic properties of the azinium class of substances. Thus XXXV in ethanolic solution reacted with amines in the presence of air to introduce a substituted amino residue at position 11, producing polybenzo analogs of the rosinduline type. For example, aniline yielded

11-anilino-9-phenyltribenzo[a,c,h]phenazinium chloride (XXXVI) as large dark violet crystals.

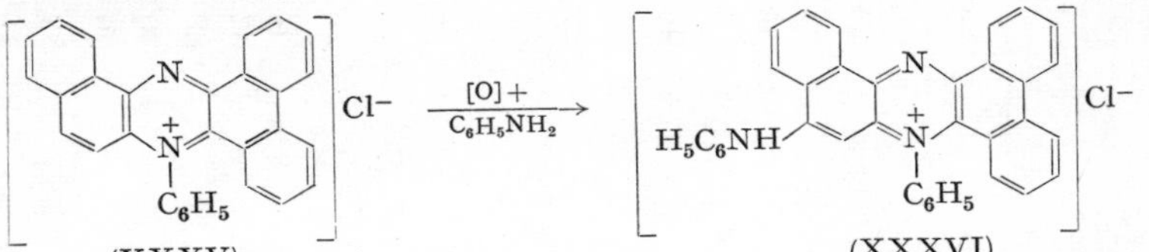

(XXXV)   (XXXVI)

These rosinduline analogs dyed silk, wool and mordanted cotton in pure blue-violet shades of good fastness to acids and washing. Dutt[44] prepared a large number of substituted 9-phenyltribenzo[a,c,h]-phenazinium salts bearing halogen, nitro, amino and hydroxy groups for evaluation as dyes for wool. These are listed in Table XLII.

Only one 16-phenyltribenzo[a,c,h]phenazinium compound (XXXVII) has been prepared and this, on treatment with alkali, readily formed a pseudo-base to which Kehrmann and Perrot[45] assigned the structure XXXVIII. The resemblance to the corresponding flav-induline series is noteworthy (see Chapter XV:2,B).

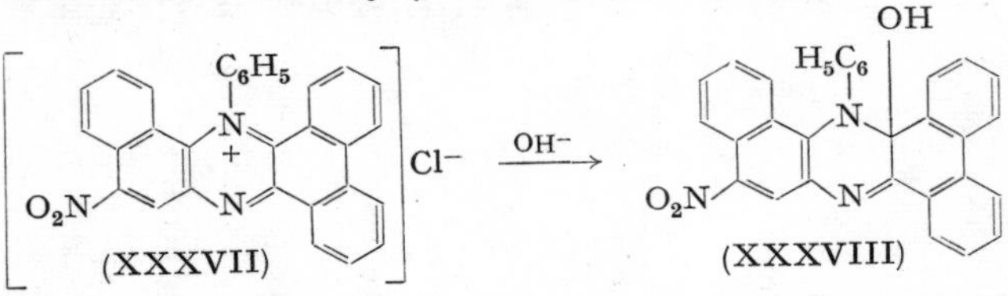

(XXXVII)   (XXXVIII)

Meisenheimer and Ditt[46] showed that the resemblance of these quaternary compounds to the flavindulines extended to the reaction with Grignard reagents. 9-Phenyltribenzo[a,c,h]phenazinium salts react with benzylmagnesium bromide, yielding two isomers, one of which is yellow and forms red salts and is accordingly said to be XXXIX, while the other is a colorless, non-basic compound thought to be XL.

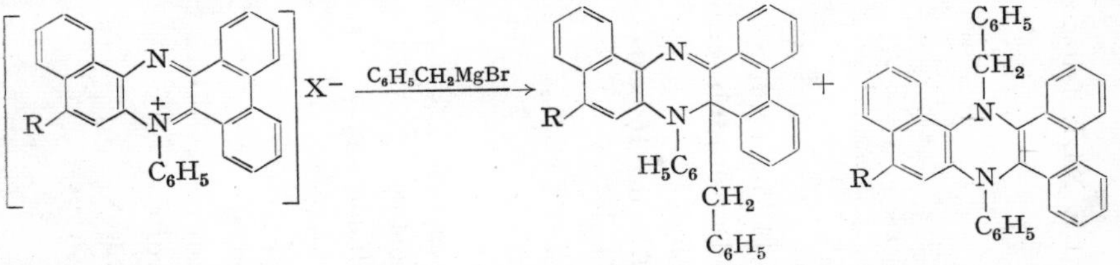

XXXV (R=H)
XXXVI (R=C₆H₅NH)

XXXIX (R=H)   XL (R=H)
XLI (R=C₆H₅NH)   XLII (R=C₆H₅NH)

TABLE XLI. Tribenzo[a,c,h]phenazines

Substituents	Physical characteristics	M.p. (°C)	Color with H_2SO_4, followed by dilution	Ref.
None	Yellow crystals	273		24–26
12,13,14,15-Tetrahydro-	Bright yellow needles	228.5–230		12
9,16b-Dihydro-16b-benzyl-9-phenyl-	Yellow crystals	186 (dec.)	Reddish-violet	46
9,16-Dihydro-16-benzyl-9-phenyl-	Colorless crystals	186 (dec.)	Bluish-violet	46
11-Methyl-	Yellow needles	341–342	Blue, lilac, rose	27
12-Methyl-	Yellow needles	254–255		85
13-Methyl-	Yellow crystals	295		86
11-Phenyl-	Small yellow needles	227–228		87
11-Bromo-	Yellow needles	314	Yellowish-brown	26
11-Sulfonic acid	Orange-red crystals		Violet, orange	28
2-Hydroxy-(?)		> 160 (dec.)		32
4-Hydroxy-(?)	Brownish-yellow needles	225 (dec.)		32
11-Benzoyl-	Yellow needles	252–255		88
10-Hydroxy-		> 200	Reddish-blue	30
11-Hydroxy-	Yellow crystals		Deep blue, red	29
12-Hydroxy-	Yellowish-brown crystals	332–332.5		33, 34
15-Hydroxy-			Greenish-blue	31

Substituents	Physical characteristics	M.p. (°C.)	Color with H_2SO_4, followed by dilution	Ref.
2,7-Dihydroxy-	Yellow-brown needles	220–221		32
4,5-Dihydroxy-	Orange-brown prismatic needles	175 (dec.)		32
13-Hydroxy-11-sulfonic acid	Needles	271–272	Olive-green	30
14-Hydroxy-11-sulfonic acid			Olive-green	30
14-Methoxy-			Reddish-violet	89
2-Nitro-(?)	Yellow needles	190 (dec.)		32
4-Nitro-(?)	Yellow needles	206–208		32
11-Nitro-		329	Yellowish-brown	26
2,7-Dinitro-	Yellow needles	> 290	Violet	32
4,5-Dinitro-	Yellow needles	275		32
2-Amino-(?)	Yellow prismatic needles	250		32
4-Amino-(?)		180–181		**32**
11-Amino-	Orange needles	309–316	Violet-red, greenish-yellow magenta	38, 39
13-Amino-	Golden lustrous leaflets		Violet, brown	36
2,7-Diamino-	Yellow needles			32
4,5-Diamino-	Yellow needles	170 (dec.)		32
11-Acetamido-	Pale yellow needles		Blue-violet, red-brown	38, 39
2,7-Dianilino-	Needles	200	Green	32
11-Anilino-9,16b-dihydro-16b-benzyl-9-phenyl-	Yellow crystals	186 (dec.)	Red salts	46
11-Anilino-9,16-dihydro-16-benzyl-9-phenyl-	Colorless needles	186 (dec.)		46

TABLE XLII. 9-Phenyltribenzo[a,c,h]phenazinium Salts

Substituents	Appearance of chloride (unless otherwise stated)	M.p. (°C.)	Color when dyed on wool and other properties*	Ref.
None	(NO₃⁻), Long dichroic (red-yellow) needles		Blue, violet, reddish-yellow*	40
3-Bromo-(?)	(NO₃⁻), orange-red needles	230	Orange	44
2,7-Dibromo-	Blue needles	> 230	Maroon	44
2-Hydroxy-(?)	Bluish-brown needles	174 (dec.)	Clay-yellow	44
4-Hydroxy-(?)	Dark-brown needles	192 (dec.)	Flesh color	44
2,7-Dihydroxy-	Brown needles	245 (dec.)	Vandyke-brown	44
4,5-Dihydroxy-	Dark-brown needles	> 290	Nut-brown	44
2-Nitro-(?)	Brownish needles		Terra-cotta	44
4-Nitro-(?)	Dark-brown needles	165 (dec.)	Maroon	44
2,7-Dinitro-	Fine brown needles	220 (dec.)	Yellowish-gray	44
4,5-Dinitro-	Brown needles	190 (dec.)	Brownish-gray	44
2-Amino-(?)	Blue needles	195 (dec.)	Dull bluish-black	44
4-Amino-(?)	Blue needles	128–130 (dec.)	Dull violet-blue	44
11-Amino-	Dark red prisms, bronze luster		Violet-blue, olive green, yellow-brown, violet red*	42, 43
2,7-Diamino-	Dark red prisms, bronze luster		Bluish-black	44
4,5-Diamino-		> 290	Violet-black	44
3-Anilino-(?)	(NO₃⁻), green amorphous solid	195 (dec.)	Olive green	44
11-Anilino-	Dark violet crystals, coppery-luster		Dirty-blue, green, violet-blue*	42, 43
2,7-Dianilino-	Bright blue powder	> 290	Blue	44
11-Methylamino-	Brassy granules			42

* This refers to color with H_2SO_4, fwd. by progressive dil. with water. No dyeing properties are given for these compounds.

In an attempt to resolve a structure of type **XL**, where optical activity would be attributable to restricted rotation, Meisenheimer and Ditt repeated the reaction of 11-anilino-9-phenyltribenzo[a,c,h]-phenazinium chloride[43] (**XXXVI**) and again observed two isomers (**XLI** and **XLII**). The colorless isomer (**XLII**) was now basic but sensitive to air, rapidly becoming blue, and, although they worked under inert atmospheric conditions, they were unable to prepare a crystalline bromocamphorsulfonate for resolution purposes. It is interesting to note that all four isomers melt at 186° with decomposition, **XXXIX** and **XL** showing no depression on admixture. Meisenheimer and Ditt were able to convert **XL** into **XXXIX** by treatment with acetic acid, but the reverse change was not realized. In the flavinduline series, the yellow isomer (corresponding to **XXXIX**) may be converted into the colorless isomer (corresponding to **XL**) by prolonged heating.

16. Phenanthro[4,5-abc]phenazine.
   R. I. 3603

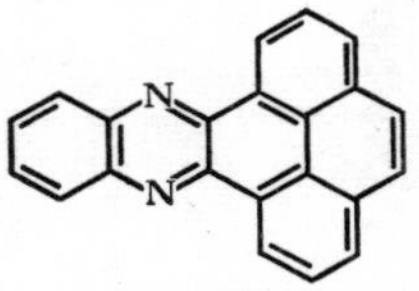

In the course of investigations of the chemistry of pyrene (*R. I.* 2813), Vollmann and his colleagues[47] prepared 4,5-pyrenequinone, which condensed with o-phenylenediamine to yield phenanthro-[4,5-abc]phenazine (**XLIII**) as weakly yellow needles, m.p. 262°, which gave a bluish-green coloration in concentrated sulfuric acid. This is, to date, the sole representative of this ring system.

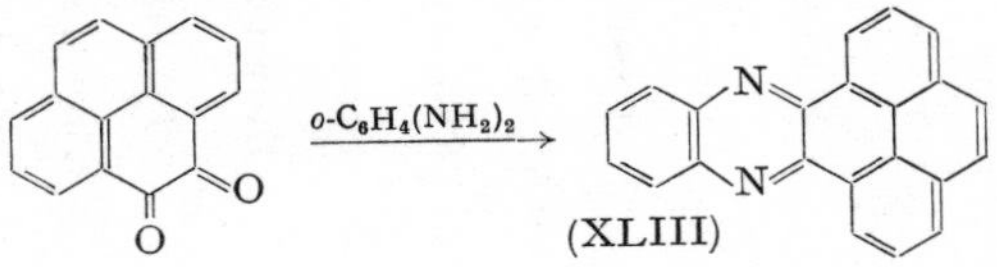

(XLIII)

17. 16-Dibenz[a,c]indeno[2,1-h]
   phenazine. R. I. 3741

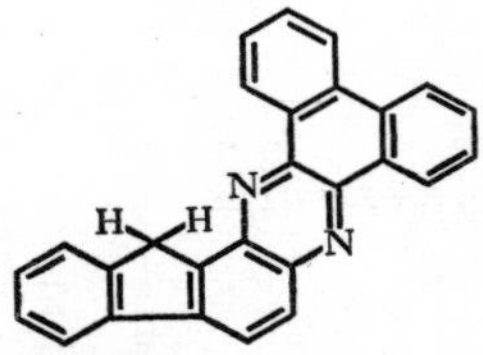

Dutta, Prasad and De[48] prepared a series of azines of this basic ring structure in order to study the effect of polycyclic hydrocarbon

TABLE XLIII. 16-Dibenz[a,c]indeno[2,1-h]phenazines

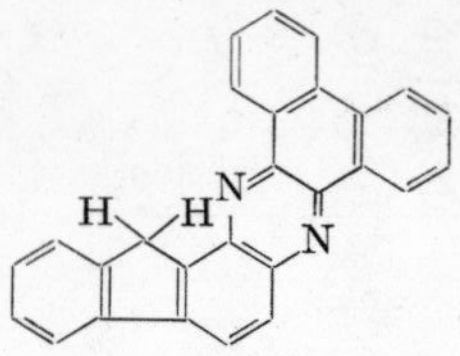

Substituents	Physical characteristics	M.p. (°C.)	Color when dyed on wool, from an acid bath*	Ref.
None	Thin brown needles	279–280	Yellow	48
2-Nitro-(?)	Chocolate needles	> 290	Chocolate-brown	48
4-Nitro-(?)	Greenish-brown crystals	> 290	Deep brown	48
2,7-Dinitro-	Yellow prismatic needles	> 290	Yellow	48
4,5-Dinitro-	Chocolate-brown needles	> 290	Chocolate-brown	48
2-Bromo-(?)	Brown crystals	> 290	Brown	48
2-Amino-(?)	Brown needles	> 290	Chocolate-brown	48
4-Amino-(?)	Brown needles	> 290	Deep brown	48
2,7-Diamino-	Brown needles	> 290	Yellow-brown	48
2-Hydroxy-(?)	Chocolate-brown needles	> 290	Chocolate	48
4-Hydroxy-(?)	Brown crystals	> 290	Greenish-brown	48
2,7-Dihydroxy-	Chocolate-brown crystals	> 290	Greenish-brown	48

*All members of this series so far described give blue colors with concentrated sulfuric acid.

residues upon the shades of monoazine dyestuffs. All the dyes were prepared similarly by condensing 1,2-diaminofluorene with 9,10-phenanthrenequinone or substitution products of this.

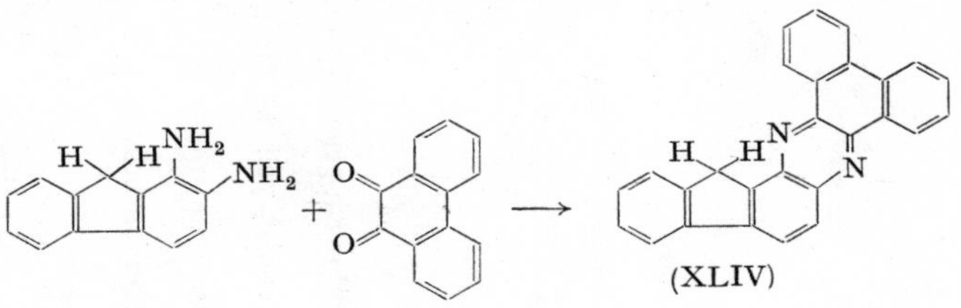

(XLIV)

The parent compound (XLIV) formed thin brown needles, m.p. 279–280°, but the substituted derivatives were all compounds melting above 290°. They all gave a blue color with concentrated sulfuric acid. They are listed in Table XLIII.

18. Dibenz[h,j]indeno[7,1-ab]phenazine.
   R. I. 3742

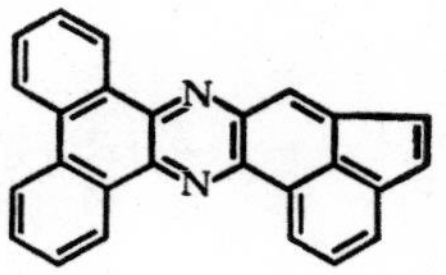

11,12-Dihydrodibenz[h,j]indeno[7,1-ab]phenazine (XLV) was prepared by Sachs and Mosebach[49] by the condensation of 4,5-diamino-acenaphthene with 9,10-phenanthrenequinone. It forms pale yellow needles, m.p. 293°, giving a purplish-red coloration in concentrated sulfuric acid.

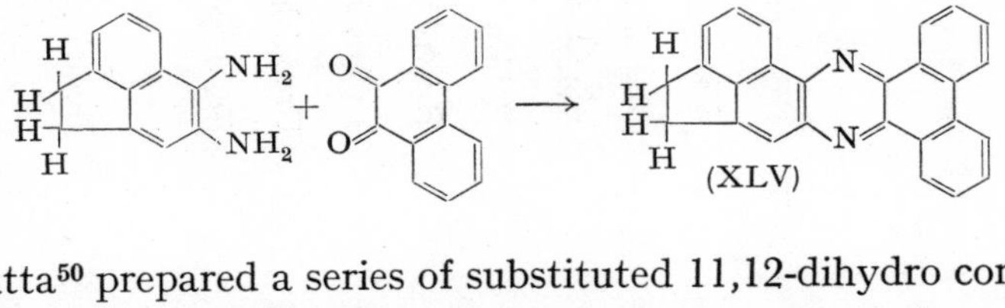

(XLV)

Dutta[50] prepared a series of substituted 11,12-dihydro compounds using substituted 9,10-phenanthrenequinones. These gave yellow to brown shades on wool when dyed from an acid bath. They are listed in Table XLIV.

There are no examples of the fully aromatic system theoretically derivable from acenaphthylene.

TABLE XLIV. 11,12-Dihydrodibenz[h,j]indeno[7,1-ab]phenazines

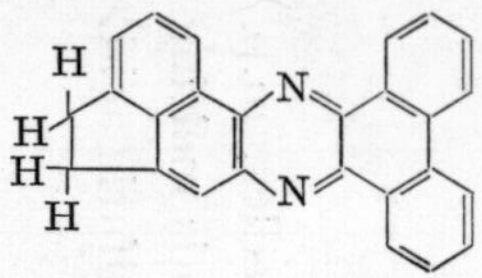

Substituents	Physical characteristics	M.p. (°C.)	Color with H_2SO_4	Color when dyed on wool, from an acid bath	Ref.
None	Pale yellow needles	293	Purplish-red		49
2-Nitro-(?)	Greenish-brown needles	274	Blue	Yellow	50
4-Nitro-(?)	Greenish-yellow needles	257–258	Dark blue	Greenish-yellow	50
2,7-Dinitro-	Yellow-brown needles	>310	Blue	Brown	50
4,5-Dinitro-	Yellow crystals	>300	Blue	Yellow	50
2-Bromo-(?)	Bright brown crystals	273	Blue	Bright yellow	50
2-Amino-(?)	Bright green needles	269–270	Blue	Yellowish-green	50
4-Amino-(?)	Greenish-brown crystals	204	Blue	Greenish-yellow	50
2,7-Diamino-	Small yellow-green needles	>300	Blue	Greenish-brown	50
4,5-Diamino-	Greenish-yellow crystals	>300	Blue	Greenish-brown	50
2-Hydroxy-(?)	Reddish-brown crystals	>300	Blue	Brown	50
4-Hydroxy-(?)	Chocolate crystals	>300	Blue	Chocolate-brown	50
2,7-Dihydroxy-	Reddish-brown crystals	>300	Greenish-blue	Chocolate-brown	50

19. Dinaphtho[2,3-a,2',3'-i]phenazine.
    R. I. 3764

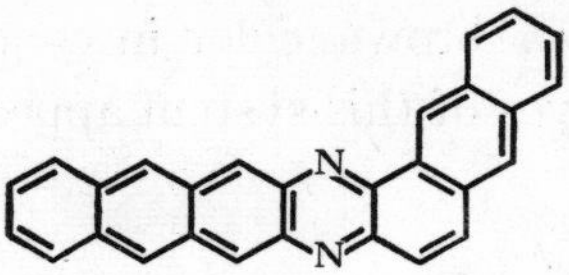

The examples of this ring system have all been prepared for use as vat dyes. Their structures are very closely related to that of indanthrone and accordingly a discussion of them is postponed till a later chapter (XVII: 9,A).

20. Dibenzo[a,c]naphtho[2,3-i]phenazine.
    R. I. 3765

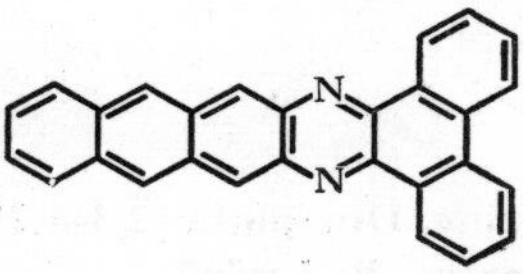

11,16-Dihydrodibenzo[a,c]naphtho[2,3-i]phenazine-11,16-dione (XLVI) was first prepared by Scholl and Kačer[9] by the condensation of 2,3-diamino-5,10-anthraquinone with 9,10-phenanthrenequinone. It formed yellow crystals, m.p. > 320°, and gave a carmine coloration in concentrated sulfuric acid. The process was later patented.[10] Reduction with sodium dithionite yielded a brown insoluble vat in contrast to the blue soluble vats of the indanthrone group (Chapter XVII).

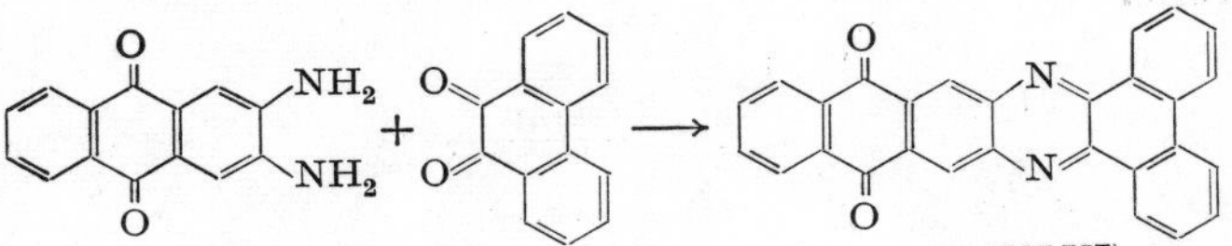

(XLVI)

21. Anthra[2,3-a]benzo[c]phenazine.
    R. I. 3766

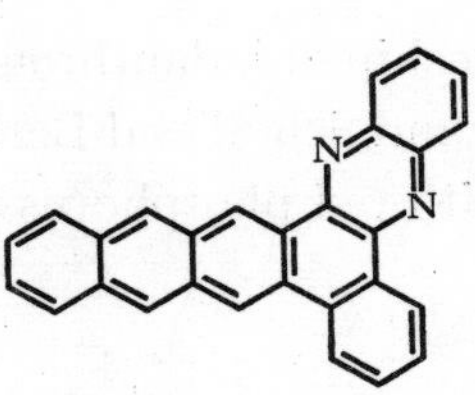

Clar.[51] in the course of studies of polynuclear hydrocarbons, oxidized benzo[a]naphthacene (R. I. 3363) in two stages with chromic acid and obtained the 5,6,8,13-diquinone (XLVII), which condensed with o-phenylenediamine in acetic acid to yield 11,16-dihydroanthra-[2,3-a]benzo[c]phenazine-11,16-dione (XLVIII) as pale yellow needles, m.p. 373°. It is readily sublimed in the form of beautiful yellow needles and gives a brown color in concentrated sulfuric acid. No other representatives of this system appear to have been prepared.

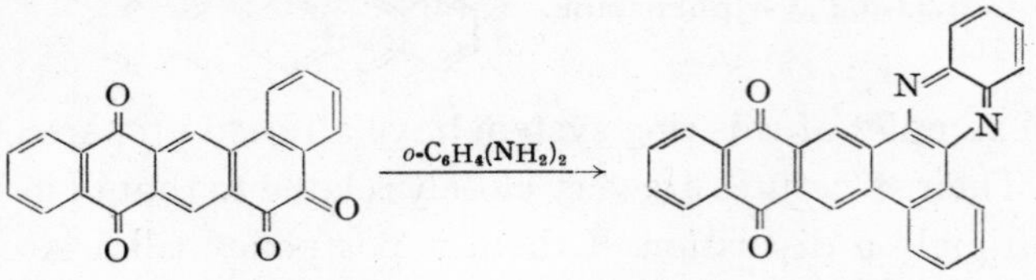

(XLVII)   (XLVIII)

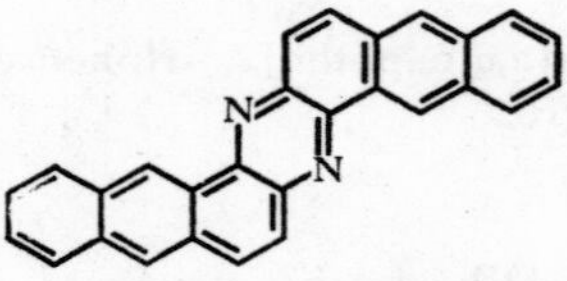

22. Anthrazine. Dinaphtho[2,3-a,2′,3′-h] phenazine. R. I. 3767

Anthrazine (XLIX) is the parent ring system of the very important series of indanthrone vat dyes. These quinone derivatives are discussed exhaustively in Chapter XVII, to which the reader is referred. At this point we shall restrict attention to the parent system and its simpler derivatives. Anthrazine is obtained by the alkaline fusion of 2-aminoanthracene at 220–230°,[52] a process akin to the formation of indanthrone.

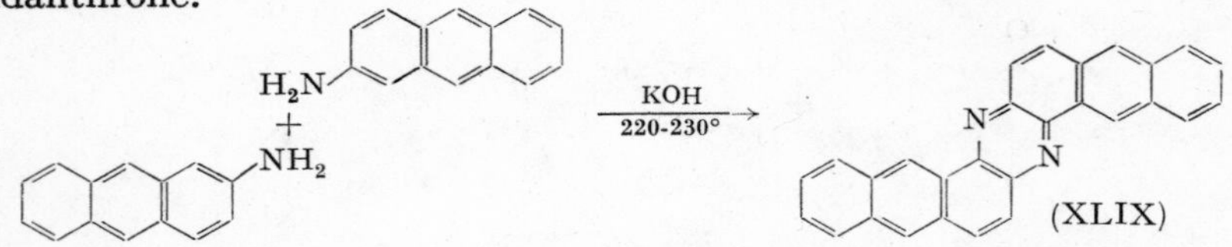

The relationship of indanthrone (L) to anthrazine was early shown by Kaufler,[53,54] and Scholl and Berblinger,[55] by the action of hydriodic acid alone or with red phosphorus when anthrazine was the product.

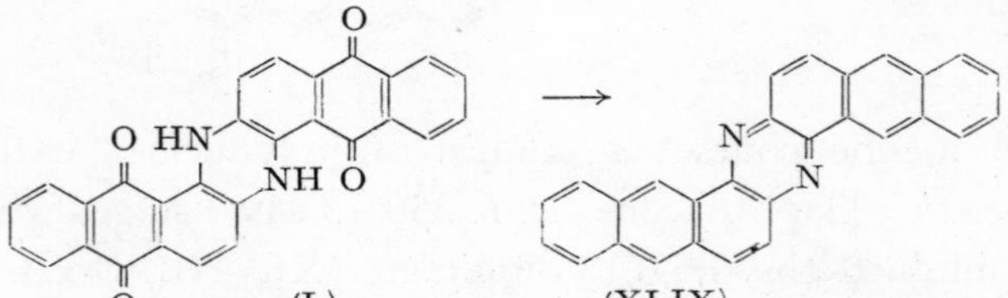

The same reaction may be brought about by zinc dust distillation[53,55] or better by distillation from a fusion mixture of zinc dust, zinc chloride and sodium chloride at 210–290°.[56] Scholl[57] showed that reduction of indanthrone with zinc dust and alkali yields 6,15-dihydro-anthrazine (LI), which readily loses hydrogen on heating alone at 360° to yield anthrazine.

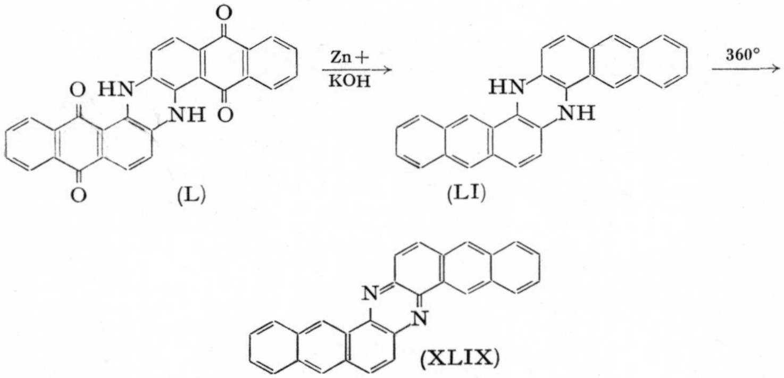

(L)   (LI)   (XLIX)

According to Schiedt,[58] anthrazine may be prepared by the reaction of 1,2-anthraquinone with formamide and acetic acid. This is an example of the "abnormal" Leuckart reaction of an o-quinone. (For other examples, see Chapter XV:3,A, Sections XVI:29 and 36, Chapter XVII:9,B and Chapter XIX:71.)

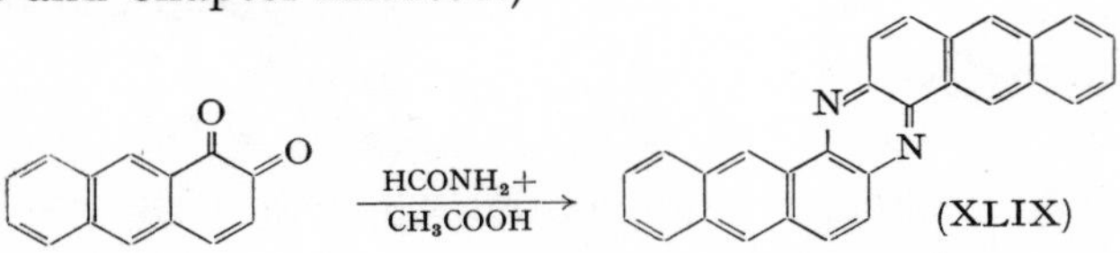

(XLIX)

Anthrazine forms vivid yellow needles, m.p. 390°. With excess bromine at 100°, it yields an octabromide in which the positions of the bromine atoms have not been determined.

5,18-Dihydroanthrazine-5,18-dione (LII) has been prepared by Terres[59] by condensing 1,2-anthraquinone with 1,2-diaminoanthra-5,10-quinone.

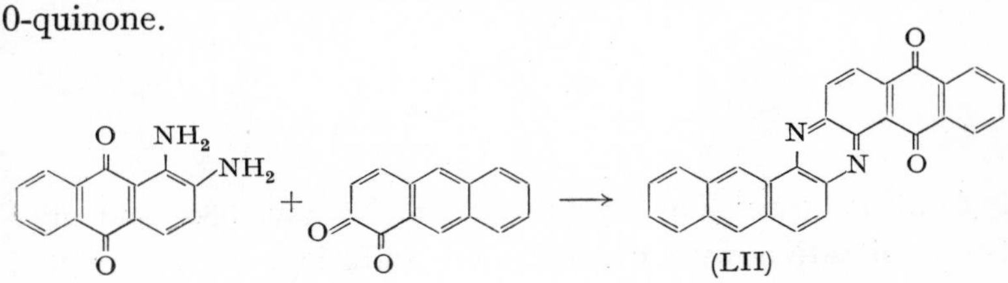

(LII)

Both XLIX and LII can be converted into indanthrone by oxidation to the 5,9,14,18-tetrahydro-5,9,14,18-tetrone (LIII), followed by
autoreduction to indanthrone by boiling with quinoline.

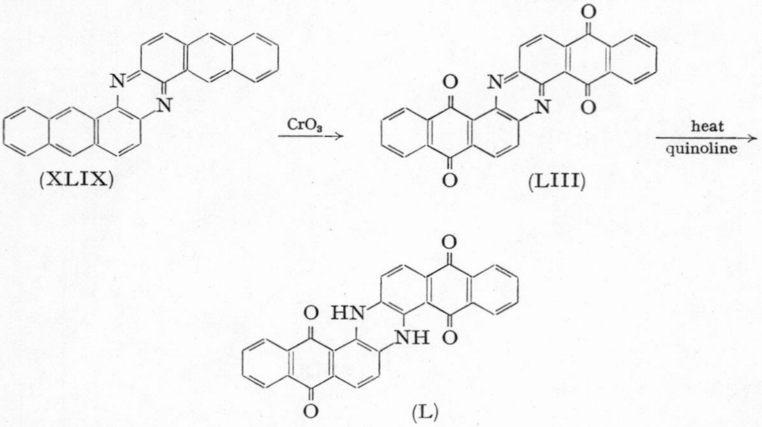

(XLIX)   (LIII)

(L)

Other derivatives of anthrazine that are obtained from indanthrone
are discussed in Chapter XVII.

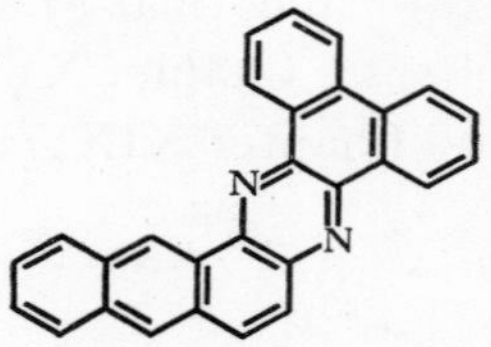

23. Dibenzo[a,c]naphtho[2,3-h]phenazine.
R. I. 3768

12,17-Dihydrodibenzo[a,c]naphtho[2,3-h]phenazine-12,17-dione
(LIV) was first described in a patent[10] and later by Terres.[59] It is
prepared by condensing 1,2-diamino-5,10-anthraquinone with 9,10-
phenanthrenequinone.

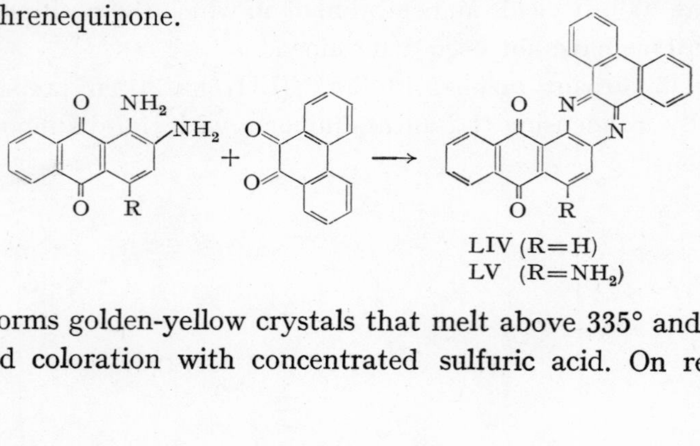

LIV (R=H)
LV (R=NH₂)

It forms golden-yellow crystals that melt above 335° and gives a
violet-red coloration with concentrated sulfuric acid. On reduction

with alkaline sodium dithionite it forms an insoluble dark greenish-blue vat.

Terres[60] later condensed 9,10-phenanthrenequinone with 1,2,4-triamino-5,10-anthraquinone and obtained LV as brown crystals, not further characterized.

24. Dinaphtho[2,3-a,2′,3′-j]phenazine.
    R. I. 3769

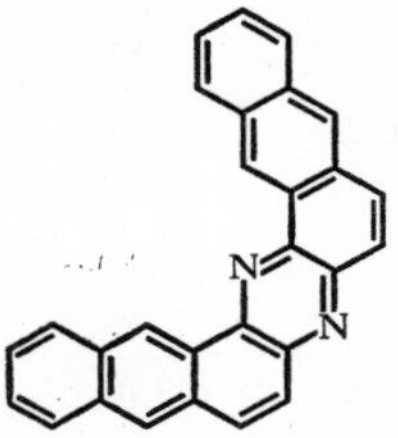

The sole representative of this system that has been unequivocally synthesized is very closely related to indanthrone and accordingly is dealt with in Chapter XVII:9,C.

It is possible that the 5,18-dihydro-5,18-dione (LVI) is formed together with 5,18-dihydroanthrazine-5,18-dione (LII) in the condensation of 1,2-diamino-5,10-anthraquinone with 1,2-anthraquinone, but the pure compound has not been isolated.[59]

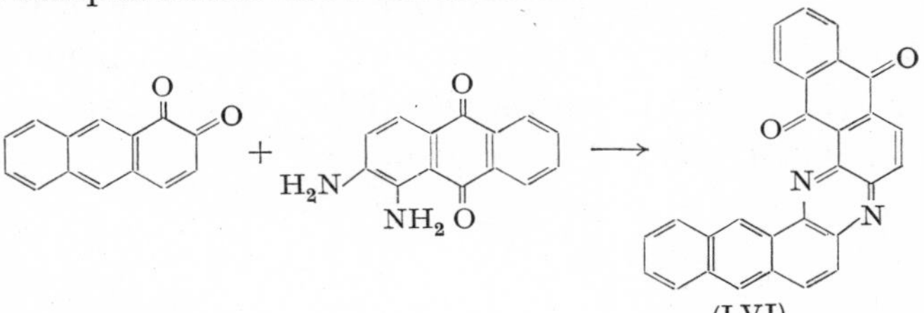

(LVI)

25. Anthra[1,2-a]benzo[c]phenazine.
    R. I. 3770

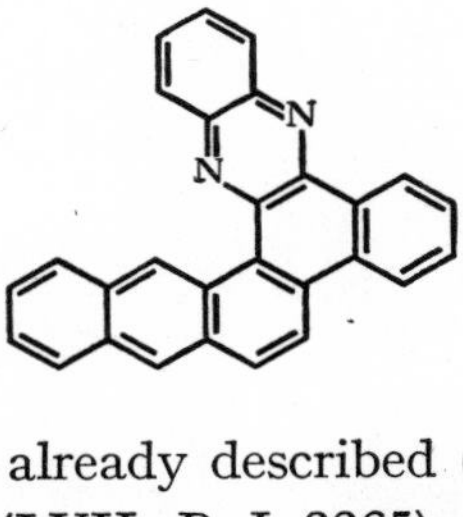

In a manner similar to that already described (Section XVI:21) Clar[51] oxidized benzo[b]chrysene (LVII, *R. I.* 3365) with chromic acid and obtained the diquinone (LVIII) as one of the products. This was condensed with o-phenylenediamine to yield 12,17-dihydroanthra-

[1,2-*a*]benzo[*c*]phenazine-12,17-dione (LIX), which formed pale yellow
needles, m.p. 350°, and gave a blood-red vat on reduction with alkaline
sodium dithionite. It gives a bright brown coloration in concentrated
sulfuric acid.

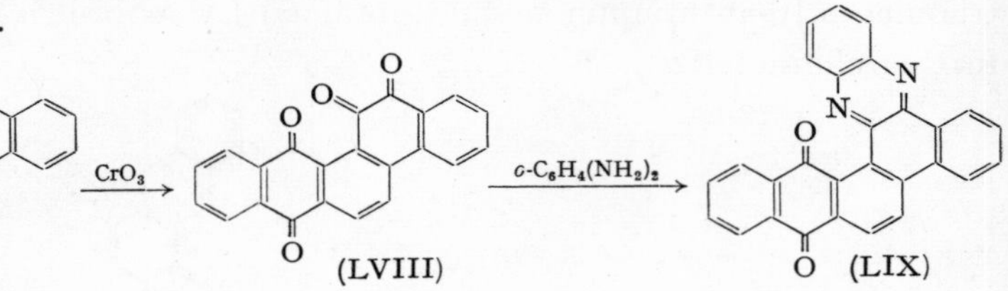

(LVII)   (LVIII)   (LIX)

26. Benzo[*a*]phenanthro[2,3-*c*]phenazine.
R. I. 3771

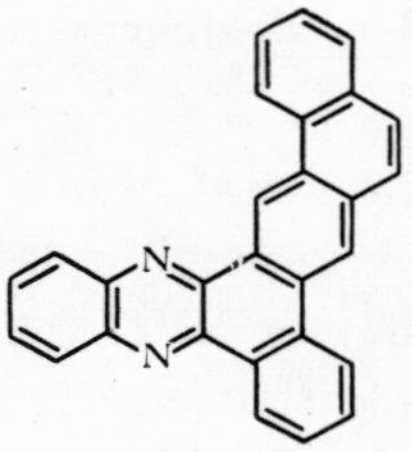

In the course of studies of carcinogenic polycyclic hydrocarbons,
Cook[61] oxidized dibenz[*a,h*]anthracene (LX, *R. I.* 3369) and obtained
a mixture of the 5.6- and 7,14-quinones. The presence of the former
o-quinone was shown by the reaction with *o*-phenylenediamine to yield
benzo[*a*]phenanthro[2,3-*c*]phenazine (LXI), which was a yellow
crystalline powder, melting above 300°.

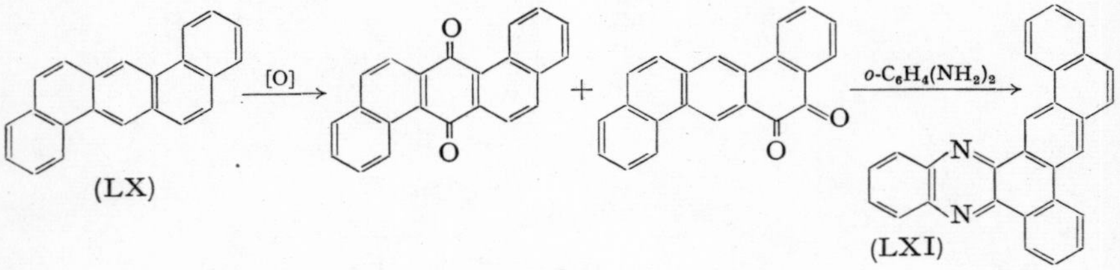

(LX)   (LXI)

27. Benzo[*a*]phenanthro[9,10-*c*]phenazine.
R. I. 3772

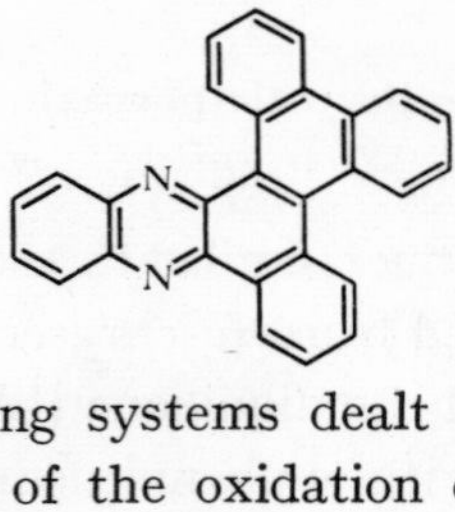

This system, like many other ring systems dealt with in this
chapter, arose as a result of studies of the oxidation of polycyclic

hydrocarbons. Hewitt[62] oxidized benzo[g]chrysene (LXII, *R. I.* 3371) with chromic acid to the 9,10-quinone (LXIII), which with *o*-phenylene-diamine yielded the parent heterocyclic system (LXIV) as canary-yellow needles, m.p. 242–243°.

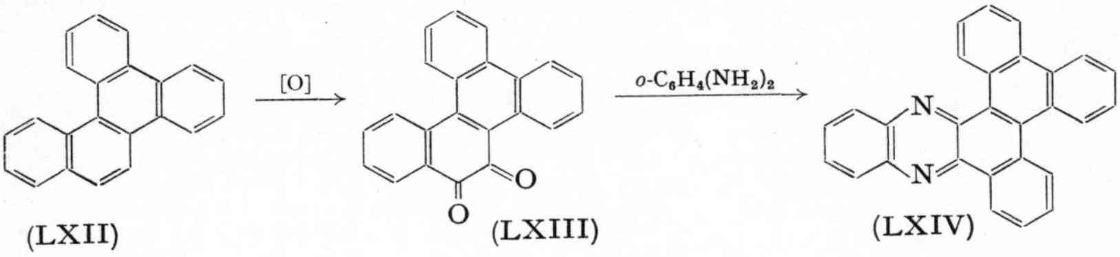

(LXII)   [O] →   (LXIII)   *o*-C$_6$H$_4$(NH$_2$)$_2$ →   (LXIV)

28. Dinaphtho[1,2-*a*,2′,1′-*c*]phenazine. R. I. 3773

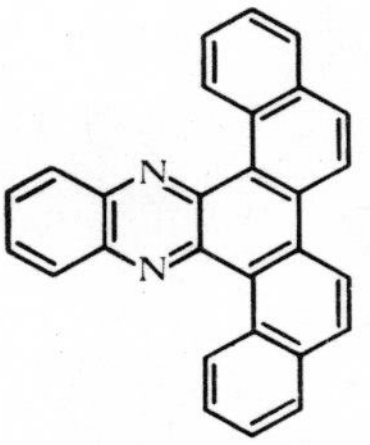

Oxidation of picene (LXV) with chromic acid yields 13,14-picene-quinone (LXVI). Meyer and Hofmann[63] showed that this condensed with *o*-phenylenediamine in glacial acetic acid to yield dinaphtho-[1,2-*a*,2′,1′-*c*]phenazine (LXVII) as yellow needles (no melting point given).

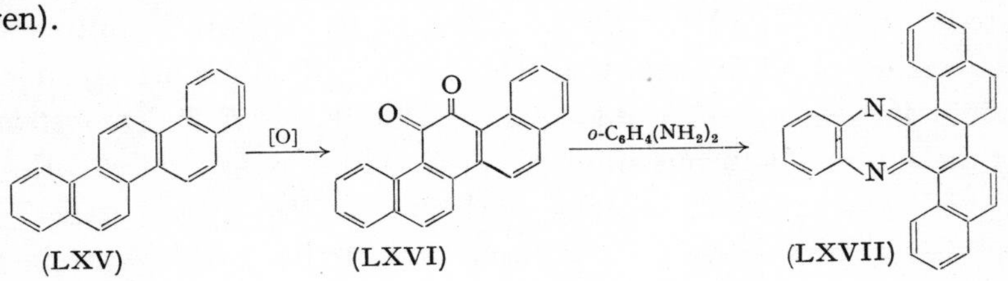

(LXV)   [O] →   (LXVI)   *o*-C$_6$H$_4$(NH$_2$)$_2$ →   (LXVII)

29. Phenanthrazine. Tetrabenzo[*a*,*c*,*h*,*j*] phenazine. R. I. 3774

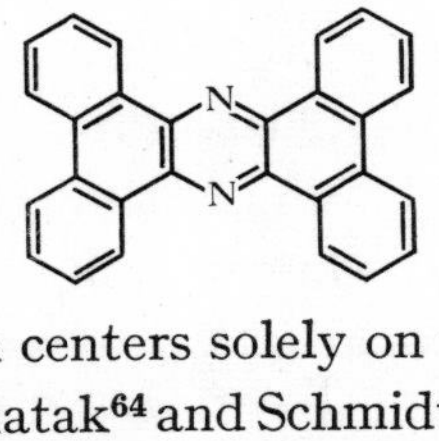

The interest of this ring system centers solely on the parent compound phenanthrazine (LXVIII). Ghatak[64] and Schmidt and Junghans[65] have prepared a number of substituted derivatives, of little intrinsic interest, and these are listed in Table XLV.

Phenanthrazine was first prepared by Graebe[91] by the action of ammonia upon 9,10-phenanthrenequinone and Sommaruga[66] obtained it later by the action of alcoholic ammonia upon 9,10-phenanthrene-quinone. Bamberger and Grob[67] showed that, when 9,10-dihydroxy-phenanthrene was heated in organic solvents at 120–130° in the presence of ammonia, phenanthrazine was formed together with 18-tetrabenzo-[a,c,h,j]phenoxazine (LXIX, R. I. 3746).

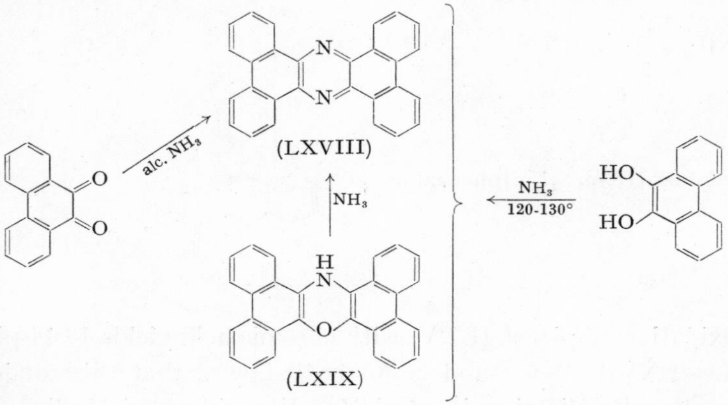

(LXVIII)

(LXIX)

Bamberger and Grob also showed that phenylhydrazine, when heated with 9,10-phenanthrenequinone, yielded the tetrabenzo-phenoxazine (LXIX) and that the action of ammonia upon this resulted in the formation of phenanthrazine. Foresti[68,69] demonstrated that the action of aqueous ammonia upon 9,10-dihydroxyphenanthrene also yielded a mixture of azine and oxazine. In a later paper[70] he suggested a mechanism for the formation of the phenoxazine in the reactions studied by Bamberger and Grob. The first step was thought to be the formation of a mixture of 9,10-dihydroxyphenanthrene and 9-amino-10-hydroxyphenanthrene. The latter compound, on short heating in ethanol, water or non-polar solvents, condenses to the oxazine with liberation of ammonia. Prolonged heating, however, led to the formation of phenanthrazine as well, which Foresti claimed arose from the action of ammonia upon 9,10-dihydroxyphenanthrene and not upon the phenoxazine, which should be stable under the conditions of the experiment.

TABLE XLV. Phenanthrazines (Tetrabenzo[a,c,h,j]phenazines)

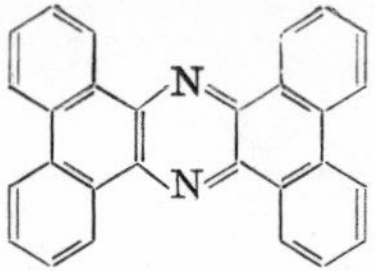

Substituents	Physical characteristics	M.p. (°C.)	Color with conc. H_2SO_4	Ref.
None	Yellow glittering rods	487	Cornflower-blue	See XVI:29
2-Bromo-	Yellow-brown needles	252–254		65
2-Nitro-	Yellowish-green crystals			64
2,11(or 2,16)-Dibromo-	Dark yellow lustrous needles	> 350	Blue-violet, cornflower-blue	65
2,7-Dibromo-	Bright yellow crystals	239–240		64
2,7-Dihydroxy-	Deep-grey crystals	205		64
2,7-Dinitro-	Yellowish-brown crystals	231–232		64
2,7-Diamino-	Deep-green crystals	177		64
4,5-Dinitro-	Golden-yellow crystals	197		64
4,5-Diamino-	Greyish-brown crystals	182		64

A somewhat similar mechanism probably accounts for the formation of phenanthrazine by heating 9,10-phenanthrenequinone with hydrazine under forcing conditions, a reaction discovered by Goldschmidt and his colleagues.[71]

Pschorr[72] prepared phenanthrazine from 9,10-diaminophenanthrene by condensing it with 9,10-phenanthrenequinone or by aerial oxidation of the diamine alone. Japp and Burton[73] obtained LXVIII by heating 2,3,5,6-tetraphenylpyrazine with soda-lime and pointed out that Erdmann[74] had unwittingly synthesized this compound in this manner seven years prior to the discovery of phenanthrene but, apart from the deep-blue color with sulfuric acid, had not characterized it.

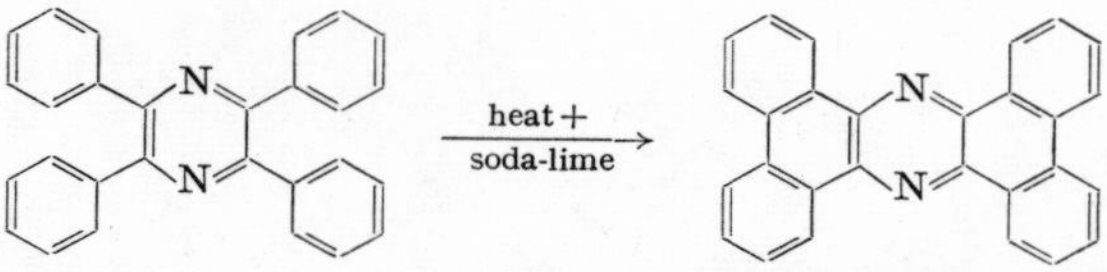

(LXVIII)

Other methods of preparing phenanthrazine are all modifications in some way or other of the "abnormal" Leuckart reaction of o-quinones (see Chapters XV:3,A; XVI:22 and 36; XVII:9,B and XIX:71). Thus Mason[75] in 1889 obtained LXVIII by heating 9,10-phenanthrenequinone with either oxamide or acetamide. Leuckart,[76] a year later, prepared it from the quinone by heating this with ammonium formate. More recently, Schiedt[58] obtained LXVIII by heating the quinone with formamide and acetic acid at 160°.

Phenanthrazine forms yellow, glittering rods, m.p. 487°, which give a cornflower-blue coloration in concentrated sulfuric acid. Ghatak[64] described the unsubstituted compound as yellow needles, m.p. 211–212°; the discrepancy is unexplained.

30. 4-Benzo[1′,2′,3′,1,10]phenanthro[4,5-abc]
    phenazine. R. I. 3776

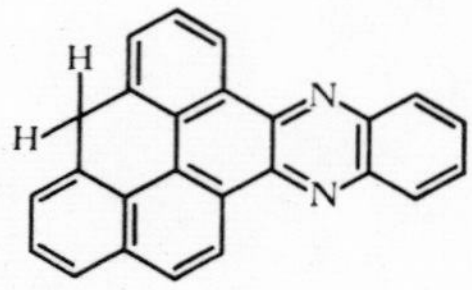

In the course of their studies of the chemistry of pyrene, Vollmann and his colleagues[47] synthesized LXX, which was condensed with *o*-phenylenediamine to yield 4-benzo[1′,2′,3′,1,10]phenanthro[4,5-*abc*]-phenazin-4-one (LXXI). This formed bright yellow crystals, m.p. 352°, and was not vatted with alkaline dithionite.

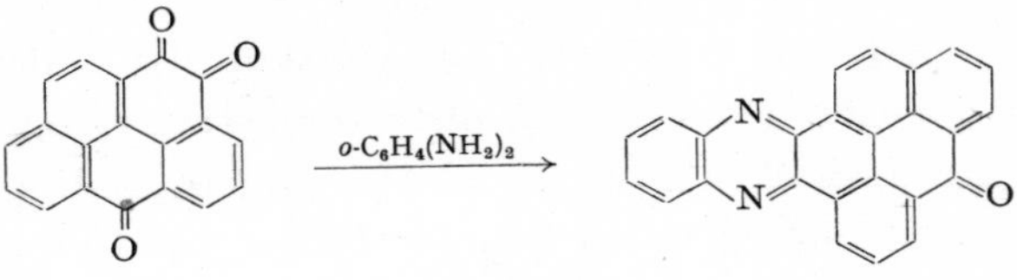

o-C$_6$H$_4$(NH$_2$)$_2$

(LXX)　　　　　　　　　　　　　　　　(LXXI)

This is the sole representative of this ring system.

31. Diphenanthro[2,3-*a*,2′,3′-*h*] phenazine. R. I. 3930

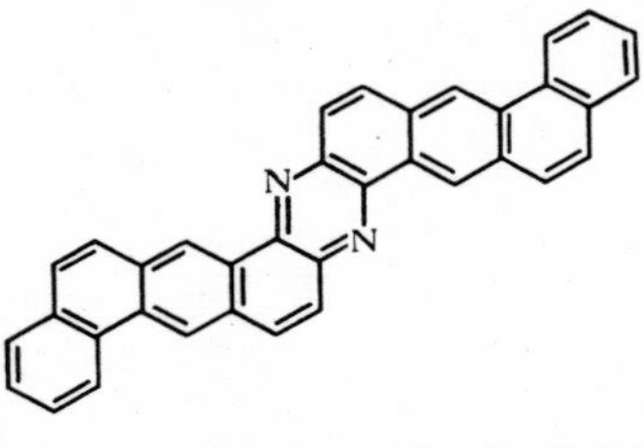

A representative of this system was synthesized by Schwenk and Waldmann[77] in the course of attempts to prepare vat dyes of the indanthrone type in which the color was other than blue. They prepared 9-aminobenz[*a*]anthra-7,12-quinone (LXXII) from the corresponding 9-chloro compound and ammonia under pressure, and this on heating at 250–270° with potassium hydroxide and potassium acetate was transformed into 7,8,11,18,19,22-hexahydrodiphenanthro[2,3-*a*,2′,3′-*h*]-phenazine-7,11,18,22-tetrone (LXXIII), which crystallized from quinoline in metallic lustrous needles. These gave a blue vat in alkaline sodium dithionite on partial reduction; the fully reduced vat was brownish-violet. Cotton was dyed in bluish-green shades from the blue vat.

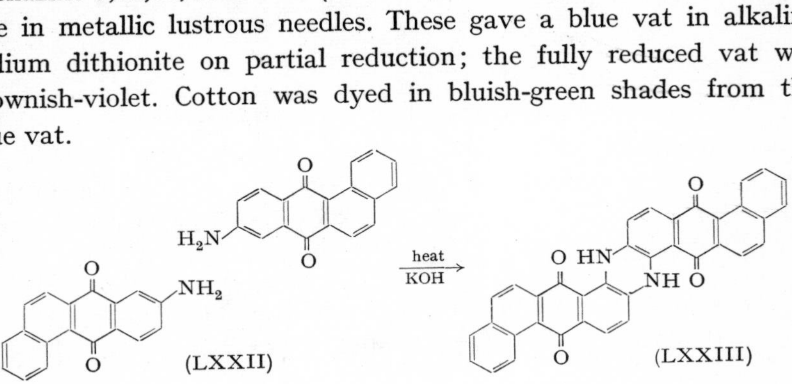

(LXXII)　　　　　　　　　　　　heat / KOH　　　　　　　　　(LXXIII)

32. Bisbenzonaphtheno[1,2-a,1',2'-h]
   phenazine. R. I. 3931

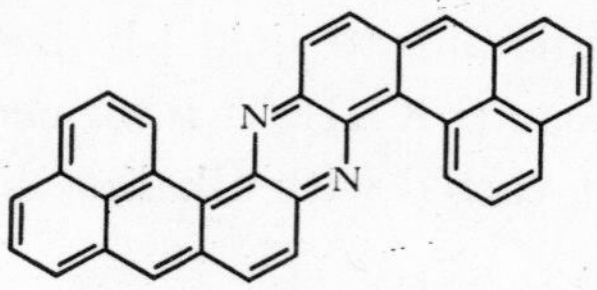

A representative of this series was prepared by Müller[78] again in search of new vat dyes modeled upon indanthrone. He took 5,6,9,14,15,18-hexahydroanthrazine-9,18-dione (LXXIV), which is obtainable from indanthrone by reduction with hydriodic acid at 150–160° (see Chapter XVII:5,C(2)) and submitted this to treatment with glycerol and sulfuric acid at 120° in the manner in which benzanthrones are prepared. The product, 7,10,17,20-tetrahydrobisbenzonaphtheno[1,2-a,-1',2'-h]phenazine-10,20-dione (LXXV) formed dark green needles. It was non-vattable with alkaline dithionite and was unchanged on alkaline fusion.

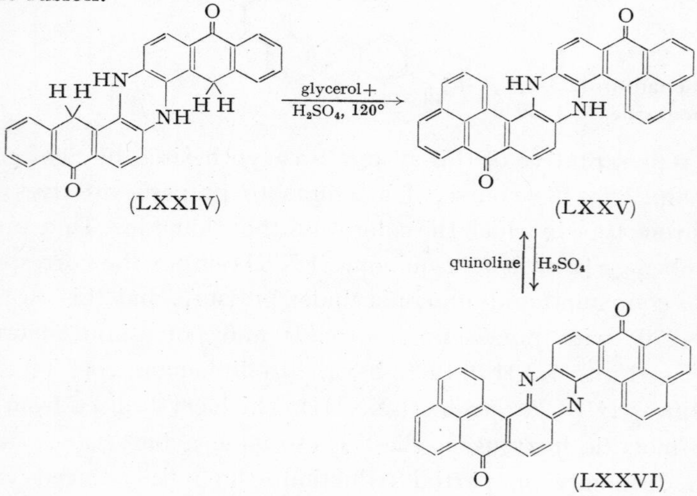

When LXXV was dissolved in concentrated sulfuric acid, the initial dark green solution became reddish-violet, sulfur dioxide was evolved and the azine (LXXVI) corresponding to LXXV was formed. This azine was readily reducible to LXXV on boiling with quinoline (see Indanthrone, Chapter XVII).

There remains a number of ring systems containing the phenazine nucleus that have not been enumerated in *The Ring Index*.

33. Dinaphtho[2,3-*b*,2′,3′-*i*]phenazine.
    7,16-Diazaheptacene.

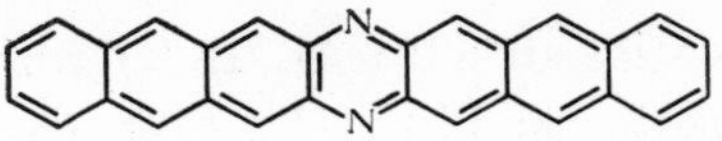

A representative of this system, prepared by Schiedt,[58] is described in Chapter XVII:9,B. This, too, is the basic structure attributed by Bradley and his coworkers[79] to Indanthrene B, a by-product of the manufacture of indanthrone (see Chapter XVII).

34. Dibenzo[*a*,*j*]naphtho
    [2,1-*c*]phenazine

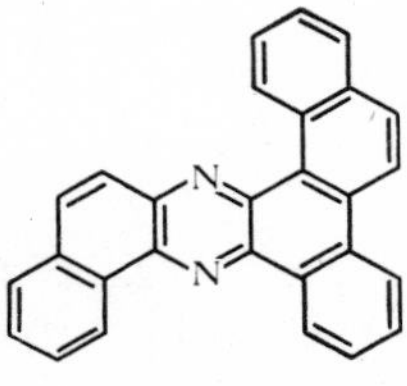

The parent substance of this system (LXXVII) was prepared by Liebermann and Witt[22] and later by Singh and Dutt,[21] by condensing 1,2-diaminonaphthalene with 5,6-chrysenequinone. It forms yellow crystals, m.p. 238°. There is an ambiguity in the manner in which the two components may unite, the alternative structure being dibenzo-[*a*,*h*]naphtho[2,1-*c*]phenazine (LXXVIII).

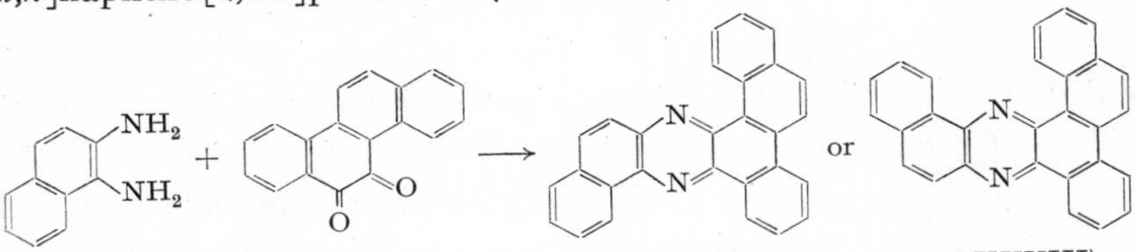

(LXXVII)   or   (LXXVIII)

35. Dibenzo[*a*,*c*]naphtho
    [1,2-*h*]phenazine

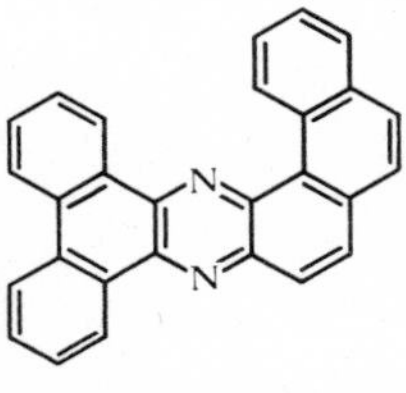

Sihlbom,[80] in the course of his investigations of the chemistry of retene, condensed 3,4-diaminoretene(3,4-diamino-7-isopropyl-1-methyl-phenanthrene) with retenequinone (7-isopropyl-1-methyl-9,10-phenan-threnequinone) and obtained 3,16-diisopropyl-7,10-dimethyldibenzo-[*a*,*c*]naphtho[1,2-*h*]phenazine (LXXIX) as canary-yellow needle-shaped prisms, m.p. 299–300°. Again, there is the possibility of an alternative structure (LXXX), which is 3,11-diisopropyl-7,17-dimethyl-dibenzo[a,c]naphtho[1,2-h]phenazine.

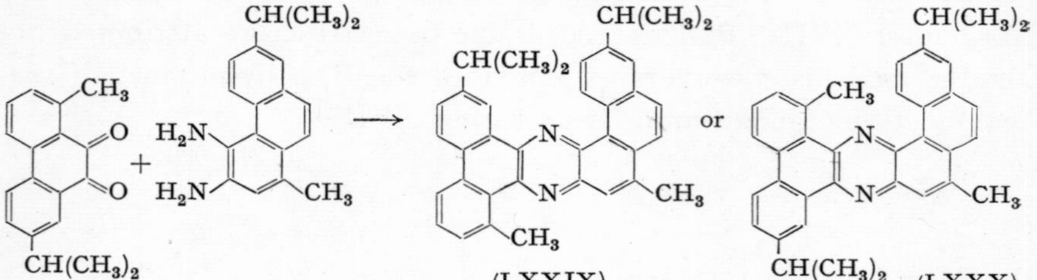

(LXXIX)   (LXXX)

No other representatives of this system have been prepared.

36. Dibenzo[a,h]dinaphtho[2,1-c,2′,1′-j]
   phenazine. "Chrysazine"

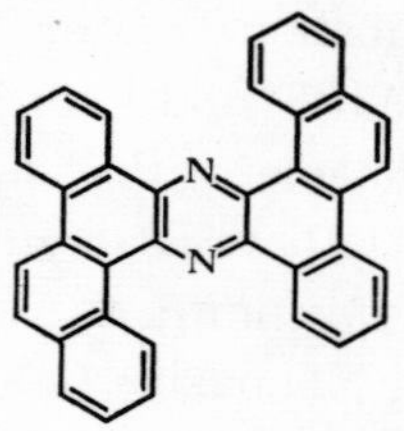

The parent substance of this ring system has been prepared by Schiedt[58] by heating 5,6-chrysenequinone with formamide and acetic acid at 170°, and forms yellow rods, m.p. 418°. It gives a deep blue color with concentrated sulfuric acid. The structure is most probably LXXXI, the alternative formulation as dibenzo[a,j]dinaphtho[2,1-c,1′2′-h]-phenazine (LXXXII) being probably incompatible with steric requirements.

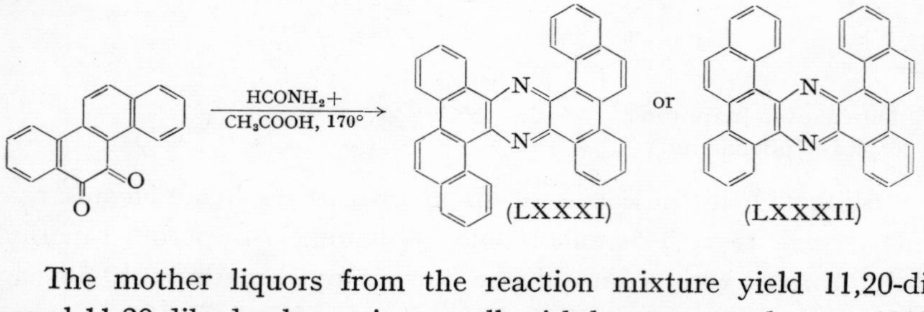

$$\xrightarrow[\text{CH}_3\text{COOH, 170°}]{\text{HCONH}_2+}$$

(LXXXI)   (LXXXII)

The mother liquors from the reaction mixture yield 11,20-di-formyl-11,20-dihydrochrysazine as yellowish-brown crystals, m.p. 190°, giving a violet-blue color in concentrated sulfuric acid (picrate, orange needles or orange-red leaflets, m.p. 205°).

37. Quinoxalo[2,3-*a*]coronene

This system was prepared recently by Zinke and Ott.[90] They oxidized coronene with chromic acid in acetic acid-nitrobenzene solution and obtained a dark violet-brown quinone, which they showed was an *o*-quinone by condensation with *o*-phenylenediamine in acetic acid-nitrobenzene. The product (LXXXIII) crystallized from a small volume of nitrobenzene in bright red-brown crystals or from a large amount of pyridine in needles that ranged in color from dark ocher-yellow to bright red-brown. It melted at 362° after sintering at 348°, sublimed readily at 300° and gave red-yellow solutions with a yellow-green fluorescence. It dissolves in cold concentrated sulfuric acid to give an emerald-green coloration that becomes blue-green on warming.

(LXXXIII)

References

1. L. I. Smith and L. R. Hac, *J. Am. Chem. Soc.*, **58**, 229 (1936).
2. B. K. Singh and B. Bhaduri, *J. Indian Chem. Soc.*, **8**, 623 (1931); *Chem. Abstracts*, **26**, 1917 (1932).
3. A. Heckendorn, *Helv. Chim. Acta*, **12**, 50 (1929).
4. L. Ruzicka, W. Bosshard, W. H. Fischer and H. Wirz, *Helv. Chim. Acta*, **19**, 1147 (1936).
5. H. H. Inhoffen, *Ber.*, **70B**, 1695 (1937).
6. Ger. Pat. 658,203; *Frdl.*, **24**, 602 (1937); *Chem. Abstracts*, **32**, 4798 (1938); *Chem. Zentr.*, **1938**, II, 422.
7. Ger. Pat. 659,095; *Frdl.*, **24**, 973 (1937); *Chem. Abstracts*, **32**, 5638 (1938); *Chem. Zentr.*, **1938**, II, 187.
8. O. Kruber, *Ber.*, **67B**, 1000 (1934).
9. R. Scholl and F. Kačer, *Ber.*, **37**, 4531 (1904).
10. Ger. Pat. 170,562; *Frdl.*, **8**, 348 (1905–1907); *Chem. Zentr.*, **1906**, II, 80.
11. R. Scholl, F. Eberle and W. Tritsch, *Monatsh.*, **32**, 1043 (1911); *Chem. Zentr.*, **1912**, I, 663.
12. G. Schroeter, *Ann.*, **426**, 17 (1922).
13. H. Goldstein and M. Streuli, *Helv. Chim. Acta*, **20**, 650 (1937).
14. E. Terres, *Ber.*, **46**, 1634 (1913).

15. Ger. Pat. 230,005; *Frdl.*, **10**, 702 (1910–1912); *Chem. Zentr.*, **1911**, I, 363.
16. Ger. Pat. 232,526; *Frdl.*, **10**, 702 (1910–1912); *Chem. Zentr.*, **1911**, I, 1094.
17. Ger. Pat. 184,391; *Frdl.*, **9**, 784 (1908–1910); *Chem. Zentr.*, **1907**, II, 766.
18. J. W. Cook, *J. Chem. Soc.*, **1931**, 2524.
19. L. F. Fieser and E. B. Hershberg, *J. Am. Chem. Soc.*, **59**, 2502 (1937).
20. M. S. Newman, *J. Am. Chem. Soc.*, **60**, 2947 (1938).
21. K. M. P. Singh and S. Dutt, *Proc. Indian Acad. Sci.*, **8A**, 187 (1938); *Chem. Abstracts*, **33**, 1943 (1939).
22. C. Liebermann and O. N. Witt, *Ber.*, **20**, 2442 (1887).
23. E. Bamberger and C. Burgdorf, *Ber.*, **23**, 2433 (1890).
24. T. A. Lawson, *Ber.*, **18**, 2422 (1885).
25. S. C. De and T. N. Ghosh, *J. Indian Chem. Soc.*, **7**, 357 (1930); *Chem. Abstracts*, **24**, 4781 (1930).
26. S. Maffei and S. Pietra, *Boll. Sci. Bologna*, **8**, 95 (1950); *Chem. Abstracts*, **46**, 119 (1952).
27. R. Lesser, *Ann.*, **402**, 1 (1914).
28. O. N. Witt, *Ber.*, **19**, 1719 (1886).
29. O. N. Witt, *Ber.*, **19**, 2791 (1886).
30. Ger. Pat. 90,213; *Frdl.*, **4**, 403 (1894–1897).
31. Ger. Pat. 90,212; *Frdl.*, **4**, 400 (1894–1897).
32. A. C. Sircar and S. Dutt, *J. Chem. Soc.*, **121**, 1944 (1922).
33. A. E. Poraï-Koshits, B. A. Poraï-Koshits and V. V. Perekalin, *J. Gen. Chem. U.S.S.R.*, **17**, 1758 (1947); *Chem. Abstracts*, **42**, 5867 (1948).
34. L. S. Efros, A. E. Poraï-Koshits and B. A. Poraï-Koshits, *J. Gen. Chem. U.S.S.R.*, **17**, 1807 (1947); *Chem. Abstracts*, **42**, 5869 (1948).
35. Swiss Pat. 259,320; *Chem. Abstracts*, **44**, 6634 (1950).
36. E. Loewe, *Ber.*, **23**, 2542 (1890).
37. E. R. Watson and S. Dutt, *J. Chem. Soc.*, **119**, 1211 (1921).
38. F. Kehrmann and I. Safar, *Helv. Chim. Acta*, **8**, 668 (1925).
39. S. Mihaéloff, *Bull. soc. chim. France, Mém.*, [5], **5**, 1655 (1938).
40. O. N. Witt, *Ber.*, **20**, 1183 (1887).
41. G. R. Levi and M. Faldino, *Gazz. chim. ital.*, **54**, 818 (1924); *Chem. Zentr.*, **1925**, I, 657; *British Abstracts*, **1925**, i, 171.
42. Ger. Pat. 97,639; *Frdl.*, **5**, 364 (1897–1900).
43. F. Kehrmann and J. Eichler, *Ber.*, **34**, 1210 (1901).
44. S. Dutt, *J. Chem. Soc.*, **121**, 1951 (1922).
45. F. Kehrmann and B. Perrot, *Helv. Chim. Acta*, **10**, 53 (1927).
46. J. Meisenheimer and F. W. Ditt, *Ann.*, **539**, 57 (1939).
47. H. Vollmann, H. Becker, M. Corell and H. Streeck, *Ann.*, **531**, 1 (1937).
48. P. C. Dutta, D. Prasad and S. C. De, *J. Indian Chem. Soc.*, **9**, 211 (1932); *Chem. Abstracts*, **26**, 5567 (1932).
49. F. Sachs and G. Mosebach, *Ber.*, **44**, 2852 (1911).
50. P. C. Dutta, *Ber.*, **66B**, 1220 (1933).
51. E. Clar, *Ber.*, **62B**, 1574 (1929).
52. Ger. Pat. 172,684; *Frdl.*, **8**, 340 (1905–1907); *Chem. Zentr.*, **1906**, II, 725.
53. F. Kaufler, *Ber.*, **36**, 930 (1903).
54. F. Kaufler, *Ber.*, **36**, 1721 (1903).
55. R. Scholl and H. Berblinger, *Ber.*, **36**, 3427 (1903).
56. E. Clar, *Ber.*, **72B**, 1645 (1939).
57. R. Scholl, *Ber.*, **40**, 933 (1907).
58. B. Schiedt, *J. prakt. Chem.*, **157**, 203 (1941).
59. E. Terres, *Ber.*, **46**, 1634 (1913).

60. E. Terres, *Monatsh.*, **41**, 603 (1920); *Chem. Zentr.*, **1921**, III, 640.
61. J. W. Cook, *J. Chem. Soc.*, **1933**, 1592.
62. C. L. Hewitt, *J. Chem. Soc.*, **1938**, 193.
63. H. Meyer and A. Hofmann, *Monatsh.*, **37**, 681 (1916); *Chem. Zentr.*, **1917**, I, 391.
64. N. Ghatak, *Allahabad Univ. Studies*, **7**, 199 (1931); *Chem. Abstracts*, **28**, 2187 (1934).
65. J. Schmidt and E. Junghans, *Ber.*, **37**, 3558 (1904).
66. E. von Sommaruga, *Monatsh.*, **1**, 145 (1880).
67. E. Bamberger and J. Grob, *Ber.*, **34**, 533 (1901).
68. B. Foresti, *Gazz. chim. ital.*, **52**, I, 278 (1922); *Chem. Zentr.*, **1922**, IV, 736.
69. B. Foresti and R. Martorelli, *Gazz. chim. ital.*, **53**, 262 (1923); *Chem. Zentr.*, **1923**, III, 927.
70. B. Foresti, *Gazz. chim. ital.*, **52**, II, 90 (1922); *Chem. Zentr.*, **1923**, I, 1399.
71. S. Goldschmidt, A. Vogt and M. A. Bredig, *Ann.*, **445**, 123 (1925).
72. R. Pschorr, *Ber.*, **35**, 2729 (1902).
73. F. R. Japp and C. I. Burton, *J. Chem. Soc.*, **49**, 843 (1886).
74. J. Erdmann, *Ann.*, **135**, 181 (1865).
75. A. T. Mason, *J. Chem. Soc.*, **55**, 107 (1889).
76. R. Leuckart, *J. prakt. Chem.*, [2], **41**, 330 (1890); *J. Chem. Soc.*, *Abstracts*, **58**, 783 (1890).
77. E. Schwenk and H. Waldmann, *J. prakt. Chem.*, **128**, 320 (1930).
78. E. J. Müller, *Ber.*, **67B**, 1799 (1934).
79. W. Bradley, E. Leete and D. S. Stephens, *J. Chem. Soc.*, **1951**, 2163.
80. L. Sihlbom, *Acta Chem. Scand.*, **2**, 486 (1948); *Chem. Abstracts*, **43**, 7470 (1949).
81. B. Schiedt, *Ber.*, **71B**, 1248 (1938).
82. K. Funke and J. Ristic, *J. prakt. Chem.*, **145**, 309 (1936).
83. M. S. Newman and J. A. Cathcart, *J. Org. Chem.*, **5**, 618 (1940).
84. E. Beschke, *Ann.*, **384**, 173 (1911).
85. V. Veselý, F. Štursa, H. Olejníček and E. Rein, *Coll. Czech. Chem. Comm.*, **1**, 493 (1929); *Chem. Abstracts*, **24**, 612 (1930).
86. V. Veselý and J. Páč, *Coll. Czech. Chem. Comm.*, **2**, 471 (1930); *Chem. Abstracts*, **24**, 5297 (1930).
87. V. Veselý and F. Štursa, *Coll. Czech. Chem. Comm.*, **5**, 343 (1933); *Chem. Abstracts*, **28**, 144 (1934).
88. K. Dziewonski and L. Sternbach, *Bull. intern. acad. polonaise, Classe sci. math. nat.*, **1933A**, 416; *Chem. Abstracts*, **28**, 2717 (1934).
89. O. Fischer and W. Kern, *J. prakt. Chem.*, **94**, 34 (1916).
90. A. Zinke and R. Ott, *Sitzungsber. Akad. Wien*, IIb, **161**, 546 (1952).
91. C. Graebe, *Ber.*, **7**, 782 (1874).

CHAPTER XVII

Indanthrone and Related Compounds

1. General

The most important member of the anthrazine (*R. I.* 3767) class of substances is Indanthrone (I) (5,6,9,14,15,18-hexahydroanthrazine-5,9,14,18-tetrone. *Chemical Abstracts* lists indanthrone as "6,15-dihydro-anthrazine-5,9,14,18-tetrone" but this nomenclature is not applicable to many derivatives of indanthrone), the parent of a number of anthra-quinone vat dyes.[1-3]

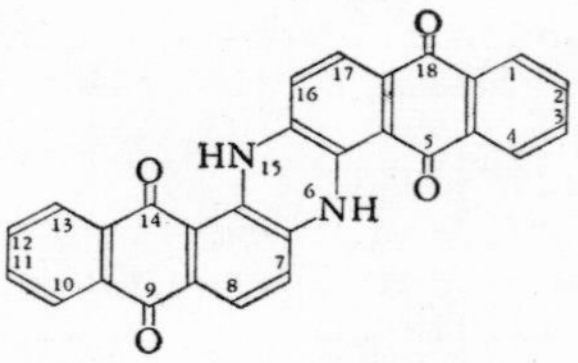

(I)

Indanthrone (*C. I.* 1106) (the name "Indanthrene" by which it was formerly known has become a trade designation for any very fast vat dye produced by I. G. Farbenindustrie A.G.; the termination "-one" is preferred also since it indicates the presence of carbonyl groups) is a blue dye of excellent stability and fastness, discovered in 1901 at Badische Anilin-und-Soda-Fabrik by René Bohn in an attempt to produce an anthraquinone analog of indigo by the alkaline fusion of 2-anthra-quinonylglycine. He showed that it was also given by the alkaline fusion of 2-aminoanthraquinone, its sulfonic acid or a hydrogenated product, for example, the corresponding 2-aminoanthranol or -anthra-hydroquinone, at 250° for one-half hour.[4] The melt was dissolved in water in the presence of air, when indanthrone separated. Owing to its insolubility, it was unsuitable in this form for dyeing, but on reduction

464

it formed a soluble vat from which direct dyeings on cotton could be made that were fast to light, air and washing.

The chemistry of indanthrone and its derivatives is complicated by the fact that many of the dyes described are mixtures of substances. Indanthrone itself is almost insoluble in most of the usual organic solvents but dissolves to a slight extent in boiling aniline or nitrobenzene to give greenish-blue solutions and crystallizes in characteristic curved, blue hair-like needles with a coppery luster, resembling indigo. The solutions are not fluorescent. On strong heating, indanthrone partly sublimes in the form of needles at 470–500°. It is very weakly basic and its salts with acids are readily hydrolyzed by water.[5,6]

2. Methods of Preparation

A.   Indanthrone is prepared commercially by many variants of the original process, for example, the fusion of 2-aminoanthraquinone with alkali at 250° alone[4,7] or at a lower temperature in mineral oil,[8] or by addition as an aqueous slurry.[9] Many patent specifications have

been filed protecting the use of various mixtures of catalysts, such as boric acid or its simple or complex salts,[10] cuprous halides,[11] alkali metal hydroxylates such as sodium phenoxide or butoxide, etc., alone[12–15] or mixed with the salt of an organic acid, for example, a mixture of sodium acetate and sodium phenoxide,[16,17] mixtures of salts of fatty acids,[17] mixtures of hydroxyaliphatic secondary or tertiary amines, such as di- and triethanolamines,[18] or oxidizing agents, such as potassium nitrate alone[19] or in a high-boiling solvent such as aniline or naphthalene,[20] or chromic acid, nitric acid or lead peroxide,[21,22] or finally with sodium chlorate in the presence of sodium phenoxide.[12] A

continuous process for indanthrone manufacture has been described.[23]
It has been claimed that the addition of soybean protein to the fusion
aids the wetting of 2-aminoanthraquinone by fused potash and
selectively accelerates the formation of indanthrone. This is said to be
due to the presence of leucine in the protein.[24]

The commercial importance of this reaction is obvious from the
extent of the above variations. The mechanism is discussed later (see
Section XVII:7).

B. A process of indanthrone formation has been described by the
fusion of 1-aminoanthraquinone with or without an added oxidizing
agent at 220–250°[25] or in the presence of metallic salts only[26] at 230–
260°.

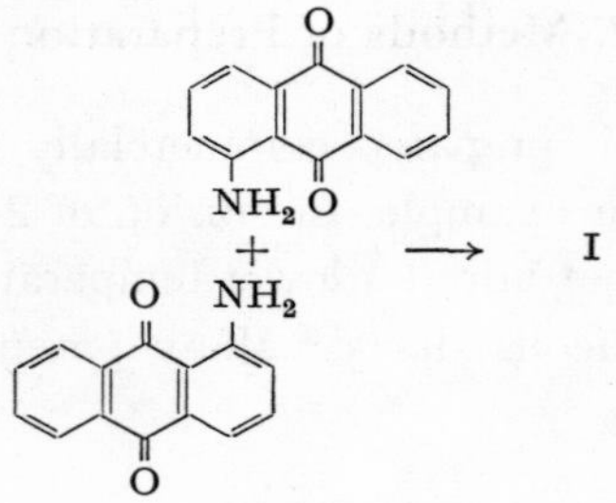

Indanthrone is also formed:

C. by heating an *o*-aminodianthraquinonylamine, produced by
heating an *o*-haloaminoanthraquinone with an aminoanthraquinone,
with oxidizing agents[27];

D. by heating 1-amino-2-bromoanthraquinone with copper
powder in naphthalene for 5 hours at the boiling point of the hydrocarbon[28];

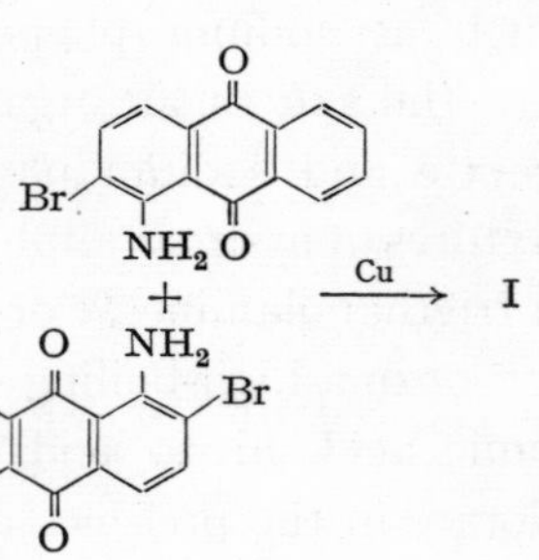

E. by heating 2-amino-1-mercaptoanthraquinone or its disulfide with an agent that removes sulfur, such as copper powder in naphthalene,[29] or with a condensing agent capable of forming a salt with the mercapto group[30];

F. by heating 2-amino-1-chloro- or 2-amino-1,3-dichloroanthraquinone with cuprous iodide, in naphthalene as an inert solvent,[31] suitably at 175° in the presence of anhydrous sodium acetate (but see reference 32);

G. by the oxidation of 2-amino-5,10-dihydroxyanthracene-5,10-disulfuric acid ester by means of cupric salts[33];

H. by the dehalogenation of haloindanthrones by heating with alcoholic potash, sodium amalgam, copper powder, etc.[34,35]

I. Indanthrone has also been prepared by the condensation of 1,2-diamino-5,10-anthraquinone with anthracene-1,2-quinone and the product (reddish-brown crystals) oxidized by potassium dichromate to anthrazine-5,9,14,18-tetrone, which on heating in quinoline yields indanthrone.[36,37] No trace of the other possible isomer, formed by combination of the units in the reverse fashion, was detected.[37]

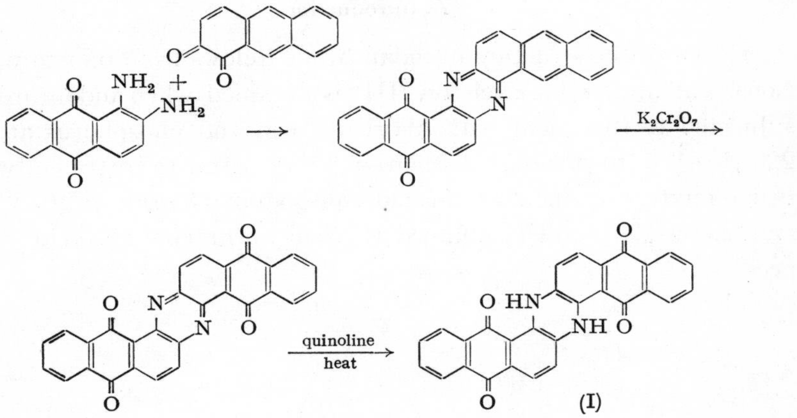

3. Structure

Indanthrone was given the formula $C_{28}H_{14}O_4N_2$, showing that it is formed by loss of four hydrogen atoms from two molecules of 2-aminoanthraquinone. It contains no free amino groups and consequently both are involved in the reaction. From these considerations and a study of the other methods of formation, it is clear that indanthrone has the structure I. The ring system is enumerated as shown in the formula. Claasz,[38] from a consideration of the chromophore in indigo, has proposed a modification of structure to include the ionic form (II) (see also Section XVII:5,C(5)). The study of indanthrone using X-rays[3,40] and electron microscopy[39] showed that there were four polymorphic modifications (designated α-, β-, γ- and δ-forms), which differ in their crystalline form and X-ray powder diagrams. The difference in tint of various dye brands, which depends upon the factors controlled during oxidation of the leuco compound or upon the purification to which the compound is submitted, are attributable to these polymorphic modifications. The α-form is the stable modification and is the one obtained by sublimation or crystallization from a high-boiling solvent. The treatment of indanthrone dyes to obtain a product of constant morphological properties has been summarized.[40]

4. Reactions

A. Introduction

Proof of the structure of indanthrone follows from its many reactions. The anthrazine skeleton (III) is obtained when indanthrone is subjected to treatment with hydriodic acid and phosphorus at 210–220°,[6,41,42] or to zinc dust distillation,[6,41] or better to treatment with a fusion mixture of zinc dust-zinc chloride-sodium chloride at 210–290°,[43] and the crude product sublimed to yield anthrazine as vivid yellow needles.

(II)   (III)

B. Oxidation

Oxidation of indanthrone, best in concentrated sulfuric acid with potassium dichromate or with hypochlorous acid, yields a dark green precipitate, said to be anthraquinoneazhydrin, the compound of an intermediate state of oxidation corresponding to the phenazhydrins (see Chapter III:2,D). This forms flat, green prisms from nitrobenzene, which on heating in aqueous solvents or alone to 400°, undergo auto-reduction to indanthrone.[6] Oxidation may be carried a stage further by the use of potassium nitrate in concentrated sulfuric acid to 5,9,14,18-tetrahydroanthrazine-5,9,14,18-tetrone (IV) (anthraquinon-azine), which separates from nitrobenzene as greenish-yellow flat prisms or hexagonal leaflets.[6] It is a somewhat stronger base than either indanthrone or the azhydrin, its salts with mineral acids being only slowly hydrolyzed by cold water.

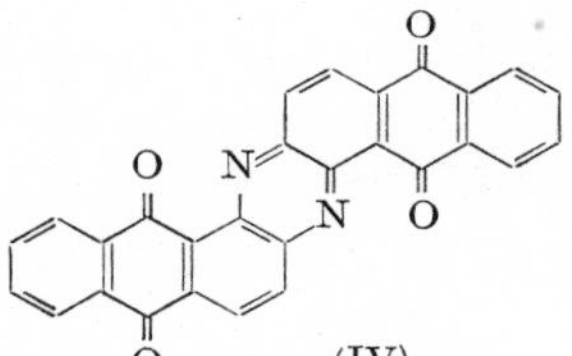

(IV)

5,9,14,18-Tetrahydroanthrazine-5,9,14-18-tetrone (IV) is reduced by sulfur dioxide to the azhydrin, but stronger reagents, or auto-reduction brought about by high temperatures (385–425°) or by attempted crystallization from wet nitrobenzene, yields indanthrone.[6] Much later, Scholl and Lamprecht[44] cast doubts on the existence of the azhydrin and concluded that it was probably a mechanical mixture of I and IV.

Prolonged oxidation of indanthrone by chromic acid in acetic acid gave a small yield of 2,3-dihydroxy-1,2-pyrazinoanthraquinone (V), the structure of which was confirmed by synthesis[45] from 1,2-diaminoanthraquinone and oxalic acid.

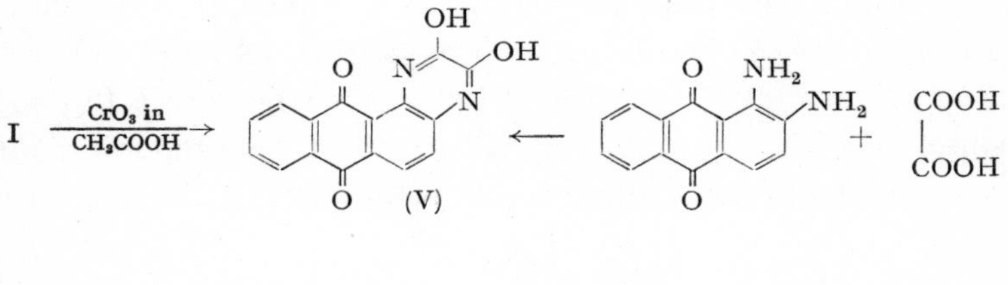

C. Reduction

(*1*) Reduction of indanthrone is highly complex, and, since it is the basis of vatting prior to dyeing, it has been intensively studied. The early investigations of Scholl and his collaborators established that reduction of indanthrone by sodium dithionite yielded a blue vat, whereas more vigorous reduction with zinc gave a brown vat, both of which were oxidized by air to indanthrone.[46] These vats were given the structures VI and VII, respectively. Benzoyl derivatives of

each compound were isolated, that from VI being a blue insoluble crystalline powder, while that from VII was a brownish-yellow powder crystallizing from pseudocumene and not melting below 300°. Scholl and Stegmüller[47] showed that heating the blue vat (VI) with sodium hydroxide for ten hours at 220–230° led to an oxidoreduction process, whereby they isolated indanthrone and an alkali-soluble, brownish-red substance, $C_{28}H_{16}O_3N_2$, giving bright red solutions in low-boiling organic solvents and a vivid red solution in hot quinoline. Its bluish-green solution in alkali was oxidized by air or by hypochlorite to a green insoluble product, a similar change occurring on cotton fabrics. This green insoluble oxidation product was a sodium salt, acidification of which yielded a brownish-violet compound giving blue solutions with hot methanolic potassium hydroxide. The oxidoreduction process was interpreted as yielding 6,9,14,15-tetrahydro-5-hydroxyanthrazine-9,14-dione (VIII) (the anthraquinone-anthranol compound), which on aerial oxidation gave 9,14-dihydro-5-hydroxyanthrazine-9,14-dione (IX). Scholl and Stegmüller[47] also showed that reduction of VIII by sodium dithionite yielded a brown vat by reduction of the remaining anthraquinone moiety to the hydroquinone, 6,15-dihydro-5,9,14-trihydroxy-anthrazine (X). This they tentatively identified as the product of reduction of indanthrone by sodium dithionite at 100°.

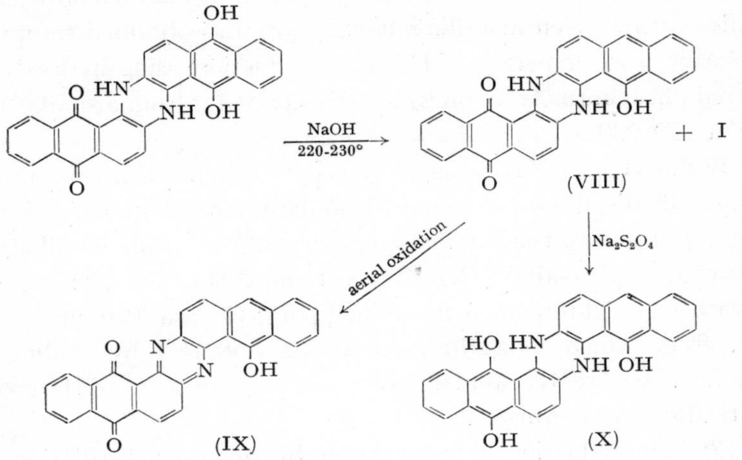

(2) Whereas reduction of indanthrone by hydriodic acid and phosphorus at 210–220° gave anthrazine,[6,41,42] heating the mixture at a lower temperature (150–160° for ten hours) yielded an hydriodide, which was readily hydrolyzed to a base, forming brown needles from nitrobenzene. This, according to Scholl and Berblinger,[6] is 5,6,9,14,15,18-hexahydroanthrazine-9,18-dione (XI), for on heating to 334–344° it lost hydrogen and yielded 5,9,14,18-tetrahydroanthrazine-9,18-dione

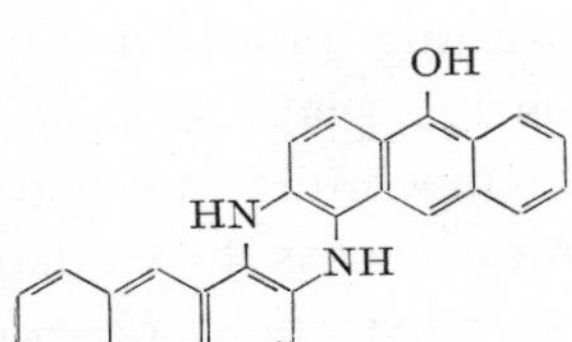

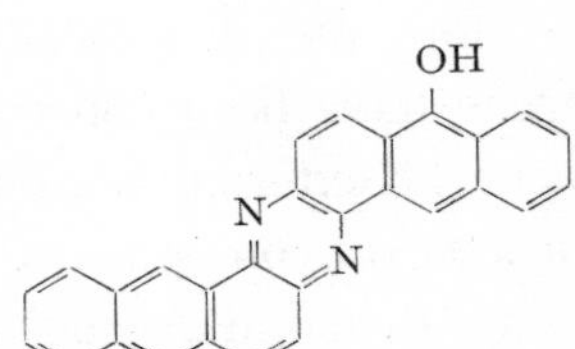

(XII) (anthranonazine), though the oxidation was better accomplished by refluxing in nitrobenzene until the originally yellowish-red solution became magenta, from which XII crystallized as lustrous brownish-red needles with a green metallic reflex. It was also obtained from indanthrone by low temperature (110–115°) reduction using hydriodic acid and red phosphorus,[6] though Kaufler[41] obtained it from a similar reduction at 250–280°.

Both XI and XII behave as cryptophenols, being insoluble in aqueous alkalis, but dissolving in alcoholic alkalis, from which solutions acids reprecipitate the original compounds. The alcoholic alkali solutions contain the salts of XIa (brown) and XIIa (blue). Treatment of XI with acid dichromate at the boiling point yields anthraquinoneazine (IV), from which indanthrone may be obtained by boiling with quinoline. An exactly similar treatment of anthrazine (III) proceeds identically to indanthrone.[6,48]

(3) The reduction of indanthrone by zinc dust distillation or by high temperature treatment with hydriodic acid and phosphorus to yield anthrazine (III) has been noted above (Section XVII:5,A). Reduction with zinc dust and caustic soda yields a dihydroanthrazine, $C_{28}H_{18}N_2$, as small, red, lustrous aggregates, which on heating at 360° yield a sublimate of anthrazine with simultaneous evolution of hydrogen.[49] Accordingly the dihydroanthrazine is formulated as 6,15-dihydroanthrazine (XIII).

(XIII)   (XIV)

(4) More recent studies of the vatting process as applied to indanthrone have been concentrated on the quantitative aspect and the influence of external factors such as temperature and concentration of the various vat components. Thus Brassard[50] has shown that vatting with sodium dithionite at 60° proceeds by reduction of two carbonyl groups only. At higher temperatures, overreduction becomes progres-

sively more pronounced, with a corresponding duller finish to the dyeing, until under extreme conditions (90°) overreduction occurs quantitatively with the consumption of four moles of dithionite (eight atomic proportions of hydrogen) per mole of indanthrone to yield a completely insoluble compound no longer reoxidizable, which Brassard considers to be 5,6,9,14,15,18-hexahydroanthrazine-9,18-dione (XI) in contrast to Scholl and Stegmüller[47] (see Section XVII:5,C(1)). Overreduction may be minimized by the addition to the vat of glucose, which forms loose addition compounds with sodium dithionite, thus providing a reserve of vatting reagent.[50] Yoe[51] had earlier arrived at the conclusion that the vat obtained by normal reduction was in colloidal suspension rather than true solution.

The oxidative titration of indanthrone vats[52,53] (in pyridine solution by means of ceric sulfate) shows that the blue vat (VI) possesses a normal redox potential at 50° of –292 mv.; that of the fully reduced vat (VII) could only be estimated roughly owing to its insolubility, but a value of –700 mv. was probable. Both halves of the titration curve were sigmoid, showing that oxidation followed a one-electron process. The inequality in the two potential steps indicated that the blue vat (VI) exists in the ion as a resonance hybrid (of which XIV is only one canonical structure) in which the negative charges are shared among the four oxygen atoms. An alternative view,[54] based on chemical rather than physical evidence, is that the two hydrogen atoms added in forming the blue vat are attached to carbonyl groups in different anthraquinone residues and the undisturbed stability and color of the molecule are attributed to hydrogen bonds between imino groups and the remaining carbonyl groups. A closely similar concept has been applied to the indanthrone molecule itself,[55] and utilizes hydrogen bonding as well as the resonance concept applied to II, but this is clearly incorrect since it is inapplicable to 6,15-dimethylindanthrone (XVII) (N,N'-dimethylindanthrone), which, although it is incapable of hydrogen bond formation, still possesses the characteristic stability and typical blue color of indanthrone.

(5)   At this point, it is appropriate to consider some of the factors governing the stability of indanthrone. In contrast to the usual properties of phenazine compounds, it is the dihydrophenazine that is here

the more stable. Thus, whereas with 5,10-dihydrophenazine oxidation to phenazine may be brought about very readily (see Chapter III:1,A), in the case of anthraquinoneazine heating in quinoline solution will bring about the facile reduction to indanthrone. Scholl[5] recognized that the peculiar stability of indanthrone was somehow connected with the presence of four carbonyl groups situated around the dihydroazine nucleus and that this stability was further improved by the introduction of halogen atoms into the molecule. One of the few drawbacks to the widespread use of indanthrone as a dye was connected with its instability towards chlorine and other bleaching agents. As will be recognized, this is not primarily due to color change attendant upon the introduction of chlorine atoms; the greening of the shade is probably to be attributed more to a partial oxidation to the yellow azine. Introduction of halogen atoms renders this oxidation less facile and hence gives a purer, more stable, blue hue. Bradley and Nursten[56] have drawn attention to the work of Fieser and Fieser[57] on the electronic effects of substituents on the stability of 1,4-naphthoquinones compared with the corresponding 1,4-dihydroxynaphthalenes and, applying this to the parallel case of dihydroazines and azines, have shown[58] that as expected the introduction of alkylsulfonyl groups enhances the stability of the dihydro form even more than do halogens, due to the greater electron-attracting properties. The stabilizing influence of the carbonyl groups on the dihydro form of the azine is also in line with the ideas of Fieser and Fieser. On the other hand, the marked electron-releasing properties of the tertiary butyl group operate in the reverse direction and the dehydrogenation of 7,16-di-*tert*-butylindanthrone occurs quite readily,[56] especially in the presence of copper salts. A solution in chlorobenzene, exposed to light, rapidly showed perceptible greening due to oxidation to the azine. 7,16-Dimethylindanthrone possesses a stability intermediate to that of indanthrone and 7,16-di-*tert*-butylindanthrone,[59] an observation in accord with the known ease of electron release in the series H,– CH_3,– $(CH_3)_3C$–.

This appears to rule out an alternative theory that the stability of the haloindanthrones was due to a steric effect, whereby the bulky halogen atoms shielded the imino groups from oxidation.[60]

D. Benzoylation

Benzoylation of indanthrone was accomplished by refluxing a suspension of the dye in benzoyl chloride.[45] 6,15-Dibenzoylindanthrone so formed crystallized from xylene as red needles, hydrolysis of which afforded indanthrone immediately. This is in contrast to the behavior of the benzoyl derivative obtained by the action of benzoyl chloride in hot quinoline,[61] which formed yellow needles from pseudocumene; these on hydrolysis yielded a blue solution from which indanthrone was obtained only following aerial oxidation. This latter benzoylation was formulated as a reductive process yielding 6,15-dihydro-5,9,14,18-tetrabenzoyloxyanthrazine (XV). The corresponding O-tetraacetyl compound, obtained by heating a mixture of indanthrone, acetyl chloride, acetic anhydride and quinoline, yielded anthranonazine (XII) on prolonged reflux in quinoline.[61] Reductive acetylation of indanthrone by heating it with zinc dust and acetic anhydride was reported[47] as giving a poorly characterized brown powder, tentatively formulated as a triacetate. 6,15-Dibenzoylindanthrone yielded 5,9,14,18-tetra-

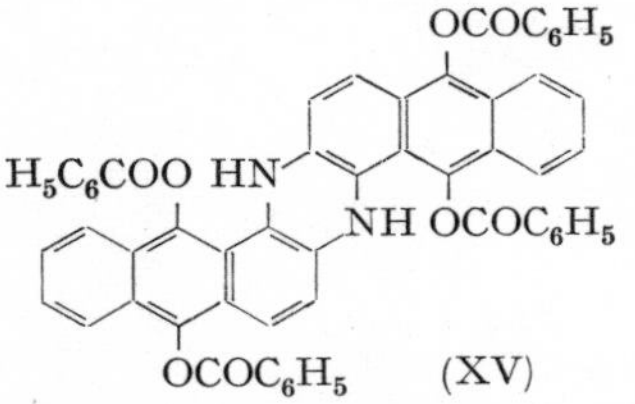

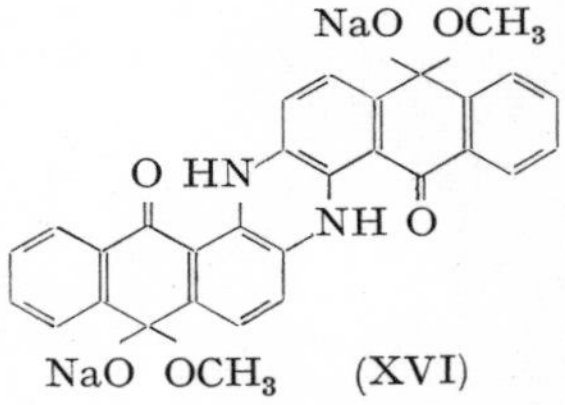

hydroanthrazine-5,9,14,18-tetrone (anthraquinoneazine) (IV) on treatment with nitric acid and may be chlorinated to yield chloroindanthrone.[45]

E. Reaction with Sodium Alkoxides

Indanthrone reacts with sodium alkoxides, such as sodium methoxide, to give a blue-black solid containing approximately two atoms of sodium per mole of indanthrone.[45] This product has been formulated as XVI.

F. Methylation

Methylation of indanthrone has only recently been reported.[62] It was accomplished by refluxing a suspension of indanthrone, methyl

4-toluenesulfonate and anhydrous potassium carbonate in trichloro-benzene for forty-eight hours. The filtered solution deposited 6,15-dimethylindanthrone (*N*,*N*'-dimethylindanthrone) (XVII), while the mother liquors on chromatography on alumina yielded a further amount together with 6-methylindanthrone (XVIII) and a blue substance to which the structure XIX was given on the basis of analysis, *N*-methyl estimation, color reactions and absorption spectra. The *N*-methyl indanthrones are dealt with more fully later (see Section XVII:6,F(2)).

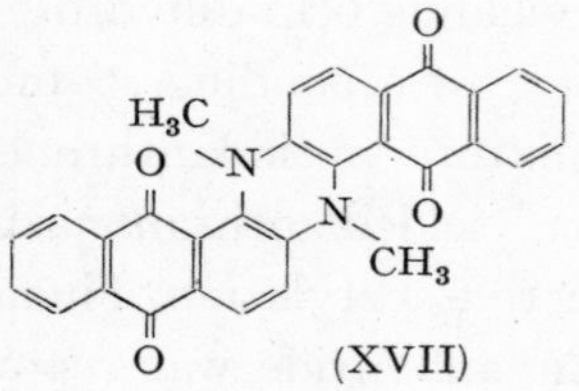

(XVII)

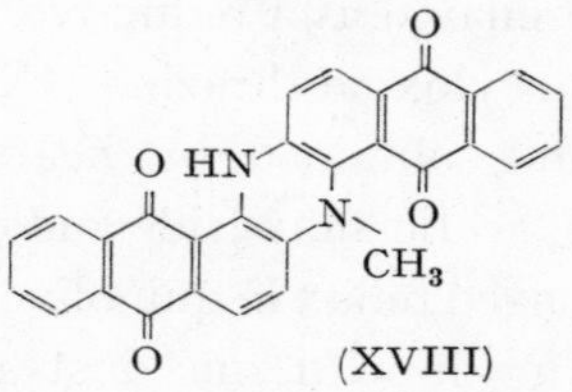

(XVIII)

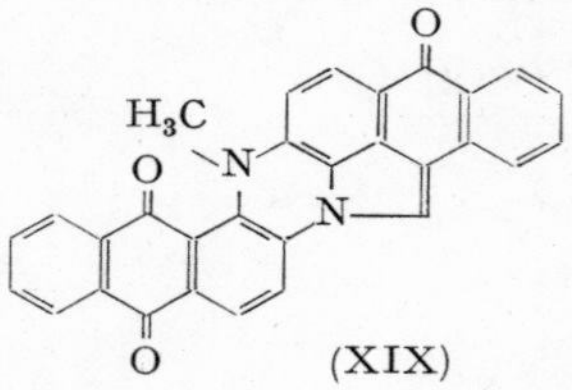

(XIX)

G. Indirect Substitution

Substituents may be introduced indirectly into the indanthrone molecule.

(*1*) Haloindanthrones may be obtained by the action of, for example, hydrochloric acid on anthraquinoneazine (IV) at high tem-peratures,[63,64] one molecule of hydrogen chloride being added, the halogen entering the 7-position (not the 8-position as stated). The mono-haloindanthrone may then be oxidized to the haloanthraquinoneazine and the process repeated to give the dihaloindanthrone. The halo-indanthrones are treated more fully later (see Section XVII:6,A).

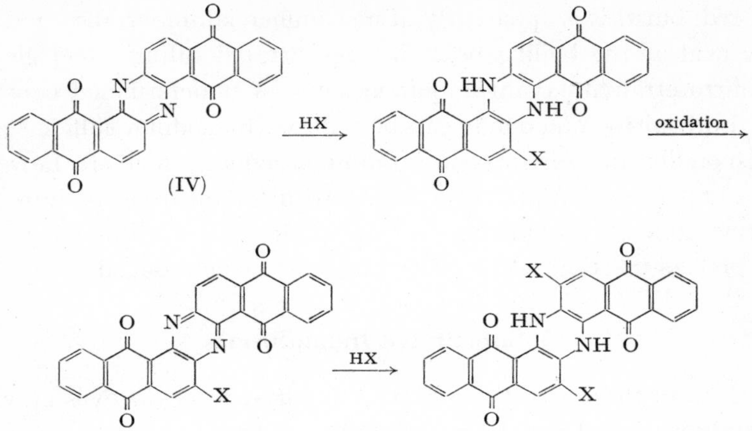

(2) Aminoindanthrones are obtained in a similar manner[6]; for example, anthraquinoneazine (IV) and ammonium hydroxide are heated under pressure when an aminoindanthrone is produced. Anilino-indanthrone was obtained similarly from anthraquinoneazine and aniline on prolonged reflux.[6] An analogy was drawn in the latter two cases between the behavior of anthraquinoneazine and 5-phenyl-phenazinium salts (Chapter II:2,D) and, on this basis, the entering groups were thought to be attached to the 8- and 17-positions, although there does not appear to be any proof of this. In the case of indirect halogenation, later patents have shown that this assumption was in error, and the entering halogen atoms are attached to the 7- and 16-positions, but there still appears to be some dubiety on this point and it has been suggested[65] that the position of the entering halogen atoms depends markedly upon the halogenating agent employed.

H. Action of Nitric Acid

The action of nitric acid on indanthrone is somewhat complex.[66] At room temperature, concentrated nitric acid acts as an oxidizing agent only, and gives anthraquinoneazine (IV). At the boiling point, however, substitution and oxidation occur to give a yellow powder, stated to be a nitrodinitrosotrihydroxyanthraquinoneazine. This gives a vat on reduction with sodium dithionite, from which cotton is dyed wine-red, but this is apparently of no commercial importance. Fuming nitric acid at the boiling point in concentrated sulfuric acid gives a tetranitrotetrahydroxyanthraquinoneazine of undetermined constitution. Both nitro compounds can be reduced by sodium sulfide to the corresponding aminohydroxyanthraquinoneazines, which are, however, of no importance. Aqua regia reacts with indanthrone to introduce chlorine atoms,[67] presumably by direct chlorination, although a step-wise process (Section XVII:5,G(1)) may also be envisaged.

5. Substituted Indanthrones

Many of these are of commercial importance as vat dyes in which the stability is enhanced towards light, washing and, in some cases, bleaches. They are best considered under their individual substituents.

A. Haloindanthrones

(1) Besides the processes noted above, for example, indirect substitution *via* anthraquinoneazine (Section XVII:5,G(1)) or by means of hydrohalic acid in sulfuric acid,[68] and by the action of aqua regia on indanthrone,[67] there are many other processes for the direct introduction of halogen atoms; by means of chlorine on indanthrone in an inert solvent[69] such as nitrobenzene alone,[70-73] or in the presence of an iron catalyst[74]; acetic acid[75]; sulfuric acid alone,[76,77] or in the presence of a catalyst,[78] preferably hydrochloric acid[79]; or in molten sulfur[80] or an inert solvent containing dissolved sulfur.[81] This latter process is clearly related to those in which the chlorinating agent is a sulfur halide[82-85] at temperatures from 20–150° and which yield mainly 7,16-dichloroindanthrone. Other sulfur compounds employed include sulfuryl chloride alone,[86] under pressure at 170°[87] or in sulfuric acid,[88] and thionyl chloride under pressure.[89] Chlorination of indanthrone has also been reported by the use of antimony pentachloride in boiling nitrobenzene[90] or by use of organic acid chlorides, such as benzoyl chloride in boiling nitrobenzene.[91] Polychloroindanthrones may be obtained by the further chlorination of chloroindanthrones.[92]

Bromination of indanthrone, for example in sulfuric acid solution at 60–80°[93] yields 7,16-dibromoindanthrone.

(2) 7,16-Dichloroindanthrones have been prepared by the direct chlorination of the corresponding dibromo compounds in inert, high-boiling solvents, such as nitrobenzene alone[94] or in the presence of sulfur[81] at temperatures above 200°. The product is the corresponding dichloroazine, which is readily reduced to the blue indanthrone. Alternatively the bromoindanthrones may be treated at low temperatures with sulfuryl chloride and then heated to 210° when partial[95,96] or complete,[96] elimination of bromine occurs.

(3) Just as indanthrone may be prepared by the self-condensation of 2-amino-1-bromoanthraquinone, so polyhalo-2-aminoanthraquinones yield haloindanthrones. Several patents protecting such a process have been granted. Thus, 2-amino-3-chloroanthraquinone is brominated (in position 1) and the product condensed in an inert solvent in the presence of an acid absorber, for example, cupric acetate.[97] The corresponding bromoindanthrone had been described much earlier,[98] at which time it had been shown[99] that milder conditions gave the corresponding azine. 7,16-Dibromoindanthrone, prepared in this way, forms small blue needles, m.p. 515°.[100] A process[101] that appears to entail simultaneous dichlorination of 2-aminoanthraquinone and condensation to the chloroindanthrone may be brought about by means of antimony pentachloride and selenium in nitrobenzene, generally with cupric acetate as catalyst; these conditions minimize the simultaneous formation of flavanthrone. 2-Aminodichloroanthraquinones may be self-condensed in the presence of cuprous iodide[31] or a mixture of copper and iodine in 1,2-dichlorobenzene.[32]

(4) Haloindanthrones do not possess such instability towards bleaching agents as does indanthrone. This is related to the electron-withdrawing properties of the halogen atoms in stabilizing the dihydro-azine (Section XVII:5,C(5)). However, the halogen atoms are moderately labile; thus chloroindanthrones are obtained by chlorination of the corresponding bromoindanthrones and, moreover, heating 7,16-di-bromoindanthrone with alcoholic potash leads to the complete elimination of bromine with formation of indanthrone.[34] It has also been shown[58,65] that, under normal vatting procedures, 7,16-dichloro-indanthrone loses much of its chlorine and on heating with piperidine in naphthalene forms 7-piperidino-16-chloroindanthrone.[102] While the

bromine atoms of 7,16-dibromoindanthrone are stable towards reflux
with dry amines, heating at a higher temperature in naphthalene largely
gives indanthrone[102] and boiling aqueous piperidine will replace 40%
of the bromine in nine hours.[58] The halogen atoms are stable towards
the action of morpholine under all conditions.[102]

By heating 7,16-dibromo-6,15-dimethylindanthrone with piperidine in naphthalene, Bradley and Nursten[102] obtained 6,15-dimethyl-
indanthrone, showing that an essential step in the removal of the
halogen atoms was the reduction of the carbonyl groups followed by
elimination of hydrogen bromide. 7,16-Dibromo-6-methylindanthrone
likewise gave 6-methylindanthrone.

B. Amino and Substituted Aminoindanthrones

Industrially, these may be produced from chloroindanthrones by
heating them with ammonia or substituted amines, such as aniline, in
the presence of an acid absorbent and a catalyst such as cuprous
chloride.[103,104] They may also be prepared by self-condensation of
2-bromo-1,4-diaminoanthraquinone in nitrobenzene at 230° in the
presence of copper bronze.[65] A process utilizing a solution of hydroxylamine in concentrated sulfuric acid, with or without the addition of
ferrous salts, has been patented[105] but the yields are said to be very
inadequate. Mixed haloaminoindanthrones have been described by the
self-condensation of 1,4-diamino-2,3-dihaloanthraquinones in the
presence of sodium acetate with either copper,[28] or cupric chloride[106]
in an inert solvent such as naphthalene or nitrobenzene. The use of
aminoindanthrones in the production of more complex vat-dyes is
described in Chapter XIX:59.

C. Cyanoindanthrones

Vat dyes, of a more greenish shade than that of the chloroindanthrones, are obtained by heating the latter substances with
cuprous cyanide in an inert solvent.[107]

D. Hydroxyindanthrones

Indanthrones containing hydroxyl groups are of less value as vat
dyes than most other indanthrones since the shade is altered by alkaline

treatment. They may be prepared by self-condensation of 1-amino-2-bromo-4-hydroxyanthraquinone, for example, by means of alkali in nitrobenzene in the presence of copper as catalyst[28] ("Indanthrene Blue 5G").

E. Alkylsulfonylindanthrones

7,16-Dialkylsulfonylindanthrones have been prepared by Bradley and Nursten,[58] who predicted (Section XVII:5,C(5)) that the presence of the alkylsulfonyl groups should exert a considerable stabilizing influence upon the dihydroazine. The compounds XX, $(R = C_2H_5)$ and XX $(R = n-C_4H_9)$ were prepared by self-condensation of 1-bromo-2-amino-3-alkylsulfonylanthraquinone in 1,2-dichlorobenzene with cupric and sodium acetates in yields of 40 and 32%, respectively.

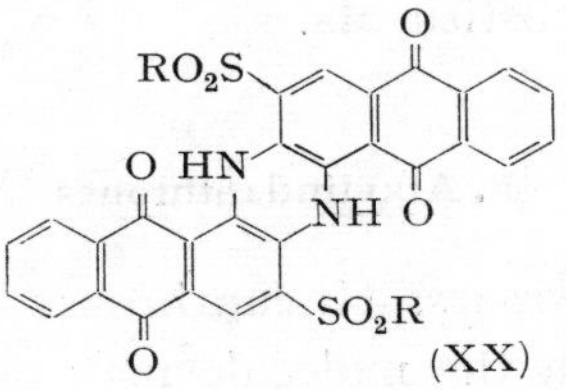

(XX)

The absorption spectra of the alkylsulfonylindanthrones in 1-chloronaphthalene closely resembled those of the corresponding 7,16-dihaloindanthrones (see Table XLVI).

TABLE XLVI. Absorption Maxima of Indanthrones in 1-Chloronaphthalene[58,59]

Substituent	Main band ($\lambda_{max.}$ in mμ)	Subsidiary band
6-Methyl-	665	
6,15-Dimethyl-	655	620(?)
7,16-Dimethyl-	770 ($\varepsilon = 2.90 \times 10^4$)	705 ($\varepsilon = 2.27 \times 10^4$)
7,16-Diethylsulfonyl-	705	652.5
7,16-Dibutylsulfonyl-	705	655
7,16-Dichloro-	720	662.5
7,16-Dibromo-	722.5	665

Chemically, the alkylsulfonylindanthrones show greater stability towards hypochlorite oxidation than do the haloindanthrones. Both are relatively strong acids and give green salts with methanolic potassium hydroxide in pyridine. Reduction with sodium dithionite gives vats, both very sparingly soluble, from which the indanthrones are regenerated unchanged by oxidation, whereas vatting in the halo-indanthrone series may lead to a loss of halogen. However, on heating the alkylsulfonylindanthrones in quinoline or dry piperidine loss of alkylsulfinic acid occurs and the resulting azine is then reduced to indanthrone itself. This is the reverse of the reaction between phenazine and benzenesulfinic acid[108] which yields 2-phenylsulfonylphenazine (see Chapter IV:4). This interpretation of the reaction has recently been questioned by Bradley and Nursten,[102] who now regard it, on analogy with the corresponding reaction of 7,16-dibromo-6,15-di-methylindanthrone, as due to a reduction of carbonyl groups, followed by elimination of the substituents.

F. Alkylindanthrones

(1) *C-Alkylindanthrones.* Indanthrones containing one or several *C*-methyl groups in the molecule may be prepared by the self-condensation of 2-aminoanthraquinones, suitably alkylated in the nucleus, by means of lead dioxide in acetic acid, or by self-condensation of the 1-bromo derivative by means of sodium acetate in boiling naphthalene in the presence of cupric oxide.[109] Kränzlein[110] prepared 7,8,16,17-tetramethylindanthrone by the self-condensation of 1-amino-2-bromo-3,4-dimethylanthraquinone and Bradley and Nursten[56] prepared 7,16-di-*tert*-butylindanthrone similarly from 2-amino-1-bromo-3-*tert*-butylanthraquinone in 1,2-dichlorobenzene in the presence of sodium acetate and copper acetate. This reaction was unusual in that the corresponding flavanthrone was formed simultaneously and was separated chromatographically. They were unable to obtain the indan-throne by alkaline fusion of 2-amino-3-*tert*-butylanthraquinone; at temperatures as low as 240°, the sole product was di-*tert*-butylflav-anthrone. In a later paper,[59] the same workers describe the preparation of 7,16-dimethylindanthrone from 2-amino-1-bromo-3-methylanthra-quinone by heating this in 1,2-dichlorobenzene in the presence of sodium acetate and cupric acetate. In contrast to the di-*tert*-butyl

homolog, 7,16-dimethylindanthrone could be prepared by the alkali fusion of 2-amino-3-methylanthraquinone at 220–300° without the simultaneous formation of the corresponding flavanthrone. This indanthrone, blue needles (no melting point) was originally described in a patent.[109] The dimethylflavanthrone was obtained by heating 2-amino-3-methylanthraquinone with antimony pentachloride in nitrobenzene.

The effect of C-alkyl substituents upon the stability of indanthrones has been discussed above (Section XVII:5,C(5)). The introduction of these groups increases the solubility in organic solvents.

The preparation of 7,16-di(trifluoromethyl)indanthrone has been described.[111] It is a stable blue dye with good fastness and is prepared as the soluble leuco tetrasulfate.

(2) *N-Alkylindanthrones.* Despite the existence of many patents on the subject of N-alkylindanthrones, it is doubtful whether any were obtained in a state of purity before the work of Bradley and his co-workers.

6-Methyl- (XVIII) and 6,15-dimethyl-indanthrone (XVII) may be obtained by the direct methylation of indanthrone by methyl 4-toluenesulfonate and anhydrous potassium carbonate in trichloro-benzene, followed by chromatographic separation.[62] 7,16-Dibromo-indanthrone has been similarly mono- and di-N-methylated. A by-product in this reaction is apparently an O-trimethyl derivative.[102]

6-Methyl- and 6,15-dimethyl-indanthrones may also be obtained by the cyclization of either 2-amino- (XXI, R = CH_3, R′ = H) or 2-methylamino-1,2′-dianthraquinonylmethylamine (XXI, R = R′ = CH_3), respectively, by heating with a suspension of potassium hydroxide in pyridine.[62]

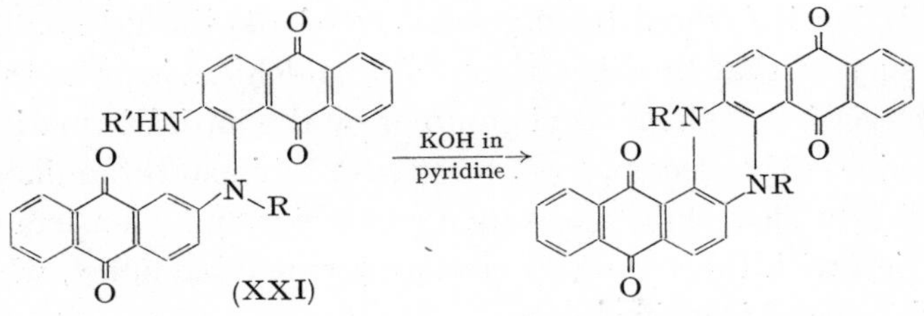

XVII (R=R′=CH_3)
XVIII (R=CH_3, R′=H)

Bradley and his team developed a color test applicable to systems containing an aromatic amino group situated ortho or para to a carbonyl group. This test, a color change generally from blue to green in the indanthrone series, depends on the formation of a potassium salt by the action of methanolic potassium hydroxide on a solution of the substance in pyridine. Indanthrone and 6-methylindanthrone give a green color, while 6,15-dimethylindanthrone, which clearly is unable to form a potassium salt, is unaffected. Application of this test to the so-called 6,15-dimethylindanthrone obtained following a patent specification[106] gave a green color, indicating the product could not be homogeneous.[112] Repetition of the patent process, namely heating purified 2-bromo-1-methylaminoanthraquinone under reflux with copper bronze, cuprous chloride or cupric acetate and either sodium acetate or potassium acetate in nitrobenzene, gave an inhomogeneous product. A clue to the failure was found in the liberation of formaldehyde corresponding in one case to 61% of the methyl groups present. Chromatographic examination of the product showed that it was mainly 6-methylindanthrone, with small amounts of indanthrone, and perhaps 6,15-dimethylindanthrone. Bradley[113] had much earlier suggested that mono-N-methylindanthrone formed the bulk of this dyestuff. Study of other patent claims,[27,114] in which an equimolar mixture of 1-amino-2-bromoanthraquinone and 2-bromo-1-methyl-aminoanthraquinone is heated in nitrobenzene with cupric chloride and an alkali to give 6-methylindanthrone, showed that here, too, methyl groups were lost as formaldehyde (11% in two hours). It was further shown that heating 6,15-dimethylindanthrone and bromomethylamino-anthraquinones with copper salts led to demethylation; with chloro-methylaminoanthraquinones dechlorination occurred as well. This demethylation is favored by the presence of alkalis and Bradley and Leete[112] suggest that the liberation of formaldehyde is preceded either by hydroxylation of the methyl group or by the initial formation of an amine oxide that decomposes to give 2-aminoanthraquinone and formaldehyde. These substances then recombine and react in a second-ary reaction with the copper to produce a copper complex, which has been isolated and identified.

Dyes, which it is claimed contain indanthrones substituted on the nitrogen atoms, are said to be formed when 1-arylamino-2-amino-3-bromoanthraquinones are heated with zinc chloride and acetic acid,[115] and when di- and tri-anthrimides are heated with metallic chlorides or alkalis and the products oxidized.[116] The latter compounds dye with yellow shades from a red vat and, hence, despite the formulas quoted in the specification, they are extremely unlikely to be phenazine derivatives and are much more probably carbazole dyestuffs. Other N-alkylindanthrones are claimed in more recent patents[117–119] by similar self-condensations to those described above; the condensing agents specified, sulfuryl chloride, benzoyl chloride, manganese dioxide, and lead dioxide, are perhaps milder in action and it may be that demethylation phenomena do not here occur. On the other hand, condensation of o-amino-αβ-anthrimides, substituted on the nitrogen atoms by alkyl groups, under vigorous conditions[117] using manganese dioxide, potassium permanganate, nitric acid or oxygen in sulfuric acid, can scarcely be expected to lead to N-alkylindanthrones. One other patent[120] describes the use of chloromethylindanthrone, which may be reacted with isothiuronium groups to produce water-soluble, direct dyes for cellulose fibers.

(3) *Properties of N-Alkylindanthrones.* Since N-alkylindanthrones still retain the anthraquinone portions of the indanthrone molecule, they may be vatted with alkaline sodium dithionite, when brown vats result, from which blue dyeings may be made. Alkylation of the nitrogen atoms increases the solubility of the dye in organic solvents and this suggests a diminution in hydrogen bonding as compared with indanthrone.[62] Indanthrone and 6-methylindanthrone both form potassium salts in pyridine, but 6,15-dimethylindanthrone does not. With nitric acid, indanthrone is rapidly oxidized to the yellow azine (IV).[6] A similar reaction occurs with 6-methylindanthrone, which rapidly gives a quaternary nitrate (XXII) as orange crystals.[62] As might be anticipated, 6,15-dimethylindanthrone is more stable and is only attacked by concentrated nitric acid, when demethylation occurs and the same quaternary nitrate (XXII) separates, together with a small quantity of unmethylated azine (IV). The quaternary nitrate may be reduced by sodium dithionite and, on subsequent aeration, yields 6-methylindanthrone (XVIII). Milder oxidizing agents, for example,

bleaches such as sodium hypochlorite, which oxidize indanthrone, are without effect upon 6,15-dimethylindanthrone. The so-called N,N'-dimethylindanthrones (for example, Algol Blue R.K.) which were prepared by patent procedures were no more stable to bleaches than was indanthrone. This curious fact now receives adequate explanation in the light of Bradley's observations.

6,15-Dimethylindanthrone is also demethylated by heating with cupric acetate and potassium carbonate in nitrobenzene, 5% of the methyl groups being lost as formaldehyde in 5 hours,[112] and also when it is heated with alumina in nitrobenzene or 1,2-dichlorobenzene.[112] This ready demethylation gives 6-methylindanthrone and indanthrone, the latter compound being strongly adsorbed by the alumina; this fact is probably the driving force in the reaction, since loss of methyl groups leads to the non-planar N-methyl compounds becoming the planar indanthrone molecule.

The absorption spectra of indanthrone, its N-alkyl derivatives and their reduced vats have been compared,[62,112] together with those of its 7,16-dihalo- and -dialkylsulfonyl derivatives[58,102] (and see Tables

TABLE XLVII.
Absorption Maxima of Indanthrones in Concentrated Sulfuric Acid[59,102]

Substituent	$m\mu$	$\varepsilon \times 10^{-4}$	$m\mu$	$\varepsilon \times 10^{-4}$	$m\mu$	$\varepsilon \times 10^{-4}$
None	470	1.25	570*	0.41	> 720	> 1.19
6-Methyl-	470	1.07	570*	0.41	720	1.15
6,15-Dimethyl-	472	1.02	580*	0.33	> 720	> 1.26
7,16-Dimethyl-†	468	1.16			840	1.76
7,16-Dibromo-	470	1.32	580	0.42	> 730	> 1.92
7,16-Dibromo-6-methyl-	< 440	> 1.69			575	1.23
7,16-Dibromo-6,15-dimethyl-	< 460	> 0.54			575	0.31

* Inflection.   † Consult reference[59] for other band maxima not listed above.

XLVI and XLVII). The distinct hypsochromic shift of the maxima for 7,16-dibromo-6-methylindanthrone and its 6,15-dimethyl homolog is attributed to steric hindrance between the bromine atoms and the methyl groups leading to non-planarity of these molecules with a consequent diminution of resonance possibilities.[102]

(4) *Halogenated N-Alkylindanthrones.* A few patent specifications relate to the preparation of dyes by halogenation of the corresponding N-alkylindanthrones by standard procedures,[117-119] or alternatively by the self-condensation of 1,3-dihalo-2-methylaminoanthraquinones in the presence of a copper catalyst and an acid-binding agent in a high-boiling solvent.[121,122] Chromatographic separation on alumina must be employed to obtain a pure product.[102] The direct methylation of haloindanthrones[102] has already been mentioned. They dye vegetable fibers in blue shades.

6. Mechanism of the Indanthrone Fusion Process

A. General

We are now in a position to survey the theories of indanthrone formation that have been advanced. An excellent account is to be found in the papers of Bradley and his co-workers,[62,112,123,124] who have done much to lighten the obscurity in which this important reaction has been shrouded.

At 150–200°, the alkaline fusion of 2-aminoanthraquinone yields alizarin; at 200–300°, the main product is indanthrone; while, above 300°, the fusion yields a mixture of indanthrone and flavanthrone (XXIII). According to Scholl and Berblinger,[6] indanthrone is a mixture of two compounds named Indanthrene A and Indanthrene B, which are differentiated by their solubilities in aniline, nitrobenzene or quinoline, Indanthrene A being the less soluble. Both give hydro derivatives, the sodium salts of which in water give blue solutions in the case of Indanthrene A and brownish-red solutions in the case of Indanthrene B. More recently, Maki[125] studied the indanthrone fusion and stated that technical Indanthrene B is a mixture of two substances, Indanthrenes B and C, and that, by using pure 2-aminoanthraquinone,[126] the formation of Indanthrene C can be suppressed. In both cases'

Indanthrene A is the bulk of the product and is the compound referred to as indanthrone (I). The structure of Indanthrene B is discussed later (Section XVII:8).

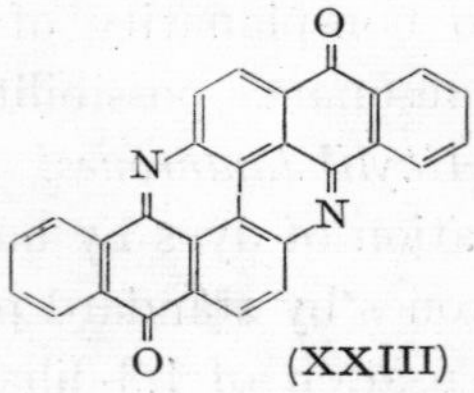

(XXIII)

Maki studied the effect of time and temperature on the decomposition of indanthrone in the alkali melt,[127] and showed that the addition of phenols or naphthols accelerated the formation of indanthrone over alizarin, thus permitting the fusion to be carried out at a lower temperature for a shorter time so that decomposition was minimized.[128–133] Under the most favorable conditions, namely, fusion of a mixture of potassium hydroxide (water content, 17–21%), phenol and 2-aminoanthraquinone for 60 minutes at 180°, Maki was able to obtain a yield of 51.5% of indanthrone.[130] Much earlier, the addition of alcohol to the alkali melt was held to be beneficial to the yield of indanthrone.[134]

B. Historical

In his original patent,[4] Bohn considered that indanthrone arises by the initial formation of 1-hydroxy-2-aminoanthraquinone (XXIV), in the manner in which alizarin is formed, followed by a dehydration to yield (I), but Scholl, Berblinger and Mansfield[63] were unable to

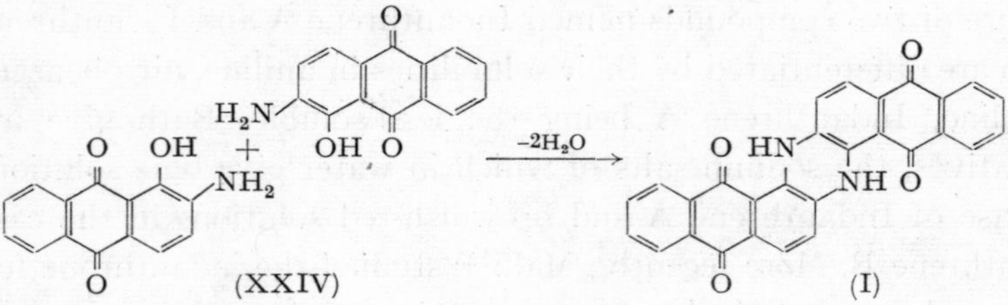

(XXIV)　　　　　　　(I)

concur with this. Scholl and Eberle[135] showed that hydroxylation of the amino group to 2-hydroxylaminoanthraquinone was not an intermediate step, since this compound on alkaline fusion was not converted to indanthrone. They suggested that the fusion proceeded by oxidation of 2-aminoanthraquinone to *sym*-di-2-anthraquinonylhydrazine (XXV), which then underwent a semidine rearrangement to yield 2-amino-5,10-dihydroxy-1-(2'-anthraquinonylamino)anthracene (XXVI), which by loss of hydrogen could yield indanthrone. However, it was later shown[136] that the hydrazine gave indanthrone only under acid conditions, when the main product was flavanthrone (XXIII). Later theories[137,138] required the formation, by migration of hydrogen, of the

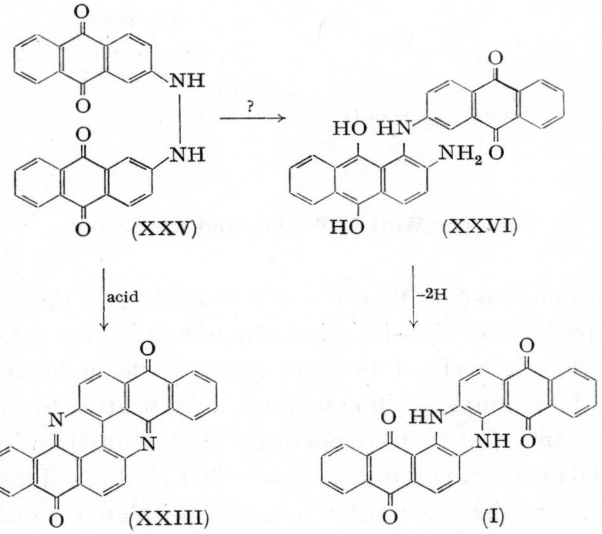

imino form of 2-aminoanthraquinone (XXVII), which should combine with a second molecule of 2-aminoanthraquinone to yield XXVI, by the normal addition of amines to quinonoid structures. A repetition of the hydrogen migration to give a second quinonoid structure (XXVIII), followed by intramolecular addition of the second amino group, would yield tetrahydroindanthrone (VII), from which indanthrone could be obtained by aerial oxidation. An alternative view was favored by Bradley and Robinson,[139] who considered it to be a case of anionoid substitution in one molecule of 2-aminoanthraquinone by the anion of a second molecule.

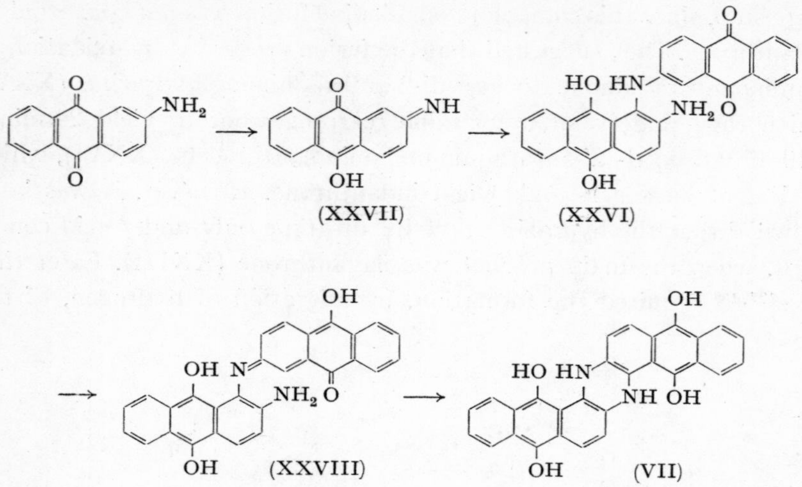

C. The Work of Bradley and His School

Bradley and his coworkers recently tested both of these hypotheses. They prepared 2-amino-1,2'-dianthraquinonylamine (XXIX) and showed[123] that it cyclized to yield indanthrone under a variety of conditions, for example, boiling in acetic acid, heating to 320° in liquid paraffin, treatment at room temperature with potassium hydroxide in pyridine and heating in carbon dioxide at 300°. Using sodium hydroxide in pyridine, a greyish-green intermediate was isolated, which, although it was reprecipitated unchanged from its solution in concentrated sulfuric acid, yielded indanthrone on boiling in quinoline. This easy oxidation excludes the possibility that the intermediate is an anthrone or anthranol and is paralleled by the fact that the reduction with alkaline sodium dithionite yields the blue vat of dihydroindanthrone (VI), which on aerial oxidation gives a blue precipitate of indanthrone. The intermediate is accordingly formulated as XXX and the easy change to dihydroindanthrone is regarded as a prototropic change induced by a base. When ring closure is brought about by heating in carbon dioxide, there was no indication of alkali-soluble products being formed, which argues against the imine-addition hypothesis.

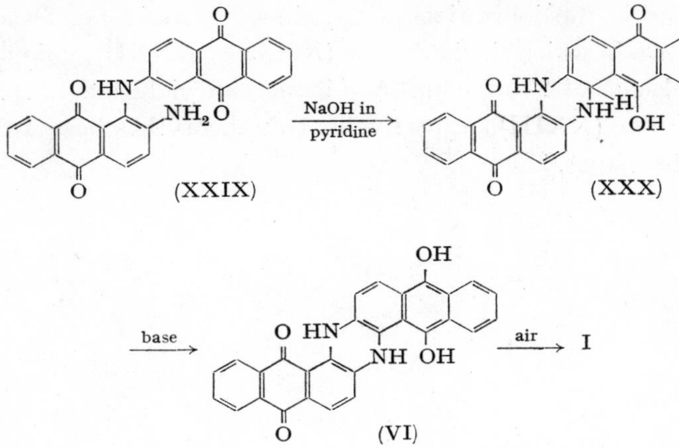

(XXIX) → NaOH in pyridine → (XXX)

base → (VI) → air → I

In another paper,[62] the imine-addition hypothesis was definitely discredited, since it was shown that 6,15-dimethylindanthrone could be obtained by heating XXI (R = R' = CH₃) with hot methanolic potassium hydroxide and 6-methylindanthrone by heating XXI (R = CH₃, R' = H) with a suspension of potassium hydroxide in pyridine. These results indicate that enolization of the anthraquinone nucleus as in XXVIII is not an essential step, and, by analogy, nor is it essential in the linking of two molecules of 2-aminoanthraquinone. In contrast to the behavior of 2-amino-1,2'-dianthraquinonylamine (XXIX), heating XXI (R = R' = CH₃ or R = CH₃, R' = H) alone or with acids did not yield indanthrone derivatives. Bradley and Leete[62] proceeded further and confirmed the statement[140] that 2-aminoanthraquinone acts as a substituting agent, reacting with nitrobenzene in the presence of potassium hydroxide to yield 2-(4'-nitroanilino)anthraquinone. They have also collected much evidence to show that 2-aminoanthraquinone will undergo anionoid substitution in the 1-position.

Clearly, these results indicate the correctness of the explanation originally advanced by Bradley and Robinson.[139] That substitution occurs exclusively in the 1-position of 2-aminoanthraquinone is ascribed by Bradley and Leete to the high stability of indanthrone, which in some way operates to favor the unique orientation.

Bradley and Nursten[56] have shown how this theory is in harmony with the related formation of flavanthrone (XXIII). The initial step in each case is the ionization of 2-aminoanthraquinone. Depending upon the form in which the ion reacts (XXXI or XXXII), union with a second molecule of 2-aminoanthraquinone can yield indanthrone (I) or flavanthrone (XXIII), respectively. This theory has been amplified in their later paper.[59]

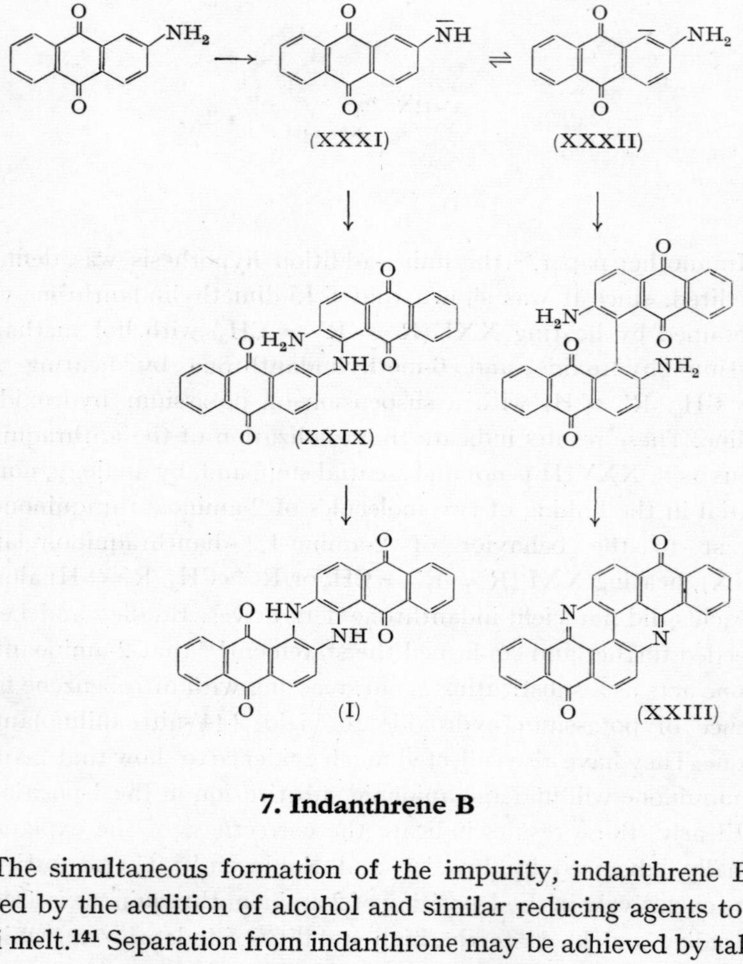

(XXXI)   (XXXII)

(XXIX)

(I)   (XXIII)

7. Indanthrene B

The simultaneous formation of the impurity, indanthrene B, is favored by the addition of alcohol and similar reducing agents to the alkali melt.[141] Separation from indanthrone may be achieved by taking account of the difference in solubility in quinoline, or by chromatography on a cellulose column.[124] In contrast to indanthrone, indanthrene B gives a brownish-red vat with alkaline sodium dithionite and its regeneration by aerial oxidation is more difficult. It yields a yellow azine on oxidation and is re-formed upon reduction.[124] Tanaka[138] claimed that it was 2-amino-5,10-dihydroxy-1-(2'-anthraquinonylamino)anthracene (XXVI) and that on fusion with alkali it formed indanthrone. This was shown to be incorrect,[123] since XXVI is readily soluble in aqueous alkali, giving a brown solution.

While the color and absorption spectrum of indanthrene B closely resembles that of indanthrone, analysis indicates the formula $C_{28}H_{14}O_{5-6}N_2$, that is, a product containing more oxygen than indanthrone.[124] The possibility that an isomer of indanthrone (e.g., XXXIII) may have been formed by an alternative route, in which cyclization occurs in the 3-position, followed by subsequent action of fused alkalis in introducing one or more hydroxyl groups, has been largely excluded. The isomer (XXXIII) was synthesized (Section XVII:9,A) and it was found that, while it resembled indanthrene B in color, color in sulfuric acid and vatting properties, it differed in the color test with methanolic potassium hydroxide in pyridine. Moreover, the action of fused alkalis upon XXXIII left it unaffected, or, in the presence of oxidizing agents, led to gross decomposition. Bradley and his coworkers[124] were therefore led to reject this hypothesis and stated that the properties of indanthrene B accorded best with its formulation as 6-hydroxy- (XXXIV) or 6,15-dihydroxy-5,7,9,14,16,18-hexahydrodinaphtho[2,3-b,2',3'-i]phenazine-5,9,14,18-tetrone (XXXV), since it is redder in shade than XXXIII, which in turn is redder than indanthrone.

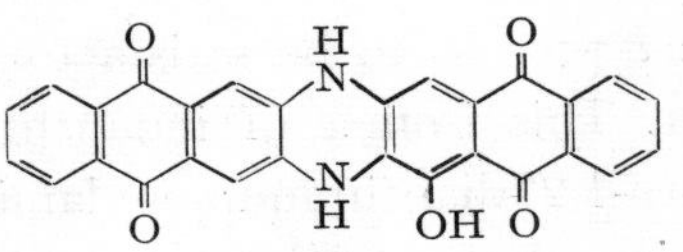

(XXXIV)

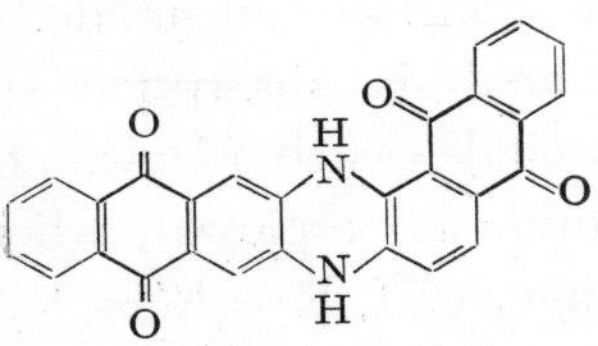

(XXXIII)

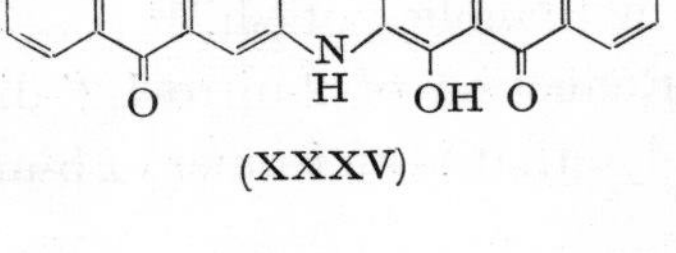

(XXXV)

8. Isomers, etc., of Indanthrone

A. 5,8,10,15,17,18-Hexahydrodinaphtho[2,3-*a*,2′,3′-*i*]phenazine-5,10,15,18-tetrone

This isomer (XXXIII, *R. I.* 3764) of indanthrone was originally described in a patent,[36] in which 2,3-diaminoanthraquinone was condensed with anthracene-1,2-quinone and the resulting anthraceno-anthraquinoneazine (XXXVI) was oxidized to 5,10,15,18-tetrahydro-dinaphtho[2,3-*a*,2′,3′-*i*]phenazine-5,10,15,18-tetrone (XXXVII) and finally reduced to the dihydroazine (XXXIII) (see Section XVII:2,I).

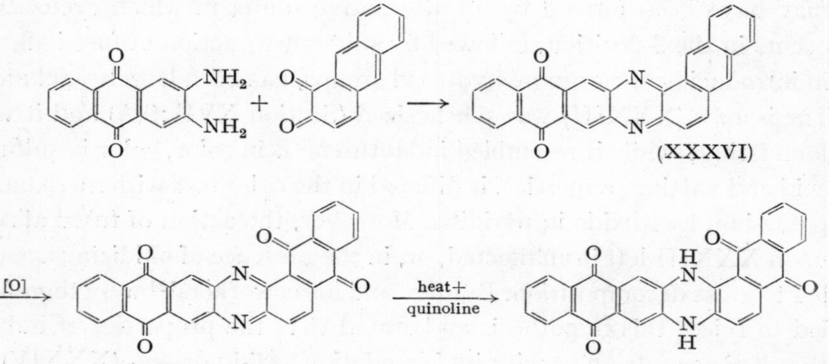

(XXXVI)

(XXXVII)   (XXXIII)

An alternative process[142] described the preparation by the condensation of alizarin with 2,3-diaminoanthraquinone in the presence of boric acid and phenol. Bradley and his coworkers[124] have found the former process to be satisfactory, but reported less success with the latter. This isomer of indanthrone also arises by the reduction of 2-nitro-1,2′-dianthraquinonylamine by alcoholic sodium sulfide.[124] The identity of the products was shown by analysis, absorption spectra and color tests. The reduction by sodium sulfide clearly follows a course different from that when stannous chloride is employed, when the product is simply the corresponding amine (XXI, R = R′ = H). It is also probably the product of heating 3-nitro-2,1′-dianthraquinonylamine with methanolic potash.[143]

Reduction of 2-nitro-1,2′-dianthraquinonylmethylamine yields a blue dye that is an isomer of 6-methylindanthrone.[124] By analogy with the related reduction mentioned above, this dye is formulated as 17-methyl-5,8,10,15,17,18-hexahydrodinaphtho[2,3-*a*,2′,3′-*i*]phenazine-5,10,15,18-tetrone (**XXXVIII**).

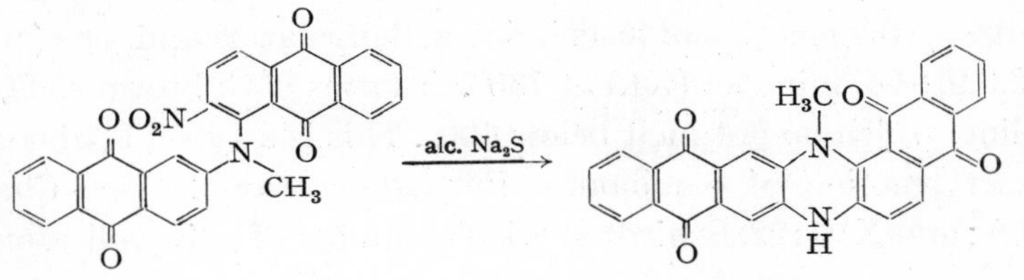

(XXXVIII)

The indanthrone isomer (**XXXIII**) closely resembles indanthrone in color, although it is redder in shade. On reduction with alkaline sodium dithionite, however, it yields a reddish-brown vat from which, on aeration, the original compound is regenerated only slowly, passing through a dull violet to a greenish-yellow color of the alkali salt, from which acidification yields the blue dye. The isomer (**XXXIII**) is clearly a stronger acid than is indanthrone. Methylation under the same conditions as are used for indanthrone affords the 8,17-dimethyl derivative (**XXXIX**), which forms blue needles from quinoline.

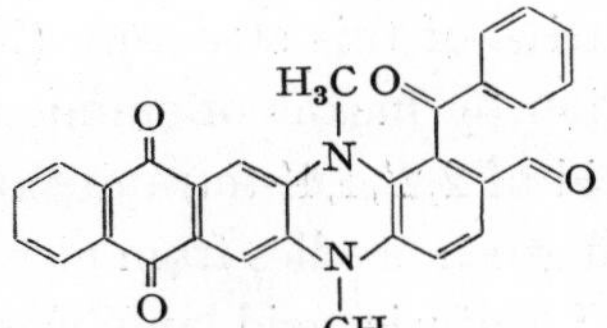

(XXXIX)

This yields an orange-red vat, from which, in contradistinction from the unmethylated parent (**XXXIII**), **XXXIX** is obtained in one stage on aeration. It resembles 6,15-dimethylindanthrone (**XVII**) in undergoing facile demethylation on heating with alumina in 1,2-dichlorobenzene.

The 6-hydroxy-1-sulfonic acid of (**XXXIII**) has been described.[142] It dyes wool greenish-blue.

B. 5,7,9,14,16,18-Hexahydrodinaphtho[2,3-b,2′,3′-i]-
phenazine-5,9,14,18-tetrone

This compound (XLI), which is the parent of the structure proposed by Bradley and his coworkers[124] for indanthrene B, was prepared by Schiedt[48] by the reaction of formamide with hystazarinquinone (anthracene-2,3,9,10-diquinone) (XL) at 130°. It forms dark brown rods, from quinoline, which do not melt below 400°. This is a typical "abnormal" Leuckart reaction of o-quinones. For other examples see Chapters XV:3,A; and XVI:22. Schiedt studied a number of polycyclic quinones

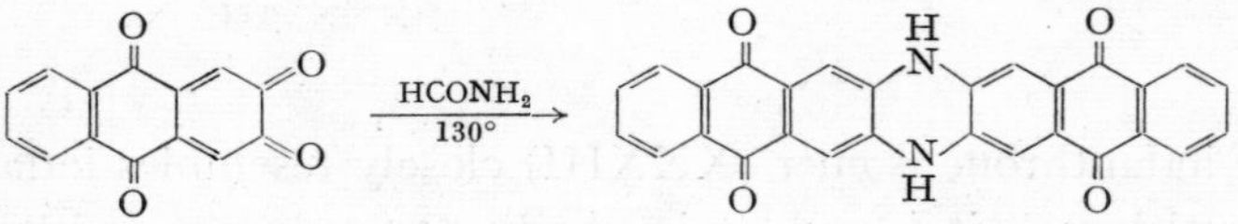

and found that, in general, the initial dihydroazine was readily dehydrogenated on heating. Clearly, the stabilizing influence of the cationoid carbonyl groups upon the dihydroazine stage (Section XVII:5,C(5)) is operative here.

C. 6,10-Diamino-5,8,11,16,17,18-hexahydrodinaphtho[2,3-a,2′,3′-i]phenazine-
5,11,16,18-tetrone

The sole representative of this structure (XLIII, R. I. 3769) was prepared by the reduction by means of stannous chloride and hydrochloric acid in acetic acid of 2,2′,4,4′-tetranitrodi-1,1′-anthraquinonylamine (XLII). It formed green needles from nitrobenzene, gave a green color with concentrated sulfuric acid and was reduced by alkaline sodium dithionite to a green vat.[144]

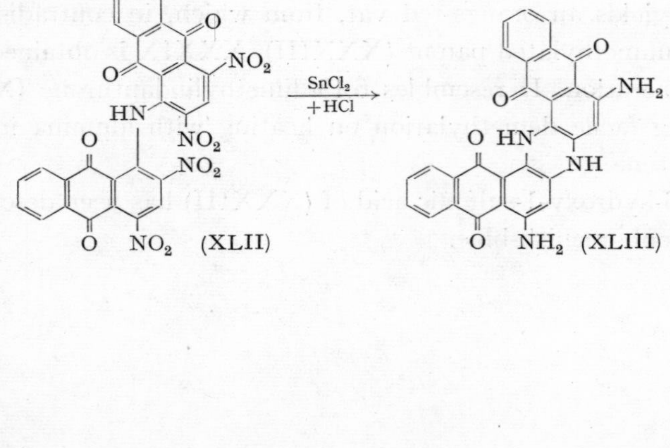

9. The Technology of Indanthrone Dyeing

On the industrial scale, the indanthrone fusion mixture may be processed in many ways. The fusion mass contains the leuco compound of indanthrone, which may be oxidized to indanthrone by solution in water and passage of air at $100°$,[145] or at lower temperatures in the presence of vatting assistants[146,147] when the dye is precipitated in a finely divided state. Alternatively the oxidation may be carried out in alkaline solution,[148] when it is claimed that iron impurities, introduced during the fusion, are removed. Other processes[149-151] depend upon the crystallization of the sodium salt of the leuco compound followed by oxidation, and finely divided or colloidal samples of indanthrone are obtained by solution in concentrated sulfuric acid followed by dilution with less concentrated sulfuric acid or by water[152-159] or by successive treatment with chlorosulfonic acid and water.[160] Such finely divided dyes find application in the "pigment pad-jig" process of dyeing, and are easily reducible on vatting. Compounds such as cyclohexanol and other cycloalkyl derivatives are claimed to be very satisfactory assistants in their preparation.[161] Processes for the removal of impurities and improvement of fastness to chlorine depend upon solution in moderately concentrated sulfuric acid and treatment with manganese dioxide or like oxidizing agents.[7,157,162-166] Purified indanthrones are sometimes known as "Brilliant Blues," as in Caledon Brilliant Blue R.N.

One of the drawbacks to indanthrone vat dyes is the limited solubility of the sodium salt of the vat. Efforts to increase this by vatting at higher temperatures led to overreduction and a duller finish to the dyeings.[50] Early attempts to increase the solubility depended upon sulfonation of the indanthrone to products which were essentially mono- or di-sulfonyl compounds,[167-170] or in forming the sulfate esters of hydroxyindanthrones.[171] Alternatively, 1-nitroanthraquinone-9-sulfonic acid was partially reduced in neutral or alkaline solution to the 1-hydroxylamino derivative, which on heating with alkali yielded the indanthrone-4,13-disulfonic acid.[172] These were fugitive dyes, however, but on electrolytic reduction the sulfonyl groups were split off, thus yielding a new route to indanthrone.

A great advance was the introduction of the sulfuric acid esters of the leucoindanthrones (Soledon Blue R). These had greatly enhanced solubilities in water, were substantive to cotton fibers and could be oxidized on the fiber when very level dyeings were obtained. Various processes for the production of these were invented. The disulfuric acid ester of 2-amino-5,10-dihydroxyanthracene was oxidized in the presence of alkali[173-175] or this process could suitably be carried out on the fabric in a printing process by using cupric salts as oxidizing agents.[176] The amino group of the leucoanthraquinone (5,10-dihydroxyanthracene) could be suitably protected, for example, as a sulfamic acid.[177] Alternatively, the sulfate acid esters of 2-(2'-nitro-1'-anthraquinonylamino)-5,10-dihydroxyanthracene could be reduced in neutral or alkaline solution.[178,179] Several processes depend upon treating the azine corresponding to indanthrone with an addition compound formed between sulfur trioxide and a strong, tertiary base in the presence of a metal,[180-182] or alternatively the azine in sulfuric acid solution is reduced by the action of a metal that gives a soluble sulfate[183] to yield what are probably the tetrasulfuric acid esters of the leuco vat of indanthrone (VII). A recent process[184] entails the prior formation of a quaternary salt between a strong tertiary base and methyl sulfate or methyl chloride. This is then treated with methyl chlorosulfonate and then with the indanthrone, for example, 7,16-dichlorindanthrone (or other vat dye) in the presence of iron powder. The reduction and esterification occur at room temperature. These substances may be oxidized on the fiber by the use of mixtures of ferrous and ferric salts.[185] The same sulfating agent, namely, the combination of sulfur trioxide and base, has been applied to 2-aminoanthraquinone and its derivatives and the products oxidized to yield similar dyes.[186] These tetrasulfuric acid esters may be isolated as their salts[187] or they may be converted into lower sulfuric acid esters by controlled hydrolysis by mild oxidizing agents, for example, alkaline hypochlorite[188,189] or by reducing agents such as alkaline sodium dithionite[188,190] The leuco derivatives of indanthrone may also be solubilized for vatting by treatment with various sulfohalides of benzoic acid.[191,192] Details of dyeing procedures using indanthrone dyes have been given.[193-195]

Modified indanthrones have been prepared by treatment of the dye with formaldehyde or agents liberating it and the products may be halogenated or oxidized and subsequently halogenated.[196-201] Such dyes may be purified by sulfuric acid treatment, which removes impurities rendering the color of the dyes fugitive to chlorine[202]; they give blue to greenish-blue dyeings. Greener shades are obtained by heating the condensation products to 250° either alone or in solvents.[203] Very fast, modified indanthrone dyes are obtained by condensing indanthrone-7,16-dicarboxylic acid with two moles of 1-aminoanthraquinone,[204] or a derivative,[205] thus combining the indanthrone series with the aroylaminoanthraquinone colors.

Besides use as a vat dye, indanthrones have been used as printing colors for textiles,[206,207] as a substitute for ultramarine in the bluing of sugar,[208] in the detection of traces of moisture in sugar,[209] in lacquer paints[210] where it was of limited utility, as a test for the presence of linseed oil in rayon[211] and in the preparation of colored cellulose diacetate films as light filters.[212] 7,16-Dibromoindanthrone (Spinning Blue BV (or 6 RA)) has been used as a pigment for viscose yarn. It is generally incorporated in the viscose prior to spinning.[213]

Note: Indanthrone dyes are sold under a variety of trade brands and abbreviations, many of which are synonymous for one compound and which indicate the manufacturing firm, for example Indanthrene (I. G. Farbenindustrie A.G.), Caledon, Soledon (I. C. I. Ltd.), Ponsol (E. I. du Pont de Nemours & Co.), the process by which the dye is produced, its purity, fastness, etc., and the use to which it may be put. To make matters more confusing, the same trade designations, for example Indanthrene, etc., suitably qualified, are applied to other, non-indanthrone, fast vat dyes.

The identity of a commercial product and in many cases its formula and method of preparation, with references to the patent literature, may often be obtained by referring to *The Colour Index* or to the review cited.[2] A less recent, but highly authoritative work, is the treatise[214] by Houben and Fischer, containing an excellent patent index of the older inventions in the anthraquinonoid dyestuff field. In view of the comprehensive character of this compilation, we have sought completeness in patent coverage only from the period 1920 to date and have given only the more important patents of the earlier period.

References

1. R. Bohn, *Ber.*, **43**, 987 (1910).
2. M. A. Kunz, *Angew. Chem.*, **52**, 269 (1939).
3. F. Mayer, *Chem.-Ztg.*, **50**, 1008 (1926); *Chem. Abstracts*, **21**, 1013 (1927).
4. Ger. Pat. 129,845–129,848; *Frdl.*, **6**, 412–414 (1900–1902); *Chem. Zentr.*, **1902**, I, 839.
5. R. Scholl, *Ber.*, **36**, 3410 (1903).
6. R. Scholl and H. Berblinger, *Ber.*, **36**, 3427 (1903).
7. Ger. Pat. 550,779; *Frdl.*, **17**, 1218 (1930); see Fr. Pat. 37,836; *Chem. Abstracts*, **25**, 4713 (1931); *Chem. Zentr.*, **1931**, II, 502.
8. Brit. Pat. 181,674; *Chem. Zentr.*, **1922**, IV, 842; *Chem. Abstracts*, **16**, 3762 (1922).
9. U. S. Pat. 1,990,954; *Chem. Abstracts*, **29**, 2367 (1935); *Chem. Zentr.*, **1935**, II, 3163.
10. Jap. Pat. 130,433; *Chem. Abstracts*, **35**, 2009 (1941).
11. Swiss Pat. 194,449; *Chem. Zentr.*, **1938**, II, 1463; see also Ger. Pat. 668,488; *Chem. Abstracts*, **33**, 2291 (1939).
12. U. S. Pat. 1,580,700; *Chem. Abstracts*, **20**, 1813 (1926); *Chem. Zentr.*, **1926**, II, 828.
13. U. S. Pat. 1,731,800; *Chem. Abstracts*, **24**, 128 (1930); *Chem. Zentr.*, **1930**, I, 597.
14. Brit. Pat. 388,043; *Chem. Abstracts*, **27**, 4684 (1933); *Chem. Zentr.*, **1933**, I, 3799.
15. Can. Pat. 329,052; *Chem. Abstracts*, **27**, 1362 (1933); *Chem. Zentr.*, **1936**, I, 1963.
16. U. S. Pat. 1,997,610; *Chem. Abstracts*, **29**, 3693 (1935); *Chem. Zentr.*, **1935**, II, 2133.
17. Ger. Pat. 548,263;*Frdl.*, **19**, 2029 (1932); see Brit. Pat. 296,106; *Chem. Zentr.*, **1929**, I, 307; *Chem. Abstracts*, **23**, 2300 (1929).
18. Russ. Pat. 33,623; *Chem. Abstracts*, **28**, 4246 (1934); *Chem. Zentr.*, **1934**, II, 3315.
19. U. S. Pat. 1,509,846; *Chem. Abstracts*, **18**, 3727 (1924); *Chem. Zentr.*, **1925**, I, 1020.
20. Brit. Pat. 166,297; *Chem. Zentr.*, **1921**, IV, 1013; *Chem. Abstracts*, **16**, 835 (1922).
21. Ger. Pat. 139,633; *Frdl.*, **7**, 227 (1902–1904); *Chem. Zentr.*, **1903**, I, 747.
22. Ger. Pat. 141,355; *Frdl.*, **7**, 227 (1902–1904); *Chem. Zentr.*, **1903**, I, 1198.
23. M. K. Bezzubets and N. G. Shakhova, *Anilinokrasochnaya Prom.*, **5**, 153 (1935); through *Chem. Abstracts*, **31**, 3281 (1937).
24. Y. Shimada, *J. Soc. Chem. Ind. Japan*, **45**, 6 (1942); **46**, 814, 817 (1943); through *Chem. Abstracts*, **43**, 5189 (1949).
25. Ger. Pat. 186,636; *Frdl.*, **9**, 777 (1908–1910); *Chem. Zentr.*, **1907**, II, 1133.
26. Ger. Pat. 186,637; *Frdl.*, **9**, 778 (1908–1910); *Chem. Zentr.*, **1907**, II, 1134.
27. Ger. Pat. 239,211; *Frdl.*, **10**, 697 (1910–1912); *Chem. Zentr.*, **1911**, II, 1396.
28. Ger. Pat. 193,121; *Frdl.*, **9**, 783 (1908–1910); *Chem. Zentr.*, **1908**, I, 573.
29. Ger. Pat. 356,922; *Frdl.*, **14**, 890 (1921–1925); *Chem. Zentr.*, **1922**, IV, 763.
30. Ger. Pat. 357,767; *Frdl.*, **14**, 891 (1921–1925); *Chem. Zentr.*, **1922**, IV, 992.
31. U. S. Pat. 2,030,876; *Chem. Abstracts*, **30**, 2204 (1936); *Chem. Zentr.*, **1936**, I, 4627.
32. T. Maki and T. Mine, *J. Soc. Chem. Ind. Japan*, **47**, 522 (1944); through *Chem. Abstracts*, **42**, 6119 (1948).

33. Brit. Pat. 338,891; *Chem. Abstracts,* **25,** 2574 (1931); *Chem. Zentr.,* **1931,** I, 1527.
34. U. S. Pat. 1,634,473; *Chem. Abstracts,* **21,** 2907 (1927); *Chem. Zentr.,* **1931,** II, 917.
35. Brit. Pat. 297,692; *Chem. Abstracts,* **23,** 2725(1929); *Chem. Zentr.,* **1929,** I, 1155.
36. Ger. Pat. 170,562; *Frdl.,* **8,** 348 (1905–1907); *Chem. Zentr.,* **1906,** II, 80.
37. E. Terres, *Ber.,* **46,** 1634 (1913).
38. M. Claasz, *Ber.,* **49,** 2079 (1916).
39. F. A. Hamm and E. Van Norman, *J. Applied Phys.,* **19,** 1097 (1948); through *Chem. Abstracts,* **43,** 2483 (1949).
40. *F. I. A. T. Final Report,* No. 1313, Vol. III, p. 441 *et seq.*
41. F. Kaufler, *Ber.,* **36,** 930 (1903).
42. F. Kaufler, *Ber.,* **36,** 1721 (1903).
43. E. Clar, *Ber.,* **72B,** 1645 (1939).
44. R. Scholl and H. Lamprecht, *Ber.,* **63B,** 2126 (1930).
45. R. Scholl and S. Edlbacher, *Ber.,* **44,** 1727 (1911).
46. R. Scholl, W. Steinkopf and A. Kabacznik, *Ber.,* **40,** 390 (1907).
47. R. Scholl and O. Stegmüller, *Ber.,* **40,** 924 (1907).
48. B. Schiedt, *J. prakt. Chem.,* **157,** 203 (1941).
49. R. Scholl (with H. Berblinger and A. Künzel), *Ber.,* **40,** 933 (1907).
50. H. A. Brassard, *J. Soc. Dyers Colourists,* **59,** 127 (1943); *Chem. Abstracts,* **37,** 5243 (1943).
51. J. H. Yoe, *J. Phys. Chem.,* **28,** 1211 (1924).
52. D. Appleton and A. Geake, *Trans. Faraday Soc.,* **37,** 60 (1941).
53. A. Geake, *Trans. Faraday Soc.,* **37,** 68 (1941).
54. V. D. Lyashenko and N. A. Kirzner, *J. Gen. Chem. (U.S.S.R.),* **16,** 583 (1946); through *Chem. Abstracts,* **41,** 1220 (1947).
55. R. Gill and H. I. Stonehill, *J. Soc. Dyers Colourists,* **60,** 183 (1944); *Chem. Abstracts,* **38,** 5497 (1944).
56. W. Bradley and H. E. Nursten, *J. Chem. Soc.,* **1951,** 2170.
57. L. Fieser and M. Fieser, *J. Am. Chem. Soc.,* **57,** 491 (1935).
58. W. Bradley and H. E. Nursten, *J. Chem. Soc.,* **1951,** 2177.
59. W. Bradley and H. E. Nursten, *J. Chem. Soc.,* **1953,** 924.
60. W. Bradley, E. Leete and H. E. Nursten, *J. Soc. Dyers Colourists,* **68,** 116 (1952).
61. R. Scholl and H. Berblinger, *Ber.,* **40,** 395 (1907).
62. W. Bradley and E. Leete, *J. Chem. Soc.,* **1951,** 2129.
63. R. Scholl, H. Berblinger and J. Mansfeld, *Ber.,* **40,** 320 (1907).
64. Ger. Pat. 147,872; *Frdl.,* **7,** 231 (1902–1904); *Chem. Zentr.,* **1904,** I, 233.
65. S. G. Bedekar, B. D. Tilak and K. Venkataraman, *Proc. Indian. Acad. Sci.,* **28A,** 236 (1948); *Chem. Abstracts,* **43,** 3399 (1949).
66. R. Scholl and J. Mansfeld, *Ber.,* **40,** 326 (1907).
67. Ger. Pat. 155,415; *Frdl.,* **7,** 230 (1902–1904).
68. Ger. Pat. 500,177; *Frdl.,* **17,** 1219 (1930); see Brit. Pat. 322,277; *Chem. Zentr.,* **1930,** I, 3249; *Chem. Abstracts,* **24,** 2891 (1930).
69. U. S. Pat. 2,026,647; *Chem. Abstracts,* **30,** 1067 (1936); *Chem. Zentr.,* **1936,** I, 4995.
70. Ger. Pat. 292,127; *Frdl.,* **13,** 426 (1916–1921); *Chem. Zentr.,* **1916,** II, 43, *Chem. Abstracts,* **11,** 1909 (1917).
71. Ger. Pat. 296,841; *Frdl.,* **13,** 424 (1916–1921); *Chem. Zentr.,* **1917,** I, 835.
72. Brit. Pat. 271,181; *Chem. Zentr.,* **1927,** II, 2120; *Chem. Abstracts,* **22,** 1691 (1928).

73. U. S. Pat. 1,847,329; *Chem. Zentr.*, **1932**, II, 130; *Chem. Abstracts*, **26**, 2469 (1932).
74. U. S. Pat. 2,205,418; *Chem. Abstracts*, **34**, 6950 (1940); *Chem. Zentr.*, **1941**, I, 3151.
75. U. S. Pat. 1,637,851; *Chem. Abstracts*, **21**, 3058 (1927); *Chem. Zentr.*, **1927**, II, 2718.
76. U. S. Pat. 1,931,646; *Chem. Abstracts*, **28**, 487 (1934); *Chem. Zentr.*, **1934**, I, 775.
77. Russ. Pat. 31,075; *Chem. Abstracts*, **28**, 3595 (1934); *Chem. Zentr.*, **1934**, I, 2491.
78. Ger. Pat. 568,635; *Frdl.*, **18**, 1294 (1931); see Brit. Pat. 291,552; *Chem. Zentr.*, **1928**, II, 1948; *Chem. Abstracts*, **23**, 1276 (1929).
79. U. S. Pat. 2,061,249; *Chem. Abstracts*, **31**, 712 (1937); *Chem. Zentr.*, **1937**, I, 3071.
80. U. S. Pat. 1,509,808; *Chem. Abstracts*, **18**, 3727 (1924); *Chem. Zentr.*, **1925**, I, 1019.
81. U. S. Pat. 2,413,483; *Chem. Abstracts*, **41**, 1711 (1947); *Chem. Zentr.*, **1947**, 1795.
82. Ger. Pat. 289,279; *Frdl.*, **12**, 481 (1914–1916); *Chem. Zentr.*, **1916**, I, 198; *Chem. Abstracts*, **11**, 891 (1917).
83. Ger. Pat. 296,192; *Frdl.*, **13**, 426 (1916–1921); *Chem. Zentr.*, **1917**, I, 461.
84. Brit. Pat. 193,200; *Chem. Zentr.*, **1925**, I, 904; *Chem. Abstracts*, **17**, 3344 (1923).
85. U. S. Pat. 2,413,514; *Chem. Abstracts*, **41**, 1847 (1947); *Chem. Zentr.*, **1947**, 1243.
86. Ger. Pat. 157,449; *Frdl.*, **8**, 351 (1905–1907); *Chem. Zentr.*, **1905**, I, 482.
87. Ger. Pat. 293,971; *Frdl.*, **13**, 423 (1916–1921); *Chem. Zentr.*, **1916**, II, 622; *Chem. Abstracts*, **11**, 2614 (1917).
88. Ger. Pat. 542,539; *Frdl.*, **18**, 1295 (1931); see Fr. Pat. 682,141; *Chem. Abstracts*, **24**, 4403 (1930); *Chem. Zentr.*, **1930**, II, 3654.
89. Ger. Pat. 287,590; *Frdl.*, **12**, 480 (1914–1916); *Chem. Zentr.*, **1915**, II, 863; *Chem. Abstracts*, **10**, 2153 (1916).
90. Ger. Pat. 168,042; *Frdl.*, **8**, 352 (1905–1907); *Chem. Zentr.*, **1906**, I, 1202.
91. Ger. Pat. 229,166; *Frdl.*, **10**, 695 (1910–1912); *Chem. Zentr.*, **1911**, I, 182; *Chem. Abstracts*, **5**, 2416 (1911).
92. Ger. Pat. 590,100; *Frdl.*, **19**, 2033 (1932); see Brit. Pat. 330,217; *Chem. Abstracts*, **24**, 6031 (1930); *Chem. Zentr.*, **1930**, II, 2838.
93. Ger. Pat. 138,167; *Frdl.*, **7**, 229 (1902–1904); *Chem. Zentr.*, **1903**, I, 268.
94. U. S. Pat. 2,377,158; *Chem. Abstracts*, **40**, 97 (1946).
95. Fr. Pat. 700,271; *Chem. Abstracts*, **25**, 3845 (1931); *Chem. Zentr.*, **1932**, I, 142.
96. Ger. Pat. 602,271; *Frdl.*, **21**, 1099 (1934); see U. S. Pat. 1,862,843, 1,862,844, 1,862,865; *Chem. Zentr.*, **1932**, II, 2246; *Chem. Abstracts*, **26**, 4063, 4068 (1932).
97. Brit. Pat. 298,248; *Chem. Abstracts*, **23**, 2832 (1929); *Chem. Zentr.*, **1929**, I, 1155.
98. Ger. Pat. 158,474; *Frdl.*, **8**, 342 (1905–1907); *Chem. Zentr.*, **1905**, I, 844.
99. Ger. Pat. 167,255; *Frdl.*, **8**, 343 (1905–1907); *Chem. Zentr.*, **1906**, I, 881.
100. F. Ullmann and W. Junghans, *Ann.*, **399**, 330 (1913).
101. Ger. Pat. 605,939; *Frdl.*, **21**, 1098 (1934); see Brit. Pat. 414,136; *Chem. Zentr.*, **1934**, II, 4023; *Chem. Abstracts*, **29**, 178 (1935).
102. W. Bradley and H. Nursten, *J. Chem. Soc.*, **1952**, 3027.
103. Brit. Pat. 330,218; *Chem. Abstracts*, **24**, 6031 (1930); *Chem. Zentr.*, **1930**, II, 2838.

104. Ger. Pat. 558,249; *Frdl.*, **19**, 2031 (1932); see Brit. Pat. 314,803; *Chem. Zentr.*, **1929**, II, 2610; *Chem. Abstracts*, **24**, 1520 (1930).
105. Ger. Pat. 287,756; *Frdl.*, **12**, 120 (1914–1916); *Chem. Zentr.*, **1915**, II, 1034; *Chem. Abstracts*, **10**, 2128 (1916).
106. Ger. Pat. 158,287; *Frdl.*, **8**, 341 (1905–1907); *Chem. Zentr.*, **1905**, I, 843.
107. Ger. Pat. 498,293; *Frdl.*, **17**, 1222 (1930); see Brit. Pat. 309,192; *Chem. Abstracts*, **24**, 504 (1930); *Chem. Zentr.*, **1929**, II, 663.
108. O. Hinsberg and A. Himmelschein, *Ber.*, **29**, 2019 (1896).
109. Ger. Pat. 238,979; *Frdl.*, **10**, 693 (1910–1912); *Chem. Zentr.*, **1911**, II, 1287; *Chem. Abstracts*, **6**, 1682 (1912).
110. P. Kränzlein, *Ber.*, **70B**, 1952 (1937).
111. *F.I.A.T. Final Report*, No. 1313, Vol. III, p. 56.
112. W. Bradley and E. Leete, *J. Chem. Soc.*, **1951**, 2147.
113. W. Bradley, *J. Soc. Dyers Colourists*, **58**, 2 (1942).
114. Ger. Pat. 234,294; *Frdl.*, **10**, 699 (1910–1912); *Chem. Zentr.*, **1911**, I, 1619; *Chem. Abstracts*, **5**, 2973 (1911).
115. Ger. Pat. 252,529; *Frdl.*, **11**, 654 (1912–1914); *Chem. Zentr.*, **1912**, II, 1793; *Chem. Abstracts*, **7**, 553 (1913).
116. Ger. Pat. 251,021; *Frdl.*, **11**, 616 (1912–1914); *Chem. Zentr.*, **1921**, II, 1245; *Chem. Abstracts*, **7**, 1296 (1913).
117. Ger. Pat. 628,230; *Frdl.*, **22**, 1066 (1935); see Fr. Pat. 782,990; *Chem. Abstracts*, **29**, 7089 (1935); *Chem. Zentr.*, **1936**, I, 2447.
118. Ger. Pat. 628,229; *Frdl.*, **22**, 1064 (1935); see Fr. Pat. 782,990 (ref. 117 preceding).
119. Ger. Pat. 628,724; *Frdl.*, **22**, 1065 (1935); see Fr. Pat. 782,990 (ref. 117 preceding).
120. Brit. Pat. 613,980; *Chem. Abstracts*, **43**, 8163 (1949).
121. U. S. Pat. 2,091,236; *Chem. Zentr.*, **1938**, I, 193; *Chem. Abstracts*, **31**, 7666 (1937).
122. U. S. Pat. 2,091,235; *Chem. Zentr.*, **1938**, I, 734; *Chem. Abstracts*, **31**, 7666 (1937).
123. W. Bradley, E. Leete and D. S. Stephens, *J. Chem. Soc.*, **1951**, 2158.
124. W. Bradley, E. Leete and D. S. Stephens, *J. Chem. Soc.*, **1951**, 2163.
125. T. Maki, *J. Soc. Chem. Ind. Japan*, **36**, Suppl. binding, No. 2, 44 (1933); through *Chem. Abstracts*, **27**, 2685 (1933).
126. T. Maki, *J. Soc. Chem. Ind. Japan*, **36**, Suppl. binding, 199 (1933); through *Chem. Abstracts*, **27**, 3709 (1933).
127. T. Maki, *J. Soc. Chem. Ind. Japan*, **32**, Suppl. binding, 300 (1929); through *Chem. Abstracts*, **24**, 2366 (1930).
128. T. Maki, *J. Soc. Chem. Ind. Japan*, **33**, Suppl. binding, 456 (1930); through *Chem. Abstracts*, **25**, 864 (1931).
129. T. Maki, *J. Soc. Chem. Ind. Japan*, **33**, Suppl. binding, 461 (1930); through *Chem. Abstracts*, **25**, 864 (1931).
130. T. Maki, *J. Soc. Chem. Ind. Japan*, **34**, Suppl. binding, 249 (1931); through *Chem. Abstracts*, **25**, 5669 (1931).
131. T. Maki, *J Soc. Chem. Ind. Japan*, **34**, Suppl. binding, 253 (1931); through *Chem. Abstracts*, **25**, 5669 (1931).
132. T. Maki, *J. Soc. Chem. Ind. Japan*, **37**, Suppl. binding, 744 (1934); through *Chem. Abstracts*, **29**, 1811 (1935).
133. T. Maki, *J. Soc. Chem. Ind. Japan*, **37**, Suppl. binding, 748 (1934); through *Chem. Abstracts*, **29**, 1811 (1935).

134. Ger. Pat. 287,270; *Frdl.*, **12**, 431 (1914–1916); *Chem. Zentr.*, **1915**, II, 935; *Chem. Abstracts*, **10**, 1934 (1916).
135. R. Scholl and F. Eberle, *Monatsh.*, **32**, 1035 (1911); *Chem. Zentr.*, **1912**, I, 662.
136. Austrian Pat. 96,687; *Chem. Zentr.*, **1924**, II, 2506.
137. E. Schwenk, *Chem.-Ztg.*, **52**, 45 (1928); *Chem. Abstracts*, **22**, 1773 (1928).
138. M. Tanaka, *J. Chem. Soc. Japan*, **56**, 192 (1935); through *Chem. Abstracts*, **29**, 4353 (1935).
139. W. Bradley and R. Robinson, *J. Chem. Soc.*, **1932**, 1254.
140. *F.I.A.T. Final Report*, No. 1313, Vol. III, p. 82.
141. Ger. Pat. 135,408; *Frdl.*, **6**, 416 (1900–1902); *Chem. Zentr.*, **1902**, II, 1231.
142. Ger. Pat. 178,130; *Frdl.*, **8**, 346 (1905–1907); *Chem. Zentr.*, **1907**, I, 775; *Chem. Abstracts*, **1**, 1650 (1907).
143. Ger. Pat. 583,715; *Frdl.*, **20**, 1369 (1933); *Chem. Zentr.*, **1933**, II, 3625; *Chem. Abstracts*, **28**, 1194 (1934).
144. A. Eckert and K. Steiner, *Monatsh.*, **35**, 1129 (1914); *Chem. Zentr.*, **1915**, I, 200.
145. U. S. Pat. 1,640,724; *Chem. Abstracts*, **21**, 3468 (1927); *Chem. Zentr.*, **1927**, II, 2718.
146. Brit. Pat. 462,548; *Chem. Abstracts*, **31**, 6027 (1937); *Chem. Zentr.*, **1937**, II, 669.
147. U. S. Pat. 2,150,109; *Chem. Abstracts*, **33**, 4796 (1939).
148. U. S. Pat. 1,509,846; *Chem. Abstracts*, **18**, 3727 (1924); *Chem. Zentr.*, **1925**, I, 1020.
149. Ger. Pat. 294,830; *Frdl.*, **13**, 429 (1916–1921); *Chem. Zentr.*, **1916**, II, 1097.
150. U. S. Pat. 1,679,230; *Chem. Abstracts*, **22**, 3787 (1928); *Chem. Zentr.*, **1928**, II, 2069.
151. U. S. Pat. 1,994,484; *Chem. Abstracts*, **29**, 2977 (1935); *Chem. Zentr.*, **1935**, II, 2133.
152. Ger. Pat. 313,724; *Frdl.*, **13**, 429 (1916–1921); *Chem. Zentr.*, **1921**, IV, 961.
153. Ger. Pat. 314,209; *Frdl.*, **13**, 430 (1916–1921); *Chem. Zentr.*, **1922**, IV, 251.
154. Ger. Pat. 347,692; *Frdl.*, **13**, 432 (1916–1921); *Chem. Zentr.*, **1922**, II, 579.
155. Ger. Pat. 355,737; *Frdl.*, **14**, 873 (1921–1925); *Chem. Zentr.*, **1922**, IV, 1034.
156. Ger. Pat. 356,607; *Frdl.*, **14**, 874 (1921–1925); *Chem. Zentr.*, **1922**, IV, 1035.
157. Ger. Pat. 515,096; *Frdl.*, **17**, 1217 (1930); *Chem. Zentr.*, **1931**, I, 1368; *Chem. Abstracts*, **25**, 1680 (1931).
158. Ger. Pat. 558,443; *Frdl.*, **18**, 1292 (1931); see Brit. Pat. 240,168; *Chem. Zentr.*, **1926**, I, 2976; *Chem. Abstracts*, **20**, 2252 (1926).
159. Ger. Pat. 614,927; *Frdl.*, **20**, 1368 (1933); see Fr. Pat. 746,227; *Chem. Abstracts*, **27**, 4547 (1933); *Chem. Zentr.*, **1933**, II, 1933.
160. Ger. Pat. 355,736; *Frdl.*, **14**, 872 (1921–1925); *Chem. Zentr.*, **1922**, IV, 1034.
161. Brit. Pat. 430,358; *Chem. Abstracts*, **29**, 7671 (1935); *Chem. Zentr.*, **1936**, I, 896.
162. Ger. Pat. 498,292; *Frdl.*, **17**, 1214 (1930); see Brit. Pat. 320,397; *Chem. Abstracts*, **24**, 2608 (1930); *Chem. Zentr.*, **1930**, I, 749.
163. Ger. Pat. 500,178; *Frdl.*, **17**, 1215 (1930); *Chem. Zentr.*, **1930**, II, 2064; *Chem. Abstracts*, **24**, 4400 (1930).
164. Ger. Pat. 502,458; *Frdl.*, **17**, 1215 (1930); *Chem. Zentr.*, **1930**, II, 2064; *Chem. Abstracts*, **24**, 4941 (1930).
165. Ger. Pat. 507,345; *Frdl.*, **17**, 1216 (1930); *Chem. Zentr.*, **1930**, II, 3654; *Chem. Abstracts*, **25**, 599 (1931).

166. Ger. Pat. 571,240; *Frdl.*, **18**, 1296 (1931); see Brit. Pat. 331,697; *Chem. Zentr.*, **1931**, II, 320; *Chem. Abstracts*, **25**, 213 (1931).
167. Ger. Pat. 216,891; *Frdl.*, **9**, 782 (1908–1910); *Chem. Zentr.*, **1910**, I, 216; *Chem. Abstracts*, **4**, 965 (1910).
168. Ger. Pat. 227,790; *Frdl.*, **10**, 694 (1910–1912); *Chem. Zentr.*, **1910**, II, 1516; *Chem. Abstracts*, **5**, 2184 (1911).
169. Ger. Pat. 544,198; *Frdl.*, **17**, 1222 (1930); see Brit. Pat. 327,087; *Chem. Zentr.*, **1930**, II, 1144; *Chem. Abstracts*, **24**, 5163 (1930).
170. U. S. Pat. 2,044,993; *Chem. Abstracts*, **30**, 5806 (1936); *Chem. Zentr.*, **1936**, II, 3361.
171. Ger. Pat. 220,361; *Frdl.*, **9**, 782 (1908–1910); *Chem. Zentr.*, **1910**, I, 1309; *Chem. Abstracts*, **4**, 2208 (1910).
172. Ger. Pat. 481,704; *Frdl.*, **16**, 1322 (1927–1929); see Brit. Pat. 274,226; *Chem. Zentr.*, **1927**, II, 2577; *Chem. Abstracts*, **22**, 1983 (1928).
173. Ger. Pat. 470,809; *Frdl.*, **16**, 1316 (1927–1929); see Brit. Pat. 272,924; *Chem. Zentr.*, **1927**, II, 2120; *Chem. Abstracts*, **22**, 1858 (1928).
174. Ger. Pat. 580,013; *Frdl.*, **20**, 1377 (1933); *Chem. Zentr.*, **1933**, II, 1599; *Chem. Abstracts*, **27**, 4934 (1933).
175. Brit. Pat. 334,902; *Chem. Zentr.*, **1931**, II, 778; *Chem. Abstracts*, **25**, 1395 (1931).
176. Ger. Pat. 563,623; *Frdl.*, **19**, 2206 (1932); see Brit. Pat. 312,404; *Chem. Zentr.*, **1929**, II, 2608; *Chem. Abstracts*, **24**, 967 (1930).
177. Ger. Pat. 584,718; *Frdl.*, **20**, 1379 (1933); see Brit. Pat. 394,887; *Chem. Zentr.*, **1933**, II, 3489; *Chem. Abstracts*, **28**, 174 (1934).
178. Ger. Pat. 739,819; *Chem. Abstracts*, **39**, 308 (1945).
179. Belg Pat. 449,295; *Chem. Abstracts*, **42**, 223 (1948).
180. Ger. Pat. 579,327; *Frdl.*, **19**, 2202 (1932); see Fr. Pat. 726,168; *Chem. Zentr.*, **1933**, I, 134; *Chem. Abstracts*, **26**, 4960 (1932).
181. Ger. Pat. 580,534; *Frdl.*, **19**, 2203 (1932); see Brit. Pat. 386,245; *Chem. Zentr.*, **1933**, I, 2876; *Chem. Abstracts*, **27**, 4404 (1933).
182. U. S. Pat. 2,200,480; *Chem. Zentr.*, **1941**, II, 813; *Chem. Abstracts*, **34**, 5855 (1940).
183. U. S. Pat. 1,847,332; *Chem. Zentr.*, **1932**, II, 130; *Chem. Abstracts*, **26**, 2469 (1932).
184. Brit. Pat. 630,459; *Chem. Abstracts*, **44**, 8128 (1950).
185. Brit. Pat. 350,499; *Chem. Zentr.*, **1932**, I, 1580; *Chem. Abstracts*, **26**, 5427 (1932).
186. U. S. Pat. 2,396,582; *Chem. Abstracts*, **40**, 3270 (1946).
187. Brit. Pat. 363,669; *Chem. Zentr.*, **1932**, II, 300; *Chem. Abstracts*, **27**, 1516 (1933).
188. Brit. Pat. 359,889; *Chem. Abstracts*, **27**, 427 (1933); *Chem. Zentr.*, **1932**, II, 3022.
189. Brit. Pat. 385,984; *Chem. Abstracts*, **27**, 4412 (1933); *Chem. Zentr.*, **1933**, I, 2320.
190. Brit. Pat. 363,668; *Chem. Abstracts*, **27**, 1515 (1933); *Chem. Zentr.*, **1932**, II, 300.
191. Ger. Pat. 583,070; *Frdl.*, **20**, 1259 (1933); see Fr. Pat. 688,748; *Chem. Zentr.*, **1931**, I, 1180; *Chem. Abstracts*, **25**, 1095 (1931).
192. Ger. Pat. 724,872; *Chem. Abstracts*, **37**, 5733 (1943); see Fr. Pat., 865,468; *Chem. Zentr.*, **1941**, II, 2382.
193. P. Hoffmann, *Deut. Wollen-Gewerbe*, **68**, 1071 (1936); through *Chem. Abstracts*, **30**, 7853 (1936).

194. R. Haller, *Bull. soc. ind. Mulhouse,* **93,** 134 (1927); *Chem. Abstracts,* **21,** 2066 (1927).
195. R. Haller, *Kolloid Z.,* **33,** 306 (1923); *Chem. Zentr.,* **1925,** I, 1963.
196. Ger. Pat. 491,430; *Frdl.,* **16,** 1321 (1927–1929); *Chem. Zentr.,* **1930,** I, 2320; *Chem. Abstracts,* **24,** 2306 (1930).
197. Ger. Pat. 518,230; *Frdl.,* **17,** 1221 (1930); *Chem. Zentr.,* **1931,** I, 2545; *Chem. Abstracts,* **25,** 2574 (1931).
198. Ger. Pat. 525,110; *Frdl.,* **18,** 1302 (1931); see Fr. Pat. 698,638; *Chem. Zentr.,* **1931,** I, 3517; *Chem. Abstracts,* **25,** 3175 (1931).
199. Ger. Pat. 526,737; *Frdl.,* **18,** 1303 (1931); *Chem. Zentr.,* **1931,** II, 2521; *Chem. Abstracts,* **25,** 4715 (1931).
200. Ger. Pat. 547,707; *Frdl.,* **18,** 1297 (1931); see Fr. Pat. 699,912; *Chem. Zentr.,* **1931,** I, 3618; *Chem. Abstracts,* **25,** 3494 (1931).
201. Ger. Pat. 548,616; *Frdl.,* **18,** 1300 (1931); see Brit. Pat. 351,032; *Chem. Zentr.,* **1931,** II, 2224; *Chem. Abstracts,* **26,** 5427 (1932).
202. Ger. Pat. 548,832; *Frdl.,* **18,** 1299 (1931); *Chem. Zentr.,* **1932,** II, 299; *Chem. Abstracts,* **26,** 4182 (1932).
203. Ger. Pat. 548,615; *Frdl.,* **18,** 1304 (1931); see Brit. Pat. 348,170; *Chem. Zentr.,* **1931,** II, 1359; *Chem. Abstracts,* **26,** 2870 (1932).
204. Swiss Pat. 255,323; *Chem. Abstracts,* **43,** 6427 (1949).
205. Swiss Pat. 249,378; *Chem. Abstracts,* **44,** 344 (1950).
206. Brit. Pat. 386,245; *Chem. Abstracts,* **27,** 4404 (1933); *Chem. Zentr.,* **1933,** I, 2876.
207. Brit. Pat. 409,029; *Chem. Abstracts,* **28,** 6321 (1934); *Chem. Zentr.,* **1934,** II, 3677.
208. F. Schubert and L. Radlberger, *Oesterr.-ungar. Z. Zuckerind. u. Landwirtsch.,* **38,** 173 (1909); *Chem. Zentr.,* **1909,** II, 1086.
209. T. Bonwetsch, *Zentr. f. Zuckerind.,* **30,** 524 (1922); through *Chem. Zentr.,* **1922,** II, 951.
210. A. P. Alekseev, *Byull. Malyarnoĭ. Tekh.,* **1938,** No. 4–5, 12; *Khim. Referat. Zhur.,* **2,** No. 5, 115 (1939); through *Chem. Abstracts,* **34,** 3509 (1940).
211. G. Antonelli, *Tinctoria,* **31,** 493 (1932); through *Chem. Abstracts,* **27,** 1759 (1933).
212. M. S. Zel'tser and G. K. Kryukova, *J. Tech. Phys. (U.S.S.R.),* **14,** 373 (1944); through *Chem. Abstracts,* **39,** 3214 (1945).
213. *F.I.A.T. Final Report,* No. 1313, Vol. III, p. 380.
214. J. Houben and W. Fischer, *Das Anthracen und die Anthrachinone, mit den zugehörigen vielkernigen Systemen,* Thieme, Leipzig, 1929.

CHAPTER XVIII

Phenazines Condensed with Other Heterocyclic Systems

Part I. Polyazines

1. Introduction

There is a very large number of heterocyclic systems containing the phenazine nucleus fused to other heterocyclic rings. Many of these are derived from *o*-quinonoid derivatives of heterocyclic compounds by condensation with *o*-phenylenediamine and these merit little attention; but a number are of somewhat greater interest. We have subdivided the heterocyclic derivatives of the phenazines into two classes: those in which the heterocyclic portion or portions consist of further azine rings and those that include the other examples of heterocyclic systems of various states of complexity. The latter group is dealt with in Chapter XIX.

The arrangement of both these chapters will be the same as that for Chapter XVI: the systems will be dealt with in the order in which they appear in *The Ring Index* classification.

2. Pyrazino[*b*]phenazine

1,4,6,11-Tetrazanaphthacene.
R. I. 2642

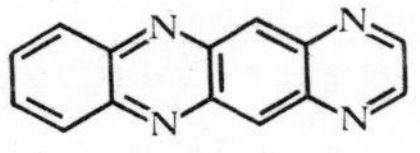

The first representative of this system was prepared by Fischer and Hepp[1] in the course of their studies of the oxidation of *o*-phenylene-diamine. They showed that the latter substance on oxidation gave 2,3-diaminophenazine (Chapter VI:3,B), which reacted with benzil to give 2,3-diphenylpyrazino[*b*]phenazine (I) as brown-red leaflets, which gave a deep blue color in concentrated sulfuric acid. On heating, I decomposed without melting.

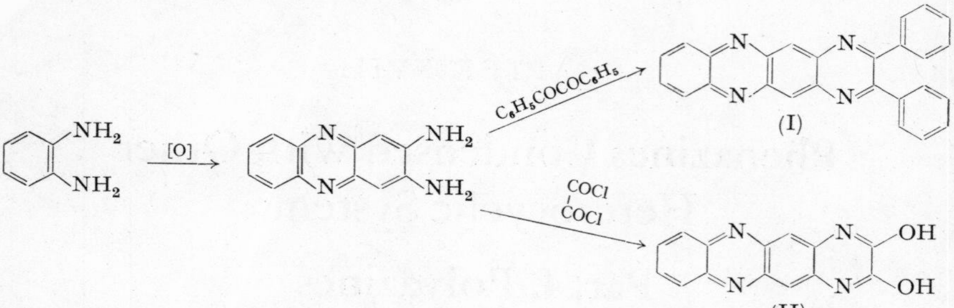

Sircar and De[2] prepared 2,3-dihydroxypyrazino[*b*]phenazine (II) by heating 2,3-diaminophenazine with oxalyl chloride. This was a brown solid, melting above 280°, which gave a blood red coloration in sulfuric acid.

A substance that is probably also a member of this group was described by Fischer and Giesen[3] by the condensation of aposafranine chloride with 1,2-ethylenediamine hydrochloride in ethanol. The product was thought to be either $C_{20}H_{18}N_4$ (III) or the compound $C_{20}H_{16}N_4$

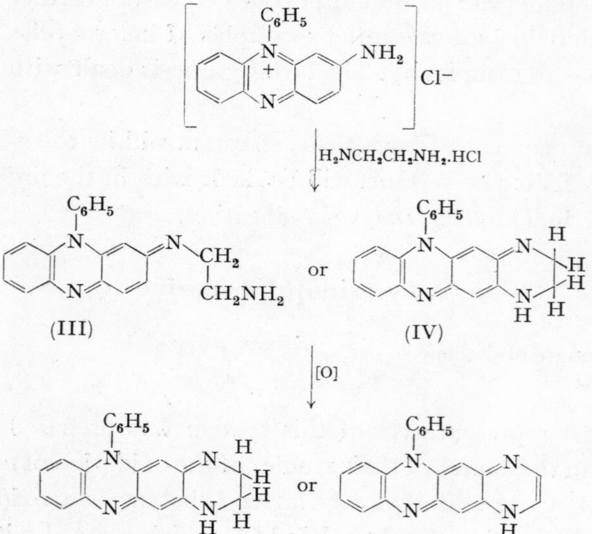

(IV) obtained by ring closure of III. This formed bluish-green lustrous crystals giving a blue color with sulfuric acid, which became red on dilution. It was transformed by oxidation with mercuric oxide in nitrobenzene or by prolonged reflux in ethanol either into $C_{20}H_{16}N_4$ (IV) if the original compound were III or else into $C_{20}H_{14}N_4$ (V) if the intermediate were IV. This is shown in the accompanying reaction scheme.

The latter compound formed green lustrous crystals that gave a yellow solution in benzene with a greenish-yellow fluorescence and a blue color in concentrated sulfuric acid. It was also obtained directly from aposafranine chloride by the action of ethylenediamine and ethylenediamine hydrochloride at 150–160°. On heating with acetic anhydride it gave a monoacetyl compound as a brownish difficultly soluble precipitate, the analysis of which did not enable Fischer and Giesen to discriminate between the two possible formulas.

3. Quinoxalo[2, 3-b]phenazine

5,7,12,14-Tetrazapentacene.
R. I. 3230

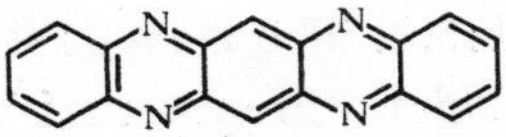

A. Introduction

Dutt[4] claimed to have prepared both this parent substance (VI) and its quinoxalo analog, diquinoxalo[2,3-b,2',3'-i]phenazine (5,7,9,14,16,18-hexazaheptacene, R. I. 3751; Section XVIII:11, VII) by condensing 2,3-diaminophenazine with o-benzoquinone in concentrated sulfuric acid and with 2,3-dihydroxyphenazine in cold 30% oleum, respectively.

At this time, Dutt held a theory that reduplication of a chromophore in this way should not lead to a shift in the position of maximum absorption of light, and it was consequently very gratifying to him that both VI and VII formed yellow needles, melting above 290°, which absorbed at 431 and 432 mμ, respectively, compared with a band at 429 mμ for phenazine. Leaving aside for a moment consideration of the stability of o-benzoquinone in concentrated sulfuric acid, or the likelihood of a condensation occurring with the dihydroxyphenazine in 30% oleum or even the nature of the phenazine maximum at 429 mμ,

it is clear that neither of the two compounds has the structure suggested
since the corresponding hydrocarbons, pentacene (deep blue) and
heptacene (dark green, almost black) would be expected to resemble

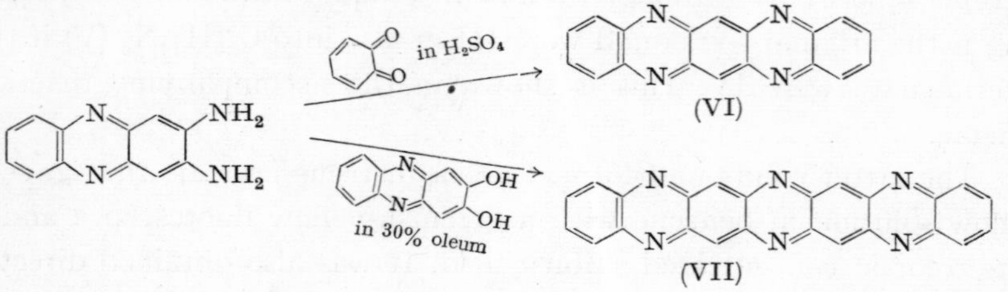

(VI)

(VII)

quite closely the aza analogs in color. This has recently been pointed
out by Badger and Pettit,[5] who have made numerous attempts to
repeat Dutt's work without any success, so that the latter's claims
must be discounted on all grounds.

Since, as will be seen in a later section, the angular isomer of VI
is well authenticated, this is a further example of the lack of stability
of extended linear quinonoid phenazine derivatives (see Chapters
XII:2, XV:6 and XVI:33). The correspondingly greater stability of
dihydro derivatives of such linear systems is nowhere better exemplified
than here (see below, Subsection B). Before turning to the series of
fluorindines, however, we may mention here a compound $C_{18}H_{18}N_4$
obtained by Morley[6] as a by-product from the condensation of o-
phenylenediamine with 1,2-cyclohexandione. This substance, isolated
as the dihydrochloride, colorless needles, m.p. 320–322° (dec.), forms
small colorless prisms, m.p. 264–265°, and gives a diacetyl compound
as small colorless needles, m.p. 245–247° (dec.). In view of the well-
known oxidation of o-phenylenediamine to 2,3-diaminophenazine,
Morley formulated the product as VIIIa, although there appears to be
no evidence that would support this against the more plausible alternative (VIIIb), that is, 1,2,3,4,4a,5,14,14a-octahydroquinoxalo[2,3-b]-
phenazine. He was unable to dehydrogenate it to any recognizable
product, however.

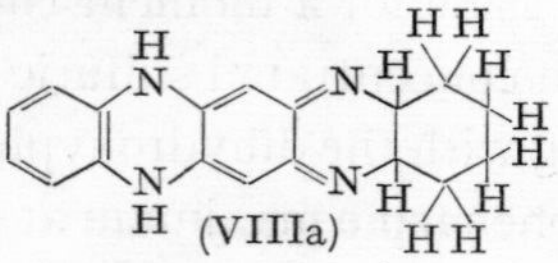

(VIIIa)

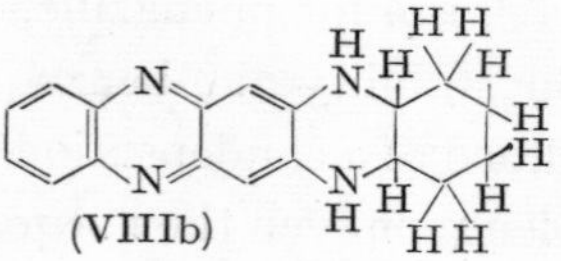

(VIIIb)

B. 5,12-Dihydroquinoxalo[2,3-b]phenazines. Fluorindines

The parent dihydro compound (IX), which was earlier referred to as phenofluoridine or homofluorindine, is now known simply as fluorindine, a name also applied to the series of related compounds. It was first prepared by Fischer and Hepp[7] by heating 2,3-diamino-phenazine with o-phenylenediamine at 200–210° and purifying the product by boiling it with dilute acid. This process has been improved by Badger and Pettit[5] by carrying out the reaction in benzyl alcohol, when a much purer product results. It is also obtained by heating together o-phenylenediamine and its hydrochloride in naphthalene in the presence of a stream of oxygen.[5]

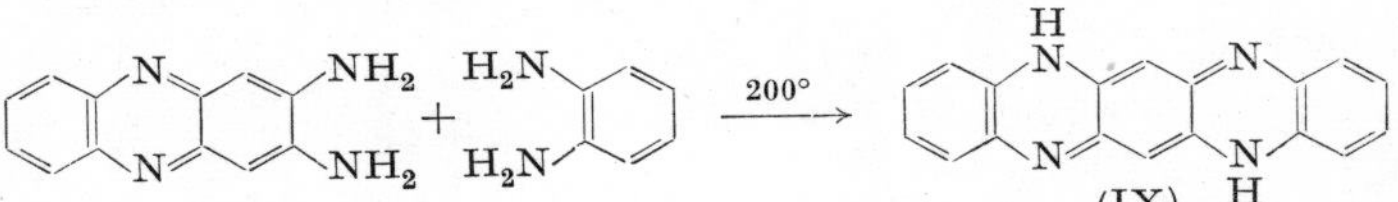

Fluorindine is also formed by heating o-phenylenediamine with 2,3-dihydroxyphenazine[8] or with 2-amino-3-hydroxyphenazine in boiling benzoic acid following Ullmann and Mauthner.[9]

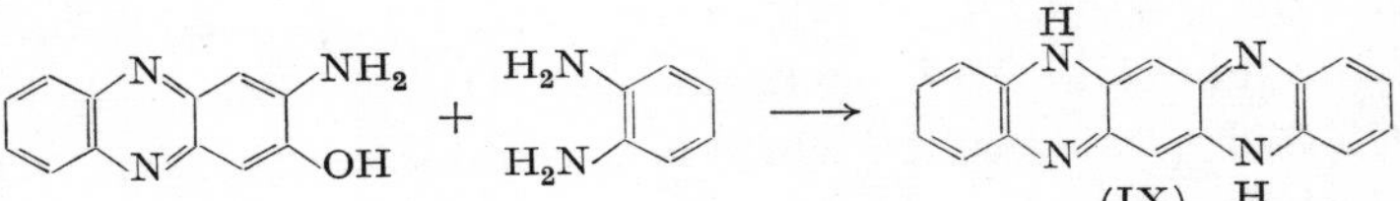

It is also produced by the condensation of 2,5-dihydroxy-1,4-benzoquinone with two molecules of o-phenylenediamine.[10] Nietzki and Slaboszewicz[11] condensed 1,5-dichloro-2,4-dinitrobenzene with o-phenylenediamine and reduced the 1,5-di(2'-aminoanilino)-2,4-dinitro-benzene (X) so obtained to the corresponding 2,4-diamino compound (XI). On heating XI in dilute acid in the presence of a stream of air, they observed the formation of fluorindine (IX). Alternatively, XI could be oxidized to 2-amino-3-(2'-aminoanilino)phenazine (XII) with ferric chloride and this on boiling with dilute acid gave fluorindine also.

When pure, fluorindine is a deep blue-purple powder that is sparingly soluble in organic solvents, giving deep blue solutions with a red fluorescence. Similar solutions are formed in concentrated sulfuric acid. With moderately concentrated acids, it forms salts that give violet-red solutions. It can be sublimed at 280–290°/0.1 mm., but does not melt. Its spectrum has been recorded by Badger and Pettit.[5] On

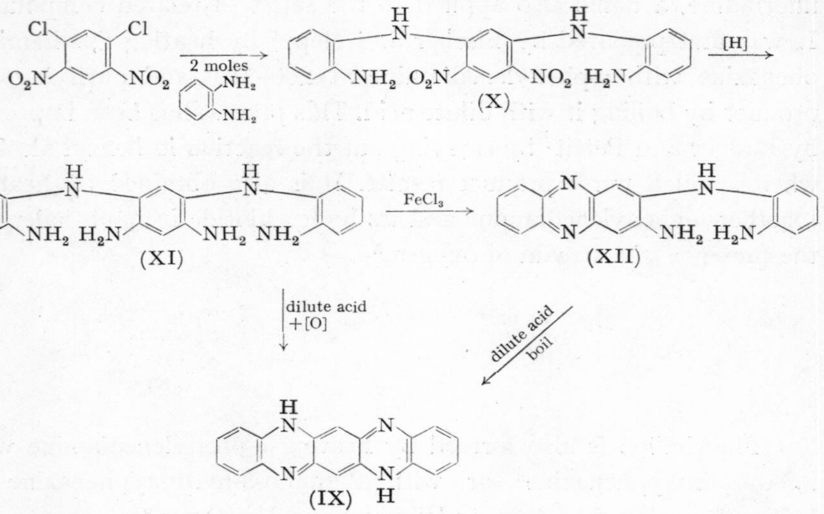

reductive acetylation, fluorindine forms 5,7,12,14-tetracetyl-5,7,12,14-tetrahydroquinoxalo[2,3-b]phenazine (XIII) as colorless needles, m.p. 375–376° (sealed tube), which is a useful means of identification.[5] On hydrolysis with mineral acid, easy aerial oxidation of the tetrahydro compound occurs to yield fluorindine.

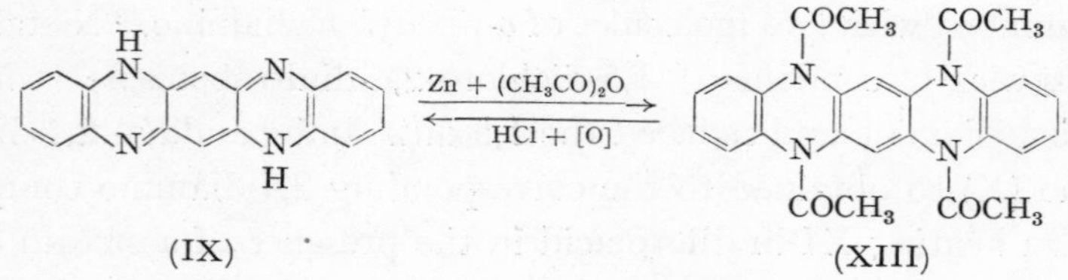

Badger and Pettit[5] made a number of unsuccessful attempts to oxidize fluorindine to the aromatic compound VI. Instead, they found that chromic acid in sulfuric acid oxidized IX to 6,13-dihydroquinoxalo-[2,3-b]phenazine-6,13-dione (XIV). Reductive acetylation of the quinone (XIV) yields 6,13-diacetoxy-5,7,12,14-tetracetyl-5,7,12,14-

tetrahydroquinoxalo[2,3-b]phenazine (XV) as small, colorless plates decomposing above 350°.

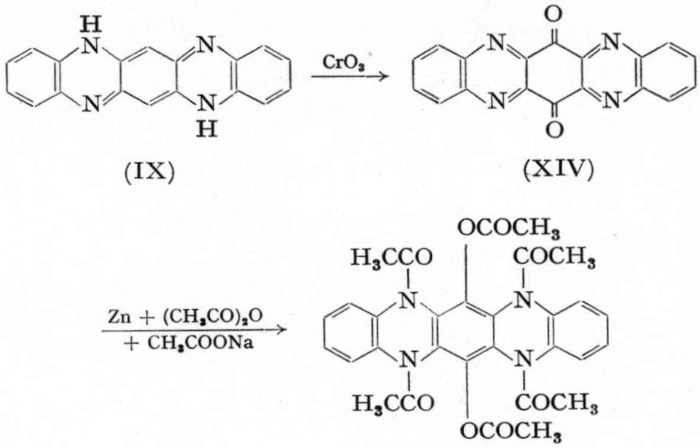

(IX)   (XIV)

(XV)

Leicester[12] claimed to have prepared the 5,12-dihydro derivative (XVI) of XIV by the addition of two molecules of o-nitroaniline to 1,4-benzoquinone, followed by reductive cyclization of the 2,5-di(2'-nitroanilino)-1,4-benzoquinone so formed. Leicester's conclusions were only supported by somewhat unsatisfactory analytical values and Badger and Pettit have shown them to be incorrect. Reductive cyclization involves the quinone oxygen atoms and the product is fluorindine, as shown by reductive acetylation to XIII.

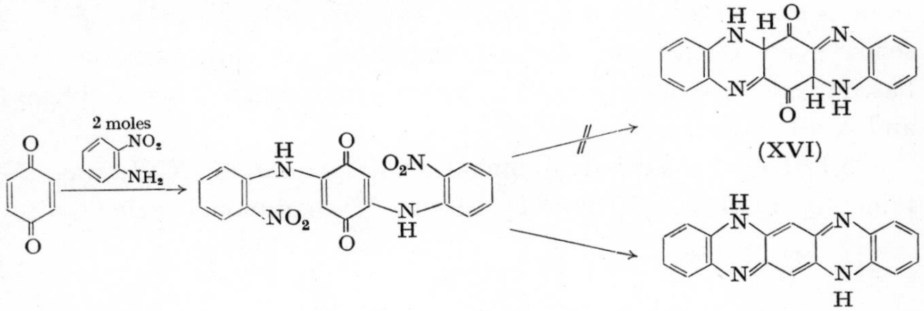

(XVI)

(IX)

A number of substituted derivatives of fluorindine have been described by Ullmann and Mauthner,[13] who oxidized monosubstituted o-phenylenediamines to the monosubstituted 2,3-diaminophenazine, with elimination of one substituent, and this was then heated in boiling benzoic acid with o-phenylenediamine or a substituted derivative of this.

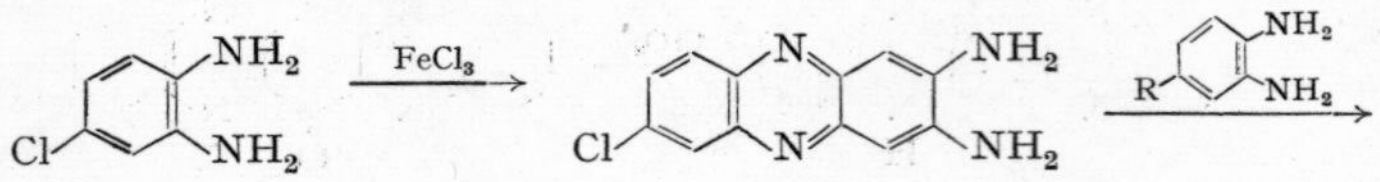

(XVII)

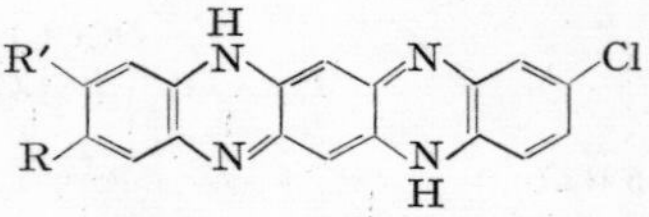

XVIII (R=R′=H)
XIX　(R=Cl, R′=H)
XX　　(R=H, R′=Cl)

Thus from 3,4-diaminochlorobenzene they obtained 2,3-diamino-7-chlorophenazine (XVII), which with o-phenylenediamine yielded 2-chlorofluorindine (XVIII) and with 3,4-diaminochlorobenzene gave 2,9-dichloro- or 2,10-dichlorofluorindine (XIX or XX, respectively). The 2-carboxylic and 2-sulfonic acids of fluorindine were prepared similarly. The relative positions of the chlorine and extra hydrogen atoms have not been determined.

The p-quinonoid structure (IX) was early attributed to fluorindine by Fischer and Hepp and was maintained over some weak criticism from Nietzki.[14] Badger and Pettit[5] have recently provided spectroscopic evidence in favor of this formulation. The early structure was based upon the similarity existing between fluorindine and its N-phenyl and N-alkyl derivatives.

5,12-Dihydro-5-methylquinoxalo[2,3-b]phenazine (XXI) was obtained by Fischer and Hepp[8] by heating 2,3-diaminophenazine hydro-

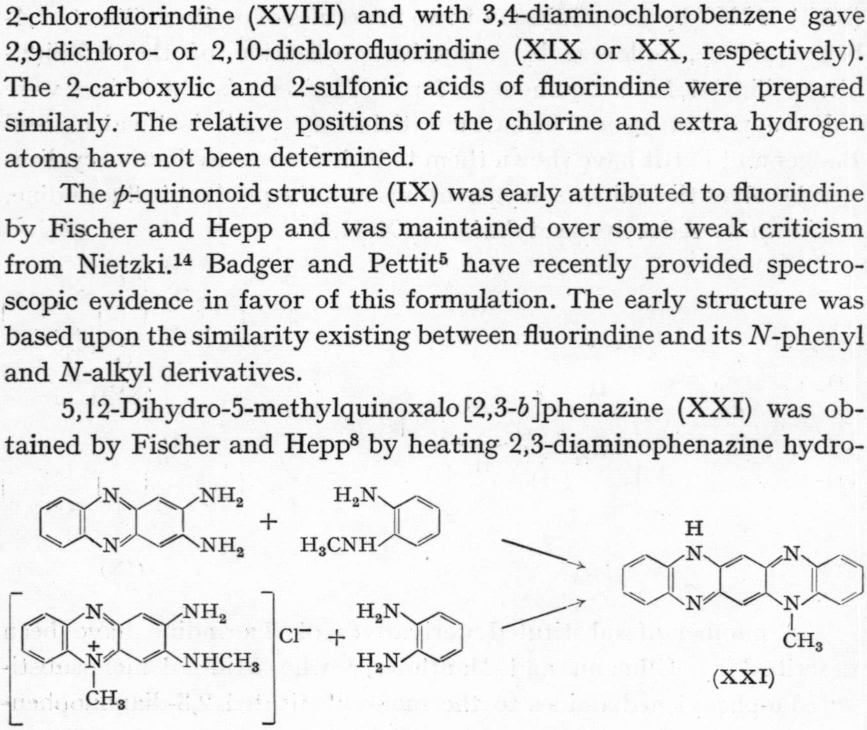

(XXI)

chloride with 2-methylaminoaniline, and by Kehrmann and Bürgin[15] by heating o-phenylenediamine hydrochloride with 2-amino-3-methyl-amino-5-methylphenazinium chloride.

The corresponding 5-phenyl derivative (XXII) was prepared by heating o-phenylenediamine hydrochloride with aposafranine chloride in ethanol[16] or with 3-anilinoaposafranine in boiling benzoic acid[15] or in the presence of ethanol at 170° under pressure.[17]

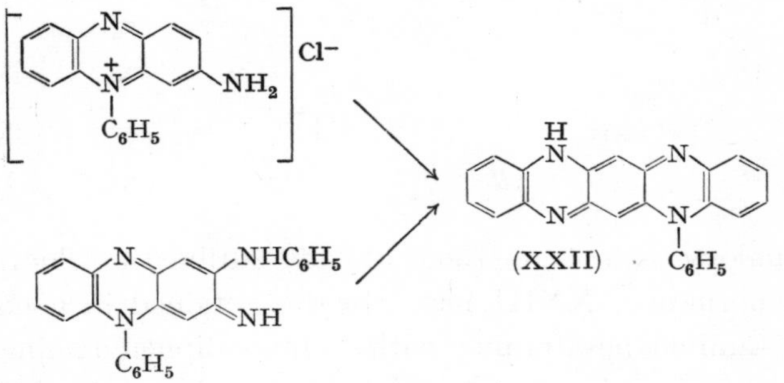

It is also obtained from o-phenylenediamine hydrochloride and 3-aminoaposafranone in ethanol at 170° under pressure[17] or from the same diamine hydrochloride and 3-hydroxyaposafranone in boiling benzoic acid.[15] The reaction with 3-anilino-aposafranine and -aposafranone and with 3-hydroxyaposafranone were valuable confirmatory proofs of the correctness of the structures of the latter compounds.

5-Phenylfluorindine itself may be rapidly crystallized from ethyl benzoate as a red lustrous powder that gives blue solutions with a red fluorescence in mineral acids. The salts are intensely colored lustrous crystals. Prolonged treatment of 5-phenylfluorindine with ethyl benzoate leads to the formation of the 12-benzoyl derivative as dark red prisms with a golden luster, the hydrochloride of which forms violet needles with a coppery luster.[15] Kehrmann and Guggenheim[18] nitrated 5-phenylfluorindine with potassium nitrate in concentrated sulfuric acid and obtained a mononitro compound as brown-red flakes with a bronze luster. Substituted 5-phenylfluorindines are also known.[19]

5,12-Diphenyl-5,12-dihydroquinoxalo[2,3-b]phenazine (5,12-di-phenylfluorindine, XXIII) was at one time known as "fluorindine," the unsubstituted compound then being known as "homofluorindine."

Care must be taken to avoid confusion when referring to the early literature. 5,12-Diphenylfluorindine was first prepared by Witt[20] and independently by Caro, according to Witt, by heating azophenine at 360°. It occurs to a small extent in the induline melt.[21] Fischer and Hepp confirmed this reaction and also showed that it was obtained by heating azophenine with zinc dust[7] or better by oxidizing it with mercuric oxide in boiling nitrobenzene.[8]

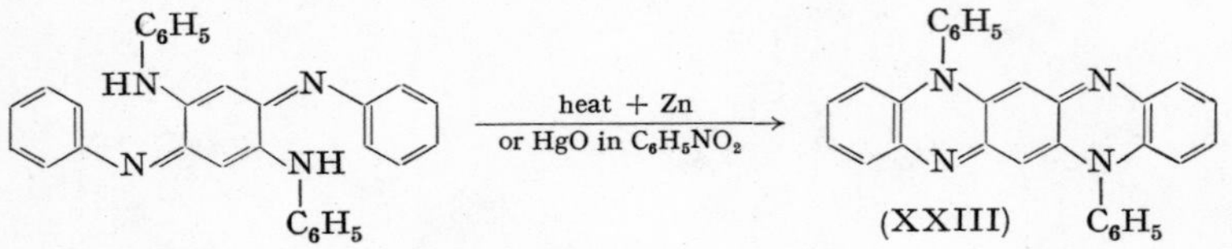

In analogy with the methods already outlined for fluorindine and 5-phenylfluorindine, XXIII may also be obtained in good yield by heating 3-anilinoaposafranine with 2-aminodiphenylamine and one equivalent of mineral acid, either alone[8] or in boiling benzoic acid.[15] It is obtained by heating 2,3-dianilino-5-phenylphenazinium anhydro-base (3-anilino-N-phenylaposafranine) alone, or better, by oxidizing it in boiling nitrobenzene with mercuric oxide.[8]

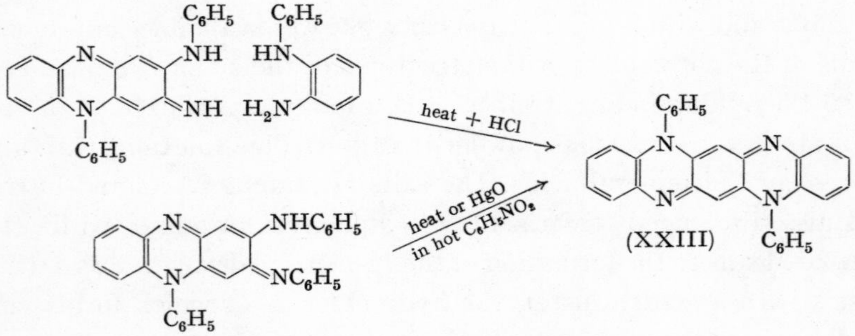

5,12-Diphenylfluorindine forms deeply colored crystals with a green or bronze luster and gives reddish-violet solutions in ethanol which exhibit a fiery red fluorescence. The salts, formed in the presence of mineral acids, give greenish-blue solutions with a brownish-red fluorescence. Kehrmann and Guggenheim[18] and Wilberg[22] have described a number of substituted derivatives of XXIII.

When 3-anilinoaposafranine chloride is condensed with 2-amino-diphenylamine in boiling benzoic acid, the two components may theoretically react in two ways. The second mode of combination yields a quaternary compound (XXIV) known as diphenylisofluorindinium hydroxide (or salt). This was isolated first by Kehrmann and Bürgin[23] in the form of the hydrochloride of the quaternary chloride (XXIV).

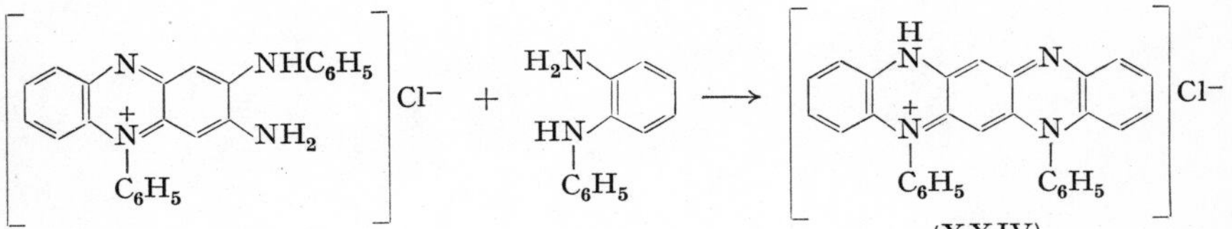

(XXIV)

Later, Kehrmann and Duret[24] showed that when this compound was basified an anhydro-base, $C_{30}H_{20}N_4$, was formed which must be formulated as a betaine in which the charges may alternate between the various nitrogen atoms so that the compound possesses a mesomeric structure, of which XXV represents two canonical forms.

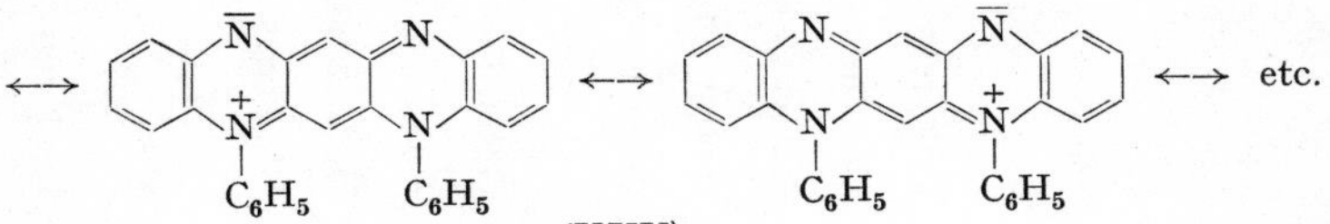

(XXV)

Processes for preparing fluorindines from alkylated or arylated o-diamines, based on the above methods, were patented,[25, 26] but the fluorindines despite their deep colors were unsuitable as dyestuffs owing to their great insolubility and the variation in shade on alkaline treatment. A patent[27] describes the modification both of fluorindines such as 5,12-diphenylfluorindine and of isofluorindines by treatment with dimethyl sulfate and similar alkylating agents in nitrobenzene at 150° to yield more soluble coloring matters that dyed cotton mordanted with tannin in purple to blue shades. These dyes, presumably quaternary salts, were said to possess good fastness properties towards light and washing and to be of great intensity of color. They do not appear to have been used commercially.

TABLE XLVIII. Quinoxalo[2,3-b] phenazines and Derivatives

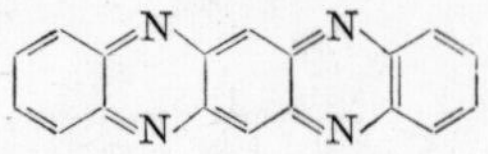

Substituents	Appearance	Color with H₂SO₄	Ref.
5,12-Dihydro-	Deep blue-purple powder	Blue, red fluorescence	See text
1,2,3,4,4a,5,14,14a-Octahydro-	Colorless prisms, m.p. 264–265°		6
1,2,3,4,4a,5,14,14a-Octahydro-5,14-diacetyl-	Colorless needles, m.p. 245–247° (dec.)		6
5,7,12,14-Tetrahydro-5,7,12,14-tetracetyl-	Colorless needles, m.p. 375–376° (dec.)		5
6,13-Dihydro-6,13-diketo-	Yellow plates, m.p. > 400°		5
5,7,12,14-Tetrahydro-6,13-diacetoxy-5,7,12,14-tetracetyl-	Colorless plates, m.p. > 350° (dec.)		5
2-Chloro-5,12-dihydro-	Green-blue needles	Blue	13
2,9(or 2,10)-Dichloro-5,12-dihydro-	Brown-red crystals	Blue	13
2-Carboxy-5,12-dihydro-	Blue crystals	Green-blue	13
2-Sulfonyl-5,12-dihydro-	Blue crystals, bronze luster	Blue	13
2,10-Dimethyl-5,12-dihydro-		Blue solution, violet fluorescence	11
5-Methyl-5,12-dihydro-	Dark red powder		15
5-Phenyl-5,12-dihydro-	Red powder, green-gold luster		15–17

Substituents	Appearance	Color with H_2SO_4	Ref.
x-Nitro-5-phenyl-5,12-dihydro-	Brown-red flakes, gold luster	Dark blue	18
5-Phenyl-12-benzoyl-5,12-dihydro-	Dark red prisms, gold luster		15
3-Chloro-5-phenyl-5,12-dihydro-	Dark red powder		18
6-Chloro-5(or 12)phenyl-5,12-dihydro-	Crystals, metallic green luster		19
6-Methyl-5(or 12)-phenyl-5,12-dihydro-	Lustrous powder		15, 19
6-Methyl-5(or 12)-phenyl-12(or 5)-benzoyl-5,12-dihydro-	Dark red prisms, gold luster		15
5,12-Diphenyl-5,12-dihydro-	Crystals, green or bronze luster		7, 8, 15, 20
3-Chloro-5,12-diphenyl-5,12-dihydro-	Red-violet needles		18
3,9(or 3,10)-Dichloro-5,12-diphenyl-5,12-dihydro-	Violet-grey needles	Cornflower-blue	18
x-Nitro-5,12-diphenyl-5,12-dihydro-	Greenish-grey crystals	Greenish-blue	18
3-Anilino-5,12-diphenyl-5,12-dihydro-	Dark blue leaflets, green luster	Blue, purple-red fluorescence	18
3,10-Dianilino-5,12-diphenyl-5,12-dihydro-	Dark blue crystals	Ultramarine, red fluorescence	18
10-Chloro-2-(4'-chloroanilino)-5,12-di(4'-chlorophenyl)-5,12-dihydro-	Bronze needles, green luster	Deep blue	22
5,7-Diphenyl-5,12-dihydro- (anhydro-base)	Grass-green crystals		23, 24
2-Amino-3-anilino-5-phenyl-5,12-dihydro-	Brown-violet crystals	Blue-green	33
6-Isopropyl-13-methyl-5,12-dihydro-	Dark powder, coppery luster	Violet-blue	36

There are a number of analogs of the fluorindines bearing one or more additional fused benzo residues. These are dealt with in the appropriate sections, although their methods of preparation, properties and reactions are very closely similar to those of the fluorindines. The same is true of the benzoxazino[2,3-*b*]phenazines and their benzo analogs.

The numerous derivatives of quinoxalo[2,3-*b*]phenazine are listed in Table XLVIII.

4. Quinoxalo[2,3-*a*]phenazine

R. I. 3232

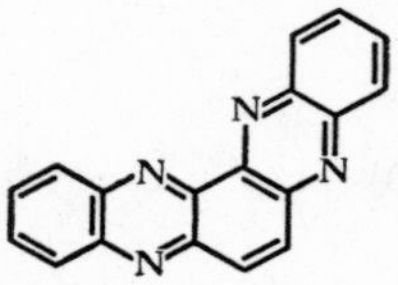

The parent compound of this series was unknown until recently; a derivative (XXVI) was prepared by Kehrmann and Duret[28] by the condensation of 2-aminodiphenylamine with rhodizonic acid when a mixture of at least three compounds resulted. These were the mono-, di- and perhaps the tri-condensation products of the *o*-diamine, the dicondensation product (XXVI) being the main constituent. It was isolated as the dibetaine anhydro-base.

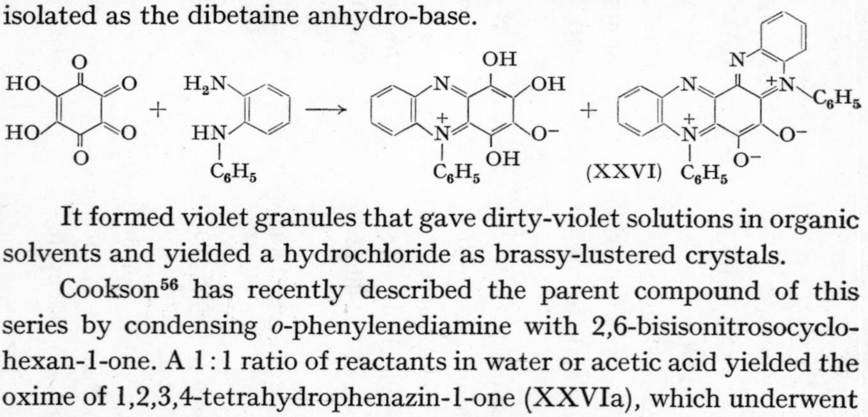

It formed violet granules that gave dirty-violet solutions in organic solvents and yielded a hydrochloride as brassy-lustered crystals.

Cookson[56] has recently described the parent compound of this series by condensing *o*-phenylenediamine with 2,6-bisisonitrosocyclo-hexan-1-one. A 1:1 ratio of reactants in water or acetic acid yielded the oxime of 1,2,3,4-tetrahydrophenazin-1-one (XXVIa), which underwent Wolff aromatization with acetic anhydride to yield 1-acetamidophen-azine; but, when two molecules of the diamine are employed for one of the bisisonitrosocyclohexanone, the product is a brown solid, which is also obtainable from the oxime (XXVIa) by heating it with *o*-phenyl-enediamine in acetic acid. The brown solid gives dark blue or green solutions in organic solvents and is perhaps a phenazhydrin or a dihydro compound, since the solutions slowly become yellow on atmospheric oxidation, a process that may be accelerated by the use of oxidizing solvents such as nitrobenzene. On standing in air, the brown crystals slowly became yellow and, after chromatographic purification and sublimation, quinoxalo[2,3-a]phenazine (XXVIb) was obtained as pale yellow needles, m.p. 304°, which form a picrate (brown rods, m.p.

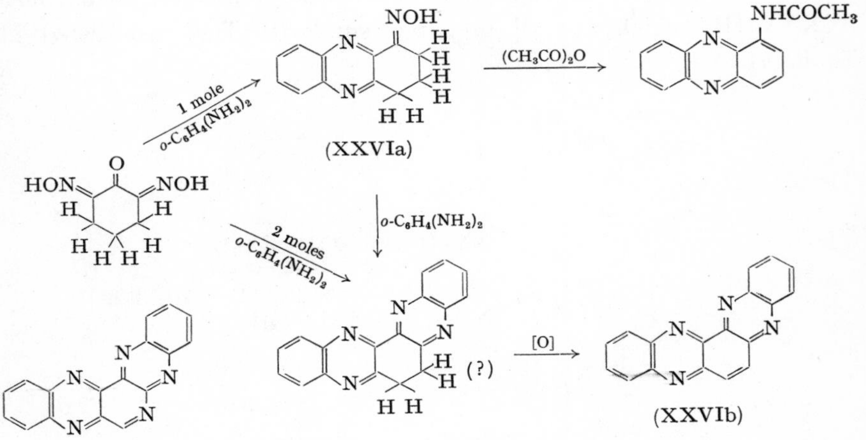

(XXVIa)

(XXVIc)

(XXVIb)

ca. 240–265°). The ultraviolet absorption spectrum of quinoxalo[2,3-a]-phenazine (XXVIb) was recorded in ethanol ($\lambda_{max.}$, 242 mμ (log ε 4.71) and 339 mμ (log ε 4.64); shifted to 246 mμ (log ε 4.64) and 348 mμ (log ε 4.56) in 3.2 N ethanolic hydrogen chloride). The 6-aza analog (XXVIc) has also been described by Cookson.[56]

5. Benzo[a]pyrazino[c]phenazine

R. I. 3233

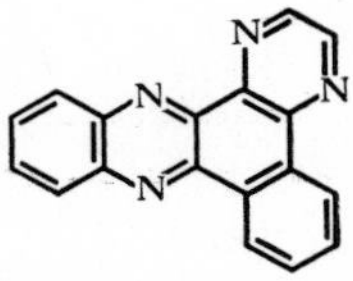

A small number of representatives of this series has been prepared by Crippa and his associates in investigations of the reaction which bears his name. The simplest member, 2-phenylbenzo[a]pyrazino[c]-phenazine (XXIX), was obtained[29] by condensing together aceto-phenone and 1-benzeneazo-2-naphthylamine to give 3-phenylbenzo[f]-quinoxaline (XXVII, R. I. 1907), which was oxidized by chromic acid to the 5,6-quinone (XXVIII); this was condensed with o-phenylene-diamine to yield XXIX. Other examples include the 2-(4'-acetamido-phenyl)-(XXXII) and 2-(4'-benzamidophenyl)benzo[a]pyrazino[c]-phenazines(XXXV)[30] and 2,3-diphenylbenzo[a]pyrazino[c]phenazine[31] (XXXVIII), which are all prepared similarly. They are listed in Table XLIX.

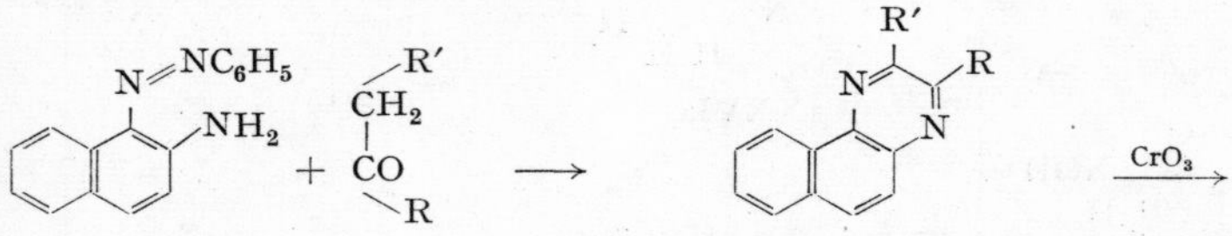

XXVII   (R=C_6H_5, R'=H)
XXX   (R=p-$CH_3CONHC_6H_4$, R'=H)
XXXIII   (R=p-$C_6H_5CONHC_6H_4$, R'=H)
XXXVI   (R=R'=C_6H_5)

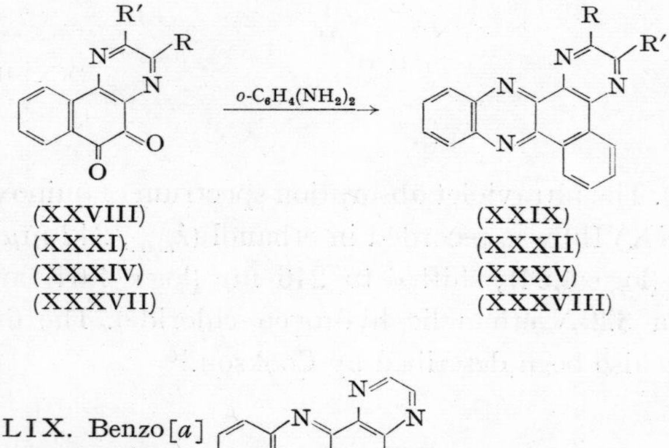

(XXVIII)   (XXIX)
(XXXI)   (XXXII)
(XXXIV)   (XXXV)
(XXXVII)   (XXXVIII)

TABLE XLIX. Benzo[a]
pyrazino[c]phenazines

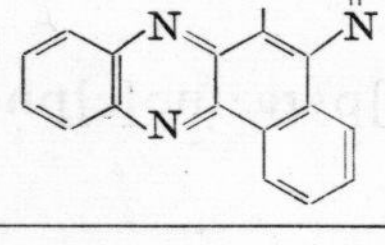

Substituents	Appearance	M.p. (°C.)	Ref.
2-Phenyl-	Light yellow crystals	272	29
2-p-Acetamidophenyl-	Light yellow crystals	> 335	30
2-p-Benzamidophenyl-		340	30
2,3-Diphenyl-	Pale yellow	> 300	31

6. Benzo[a]quinoxalo[2,3-i]phenazine

R. I. 3577

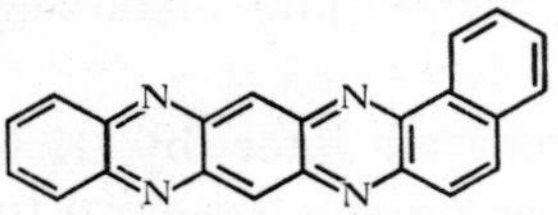

This system is unknown in the fully aromatic state, but numerous examples of dihydro compounds are known. These benzo analogs of fluorindine (see Section XVIII:3,B) resemble the latter compound very closely. Because of the presence of an extra benzo residue in an asymmetrical position, there arises the possibility of positional isomers for the two additional hydrogen atoms or substituting groups.

A. 7,14-Dihydrobenzo[a]quinoxalo[2,3-i]phenazine

This unsubstituted isomer (XL) (or the alternative 9,16-dihydro compound, XLI) was first prepared by Nietzki and Vollenbruck,[32] who condensed 1,5-dichloro-2,4-dinitrobenzene first with one mole of 1,2-naphthalenediamine and then reacted the remaining chloro group with one mole of o-phenylenediamine. Reduction of the product gave the tetramino compound (XXXIX), which on aerial oxidation underwent

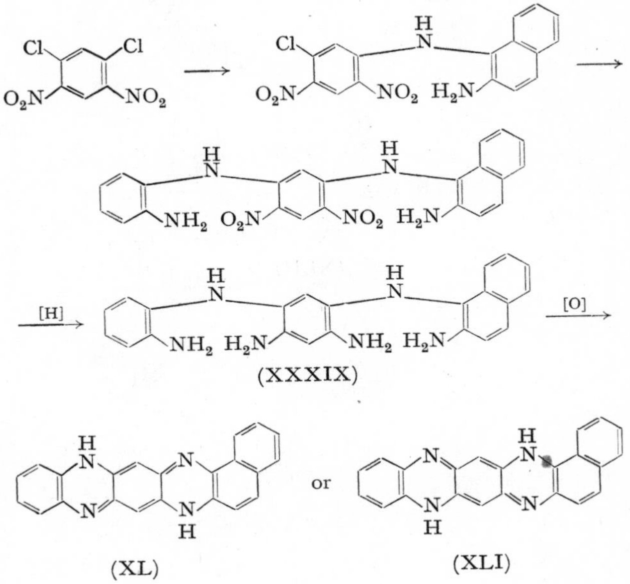

(XXXIX)

(XL)   or   (XLI)

ring closure to the 1,2-benzofluorindine (XL). The reaction scheme is very similar to that employed by Nietzki and Slaboszewicz[11] in the synthesis of fluorindine.

The same compound was prepared later by Kehrmann and Schedler[33] in a much simpler manner by condensing 9,10-dihydroxy-benzo[a]phenazine (Section XIII:3,B) with o-phenylenediamine in boiling benzoic acid. The base (XL) forms greenish lustrous needles, sparingly soluble in organic solvents, to give weak violet-red solutions with a strong fiery red fluorescence. With concentrated sulfuric acid, a blue color is obtained that deepens on the addition of water. The 5-acetamido compound was described by Kehrmann and Logoz.[34]

The 7-phenyl derivative of XL was of some importance in elucidating the course of the reaction of hydroxylamine with isorosindone (7-phenyl-9(7)-benzo[a]phenazinone, Chapter XIV:2,C(2) and 6,B).

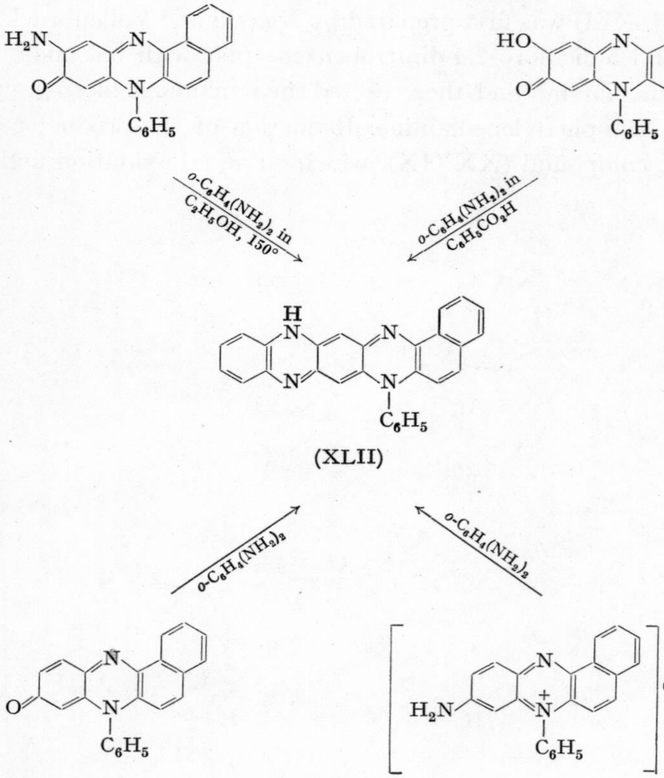

(XLII)

After it was realized that the product of this reaction was an amino-isorosindone, it was at first concluded that the amino group had entered position 5. That in fact it was 10-aminoisorosindone followed from the observation of Fischer and Römer[35] that, on heating with o-phenylene-diamine in ethanol at 150° under pressure, it yielded 7-phenyl-7,14-dihydrobenzo[a]quinoxalo[2,3-i]phenazine (XLII), which was also obtained from o-phenylenediamine and isorosindone chloride or more readily from isorosinduline chloride. Much later, Kehrmann and Logoz[34] showed that 10-hydroxy-7-phenyl-9(7)-benzo[a]phenazinone (10-hydroxyisorosindone, Chapter XIV:3,B) and o-phenylenediamine in boiling benzoic acid yielded 7-phenyl-1,2-benzofluorindine (XLII).

The base forms dark violet needles with a metallic luster, slightly soluble in benzene to give a reddish-violet solution with a vermilion fluorescence and yielding a bluish-green color in concentrated sulfuric acid.

Kehrmann and Collaud[36] reacted 5-acetamido-9,10-dihydroxy-benzo[a]phenazine with 2-aminodiphenylamine hydrochloride in boiling benzoic acid and obtained either 5-acetamido-14-phenyl-7,14-dihydrobenzo[a]quinoxalo[2,3-i]phenazine (XLIII) or the corresponding 5-acetamido-9-phenyl-9,16-dihydrobenzo[a]quinoxalo [2,3-i]phenazine (XLIV) as brownish-red microscopic crystals.

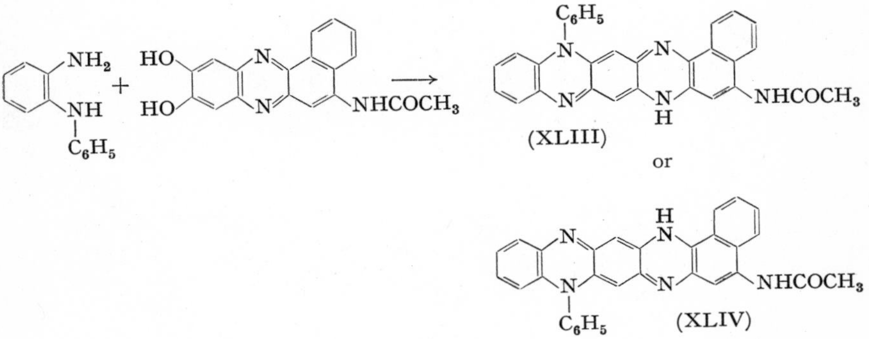

(XLIII)

or

(XLIV)

Kehrmann and Schedler[33] reacted 9,10-dihydroxybenzo[a]phen-azine with 2-aminodiphenylamine and obtained two isomers, presumably XLV and XLVI, but they were unable to decide which structure to allocate to which compound. Fischer and Giesen[3] briefly described a "fluorindine-like product" obtained by the condensation of 1,2-diaminonaphthalene and aposafranine; this also may be either XLV or XLVI.

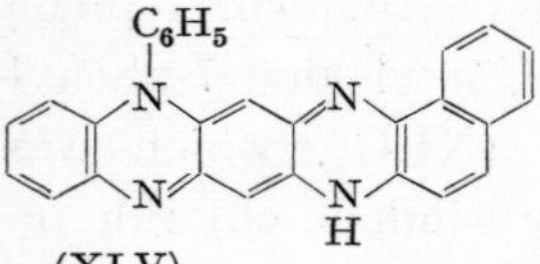

(XLV) C_6H_5 (XLVI)

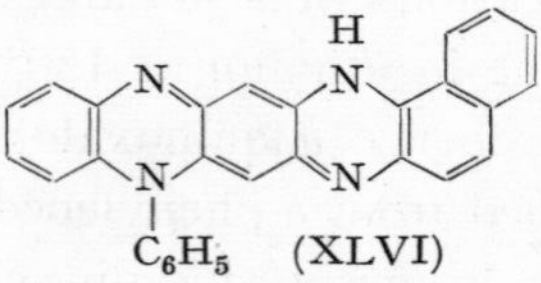

Fischer and Römer[35] formulated as 7,14-diphenyl-7,14-dihydro-benzo[a]quinoxalo[2,3-i]phenazine (XLVII) a compound that formed dark green prisms, sparingly soluble in benzene to give a greenish-brown solution, and giving a blue-green solution in sulfuric acid, and which they obtained by heating 2-aminodiphenylamine hydrochloride with 10-aminoisorosindone or even with isorosindone itself in ethanol at 150° under pressure. Kehrmann and Logoz,[34] however, condensed 2-aminodiphenylamine with 10-hydroxyisorosindone in benzoic acid and obtained two isomeric compounds, the one that was produced in smaller yield being formulated as XLVII. This formed dark blue crystals with a green luster and was soluble in benzene to give red-violet solutions with the typical crimson fluorescence of fluorindines;

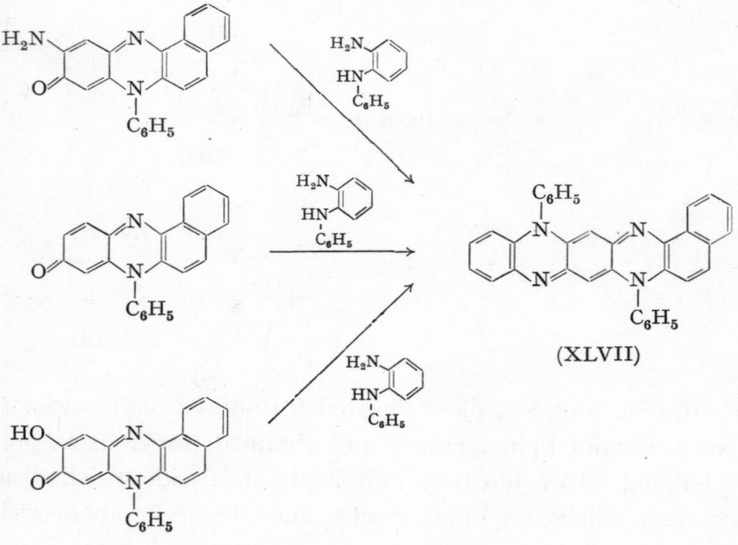

(XLVII)

it gave a bluish-green solution in concentrated sulfuric acid. The compound of Fischer and Römer is therefore more probably the isomeric XLIX (see Section XVIII:6,C).

B. 9,16-Dihydrobenzo[a]quinoxalo[2,3-i]phenazine (XLI)

The unsubstituted compound may be the product described above as XL or XLI. The only certain member of this series is that described by Kehrmann and Levy[37] as formed by the action of o-phenylenediamine upon 9-amino-10-dimethylamino-12-phenylbenzo[a]phenazinium chloride. The product, 16-phenyl-9,16-dihydrobenzo[a]quinoxalo-[2,3-i]phenazine (XLVIII) was violet-red and was weakly fluorescent in solution.

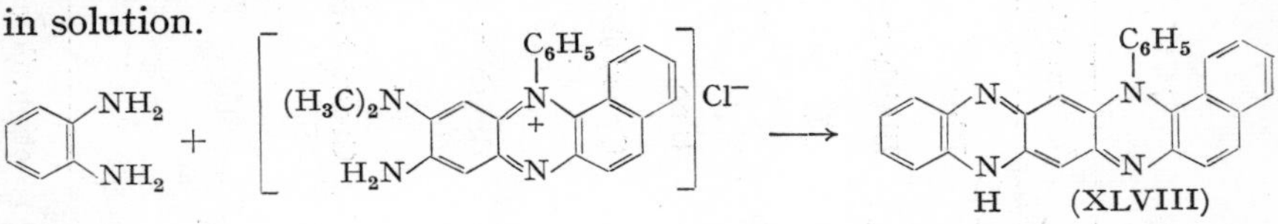

For possible 9-phenyl-9,16-dihydro compounds in this series, see XLIV and XLVI, above.

C. 7,9-Diphenyl-1,2-benzoisofluorindine

In the reaction between 2-aminodiphenylamine and 10-hydroxy-isorosindone mentioned above (Section XVIII:6,A), the major product was described by Kehrmann and Logoz[34] as olive-green crystals with a feeble blue reflex. In analogy with the isofluorindine structure (Section XVIII:3,B), they suggested this was the mesomeric betaine of which XLIX is only one of the possible charge structures. When XLIX was warmed with dimethyl sulfate, a soluble quaternary salt was formed and isolated as the almost black platinichloride.

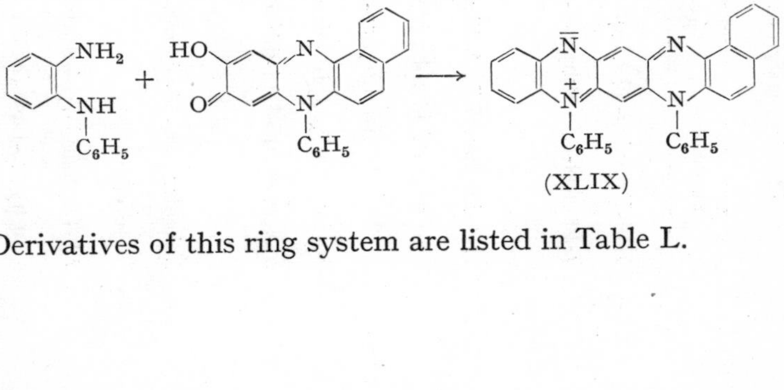

Derivatives of this ring system are listed in Table L.

TABLE L. Benzo[a]quinoxalo[2,3-i]phenazines

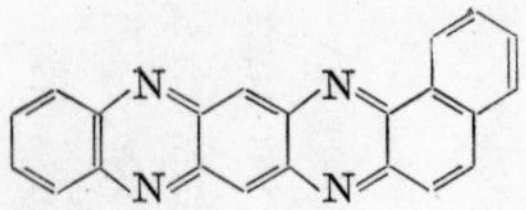

Substituents	Appearance	Color with H_2SO_4	Color of solutions	Ref.
7,14-Dihydro- (?9,16)	Greenish lustrous needles	Blue	Violet-red	32, 33
7-Phenyl-7,14-dihydro-	Dark violet needles, metallic luster	Bluish-green	Red-violet	34, 35
7,14-Diphenyl-7,14-dihydro-	Dark blue needles, green reflex		Violet-red	34, 35
14-Phenyl-7,14-dihydro-*	Dark red crystals	Blue	Red	3, 33
9-Phenyl-9,16-dihydro-	Red needles	Greenish-blue	Violet-red	3, 33
16-Phenyl-9,16-dihydro-	Violet-red crystals			37
5-Acetamido-7,14-dihydro-	Dark violet needles, coppery luster	Bluish-green	Violet-red	34
5-Acetamido-14-phenyl-7,14-dihydro-	Brownish-red crystals	Greenish-blue	Red-violet	36
7,9-Diphenyl-7,14-dihydro-, anhydro-base (isofluorindine)	Olive-green crystals, blue reflex	Greenish-blue		34, 35

* These two isomeric substances have been isolated from the same reaction. Complete structural identification is lacking.

7. Naphtho[1,2-b,3,4-b']diquinoxaline

R. I. 3580

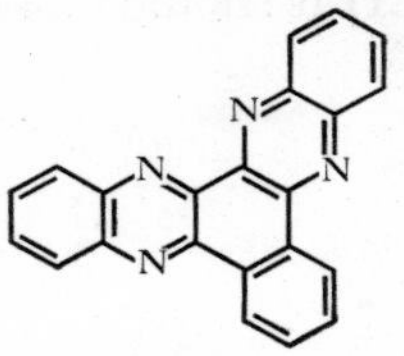

This system (L) was originally prepared by Zincke and Wiegand[38] by the action of o-phenylenediamine upon benzo[a]phenazine-5,6-quinone (Chapter XII:3,F) or by the action of excess o-phenylenediamine upon 1a,7a-dihydroöxiro[b]naphthalene-2,7-quinone.

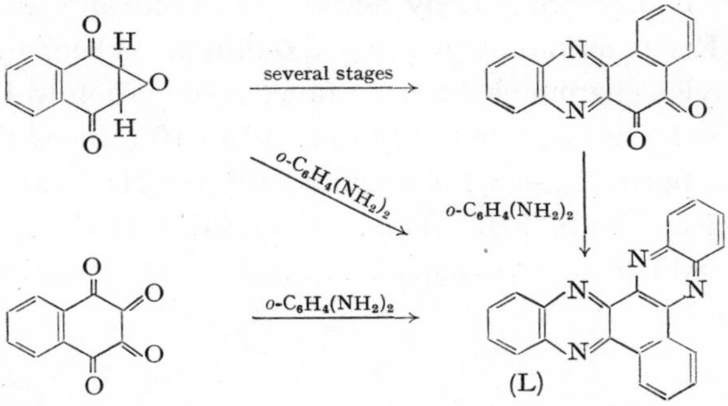

Zincke and Ossenbeck[99] obtained L by heating o-phenylenediamine with 1,2,3,4-tetrahydronaphthalene-1,2,3,4-tetrone. Badger and Pettit[40] repeated Zincke's preparation from benzo[a]phenazine-5,6-quinone and report that L forms very pale yellow needles, m.p. 320–321°.

Kehrmann[41] claimed to have obtained 5,16-dihydronaphtho-[1,2-b,3,4-b']diquinoxaline (LI) by the fusion of o-phenylenediamine with 6-chloro-5-hydroxybenzo[a]phenazine in naphthalene and described it as pure golden-yellow leaflets, m.p. 263°. He also isolated fluorindine as a by-product of the oxidation of the o-phenylenediamine. He was unable to carry out the oxidation of his product LI to L.

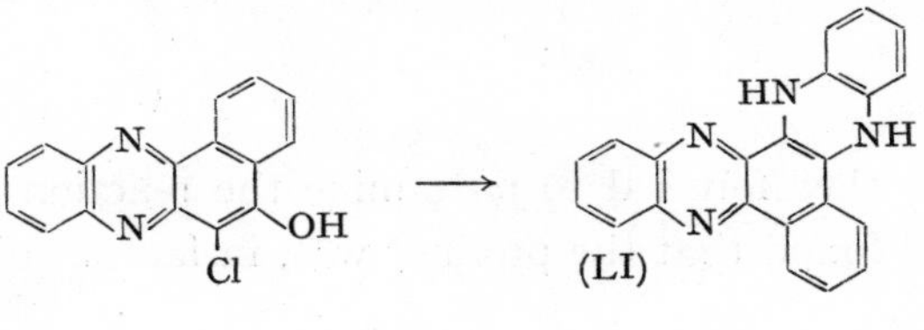

(LI)

Badger and Pettit[40] attempted to prepare such a dihydro compound, since in a tautomeric form such as LII it should closely resemble fluorindine.

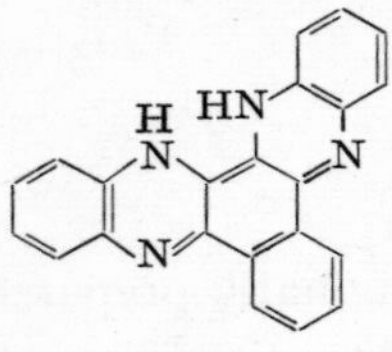

(LII)

Catalytic reduction of L was unsuccessful, the colorless solution obtained soon depositing L by aerial oxidation, and an attempt to apply the Ris reaction by heating 5,6-dihydroxybenzo[a]phenazine with o-phenylenediamine led to spontaneous oxidation to L. Reductive acetylation of L proceded smoothly and 5,10,15,16-tetracetyl-5,10,15,16-tetrahydronaphtho[1,2-b,3,4-b']diquinoxaline (LIII) was obtained as colorless prisms, m.p. 318°. This on careful hydrolysis gave a red compound, which was perhaps LII, but which readily underwent oxidation to L.

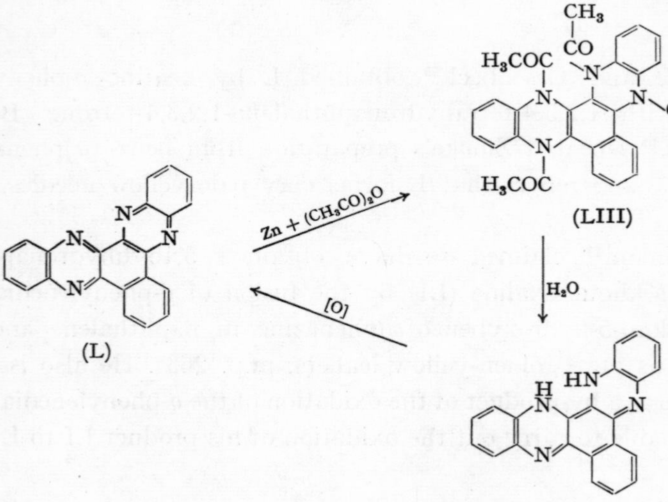

(LIII)

(L)

Zn + (CH₃CO)₂O

[O]

H₂O

(LII)

They were therefore led to reëxamine the reaction described by Kehrmann and found that the product was, in fact, a mixture of two compounds; the presence of fluorindine in the reaction mixture, as reported by Kehrmann, was also confirmed. Fractional crystallization of the product from chloroform resolved the mixture into a less soluble compound, golden plates, m.p. 272°, and a more soluble fraction that was identified as L. Analysis of the compound, m.p. 272°, which was clearly the compound with which Kehrmann had worked, showed it could not possess the formula of LI and after intensive study they proposed LIV.

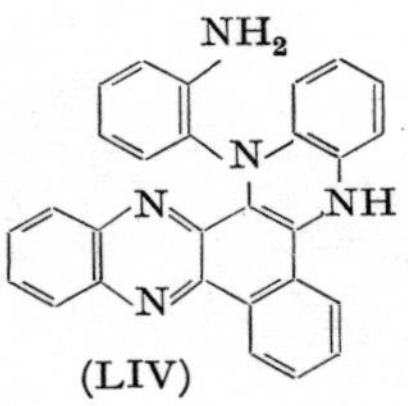

(LIV) 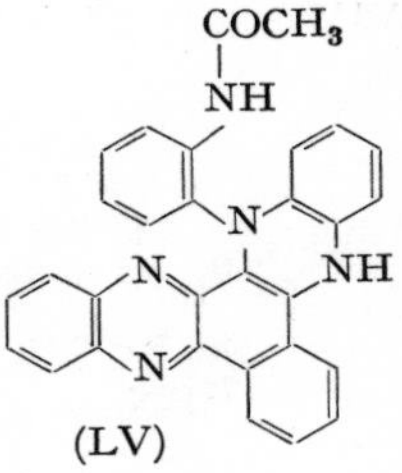   (LV)

Oxidation gave L, and the presence of a primary amino group was shown by the formation of an alkali-soluble tosyl derivative, orange prisms, m.p. 228–229°. Acetylation with acetyl chloride in pyridine gave a normal N-acetyl derivative, presumably LV, as yellow needles, m.p. 250–252°, but with acetic anhydride the product was an anhydro-acetyl derivative, $C_{30}H_{19}N_5$, which formed pale yellow plates, m.p. 260°, to which they attributed structure LVI.

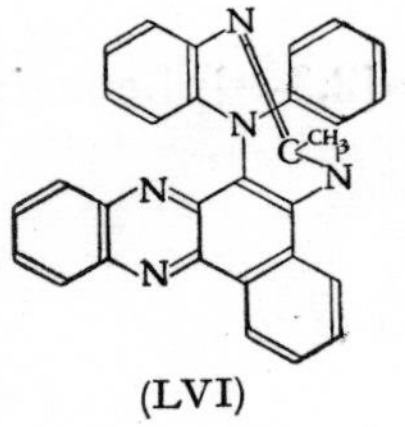

(LVI) 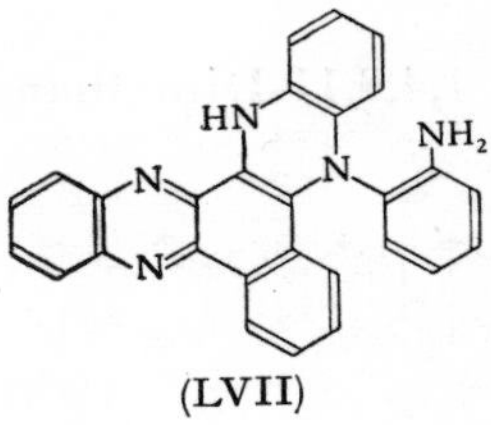   (LVII)

The alternative formulation (LVII) for the initial product was ruled out on spectroscopic considerations. The mechanism of formation appears to be based on the initial substitution of the chlorine atom by one molecule of o-phenylenediamine, 6-chloro-5-hydroxybenzo[a]-phenazine reacting in the keto form (LVIII), a fact which its deep-red color supports, followed by either ring closure to L or reaction with a second molecule of *o*-phenylenediamine as shown in the accompanying reaction scheme.

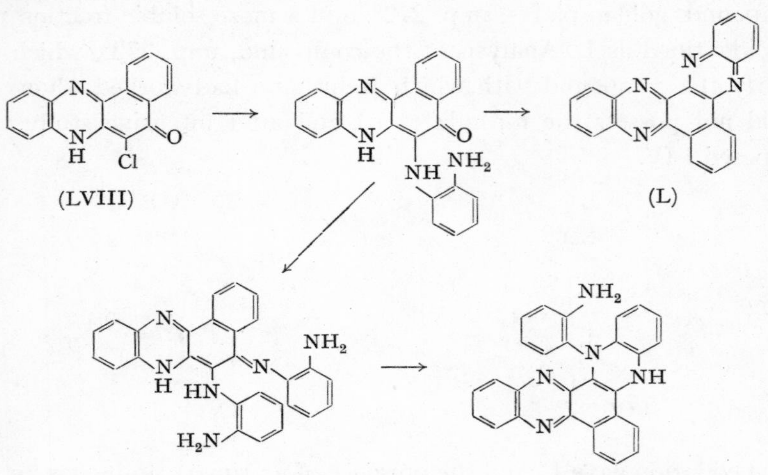

(LVIII)   (L)

(LIV)

This mechanism is supported by the fact that *o*-phenylenediamine reacts under similar conditions with 5-chloro-6-hydroxybenzo[*a*]-phenazine, which does not exist in the keto form (color, pale yellow), to yield only naphtho[1,2-*b*,3,4-*b'*]diquinoxaline (L). No trace of a compound resembling LIV could be detected.

8. 1,4,8,11-Dimethanoquinoxalo[2,3-*b*]phenazine

R. I. 3705

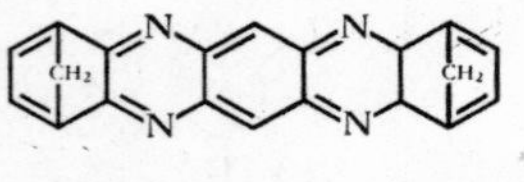

Heckendorn[42] claimed to have prepared an example (LIX) of this series by reacting two moles of camphorquinone with one mole of 1,2,4,5-tetraminobenzene. The initial product of the reaction, in which probably only one of the azine rings was closed, was allowed to stand with concentrated sulfuric acid when a colorless substance, m.p. 333–335°, was obtained. This was thought to be 1,8,15,15,16,16-hexamethyl-1,2,3,4,8,9,10,11-octahydro-1,4,8,11-dimethanoquinoxalo[2,3-*b*]-phenazine or the 1,11,15,15,16,16-hexamethyl isomer (**LIX**).

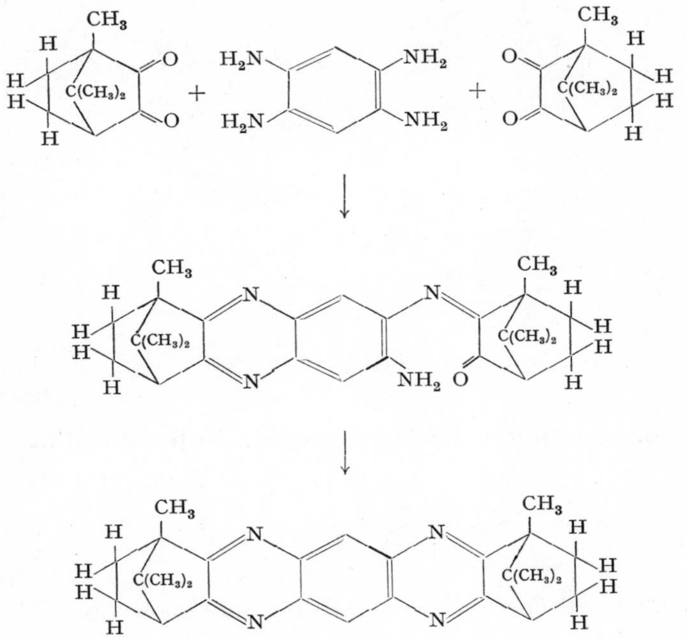

(LIX)

9. 1,4,9,12-Dimethanoquinoxalo[2,3-*a*]phenazine

R. I. 3706

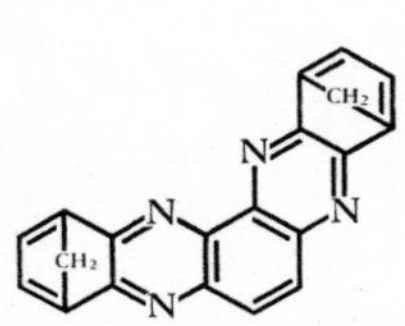

In a similar fashion to that described above (Section XVIII:8), Heckendorn[42] condensed camphorquinone with 1,2,3,4-tetramino-benzene and obtained a derivative of this system as colorless crystals, m.p. 245°. This may be one of three possible isomers, the structures of which the reader may deduce from that of one, **LX**.

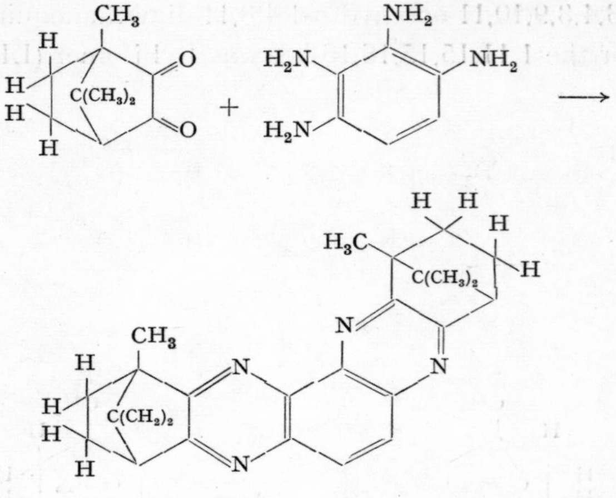

(LX)

10. Acenaphtho[1,2-b]quinoxalo[2,3-g]quinoxaline

R. I. 3740

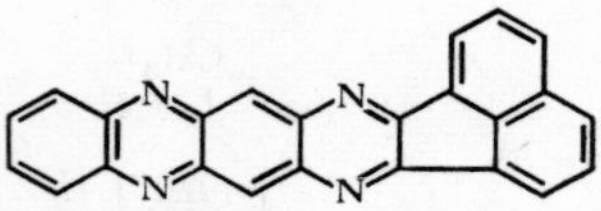

Ullmann and Cassirer[43] described the only known example of this series by condensing 1,2-acenaphthoquinone with 2,3-diaminophenazine. The product, acenaphtho[1,2-b]quinoxalo[2,3-g]quinoxaline (LXI), formed sparingly soluble red crystals, melting above 320°, and giving a red-brown color in concentrated sulfuric acid.

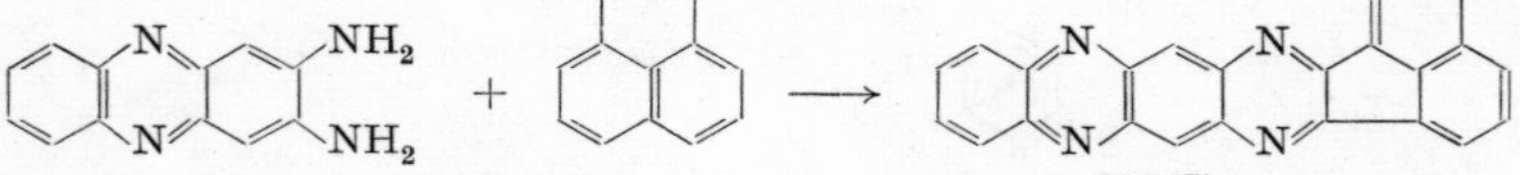

(LXI)

11. Diquinoxalo[2,3-b,2',3'-i]phenazine

5,7,9,14,16,18-Hexazaheptacene.
R. I. 3751

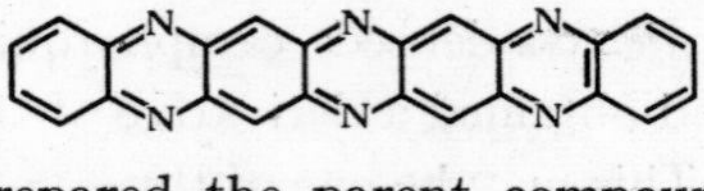

Dutt[4] claimed to have prepared the parent compound of this series by the reaction between 2,3-dihydroxyphenazine and 2,3-diaminophenazine in cold 30% oleum. The reader is referred to Section XVIII:3,A, in which the reaction product is discussed in detail, and in which Dutt's claim is disallowed.

12. Diquinoxalo[2,3-*a*,2′,3′-*c*]phenazine

R. I. 3752

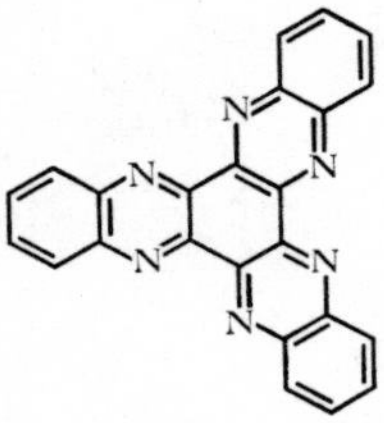

The first representative of this system to be prepared was the 2,8,14-trimethyl derivative (LXII) or an isomer of this that Nietzki and Kehrmann[44] obtained by condensing rhodizonic acid with 3,4-diaminotoluene and oxidizing the monoazine to 1,2,3,4-tetrahydro-7-methylphenazin-1,2,3,4-tetrone, which was then condensed with more of the diamine to yield LXII as sulfur-yellow needles.

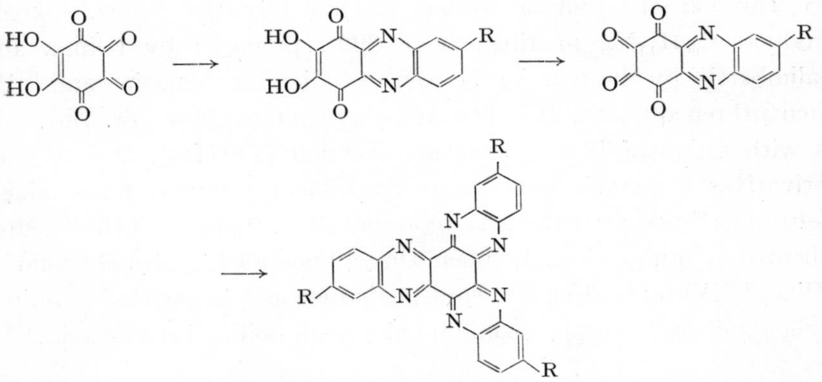

LXII (R=CH$_3$)
LXIII (R=H)

The following year, Nietzki and Schmidt[45] repeated the synthesis using *o*-phenylenediamine instead of the toluene derivative and obtained the parent substance (LXIII) as greenish-yellow needles.

Later, Kehrmann and Duret[28] described a substance obtained in very small yield in the condensation of rhodizonic acid with 2-amino-diphenylamine (see Section XVIII:4). This compound, which formed dark, greenish-blue needles, was not analyzed but was tentatively held to be 5,11,17-triphenyldiquinoxalo[2,3-*a*,2',3'-*c*]phenazinium trihydroxide (LXIV).

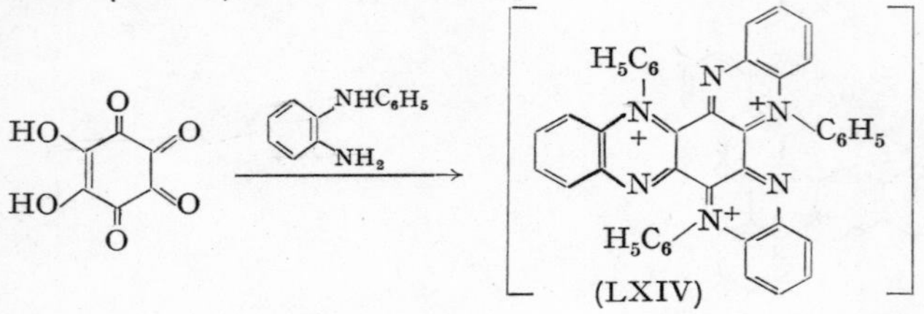

13. Dibenzo[*a*,*c*]quinoxalo[2,3-*i*]phenazine

R. I. 3753

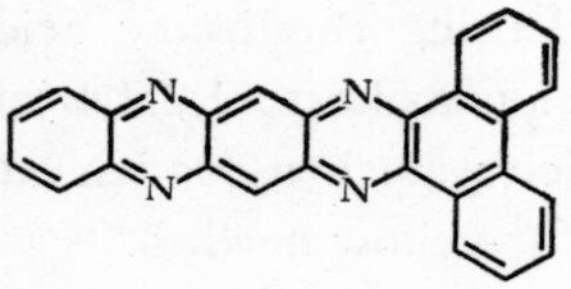

The parent aromatic system is probably the brownish-green product, $C_{26}H_{14}N_4$, melting above 300°, prepared by Crippa and Galimberti[46] by the reaction between 2,3-diaminophenazine and 9,10-phenanthrenequinone. It is not well-characterized however. But, just as with quinoxalo[2,3-*b*]phenazine (Section XVIII:3), the dihydro derivatives are stable and closely resemble the parent fluorindines. Kehrmann[47] prepared the first representative, 9-phenyl-9,16-dihydro-dibenzo[*a*,*c*]quinoxalo[2,3-*i*]phenazine (9-phenyl-1,2,3,4-dibenzofluor-indine, LXV) by heating *o*-phenylenediamine and 12-amino-11-anilino-9-phenyldibenzo[*a*,*c*]phenazinium chloride in boiling benzoic acid. The

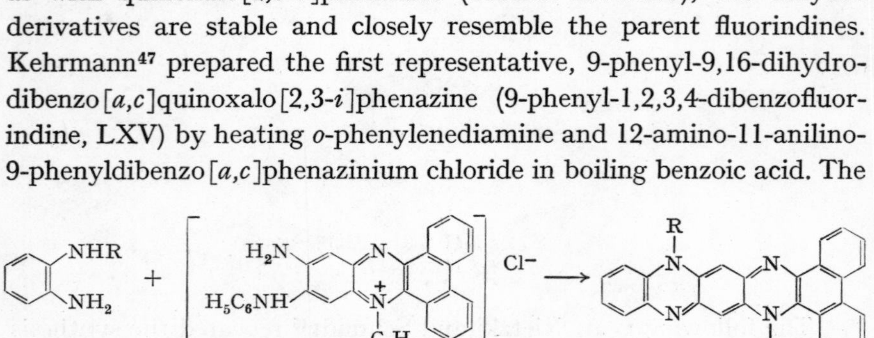

LXV (R=H)
LXVI (R=C_6H_5)

product formed minute flakes with a golden luster giving a bluish-green color in concentrated sulfuric acid. It gives violet-blue solutions in nitrobenzene without any marked fluorescence.[33]

Much later, Kehrmann and Schedler[33] repeated this preparation and extended it to the 9,16-diphenyl compound (LXVI) by using the 2-aminodiphenylamine in place of o-phenylenediamine. This compound (LXVI) formed dark violet coppery crystals giving a violet, non-fluorescent solution in hot benzene and a dirty-green color in concentrated sulfuric acid. They converted LXVI into a water-soluble quaternary salt by methylation with dimethyl sulfate in nitrobenzene at 150°. This dyed cotton mordanted with tannin in blue-green shades of moderate light-fastness, but does not appear to have had any commercial application.

14. 7,9,16,18-Tetrazadibenzo[a,n]pentacene

R. I. 3754

There are a number of dihydro compounds of the fluorindine type recorded for this series. In many cases the reactions are ambiguous and the products can equally well be derivatives of 7,9,16,18-tetrazadibenzo[a,l]pentacene, a ring system not listed in *The Ring Index*.

Nietzki and Vollenbruck[32] prepared 7,16-dihydro-7,9,16,18-tetrazadibenzo[a,n]pentacene (LXVII) by reacting 1,5-dichloro-2,4-dinitrobenzene with two parts of 1,2-diaminonaphthalene, reducing the product and then cyclizing to LXVII by oxidation with air or ferric chloride in hot aqueous hydrochloric acid. The synthesis is not unambiguous, however, and the product could also be either LXVIII or LXIX. The free base gives red solutions, while those of the salt are blue. They are non-fluorescent.

A similar product, which may be any of the three possible isomers mentioned above, was obtained by Kehrmann and Schedler[33] by the condensation of 1,2-diaminonaphthalene with 9,10-dihydroxybenzo-[a]phenazine in boiling benzoic acid. The base, brownish-violet crystals, which could not be recrystallized without oxidation to a brown compound thought to be the azine, gave a crystalline hydrochloride with a bluish metallic luster. Kehrmann and Logoz[34] isolated

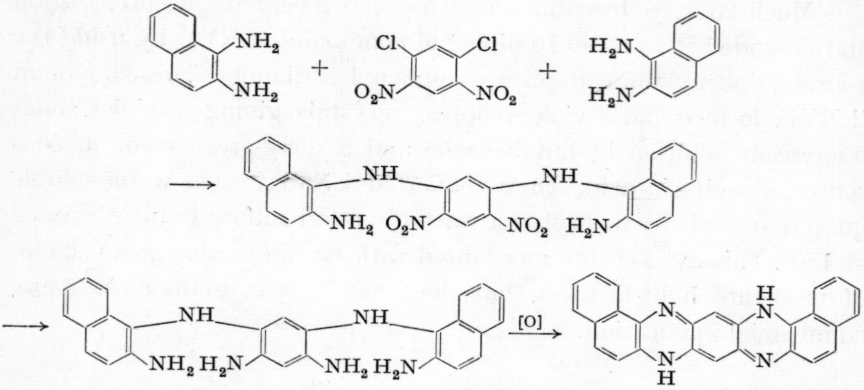

(LXVII)

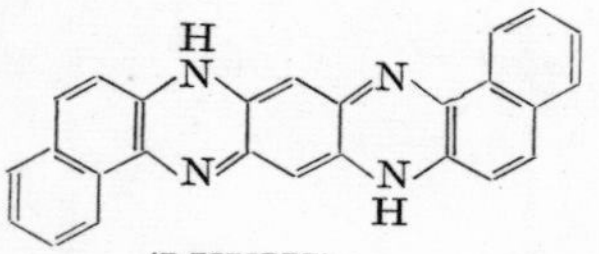

(LXVIII)

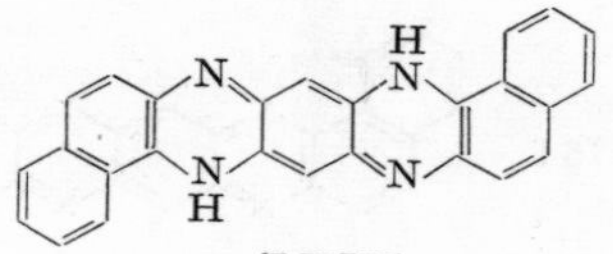

(LXIX)

the azine as red-brown crystals, readily reduced by stannous chloride to the dibenzofluorindine (LXVII–LXIX). They also obtained the 5-acetamido derivative as violet-blue crystals that also were oxidized in solution, probably to the azine although, in this case, the azine was not isolated. The 5,11-(or 5,14)-diacetamido derivative of LXVII–LXIX was described by Kehrmann and Collaud.[36]

These observations on the lack of stability of the fluorindines when benzo residues are fused in an angular position recalls the fact that, whereas dibenzo[b,i]phenazine is unknown, dibenzo[a,i]phenazine may be prepared (Chapter XV:4 and 6) and is a further example of the increased stability of linear dihydroazines over their angular isomers.

Fischer and Römer[35] noted that the condensation of 1,2-diaminonaphthalene and 10-aminoisorosindone yielded a green dye which they stated was of the fluorindine type, although they did not characterize it apart from noting it was non-fluorescent. Much later, Kehrmann and

Logoz[34] condensed 1,2-diaminonaphthalene with 10-hydroxyrosindone and obtained a product which they showed was either 7-phenyl-7,16-dihydro-7,9,16,18-tetrazadibenzo[a,n]pentacene (LXX) or 7-phenyl-7,16-dihydro-7,9,16,18-tetrazadibenzo[a,l]pentacene (LXXI). The same product was formed in very poor yield from 2-anilino-1-naphthylamine and 9,10-dihydroxybenzo[a]phenazine. It gave dark greenish-blue crystals of the hydrochloride and an inky black color with concentrated sulfuric acid.

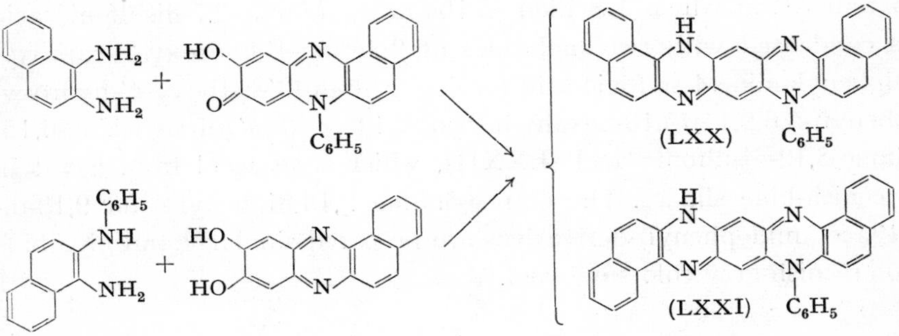

Kehrmann and Collaud[36] described the 11- or 14-acetamido derivative of LXX or LXXI, respectively. The compounds prepared in this series are listed in Table LI.

TABLE LI. 7,9,16,18-Tetrazadibenzo[a,n]pentacenes or the Corresponding [a,l] Isomers

Substituents	Appearance	Color with H_2SO_4	Color of solutions	Ref.
None	Red-brown crystals			34
7,16-Dihydro-	Brownish-violet crystals	Blue	Red	32–34
5-Acetamido-7,16-dihydro-	Violet-blue crystals	Green	Blue	34
5,11-Diacetamido-7,16-dihydro-	Red-brown crystals	Violet-blue		36
7-Phenyl-7,16-dihydro-	Red-violet crystals	Inky black		34, 35
11-Acetamido-7-phenyl-7,16-dihydro-	Violet-black needles	Green	Violet	36

15. Benzo[1,2-a,4,5-a']diphenazine

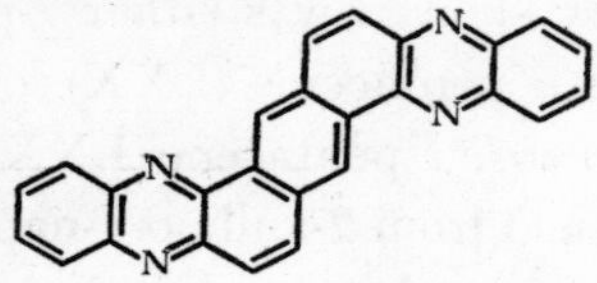

R. I. 3755

Representatives of this system have been described as potential vat dyes in which the anthraquinone and dihydroazine functions of indanthrone are interchanged. For example, a process has been patented[48] in which 1,6-diiodo-5,10-anthraquinone-2,7-disulfonic acid is condensed with two molecules of 2-amino-4'-hydroxy-3'-carboxy-diphenylamine-4-sulfonic acid to yield 9,18-di-(3'-carboxy-4'-hydroxy-phenyl)-5,6,9,14,15,18-hexahydrobenzo[1,2-a,4,5-a']diphenazine-6,15-dione-3,12-disulfonic acid (LXXII), which dyes wool from a vat in greenish-blue shades. The corresponding 9,18-diphenyl- and 9,18-di-(4'-acetamidophenyl)-derivatives are prepared similarly and give blue to greenish-grey colors on wool.

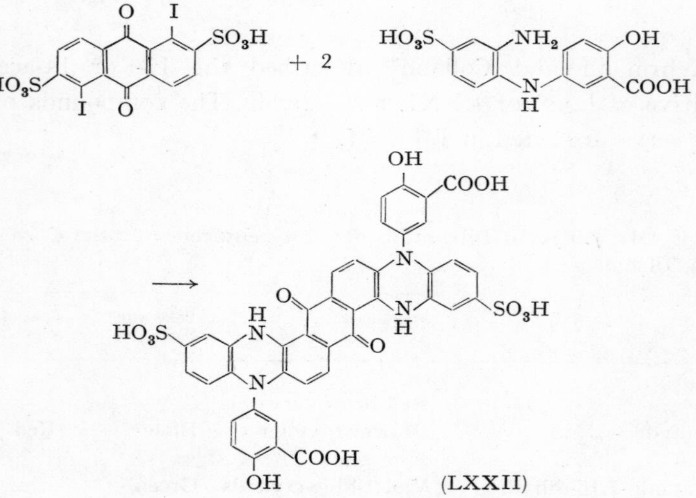

(LXXII)

Another patent[49] describes similar compounds that are prepared by condensing 1,6-dichloro-5,10-anthraquinones with o-nitroaniline or 1,6-diamino-5,10-anthraquinones with o-chloronitrobenzene, the condensations being effected by heating in an inert solvent in the presence of an acid-absorbing agent and a copper catalyst. The intermediates so obtained are then reduced with alcoholic sodium sulfide to 5,6,9,14,15,18-hexahydrobenzo[1,2-a,4,5-a']diphenazine-6,15-diones (LXXIII) and these may in turn be oxidized to the 6,15-dihydro-6,15-diones (LXXIV).

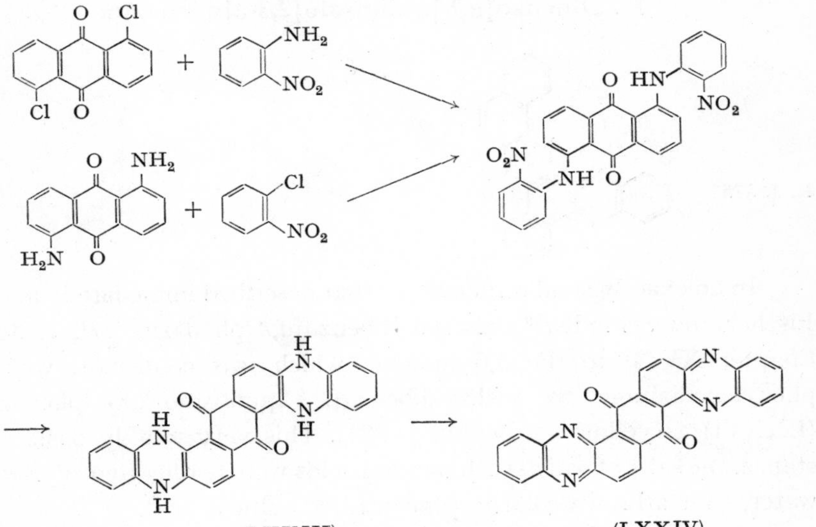

(LXXIII)   (LXXIV)

16. Dibenzo[c,h]quinoxalo[2,3-a]phenazine

R. I. 3756

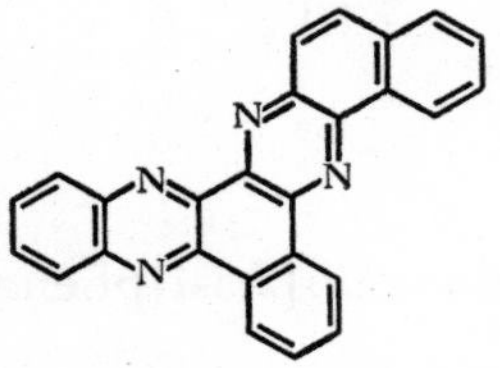

The parent ring system (LXXV) was prepared by Fischer and Schindler[50] by oxidizing dibenzo[a,j]phenazine (R. I. 3253, Chapter

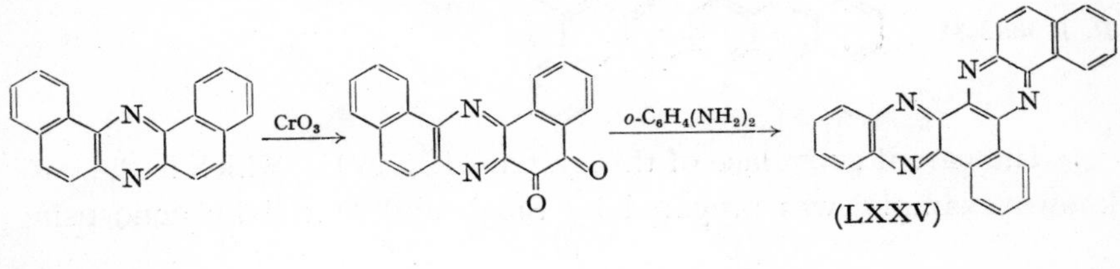

(LXXV)

XV:5) to the 5,6-quinone, which yielded LXXV by condensation with
o-phenylenediamine. Dibenzo[c,h]quinoxalo[2,3-a]phenazine formed
dark yellow needles from pyridine and gave a blood-red coloration with
concentrated sulfuric acid.

17. Dibenzo[a,h]quinoxalo[2,3-c]phenazine

R. I. 3757

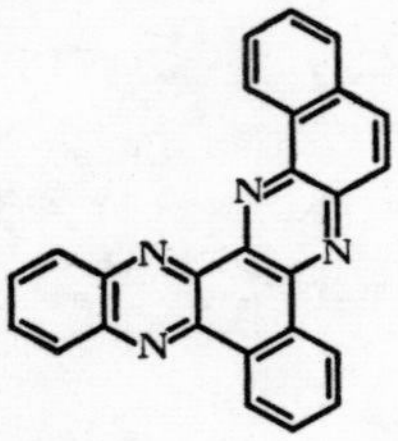

In an exactly similar manner to that described immediately above,
Fischer and Schindler[50] oxidized dibenzo[a,h]phenazine (R. I. 3254,
Chapter XV:3) to the 5,6-quinone, which was condensed with o-
phenylenediamine to yield dibenzo[a,h]quinoxalo[2,3-c]phenazine
(LXXVI) as yellow needles, m.p. 284°. This very weakly basic substance, the salts of which with mineral acids were readily hydrolyzed by
water, gave a brown color in concentrated sulfuric acid.

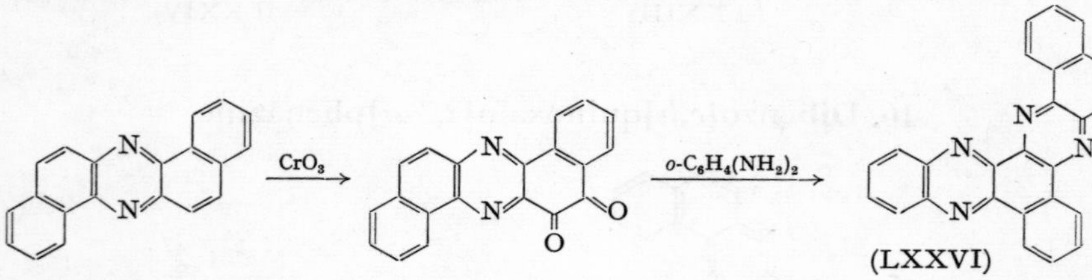

18. Benzo[a]naphtho[2,1-c]quinoxalo[2,3-i]phenazine

R. I. 3882 M

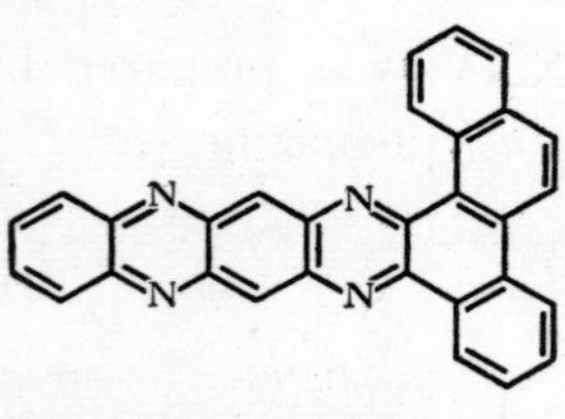

The parent substance of this system (LXXVII), which is the only
known example, was prepared by Singh and Dutt[51] by condensing

2,3-diaminophenazine with 5,6-chrysenequinone. It forms almost black crystals, which melt above 300°.

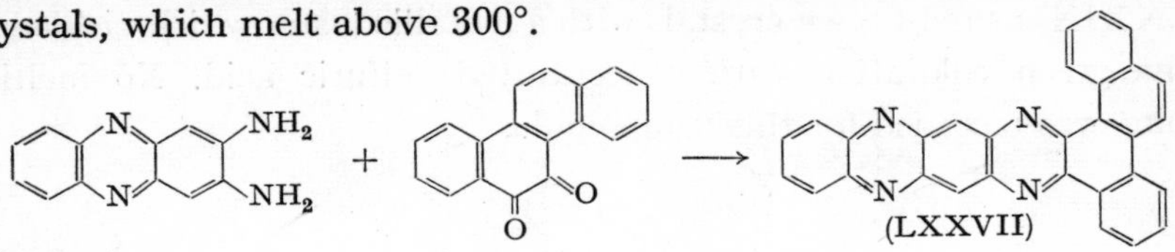

(LXXVII)

19. Dibenzo[c,c']benzo[1,2-a,4,3-a']diphenazine

R. I. 3926

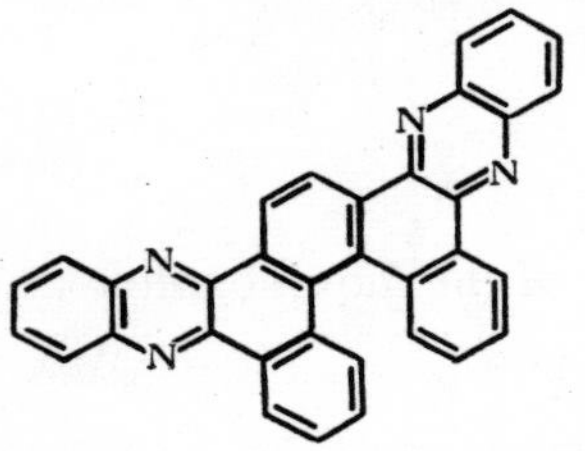

In the course of studies of carcinogenic polycyclic hydrocarbons, Cook[52] oxidized dibenzo[c,g]phenanthrene-2,5-dicarboxylic acid to the 1,2,5,6-di-o-quinone, which with o-phenylenediamine yielded dibenzo-[c,c']benzo[1,2-a,4,3-a']diphenazine (LXXVIII). This formed microscopic yellow needles, melting above 360°.

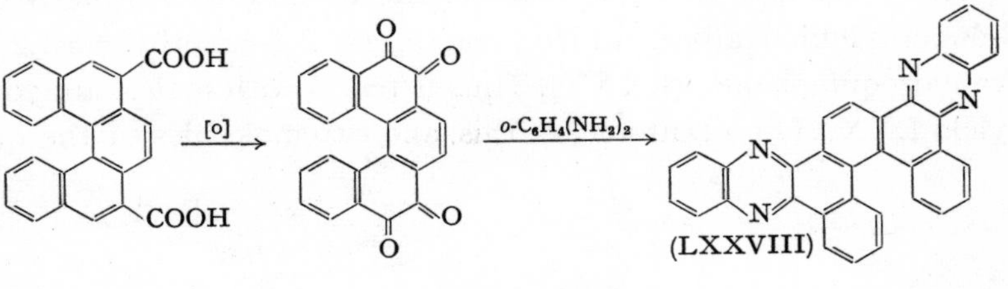

(LXXVIII)

20. Perylo[2,3-b,10,11-b']diquinoxaline

R. I. 3927

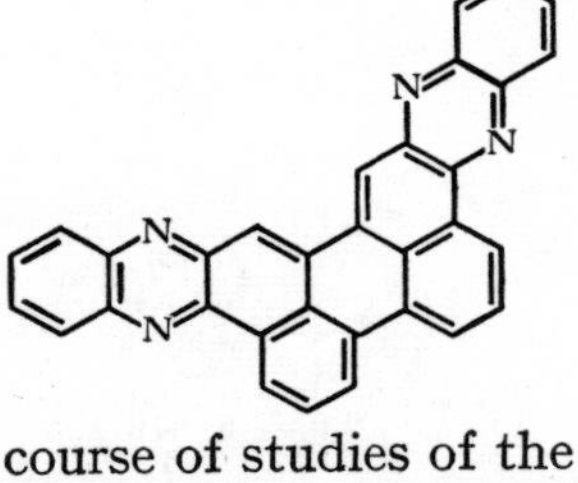

In the course of studies of the chemistry of perylene, Zincke and his colleagues[53] heated 2,11-dihydroxyperylene-3,10-quinone with *o*-phenylenediamine and obtained the parent aromatic ring system (LXXIX) as red-brown crystals with a metallic luster which yielded an olive-green coloration with concentrated sulfuric acid. No melting point was recorded for this compound.

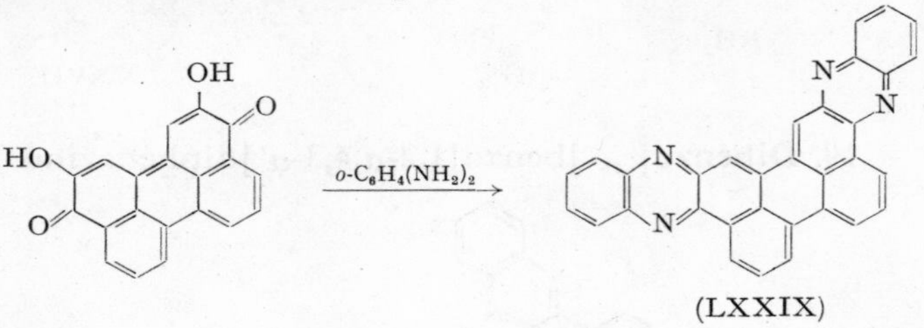

$o\text{-}C_6H_4(NH_2)_2 \longrightarrow$

(LXXIX)

There remain two ring systems of the diquinoxaline type that have not been listed in *The Ring Index*.

21. Diquinoxalo[2,3-*b*,2′,3′-*i*]anthracene

5,9,14,18-Tetrazaheptacene. Benzo-
[1,2-*b*,4,5-*b*′]diphenazine

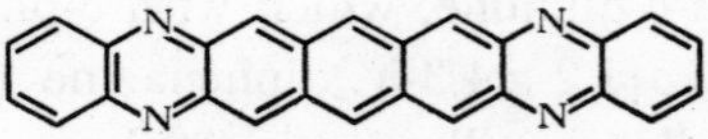

Schönberg and Mostafa[54] studied the Diels-Alder synthesis with 2,3-dimethylquinoxaline, which reacts as 2,3-dimethylene-1,2,3,4-tetrahydroquinoxaline (LXXX). Thus it reacts with maleic anhydride to yield LXXXI or a tautomer of this, and two molecules of the quin-

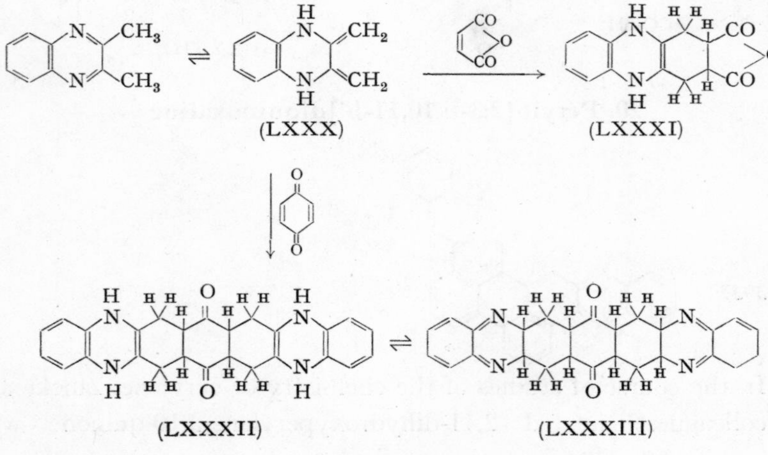

(LXXX)   (LXXXI)

(LXXXII)   (LXXXIII)

oxaline readily react with one of 1,4-benzoquinone to yield 5,6,6a,7,7a-8,9,14,15,15a,16,16a,17,18-tetradecahydrodiquinoxalo [2,3-b,2′,3′-i]-anthracene-7,16-dione (LXXXII) or a tautomer (LXXXIII), which forms colorless needles, m.p. 190°.

The maleic anhydride adduct (LXXXI), which properly does not belong in this section, forms slightly greenish-yellow crystals melting above 305°. Owing to its anhydride function, it is soluble in dilute alkali on warming but is reprecipitated by acidification (see Chapter XIX:65).

22. Diquinoxalo[2,3-e,2′,3′-l]pyrene

Dibenzo[hi,uv]5,9,14,18-
tetrazahexacene

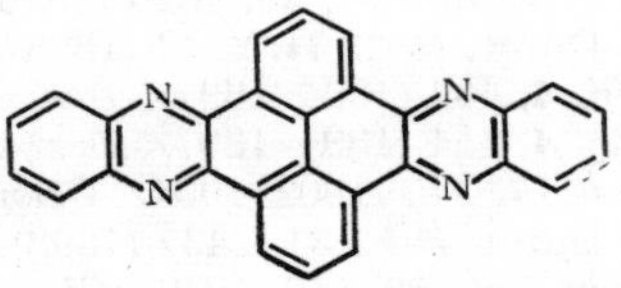

Vollmann and his colleagues,[55] in studying the chemistry of pyrene, oxidized this hydrocarbon to the 4,5,9,10-di-o-quinone (LXXXIV), which condensed with o-phenylenediamine to give a derivative forming bright yellow needles, melting above 420°. This was not analyzed, but did not vat and so was presumably the diazine, the parent compound of this structure (LXXXV).

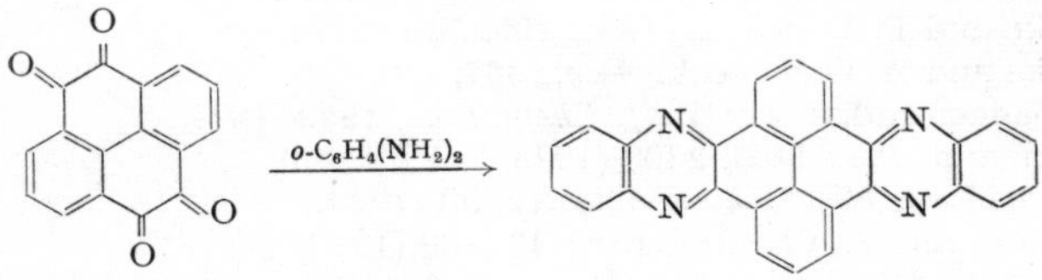

(LXXXIV)   (LXXXV)

References

1. O. Fischer and E. Hepp, *Ber.*, **23**, 841 (1890).
2. A. C. Sircar and P. K. De, *Quart. J. Indian Chem. Soc.*, **2**, 312 (1925); *Chem. Abstracts*, **20**, 1805 (1926); *Chem. Zentr.*, **1926**, I, 2697.
3. O. Fischer and C. Giesen, *Ber.*, **30**, 2489 (1897).
4. S. Dutt, *J. Chem. Soc.*, **1926**, 1171.
5. G. M. Badger and R. Pettit, *J. Chem. Soc.*, **1951**, 3211.
6. J. S. Morley, *J. Chem. Soc.*, **1952**, 4008.
7. O. Fischer and E. Hepp, *Ber.*, **23**, 2789 (1890).

8. O. Fischer and E. Hepp, *Ber.*, **28**, 293 (1895).
9. F. Ullmann and F. Mauthner, *Ber.*, **35**, 4302 (1902).
10. F. Kehrmann, *Ber.*, **27**, 3348 (1894).
11. R. Nietzki and J. Slaboszewicz, *Ber.*, **34**, 3727 (1901).
12. J. Leicester, *Ber.*, **23**, 2793 (1890).
13. F. Ullmann and F. Mauthner, *Ber.*, **36**, 4026 (1903).
14. R. Nietzki, *Ber.*, **28**, 1357 (1895).
15. F. Kehrmann and H. Bürgin, *Ber.*, **29**, 1246 (1896).
16. O. Fischer and E. Hepp, *Ber.*, **29**, 361 (1896).
17. O. Fischer and A. Dischinger, *Ber.*, **29**, 1602 (1896).
18. F. Kehrmann and B. Guggenheim, *Ber.*, **34**, 1217 (1901).
19. F. Kehrmann, *Ber.*, **28**, 1543 (1895).
20. O. N. Witt, *Ber.*, **20**, 1538 (1887).
21. O. Fischer and E. Hepp, *Z. Farben u. Textil Chem.*, **1**, 457 (1902); through *Chem. Zentr.*, **1902**, II, 902.
22. E. Wilberg, *Ber.*, **35**, 954 (1902).
23. F. Kehrmann and H. Bürgin, *Ber.*, **29**, 1820 (1896).
24. F. Kehrmann and A. Duret, *Ber.*, **31**, 2442 (1898).
25. Ger. Pat. 78,601; *Frdl.*, **4**, 452 (1894–1897); *Ber., Ref.*, **28**, 257 (1895).
26. Ger. Pat. 78,852; *Frdl.*, **4**, 454 (1894–1897); *Ber., Ref.*, **28**, 258 (1895).
27. Ger. Pat. 142,565; *Frdl.*, **7**, 345 (1902–1904); *Chem. Zentr.*, **1903**, II, 84.
28. F. Kehrmann and A. Duret, *Ber.*, **31**, 2437 (1898).
29. G. B. Crippa, *Gazz. chim. ital.*, **59**, 330 (1929); *Chem. Abstracts*, **24**, 121 (1930).
30. G. B. Crippa, P. Axerio and M. Long, *Gazz. chim. ital.*, **60**, 301 (1930); *Chem. Abstracts*, **24**, 4041 (1930).
31. G. B. Crippa and G. Perroncito, *Gazz. chim. ital.*, **64**, 91 (1934); *Chem. Abstracts*, **28**, 4733 (1934).
32. R. Nietzki and A. Vollenbruck, *Ber.*, **37**, 3887 (1904).
33. F. Kehrmann and J. A. Schedler, *Helv. Chim. Acta*, **8**, 3 (1925).
34. F. Kehrmann and R. Logoz, *Helv. Chim. Acta*, **10**, 339 (1927).
35. O. Fischer and F. Römer, *Ber.*, **40**, 3406 (1907).
36. F. Kehrmann and C. Collaud, *Helv. Chim. Acta*, **11**, 1028 (1928).
37. F. Kehrmann and A. Levy, *Ber.*, **31**, 3097 (1898).
38. T. Zincke and P. Wiegand, *Ann.*, **286**, 58 (1895).
39. T. Zincke and A. Ossenbeck, *Ann.*, **307**, 1 (1899).
40. G. M. Badger and R. Pettit, *J. Chem. Soc.*, **1952**, 1877.
41. F. Kehrmann, *Ber.*, **56 B**, 2390 (1923).
42. A. Heckendorn, *Helv. Chim. Acta*, **12**, 50 (1929).
43. F. Ullmann and E. Cassirer, *Ber.*, **43**, 439 (1910).
44. R. Nietzki and F. Kehrmann, *Ber.*, **20**, 322 (1887).
45. R. Nietzki and A. W. Schmidt, *Ber.*, **21**, 1227 (1888).
46. G. B. Crippa and P. Galimberti, *Gazz. chim. ital.*, **61**, 91 (1931); *Chem. Abstracts*, **25**, 3343 (1931).
47. F. Kehrmann, *Ber.*, **33**, 395 (1900).
48. Ger. Pat. 652,772; *Frdl.*, **24**, 814 (1937); *Chem. Abstracts*, **32**, 1487 (1937); see also Brit. Pat., 469,016; *Chem. Zentr.*, **1937**, II, 3238; *Chem. Abstracts*, **32**, 799 (1938).
49. Brit. Pat. 338,486; *Chem. Abstracts*, **25**, 2438 (1931); *Chem. Zentr.*, **1931**, I, 1684.
50. O. Fischer and E. Schindler, *Ber.*, **41**, 390 (1908).
51. K. M. P. Singh and S. Dutt, *Proc. Indian Acad. Sci.*, **8A**, 187 (1938); *Chem. Abstracts*, **33**, 1943 (1939).

52. J. W. Cook, *J. Chem. Soc.*, **1933,** 1592.
53. A. Zincke, F. Stimler and E. Reuss, *Monatsh.*, **64,** 415 (1934); *Chem. Abstracts*, **29,** 1414 (1935).
54. A. Schönberg and A. Mostafa, *J. Chem. Soc.*, **1943,** 654.
55. H. Vollmann, H. Becker, M. Corell and H. Streeck, *Ann.*, **531,** 1 (1937).
56. G. H. Cookson, *J. Chem. Soc.*, **1953,** 1328.

CHAPTER XIX

Phenazines Condensed with Other Heterocyclic Systems

Part II. Miscellaneous Systems

The very numerous miscellaneous systems in which phenazine and its polybenzo analogs are fused to heterocyclic systems other than the azine nucleus are in the main of little intrinsic interest. They will be dealt with in the order of their *Ring Index* enumeration.

1. Phenazino[2,3]-1,3,2-diaziodolium hydroxide. R. I. 2339

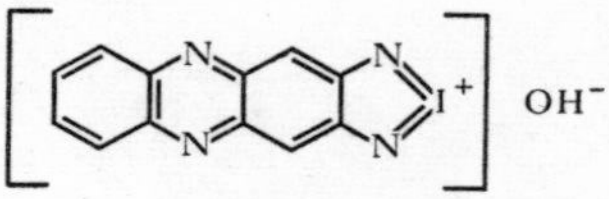

Hugel[1] discovered that *o*-diamines react with iodic acid in aqueous solution to yield heterocyclic compounds containing a quaternary iodine atom. In the course of his brief memoir he mentioned that 2,3-diaminophenazine gave such a compound, presumably of the above formula, although it was not characterized at all. It is probably a "mesoionic" structure[2] and therefore may be represented as I.

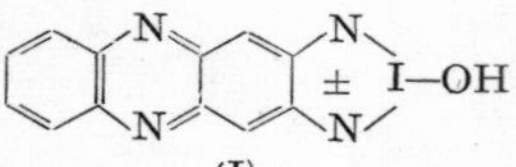

(I)

2. Phenazino [2,3-*d*]-1,3,2-oxazthiolium hydroxide. R. I. 2340

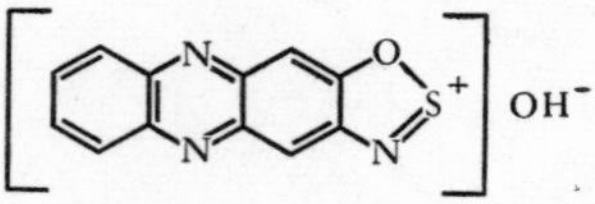

Sircar and Sen[3] reacted 2-amino-3-hydroxyphenazine with thionyl chloride and obtained a black, microscopically crystalline product

548

melting above 300°. It was sparingly soluble in water and gave a greenish-yellow color in concentrated sulfuric acid. They formulated this as the quaternary hydroxide (II). It is probably partially mesoionic.

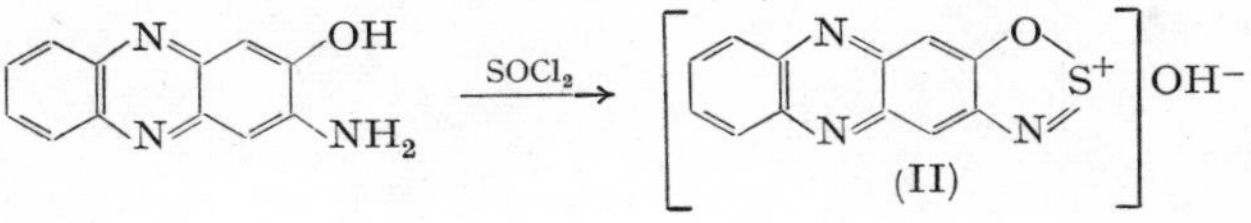

3. **[1,2,3]Thiadiazolo[4,5-*a*] phenazine. R. I. 2342**

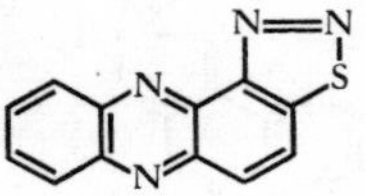

Fries and his coworkers[4] in the course of extensive studies of bicyclic heterocyclic compounds prepared 6,7-dichlorobenzothia-diazole-4,5-quinone (III) which reacted with *o*-phenylenediamine in acetic acid to give 4,5-dichloro[1,2,3]thiadiazolo[4,5-*a*]phenazine (IV) as greenish-yellow leaflets, m.p. 287°. This is the only example of this system.

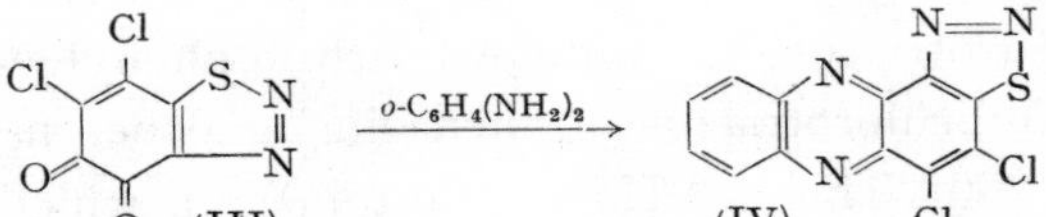

4. **1-Triazolo[*b*]phenazine. R. I. 2345**

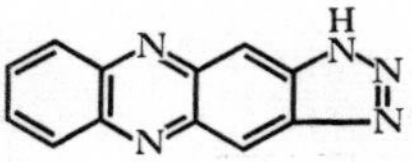

Karrer[5] prepared the first example of this system by treating 2,3-diaminophenazine-7-arsonic acid with sodium nitrite and dilute acetic acid. The product was a poorly characterized brown powder, probably V or a tautomer.

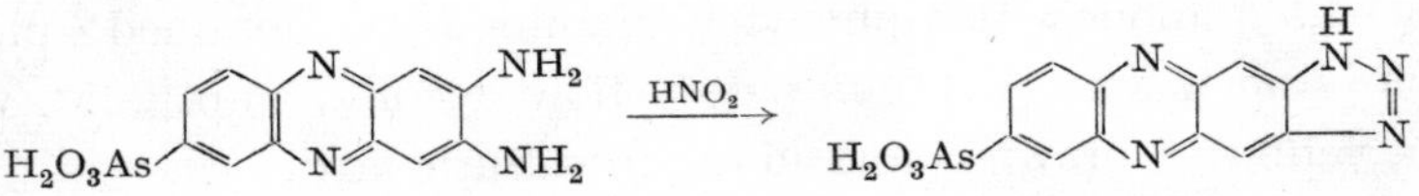

The parent system (VI) was obtained by Sircar and De[6] by di-azotization of 2,3-diaminophenazine. It formed golden-yellow needles, m.p. 280°, and gave a blood-red color in concentrated sulfuric acid.

Steigmann[7] has described the preparation of VI and its use as a photographic desensitizer and fog restrainer in photographic development,
in which it is very efficient.

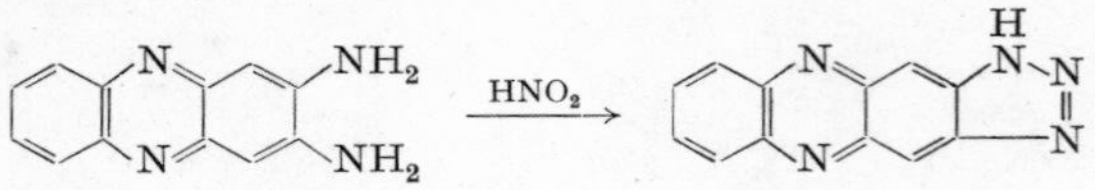

(VI)

5. 2-Triazolo[a]phenazine.
   R. I. 2346

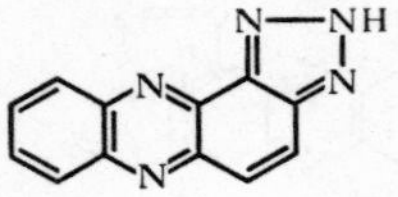

Zincke carried out an extensive study of the chemistry of benzotriazole and its derivatives. When the nitrogen atom is unsubstituted,
it is not possible to distinguish between the tautomeric forms. The same
is true of the triazolo[a]phenazine obtained by condensing o-phenylenediamine with a quinone of the benzotriazole series containing an
unsubstituted nitrogen atom. Zincke and his coworkers[8] condensed
4,5-dichlorobenzotriazole-6,7-quinone with o-phenylenediamine and
obtained a 4,5-dichlorotriazolo[a]phenazine as ocher needles, decomposing above 260°. This is VII or a tautomer, in which latter case it
properly belongs in Section XIX: 6 (see below).

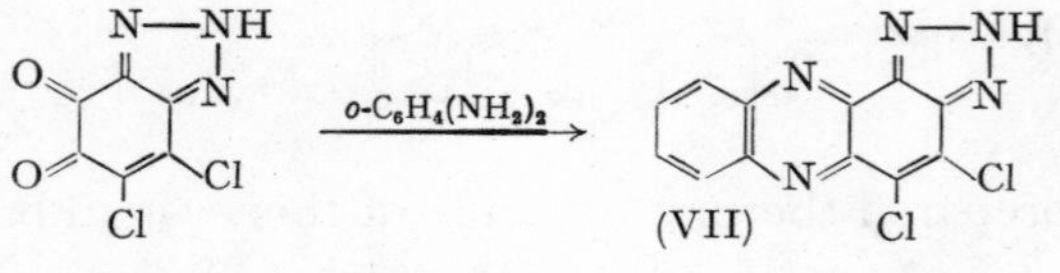

When the nitrogen atom is substituted there is no ambiguity about
the nature of the product. Fries and Roth[9] treated 2-phenylbenzo-
triazole-4,5-quinone with o-phenylenediamine and so obtained 2-phenyl-
triazolo[a]phenazine (VIII) as pale yellow needles, m.p. 225°, which
gave a yellowish-brown coloration with sulfuric acid.

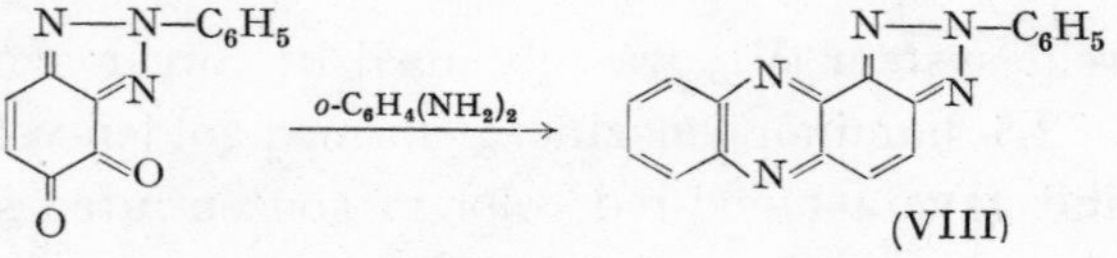

6. 3-Triazolo[a]phenazine.
   R. I. 2347

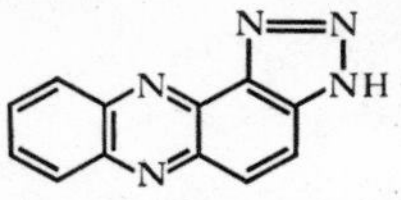

As has been pointed out in the previous section, there is no means of discriminating between triazolo[a]phenazines that are not substituted on one of the triazole nitrogen atoms, so that VII may belong in this section. Of the compounds about which there can be no dubiety, Zincke and Petermann[10] prepared the first examples. 6,7-Dichloro-1-phenylbenzotriazole-4,5-quinone was condensed with o-phenylenediamine in acetic acid and yielded 4,5-dichloro-3-phenyltriazolo[a]-phenazine (IX) as silky, colorless needles, melting above 250°.

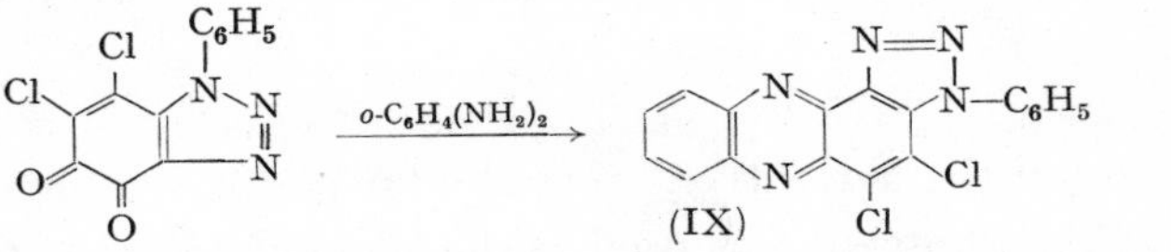

When the chlorohydroxyquinone (X) was used, the product (XI) was a bordeaux-red crystalline powder, decomposing above 200°, and, when 6,6-dichloro-4,5,6,7-tetrahydro-1-phenylbenzotriazole-4,5,7-trione (XII) was used, the product (XIII) formed gray, glistening needles, decomposing by 238°.

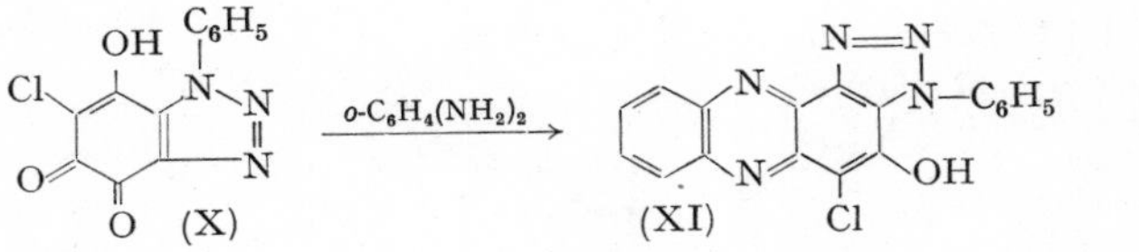

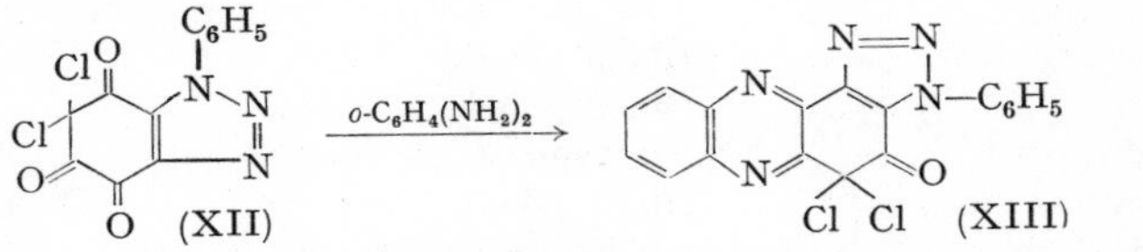

Fries and Empson[11] obtained the unsubstituted 3-phenyltriazolo-[a]phenazine (XIV) from the corresponding quinone as pale yellow needles, m.p. 250°.

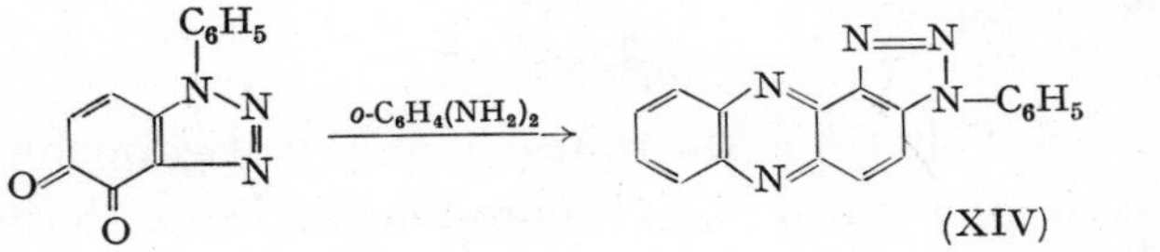

7. Oxazolo[*b*]phenazine.
   R. I. 2355

Sircar and Sen[3] prepared a number of derivatives of this system by reacting 2-amino-3-hydroxyphenazine with a series of carboxylic acids, anhydrides or acid chlorides. As an example, we may consider the formation of the parent heterocycle (XV) by the reaction of the aminohydroxyphenazine with anhydrous formic acid at 280–300° under pressure for a prolonged period. It formed a black, micro-crystalline powder, melting above 300°.

$$\xrightarrow{\text{HCOOH}}$$

(XV)

Nearly all the derivatives were similar poorly characterized compounds. When phosgene was used as the acid chloride, the product was 2-hydroxyoxazolo[*b*]phenazine and the 2-mercapto derivative was obtained from the aminohydroxyphenazine and potassium ethyl xanthate.

The derivatives prepared are listed in Table LII.

TABLE LII. Derivatives of
   Oxazolo[*b*]phenazine[3]

Substituent	Appearance	M.p. (°C.)
None	Black powder	> 300
2-Methyl-	Black powder	> 300
2-Phenyl-	Fine yellow needles	> 300
2-Hydroxy-	Black powder	> 300
2-Sulfhydryl-	Black powder	> 300

8. Thiazolo[4,5-*a*]phenazine.
   R. I. 2369

Fries and Wolter[12], in the course of an investigation of the benzo-thiazole series, obtained 6,7-dichloro-2-methylbenzothiazole-4,5-quinone. This reacted with *o*-phenylenediamine to yield 4,5-dichloro-2-methylthiazolo[4,5-*a*]phenazine (XVI) as crystals, m.p. 270°, but the product was not characterized by an analysis.

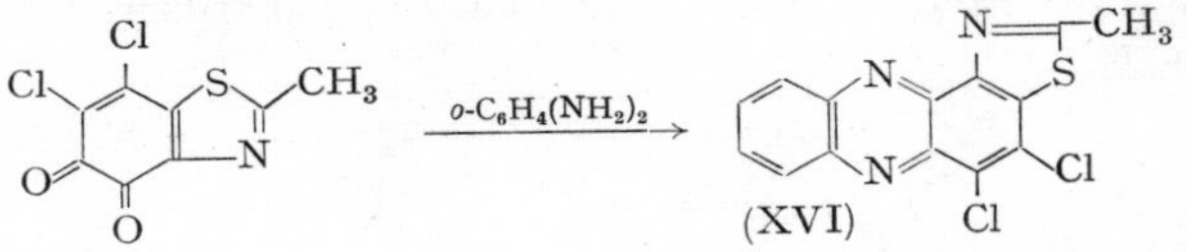

9. 1-Imidazo[*b*]phenazine.
R. I. 2381

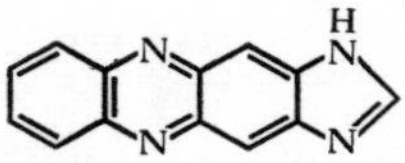

Representatives of this series were prepared by Sircar and De[6] by the reaction between 2,3-diaminophenazine and a series of aromatic aldehydes. As a typical example we may consider the reaction using benzaldehyde when the product, 2-phenyl-1-imidazo[*b*]phenazine (XVII) formed brown needles, melting above 290°.

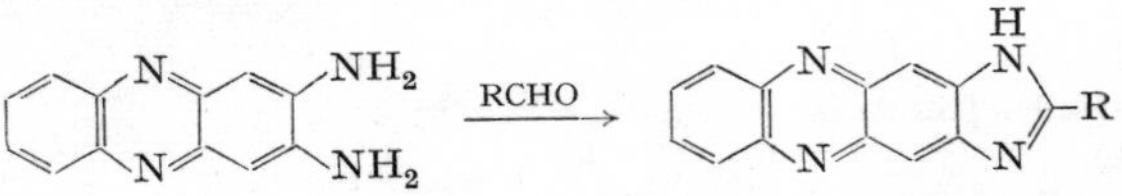

XVII (R=C₆H₅)

Crippa and Galimberti[13] obtained a derivative of this system by reacting 2,3-diaminophenazine with phthalic anhydride to obtain 12-isoindolo[2,1-*a*]phenazino[2,3-*d*]imidazol-12-one (XVIII, *R. I.* 3464; see Section XIX:29) and refluxing this with 30% potassium hydroxide solution when the amide link was hydrolyzed. Acidification of the deep

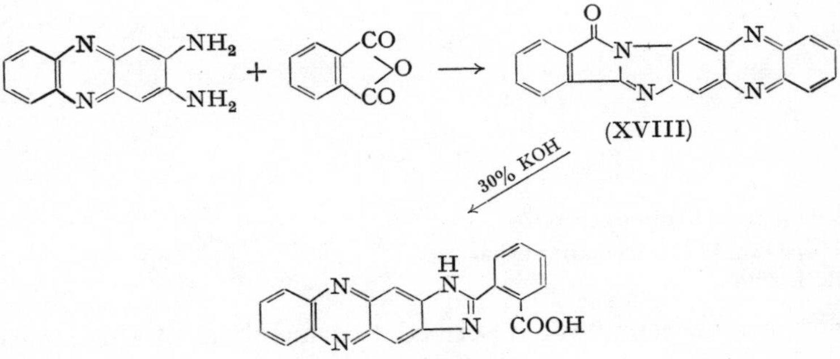

(XVIII)

(XIX)

red solution of the potassium salt liberated 2-(2'-carboxyphenyl)-1-imidazo[b]phenazine (XIX).

The initial stage of the reaction (to XVIII) had already been accomplished by Sircar and De.[6] The examples of this system are listed in Table LIII.

TABLE LIII. Derivatives of 1-Imidazo[b]phenazine

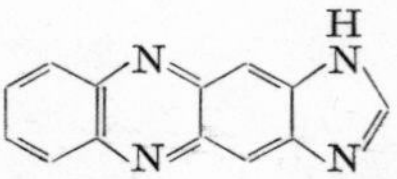

Substituent	Appearance	M.p. (°C.)	Ref.
2-Phenyl-	Brown needles	> 290	6
2-(3'-Nitrophenyl)-	Yellow needles	> 300	6
2-(4'-Methoxyphenyl)-	Orange-yellow plates	> 270	6
2-(4'-Dimethylaminophenyl)-	Chocolate-brown needles	> 290	6
2-(2'-Carboxyphenyl)-	Blackish crystals	> 300	13

10. 1-Pyrazolo[3,4-a]phenazine.
   R. I. 2382

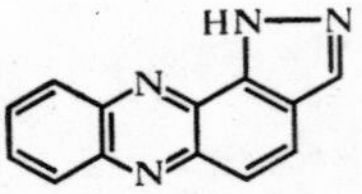

5-Chloro-4-hydroxy-1-pyrazolo[3,4-a]phenazine (XXII) was obtained by Fries and Weldert[14] by condensing o-phenylenediamine with a dichlorotriketo derivative (XXI) obtained by the chlorination of 5-chloro-6-hydroxyisoindazole-4,7-quinone (XX). The azine formed yellow needles, which did not melt below 300°. No other examples appear to be known.

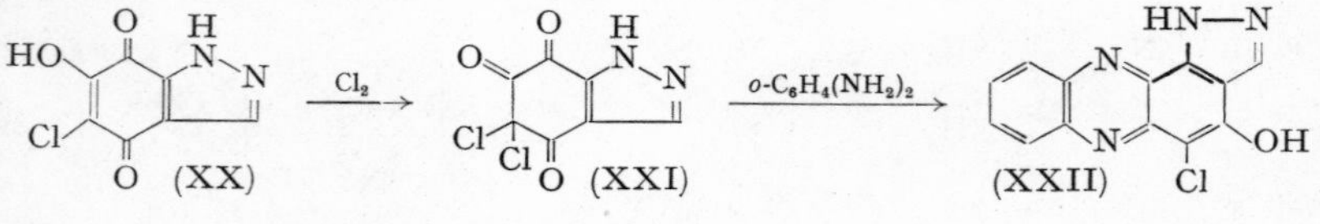

11. 2-p-Oxazino[b]phenazine.
   1(2)-Oxa-4,6,11-triazanaphthacene.
   R. I. 2606

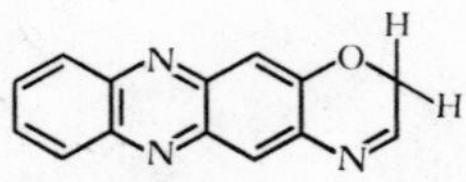

Sircar and Sen[3] have described two members of this series. By heating 2-amino-3-hydroxyphenazine with 1,2-dibromoethane (ethylene dibromide) they obtained 3,4-dihydro-2-*p*-oxazino[*b*]phenazine (**XXIII**) as a black crystalline powder, melting above 300°. Reaction of the same aminohydroxyphenazine with oxalyl chloride gave 3-hydroxy-2-*p*-oxazino[*b*]phenazin-2-one (**XXIV**). This formed a yellow crystalline powder, melting above 300° and soluble in alkali, for which reason it was given the hydroxy-keto structure shown.

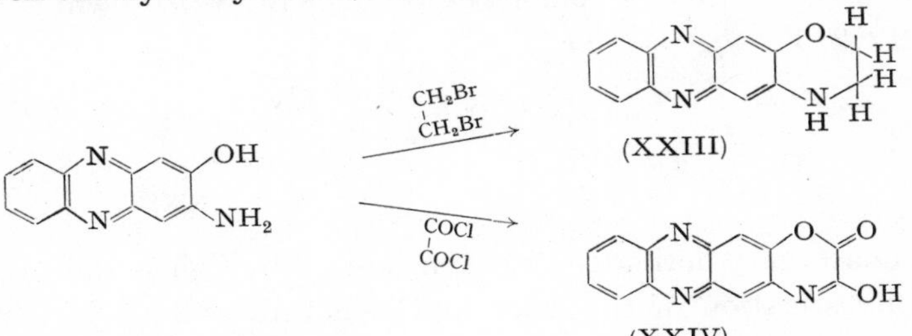

(XXIII)

(XXIV)

12. 7-*p*-Oxazino[*de*]phenazine.
    R. I. 2608

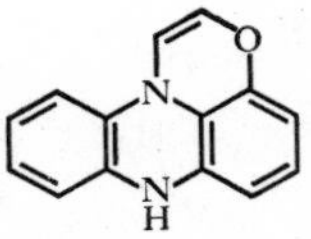

This system is represented by the compound prepared by Hille-mann[15] in his proof of the structure of pyocyanine (Chapter X:1). It had been shown that this bacterial pigment was an *N*-methylphenazinone or the betaine of a hydroxy-*N*-methylphenazinium compound, but the relative positions of the methyl group and oxygen atom had not been established. Hillemann reduced pyocyanine (**XXV**) to leuco-pyocyanine (**XXVI**) and this reacted with oxalyl chloride in chloroform solution in the presence of pyridine to yield 1,2-dihydro-7-methyl-*p*-oxazino[*de*]phenazine-1,2-dione (**XXVII**). This formed brown needles, m.p. 218–220° (dec.) after preliminary sintering. Its formation was the ultimate step in determining the constitution of the pigment.

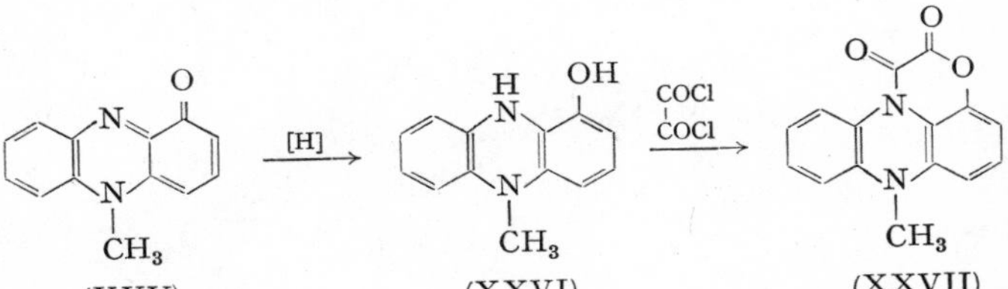

(XXV)   (XXVI)   (XXVII)

13. Pyrido[2,3-b]phenazine.
1,6,11-Triazanaphthacene.
R. I. 2654

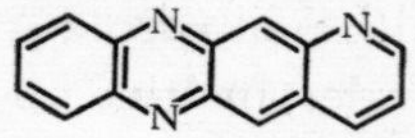

The parent of this ring system is unknown. Borsche and Barthen-heier[16] prepared 2-phenylpyrido[2,3-b]phenazine (XXVIII) by heating o-phenylenediamine with 6,7-dihydroxy-2-phenylquinoline in a sealed tube at 210–220° for 36 hours. The product formed brownish leaflets, m.p. 212–213°.

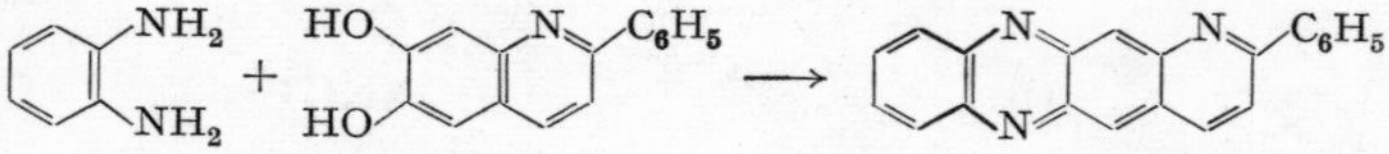

(XXVIII)

A quaternary derivative was synthesized by Cohen and Crabtree[17] in an investigation of the color and structure of dyes of the Azine Scarlet type. These workers condensed 1-methyl-6-nitroso-1,2,3,4-tetrahydroquinoline with "p-dimethylamino-o-toluidine" and formulated their product as XXIX.

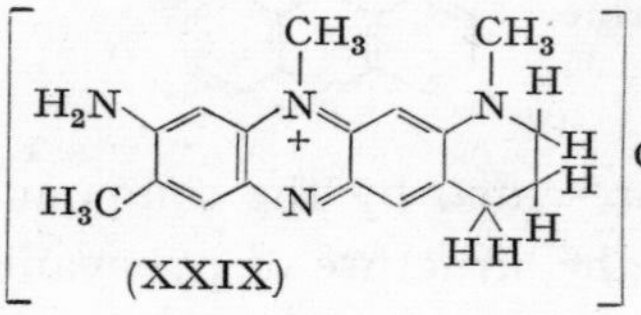

(XXIX)

From their paper, however, it is clear that this is incorrect. The "p-dimethylamino-o-toluidine" was prepared by coupling diazotized sulfanilic acid with 2-dimethylaminotoluene and splitting the azo derivative by reduction, so that the diamine was in all probability

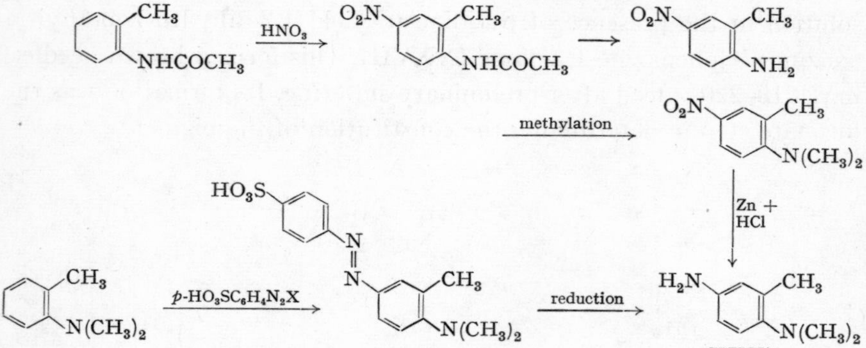

(XXX)

XXX, a view upheld by an alternative synthesis due to Bernthsen.[18] This consists in the nitration of 2-acetamidotoluene, hydrolysis of the acetyl group, methylation and finally reduction of the nitro group.

Consequently the reaction between the diamine and 1-methyl-6-nitroso-1,2,3,4-tetrahydroquinoline will yield XXXI.

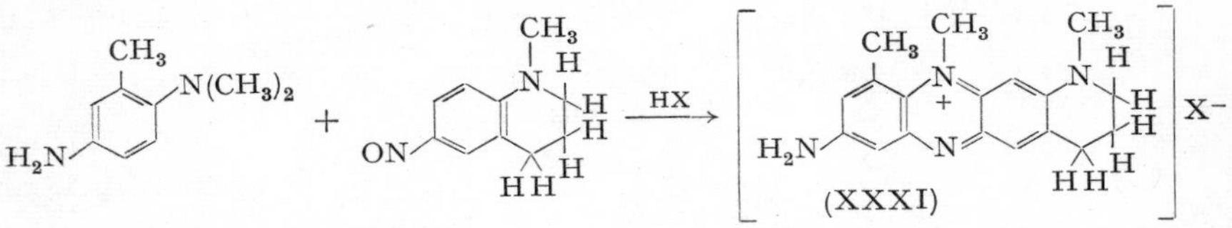

The dye salt formed a green iridescent mass when precipitated from the reaction mixture and dissolved in water to yield a magenta solution.

The above discrepancies have been pointed out on pages 43–44 of *Six-Membered Heterocyclic Nitrogen Compounds with Four Condensed Rings* by C. F. H. Allen and associates, published in this series, but in error the incorrect formula and chemical name were given for the product (XXXI). We wish, with Dr. Allen's permission, to correct that error here.

14. Pyrido[3,2-*a*]phenazine.
    R. I. 2656

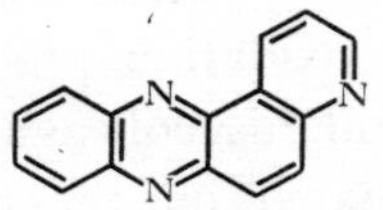

Representatives of this system were synthesized by Zincke and Wiederhold.[19] 5,6-Dichloropyrido[3,2-*a*]phenazine (XXXII) was obtained by condensing 7,8-dichloroquinoline-5,6-quinone with *o*-phenylenediamine in methanolic acetic acid. It formed a yellow powder, m.p. 239–240°.

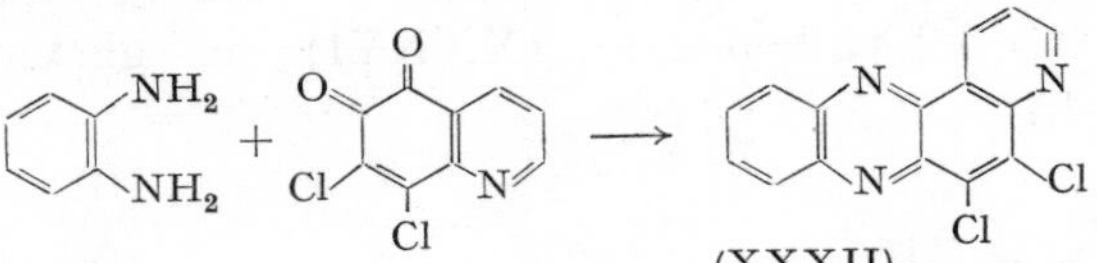

When the chlorohydroxyquinolinequinone (XXXIII) was used, the product, 6-chloro-5-hydroxypyrido[3,2-*a*]phenazine (XXXIV), formed yellow needles, decomposing above 200° without melting. It

yielded red salts with both acids and alkalis. Oxidation of a solution
of **XXXIV** in acetic acid by nitric acid yielded pyrido [3,2-*a*]phenazine-
5,6-quinone (**XXXV**), which formed yellow crystals, decomposing
above 270°. Analysis of **XXXV** indicated it was a monohydrate.

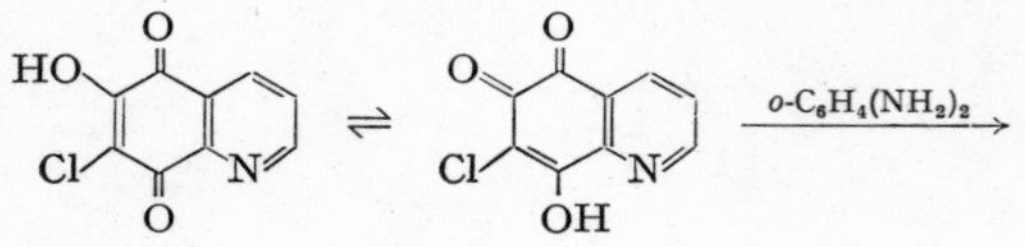

(XXXIII)

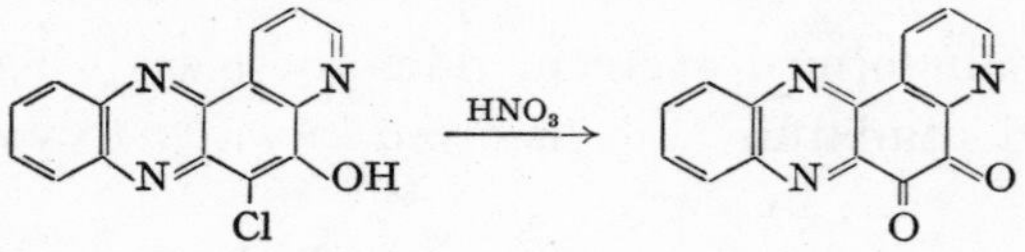

(XXXIV)   (XXXV)

15. 1-Pyrano[3,2-*a*]phenazine.
R. I. 2660 M (Modified)

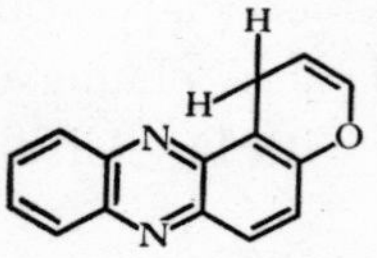

In the course of studies of the structure of tocopherol (Vitamin E),
attention was paid to the oxidation products known as α- and β-
Tocopherol Reds. Smith and his colleagues[20, 21] held these to be *o*-
quinones, a view substantiated by the reaction with *o*-phenylene-
diamine to give phenazine derivatives which, however, were oils. Model
chromans on oxidation behaved similarly; for example, 3,4-dihydro-
2,2,7,8 - tetramethyl-1,2 - benzopyran - 5,6 - quinone yielded crystalline
phenazines with *o*-phenylenediamine and 1,2-diamino-3,4,5,6-tetra-
methylbenzene, the former reagent giving 2,3-dihydro-3,3,5,6-tetra-
methyl-1-pyrano[3,2-*a*]phenazine (**XXXVI**) as glistening yellow
needles, m.p. 151–151.5°.

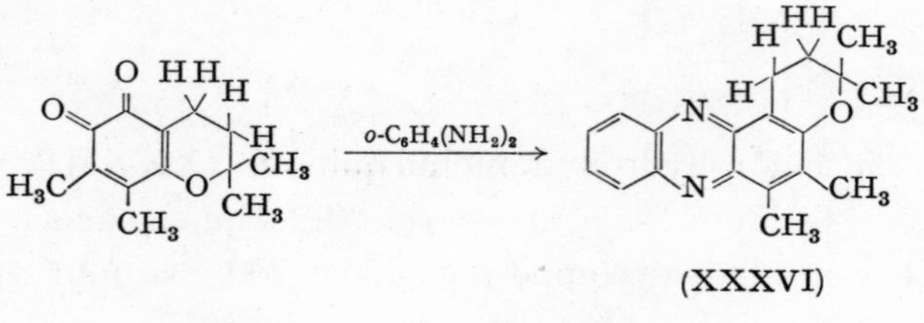

(XXXVI)

John and Emte[22] carried the investigation a stage further and showed that the tocopherol reds were isomerized by treatment with hot acids to yellow *p*-quinones, which did not react with *o*-phenylenediamine. On treatment with nitric acid, both the tocopherol reds and the model chroman compounds (**XXXVII** and **XXXVIII**) suffered oxidation and isomerization to yield hydroxy-*p*-quinones (**XXXIX** and **XL**). These reacted much more slowly with *o*-phenylenediamine to yield brownish-yellow crystalline products. These are either the 1-pyrano[3,2-*a*]phenazines (**XLI** and **XLII**) or the structural isomers of the otherwise unknown 4-pyrano[2,3-*a*]phenazine system (**XLIII** and **XLIV**).

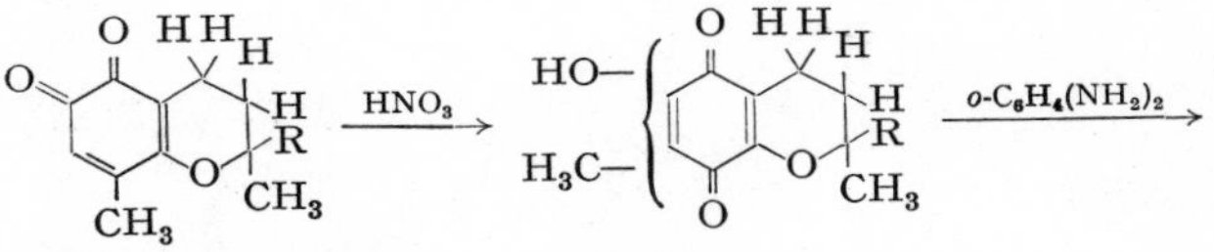

XXXVII (R=H)
XXXVIII (R=CH₃)

XXXIX (R=H)
XL (R=CH₃)

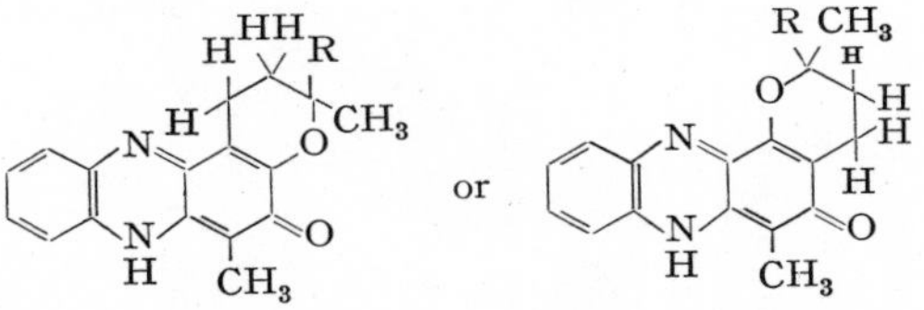

XLI (R=H)
XLII (R=CH₃)

or

XLIII (R=H)
XLIV (R=CH₃)

The derivatives of the 1-pyrano[3,2-*a*]phenazine system are listed in Table LIV.

16. 1-Benzo[*a*]triazolo[*c*]phenazine.
R. I. 3026

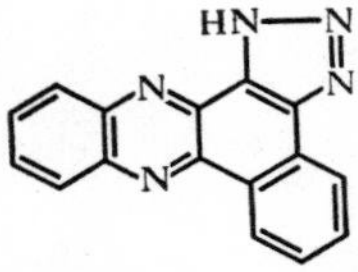

Only one example of this system is known, of which the position of the mobile hydrogen atom (see Section XIX:5,6) is fixed by substitution. Charrier and Beretta[23] oxidized 3-phenylnaphtho[1,2]triazole (**XLV**), obtained by the action of nitrous acid upon 2-anilino-1-

TABLE LIV. Derivatives of 2,3-Dihydro-1-pyrano[3,2-a]phenazine

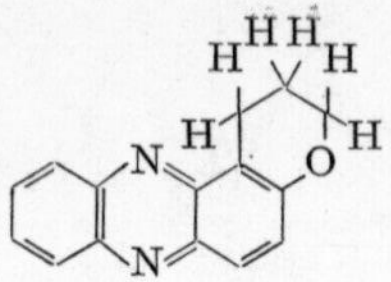

Substituents	Appearance	M.p. (°C.)	Remarks	Ref.
3,5,6-Trimethyl-	Yellow needles	180		22
3,3,5,6-Tetramethyl-	Glistening yellow needles	151–151.5	Green-yellow fluorescence in u.v.	20–22
3,3,5,6,8,9,10,11-Octamethyl-	Yellow crystals	204–205		21
3,5-Dimethyl-3(4′,8′,12′-trimethyl-tridecyl)- (β-Tocopherol red phenazine)	Yellow oil		λ_{max} 265, 365 mμ	22
3,5,6-Trimethyl-3(4′,8′,12′-trimethyl-tridecyl)- (α-Tocopherol red phenazine)	Yellow oil		λ_{max} 270, 365 mμ	20–22
3,6-Dimethyl-5(7H)-keto-*	Brownish-yellow needles	158		22
3,3,6-Trimethyl-5(7H)-keto-*	Brownish-yellow needles	142		22

* These structures are ambiguous. See XLI–XLIV in text.

naphthylamine, and reacted the 4,5-quinone (XLVI) so produced with
o-phenylenediamine. 1-Phenylbenzo[*a*]triazolo[*c*]phenazine (XLVII),
so prepared, formed bright yellow needles, m.p. 268°.

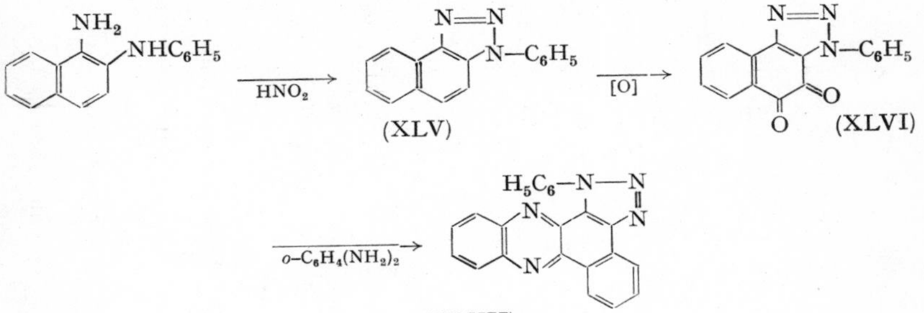

(XLV)   (XLVI)

(XLVII)

17. 2-Benzo[*a*]triazolo[*c*]phenazine.
   R. I. 3027

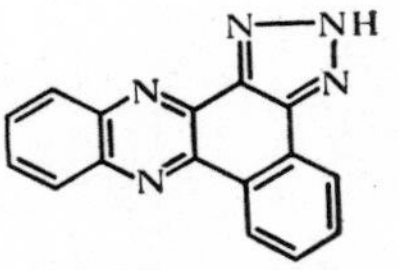

2-Phenylnaphtho[1,2]triazole-4,5-quinone (XLVIII), prepared by
the chromic acid oxidation of 1-benzeneazo-2-naphthylamine, was
reacted with 2-aminodiphenylamine hydrochloride by Charrier[24] and
Charrier and Manfredi.[25] The product, 2,8-diphenylbenzo[*a*]triazolo-
[*c*]phenazinium chloride (XLIX), or the 13-phenyl isomer, formed
reddish-yellow crystals, m.p. 238°, which dyed cotton mordanted with
tannin in yellowish-red shades.

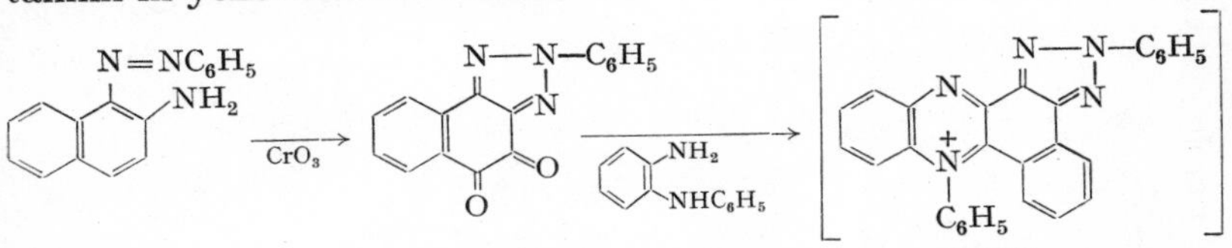

(XLVIII)   (XLIX)

Using other substituted 2-aminodiphenylamines, other dyes were
described. Gallotti and Ercoli[26] described 2-(2′,3′- and 4′-nitrophenyl)-
derivatives obtained from *o*-phenylenediamine and the corresponding
2-(nitrophenyl)naphtho[1,2]triazole-4,5-quinones and Charrier[27] recorded the properties of other 2-substituted phenyl derivatives in this
series, similarly synthesized. Table LV lists these compounds.

TABLE LV. 2-Benzo[a]triazolo[c]phenazines

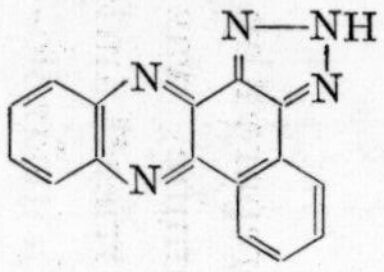

Substituents	Appearance	M.p. (°C.)	Remarks	Ref.
2-(2'-Nitrophenyl)-	Light yellow crystals	277–278		26
2-(3'-Nitrophenyl)-	Yellowish crystals	328		26
2-(4'-Nitrophenyl)-	Yellow crystals	312		26
2-(2'-Methylphenyl)-	Yellowish crystals	209–210		27
2-(3'-Methylphenyl)-	Light yellow crystals	251–252		27
2-(4'-Methylphenyl)-	Light yellow crystals	258		27
2-(4'-Bromophenyl)-	Light yellow crystals	306		27
2-(4'-Dibromomethylphenyl)-	Yellow crystals	282		27
2,8(or 2,13)-Diphenyl-	Chloride, reddish-yellow crystals	238	Dyes tannined cotton yellow-red	24, 25
8(or 13)-4''-Benzeneazophenyl-11-nitro-2-phenyl-	Chloride, brick-red	138	Dyes tannined cotton yellow-brown	25

18. 3-Benzo[a]triazolo[c]phenazine.
R. I. 3028

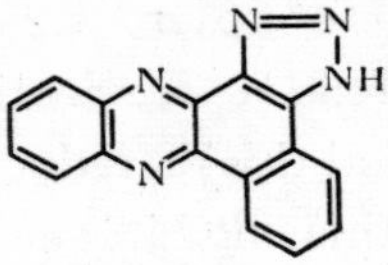

Zincke and Noack[28] prepared the parent ring system by oxidizing 1,2-diamino-3,4-dihydroxynaphthalene with nitric acid and condensing the 1-naphtho[1 2]triazole-4,5-quinone (L) with *o*-phenylenediamine. The product, 3-benzo[a]triazolo[c]phenazine (LI), formed small, fine bright yellow needles, which did not melt below 250°. There seems to be no reason why the compound should be given this structure rather than that of a tautomer such as 1-benzo[a]triazolo[c]phenazine (Section XIX:16).

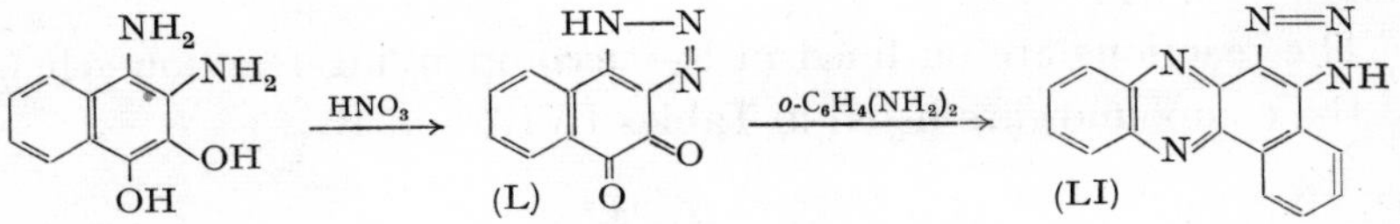

19. 5[1,2]Benzisothiazolo[4,3-ab]
phenazine. R. I. 3033

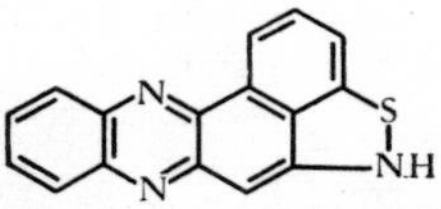

The members of this ring system are derived from naphthosultam (2-naphtho[1,8-*cd*]isothiazole-1,1-dioxide, *R. I.* 1546). Zincke[29] prepared the first member by reacting 3-hydroxy-4-naphthosultamquinone (4-hydroxy-5-naphtho[1,8-*cd*]isothiazole-1,1-dioxide-5-one, LII, *R. I.* 1548) with *o*-phenylenediamine to give 5[1,2]benzisothiazolo[4,3-*ab*]-phenazine-4,4-dioxide (LIII), which crystallized from acetic acid in dark red needles, melting above 260° with decomposition.

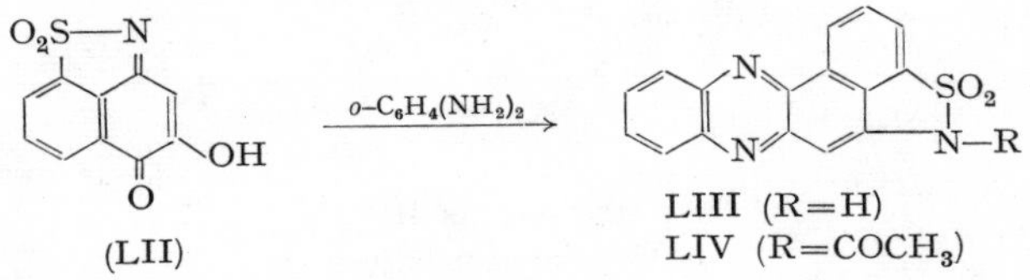

LIII (R=H)
LIV (R=COCH₃)

The *N*-acetyl derivative (LIV) formed yellowish needles, m.p. 270°. By condensing *o*-phenylenediamine with 3,3-dichloro-3,4-dihydro-5-naphth[1,8-*cd*]isothiazole-4,5-dione-1,1-dioxide (LV), Zincke obtained the corresponding 6,6-dichloro[1,2]benzisothiazolo[4,3-*ab*]phenazine-4,4-dioxide (LVI, *R. I.* 3034; see Section XIX:20) as reddish-white needles, m.p. 265–266°, and this on reduction with stannous chloride gave 6-chloro-5[1,2]benzisothiazolo[4,3-*ab*]phenazine-4,4-dioxide (LVII) as red-brown needles with a bronze luster, which decomposed above 290°. This compound was also one of the products from the reaction between LV and *o*-phenylenediamine. Oxidation of LVII with concentrated nitric acid gave 6[1,2]benzisothiazolo[4,3-*ab*]phenazin-6-one-4,4-dioxide (LVIII) as yellow-red plates, melting above 280°, and this upon stannous chloride reduction yielded 6-hydroxy-5[1,2]benzisothiazolo-[4,3-*ab*]phenazine-4,4-dioxide (LIX), small dark green plates, decomposing above 270°. The diacetyl derivative of LIX formed yellowish needles, m.p. 245–246°.

The reactions are outlined in the accompanying reaction scheme and the compounds are listed in Tables LVIA and B.

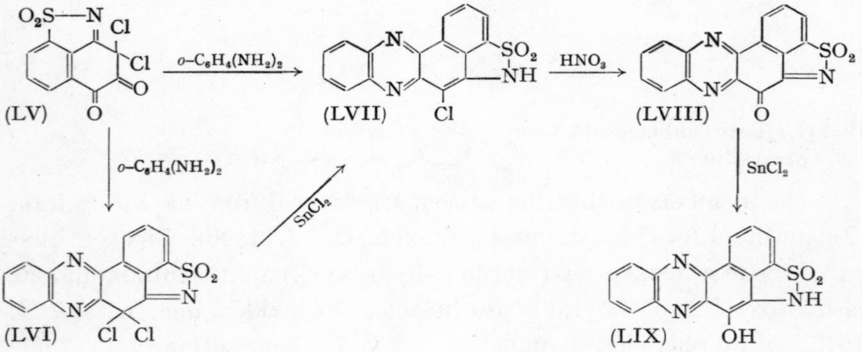

TABLE LVIA. 5[1,2]Benzoisothiazolo [4,3-*ab*]phenazine-4,4-dioxides[29]

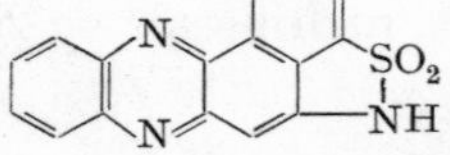

Substituent	Appearance	M.p. (°C.)
None	Dark red needles	> 260
5-Acetyl-	Yellowish needles	270
6-Chloro-	Red-brown needles, bronze luster	> 290
6-Hydroxy-	Dark green plates	> 270
5-Acetyl-6-acetoxy-	Yellowish needles	245–246

TABLE LVIB. 6[1,2]Benzoisothiazolo
[4,3-*ab*]phenazine-4,4-dioxides[29]

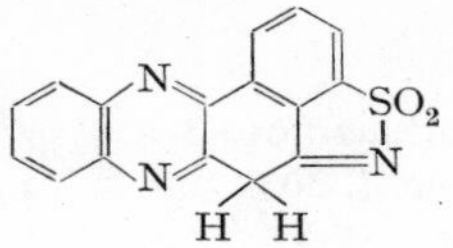

Substituent	Appearance	M.p. (°C.)
6,6-Dichloro-	Reddish-white needles	265–266
6-Keto-	Yellow-red plates	> 280

A number of patents deal with dyestuffs based upon this system. The parent compound (LIII) may be treated with 2,3-dichloro-1,4-naphthoquinone in the presence of sodium acetate in nitrobenzene, when a dye is obtained which forms brownish-yellow needles. This dyes cotton from a sodium dithionite vat in fast, clear greenish-yellow shades (see also Section XIX:76). 2,3-Dichloronaphthosultam-4-quinone (3,4-dichloro-5-naphth[1,8-*cd*]isothiazol-4-one-1,1-dioxide) may be substituted for the naphthoquinone in this process,[30] when a golden-yellow dye for cotton is obtained. Further reaction with LIII yields a brown-yellow vat dye.

Other patents deal with anhydro-bases of 7-phenyl-5[1,2]benziso-thiazolo[4,3-*ab*]phenazinium salts such as LX. These may be prepared by condensing, for example, 3-anilinonaphthosultam-6-sulfonic acid with 4-nitrosoaniline or by the joint oxidation of the naphthosultam compound with *p*-diamines, of which one amino group must be primary.[31,32]

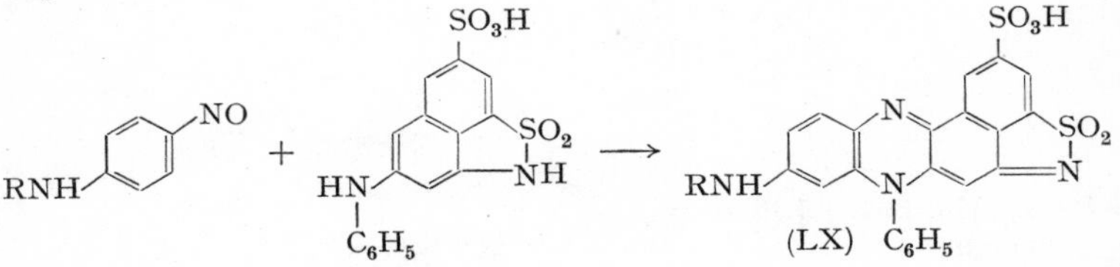

These modifications of the Wool Fast Blues (Chapter XIV:5,A) give reddish-violet or violet shades when dyed on wool from an acid bath.

20. 6[1,2]Benzisothiazolo[4,3-ab]
phenazine. R. I. 3034

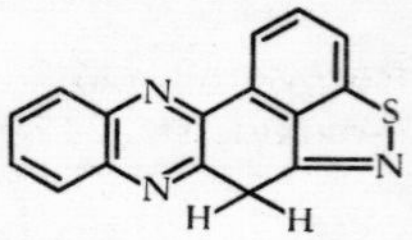

The examples of this ring system have already been discussed in the preceding section. They are LVI and LVIII and are included in Table LVI B.

21. Benzo[a]pyrazolo[4,3-c]
phenazine. R. I. 3037 R

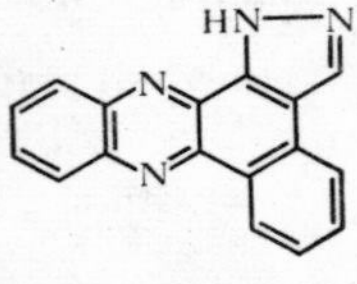

Corbellini, Capucci and Tommasini,[33] in their efforts to elucidate the dehydrating action of sulfuryl chloride upon cis-o-[4,5-(1′,2′-naphtho)-3-pyrazolyl]cinnamic acid (LXI) (see Section XIX:44), oxidized the methyl and ethyl esters of this to the corresponding o-quinones and condensed these with o-phenylenediamine. The products (LXII, m.p. 292°) and (LXIII, m.p. 265°) were both light yellow crystalline substances.

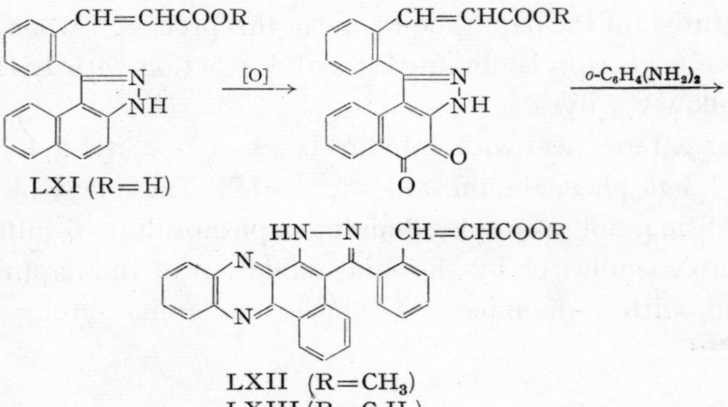

LXI (R=H)

LXII (R=CH₃)
LXIII (R=C₂H₅)

22. 3-Benz[a]imidazo[c]phenazine.
R. I. 3038

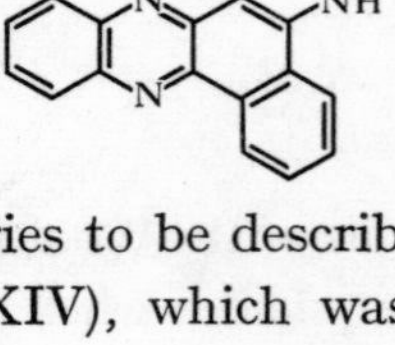

The first member of this series to be described was 2,3-dimethyl-benz[a]imidazo[c]phenazine (LXIV), which was prepared by Kehrmann and Zimmerli[34] by the condensation of 3-acetamido-4-methyl-amino-1,2-naphthoquinone with *o*-phenylenediamine hydrochloride in aqueous ethanol at room temperature. During the reaction, ring closure of the imidazole nucleus occurred and LXIV was obtained as orange needles, m.p. 264°. It dissolved in concentrated sulfuric acid to give a violet-brown color and this, on dilution, passed through orange to bright yellow. Owing to the imidazole ring, LXIV is basic and forms a stable hydrochloride. Kehrmann and Zimmerli also mentioned the formation of 2-methyl-3-phenylbenz[*a*]imidazo[*c*]phenazine (LXVI) from 1-phenyl-2-methylnaphth[1,2]imidazol-4,5-quinone (LXV). This compound (LXVI) forms orange-yellow needles. Goldstein and Gentoñ[35] similarly prepared the 2,3-diphenyl analog (LXVII) starting from 4-anilino-3-benzamido-1,2-naphthoquinone. It formed small yellow needles, m.p. 295°.

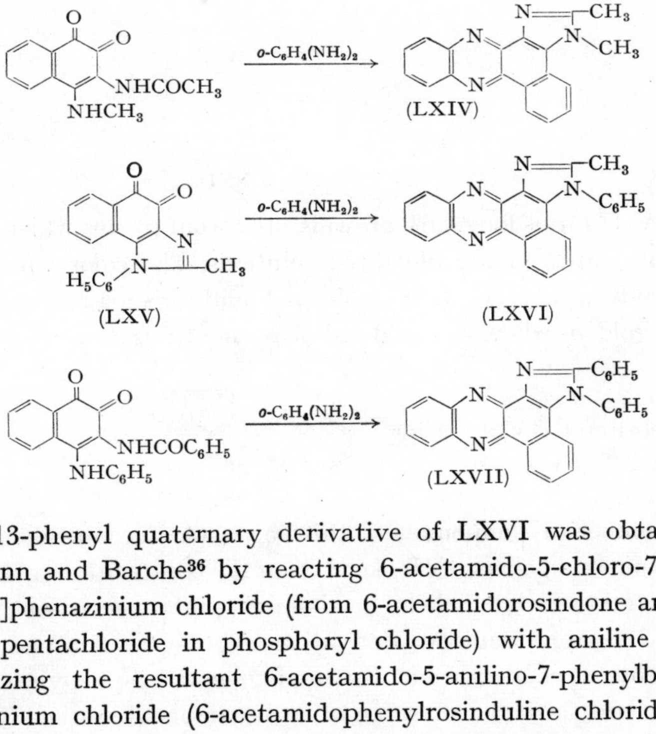

A 13-phenyl quaternary derivative of LXVI was obtained by Kehrmann and Barche[36] by reacting 6-acetamido-5-chloro-7-phenyl-benzo[*a*]phenazinium chloride (from 6-acetamidorosindone and phosphorus pentachloride in phosphoryl chloride) with aniline and recrystallizing the resultant 6-acetamido-5-anilino-7-phenylbenzo[*a*]-phenazinium chloride (6-acetamidophenylrosinduline chloride) when spontaneous ring closure occurred to LXVIII. This compound was also prepared by Kehrmann and Cordone[37] by the action of aniline in the access of air upon 6-acetamido-7-phenylbenzo[a]phenazinium chloride in ethanolic solution.

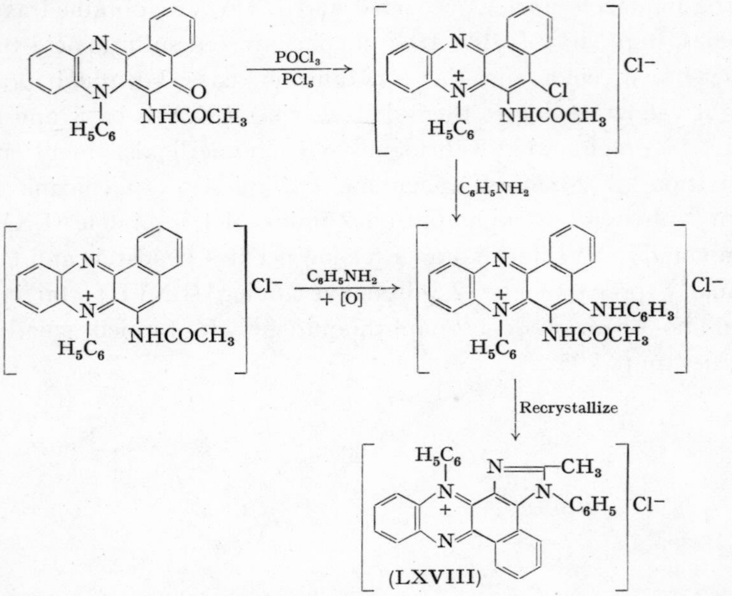

LXVIII forms long dark brownish-red stout prisms which are very soluble in water, giving blood-red solutions. The color with concentrated sulfuric acid is dirty violet-red and this passes on dilution through golden-yellow to blood-red (after neutralization).

23. Benzo[a]furo[2,3-c]phenazine.
    R. I. 3089

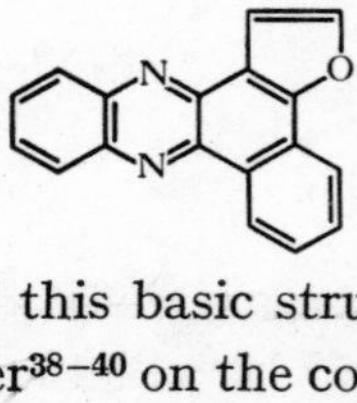

A number of compounds of this basic structure are described in the posthumous papers of Hooker[38-40] on the constitutions of lomatiol, lapachol and the related chemistry involving interconversions between 1,2- and 1,4-naphthoquinone derivatives. The representatives were all prepared by the condensation of an o-quinone with o-phenylenediamine and served to show the presence of an o-quinonoid system. They are listed in Table LVII.

TABLE LVII. Benzo[*a*]furo
[2,3-*c*]phenazines

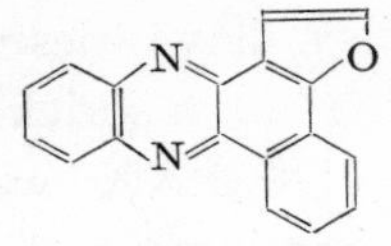

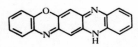

Substituents	Appearance	M.p. (°C.)	Ref.
None		195–196	40
2-Methyl-		209.5–210.5	40
2-Ethyl-		159–160	40
2-Phenyl-		237–238	40
1-Bromo-2-phenyl-1,2-dihydro-		237–238	40
2,2-Dimethyl-1,2-dihydro-	Golden yellow needles	154–155	38
2-Isopropenyl-1,2-dihydro-	Yellow needles	157.5–158	39

**24. 12-Quinoxalo[2,3-*b*]phenoxazine.
R. I. 3195**

The parent compound (LXIX) of this series was first prepared by
Fischer and Hepp[41] by heating 2,3-dihydroxyphenazine with 2-amino-
phenol hydrochloride at 170–200° (compare the formation of fluorindine
using *o*-phenylenediamine, Chapter XVIII:3,B).

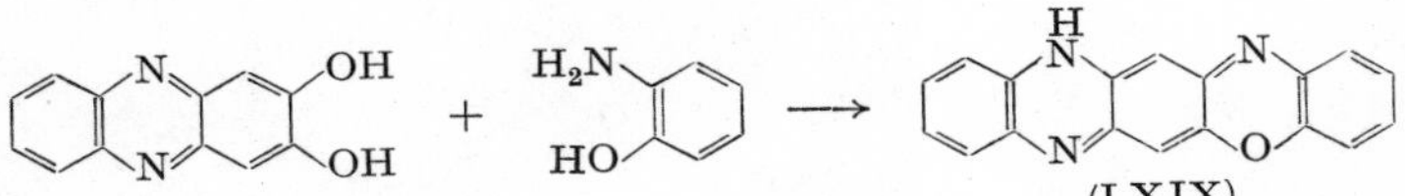

(LXIX)

It may also be prepared from 2-amino-3-isophenoxazone (*R. I.*
1846) or from 2-hydroxy-3-isophenoxazone and *o*-phenylenediamine
following Diepolder.[42]

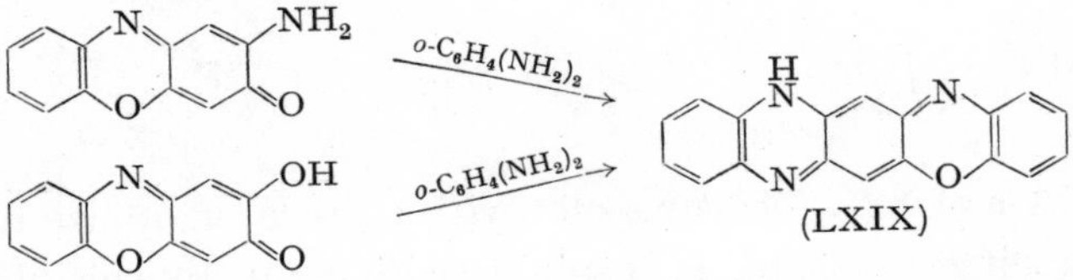

(LXIX)

It forms crystals with a green metallic luster which are difficultly
soluble in ethanol to give a dark red solution with a greenish-yellow
fluorescence. The solutions of the salts are violet with a blood-red
fluorescence.

Kehrmann and pupils[43] have described 3-dimethylamino-12-quinoxalo[2,3-*b*]phenoxazine as a brick-red crystalline solid. The 12-phenyl derivative of LXIX (LXX) was prepared by Fischer and Giesen[44] by the action of 2-aminophenol upon aposafranine chloride. Later, Kehrmann and Schedler[45] obtained LXX by the action of 2-aminophenol hydrochloride upon hydroxyaposafranone. Deipolder[42] prepared LXX by the action of 2-aminodiphenylamine hydrochloride upon 2-hydroxy-3-isophenoxazone (formation of the azine ring) and it is also obtained by the action of alkali upon 14-methyl-12-phenyl-12-quinoxalo[2,3-*b*]phenoxazinium chloride[42] (LXXI, *R. I.* 3196; see Section XIX:25) although Diepolder[46] was at first mistaken about the course of the reaction.

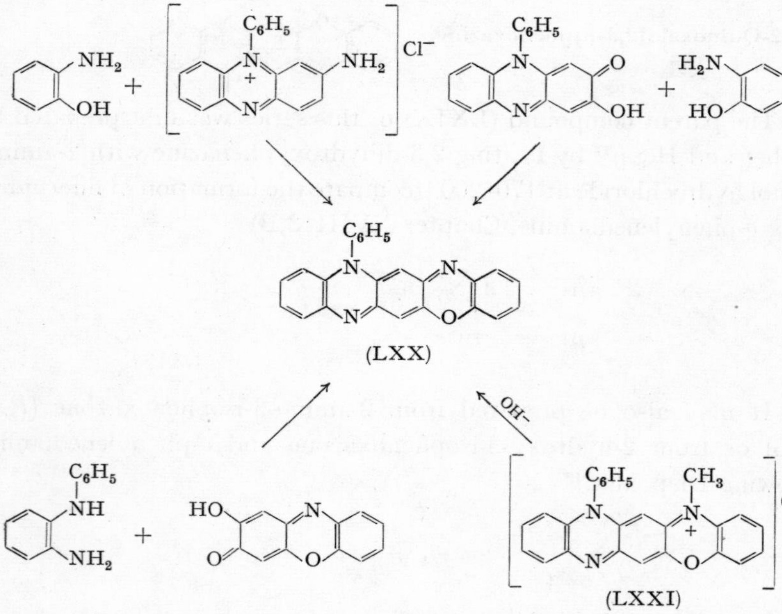

(LXX)

(LXXI)

The base (LXX) forms needles with a green or bronze luster and does not melt below 330°. It is soluble with great difficulty in ethanol to give a cherry-red color with a blood-red fluorescence and gives a green-blue color in concentrated sulfuric acid.

The 10-chloro derivative of LXX is also known.[45] Table LVIII lists representatives of this system.

TABLE LVIII. Derivatives of 12-Quinoxalo [2,3-*b*]phenoxazine

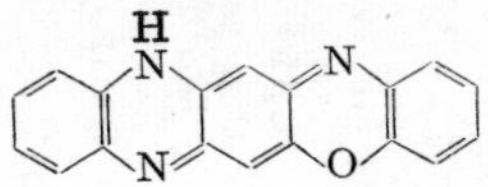

Substituents	Appearance	M.p. (°C.)	Color with H_2SO_4, followed by dilution	Ref.
None	Crystals, green luster			41, 42
3-Dimethylamino-	Brick-red		Blue, red fluorescence	43
12-Phenyl-	Needles, green luster	> 330 dec. 314	Green-blue, violet-blue	42, 44–46
10-Chloro-12-phenyl-	Brown-red crystals, green luster		Green-blue, blue-violet	45
14-Methyl-12-phenyl-	Cl⁻, bronze lustrous needles		Green-blue, violet-blue	45, 47
10-Chloro-14-methyl-12-phenyl-	NO₃⁻, crystals, gold luster		Green-blue, blue-violet	45

25. 14-Quinoxalo[2,3-b]phenoxazine.
R. I. 3196

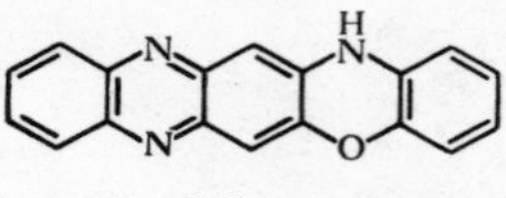

This tautomer of the system described in the previous section is represented by a number of compounds Diepolder prepared in the course of a short series of researches on the oxidation of 2-alkylamino-phenols. He showed[48] that 2-ethylaminophenol on oxidation gave 10-ethylphenoxazine-2,3-quinone (LXXII) and this reacted with o-phenylenediamine to yield 14-ethylquinoxalo[2,3-b]phenoxazine (LXXIII) as orange needles, giving dark yellow solutions with a strong green fluorescence. Diepolder[47] also showed that the oxidation of 2-methylaminophenol proceeded similarly and the quinone (LXXIV) gave the corresponding 14-methylquinoxalo[2,3-b]phenoxazine(LXXV) as orange-yellow needles.

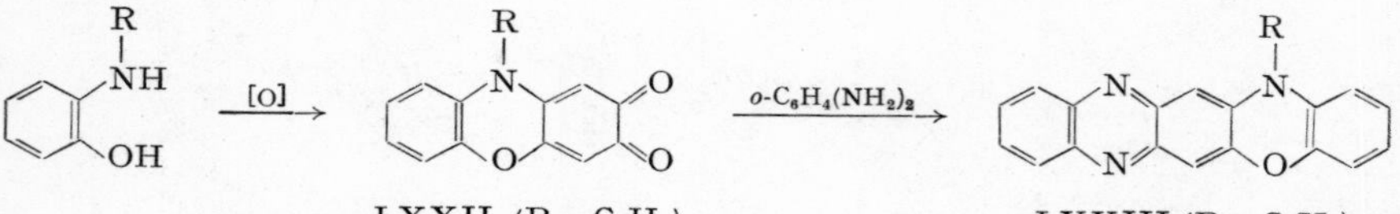

LXXII (R=C$_2$H$_5$) LXXIII (R=C$_2$H$_5$)
LXXIV (R=CH$_3$)   LXXV (R=CH$_3$)

When LXXIV was condensed with 2-aminodiphenylamine hydro-chloride,[46,47] the quaternary 14-methyl-12-phenyl-12-quinoxalo[2,3-b]-phenoxazinium chloride (LXXI) resulted. This formed bronze lustrous needles, soluble in ethanol to give violet-blue solutions with a red

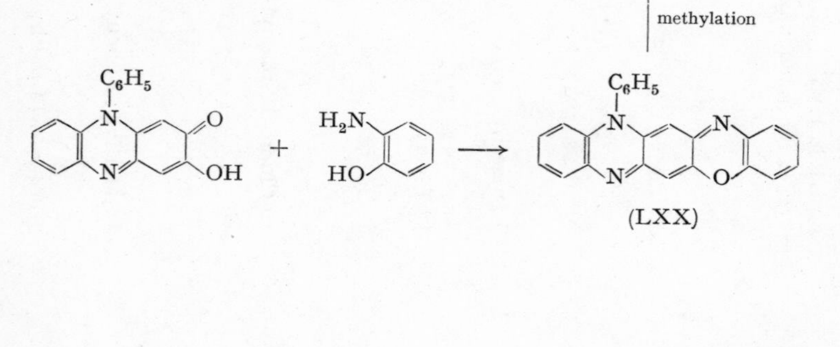

(LXXI)

methylation

(LXX)

fluorescence. The reaction of this compound with alkali has been dealt with in the previous section. Diepolder[47] formulated the product as *o*-quinonoid, but Kehrmann and Schedler[45] showed that LXXI could also be obtained from hydroxyaposafranone and 2-aminophenol hydrochloride in boiling benzoic acid, followed by methylation of the intermediate (LXX) with methyl sulfate in boiling nitrobenzene. It dyes cotton mordanted with tannin in violet-blue shades, fugitive to light.

The representatives of this series are listed in Table LIX.

TABLE LIX. Derivatives of 14-Quinoxalo [2,3-*b*]phenoxazine

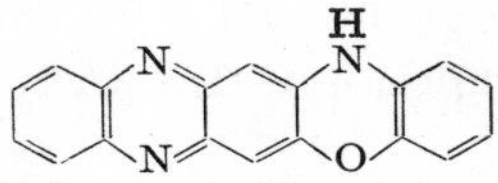

Substituent	Appearance	M.p. (°C.)	Color with H₂SO₄	Ref.
14-Methyl-	Orange-yellow needles	250	Blue, violet	47
14-Ethyl-	Orange needles	229		48

26. Dipyrido[3,2-*a*,3′,2′-*h*] phenazine. R. I. 3240

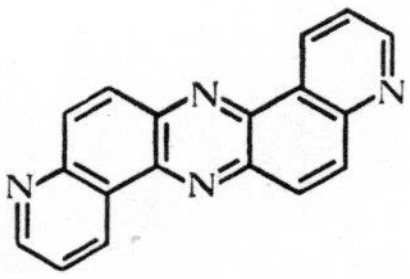

It will be remembered that one method of preparing dibenzo-[*a,h*]phenazine (Chapter XV:3) consisted in the oxidation of 2-naphthylamine with sodium hypochlorite or bleaching powder. Meigen and Nottebohm[49] extended this to the heterocyclic analog (LXXVI) by oxidizing 6-aminoquinoline with sodium hypobromite. The same product was obtained when 6-amino-5-bromoquinoline was used and hence it was shown to be dipyrido[3,2-*a*,3′,2′-*h*]phenazine. It formed yellow lustrous needles, which melted above 420°. Reduction yielded a product that was readily reoxidized to LXXVI, but which was not characterized. It was presumably the 7,14-dihydro derivative.

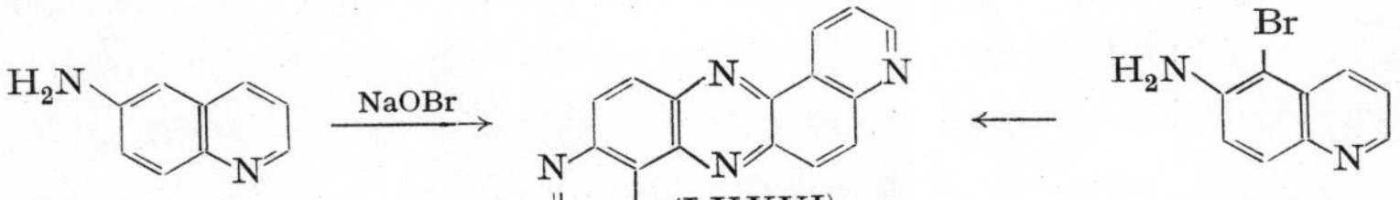

(LXXVI)

27. Dipyrido[*de,kl*]phenazine.
    R. I. 3242

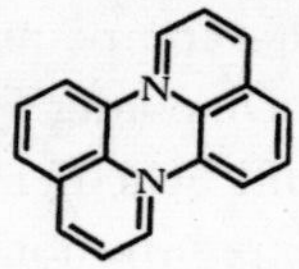

Wieland and Haas[50] studied the rearrangement products obtained by the action of ethereal hydrogen chloride upon ethereal solutions of the ditertiary hydrazines obtained by the oxidation of 1,2,3,4-tetrahydroquinolines. 1,1'-Di(1,2,3,4-tetrahydroquinolyl) (LXXVII), obtained by the permanganate oxidation of 1,2,3,4-tetrahydroquinoline, underwent a normal "benzidine" rearrangement to 6,6'-di(1,2,3,4-tetrahydroquinolyl) (LXXVIII).

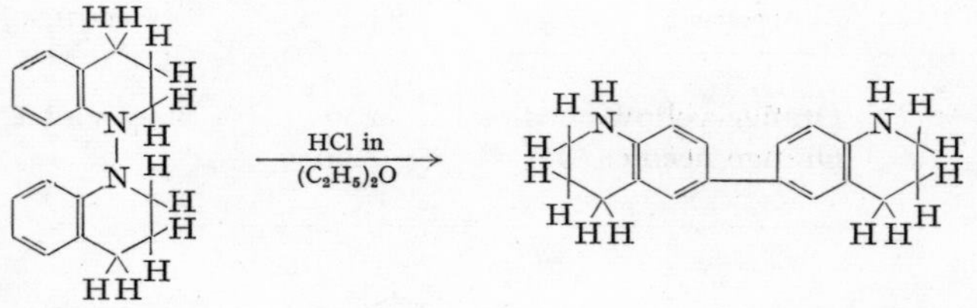

$$\xrightarrow{\text{HCl in } (C_2H_5)_2O}$$

(LXXXVII)   (LXXVIII)

When, however, the 6-position was blocked, for example by methoxyl groups, this type of rearrangement could not occur. Instead, the product was a compound, $C_{20}H_{22}O_2N_2$, together with the initial starting material, 6-methoxy-1,2,3,4-tetrahydroquinoline. They identified the C_{20} compound as 1,2,3,8,9,10-hexahydro-5,12-dimethoxydipyrido[*de, kl*]phenazine (LXXIX). The reaction mixture was basified and the dried precipitate extracted with ethanol to remove the tetrahydroquinoline. The residue (LXXIX) crystallized from ethyl acetate in stellate clusters of yellow needles m.p. 160°. A very characteristic reaction of LXXIX was noted when it was treated with ethereal hydrogen chloride. It underwent a rapid autoxidation and the solution became red from which on standing scarlet-red needles of a salt were deposited. Wieland and Haas interpreted this as the meriquinonoid salt (LXXX). It is perhaps a semiquinone chloride (LXXXa), but see

Chapter III:2,B for a full discussion of the oxidation products of similar perazines.

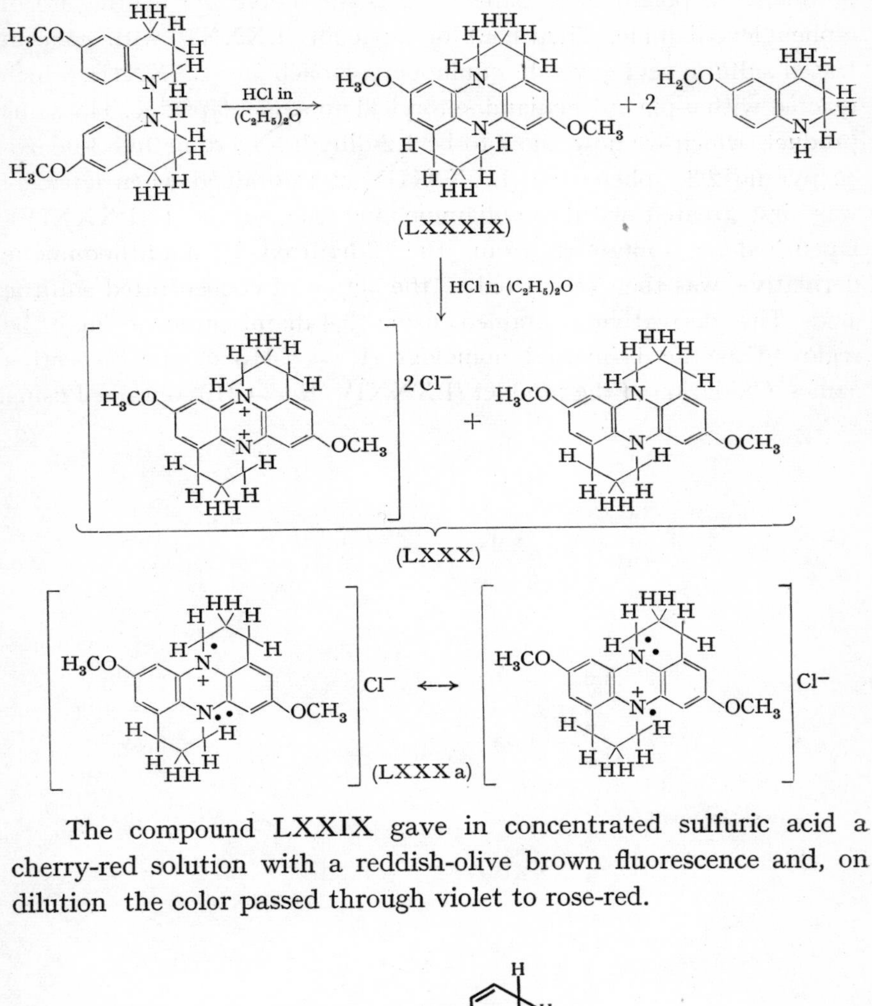

(LXXXIX)

(LXXX)

(LXXX a)

The compound LXXIX gave in concentrated sulfuric acid a cherry-red solution with a reddish-olive brown fluorescence and, on dilution the color passed through violet to rose-red.

28. 3-Benzo[*a*]pyrano[2,3-c]
    phenazine. R. I. 3248

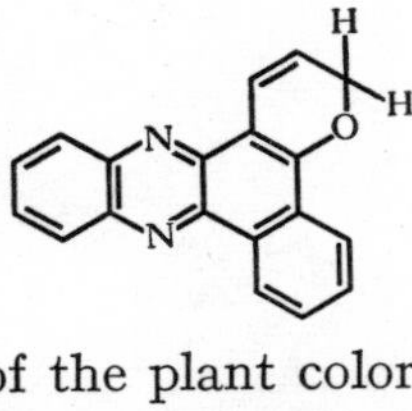

In his investigations of the plant coloring matters, lapachol and lomatiol, Hooker prepared a number of examples of this ring system.

In his early paper,[51] he employed 3,4-diaminotoluene for the characterization of *o*- and *p*-quinones introducing an ambiguity about the products. In posthumous papers,[52] this was overcome by the use of *o*-phenylenediamine. Treatment of lapachol (LXXXI) with concentrated sulfuric acid gave an *o*-quinone, *β*-lapachone (LXXXII), which reacted with *o*-phenylenediamine to yield an azine, lapazine. The same product, which we now know to be 1,2-dihydro-3,3-dimethyl-3-benzo-[*a*]pyrano[2,3-*c*]phenazine (LXXXIII) was obtained when lapachol was first treated with the diamine and the eurhodol (LXXXIV) lapeurhodone, obtained from the 2-hydroxy-1,4-naphthoquinone derivative, was then submitted to the action of concentrated sulfuric acid. The derivatives obtained using 3,4-diaminotoluene may be regarded as the 11-methyl homologs (R = CH_3) of the respective azines. Oxidation of the product (LXXXIV, R = CH_3), obtained using

(LXXXI) (LXXXII) (LXXXIV) (LXXXIII) (LXXXV) (LXXXVI)

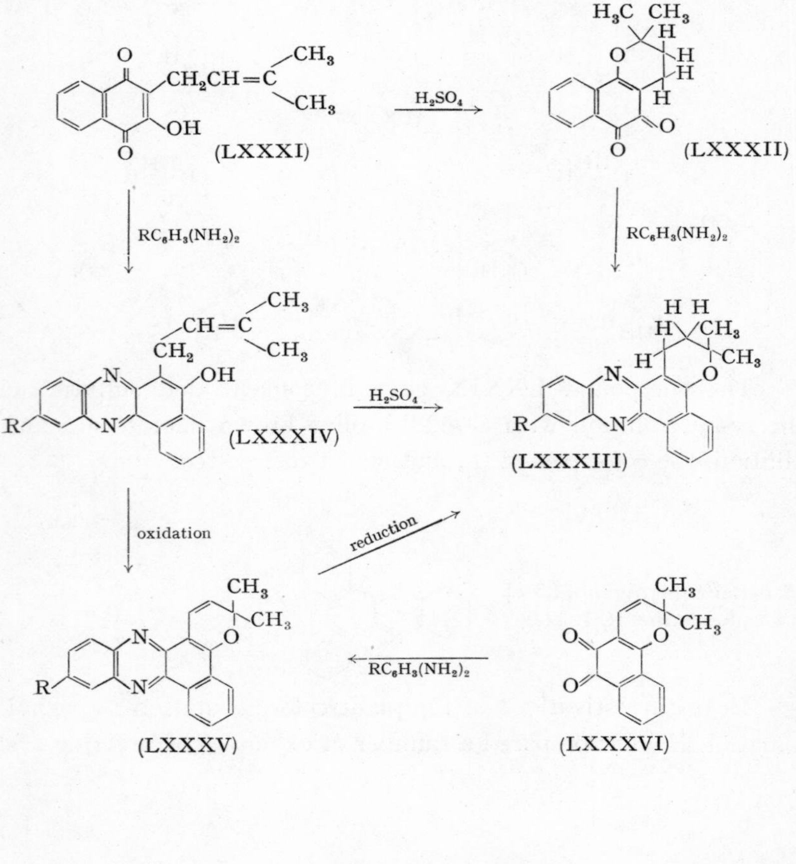

this latter diamine, by means of the action of the atmosphere upon an ethereal alkaline solution, yielded 3,3,11(or 12)-trimethyl-3-benzo[a]-pyrano[2,3-c]phenazine (LXXXV), which could be separated into two forms, presumably isomers, although it was not decided whether this was due to a difference in the position of the 11- (or 12-)methyl group.[52] The compounds (LXXXV) could also be obtained by the action of 3,4-diaminotoluene upon dehydrolapachone (LXXXVI). Reduction of the compound (LXXXV, R = H), obtained by the action of o-phenyl-enediamine upon LXXXVI gave the lapazine (LXXXIII, R = H).

These reactions are summarized in the accompanying reaction scheme.

With lapachol and lomatiol (LXXXVII), which is hydroxy-lapachol, Hooker[38, 53, 54] advanced the ingenious and now well-known mechanism to explain the apparent loss on oxidation of a carbon atom from midway in the side chain. The product, (LXXXVIII) from lomatiol,[39] readily underwent ring closure on heating to yield a red *p*-quinone, 3-methyl-2-naphtho[2,3-*b*]pyran-5,10-quinone (LXXXIX,

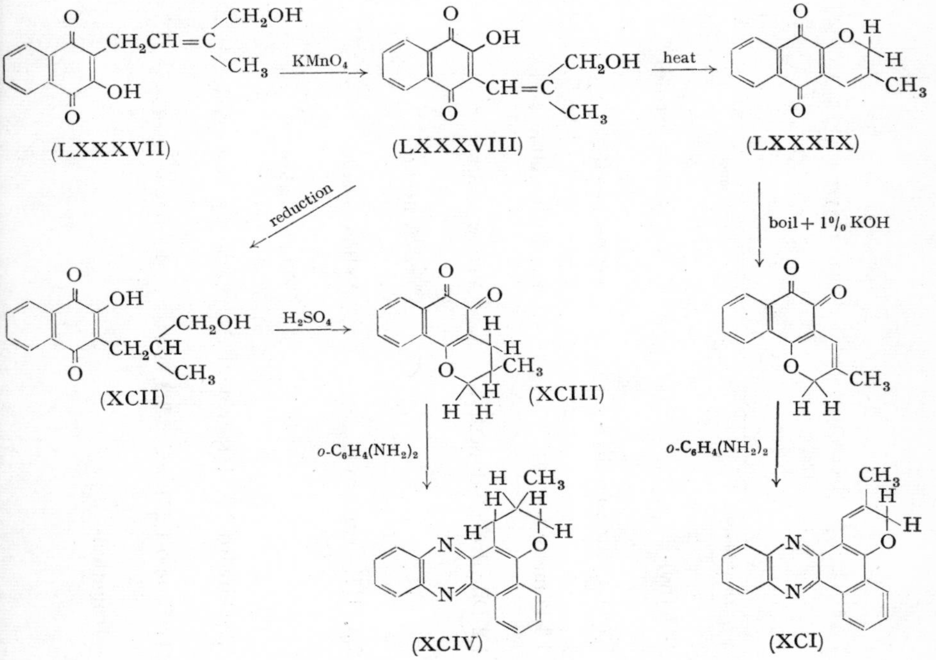

TABLE LX. Derivatives of 3-Benzo[a]pyrano[2,3-c]phenazine

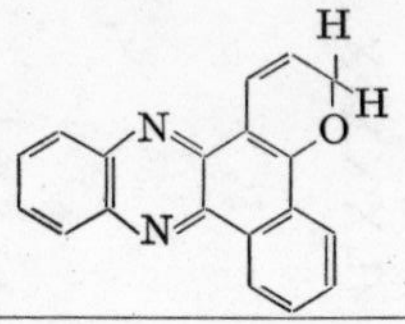

Substituents	Appearance	M.p. (°C.)	Color with H_2SO_4	Ref.
2-Methyl-	Golden-yellow needles	163–163.5	Yellow-green	55
1,2-Dihydro-2-methyl-	Yellow needles	160–161	Deep green	56
3,3-Dimethyl-	Brownish-yellow scales	156.5–157	Green	52
1,2-Dihydro-3,3-dimethyl-	Yellow scales	130.5–131.5	Dimorphic	52
	Yellow needles	121.5–122.5		
3,3,11(?)-Trimethyl-	Yellow needles	149–151.5	Two isomers; both give green color	52
	Yellow scales	169.5–171.5		
1,2-Dihydro-3,3,11(?)-trimethyl-	Canary yellow crystals	135	Deep green	51
2(?)Bromo-1,2-dihydro-3,3,11(?)-trimethyl-	Light yellow needles		Deep green	51

R. I. 1996), and this rearranged with very dilute alkali to the violet o-quinone, 3-methyl-2-naphtho[1,2-*b*]pyran-5,6-quinone[55] (XC). This reacted with o-phenylenediamine to yield 2-methyl-3-benzo[*a*]pyrano-[2,3-*c*]phenazine (XCI). Reduction of the intermediate (LXXXVIII) to the dihydro compound (XCII), followed by ring closure with sulfuric acid, gave the o-quinone, 3,4-dihydro-3-methyl-2-naphtho[1,2-*b*]pyran-5,6-quinone (XCIII), which reacted with o-phenylenediamine to yield 1,2-dihydro-2-methyl-3-benzo[*a*]pyrano[2,3-*c*]phenazine (XCIV).[56]

The members of this ring system are listed in Table LX.

29. 12-Isoindolo[2,1-*a*]phenazino [2,3-*d*]imidazole. R. I. 3464

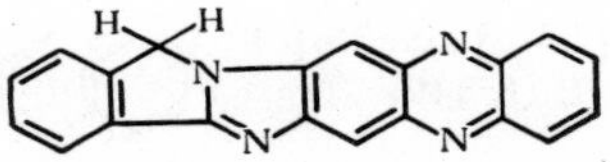

Sircar and De[6] reacted 2,3-diaminophenazine with a number of cyclic aromatic anhydrides, when one carboxyl residue was used to close the imidazole ring and the carboxyl group remaining formed an amide link with the basic imidazole center. This led to a number of different heterocyclic systems derived from phenazine (see Sections XIX:30, 45, 52) besides the present one, which was the product when phthalic anhydride was used. This compound, 12-isoindolo[2,1-*a*]-phenazino[2,3-*d*]imidazol-12-one (XCV), was also obtained by Crippa and Galimberti[13] in the same way. It crystallized from xylene in lemon-yellow needles, m.p. 358°. (For the ring opening with alkali, see Section XIX:9.)

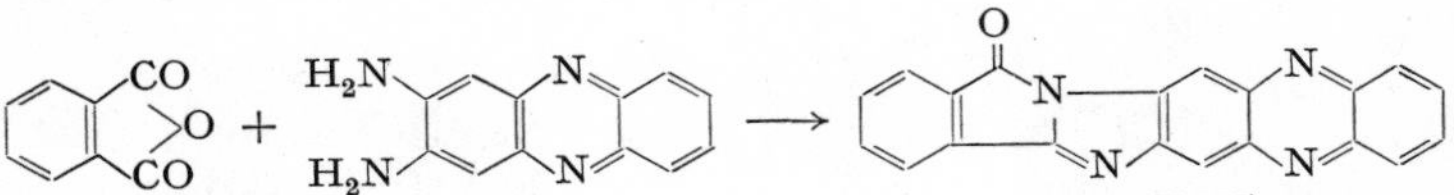

(XCV)

30. 8,11-Methano-8-azepo[1,2-*a*]quinoxalo [2,3-*f*]benzimidazole. R. I. 3466

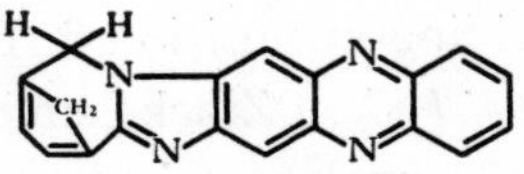

A derivative (XCVI) of this complicated ring system was obtained by Sircar and De[6] by the reaction of camphoric anhydride with 2,3-

diaminophenazine (see Section XIX:29). It formed yellow needles, m.p. 215–219°. No other representatives are known.

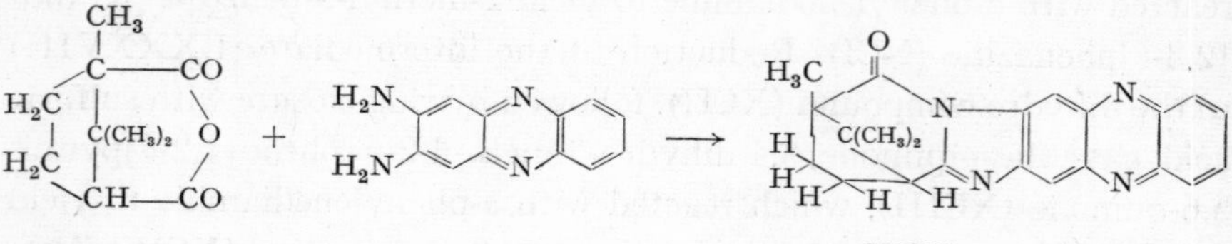

(XCVI)

31. 6-Quinoxalo[2,3-a]triazolo[c] phenazine. R. I. 3491

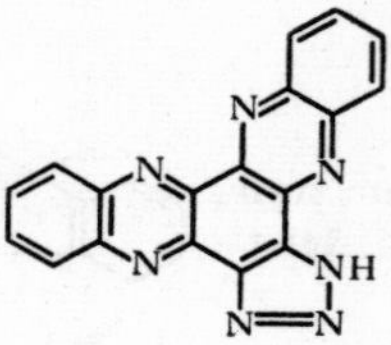

In the course of their studies of the chemistry of benzotriazole, Zincke and his coworkers[8] obtained 4,5,6,7-tetrahydrobenzotriazol-4,5,6,7-tetrone, which condensed with o-phenylenediamine to give the parent structure (XCVII) of this system as a very insoluble grey-white powder, which melts above 260°. The same product is obtained from the chlorohydroxy-4,7-quinone and o-phenylenediamine.

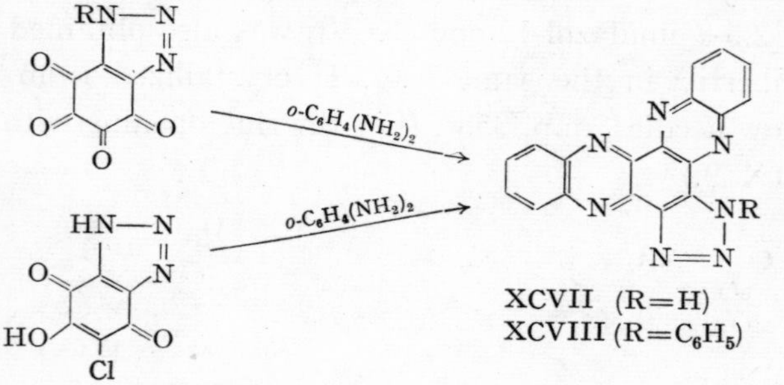

XCVII (R=H)
XCVIII (R=C$_6$H$_5$)

The hydrogen atom of the triazole ring is mobile and cannot be fixed as residing at position 6. This is merely the "low H" convention of *The Ring Index*. Zincke and Petermann[10] repeated this synthesis using 4,5,6,7-tetrahydro-1-phenylbenzotriazole-4,5,6,7-tetrone and obtained the 6-phenyl derivative (XCVIII) as nearly colorless needles, melting above 260°.

32. 2-Dibenzo[*a,h*]triazolo[*c*] phenazine. R. I. 3492

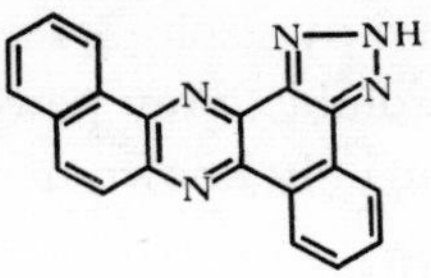

Just as 2-phenylnaphtho[1,2]triazole-4,5-quinone (XLVIII) will react with *o*-phenylenediamine to give derivatives of 2-benzo[*a*]-triazolo[*c*]phenazine (Section XIX:17), so too will it condense with 1,2-diaminonaphthalene as Charrier[57] showed. The product is formulated as 2-phenyldibenzo[*a,h*]triazolo[*c*]phenazine (XCIX), although it may just as easily be 2-phenyldibenzo[*a,j*]triazolo[*c*]phenazine (C).

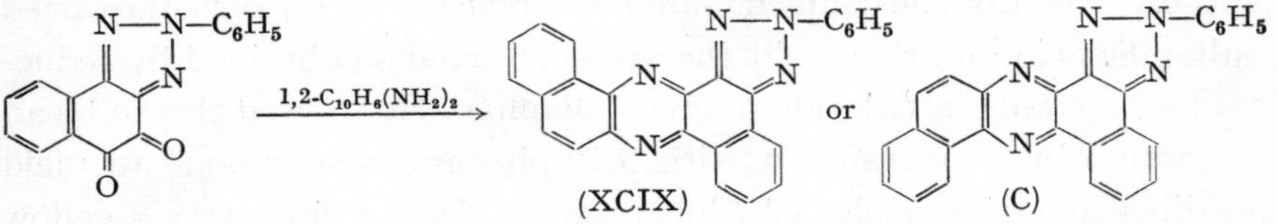

(XCIX)   or   (C)

The compound (XCIX or C) forms a yellow crystalline powder, m.p. 262°, which yields intensely red salts and gives a violet coloration with concentrated sulfuric acid. The 2-*p*-chlorophenyl analog, prepared similarly, melted at 280°.

33. 6-Pyrazolo[3,4-*a*]quinoxalo[2,3-c] phenazine. R. I. 3494

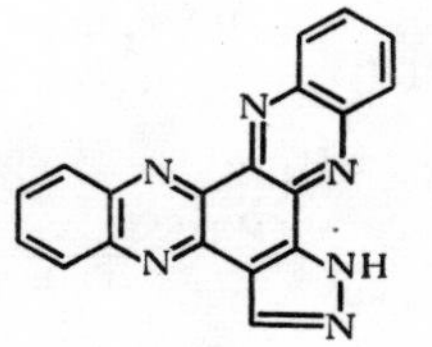

It will be recalled that 1-pyrazolo[3,4-*a*]phenazine (Section X1X:10) was prepared by Fries and Weldert[14] from 5-chloro-6-hydroxy-isoindazole-4,7-quinone (XX). If this quinone is first oxidized with nitric acid, it yields 4,5,6,7-tetrahydroisoindazole-4,5,6,7-tetrone (CI) and this, with two sets of *o*-quinonoid functions, condenses with *o*-

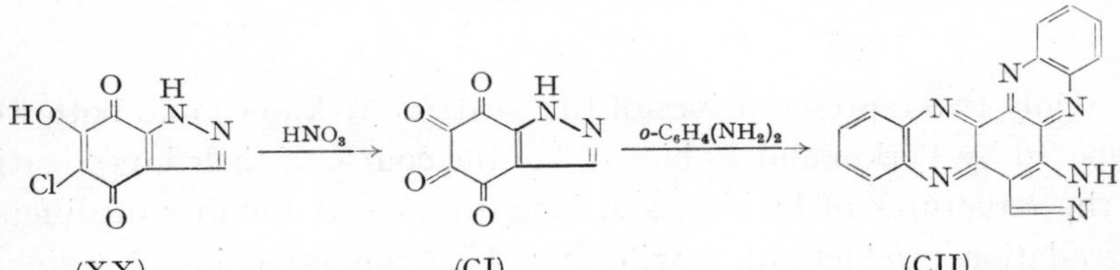

(XX)   (CI)   (CII)

phenylenediamine to form 6-pyrazolo[3,4-*a*]quinoxalo[2,3-*c*]phenazine (CII). This is a sparingly soluble, grey powder, melting above 300°.

Compound (CII) is the only known member of this ring system.

34. 14-Dibenzo[*a,c*]pyrazolo[3,4-*h*] phenazine. R. I. 3496

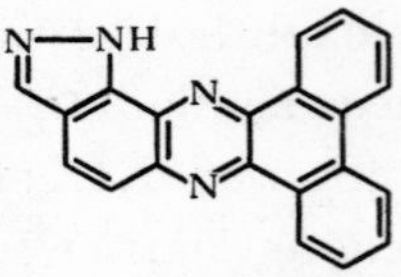

Fieser[58] has prepared the sole representative of this ring system, in the course of his study of the chemistry of isoindazole (*R. I.* 773). In this investigation, he coupled 6-aminoisoindazole (CIII) with diazotized sulfanilic acid and then split the azo compound so obtained by reduction with stannous chloride to give a diamine. He showed this to be an *o*-diamine by condensing it with 9,10-phenanthrenequinone to yield 14-dibenzo[*a,c*]pyrazolo[3,4-*h*]phenazine (CIV) as fine, lemon-yellow needles, m.p. 364°, which gave a carmine-red solution in concentrated sulfuric acid.

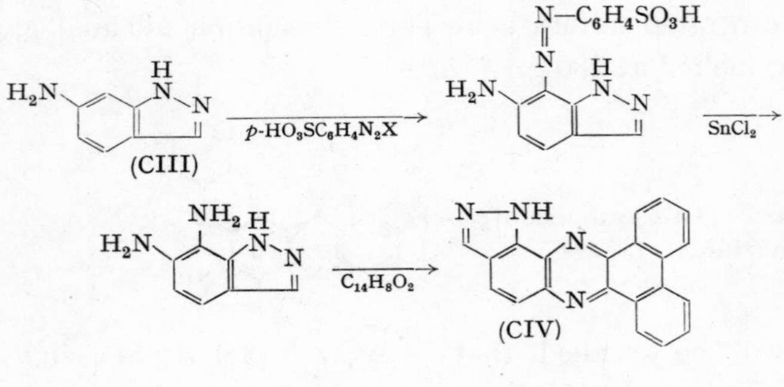

35. Benzo[*a*]benzofuro[3,2-*c*] phenazine. R. I. 3516

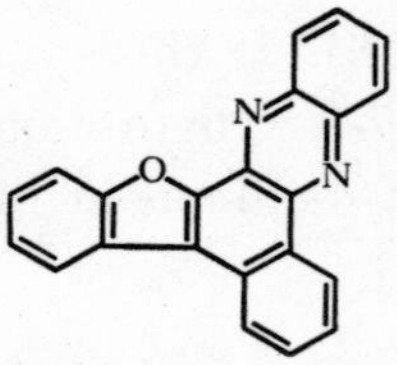

Only two representatives of this system are known and both were prepared by Perkin and Robinson[59] in the course of their investigation of the structures of brazilin and hematoxylin. A number of different degradation products of brazilin could be converted into a quinone,

trimethoxy-α-brazanquinone (CV). This reacted with 3,4-diamino-
toluene to yield 2(or 3)-methyl-7,8,12-trimethoxybenzo[*a*]benzofuro-
[3,2-*c*]phenazine (CVI) as glistening orange-brown needles, m.p. 257°,
thus proving CV to be an *o*-quinone.

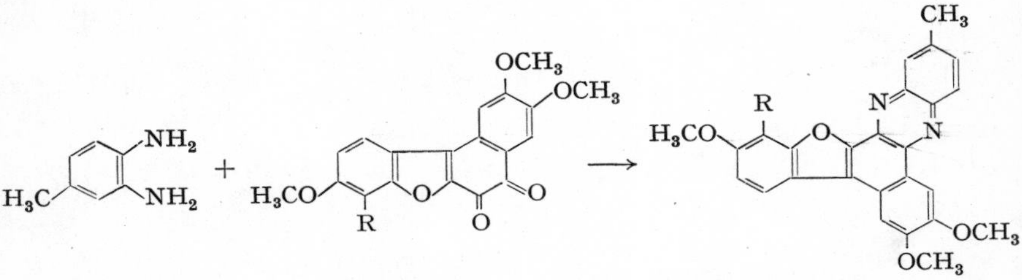

CV   (R=H)
CVII (R=OCH₃)

CVI   (R=H)
CVIII (R=OCH₃)

The azine (CVI) gave a royal blue color in concentrated sulfuric
acid and this on dilution became crimson. Hematoxylin, which is a
methoxybrazilin, on similar degradation yielded the corresponding
quinone (CVII) and this gave the azine (CVIII) as coffee-colored
needles, shrinking at 205–210°. It closely resembled CVI in properties.

**36. Furo[4,5]phenanthro[9,10-*b*]
quinoxaline. R. I. 3517**

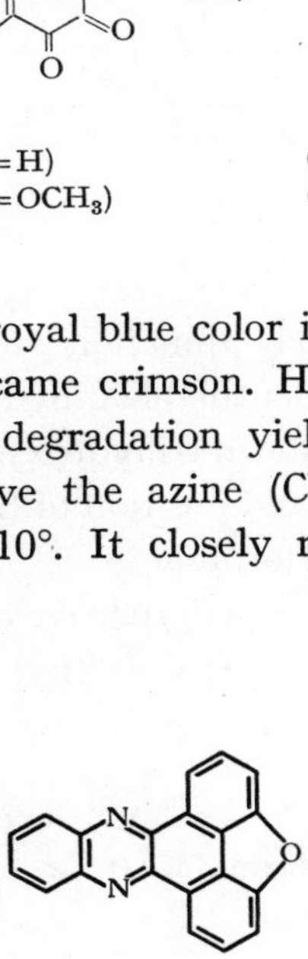

A few members of this ring system were reported by Vongerichten[60]
at the turn of the century in the course of his investigations of the structure of morphine. By application of the Hofmann degradation to morphine. it was possible to obtain morphenol methyl ether (3-methoxy-
phenanthro[4,5-*bcd*]furan, CIX, *R. I.* 2496), which after demethylation
gave morphenol (CX). This was shown to be related to phenanthrene by
zinc dust distillation and confirmed by oxidation of acetylmorphenol
to the quinone (CXI), which condensed with 3,4-diaminotoluene to give
3-hydroxy-10(or 11)-methylfuro[4,5]phenanthro[9,10-*b*]quinoxaline

(CXII) as yellow needles. Acetylation of CXII gave the corresponding acetoxy compound (CXIII) as yellow needles, m.p. 231–232°.

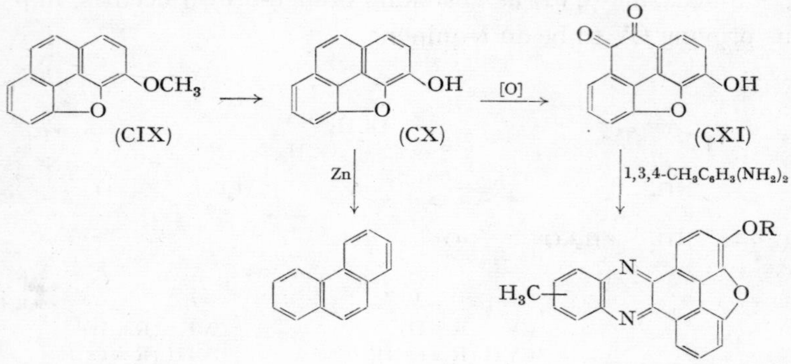

This work, taken in conjunction with the reductive opening of the furan ring to yield an identifiable dihydroxyphenanthrene and hydrolytic ring scission to a known trihydroxyphenanthrene, established with certainty the presence and position of the ether ring in morphenol and hence, presumably, in morphine.

An unorientated bromo derivative of CXIII was later obtained by Vongerichten[61] as yellow crystals that gave a blue solution in concentrated sulfuric acid.

37. 7-Benzo[a]-[1,4]benzoxazino[3,2-i] phenazine. R. I. 3573

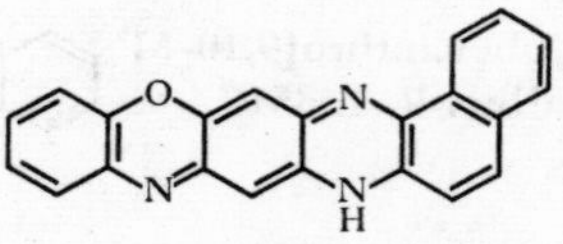

This ring system has a very close connection with that described in Section XIX:24, of which it is the 8,9-benzo analog. This is well emphasized in the similar methods of synthesis and properties of the members. Kehrmann and Wild[62] extended Diepolder's original synthesis[46, 47] to this series by condensing 10-methylphenoxazine-2,3-quinone (LXXIV) with 2-anilino-1-naphthylamine hydrochloride in boiling benzoic acid. Owing to the high temperature employed, a certain amount of demethylation occurred. The products were separated by solvent partition between ethanolic hydrochloric acid and benzene.

The benzene layer, which undoubtedly contained CXIV, was wine-red with a yellow fluorescence; the compound was not isolated, however. From the acid solution, they isolated 9-methyl-7-phenyl-7-benzo[a]-[1,4]benzoxazino[3,2-i]phenazinium nitrate (CXV) as needles with a green metallic luster, giving a blue solution in ethanol. This, on boiling with alkali, underwent oxidative demethylation to give a product identical with that in the benzene layer (CXIV).

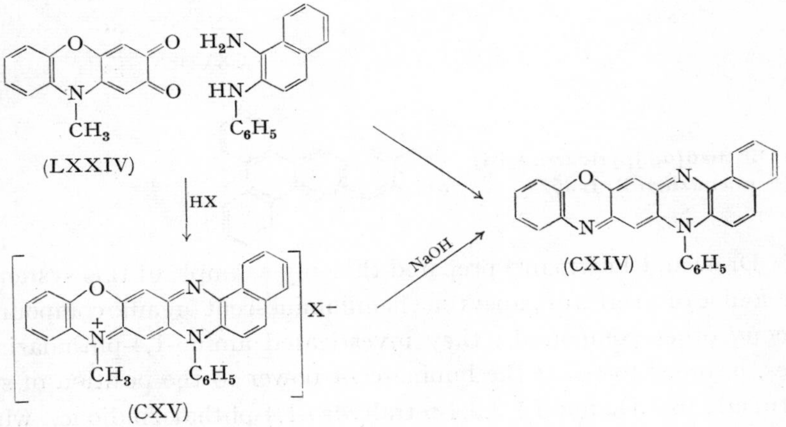

O   O   H₂N

N

CH₃   HN

     C₆H₅

(LXXIV)

| HX

NaOH

(CXIV)   C₆H₅

O   N

N⁺   N   X⁻

CH₃   C₆H₅

(CXV)

When 1,2-diaminonaphthalene was employed as diamine, the corresponding parent system (CXVI) was obtained, but was not characterized, except as being very weakly basic.

Later, Kehrmann and Collaud[63] synthesized CXVI by a different route involving formation of the oxazine ring. 9,10-Dihydroxybenzo-[a]phenazine (Chapter XIII:3,B) was heated with 2-aminophenol in boiling benzoic acid. The product crystallized from nitrobenzene in orange-red crystals, sparingly soluble in benzene to give yellow solutions with a feeble green fluorescence. It gave a bluish-green color in concentrated sulfuric acid. When 10-hydroxy-7-phenyl-9(7)-benzo[a]-phenazinone (10-hydroxyisorosindone, Chapter XIV:3,B) was used, the product (CXVII) formed almost black microscopic crystals, which were difficultly soluble in organic solvents to give violet solutions which did not fluorescence. Concentrated sulfuric acid dissolved a trace of this substance to give a pure blue solution, from which a violet-blue quaternary sulfate was precipitated on dilution.

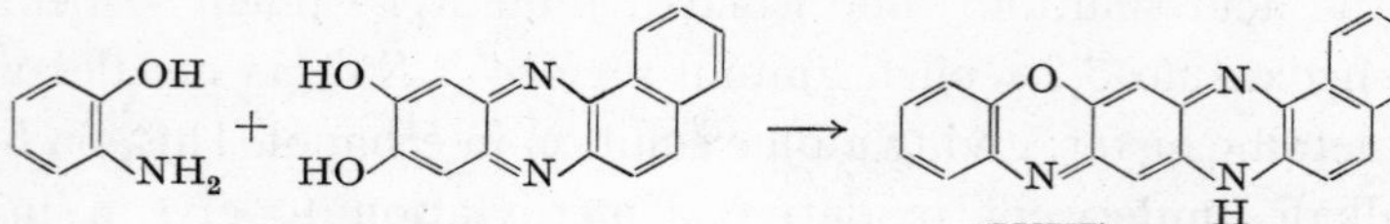

(CXVI)

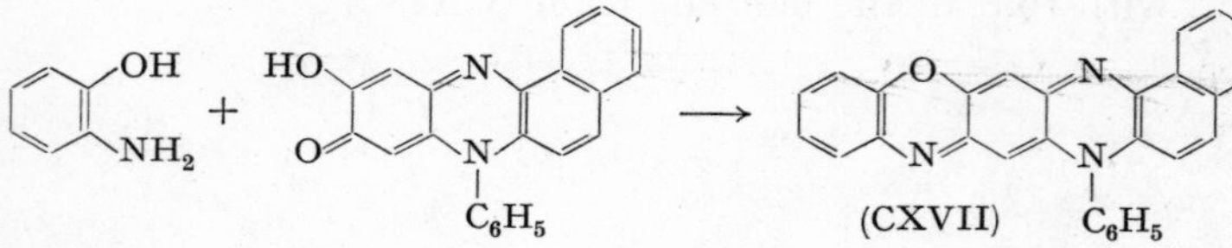

(CXVII) C_6H_5

38. Dibenzo[a,c]pyridazo[4,5-i] phenazine. R. I. 3579

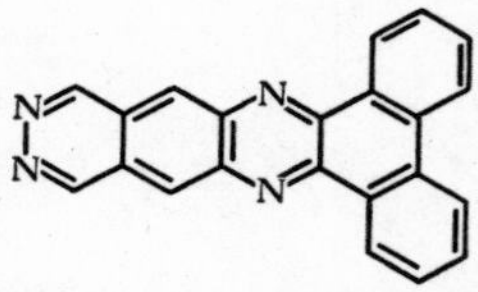

Drew and Pearman[64] prepared the only example of this system in the course of a series of papers on chemiluminescent organic compounds. Among other compounds, they investigated amino-1,4-phthalazindi-ones, in order to relate the luminescent power to the position of sub-stituents. 6,7-Diamino-1,2,3,4-tetrahydro-1,4-phthalazindione, which was required for this work, was condensed with 9,10-phenanthrene-quinone to yield 11,12,13,14-tetrahydrodibenzo[a,c]pyridazo[4,5-i]-phenazine-11,14-dione (CXVIII) as orange crystals, apparently a dihydrate, melting above 340°.

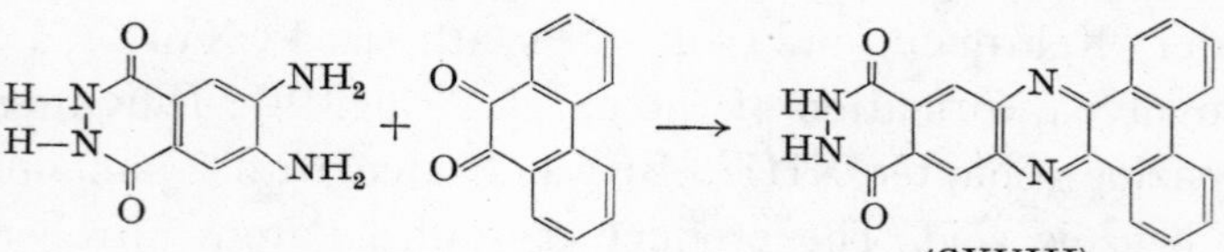

(CXVIII)

39. Dibenzo[a,c]-p-dioxino[i] phenazine. R. I. 3582

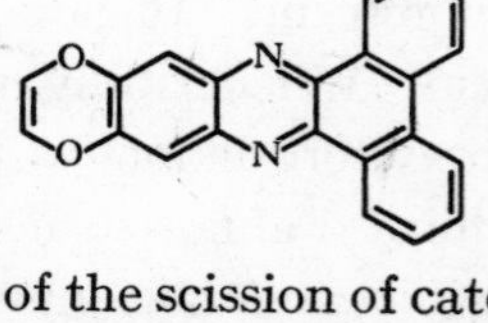

In the course of a study of the scission of catechol ethers, Robinson and Robinson[65] prepared 2,3-dihydro-6-nitro-1,4-benzodioxin (CXIX), which on nitration yielded the 6,7-dinitro compound (CXX). Reduction of CXX to the corresponding diamine and condensation of this with 9,10-phenanthrenequinone yielded 12,13-dihydrodibenzo[a,c]-p-di-oxino[i]phenazine (CXXI) as clusters of yellow needles, m.p. 239–240°.

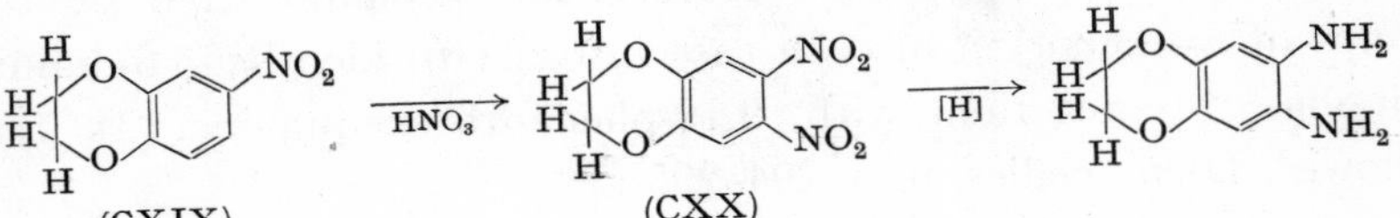

(CXIX)   (CXX)

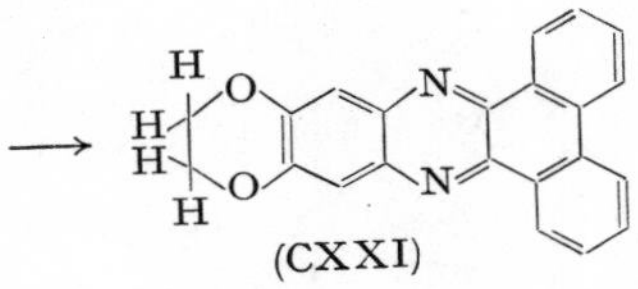

(CXXI)

40. **Benzo[a]quino[2,3-c]phenazine.**
    R. I. 3583

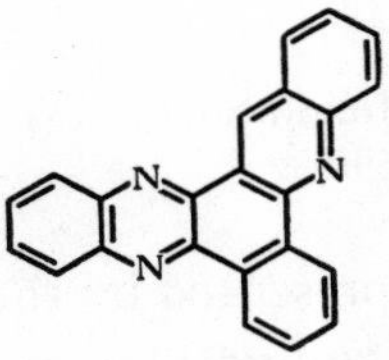

Lagodzinski and Hardine[66] prepared the only example of this system, 5,16-dihydrobenzo[a]quino[2,3-c]phenazine-16-one (CXXII), in the manner shown below. It formed lustrous, stout, dark yellow needles, m.p. 276°.

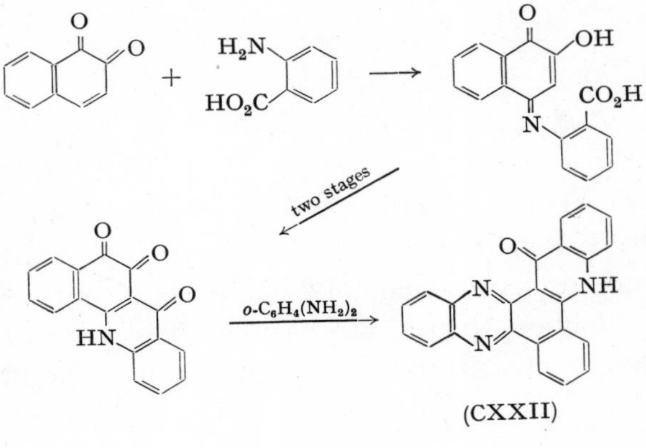

(CXXII)

41. Dibenzo[a,c]pyrido[3,2-h] phenazine. R. I. 3584

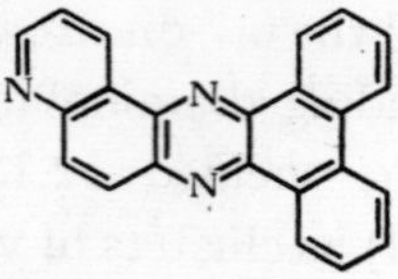

This basic ring system (CXXIII) has been prepared by three groups of workers,[67-69] in each case in order to identify 5,6-diaminoquinoline by reaction with 9,10-phenanthrenequinone. It forms yellowish-fawn needles, m.p. 294–295°.

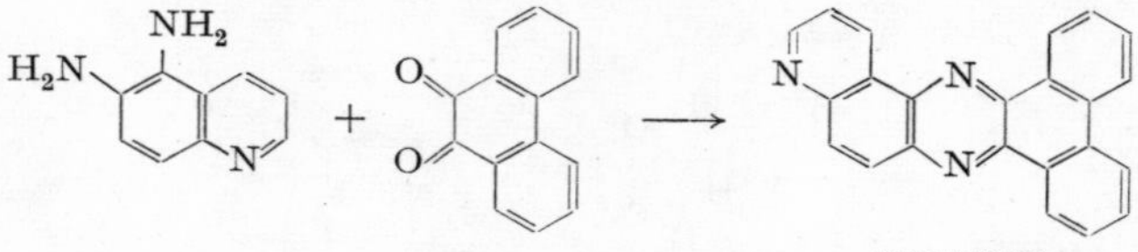

(CXXIII)

42. 2-Pyrano[3',4',5',4,5]naphtho[1,8-ab] phenazine. R. I. 3590

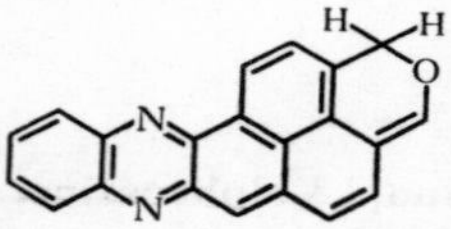

This system is represented by the 3,6-dihydro-1,3,6-trione (CXXV) which is the cyclic anhydride of 3,4-dicarboxy-7-naphtho[1,8-ab]-phenazin-7-one (Chapter XV:8), and is obtained by the oxidation of 5-acenaphtho[5,6-ab]phenazin-5-one (CXXIV).

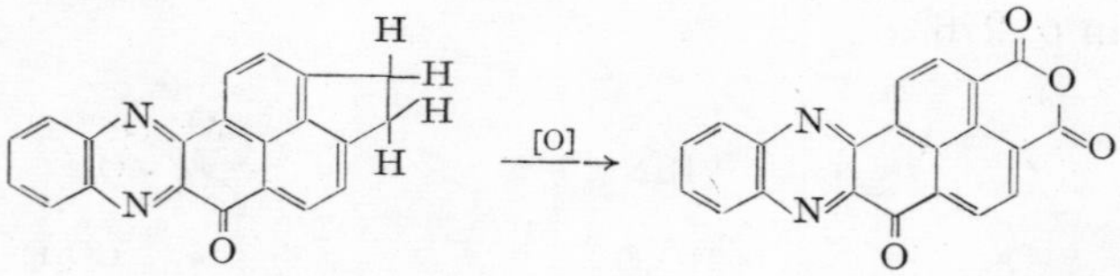

(CXXIV)   (CXXV)

This oxidation is described in a patent[70] in which are given details of the condensation of CXXV, or its derived dicarboxylic acid, with ammonia, primary amines, 1,2-diamines or o-nitroanilines (with subsequent reduction) to yield very fast vat dyes of various colors, but of undetermined constitution. (See also Chapter XV:8 and Table XXXIX.)

43. Oxepo[3′,4′,5′,6′,4,5]phenanthro [9,10-*b*]quinoxaline. R. I. 3663

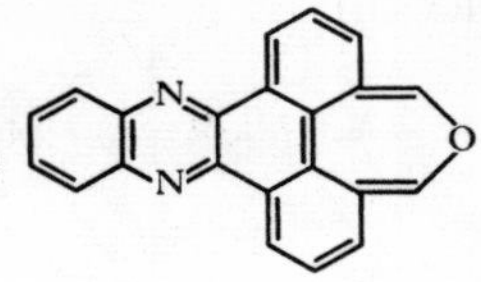

Vollmann and his collaborators[71] prepared the only member of this series, 4,6-dihydroöxepo[3′,4′,5′,6′,4,5]phenanthro[9,10-*b*]quinoxal-ine-4,6-dione (CXXVII), by condensing 4,5-dicarboxy-9,10-phenan-threnequinone with *o*-phenylenediamine and cyclizing the 4,5-di-carboxydibenzo[*a,c*]phenazine (CXXVI, m.p. 330°) to the acid an-hydride (CXXVII) by prolonged reflux in nitrobenzene. It forms long yellowish needles, m.p. 340°, and gives a reddish-orange coloration with concentrated sulfuric acid.

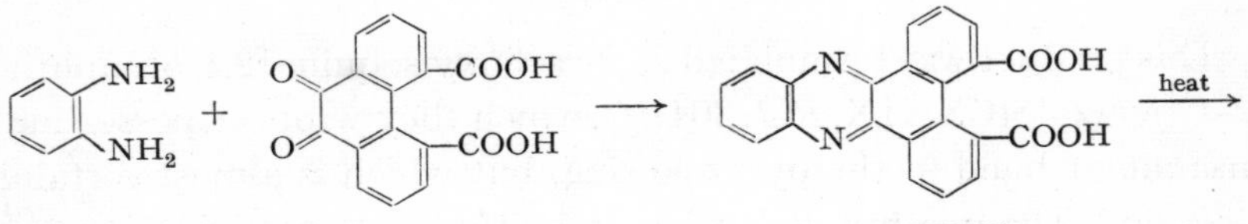

(CXXVI)

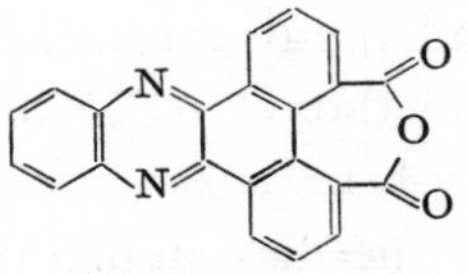

(CXXVII)

44. Benz[*a*]isoquino[2′,1′,1,5]pyrazolo [4,3-*c*]phenazine. R. I. 3712 M

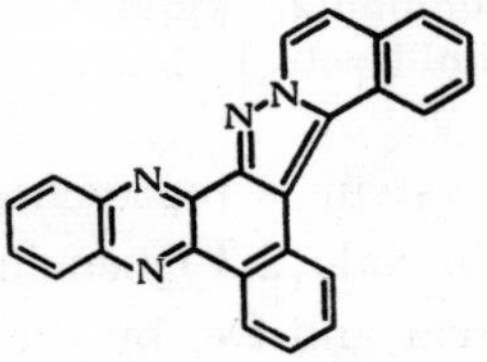

Corbellini and his associates[33] prepared a number of represent-atives of this complicated ring system in their efforts to elucidate the constitution of the product obtained by the dehydrogenating action of sulfuryl chloride upon *cis-o*-[4,5,1′,2′]-naphtho-3-pyrazolylcinnamic acid (CXXVIII).

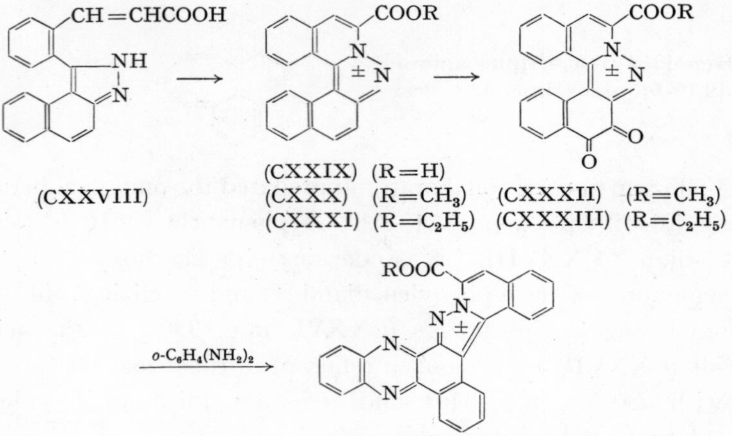

(CXXVIII)

(CXXIX) (R=H)
(CXXX) (R=CH₃)   (CXXXII) (R=CH₃)
(CXXXI) (R=C₂H₅)   (CXXXIII) (R=C₂H₅)

o-C₆H₄(NH₂)₂

(CXXXIV) (R=CH₃)
(CXXXV) (R=C₂H₅)

This product was formulated as 9-carboxyisoquino[2,1-*h*]naphtho-[1,2-*d*]pyrazole (CXXIX, *R. I.* 3041 J), which they wrote as possessing a transannular bond in the pyrazole ring, but which is almost certainly mesoionic.[2] The methyl (CXXX) and ethyl esters (CXXXI) were oxidized to the 5,6-quinones (CXXXII and CXXXIII, respectively) by means of chromic acid and these were condensed with *o*-phenylene-diamine to give 17-carbomethoxy- (CXXXIV, yellow needles, m.p. 327°) and 17-carboethoxy-benz[*a*]isoquino[2′,1′,1,5]pyrazolo[4,3-*c*]-phenazine (CXXXV, yellow needles, m.p. 281°).

45. 7-Benz[4,5]isoquino[2,1-*a*]quinoxalo
[2,3-*f*]benzimidazole. R. I. 3713

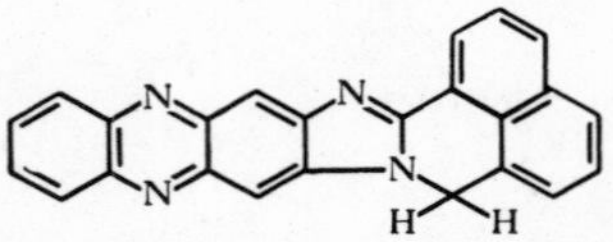

This ring system is represented by the product, 7-benz[4,5]iso-quino[2,1-*a*]quinoxalo[2,3-*f*]benzimidazol-7-one (CXXXVI). This was prepared by Sircar and De[6] by the action of 1,8-naphthalic anhydride upon 2,3-diaminophenazine. It forms yellow needles that do not melt below 300°.

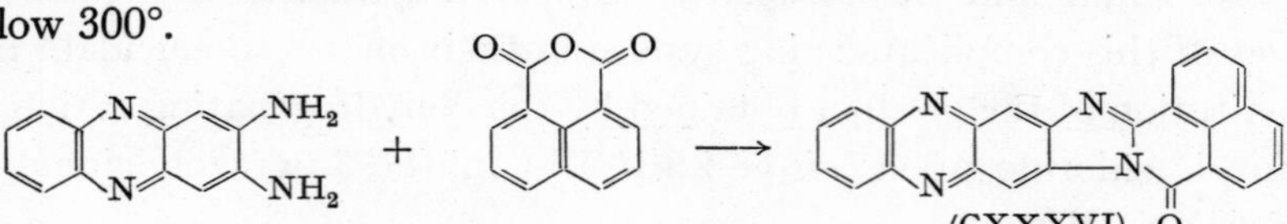

(CXXXVI)

**46. Dibenzo[*a,c*]benzofuro[2,3-*i*]
  phenazine. R. I. 3721**

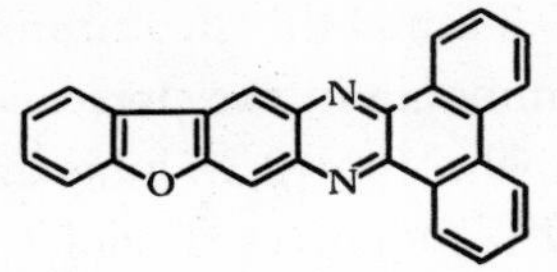

This system was first prepared by Borsche and Schacke[72] in the course of orientation studies on the dibenzofuran series. 3-Diacetamido-dibenzofuran (CXXXVII) was nitrated and the nitroamine reduced to an *o*-diamine, which condensed with 9,10-phenanthrenequinone. The nitro group was thought to enter position 2 to give CXXXVIII and consequently the diamine (CXXXIX) and the corresponding azine (CXL), but it was not possible to exclude the alternative possibility of the diamine being 3,4-diaminodibenzofuran (CXLI), with a corresponding alteration of the structure of the azine.

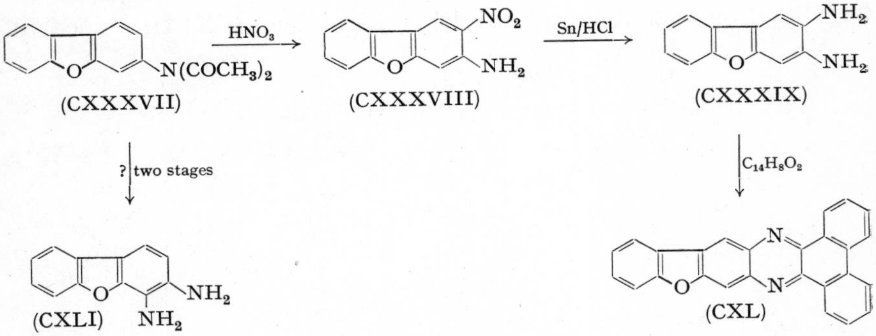

(CXXXVII) $\xrightarrow{\text{HNO}_3}$ (CXXXVIII) $\xrightarrow{\text{Sn/HCl}}$ (CXXXIX)

? two stages

$C_{14}H_8O_2$

(CXLI)

(CXL)

However, the correctness of Borsche's assumption was later proved by Gilman and his colleagues,[73] who synthesized CXXXIX

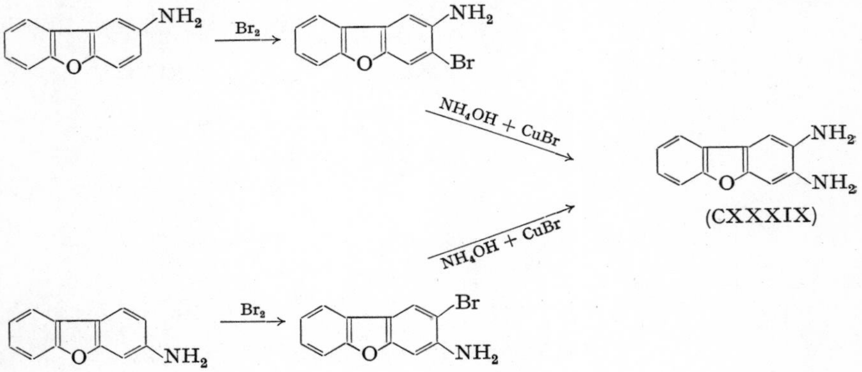

$\xrightarrow{\text{Br}_2}$

$\xrightarrow{\text{NH}_4\text{OH} + \text{CuBr}}$

(CXXXIX)

$\xrightarrow{\text{NH}_4\text{OH} + \text{CuBr}}$

$\xrightarrow{\text{Br}_2}$

from both 2- and 3-aminodibenzofurans by bromination, followed by treatment with ammonia in the presence of cupric bromide.

Dibenzo[a,c]benzofuro[2,3-i]phenazine (CXL) forms yellow, felted needles, m.p. 297°, and gives a violet-blue color with concentrated sulfuric acid.

47. Benzo[a]naphtho[2′,3′,4,5]furo[2,3-c] phenazine. R. I. 3722

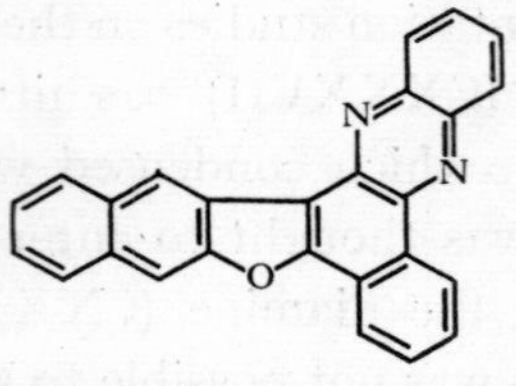

Hooker for many years investigated the nature of the product obtained by the action of light upon 2-hydroxy-1,4-naphthoquinone; in a paper published posthumously,[74] it was shown that this was 2,2′-dihydroxy-3,3′-dinaphthyl-1,4,1′,4′-diquinone (CXLII), since it

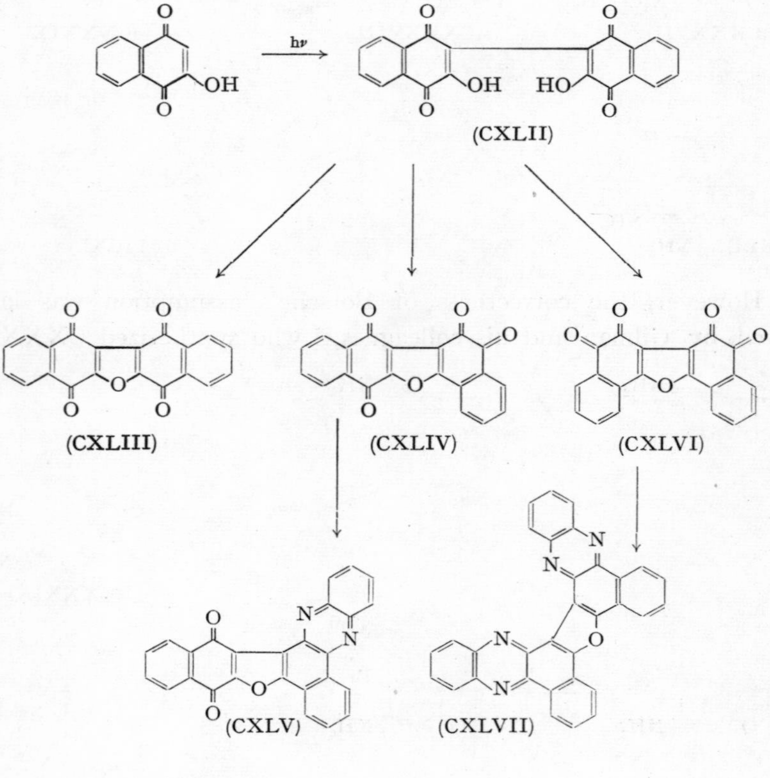

(CXLII)

(CXLIII)   (CXLIV)   (CXLVI)

(CXLV)   (CXLVII)

was dehydrated to yield three isomeric diquinones, one of which gave no azine derivative with o-phenylenediamine and was accordingly given structure CXLIII. The second isomer gave a monoazine, benzo-[a]naphtho[2′,3′,4,5]furo[2,3-c]phenazine-11,16-quinone (CXLV), indicating the presence of one o-quinonoid group and so was given structure CXLIV. The third isomer (CXLVI) contained two o-quinonoid functions, as indicated by the formation of the diazine, dibenzo-[c,c′]furo[3,2-a,4,5-a′]diphenazine (CXLVII, *R. I.* 3922; Section XIX:62).

The monoazine (CXLV) formed golden yellow plates, m.p. 329–330°, while the diazine (CXLVII) gave small dull yellow needles, m.p. 409–410°.

48. Dibenzo[a,c]benzofuro[2,3-h] phenazine. R. I. 3723

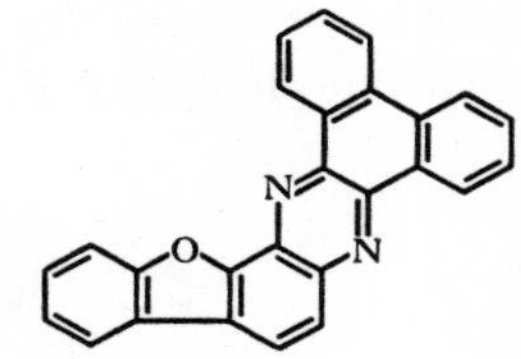

In a series of investigations of the orientation of dibenzofuran substitution (see also Section XIX:46), Gilman and his collaborators[75] nitrated 4-acetamidodibenzofuran and reduced the nitroamine so obtained to 3,4-diaminodibenzofuran (CXLVIII). This condensed with 9,10-phenanthrenequinone to yield dibenzo[a,c]benzofuro[2,3-h]phenazine (CXLIX) as yellow crystals, m.p. 277–278°.

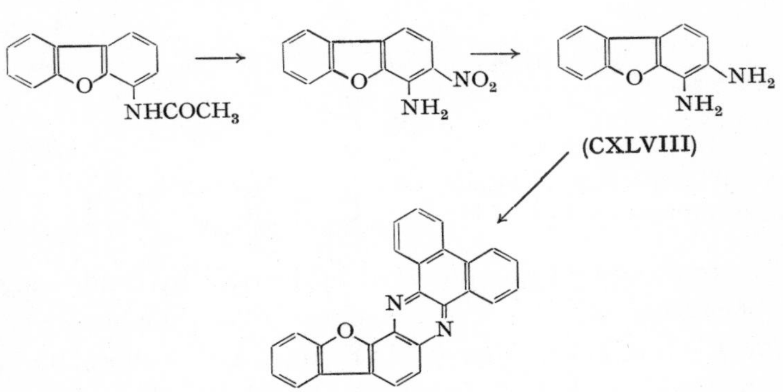

(CXLVIII)

(CXLIX)

**49. Benzo[a]naphtho[1′,2′,4,5]furo[2,3-c]
phenazine. R. I. 3724**

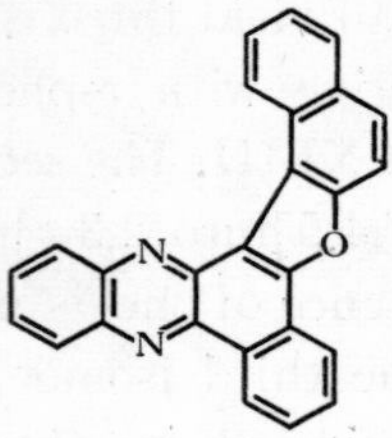

The parent compound (CLII) of this system was prepared by
Clemo and Spence[76] in the course of a study of the isomeric dinaphtho-
furans obtained by heating naphthols with metallic oxide catalysts.
They showed that 2-naphthol, when heated with calcium oxide at
270–340°, yielded dinaphtho[1,2,2′,3′]furan (CL). This was oxidized
with chromic acid to a *p*-quinone, which could be rearranged by alkaline
hydrolysis and subsequent thermal dehydration to an *o*-quinone (CLI).
This quinone reacted with *o*-phenylenediamine to give (CLII) as yellow
needles, m.p. 240°.

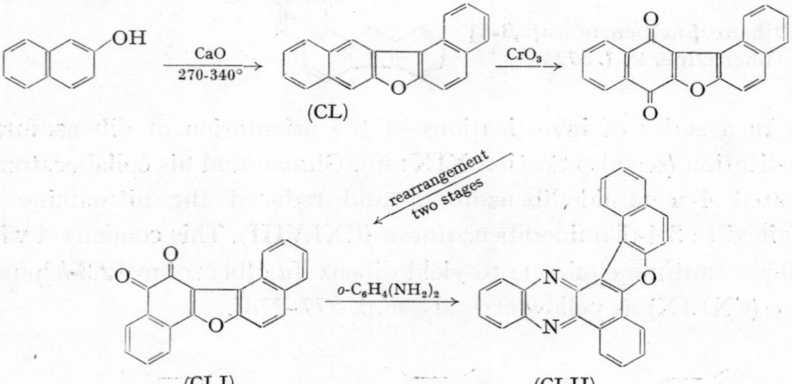

**50. Naph[2′,1′,4,5]thieno[2,3-b]quinoxalo
[2,3-g]quinoxaline. R. I. 3738**

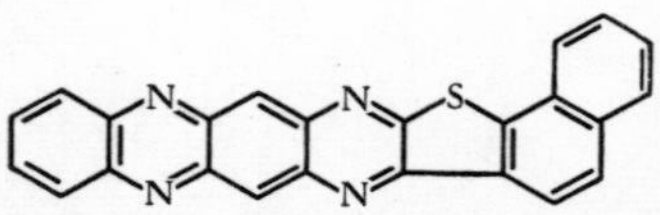

This parent system was prepared by Dutta[77] by condensing 2,3-
diaminophenazine with 2,3-dihydronaphtho[1,2-b]thiophene-2,3-dione
(CLIII, *R. I.* 1744). The product (CLIV) formed a dark chocolate-brown
powder, melting above 295°. It gave a blue-black color with concen-

trated sulfuric acid and dyed wool from an acid bath in chocolate-brown shades. (See also Section XIX:51.)

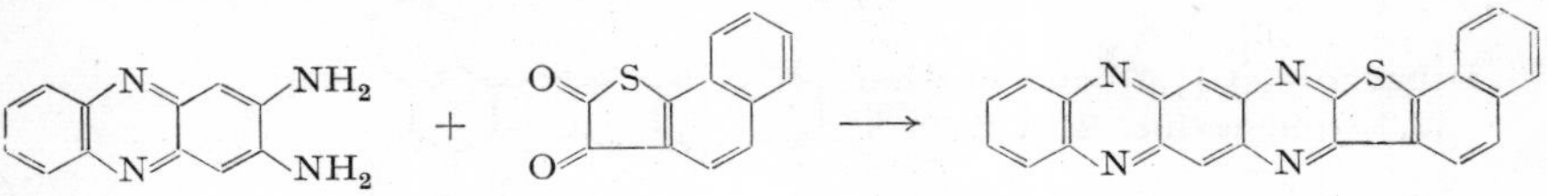

(CLIII)   (CLIV)

51. Naph[1′,2′,4,5]thieno[2,3-b]quinoxalo [2,3-g]quinoxaline. R. I. 3739

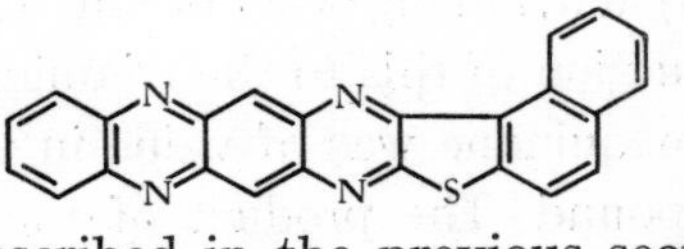

In a manner identical to that described in the previous section (XIX:50), Dutta[77] condensed 2,3-diaminophenazine with 1,2-dihydro-naphtho[2,1-*b*]thiophene-1,2-dione (CLV, *R. I.* 1745) to obtain naph-[1′,2′,4,5]thieno[2,3-*b*]quinoxalo[2,3-*g*]quinoxaline (CLVI) as a brown-violet powder, melting above 295° and giving a brownish-violet color in concentrated sulfuric acid. It dyed wool from an acid bath in brownish-violet shades.

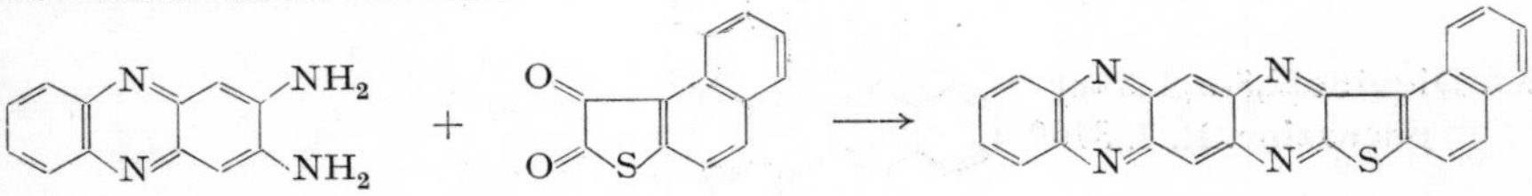

(CLV)   (CLVI)

52. 19-Dibenzo[c,e]quinoxalo [2′,3′,5,6]benzimidazo [1,2-a]azepine. R. I. 3744

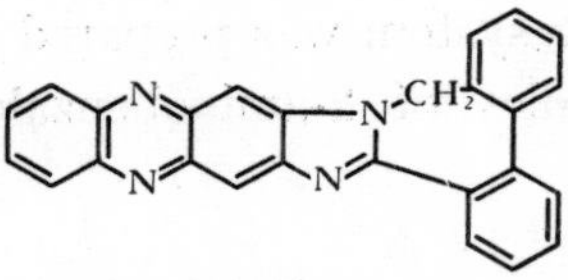

This ring system is represented by the product obtained by Sircar and De[6] by reacting 2,3-diaminophenazine with 2,2′-diphenic anhydride. 19-Dibenzo[*c,e*]quinoxalo[2′,3′,5,6]benzimidazo[1,2-*a*]azepin-19-one (CLVII) crystallized in greenish-yellow needles, which did not melt below 290° and which gave a blood-red coloration with concentrated sulfuric acid.

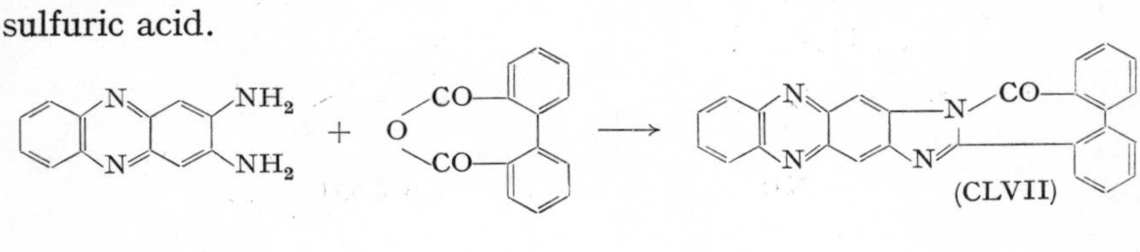

(CLVII)

For similarly derived ring systems using different acid anhydrides, see Sections XIX:29, 30 and 45.

53. Dibenzo[a,c]-[1,4]benzodioxino [2,3-i]phenazine. R. I. 3759

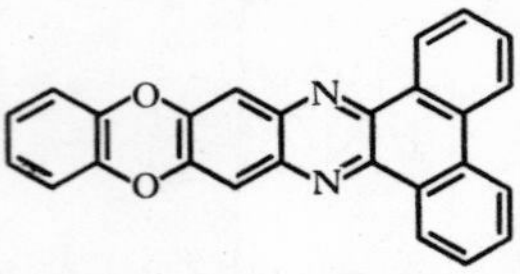

Tomita[78] studied the nitration of dibenzo-*p*-dioxin (CLVIII, *R. I.* 1931) and, among other products, described the 2,3,7-trinitro derivative. Reduction of this to the triamine and condensation with 9,10-phenanthrenequinone was of value in indicating the orientation of the nitro compound The product of the condensation, 13-aminodibenzo[a,c]-[1,4]benzodioxino[2,3-i]phenazine (CLIX), formed yellow crystals, m p. 339°.

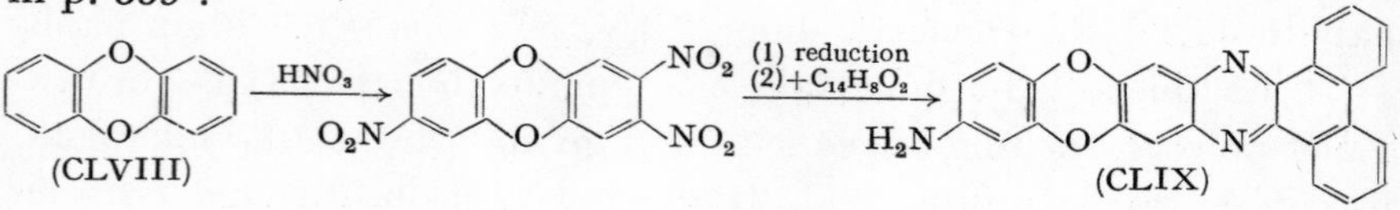

(CLVIII) $\xrightarrow{\text{HNO}_3}$ (1) reduction $\xrightarrow{(2)+C_{14}H_8O_2}$ (CLIX)

54. Diquino[2,3-a,2',3'-c] phenazine. R. I. 3760

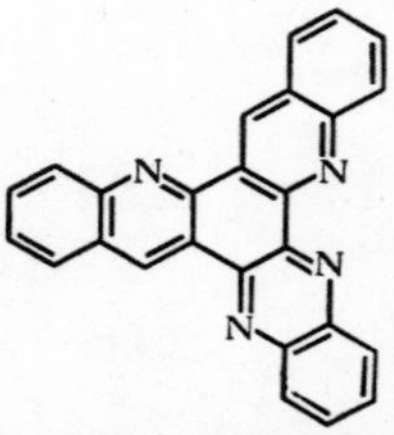

This basic ring system was prepared by von Niementowski.[79] He condensed two moles of 2-aminobenzaldehyde with one mole of

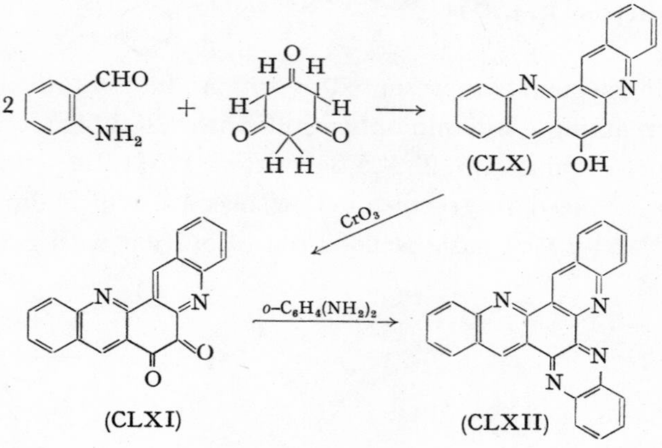

2   (CLX)   OH

$\xdownarrow{\text{CrO}_3}$

(CLXI) $\xrightarrow{o-C_6H_4(NH_2)_2}$ (CLXII)

phloroglucinol under the conditions of the Friedländer synthesis to yield 7-hydroxyquin[2,3]acridine (CLX, *R. I.* 3280). This was oxidized by chromic acid to the 6,7-quinone (CLXI), which was then condensed with *o*-phenylenediamine. Diquino[2,3-*a*,2′,3′-*c*]phenazine (CLXII) formed yellow needles, m.p. 420°.

55. Diisoquino[5,4-*ab*,5′,4′-*hi*]
      phenazine. R. I. 3761

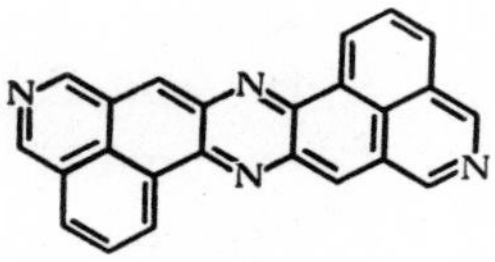

This is one of the structures attributed by Francis and Simonsen[80] to products obtained in the condensation of 5-amino-2,3-dihydro-2-methyl-1-benz[*de*]isoquinolin-1,3-dione (CLXIII, *R. I.* 1980, *N*-methyl-1,8-naphthalimide) with 1-chloro-5,10-anthraquinones, which may also be substituted with 4- or 6-benzamido groups.

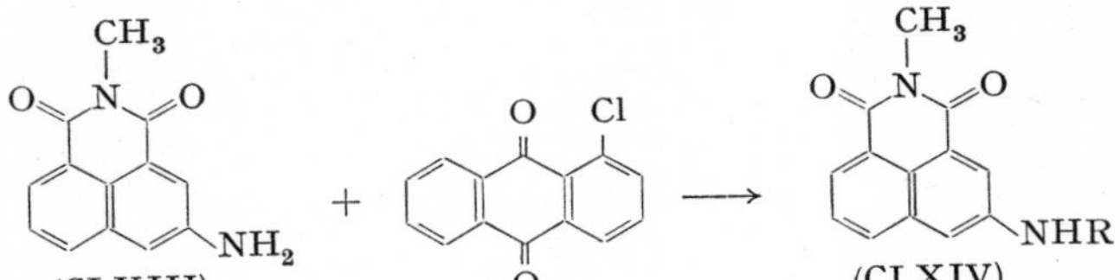

(CLXIII)   +   (CLXIV)

This reaction under normal conditions gives the 1-anthraquinonyl-amino compound (CLXIV, R = 1-anthraquinonyl) or a substitution product of this. When, however, the reaction is conducted in nitrobenzene at 200–210°, it takes an abnormal course and the chloroanthraquinone appears to act as a dehydrogenating agent. The products are 5,10-anthraquinone and a compound crystallizing in purple-red plates that does not melt below 400°. Francis and Simonsen suggested this was 4,5,6,8,12,13,14,16-octahydro-5,13-dimethyldiisoquino[5,4-*ab*,5′,4′-*hi*]-phenazine-4,6,12,14-tetrone (CLXV).

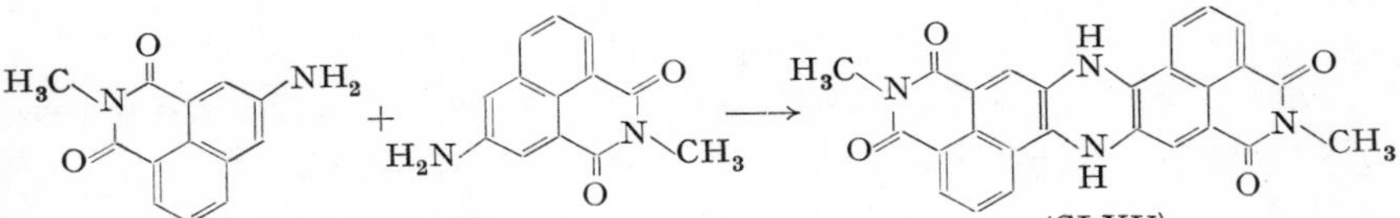

(CLXIII)   (CLXV)

With the 4- and 6-benzamido-1-chloro-5,10-anthraquinones and CLXIII, the reaction seemed to occur in yet a different way. The products were isomeric substances, $C_{47}H_{27}O_7N_5$. In analogy with CLXV, they could be the corresponding 8,1'-(4' or 6'-benzamido-5',10'-anthraquinonyl) compounds (CLXVI), in which R represents the 1'-(4'-benzamido-) and 1'-(6'-benzamido-5',10'-anthraquinonyl) residues. Alternatively, Francis and Simonsen suggested that the reaction took a different path and yielded representatives of another ring system. These would be 4- or 6-benzamido-8,12,13,14,16,17-hexahydro-13-methyl-8-(3'-N-methyl-1',8'-naphthalimido)-5-isoquino[5,4-ab]naphtho[2,3-h]phenazine-5,12,14,17-tetrones. Structure CLXVII represents the 4-benzamido isomer.

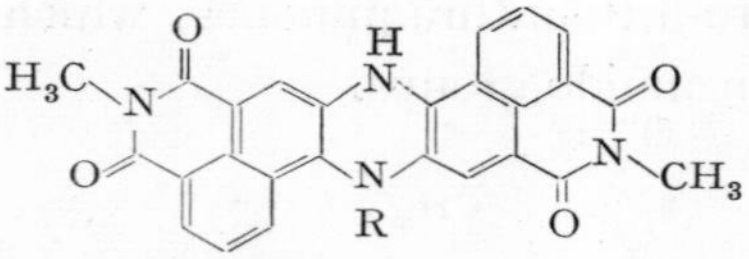

(CLXVI)

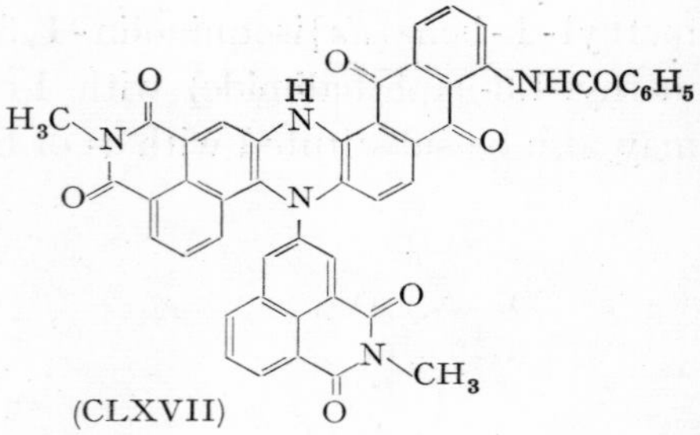

(CLXVII)

This structure (CLXVII) is a representative of the 5-isoquino-[5,4-ab]naphtho[2,3-h]phenazine system (R. I. 3762; Section XIX: 56). The compound (CLXVI or CLXVII) from 4-benzamido-1-chloro-5,10-anthraquinone and CLXIII forms purple needles, m.p. 320–323°, while that from the 6-benzamido isomer crystallizes in red needles, m.p. 331–333°.

56. 5-Isoquino[5,4-ab]naphtho[2,3-h] phenazine. R. I. 3762

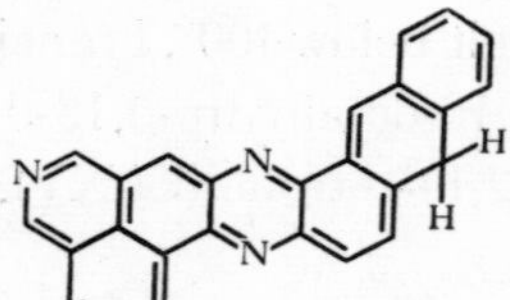

Two compounds that may possess this skeleton have been discussed in the previous section (Section XIX:55), to which the reader is referred.

57. 16-Benzo[*a*]naphtho[2′,1′,5,6]pyrano [2,3-c]phenazine. R. I. 3763

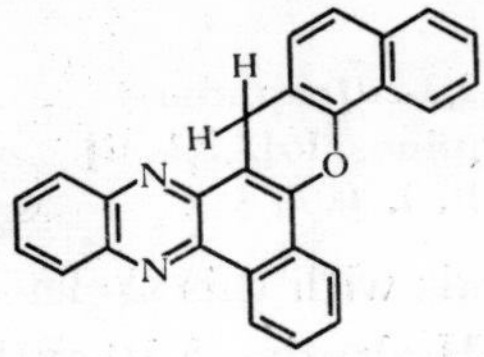

Sen-Gupta and Tucker[81] prepared a number of 7-dibenzo[*c,h*]-xanthenes (CLXVIII, *R. I.* 3344) by condensing aliphatic ketones with 1-naphthol. One of the products of the chromic acid oxidation of these compounds was, in each case, the 5,6-quinone. These were condensed with *o*-phenylenediamine to yield a number of substituted derivatives of 16-benzo[*a*]naphtho[2′,1′,5,6]pyrano[2,3-*c*]phenazine (CLXIX), which are listed in Table LXI.

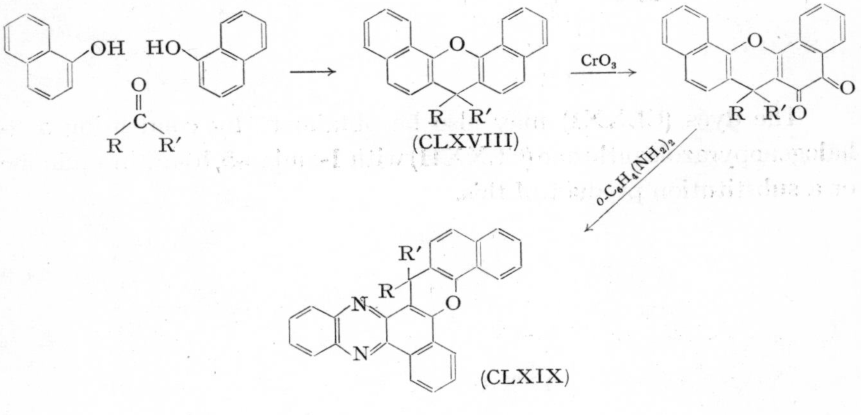

TABLE LXI. 16-Benzo[*a*]naphtho [2′,1′,5,6]pyrano[2,3-*c*]phenazines[81]

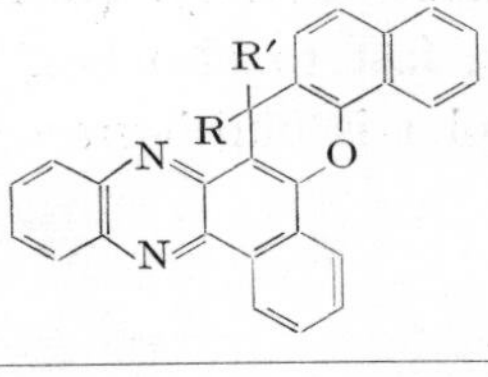

Substituents	Appearance	M.p. (°C.)
16,16-Dimethyl-	Brown needles	251–252
16-Ethyl-16-methyl-	Yellow rods	236–241
16,16-Diethyl-	Yellow rods	218–219

58. Naphtho[1,2,3-cd]naphtho [2′,3′,5,6]quinoxalo[3,2,1-hi] indazole. R. I. 3868

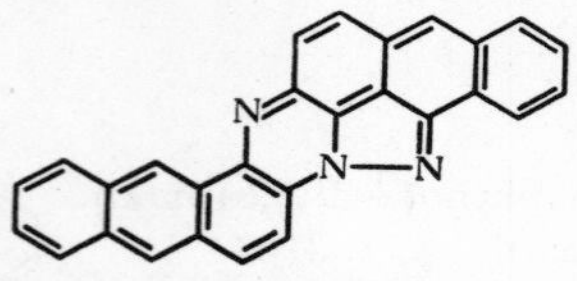

Compounds with this skeleton are described as new vat dyes in a patent.[82,83] 1-Hydrazino-5,10-anthraquinones are first converted to the corresponding pyrazoleanthrone (CLXX) and these are then condensed, in the presence of alkaline reagents such as potassium carbonate and copper powder in hot nitrobenzene, with 1-amino-2-halogeno-5,10-anthraquinones or their substitution products.

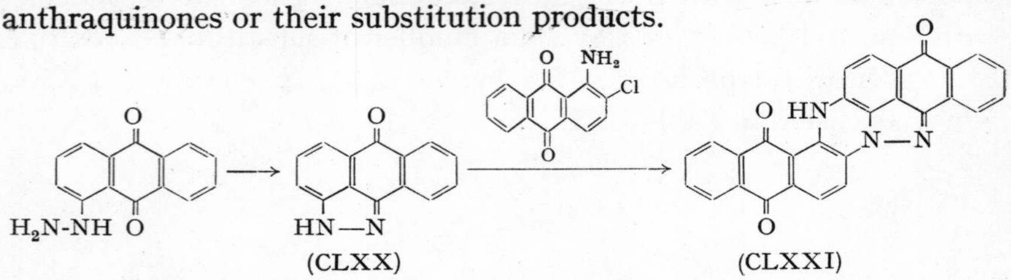

(CLXX)   (CLXXI)

The dyes (CLXXI) may also be obtained[82] by condensing a 2-halogenopyrazoleanthrone (CLXXII) with 1-amino-5,10-anthraquinone or a substitution product of this.

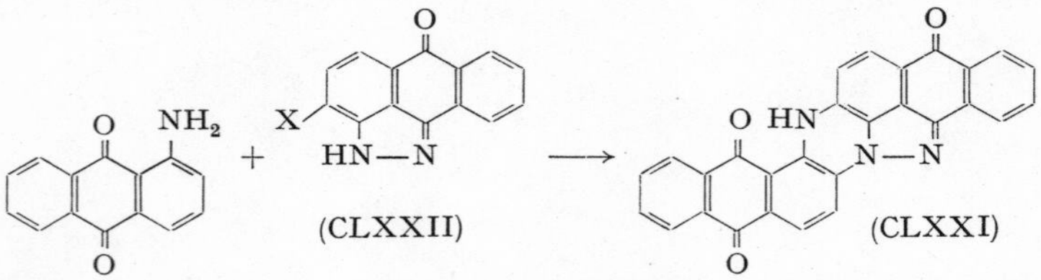

(CLXXII)   (CLXXI)

The unsubstituted dye (CLXXI) dyes cotton from a vat in blue-violet shades, fast to bleaches. When it is substituted by hydroxyl groups the color is bluish-green and this on chlorination becomes a grey dye.

59. Dinaphtho[2,3-a,2′,3′-i]pyrido [3,2-c]phenazine. R. I. 3884

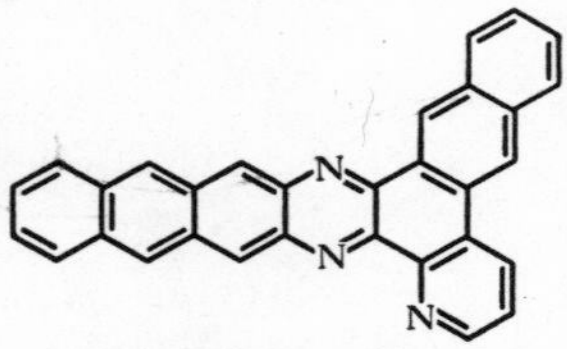

A representative of this system is described in a patent.[84] It is obtained by the condensation of 2,3-diamino-5,10-anthraquinone with

Alizarin Blue (7,12 - dihydro - 5,6 - dihydroxynaphtho [2,3 -*f*]quinoline-7,12-dione, *R. I.* 2733, *C. I.* 1066) in the presence of boric acid in phenol. The dye, 5,10,12,17,19,20-hexahydrodinaphtho [2,3-*a*,2′,3′-*i*]-pyrido [3,2-*c*]phenazine-5,12,17,20-tetrone (CLXXIII), is difficultly soluble in organic solvents and gives green solutions in concentrated sulfuric acid. It dyes cotton from a vat in green shades.

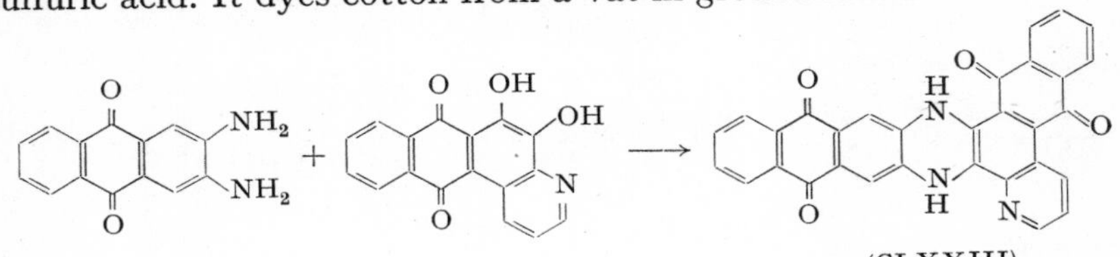

(CLXXIII)

60. 7,9,18-Triaza-19-dinaphtho [2,3-*a*,3′,2′,1′-*hi*] naphthacene.
Pyrido [2,3,4-*lm*]anthrazine.
R. I. 3885

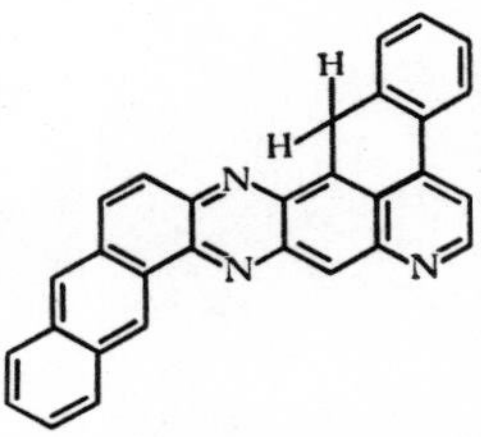

This polycyclic system is a derivative of the anthrazine system. The sole representative (CLXXVII) is derived from indanthrone (Chapter XVII) and is sometimes known as "pyridinoindanthrone." A group of patents deal with its production from 2,1′-dianthraquinonylamine (CLXXIV). This compound is nitrated[85] to the 1,4′-dinitro-2,1′-di-anthraquinonylamine (CLXXV), which may be reduced[85,86] to the 1,4′-diamino compound (CLXXVI) by aqueous sodium sulfide and this, on warming to 45° with acetic anhydride in the presence of concentrated or fuming sulfuric acid,[86] undergoes dehydration and ring closure to CLXXVII. Alternatively, the dinitrodianthraquinonylamine (CLXXV) is reduced and ring closed in one stage to 8-aminoindanthrone (CLXXVIII) by fusion with a mixture of sodium sulfide and sodium hydroxide.[85,86] 8-Aminoindanthrone on warming with acetic anhydride in the presence of concentrated or fuming sulfuric acid[86] then undergoes acetylation and subsequent dehydration to CLXXVII. A third route to CLXXVII is described in another patent[87] in which the dinitrodi-anthraquinonylamine (CLXXV) is treated with a mixture of sulfur, acetic anhydride and fuming sulfuric acid at 30°, when reduction, ring closure, acetylation and dehydration occurs in one stage. The routes are outlined in the accompanying reaction scheme.

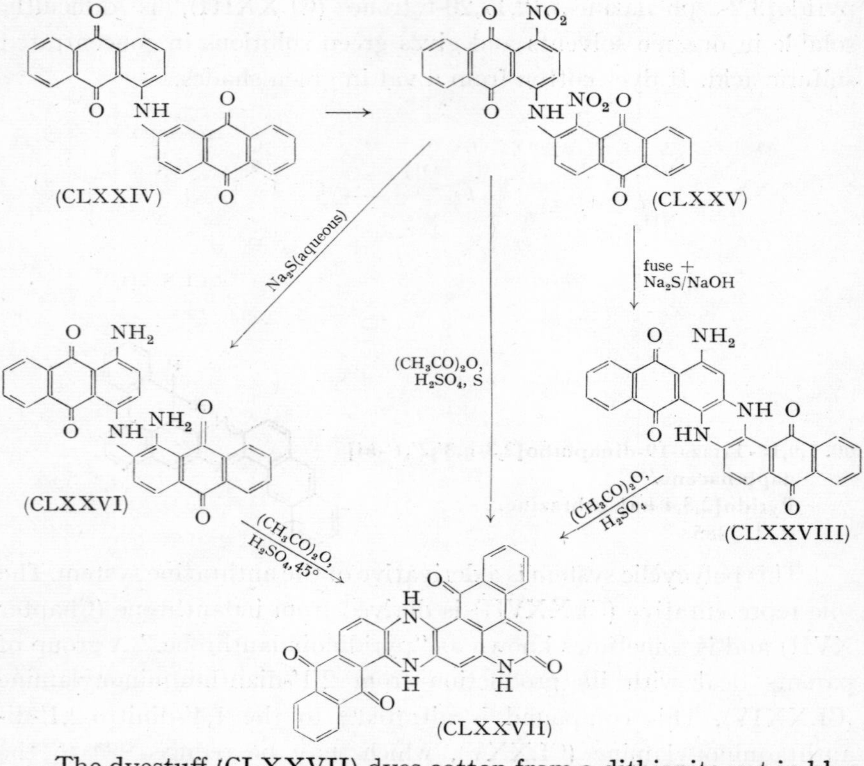

(CLXXIV) → (CLXXV)

Na$_2$S(aqueous)

fuse + Na$_2$S/NaOH

(CH$_3$CO)$_2$O, H$_2$SO$_4$, S

(CLXXVI)

(CLXXVIII)

(CH$_3$CO)$_2$O, H$_2$SO$_4$, 45°

(CH$_3$CO)$_2$O, H$_2$SO$_4$

(CLXXVII)

The dyestuff (CLXXVII) dyes cotton from a dithionite vat in blue colors and gives an emerald-green solution in concentrated sulfuric acid. A related dyestuff is described in Section XIX:63.

61. Dibenzo[c,c′]furo[2,3-a,4,5-a′] diphenazine. R. I. 3921

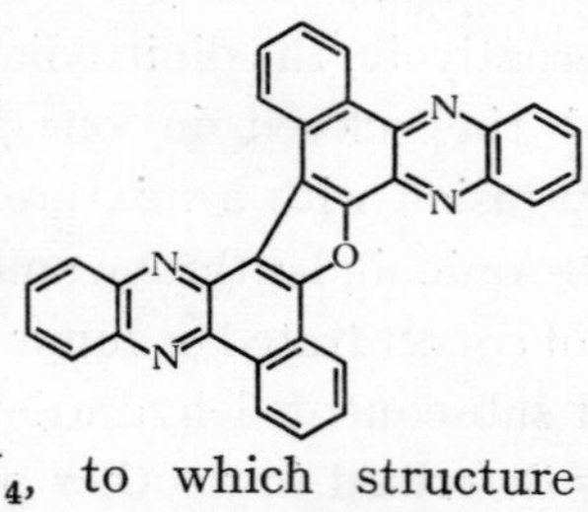

A compound, C$_{32}$H$_{16}$ON$_4$, to which structure CLXXX was attributed, was described by Lindenbaum.[88] By heating 6-bromo-5-

hydroxybenzo[a]phenazine in nitrobenzene he obtained the ether (CLXXIX) and this was heated with sodium ethoxide in ethanolic solution when the compound said to be dibenzo[c,c']furo[2,3-a,4,5-a']-diphenazine (CLXXX) was obtained as greenish-yellow needles, melting above 300°. The loss of the elements of hypobromous acid under these reaction conditions is surprising and the reaction may be worthy of reinvestigation.

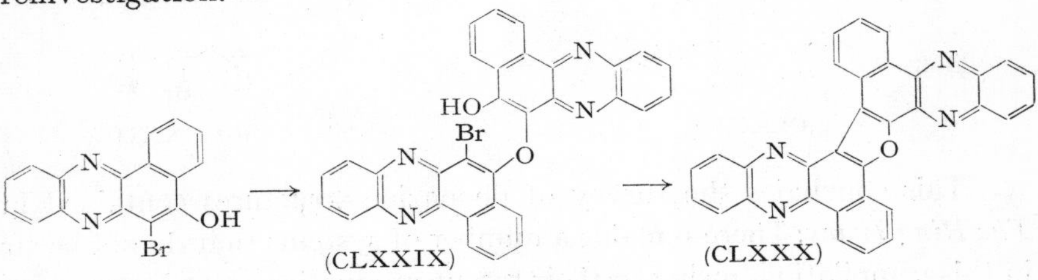

(CLXXIX)   (CLXXX)

62. Dibenzo[c,c']furo[3,2-a,4,5,-a']
diphenazine. R. I. 3922

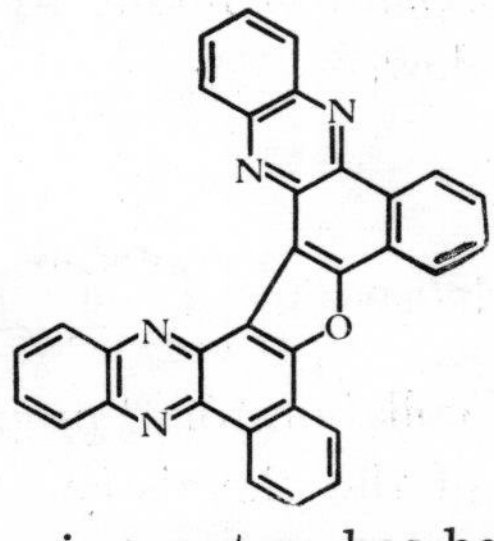

The basic compound of this ring system has been synthesized by Hooker.[74] It is described together with a related system in Section XIX:47, to which the reader is referred.

63. 7,9,17,19-Tetrazadinaphtho
[1,2,3-de,1',2',3'-op]
pentacene. R. I. 3929

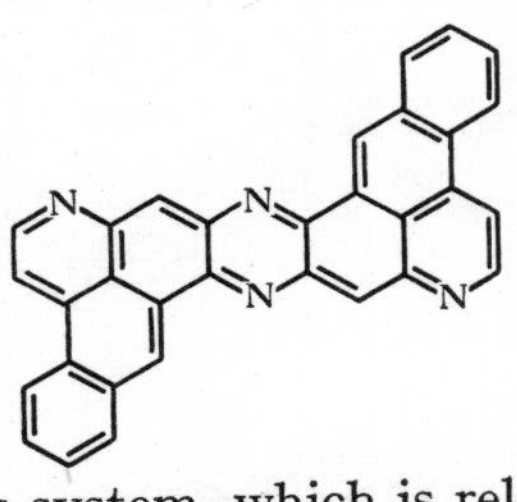

A representative of this system, which is related to 7,9,18-triaza-19-dinaphtho[2,3-a,3',2',1'-hi]naphthacene (*R. I.* 3885; Section XIX: 60) is described in a patent[86] dealing with the production of vat dyes. Like its less complicated relative, this dye (CLXXXII) is obtained by warming a mixture of acetic anhydride and fuming sulfuric acid with a derivative of indanthrone, in this particular case, 8,17-diamino-7,16-dibromoindanthrone (CLXXXI). It gives a green coloration in concentrated sulfuric acid.

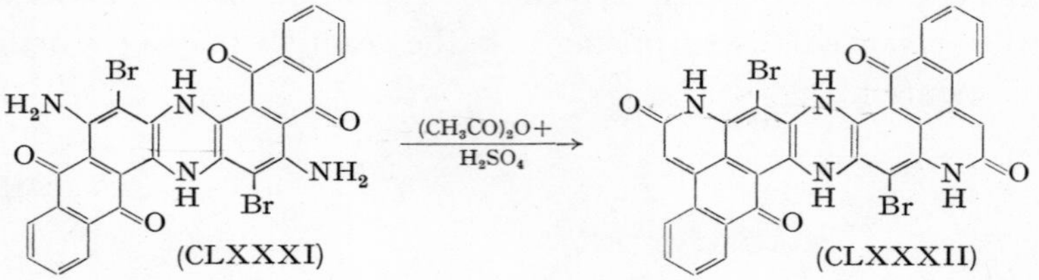

This concludes the survey of phenazine structures contained in *The Ring Index*. There remains a number of systems that do not occur in this compilation, owing to their recent production or to inadvertent omission from the *Index* or finally to their complex polymeric nature. These are listed below.

64. 3-Pyrazolo[4,3-a]phenazine

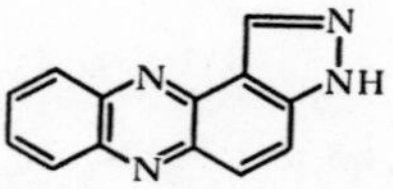

Fries and his collaborators[89] prepared this system in 1941 in the course of studies of the chemistry of isoindazole. 5-Hydroxy-1,3-diphenylisoindazole was converted to the 4,5-quinone by bromination and hydrolysis. This quinone reacted with o-phenylenediamine to yield 1,3-diphenyl-3-pyrazolo[4,3-a]phenazine (CLXXXIII) as sheaves of yellow needles that possessed a double m.p. at 165° and 185°.

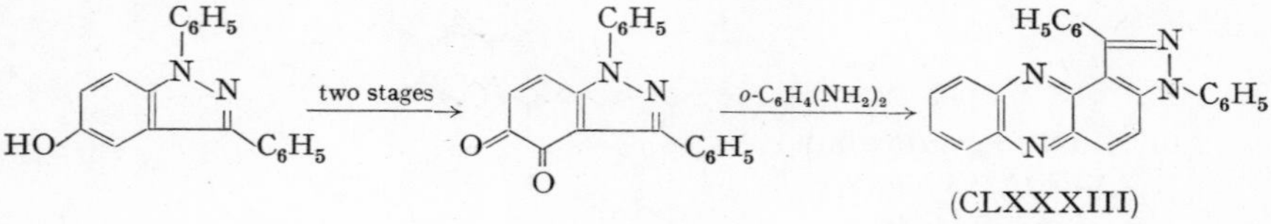

65. Furo[3,4-b]phenazine

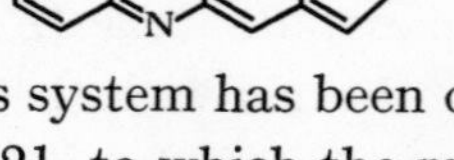

A derivative of this system has been discussed in another connection in Chapter XVIII:21, to which the reader is referred.

66. 10-*p*-Benzoxazino[2,3,4-*de*] phenazine

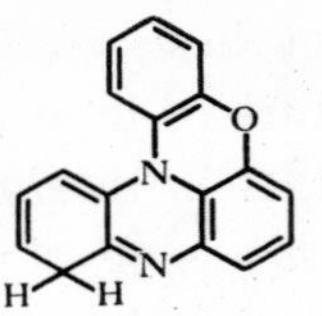

A derivative of this ring system has been proposed by Pavolini and his coworkers[90] as the structure of *p*-phenetidine brown, the oxidation product obtained by Kinzel[91] by the action of 3% hydrogen peroxide solution upon a solution of *p*-phenetidine in dilute sulfuric acid. The oxidation product, $C_{24}H_{22}O_5N_2$, forms a pale cinnamon-brown crystalline powder, decomposing at 280° and gives an intense blue coloration with concentrated sulfuric acid.

Kinzel proposed a structure (CLXXXIV) that contains a *m*-bridged benzene ring. Pavolini pointed out the strain such a structure would involve and since Kinzel had shown that the product was also formed by the action of *p*-phenetidine upon 4,4′-diethoxyazobenzene, which was found as a by-product in the oxidation, he accordingly proposed CLXXXVII as the structure of *p*-phenetidine brown and

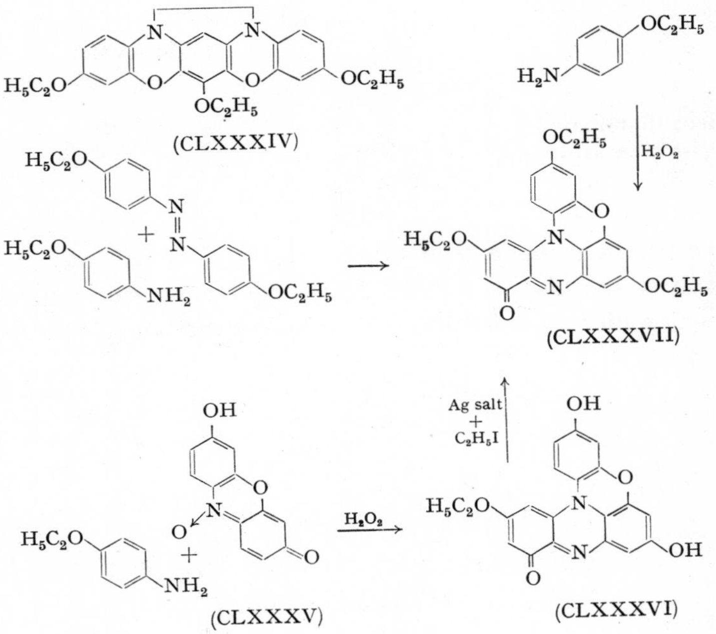

(CLXXXIV)

(CLXXXVII)

(CLXXXV)

(CLXXXVI)

based this upon a partial synthesis from resazurin (CLXXXV), by oxidation of this with a mixture of hydrogen peroxide in acetic acid. The intermediate (CLXXXVI) thus obtained is converted to the silver salt and this is ethylated by means of ethyl iodide.

The corresponding 3,7,12-trimethoxy-10-*p*-oxazino[2,3,4-*de*]phenazinone, *p*-anisidine brown, is obtained by the similar oxidation of *p*-anisidine. It forms a brown powder, m.p. 290° (dec.).

67. Quino[2,3-*b*]phenazine.
5,7,12-Triazapentacene

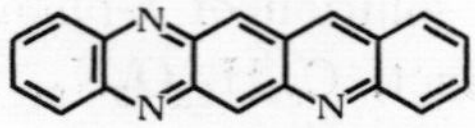

Borsche and Barthenheier[16] prepared a member of this series by condensing 1,2,3,4-tetrahydro-6,7-dihydroxyacridine with *o*-phenylenediamine by heating a mixture of the components in a sealed tube at 210°; the product was purified by repeated sublimation. 1,2,3,4-Tetrahydroquino[2,3-*b*]phenazine (CLXXXVIII) formed yellowish-white crystals, m.p. 350°.

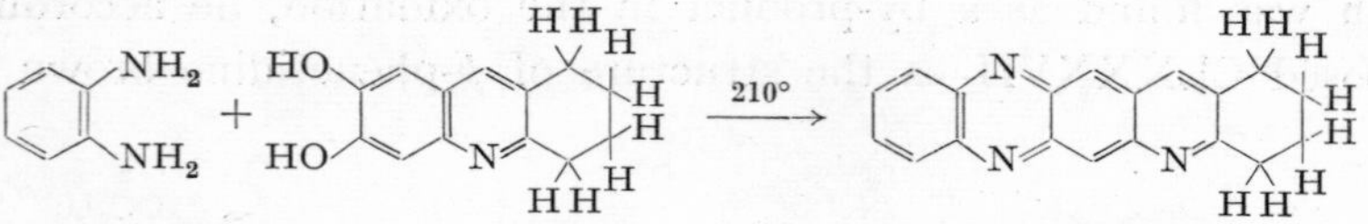

(CLXXXVIII)

68. Dibenzo[*a*,*c*]pyrido
[2,3-*h*]phenazine

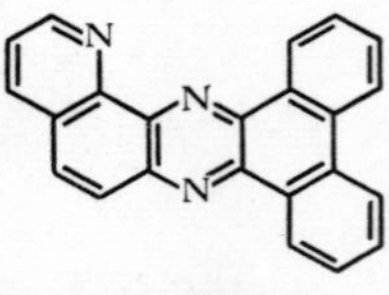

The parent compound of this series (CLXXXIX) was prepared by Renshaw and his associates.[68] 7-Aminoquinoline was coupled with benzenediazonium chloride and the aminoazo compound was reduced

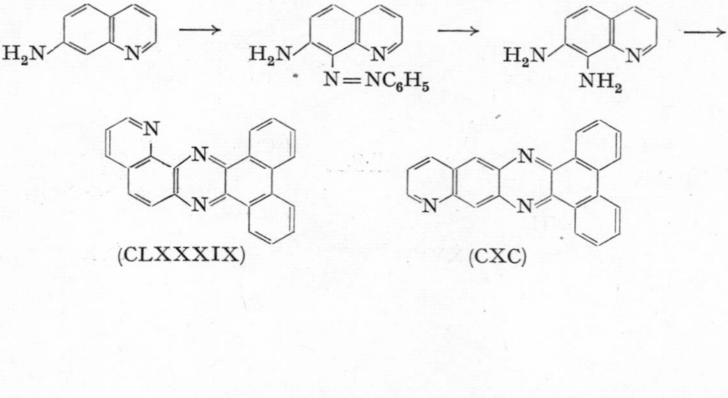

(CLXXXIX)   (CXC)

to what was probably 7,8-diaminoquinoline. This was condensed with 9,10-phenanthrenequinone to give CLXXXIX as crystals, m.p. 314°. The alternative formulation of the product as dibenzo[*a,c*]pyrido-[2,3-*i*]phenazine (CXC) is much less probable.

69. Phenanthro[9',10',4,5]thieno[2,3-*b*] quinoxalo[2,3-g]quinoxaline

The parent compound (CXCI), which forms a chocolate-brown mass, melting above 290°, was prepared by Dutta and Sinha[92] by the condensation of 2,3-diaminophenazine with 2,3-dihydrophenanthro-[9,10-*b*]thiophene-2,3-dione. It gives a blue-black coloration with concentrated sulfuric acid.

(CXCI)

70. 1,3,8,11,13,18-Hexazabis-benzonaphtheno[2,1-*a*,2',1'-*h*] anthracene*
Bisperimido[5,4-*a*,5',4'-*h*] phenazine

A dyestuff with this basic structure is described in a report, dated 3 June, 1939, from an I. G. Farben research laboratory and reissued by the U. S. Publications Board.[93] It is prepared by the aerial oxidation

---

* These reactions are discussed by Allen in the companion volume in this series, *Six-Membered Heterocyclic Nitrogen Compounds with Four Condensed Rings*, p. 283. It appears to us that there is an error in his interpretation of the original German report. The compound, which he calls 6-amino-1,3-diazabenzanthrone, is not identical with the German 5-amino-1,9-anthrapyrimidine. The resulting dye from the latter compound possesses structure XXXb according to the report, not XXXa. In agreement with this view is the statement in the report that 5-methylamino-1,9-anthrapyrimidine does not react. The second reaction involved 8-amino-1,9-anthrapyrimidine and this cannot yield either structure XXXa or XXXb. Structure XXXa ,in Allen's volume, would be produced from 4-amino-1,9-anthrapyrimidine, but in fact this reaction is not mentioned in the German report.

of a solution of 8-amino-1,3-diazabenzanthrone in pyridine at 50–55° in the presence of potassium hydroxide.

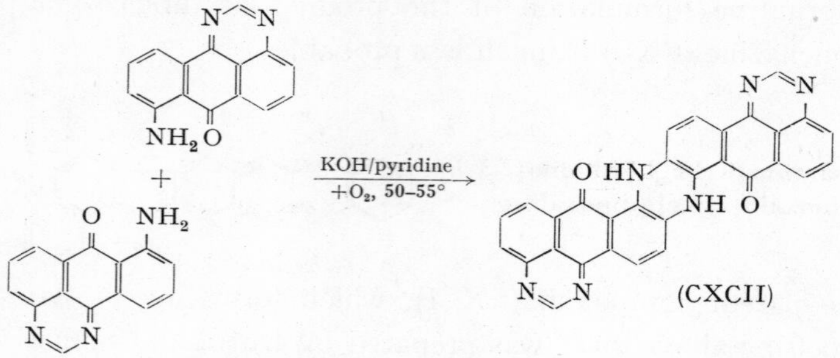

(CXCII)

From its preparation and analysis, it was given structure CXCII. A related dyestuff is described in the next section (XIX:71). The 8-methylaminodiazabenzanthrone failed to react to give the N,N'-di-methyl homolog of CXCII. C-Methyl and C-phenyl derivatives were mentioned but no details are available. The dyestuff is unstable when vatted, but by a special procedure gave deep sea-blue dyeings of poor stability.

71. 4,6,7,14,16,17-Hexazabisbenzonaphtheno[1,2-a,1′,2′-h]anthracene.* Bisperimido[4,5-a,4′,5′-h] phenazine.

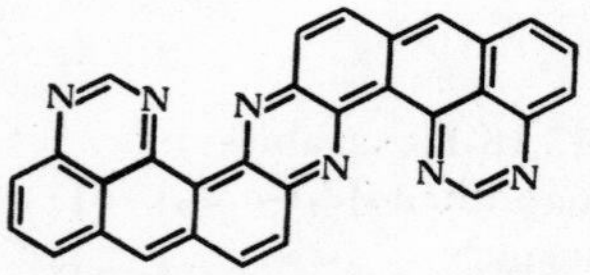

This structure is closely related to that described in the preceding section. Both are described in the same report[93] and both are prepared in the same manner. The dyestuff of which this is the basic structure was prepared by aeration of a pyridine solution of 11-amino-1,3-diaza-

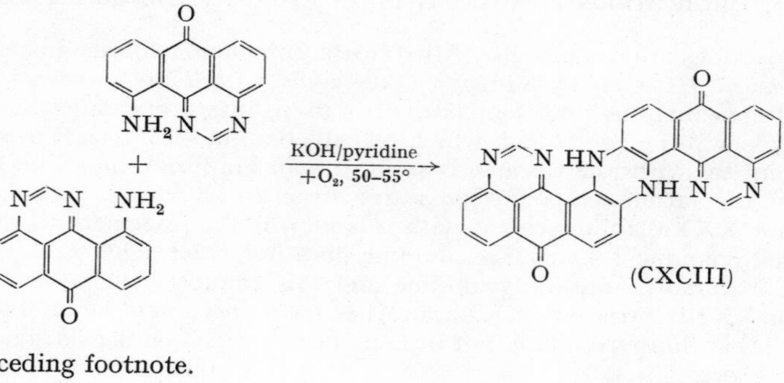

(CXCIII)

* See preceding footnote.

benzanthrone, heated to 50–55° in the presence of potassium hydroxide. The product, 7,10,17,20 - tetrahydro - 4,6,7,14,16,17 - hexazabisbenzo-naphtheno [1,2-*a*,1′,2′-*h*]anthracene-10,20-dione (CXCIII) was a weakly violet dyestuff of very poor fastness.

Neither CXCII nor CXCIII has any commercial value as vat dyes.

72. Dibenzo[*a,j*]diquinoxalo [2,3-*c*,2′,3′-*h*]phenox-azine or Dibenzo[*a,h*] diquinoxalo[2,3-*c*,2′,3′-*j*] phenoxazine

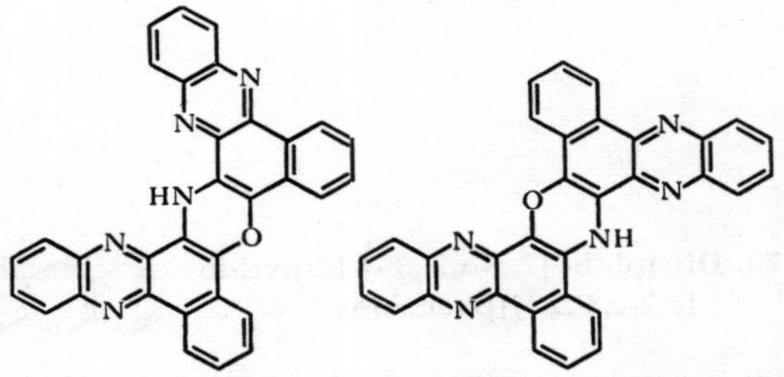

A compound, which has been omitted from *The Ring Index* presumably inadvertantly, was obtained by Lindenbaum,[88] who found that heating 6-bromo-5-hydroxybenzo[*a*]phenazine with alcoholic ammonia gave $C_{32}H_{19}O_2N_5$. This, he concluded, was either 5,5′-di-hydroxy-6,6′-di(benzo[*a*]phenazinyl)amine (CXCIV) or 6-amino-5′-hydroxy-5,6′-di(benzo[*a*]phenazinyl) ether (CXCV). When the com-

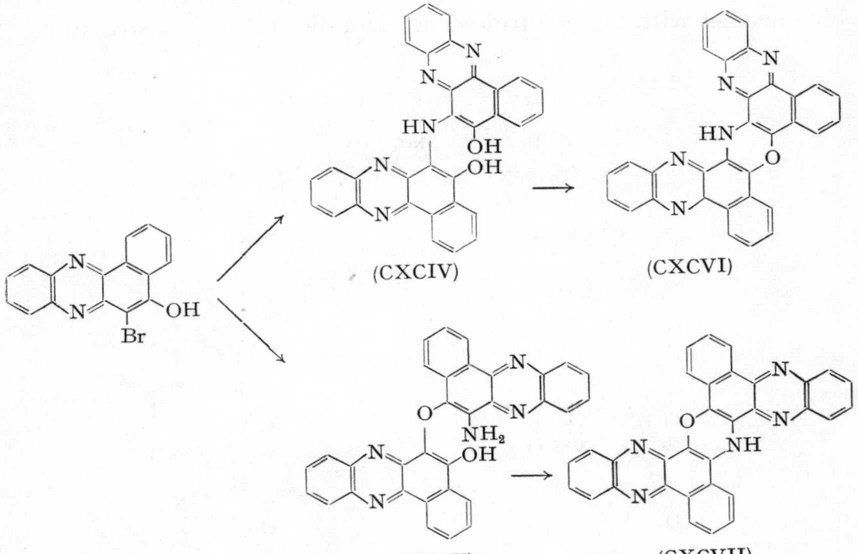

(CXCIV)

(CXCVI)

(CXCV)

(CXCVII)

pound $C_{32}H_{19}O_2N_5$ was heated in nitrobenzene, water was expelled and a new compound $C_{32}H_{17}ON_5$ was obtained as lustrous blue-black needles, which did not melt below 300°. This may be either dibenzo-[a,j]diquinoxalo[2,3-c,2′,3′-h]phenoxazine (CXCVI) or dibenzo[a,h]-diquinoxalo[2,3-c,2′,3′-j]phenoxazine (CXCVII), respectively, depending upon the exact nature of the intermediate.

73. Dinaphtho[2,3-a,2′,3′-h]dipyrido [3,2-c,3′,2′-j]phenazine

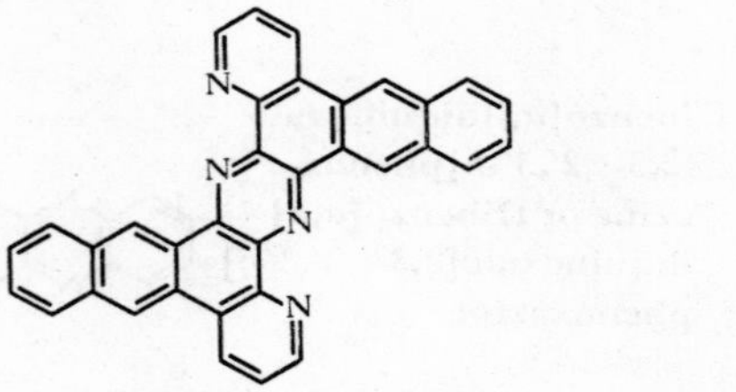

Schiedt[94] prepared an example of this ring system by means of the anomalous Leuckart reaction (see Chapter XVI:22) of o-quinones. He oxidized Alizarin Blue (CXCVIII) to the diquinone (CXCIX) by means of nitric acid and then this was heated with formamide at 150° under pressure. The product, 5,10,11,16,21,22-hexahydrodinaphtho[2,3,-a, 2′,3′-h]dipyrido[3,2-c,3′,2′-j]phenazine-5,10,16,21-tetrone (CC), formed blue needles with a green iridescence and did not melt below 400°.

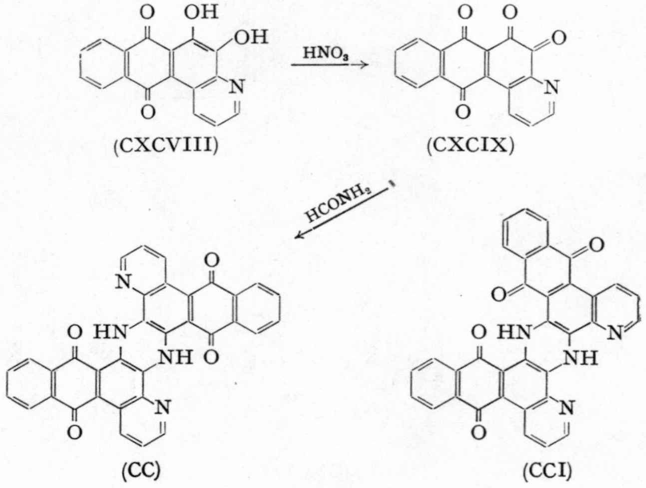

(CXCVIII)   (CXCIX)

(CC)   (CCI)

The alternative formulation of the product as 5,10,15,20,21,22-hexahydrodinaphtho[2,3-*a*,2′,3′-*j*]dipyrido[3,2-*c*,2′,3′-*h*]phenazine (CCI) was not considered by Schiedt, but is equally feasible.

74. Nigrosulfine

A black sulfur-containing dye called Nigrosulfine, which is water-soluble and suitable for dyeing cotton and chrome-mordanted leather, is formed by fusing 2,4-dinitrophenol with sulfur and treating the melt with sodium hydrogen sulfite in the presence of air.[95,96] The pure dye $(C_{24}H_4N_6O_{12}S_{10}Na_4.5H_2O)_n$ was shown to contain two sulfite and two thiosulfite groups per repeating unit by means of acid and alkaline hydrolysis experiments. The complex reactions occurring on oxidation in the presence of sulfides, sulfites and thiosulfites are discussed fully in the papers and on this basis the conjectural process shown below was advanced, leading to structure (CCII) for Nigrosulfine. Ufimtsev[97] has adversely criticized the hydrolysis data and the conclusions drawn therefrom. The improbable nature of the sulfur-sulfur links shown in the intermediate stages is a further point against the proposed mechanism.

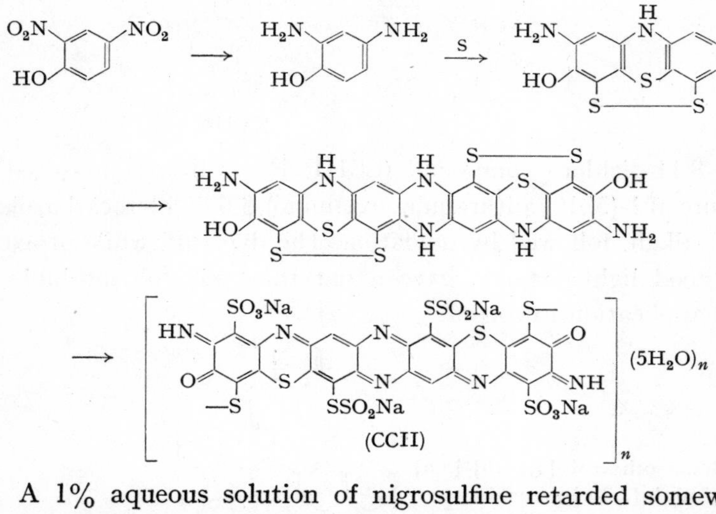

(CCII)

A 1% aqueous solution of nigrosulfine retarded somewhat the development of experimental tuberculosis in rabbits according to another group of Soviet workers.[98]

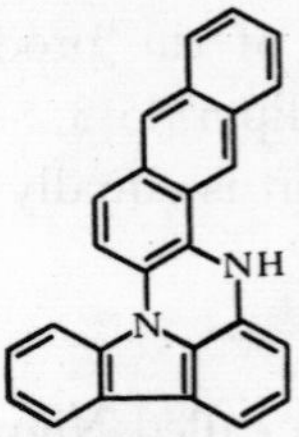

**75. 6-Naphth[2,3-a]indolo
    [1,2,3-fg]phenazine**

Dyestuffs containing this ring system are mentioned in a review of German wartime research on dyestuffs.[99] The simplest representative (CCIII, R = H) was prepared by reacting 1-chloro-5,10-anthraquinone-2-carboxylic acid with 1-aminocarbazole in the presence of methanolic potassium hydroxide at 130–150°, and completing the reaction by oxidation. The dyestuff, obtained in 80% yield, gave blue shades with excellent light-fastness properties but it showed only poor affinity for cotton.

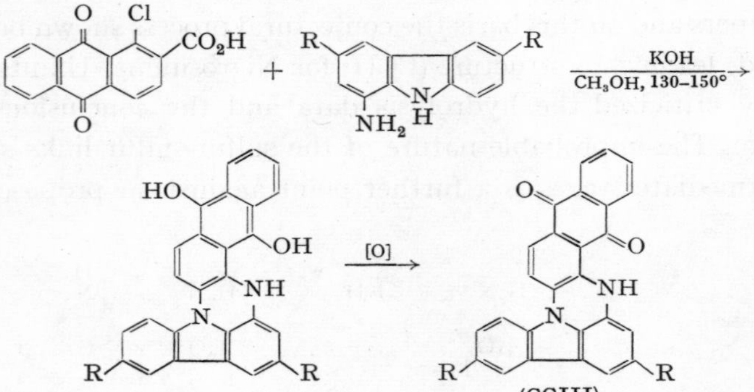

The 8,11-dichloro compound (CCIII, R = Cl) was produced by ring closure of 1-(5′,10′-anthraquinonylamino)-3,6-dichlorocarbazole by means of alkali, followed by oxidation. The dyestuff, while of exceptionally good light-fastness, gave a vat that was too insoluble for practical application to cotton.

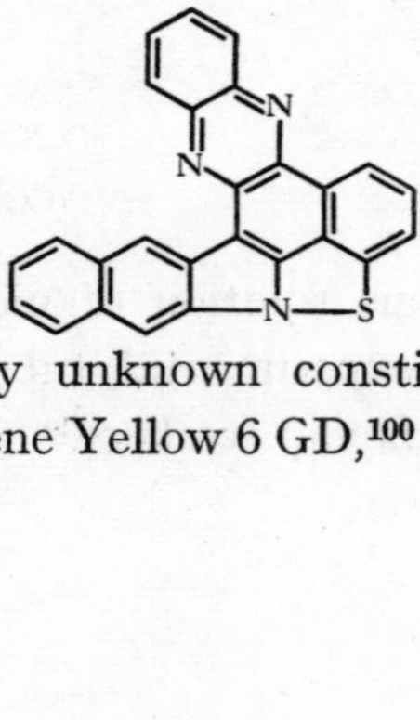

**76. [1,2]Benzisothiazolo[4,3-ab]-[5,6]
    benzindolo[2,3-c]phenazine**

A vat dyestuff of previously unknown constitution, produced under the trade name of Indanthrene Yellow 6 GD,[100] has been revealed to be CCIV. Because of its non-tendering, light-fast greenish-yellow shade, it was revived by I. G. Farbenindustrie A.G. and numerous substituted derivatives were prepared. All were less light-fast than the standard shade.[101] It seems very probable[102] that Indanthrene Yellow 6 GD is the product dyeing cotton from a vat in fast, clear greenish-yellow shades, described in a patent[30] as being produced by the action of 2,3-dichloro-1,4-naphthoquinone upon 5[1,2]benzisothiazolo[4,3-*ab*]-phenazine-4,4-dioxide (*R. I.* 3033) in nitrobenzene in the presence of sodium acetate (see Section XIX:19).

(CCIV)

References

1. G. Hugel, *Compt. rend.*, **182,** 65 (1926); *Chem. Abstracts*, **20,** 1239 (1926); *Chem. Zentr.*, **1926,** I, 1995.
2. A. W. Johnson, *Ann. Repts. Progress Chem.*, **48,** 213 (1951).
3. A. C. Sircar and S. C. Sen, *J. Indian Chem. Soc.*, **11,** 363 (1934); *Chem. Abstracts*, **28,** 6151 (1934).
4. K. Fries, M. Vorbrodt and G. Siebert, *Ann.*, **454,** 172 (1927).
5. P. Karrer, *Ber.*, **46,** 255 (1913).
6. A. C. Sircar and P. K. De, *Quart. J. Indian Chem. Soc.*, **2,** 312 (1925); *Chem. Abstracts*, **20,** 1805 (1926); *Chem. Zentr.*, **1926,** I, 2697.
7. A. Steigmann, *Brit. J. Phot.*, **93,** 256 (1946); *Chem. Abstracts*, **40,** 5347 (1946).
8. T. Zincke, E. Stoffel and E. Petermann, *Ann.*, **311,** 276 (1900).
9. K. Fries and E. Roth, *Ann.*, **389,** 318 (1912).
10. T. Zincke and E. Petermann, *Ann.*, **313,** 251 (1900).
11. K. Fries and J. Empson, *Ann.*, **389,** 345 (1912).
12. K. Fries and A. Wolter, *Ann.*, **527,** 60 (1936).
13. G. B. Crippa and P. Galimberti, *Gazz. chim. ital.*, **61,** 91 (1931); *Chem. Abstracts*, **25,** 3343 (1931).
14. K. Fries and R. Weldert, *Ann.*, **454,** 314 (1927).
15. H. Hillemann, *Ber.*, **71B,** 46 (1938).
16. W. Borsche and J. Barthenheier, *Ann.*, **548,** 50 (1941).
17. J. B. Cohen and H. G. Crabtree, *J. Chem. Soc.*, **119,** 2055 (1921).
18. A. Bernthsen, *Ber.*, **25,** 3128 (1892).
19. T. Zincke and K. Wiederhold, *Ann.*, **290,** 359 (1896).

20. L. I. Smith, W. B. Irwin and H. E. Ungnade, *Science*, **90**, 334 (1939).
21. L. I. Smith, W. B. Irwin and H. E. Ungnade, *J. Am. Chem. Soc.*, **61**, 2424 (1939).
22. W. John and W. Emte, *Z. physiol. Chem.*, **268**, 85 (1941).
23. G. Charrier and A. Beretta, *Gazz. chim. ital.*, **56**, 191 (1926); *Chem. Abstracts*, **20**, 2859 (1926).
24. G. Charrier, *Atti accad. Lincei*, [5], I, **33**, 346 (1924); *Chem. Zentr.*, **1924**, II, 2261.
25. G. Charrier and A. Manfredi, *Gazz. chim. ital.*, **56**, 196 (1926); *Chem. Abstracts*, **20**, 2859 (1926).
26. M. Gallotti and A. Ercoli, *Gazz. chim. ital.*, **59**, 207 (1929); *Chem. Abstracts*, **23**, 4216 (1929).
27. G. Charrier, *Gazz. chim. ital.*, **59**, 479 (1929); *Chem. Abstracts*, **24**, 366 (1930).
28. T. Zincke and H. Noack, *Ann.*, **295**, 6 (1897).
29. T. Zincke, *Ann.*, **412**, 78 (1917).
30. Ger. Pat. 368,172; *Chem. Zentr.*, **1923**, II, 1187.
31. Brit. Pat. 275,301; *Chem. Zentr.*, **1927**, II, 2718; see also U. S. Pat., 1,723,199; *Chem. Abstracts*, **23**, 4578 (1929).
32. Fr. Pat. 634,232; *Chem. Abstracts*, **22**, 3785 (1928); *Chem. Zentr.*, **1928**, I, 2544.
33. A. Corbellini, F. Capucci and G. Tommasini, *Gazz. chim. ital.*, **69**, 137 (1939); *Chem. Abstracts*, **33**, 7780 (1939).
34. F. Kehrmann and F. Zimmerli, *Ber.*, **31**, 2405 (1898).
35. H. Goldstein and G. Genton, *Helv. Chim. Acta*, **21**, 56 (1938).
36. F. Kehrmann and G. Barche, *Ber.*, **33**, 3067 (1900).
37. F. Kehrmann and M. Cordone, *Ber.*, **46**, 2974 (1913).
38. S. C. Hooker, *J. Am. Chem. Soc.*, **58**, 1168 (1936).
39. S. C. Hooker, *J. Am. Chem. Soc.*, **58**, 1181 (1936).
40. S. C. Hooker and A. Steyermark, *J. Am. Chem. Soc.*, **58**, 1202 (1936).
41. O. Fischer and E. Hepp, *Ber.*, **28**, 293 (1895).
42. E. Diepolder, *Ber.*, **35**, 2816 (1902).
43. F. Kehrmann, E. Grillet and P. Borgeaud, *Helv. Chim. Acta*, **9**, 866 (1926).
44. O. Fischer and C. Giesen, *Ber.*, **30**, 2489 (1897).
45. F. Kehrmann and J. A. Schedler, *Helv. Chim. Acta*, **8**, 9 (1925).
46. E. Diepolder, *Ber.*, **34**, 2272 (1901).
47. E. Diepolder, *Ber.*, **32**, 3514 (1899).
48. E. Diepolder, *Ber.*, **31**, 495 (1898).
49. W. Meigen and E. Nottebohm, *Ber.*, **39**, 744 (1906).
50. H. Wieland and E. Haas, *Ber.*, **53**, 1336 (1920).
51. S. C. Hooker, *J. Chem. Soc.*, **63**, 1376 (1893).
52. S. C. Hooker, *J. Am. Chem. Soc.*, **58**, 1190 (1936).
53. S. C. Hooker, *J. Am. Chem. Soc.*, **58**, 1174 (1936).
54. S. C. Hooker and A. Steyermark, *J. Am. Chem. Soc.*, **58**, 1179 (1936).
55. S. C. Hooker and A. Steyermark, *J. Am. Chem. Soc.*, **58**, 1207 (1936).
56. S. C. Hooker and A. Steyermark, *J. Am. Chem. Soc.*, **58**, 1198 (1936).
57. G. Charrier, *Gazz. chim. ital.*, **54**, 610 (1924); *Chem. Zentr.*, **1924**, II, 2656.
58. L. F. Fieser, *J. Am. Chem. Soc.*, **48**, 1097 (1926).
59. W. H. Perkin and R. Robinson, *J. Chem. Soc.*, **95**, 381 (1909).
60. E. Vongerichten, *Ber.*, **33**, 352 (1900).
61. E. Vongerichten, *Ber.*, **38**, 1851 (1905).
62. F. Kehrmann and G. Wild, *Helv. Chim. Acta*, **8**, 13 (1925).
63. F. Kehrmann and C. Collaud, *Helv. Chim. Acta*, **11**, 1028 (1928).

64. H. D. K. Drew and F. H. Pearman, *J. Chem. Soc.*, **1937**, 586.
65. G. M. Robinson and R. Robinson, *J. Chem. Soc.*, **111**, 929 (1917).
66. K. Lagodzinski and D. Hardine, *Ber.*, **27**, 3068 (1894).
67. A. Kaufmann and O. Zeller, *Ber.*, **50**, 1626 (1917).
68. R. R. Renshaw, H. L. Friedman and F. J. Gajewski, *J. Am. Chem. Soc.*, **61**, 3322 (1939).
69. D. M. Hall and E. E. Turner, *J. Chem. Soc.*, **1945**, 699.
70. Ger. Pat. 659,095; *Chem. Abstracts*, **32**, 5638 (1938).
71. H. Vollmann, H. Becker, M. Corell and H. Streeck, *Ann.*, **531**, 1 (1937).
72. W. Borsche and B. Schacke, *Ber.*, **56B**, 2498 (1923).
73. H. Gilman, G. E. Brown, W. G. Bywater and W. H. Kirkpatrick, *J. Am. Chem. Soc.*, **56**, 2473 (1934).
74. S. C. Hooker, *J. Am. Chem. Soc.*, **58**, 1212 (1936).
75. H. Gilman, A. L. Jacoby and J. Swislowsky, *J. Am. Chem. Soc.*, **61**, 954 (1939).
76. G. R. Clemo and R. Spence, *J. Chem. Soc.*, **1928**, 2811.
77. P. C. Dutta, *Ber.*, **66B**, 1223 (1933).
78. M. Tomita, *J. Pharm. Soc. Japan*, **55**, 205 (1935); *Chem. Zentr.*, **1936**, I, 2552.
79. S. von Niementowski, *Ber.*, **39**, 385 (1906).
80. E. M. Francis and J. L. Simonsen, *J. Chem. Soc.*, **1935**, 496.
81. H. K. Sen-Gupta and S. H. Tucker, *J. Chem. Soc.*, **121**, 557 (1922).
82. Ger. Pat. 498,067; *Chem. Zentr.*, **1930**, II, 995.
83. Ger. Pat. 493,813; *Chem. Zentr.*, **1930**, I, 3489.
84. Ger. Pat. 178,130; *Chem. Zentr.*, **1907**, I, 775; *Frdl.*, **8**, 346 (1905–1907).
85. Ger. Pat. 186,465; *Chem. Zentr.*, **1907**, II, 866; *Frdl.*, **9**, 779 (1908–1910).
86. Ger. Pat. 198,025; *Chem. Zentr.*, **1908**, I, 1814; *Frdl.*, **9**, 779 (1908–1910).
87. Ger. Pat. 200,015; *Chem. Zentr.*, **1908**, II, 463; *Frdl.*, **9**, 780 (1908–1910).
88. S. Lindenbaum, *Ber.*, **34**, 1050 (1901).
89. K. Fries, K. Fabel and H. Eckhardt, *Ann.*, **550**, 31 (1942).
90. T. Pavolini, F. Gambarin and W. Manzini, *Ann. chim. (Rome)*, **40**, 647 (1950); *Chem. Abstracts*, **46**, 4550 (1952); *Chem. Zentr.*, **1952**, 2000.
91. Kinzel, *Arch. Pharm.*, **229**, 329 (1891).
92. P. C. Dutta and R. M. Sinha, *J. Indian Chem. Soc.*, **18**, 477 (1941); *Chem. Abstracts*, **36**, 4505 (1942).
93. U. S. Publications Board Report (PB Report) 70342, pp. 14423–14425 (on microfilm).
94. B. Schiedt, *J. prakt. Chem.*, **157**, 203 (1941).
95. I. Khmel'nitzkaya and V. Verkhovskaya, *Anilinokrasochnaya Prom.*, **5**, 3 (1935); *Chem. Abstracts*, **29**, 3519 (1935); *Chem. Zentr.*, **1935**, II, 282.
96. I. Khmel'nitzkaya and V. Verkhovskaya, *Anilinokrasochnaya Prom.*, **5**, 67 (1935); *Chem. Abstracts*, **29**, 4943 (1935); *Chem. Zentr.*, **1935**, II, 2129.
97. V. N. Ufimtsev, *Org. Chem. Ind. (U.S.S.R.)*, **3**, 354 (1937); *Chem. Abstracts*, **31**, 6885 (1937); *Chem. Zentr.*, **1938**, II, 595.
98. F. L. Shpanir, E. D. Chertkova and L. I. Serebrennikova, *Problemy Tuberk*, **1940**, No. 3–4; *Chem. Abstracts*, **39**, 1223 (1945).
99. *F.I.A.T. Final Report*, No. 1313, Vol. III, pp. 31, 32.
100. Schultz, *Farbstofftabellen*, Ergänzungsband II, Akademische Verlag, Leipzig, 1939, p. 206.
101. *F.I.A.T. Final Report*, No. 1313, Vol. III, p. 35.
102. B. Suryanarayana and B. D. Tilak, *Proc. Indian Acad. Sci.*, **37A**, 81 (1953).

Addenda

Part I

G. A. Swan

Part II

D. G. I. Felton

Addendum to Chapter I

5. Rozum has reduced 2,2'-dinitrodiphenylamines to 5,10-dihy-drophenazines with sodium and methanol.[1]

8. Serebryanyĭ has shown that the action of aniline, in the presence of potassium hydroxide in a hydrocarbon solvent, on 2-nitro-diphenylamine, gives phenazine in 40–50% yield; whereas with the 4-isomer, 4-nitrosodiphenylamine results. This is taken as an indication of the participation of 2-nitrosodiphenylamine as an intermediate in the Wohl-Aue reaction.[2]

For further work on the preparation of phenazine-5-oxides by the Wohl-Aue reaction see reference 3.

References

1. Yu. S. Rozum, *Ukrain. Khim. Zhur.*, **16**, 434 (1950); through *Chem. Abstracts*, **49**, 1063 (1955).
2. S. B. Serebryanyĭ, *Ukrain. Khim. Zhur.*, **21**, 350 (1955); through *Chem. Abstracts*, **49**, 14773 (1955).
3. Y. Kidani, *Pharm. Bull.* (Japan), **2**, 292 (1954); through *Chem. Abstracts*, **50**, 1033 (1956).

Addendum to Chapter II

1A. A low temperature refinement of the crystal structure (Fourier projection) of phenazine has been published.[1]

1D. Phenazine failed to undergo the Diels-Alder reaction with anethole or maleic anhydride.[2]

1E. A recently published melting point (129–130°) for 1-methyl-phenazine-5-oxide is lower than that (142°) mentioned on pages 18 and 24.[3] In an abstract of another paper, the melting points of 1-methyl-phenazine-5-oxide and 2-phenazinecarboxylic acid-*N*-oxide are given as 263° and 129°, respectively; but it is presumed that these have been erroneously reversed.[4]

The polarography of phenazine-5-oxide and phenazine-5,10-dioxide have been studied.[5]

3. 2,2'-Biphenazine (orange plates, m.p. 229°) has been obtained by the Wohl-Aue reaction between 4,4'-diaminodiphenyl and nitrobenzene. Various substitution products have also been obtained.[6]

Additions to Table I. (p. 24)

Name of compound	M.p. (°C.)	Salts, derivatives, remarks	Ref.
1-Methylphenazine			3, 4, 7
2-Methylphenazine			7, 8
2-*tert*-Butylphenazine	84	I.R. Spectrum	8
(2-(*a,a,γ,γ*-Tetramethyl-butyl)-phenazine	98		8
1,3-Dimethylphenazine	123		8
2,3-Dimethylphenazine			8
2,8-Dimethylphenazine	154–155	5,10-Dihydro, m.p. 218°	9
2-Methyl-3-isopropyl-phenazine	94		8
1,2,3-Trimethylphenazine	161.5		8
1,2,4-Trimethylphenazine	120–120.5		8

References

1. F. L. Hirshfeld and G. M. J. Schmidt, *Acta Cryst.*, **7**, 129 (1954).
2. M. Lora Tamayo, R. Pérez Ossorio and M. Sanz Burata, *Anales real soc. españ. fís. y quím.* (*Madrid*), **50B**, 865 (1954); through *Chem. Abstracts*, **50**, 361 (1956).
3. S. Maffei, S. Pietra and A. M. Rivolta, *Ann. chim.* (*Rome*), **42**, 519 (1952); through *Chem. Abstracts*, **49**, 6968 (1955).
4. S. Maffei, S. Pietra and A. M. Rivolta, *Ann. chim.* (*Rome*), **43**, 611 (1953); through *Chem. Abstracts*, **49**, 1065 (1955).
5. R. Curti and S. Locchi, *Atti accad. nazl. Lincei, Rend., Classe sci. fis., mat. e nat.*, **14**, 796 (1953); through *Chem. Abstracts*, **48**, 8674 (1954).
6. Yu. S. Rozum, *Ukrain. Khim. Zhur.*, **21**, 491 (1955); through *Chem. Abstracts*, **50**, 7812 (1956).
7. Yu. S. Rozum, *Zhur. Obshchei Khim.*, **25**, 611 (1955); *J. Gen. Chem.* (*U.S.S.R.*), **25**, 583 (1955); through *Chem. Abstracts*, **50**, 3462 (1956).
8. H.-J. Teuber and G. Staiger, *Chem. Ber.*, **88**, 802 (1955).
9. Yu. S. Rozum, *Ukrain. Khim. Zhur.*, **16**, 434 (1950); through *Chem. Abstracts*, **49**, 1063 (1955).

Addendum to Chapter III

1A.   5,10-Dihydrophenazine is much less effective than *N*-methyl-aniline as an antioxidant.[1]

For a preparative method, see addendum to Chapter 1:5.

1F. The diphenylamine blue color reaction has been studied as a test for aliphatic nitro-compounds; and its mechanism has been further discussed. The possibility that a perazine is formed appears not to be entirely excluded.[2]

2C. The paramagnetism of 5-ethyl-5(10)-phenazyl decreases as the temperature is lowered; and, simultaneously, a new absorption band, for which Beer's Law does not hold, is produced at 800 mμ. Thus, at room temperature, the material exists as free radicals, which dimerize at low temperatures, presumably giving a dimer in which the two phenazine nuclei lie parallel to one another, allowing of the overlap of their π electrons (cf. phenazhydrin).[3,4]

Phenazyls have found application in the stabilization of polymeric organic materials which tend to deteriorate because of the effects of heat, light, and oxidation.[5]

2D. When phenazhydrin, which had been prepared from deuterium-labelled phenazine and unlabelled dihydrophenazine, was separated into its components, equal concentration of deuterium was found.[6] A similar result has also been obtained, using phenazine labelled with ^{15}N instead of deuterium.[7]

Although phenazhydrin-type compounds are formed from 1-methoxyphenazine and its dihydro derivative in the ratios 3:1 and 1:1 and from 1-phenazinol and its dihydro derivative in the ratio 3:1, it seems that in the cases of 2-phenazinol and 2-methoxyphenazine, combination occurs only in the ratio 7:1.[8]

3A. The condensation of o-phenylenediamine with 2-hydroxy-cyclohexanone gives a mixture of 1,2,3,4-tetrahydrophenazine and cis-1,2,3,4,4a,5,10,10a-octahydrophenazine[7,9]. 2-Chlorocyclohexanone appears to behave similarly to 2-hydroxycyclohexanone.[7]

4A. 1,2,3,4,6,7,8,9-Octahydrophenazine has been isolated as a by-product in the Beckmann rearrangement of cyclohexanoneoxime.[10] 1,2,3,4,6,7,8,9-Octahydrophenazine-1,6-diacetic acid has been described.[11]

4B. Crystalline mono- and diacetyl derivatives of 1,2,3,4,4a,5,10,10a-octahydrophenazine have been obtained and these have been brominated.[9]

References

1. G. S. Hammond, C. E. Boozer, C. E. Hamilton and J. N. Sen, *J. Am. Chem. Soc.*, **77**, 3238 (1955).
2. K. Grebber and J. V. Karabinos, *J. Research Natl. Bur. Standards*, **49**, 163 (1952).
3. K. H. Hausser and L. Birkofer, *Naturwissenschaften*, **42**, 97 (1955).
4. K. H. Hausser, *Naturwissenschaften*, **43**, 14 (1956).
5. U. S. Pat., 2,619,479; *Chem. Abstracts*, **47**, 4652 (1953).
6. I. P. Gragerov, *Zhur. Obshcheǐ Khim.*, **24**, 1769 (1954); through *Chem. Abstracts*, **49**, 12490 (1955).
7. G. A. Swan, unpublished work.
8. C. Dufraisse, E. Toromanoff and Y. Fellion, *Compt. rend.*, **241**, 1673 (1955).
9. P. J. Earle and M. L. Tomlinson, *J. Chem. Soc.*, **1956**, 794.
10. A. Schäffler and W. Ziegenbein, *Chem. Ber.*, **88**, 767 (1955).
11. F. Ramirez and J. W. Sargent, *J. Amer. Chem. Soc.*, **77**, 6297 (1955).

Addendum to Chapter IV

2.   The reason for the preferential replacement of the 7-chlorine atom of 2,7-dichlorophenazine-5-oxide by hydroxyl has been discussed.[1] The synthetic use of the replacement of the chlorine atom of 2-chloro-

Additions to Table V. (p. 69)

Substituents	M.p. (°C.)	Derivatives	Ref.
1-Fluoro-	208–209	10-Oxide, m.p. 203–204°	15
2-Fluoro-	181–182		15
1-Chloro-			2–5
2-Chloro-			3–7
1,2-Dichloro-	175–177	N-Oxide, m.p. 217–219°	2
1,3-Dichloro-		N-Oxide, m.p. 236–237° (dec.)	2
1,4-Dichloro-			2
1,6-Dichloro-			3
1,7-Dichloro-	171–174		3
1,8-Dichloro-	222–223		3
1,9-Dichloro-	211–212		3
2,3-Dichloro-	250–251		2
2,7-Dichloro-			6
2,8-Dichloro-	229–230	N-Oxide, m.p. 232–233°	2
2,3,7,8-Tetrachloro-	330		4
8-Chloro-1-methyl-	153		8
6,9-Dichloro-1-methyl-	193.5		8

phenazine-5,10-dioxide is limited by the fact that with oxidizable reagents reduction of the *N*-oxide occurs.[16] 1- and 2-Trifluoromethylphenazines (m.p. 125–126° and 177–178°, respectively) have been prepared.[15]

3. Nitration of phenazine-5-oxide with concentrated sulfuric acid and potassium nitrate at 0° yields a mixture of 3-nitrophenazine-5-oxide (m.p. 204°) and 1-nitrophenazine-5-oxide (m.p. 213°), which have been hydrogenated catalytically to 2- and 1-aminophenazines, respectively.[7,17] 3-Nitrophenazine-5-oxide is also obtained by nitration of phenazine-5,10-dioxide and when it is refluxed with a mixture of *N*,*N*-dimethylaniline and acetic anhydride, it yields 2-nitrophenazine (m.p. 225°).[7]

The nitration of 1-methoxyphenazine, 1-methoxyphenazine-5-oxide, 2-methoxyphenazine-5-oxide and 2-methoxyphenazine-10-oxide has also been studied.[7]

6A. Many derivatives[6,9,18] of 1-phenazinecarboxylic acid, including the nitrile (m.p. 170–172°)[10] and the anhydride (m.p. 234°),[11] have been described. 1-Phenazinecarboxaldehyde has been obtained from 1-methylphenazine by oxidation with selenium dioxide; its absorption spectrum has been recorded.[12]

6B. Although both Maffei (see Chapter IV:5) and Rozum[11] have reported 160° as the melting point of 2-phenazinecarbonitrile, Vivian, Hartwell, and Waterman[10] record a value of 232–234°. Other derivatives of 2-phenazinecarboxylic acid have also been prepared.[8,13]

2-Phenazinecarboxaldehyde (yellow, m.p. 185°, derivatives and absorption spectrum recorded) has been obtained from 2-methylphenazine by oxidation with selenium dioxide. The action of methylmagnesium iodide on it yields methyl 2-phenazylcarbinol (yellow, m.p. 116°), which is oxidized by chromic acid to methyl 2-phenazylketone (yellow-green, m.p. 168°, derivatives and U.V. spectrum recorded).[12]

6C. Phenazine-1,6-dicarboxylic acid has been further characterized.[11]

The action of phosgene on 5,10-dihydro-5-methylphenazine gives 5,10-dihydro-5-methylphenazine-10-carboxylic acid chloride (m.p. 188–190°).[14]

References

1. G. W. Wheland, *Resonance in Organic Chemistry*, Wiley, New York, 1955, p. 503.
2. V. P. Chernetskiĭ and A. I. Kiprianov, *Zhur. Obshcheĭ Khim.*, 23, 1743 (1953); through *Chem. Abstracts*, 48, 13695 (1954).
3. V. P. Chernetskiĭ and S. B. Serebryanyĭ, *Sbornik Stateĭ Obshcheĭ Khim., Akad. Nauk. S.S.S.R.*, 1, 646 (1953); through *Chem. Abstracts*, 49, 1066 (1955).
4. S. Maffei, S. Pietra and A. Cattaneo, *Gazz. chim. ital.*, 84, 746 (1954).
5. S. B. Serebryanyĭ and N. A. Il'yushina, *Zhur. Obshcheĭ Khim.*, 23, 1776 (1953); through *Chem. Abstracts*, 49, 338 (1955).
6. I. Ya. Postovskiĭ and A. I. Abramova, *Zhur. Obshcheĭ Khim.*, 24, 485 (1954); through *Chem. Abstracts*, 49, 6273 (1955).
7. H. Otomasu, *Pharm. Bull.* (Japan), 2, 283 (1954); through *Chem. Abstracts*, 50, 1033 (1956).
8. S. Maffei, S. Pietra and A. M. Rivolta, *Ann. chim.* (*Rome*), 43, 611 (1953); through *Chem. Abstracts*, 49, 1065 (1955).
9. Yu. S. Rozum, *Ukrain. Khim. Zhur.*, 20, 661 (1954); through *Chem. Abstracts*, 29, 14771 (1955).
10. D. L. Vivian, J. L. Hartwell and H. C. Waterman, *J. Org. Chem.*, 20, 797 (1955).
11. Yu. S. Rozum, *Ukrain. Khim. Zhur.*, 21, 361 (1955); through *Chem. Abstracts*, 49, 14772 (1955).
12. Yu. S. Rozum, *Zhur. Obshcheĭ, Khim.*, 25, 611 (1955); *J. Gen. Chem. U.S.S.R.*, 25, 583 (1955); through *Chem. Abstracts*, 50, 3462 (1956).
13. S. Maffei, S. Pietra and A. M. Rivolta, *Ann. chim.* (*Rome*), 42, 519 (1952); through *Chem. Abstracts*, 49, 6968 (1955).
14. A. W. Weston, R. W. DeNet and R. J. Michaels, Jr., *J. Am. Chem. Soc.*, 75, 4006 (1953).
15. V. P. Chernetskiĭ, L. M. Yagupol'skiĭ and S. B. Serebryanyĭ, *Zhur. Obshcheĭ Khim.*, 25, 2161 (1955); through *Chem. Abstracts*, 50, 8661 (1956).
16. J. K. Landquist, *J. Chem. Soc.*, 1956, 2550.
17. A. D. Grabenko and S. B. Serebryanyĭ, *Ukrain. Khim. Zhur.*, 21, 249 (1955); through *Chem. Abstracts*, 50, 9426 (1956).
18. Yu. S. Rozum, *Ukrain. Khim. Zhur.*, 20, 381 (1954); through *Chem. Abstracts*, 50, 9426 (1946).

Addendum to Chapter V

2B. A further paper on the solvatochromism of 1,3,4-trimethyl-2-phenazinol has appeared.[1] A study has been made of the absorption spectra of the oxidation products of the quaternary salts derived from alkoxyphenazines (N-alkylphenazinones).[2]

3A. 1,4- 1,6- and 1,8-Phenazinediols have been oxidized to their respective quinones by lead tetracetate.[11] The alleged 2,7-diethoxyphenazine of Neu is probably "*p*-phenetidine black."[12]

Additions to Table VI. (p. 83)

Substituents	M.p. (°C.)	Derivatives, etc.	Ref.
1-Methoxy-			2, 3, 8
2-Methoxy-		5,10-Dihydro, m.p. 192°	3–8
2-Benzyloxy-	111		5
1-Methoxy-3-methyl-	152–153		5
1-Methoxy-3-ethyl-	100–101		5
1-Methoxy-3-allyl-	122		5
1-Ethoxy-9-methyl-	115		2
1-Methoxy-4-nitro-	224	5-Oxide, m.p. 223° (dec.)	7
1-Methoxy-7-chloro-	165–166		9
1-Methoxy-8-chloro-	209–210		9
1-Methoxy-8-fluoro-	148–150		17
1-Methoxy-9-chloro-	184–185		9
2-Methoxy-8-methyl-		5,10-Dihydro, m.p. 133–134°	4
2-Hydroxy-1-nitro-			7
2-Methoxy-1-nitro-	238	10-Oxide, m.p. 243°(dec.)	7
2-Methoxy-8-chloro-			9
2-Methoxy-7-cyano-	267–268		10
2-Methoxy-8-cyano-	224–225.5		10

Additions to Table VII. (p. 89)

Substituents	M.p. (°C.)	Derivatives, etc.	Ref.
1,2-Dihydroxy-			6
1,2-Dimethoxy-			6
1,3-Dihydroxy-		Diacetyl, m.p. 263–266°; 5,10-dioxide, m.p. 280°	6
1,3-Dimethoxy-	145 or 228		2, 6
1,4-Dihydroxy-		5,10-Dioxide, m.p. > 340°	6, 7, 11
1,4-Dimethoxy-			6
1,4-Dihydroxy-6-methyl-	174	Diacetyl, m.p. 160°	11
1,4-Dimethoxy-6-methyl-	189		11
1,6-Dimethoxy-			13
1,7-Dihydroxy-		5-Oxide, m.p. 177–178°; 5,10-dioxide, m.p. > 330°	3
1,7-Dimethoxy-	153	5-Oxide, m.p. 211°	2, 3

(Table Continued)

Table VII. *(continued)*

Substituents	M.p. (°C.)	Derivatives, etc.	Ref.
1,8-Dihydroxy-	247–248 (dec.) or 216	Diacetyl, m.p. 181° or 166°	11, 14
1,8-Dimethoxy-	154–155		9, 14
1,9-Dihydroxy-		5-Oxide, m.p. 258° (dec.)	3
1,9-Dimethoxy-			9, 13
2,3-Dihydroxy-	> 340		6
2,3-Dimethoxy-	226		6
2,7-Dihydroxy-	> 330	Diacetyl, m.p. 266–267° (dec.); 5,10-dioxide, m.p. 234–236°	14
2,7-Dimethoxy-	246	5-Oxide, m.p. 236° (dec.)	14
2,8-Dimethoxy-		5-Oxide, m.p. 229°; 10-oxide, m.p. 216°; 5,10-dihydro, m.p. 215°	3, 4
1,2,4-Trihydroxy-		Triacetyl, m.p. 259–260°	11
1,3,6-Trimethoxy-	209		2
1,7,8-Trimethoxy-	215		2

Additions to Table VIII. (p. 95)

4-Amino-5,10-dihydro-1-hydroxy-3-methylphenazine, m.p. 230°.[15]
8-Amino-2-hydroxyphenazine, m.p. > 350°.[16]
4-Amino-1-methoxyphenazine, m.p. 214°.[7]

References

1. R. Suhrmann and H. H. Perkampus, *Z. Elektrochem.*, **56**, 743 (1952).
2. Yu. S. Rozum, *Sbornik Statei Obshchei Khim., Akad. Nauk S.S.S.R.*, **1**, 600 (1953); through *Chem. Abstracts*, **49**, 1065 (1955).
3. I. Yoshioka, *Pharm. Bull.* (Japan), **2**, 25 (1954); through *Chem. Abstracts*, **50**, 357 (1956).
4. Yu. S. Rozum, *Ukrain. Khim. Zhur.*, **16**, 434 (1950); through *Chem. Abstracts*, **49**, 1063 (1955).
5. H. -J. Teuber and G. Staiger, *Chem. Ber.*, **88**, 802 (1955).
6. I. Yoshioka and H. Otomasu, *Pharm. Bull.* (Japan), **2**, 53 (1954); through *Chem. Abstracts*, **50**, 358 (1956).
7. H. Otomasu, *Pharm. Bull.* (Japan), **2**, 283 (1954); through *Chem. Abstracts*, **50**, 1033 (1956).
8. Y. Kidani, *Pharm. Bull.* (Japan), **2**, 292 (1954); through *Chem. Abstracts*, **50**, 1033 (1956).

9. S. B. Serebryanyĭ and N. A. Il'yushina, *Zhur. Obshcheĭ Khim.*, **23,** 1776 (1953); through *Chem. Abstracts*, **49,** 338 (1955).

10. D. L. Vivian, J. L. Hartwell and H. C. Waterman, *J. Org. Chem.*, **20,** 797 (1955).

11. Yu. S. Rozum, *Zhur. Obshcheĭ Khim.*, **25,** 611 (1955); *J. Gen. Chem. U.S.S.R.*, **25,** 583 (1955); through *Chem. Abstracts*, **50,** 3462 (1956).

12. J. Mitchell and K. H. Pausacker, *J. Chem. Soc.*, **1954,** 4502.

13. S. Maffei and M. Aymon, *Gazz. chim. ital.*, **84,** 667 (1954).

14. I. Yoshioka and H. Otomasu, *Pharm. Bull.* (Japan), **1,** 66 (1953); through *Chem. Abstracts*, **49,** 12492 (1955).

15. M. Lora Tamayo, R. Pérez Ossorio and M. Sanz Burata, *Anales real soc. españ. fís. y quím. (Madrid)*, **50B,** 865 (1954); through *Chem. Abstracts*, **50,** 361 (1956).

16. D. L. Vivian, *J. Org. Chem.*, **21,** 565 (1956).

17. V. P. Chernetskiĭ, L. M. Yagupol'skiĭ and S. B. Serebryanyĭ, *Zhur. Obshcheĭ Khim.*, **25,** 2161 (1955); through *Chem. Abstracts*, **50,** 8661 (1956).

Addendum to Chapter VI

2A. *o*-Phenylenediamine condenses with bishydroxyiminocyclohexanone to give 1,2,3,4-tetrahydro-1-hydroxyiminophenazine, which is dehydrated by acetic anhydride to 1-acetamidophenazine (bright yellow, m.p. 170–172°) in 30% overall yield from the diamine.[1] The cyclization of 2-amino-6-nitrodiphenylamine gives 1-aminophenazine in 30% yield;[2] the latter has also been obtained by catalytic hydrogenation of 1-nitrophenazine-5-oxide.[3] Some halogen-substituted *N,N*-dimethylaminophenazines are described in reference 2.

2B. 2-Aminophenazine, obtained by catalytic hydrogenation of 3-nitrophenazine-5-oxide, has been converted into 2-chlorophenazine by the Sandmeyer reaction.[3]

Additions to Table X. (p. 107)

Substituents	M.p. (°C.)	Ref.
1,6-Diamino-	245	4
1,9-Diamino-	264–265	4
2-Amino-7-dimethylamino-	>310	2
2-Amino-8-dimethylamino-	232.5	2
2-Amino-8-dimethylamino-3-methyl-	171–187 (dec.)	2
2,3-Dimorpholino-	221.5	5

3E. A compound possessing the structure hitherto accepted for neutral red has been synthesized; but apparently this has to undergo some modification before it becomes identical with the dye. Details of this structural anomaly have not yet been disclosed.[2]

Further work on the polarography[6] of neutral red and on the use of neutral red in staining[7,8] and in studies of gastric secretion[9,10] have been published.

References

1. G. H. Cookson, *J. Chem. Soc.*, **1953**, 1328.
2. a). D. L. Vivian, *J. Org. Chem.*, **21**, 565 (1956).
2. b). D. L. Vivian and M. Belkin, *Nature*, **178**, 154 (1956).
3. H. Otomasu, *Pharm. Bull.* (Japan), **2**, 283 (1954); through *Chem. Abstracts*, **50**, 1033 (1956).
4. S. Maffei and M. Aymon, *Gazz. chim. ital.*, **84**, 667 (1954).
5. W. Brackman and E. Havinga, *Rec. trav. chim.*, **74**, 937 (1955).
6. V. Vojíř, *Chem. Listy*, **47**, 634 (1953); through *Chem. Abstracts*, **48**, 3813 (1954).
7. K. S. Bhargava, *Cytologia* (*Tokyo*), **16**, 72 (1950); through *Chem. Abstracts*, **47**, 10630 (1953).
8. O. Geschöpf, *Österr. botan. Z.*, **99**, 1 (1952); *Chem. Abstracts*, **48**, 9480 (1954).
9. M. S. Rudoï and E. E. Giler, *Klin. Med.* (*U.S.S.R.*), **32**, No. 5, 83 (1954); through *Chem. Abstracts*, **48**, 12289 (1954).
10. S. Woislawski, *Proc. Soc. Explt. Biol. Med.*, **83**, 130 (1953).

Addendum to Chapter VII

1B. A mechanism for indamine-formation, similar to that shown in Eq. (5) on p. 120, has been put forward by Bradley and Watkinson.[1]

2B. Further work on the photographic desensitizing action of phenosafranine[2-4] and of the photoconductivity of alkali halide crystals with adsorbed phenosafranine has been published. Phenosafranine protects cardiac glycosides from the action of light.[6] Safranine has been used in a differential staining method.[7]

2H. New phenazine dyes, including wool dyes[8] and one which is said to be deeper in color than safranine and capable of dyeing cotton directly from aqueous solution,[9] have been described.

2I. Additions to the series of patents on color photography by General Aniline and Film Corporation have appeared.[10-12]

References

1. W. Bradley and L. J. Watkinson, *Chem. & Ind.*, **1954**, 1482.
2. L. Falla, *Colloq. sensibilité phot.*, *Paris, 1951, Science et inds. phot.*, **23A,** 128 (1952); through *Chem. Abstracts*, **47,** 4772 (1953).
3. A. Hautot and H. Sauvenier, *Bull. soc. roy. sci. Liège*, **21,** 79, 95, 180 and 497; through *Chem. Abstracts*, **47,** 4229 and 4230 (1953); **48,** 482 and 5695 (1954).
4. L. Cohen-Solal, *Science et inds. phot.*, **23,** 388 (1952); *Chem. Abstracts*, **47,** 428 (1953).
5. H. Yagi, *Mem. Coll. Sci., Univ. Kyoto, Ser. A.*, **26,** 75 (1950); through *Chem. Abstracts*, **47,** 6770 (1953).
6. T. M. Feinblatt and E. A. Ferguson, Jr., *New Engl. J. Med.*, **246,** 905 (1952); *Chem. Abstracts*, **47,** 12751 (1953).
7. J. H. D. Bryan, *Stain Technol.*, **30,** 153 (1955).
8. U.S. Pat., 2,613,209; *Chem. Abstracts*, **47,** 3577 (1953).
9. A. A. Kharkharov, *Izvest. Akad. Nauk S.S.S.R., Otdel. Khim. Nauk*, **1954,** 117; through *Chem. Abstracts*, **49,** 6262 (1955).
10. U.S. Pat., 2,656,272; *Chem. Abstracts*, **48,** 486 (1954).
11. U.S. Pat., 2,657,139; *Chem. Abstracts*, **48,** 68 (1954)
12. U.S. Pat., 2,701, 766; *Chem. Abstracts*, **49,** 10777 (1955).

Addendum to Chapter VIII

3B. Barry and his collaborators[1] have shown (by chromatographic separation of the anhydro-bases) that the crude product of oxidation of 2-aminodiphenylamine hydrochloride with ferric chloride contains not only 2-amino-3-anilino-10-phenylphenazinium chloride (A), but also 5–10% of the isomeric 3-amino-2-anilino-compound (B). When the ferric chloride is replaced by *p*-benzoquinone, these two compounds result in approximately equal amounts, and a small amount of aposafranone is also formed. The anhydrobase of A (m.p. 203–204°) gives absorption maxima at 280 and 480 mμ and in concentrated sulfuric acid gives a brown-red solution; whereas that of B (m.p. 257–259°) gives maxima at 230, 272, and 455 mμ, and a green-brown solution in sulfuric acid. When heated with alcoholic sulfuric acid in a sealed tube, both isomers give, among other products, anilinoaposafranone and hydroxyaposafranone. The former cannot be a direct degradation product of B; it must be formed by a reversion of hydroxyaposafranone and aniline.

Various substitution products of these two isomers, as well as compounds containing an alkyl or cyclohexyl residue in place of the phenyl group, have also been prepared.[1-3]

References

1. V. C. Barry, J. G. Belton, J. F. O'Sullivan and D. Twomey, *J. Chem. Soc.*, 1956, 888.
2. V. C. Barry, J. G. Belton, J. F. O'Sullivan and D. Twomey, *J. Chem. Soc.*, 1956, 893.
3. V. C. Barry, J. G. Belton, J. F. O'Sullivan and D. Twomey, *J. Chem. Soc.*, 1956, 896.

Addendum to Chapter X

1A. Further information on the staining of wool by pyocyanine has been published.[1]

1B. The infra-red spectra of pyocyanine and its semiquinonoid perchlorate have been recorded.[2]

1C. Further studies have been made of the nutritive requirements of *Pseudomonas aeruginosa* for pyocyanine production.[3,4] Certain phenanthrene alkaloids, such as codeine, have been found to stimulate pigmentation.[5]

References

1. I. E. B. Fraser and A. P. Mulcock, *Nature*, **177**, 628 (1956).
2. W. Otting and H. Kainer, *Chem. Ber.*, **87**, 1205 (1954).
3. E. Hellinger, *J. Gen. Microbiol.*, **5**, 633 (1951); through *Chem. Abstracts*, **47**, 2828 (1953).
4. M. M. Nemes, *Univ. Microfilms* (Ann Arbor, Mich.), **Pub.** No. **5824**, 107; through *Chem. Abstracts*, **48**, 2832 (1954).
5. J. Kwapínski and H. Pietraszkiewicz, *Med. Dóswiadczalna i Mikrobiol.*, **5**, 159 (1953); through *Chem. Abstracts*, **47**, 8185 (1953).

Addendum to Chapter XI

1. The selective staining of mitochondria by Janus green may be due to the selective localization of the cytochrome oxidase system within the mitochondria, and hence more rapid reduction of the dye in nonmitochondrial cell components.[1-4] Virulent strains of *Mycobacterium tuberculosis* are stained by neutral red, while avirulent varieties are not.[5-7]

3A. References 8 and 9 are relevant to work on pyocyanine acting as carrier in enzyme systems.

3B.   The increase in oxygen uptake which pyocyanine produces in certain bacteria is not inhibited by potassium cyanide.[10] The addition of neutral red to cultures of *Azotobacter* produces greater repression of respiration than of nitrogen fixation.[11] Janus green is reduced in a Hill-type reaction with illuminated chloroplasts.[12] *In vitro* experiments on the effect of phenazine dyes on hyaluronidase in serum have been carried out.[13]

3C.   The effect of adding pyocyanine to the soil in which wheat and peas are growing has been investigated.[14]

A series of arylamides of phenazine-1-carboxylic acid has been tested for antitubercular activity.[15]

The inactivation of viruses by phenazine dyes has been further investigated.[16–19] Neutral red was found to inactivate bacteriophages.[20]

It is claimed that amino- and hydroxy-phenazines have fungicidal properties. In one case destruction of mildew and black rot is obtained at a concentration of 1:10,000.[21] The action of neutral red, Janus green, nigrosine, and pyocyanine on the development of *Aspergillus* has been studied.[22,23]

Neutral red accelerates the metamorphosis of *Bugula* larvae.[24] Phenazine and pyocyanine killed, or prevented the development of horse strongyle larvae and eggs.[25]

2,8-Phenazinediarsonic acid induced damage in sarcoma 37;[26] a drop in cytochrome oxidase also occurred.[27] Phenazine has been shown to produce bladder-cancer in experimental animals.[28] Janus green increases the tumor-formation produced by carcinogenic hydrocarbons.[29]

Neutral red and phenosafranine have been found to have only doubtful mutagenic activity against *Drosophila melonagaster*.[30]

Neutral red and neutral violet are depressors.[31] Their effect on the isolated ileum has been studied.[32] Other studies deal with the sorption of neutral red by the nerve cells of rat brain under the influence of conditioned reflex stimulant[33,34] and of the effect of neutral red and Janus green on the resting potential of surviving frog muscle fibers.[35] A dihydrophenazine ester has been found to have a slight antispasmodic effect.[36]

References

1. A. Lazarow and S. J. Cooperstein, *Exptl. Cell Research*, **5,** 56 (1953); through *Chem. Abstracts*, **48,** 2788 (1954).
2. S. J. Cooperstein, A. Lazarow and J. W. Patterson, *Exptl. Cell Research*, **5,** 69 (1953); through *Chem. Abstracts*, **48,** 2788 (1954).
3. S. J. Cooperstein and A. Lazarow, *Exptl. Cell Research*, **5,** 82 (1953); through *Chem. Abstracts*, **48,** 2789 (1954).
4. A. Lazarow and S. J. Cooperstein, *J. Histochem. and Cytochem.*, **1,** 234 (1953).
5. D. E. Hughes, E. S. Moss, M. Hood and M. Henson, *Am. J. Clin. Pathol.*, **24,** 621 (1954); through *Chem. Abstracts*, **48,** 8868 (1954).
6. J. Desbordes and E. Fournier, *Ann. inst. Pasteur*, **86,** 657 (1954).
7. H. Hein, *Z. Tuberk.*, **103,** 339 (1954); through *Chem. Abstracts*, **48,** 10104 (1954).
8. H. Beinert, R. M. Bock, D. S. Goldman, D. E. Green, H. R. Mahler, S. Mii, P. G. Stansly and S. J. Wakil, *J. Am. Chem. Soc.*, **75,** 4111 (1953).
9. D. E. Green, S. Mii, H. R. Mahler and R. M. Bock, *J. Biol. Chem.*, **206,** 1 (1954).
10. Y. Kimura, *Osaka Daigaku Igaku Zassi*, **5,** 323 (1953); through *Chem. Abstracts*, **47,** 8188 (1953).
11. M. V. Fedorov, *Doklady Akad. Nauk S.S.S.R.*, **72,** 1139 (1950); through *Chem. Abstracts*, **48,** 6504 (1954).
12. L. Horowitz, *Plant Physiol.*, **30,** 10 (1955).
13. D. Glick and M. J. Ochs, *Proc. Soc. Exptl. Biol. Med.*, **81,** 363 (1952).
14. N. A. Krasil'nikov, *Agrobiologiya*, **1952,** No. 6, 57; through *Chem. Abstracts*, **47,** 7144 (1953).
15. Yu. S. Rozum, *Ukrain. Khim. Zhur.*, **20,** 661 (1954); through *Chem. Abstracts*, **49,** 14771 (1955).
16. S. Okubo, *Bull. Physiog. Sci. Research Inst., Tokyo Univ.*, **No. 6,** 13 (1950); through *Chem. Abstracts*, **48,** 7695 (1954).
17. G. Ciaccio, G. Gasparini and N. Ercoli, *J. Immunol.*, **72,** 299 (1954).
18. W. Ginoza and D. E. Atkinson, *J. Am. Chem. Soc.*, **78,** 2401 (1956).
19. E. W. Hurst, J. K. Landquist, P. Melvin, J. M. Peters, N. Senior, J. A. Silk and G. J. Stacey, *Brit. J. Pharmacol.*, **8,** 297 (1953).
20. M. Goto and S. Iwahara, *Bull. Physiog. Sci. Research Inst. Tokyo Univ.*, **No. 4,** 15 (1950); through *Chem. Abstracts*, **48,** 7695 (1954).
21. Fr. Pat. 887,820; *Chem. Abstracts*, **47,** 4033 (1953).
22. F. Aiquel and F. J. Herrero, *Arch. farm. y bioquím. Tucuman*, **4,** 149 (1948); through *Chem. Abstracts*, **47,** 10064 (1953).
23. J. Alkiewicz and Z. Graczykòwna, *Med. Dóswiadczalna i Mikrobiol.*, **4,** 257 (1952); through *Chem. Abstracts*, **47,** 1234 (1953).
24. W. F. Lynch, *Biol. Bull.*, **103,** 369 (1952); through *Chem. Abstracts*, **47,** 4000 (1953).
25. N. D. Levine and V. Ivens, *Am. J. Vet. Research*, **15,** 349 (1954); through *Chem. Abstracts*, **48,** 10936 (1954).
26. J. Leiter, V. Downing, J. L. Hartwell and M. J. Shear, *J. Natl. Cancer Inst.*, **13,** 365 (1952); through *Chem. Abstracts*, **47,** 1851 (1953).
27. J. Leiter, A. D. Paradis and V. S. Waravdekar, *J. Natl. Cancer Inst.*, **14,** 177 (1953); through *Chem. Abstracts*, **47,** 11555 (1953).
28. G. Rudali, H. Chalvet and F. Winternitz, *Compt. rend.*, **240,** 1738 (1955).
29. H. Bielka, *Naturwissenschaften*, **42,** 299 (1955).
30. A. M. Clark, *Am. Naturalist*, **87,** 295 (1953).

31. T. J. Haley and J. L. Leitch, *Arch. intern. pharmacodynamie*, **93**, 341 (1953); through *Chem. Abstracts*, **47**, 11506 (1953).
32. J. L. Leitch and T. J. Haley, *J. Am. Pharm. Assoc.*, **41**, 559 (1952); through *Chem. Abstracts*, **47**, 779 (1953).
33. S. N. Romanov, *Doklady Akad. Nauk S.S.S.R.*, **90**, 117 (1953); through *Chem. Abstracts*, **47**, 8208 (1953).
34. S. N. Romanov, *Doklady Akad. Nauk S.S.S.R.*, **89**, 753 (1953); through *Chem. Abstracts*, **47**, 10721 (1953).
35. H. J. Lehmann, *Pflügers Arch. ges. Physiol.*, **259**, 294 (1954).
36. A. W. Weston, R. W. DeNet and R. J. Michaels, Jr., *J. Am. Chem. Soc.*, **75**, 4006 (1953).

Addendum to Chapter XII

3D. Benzo[a]phenazine, in solution in a mixture of dilute sulfuric acid and acetone (2:1) at pH 0.4–0.9, has been reduced electrolytically at —120 mV between mercury electrodes to yield a mixture of the paramagnetic semiquinone with the diamagnetic dimer.[1]

3E. The polarographic reduction of benzo[a]phenazine-7- and -12-oxides,[2] of 1-chlorobenzo[a]phenazine-7- and -12-oxides and of 4-chlorobenzo[a]phenazine-12-oxide[3] has been studied. Plots of the half-wave potential against pH showed that the oxygen atom in the 12-position increased the stability of the free hydroxylic radical compared with that of the 7-oxides, while the stability was enhanced by a chlorine atom in the 1-position and decreased by a 4-chloro group. The equilibrium constant (stability constant) of the respective semiquinones at various pH values showed a steady increase in the series 1-chlorobenzo[a]phenazine-7-oxide, benzo[a]phenazine-7-oxide, 4-chlorobenzo[a]phenazine-12-oxide, benzo[a]phenazine-12-oxide, 1-chlorobenzo[a]phenazine-12-oxide.[4]

Additions to Table XIII. (p. 236)

Substituents	Derivatives	Ref.
1-Chloro-	7-oxide, m.p. 223°	3
	12-oxide, m.p. 177° (dec.)	
4-Chloro-	12-oxide, m.p. 193°	3

References

1. R. Curti, S. Locchi and U. Landini, *Ricerca Sci.,* **24,** 2053 (1954); *Chem. Abstracts,* **50,** 12066 (1956).
2. R. Curti and S. Locchi, *Atti accad. nazl. Lincei, Rend., Classe sci. fis., mat. e nat.,* **14,** 796 (1953); *Chem. Abstracts,* **48,** 8674 (1954).
3. R. Curti, S. Locchi and U. Landini, *Atti accad. nazl. Lincei, Rend. Classe sci. fis., mat. e nat.,* **18,** 78 (1955); *Chem. Abstracts,* **50,** 4159 (1956).
4. R. Curti and S. Locchi, *Atti. accad. nazl. Lincei, Rend., Classe sci. fis., mat. e nat.,* **18,** 179 (1955); *Chem. Abstracts,* **50,** 4159 (1956).
5. Add to Ref. 131 (p. 254). *Chem. Abstracts,* **49,** 6968 (1955).

Addendum to Chapter XIII

2E.   8-Methoxy- and 11-methoxy-benzo[a]phenazines have been prepared by the condensation of 2,3-diaminoanisole with 1,2-naphthoquinone, followed by chromatographic separation. The orientation of the isomers follows from the synthesis of the 8-methoxy isomer by the Wohl-Aue modified procedure from 2-nitroanisole and 1-naphthylamine and from the synthesis of the 11-methoxy compound by the reaction between 3-aminoanisole and 1-nitronaphthalene. The reaction between 3-nitroanisole and 1-naphthylamine yields 11-methoxybenzo[a]phenazine-7-oxide, which on heating with acetic anhydride is reduced to 11-methoxybenzo[a]phenazine. The mother liquor of the latter Wohl-Aue reaction also contains 9-methoxybenzo[a]phenazine. 10-Methoxybenzo[a]phenazine is similarly obtained from 4-aminoanisole and 1-nitronaphthalene. Most of these methoxy compounds have been demethylated to the corresponding hydroxy compounds by means of hydrobromic acid in acetic acid.[1]

Additions to Table XIV. (p. 261)

Substituents	Physical characteristics	M.p. (°C.)	Derivatives, etc.	Ref.
8-Hydroxy-	Yellow needles	188–190	MeO-, m.p. 213–214°	1
9-Hydroxy-		> 300	MeO-, m.p. 206°	1
10-Hydroxy-			MeO-, m.p. 214–216°	1
11-Hydroxy-	Yellow needles	202–204	MeO-, m.p. 179–180°	1
			MeO-7-oxide, m.p. 239–240° (dec.)	

Addition to Table XV. (p. 274)

Substituent	M.p. (°C.)	Ref.
5-Morpholino-	164–177	2

References

1. I. Yoshioka, T. Ikeda and K. Kometani, *J. Pharm. Soc. Japan*, **76,** 30 (1956); through *Chem. Abstracts*, **50,** 13042 (1956).
2. W. Brackmann and E. Havinga, *Rec. trav. chim.*, **79,** 937 (1955).

Addendum to Chapter XV

2A and B. 10-Hydroxy- and 11-hydroxy-dibenzo[*a, c*]phenazines have been prepared by demethylation of the corresponding methoxy compounds. The action of sodium carbonate upon the metho-*p*-toluene sulfonates of these hydroxy compounds has afforded 14-methyl-10(14)-dibenzo[*a, c*]phenazinone and 9-methyl-11(9)-dibenzo[*a, c*]phenazinone respectively.[1]

Additions to Table XXX. (pp. 366 *et seq.*)

Substituents	Physical characteristics.	M.p. (°C.)	Derivatives	Ref.
10-Hydroxy-		255–256 257–258	*N*-Methyl anhydro-base, m.p. 192–193° Methiodide, m.p. > 300°	1,2
10-Methoxy-		270–271		1
11-Hydroxy-		305–306	*N*-Methyl anhydro-base, m.p. 215–216° Methiodide, m.p. > 300°	1
11-Methoxy-		201–202		1
10,13-Dihydroxy-	Orange-red	282	Blue ppt. with Pb^{++}, red-violet ppt. with Cu^{++}	3
10,13-Dimethoxy-	Orange-yellow	226–227		3

Addition to Table XXXVIII. (p. 415)

Substituents	Physical characteristics	M.p. (°C.)	Ref.
6-Hydroxy-8,13-diphenyl-	Yellow-orange prisms	279–280	4

9. **Naphtho[2,3-b]phenazine**
   5,14-Diazapentacene
   No R. I.

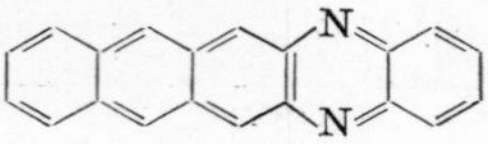

A derivative of this previously undescribed ring system has been reported.[4] 9,10-Diphenylanthracene-2,3-diol was fused at 160–170° with o-phenylenediamine and the product recrystallized from cyclohexane. 7,12-Diphenyl-5,14-dihydronaphtho[2,3-b]phenazine formed yellow needles, m.p. 260°, containing cyclohexane. The unsolvated compound, which melted at 300–315° and resolidified to form a green compound, was unstable and oxidized readily to green and blue products, probably phenazhydrins. The solutions exhibited a vivid green fluorescence.

References

1. A. I. Kiprianov and M. M. Kroshchenko, *Ukrain. Khim. Zhur.*, **19**, 302 (1953); *Referat. Zhur., Khim.*, 1954, No. 12731; through *Chem. Abstracts*, **49**, 11667 (1955).
2. I. Yoshioka, T. Ikeda and K. Kometani, *J. Pharm. Soc. Japan*, **76**, 30 (1956); through *Chem. Abstracts*, **50**, 13042 (1956).
3. S. Kawai, J. Kosaka and M. Hatano, *Proc. Jap. Acad.*, **30**, 774 (1954); through *Chem. Abstracts*, **49**, 10973 (1955).
4. A. Etienne and J. Bourdon, *Bull. soc. chim. France, Mém.*, **22**, 380 (1955).

Addendum to Chapter XVI

12. Another preparation[1] of benzo[a]naphtho[1,2-c]phenazine, in the same way as that already reported, has given the product as canary-yellow needles, m.p. 168°.

22. The photo-conductivity of anthrazine, specially purified by repeated sublimation, has been measured.[2]

38. **1-Indeno[5,6-b]quinoxaline**
    No R. I.

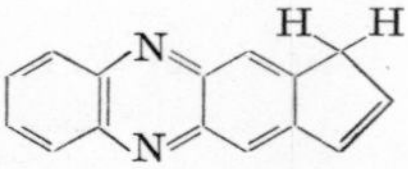

2,3-Dihydro-1-indeno[5,6-b]quinoxaline, a member of this hitherto-undescribed ring system, has been synthesized[3] by the condensation of o-phenylenediamine with hydrindane-5,6-quinone. It forms bright yellow needles, m.p. 139°.

39. 5,12-Ethenobenzo[b]phenazine
No R. I.

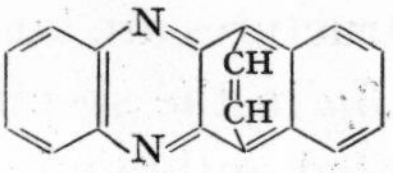

This new ring system is represented by 2,4a,5,12-tetrahydro-4,4a-13,14-tetramethyl-5,12-ethenobenzo[b]phenazin-1-ol-2-one (II). 4,5-Dimethyl-o-benzoquinone dimerizes in nitromethane to yield (I), which with o-phenylenediamine affords a mixture of 2,3-dimethylphenazine and (II).[4] The latter compound forms yellow crystals, m.p. 171°, and gives a yellow acetyl derivative, m.p. 204°.

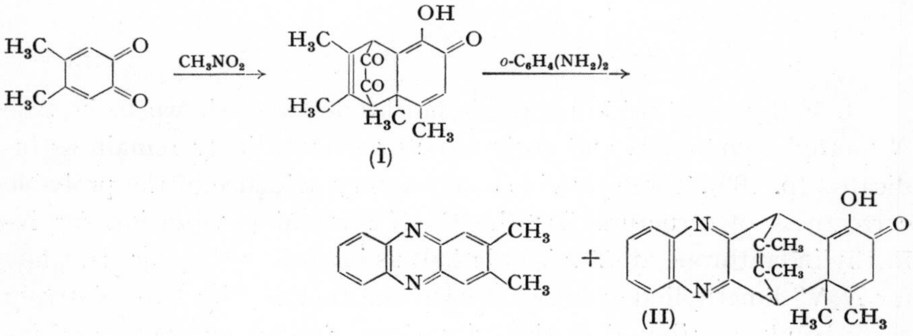

References

1. H. Dannenberg and S. Läufer, *Chem. Ber.*, **89**, 2242 (1956).
2. H. Inokuchi, *Bull. Chem. Soc. Japan*, **27**, 22 (1954).
3. H. J. Teuber and G. Staiger, *Chem. Ber.*, **88**, 802 (1955).
4. L. Horner and K. Sturm, *Ann.*, **597**, 1 (1955).

Addendum to Chapter XVII

3. A very recent contribution by Wyman[1] to the structural studies on indanthrone describes the infrared absorption spectra of indanthrone and of some of its derivatives, both in mulls and in potassium bromide pellets. None of these spectra exhibit the expected -NH-stretching frequency around 3μ. That the absence of this is not due to hydrogen bonding of the imino group with an adjacent carbonyl function follows from the observation of such a stretching mode at this frequency in indigo and in 1-aminoanthraquinone, where such hydrogen bonded structures are known to occur. There is a very strong vibration around 6.3μ in the spectra of most indanthrone derivatives and also in the related anthraquinoneazines and this is attributed to the C=N bond stretching mode.

For this reason, Wyman has proposed an alteration to the structure of indanthrone to (I).

(I)

6-Methyl- and 6,15-dimethylindanthrones were shown to be true N-methyl compounds and their structures accordingly remain as indicated (p. 483). These provide confirmatory evidence of the probable correctness of structure (I); the C=N stretching vibration for N-methylindanthrone at 6.3μ is only half as intense as that for (I), while for N,N'-dimethylindanthrone it has been replaced by two relatively weak bands, attributed to ring vibrations. Studies on deuterated indanthrones, in which 35 % of the active hydrogen is replaced by deuterium, lends further support to (I).

This structure explains seemingly anomalous chemical properties of indanthrone according to Wyman, for example the behavior in the vatting reaction with sodium dithionite (p. 470). The two-step reduction process of the carbonyl groups is inconsistent with the behavior of all other polyanthraquinone dyes. On the basis of (I), Wyman postulates that the first stage of reduction, to a blue vat, is reduction of the two carbonyl groups in (I) to yield a sodium salt of 5,9,14,18-tetrahydroxyanthrazine, while the second step of reduction, to a brown vat, involves the reduction of the azine ring to the dihydroazine. In harmony with this view, he points out, is the fact that N,N'-dimethylindanthrone only gives a brown vat; clearly, it is not possible in this case to obtain a vat containing the anthrazine nucleus in the lower state of reduction.

Wyman suggests that the noteworthy stability of indanthrone and its deep blue color are more readily explained on the basis of the fully conjugated structure (I) and in the paper, to which the reader is referred, he discusses other anomalies which now receive an explanation.

Further details have been given of the differentiation of polymorphic modifications of indanthrone by X-ray powder photographs.[2] The photo-conductivity of highly-purified indanthrone and the optical absorption by a thin film of the solid material have been measured.[3]

References

1. G. M. Wyman, *J. Am. Chem. Soc.*, **78**, 4599 (1956).
2. S. Susich, *Anal. Chem.*, **22**, 425 (1950).
3. H. Inokuchi, *Bull. Chem. Soc. Japan*, **27**, 22 (1954).

Addendum to Chapter XVIII

2.   2,3-Dimethylpyrazino[b]phenazine is said to be the compound formed in a reaction used for the colorimetric determination of diacetyl in biological materials.[1] In this procedure the reagent is 2,3-diaminophenazine which is used in concentrated sulfuric acid. After reaction, the excess of reagent is removed by tetrazotization and reduction of the tetrazonium salt by hypophosphorous acid. The blue color remaining is measured colorimetrically. A similar color is formed by methylglyoxal and this is presumably due to 2-methylpyrazino[b]phenazine. A free radical is postulated as the colored product.

3A.   Landquist[2] has cast doubt on the structures attributed by Morley to the compound $C_{18}H_{18}N_4$ obtained by the latter as a by-product from the condensation of o-phenylenediamine with 1,2-cyclohexandione (p. 510). Landquist has isolated a by-product from a similar reaction between 3,4-diaminochlorobenzene and the dione, to which he attributed the formula $C_{18}H_{18}N_4Cl_2$; he states that Morley's product was $C_{18}H_{20}N_4$, although this is an error and in disagreement with the proposed structures. However, Landquist gives analytical figures (C, H and N only) which are equally compatible with the alternative formula, $C_{18}H_{16}N_4Cl_2$, for his product, which would make it analogous to Morley's compound. If this is so, as seems probable, then it is not possible to sustain the structures suggested by Morley and the question must remain open.

63. Naphtho[2,1-h]quinoxalo-
     [2,3-a]phenazine
     No R. I.

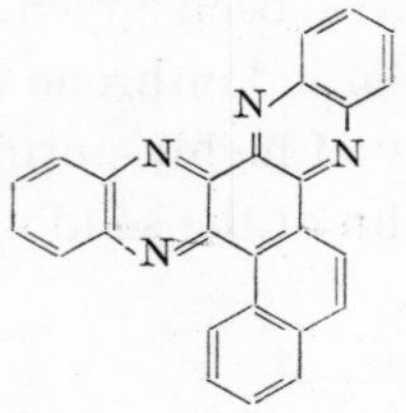

A member of this new ring system has been described[3] by the action of o-phenylenediamine upon 2,9-dichlorophenanthrene-3,4-quinone, which is obtainable from 3-phenanthrol. The formula of the product of the reaction, $C_{26}H_{13}N_4Cl$, suggests the involvement of two molecules of o-phenylenediamine with one of the quinone, with concomitant loss of a chlorine atom. The product, which formed small, light yellow pellets of indefinite crystalline character, m.p. 320–321°, was formulated as 7-chloronaphtho[2,1-h]quinoxalo[2,3-a]phenazine.

References

1. J. M. Dechary, E. Kun and H. C. Pitot, *Anal. Chem.*, 26, 449 (1954).
2. J. K. Landquist, *J. Chem. Soc.*, 1956, 2551.
3. C. K. Bradsher, F. C. Brown and P. H. Leake, *J. Am. Chem. Soc.*, 78, 4400 (1956).

Addendum to Chapter XIX

9. During their studies of certain indulines (see Chapter VII: 3, **B** and Addendum), Barry and his collaborators[1] remarked that the oxidation of 2-aminodiphenylamine hydrochloride in acetone solution with p-benzoquinone afforded an orange-yellow base giving a striking green-yellow fluorescence in solution. The same product could be obtained by heating 3-anilinoaposafranine in excess of acetone in the presence of syrupy phosphoric acid. They formulated the product as 2,10-dihydro-2,2-dimethyl-1,10-diphenyl-1-imidazo[b]phenazine. This work has been extended[2] and the structures confirmed by catalytic hydrogenation and by ultraviolet and infrared spectroscopic measurements. These compounds are most readily formed by the oxidation of 2-aminodiphenylamines, and, moreover, can be obtained in cases where oxidation of the diphenylamine in the absence of ketone does not yield a 3-anilinoaposafranine, so that the latter class of compound probably does not function as an intermediate. The highest yields (50 %) are obtained with dialkyl- or cycloalkyl-ketones; alkyl aryl ketones give this class of compound in yields of less than 20 % while diarylketones fail to react. The hydrogenation of these dihydro-imidazo[b]phenazines yields 3-anilinoaposafranines, with an additional substituent on the anilino nitrogen atom, and these products have shown greater protective activity than any other class of compound examined when tested on experimental murine tuberculosis.

TABLE LIIIa. 2,10-Dihydro-1-imidazo[b]phenazines

stituents	Appearance	M.p. (°C.)	Derivatives, etc.	Ref.
2-Dimethyl-1,10-diphenyl-	Orange-yellow needles	236–237 230–232	HCl, red crystals, m.p. 245° (dec.); methosulfate, red-brown, m.p. 265° (dec.)	1,2
Ethyl-2-methyl-1,10-diphenyl-		173–176		2
2-Diethyl-1,10-diphenyl-		216–218	Double m.p.; also melts at 145–147°	2
sec-Butyl-2-methyl-1,10-diphenyl-		182–183		2
Carbethoxymethyl-2-methyl-1,10-diphenyl-		151–152		2
β-Hydroxyethyl-2-methyl-1,10-diphenyl-		197–200		2
Chloromethyl-2-methyl-1,10-diphenyl-		187–190		2
Methyl-1,2,10-triphenyl-		223–225		2
Methyl-1,10-diphenyl-2(4′-pyridyl)-		265–266		2
10-Di-(4′-chlorophenyl)-2,2-dimethyl-		246–247		2
2-Dimethyl-1,10-di(4′-tolyl)-		211–213		2
10-Di(cyclohexyl)-2,2-dimethyl-		257–258		2
10-Dibenzyl-2,2-dimethyl-		224–225		2
10-Diphenyl-2,2-spirocyclohexyl-		292–294		2
10-Di(4′-chlorophenyl)-2,2-spirocyclohexyl-		299 (dec.)		2
10-Di(4′-isopropoxyphenyl)-2,2-spirocyclohexyl-		289		2

14. 10-Chloropyrido[3,2-a]phenazine has been obtained by the ring closure of 6-(4'-chloro-2'-nitroanilino)quinoline using a mixture of ferrous oxalate and lead at 256°. The product crystallizes from benzene as very pale yellow needles, m.p. 242–247°, after preliminary softening and darkening.[3]

New Ring Systems

77.   Pyrrolo[3,4-b]phenazine

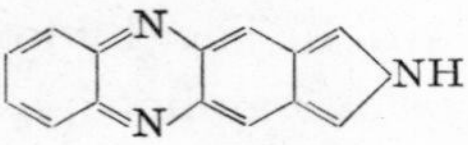

A member of this ring system, 1,3,3a,4,4a,10a,11,11a-octahydro-1,3-diketo-2-phenylpyrrolo[3,4-b]phenazine, has been obtained[4] by the reaction of N-phenylmaleimide with 2,3-dimethylquinoxaline, which functions as if it were 1,2,3,4-tetrahydro-2,3-dimethylenequinoxaline. The product forms colorless crystals, m.p. 184°. The position of the hydrogen atoms has not been fixed definitely and a tautomeric structure is 1,3,3a,4,5,10,11,11a-octahydro-1,3-diketo-2-phenylpyrrolo-[3,4-b]phenazine. For a similar reaction, the reader is referred to Chapter XVIII: 21.

78.   Pyrido[2,3-a]phenazine

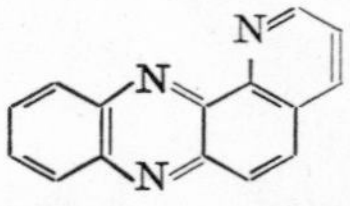

A representative of this ring system has been obtained by the ring closure, using ferrous oxalate and metallic lead, of 8-(4'-chloro-2'-nitroanilino)-quinoline.[3] 9-Chloropyrido[2,3-a]phenazine, thus obtained, forms very pale yellow needles, m.p. 272–273° (dec.).

79.   Benzofuro[2,3-a]phenazine

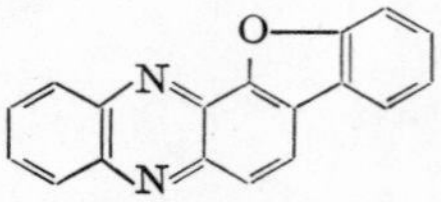

By a reaction similar to that described in the preceding section, 2-(4'-chloro-2'-nitroanilino)-diphenyleneoxide has been converted[3] into 10-chlorobenzofuro[2,3-a]phenazine, which forms very small, light yellow needles, m.p. 277–286°, from benzene.

References

1. V. C. Barry, J. G. Belton, J. F. O'Sullivan and D. Twomey, *J. Chem. Soc.*, **1956**, 888.
2. V. C. Barry, J. G. Belton, J. F. O'Sullivan and D. Twomey, *J. Chem. Soc.*, **1956**, 3347.
3. D. L. Vivian, J. L. Hartwell and H. C. Waterman, *J. Org. Chem.*, **19**, 1641 (1954).
4. A. Mustafa and M. Kamel, *J. Am. Chem. Soc.*, **77**, 1828 (1955).

SUBJECT INDEX

A

I